DATE DUE

APR 4 1998	

GAYLORD   PRINTED IN U.S.A.

ETHYLENIMINE AND OTHER AZIRIDINES

CHEMISTRY AND APPLICATIONS

ETHYLENIMINE AND OTHER AZIRIDINES

CHEMISTRY AND APPLICATIONS

O. C. Dermer

DEPARTMENT OF CHEMISTRY
OKLAHOMA STATE UNIVERSITY
STILLWATER, OKLAHOMA

AND

G. E. Ham

TEXAS DIVISION
THE DOW CHEMICAL COMPANY
FREEPORT, TEXAS

 1969

ACADEMIC PRESS   New York and London

ACADEMIC PRESS, INC.
111 Fifth Avenue, New York, New York 10003

United Kingdom Edition published by
ACADEMIC PRESS, INC. (LONDON) LTD.
Berkeley Square House, London W1X 6BA

LIBRARY OF CONGRESS CATALOG CARD NUMBER: 69-13474

PRINTED IN THE UNITED STATES OF AMERICA

PREFACE

   This book is intended to meet the need for a comprehensive and up-to-date discussion and bibliography on compounds that contain rings consisting of two carbon atoms and one nitrogen atom (ethylenimines or aziridines, and azirines) and their derivatives. Although this field has been reviewed repeatedly in the past, sometimes fairly comprehensively, many of the reviews are not current and are usually weak in their treatment of the applications of aziridines, and the most complete one is not in English.

   The literature coverage is intended to be substantially covered to late 1968. The few references deliberately excluded are those dealing only with specific physiological effects and clinical testing, and a handful, mostly patents, in which aziridines are merely mentioned among many other amines. On the other hand, the work is not a catalogue of all compounds containing aziridine rings, nor of their reactions.

Both the nomenclature and the abbreviations of group names employed by *Chemical Abstracts* are used extensively in this book. However, conservation of space, especially in tables, has dictated some departures from *Chemical Abstracts* rules, and has motivated the use of a number of trivial and trade names for aziridinyl compounds. Such names, which largely follow those used in the field of cancer chemotherapy, are defined in the index and in the List of Abbreviations. The abbreviations, with few exceptions, are the ones used in technological and biomedical literature. Occasionally these differ by fields, as when tris(1-aziridinyl)phosphine oxide is called APO in technology and tepa or TEPA (from a less satisfactory name, TriEthylenePhosphorAmide) in chemotherapy.

We are indebted to The Dow Chemical Company for authorizing and sponsoring the writing of this book, and to colleagues in both our organizations for many helpful suggestions.

Freeport, Texas   O. C. DERMER
May, 1969   G. E. HAM

CONTENTS

ix

2. Physical Properties of Aziridines

3. Reactions of Aziridines

4. Polymerization and Polymers of Aziridines

5. Industrial Applications of Aziridines

6. Biological Properties and Uses of Aziridines

7. Analytical Methods for Aziridines and Derivatives

8. Handling and Storage of Aziridines

References

LIST OF ABBREVIATIONS

Abbreviation	*Chemical Abstracts* index name
Apholate	1,3,5-Triazatriphosphorine, 2,2,4,4,6,6-hexakis-(1-aziridinyl)-2,2,4,4,6,6-hexahydro-
Aphamide, aphomide	Phosphinic amide, N,N'-ethylenebis [p,p-bis(1-aziridinyl)-N-methyl]-
Aphoxide	Phosphine oxide, tris(1-aziridinyl)-
APO	Phosphine oxide, tris(1-aziridinyl)-
APS	Phosphine sulfide, tris(1-aziridinyl)-
EI	Ethylenimine
Metepa	Phosphine oxide, tris(2-methyl-1-aziridinyl)-
PEI	Polyethylenimine
Tepa, TEPA	Phosphine oxide, tris(1-aziridinyl)-
TEM, trimethylenemelamine	Triazine, 2,4,6-tris(1-aziridinyl)-
Thiotepa	Phosphine sulfide, tris(1-aziridinyl)-
Tretamine	Triazine, 2,4,6-tris(1-aziridinyl)-

SYMBOLS USED ONLY IN FORMULAS (these in addition to the ones in *Chemical Abstracts*)

Az	1-Aziridinyl
Ms	Methanesulfonyl
Q	A polyvalent atom or group
R, R′, R″	Monovalent organic groups
Ts	*p*-Toluenesulfonyl
Y	A divalent atom or group

FORMATION OF THE AZIRIDINE RING

Historical Background

The earliest assignment of an aziridine structure to a compound was by Sabaneyev (*3084*) in 1875. He believed that the crystalline compound obtained from 1,1,2,2-tetrabromoethane, aniline, and alcoholic alkali was 2,3-dianilino-1-phenylaziridine (**1**). However, it was later shown to have the isomeric form PhNHCH₂C(=NPh)NHPh, an acetamidine derivative.

In 1881 Lehrfeld (*2287*) warmed ethyl 2,3-dibromosuccinate with alcoholic ammonia and obtained what he considered was probably ethyl 3-carbamoyl-aziridine-2-carboxylate (**2**), and thence made other aziridine derivatives. His observations have been confirmed (*1677*), but it still remains uncertain whether he had aziridines or the isomeric enamines, e.g., **3**.

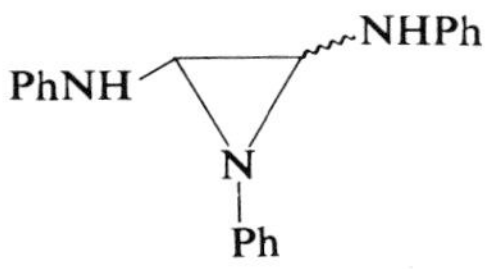

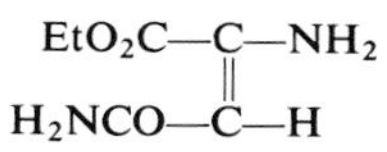

Apparently without knowledge of the earlier work, Ladenburg (*2253*) conceived and pointed out the probable existence of ethylenimine (EI) and homologous imines. He predicted that they should be obtainable from diamines by loss of ammonia. With this idea he tried for several years to prepare EI (*2252*). In 1888 he and Abel (*2251*) reported pyrolysis of ethylenediamine dihydrochloride to give small yields of the hydrochloride of a base believed to be EI, although its vapor density indicated that it was the dimer, piperazine. Preparation and properties of authentic piperazine led Sieber (*3260*) and von Hofmann (*1748*) to think that this was different from Ladenburg and Abel's product; but Majert and Schmidt (*2398*) soon showed that this product was indeed piperazine, and von Hofmann (*1749*) agreed.

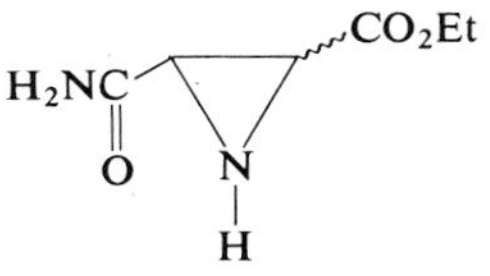

In the meantime Gabriel had prepared and characterized what he considered to be vinylamine, by the rearrangement of 2-bromoethylamine to "vinylamine" hydrobromide and liberation of the free base with silver oxide (*1385*) or potassium hydroxide (*1391*). This preparation was improved (*1392*) and applied to 2-bromopropylamine (*1388, 1723*) and 2-chloro-3-camphanamine (*1006*). However, the insolubility of the benzenesulfonyl derivative of "vinylamine" in aqueous alkali and the failure of the free base to react rapidly with aqueous potassium permanganate led Marckwald (*1771, 2429*) to conclude that it was really EI. The further evidence for the EI structure adduced by Marckwald and Frobenius (*2428*) pretty well settled the question, although some uneasiness about whether 2-phenylaziridine was really 2-phenylvinylamine was expressed in 1934 (*1340*), and vinylamine structures were written for what were surely aziridines as recently as 1939 (*381*) and 1949 (*2265*).

Intramolecular Displacement by the Amino Group

INTRODUCTION

The most general method of generating an aziridine ring is the unimolecular rearrangement of a vicinally substituted amine (**4**) to an iminium salt (**5**). This intramolecular alkylation occurs more or less readily depending on the structure of the substituted amine and the nature of the solvent. The reaction has both theoretical and preparative importance; these will be discussed in that order.

$$
\begin{array}{ccc}
\underset{\displaystyle \overset{\displaystyle \text{L}}{\underset{\displaystyle \text{N}}{\overset{|}{\underset{\diagdown\diagup}{\text{C}}}}\!\!-\!\!\overset{|}{\underset{|}{\text{C}}}}{} & \longrightarrow & \underset{\displaystyle \underset{\diagup\diagdown}{\overset{\displaystyle N^+}{\diagdown\diagup}}}{-\overset{|}{\text{C}}\!-\!\overset{|}{\text{C}}\!-} \quad \text{L}^- \\
\mathbf{4} & & \mathbf{5} \qquad (\text{L}^- = \text{leaving group})
\end{array}
$$

Kinetics of the cyclization were first studied by Freundlich and his students (*1338–1344, 3092, 3093, 3095*). The investigation of the mode of physiological action of nitrogen mustards during World War II soon was concerned with the rate of formation and decomposition of quaternary aziridinium intermediates of type **5** (*1473*). Since then, interest in such ions has been maintained by their connection with 2-haloalkylamines as antitumor drugs and as sympatholytic agents (*744, 3647*). The cyclization also represents an interesting example of those nucleophilic displacements on carbon that involve neighboring group participation (*1720, 2364, 3395, 3397*).

The first postulation of a quaternary aziridinium salt was by Marckwald and Frobenius (*2428*) in 1901; the salt was considered to be the spiro salt **6**, presumably formed from 1-(2-chloroethyl)piperidine.

This structural assignment was rejected by Knorr (*2118*, *2119*) and definitely disproved recently (*2294*, *2295*), the compound being the dimeric

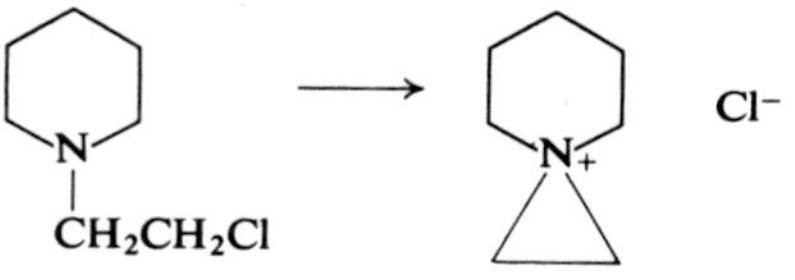
N
CH_2CH_2Cl
N+
Cl⁻

6

piperazine. The next, and more acceptable, suggestions were that such quaternary salts constitute reactive intermediates, such as **7** and **8**, in many

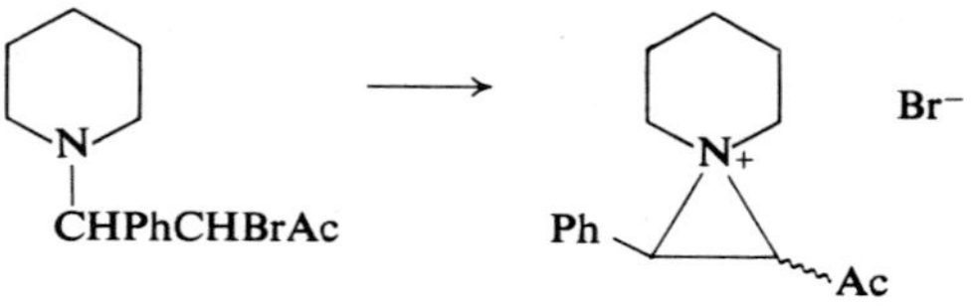
N
CHPhCHBrAc
N+
Ph
Ac
Br⁻

(*786, 787, 2620, 2621*)

7

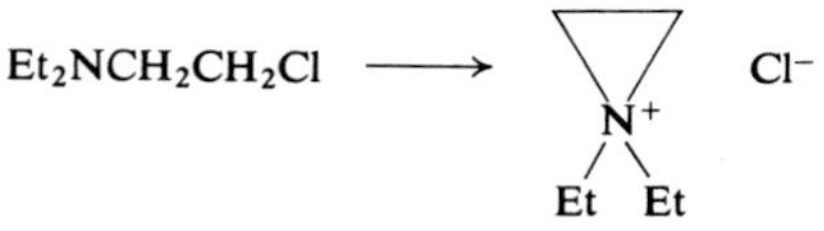
$Et_2NCH_2CH_2Cl$
N+
Et Et
Cl⁻

(*1479*)

8

of the reactions of (2-haloalkyl)dialkylamines. This theme was expanded rapidly when it was found that toxicity of the nitrogen mustards could be correlated with the extent to which they had so cyclized (*490*, *1355–1357*, *1489–1492*, *1556*, *1557*). It was also reassuring that the aziridinium ions, though unstable, could be isolated as the insoluble picrylsulfonates (*1355*, *1490–1492*).

Association of other physiological effects of nitrogen mustards with their aziridinium forms soon followed. The antitumor action of such alkylating agents has had major study (*139*, *744*, *2870*), and many cyclizations, including those of *N*,*N*-bis(2-chloroethyl)amino acids (*1941*, *2966*), *N*,*N*-bis(2-chloroethyl)amino sugars (*3687*), and *N*,*N*-bis(2-chloroethyl)purines (*2377*, *3190*), have been noted. 3-Carbamoyl-1-(2-chloroethyl)pyridinium chloride cannot thus cyclize, but its reduction with sodium hyposulfite yields a 1,4-dihydropyridine derivative (**9**) that can do so (Eq 1) (*1349*). Indeed many aziridines have antitumor action (see Chapter 6). However, there is no clear correspondence of such action in nitrogen mustards to their rate or extent of cyclization. Such correlation has also been sought in the mutagenic effects of

$$\text{(1)}$$

these mustards (*2918, 3269–3271, 3347*). The case for aziridinium ion intermediates as active agents in the sympatholytic action of the mustards is much better (*744, 3647*). The pressor action of adrenaline and noradrenaline is counteracted by "one-armed" nitrogen mustards such as dibenamine $[(PhCh_2)_2NCH_2CH_2Cl]$ and dibenzyline $[PhOCH_2CHMeN(CH_2Ph)CH_2-CH_2Cl]$ and good, though inexact, correlation between their existence in aziridinium form and their blocking potency has repeatedly been demonstrated (*64, 65, 317–319, 642–644, 1056, 1442, 1514, 1515, 1517, 1518, 1620, 1764, 2073, 2075, 2695, 2696, 2698, 2918, 3145*).

RATES OF REACTION

Analytical Methods. Since compounds containing aziridinium nitrogen atoms are as a rule difficult to isolate, much of the work just discussed has had to develop and rely on analytical methods for following the rate of the cyclization forming **5**.

1. Determination of L⁻ formed. This is very simple and common, at least when L⁻ is a halide and an argentometric method can be used. It is untrustworthy if any other L⁻-forming process is significant, e.g., displacement of L⁻ by a solvent molecule, usually water, or by a second molecule of substituted amine. If no substantial buildup of acidity accompanies formation of L⁻, direct hydrolysis (Eq 2) can be ruled out; if the reaction is first order in amine,

$$\text{(2)}$$

attack by a second molecule of amine is excluded. If hydrogen ions do form, a correction for the extent of direct hydrolysis can be made (*1355, 1620, 3647*). In the cyclization of *N*-(2-bromoethyl)aniline a second-order reaction with base can compete significantly with intramolecular displacement of the halogen (*1668*).

The reversal of the cyclization, to form the substituted amine, is likely to be kinetically significant as the concentration of L⁻ builds up.

2. Determination of aziridinium ion with thiosulfate ion. The aziridinium ring is quantitatively opened by thiosulfate, and excess thiosulfate can readily be determined (*1492, 1602, 1802*). However, the ring opening is sometimes too slow to be satisfactory for rate studies (*280, 3269, 3270*). One technique is to have thiosulfate present continuously during the cyclization, to trap the aziridinium ions (*1442, 2343, 2426*). The method assumes that no direct displacement of L^- by thiosulfate occurs. Recent work (*2109*) shows that this is an unsafe assumption, especially for primary halides, but the validity of the method can be established by showing the rate of reaction independent of thiosulfate concentration. Complete reaction of thiosulfate with a nitrogen mustard uses up one equivalent of thiosulfate per $-CH_2CH_2Cl$ group except for that part of the chloro amine that undergoes direct hydrolysis; the extent of the latter can thus be estimated. Because of the consecutive ring openings and recyclizations that can occur with bis- and tris(2-haloalkyl)amines, the thiosulfate method is less reliable in application to them except to measure total cyclization.

3. Determination of unreacted amine by titration with standard acid. This has been used but little (*1639, 3540*).

4. In a tertiary amine, the protonated form (e.g., $LCH_2CH_2NHR_2^+$) cannot cyclize, but in solution the aminium ion is in equilibrium with the free base, which can undergo cyclization. Titration of hydrogen ions to keep the pH near the pK_a permits calculation or at least estimation of the amount of amine that has cyclized (*281, 1607, 3670*).

5. The direct polarographic reduction of aziridinium intermediates has been shown suitable for their determination (*2427*) and used in rate studies (*3869*).

6. Other instrumental methods can be specific for determination of aziridinium ions: ultraviolet spectrophotometry (*3345, 3670*) and nuclear magnetic resonance spectrometry (*2310, 3347*).

Observed Rates of Cyclization. The interest in studying correlation between sympatholytic effect and aziridinium ion content led to a series of measurements of the maximum concentrations of such ions attained in solutions of appropriate 2-haloalkylamines. While the data are the resultants of the rate of formation of the ring and the rates of destruction of the ring, and therefore essentially empirical, they are reproduced in Table 1-I. It will be noted that maximum concentration of aziridinium ions is usually found for bromides; the corresponding fluorides do not cyclize at measurable rates, the chlorides cyclize so slowly that the rings are exposed to various nucleophilic attacks, and the iodides necessarily give the very nucleophilic iodide ion which keeps the "steady state" concentration of aziridinium ions low.

As a unimolecular reaction, the formation of aziridinium ions by ring closure follows a very simple rate law, and many such rate constants have

Table 1-I

MAXIMUM CONCENTRATIONS OF AZIRIDINIUM IONS FROM 2-HALOALKYLAMINES, $XCHR^1CH_2NR^2R^3$

X	Amine			Solvent	Temp. (°C)	Time (min)	Ion formed (% of theory)[a]	References
	R^1	R^2	R^3					
Cl	H	H	CH_2CH_2Cl	0.2M phosphate buffer, pH 7.3	37	90	≈ 80	2988
Br	H	H	CH_2CH_2Cl	0.2M phosphate buffer, pH 7.3	37	15	≈ 90	2988
Br	H	H	CH_2CH_2Cl	0.2M phosphate buffer, pH 6.0	37	30	≈ 80	2988
Br	H	H	CH_2CH_2Br	0.2M phosphate buffer, pH 7.3	37	3	≈ 95	2988
Br	H	H	CH_2CH_2Br	0.2M phosphate buffer, pH 6.0	37	20	≈ 80	2988
Cl	H	Me	Me	D_2O, excess Na_2CO_3	27	5	22	3347
Cl	Me	Me or Et	CH_2CH_2F	Aq. buffer	36.7	—	Some	2691
Cl	H	Me	CH_2CH_2Cl	1M Na_2CO_3	30	20	57	3347
Cl	H	Et	Et	D_2O, excess Na_2CO_3	0	35	≈ 100	3347
Cl	Ph	Me	Me	0.16M $NaHCO_3$	37	0	98	1286
Cl	Ph	Me	Me	H_2O	37	0	96	1286
Cl	Ph	Me	Me	50% Me_2CO	31	—	92	645
Br	H	c-C_6H_{11}	c-C_6H_{11}	70% EtOH	27	—	≈ 50	1620
Br	H	CH_2Ph	CH_2Ph	67% Me_2CO	30	—	0	641
Br	H	CH_2Ph	CH_2Ph	67% Me_2CO	30	—	2	642
Br	H	CH_2Ph	CH_2Ph	70% EtOH	4	—	≈ 50	1620
Br	H	CH_2Ph	CH_2Ph	70% EtOH	27	—	4–10	642
Br	H	CH_2Ph	CH_2Ph	70% EtOH	37	—	15	1620
Br	H	CH_2Ph	CH_2Ph	70% EtOH	37	—	2–8	642

				Solvent				Refs
Br	H	CH$_2$Ph	CH$_2$Ph	70% EtOH + KHCO$_3$	37	15	5	318, 3647
Br	H	CH$_2$Ph	CH$_2$Ph	67% Me$_2$CO	30	—	16	642
I	H	CH$_2$Ph	CH$_2$Ph	67% Me$_2$CO	30	—	4.5	642
Cl	Me	CH$_2$Ph	CH$_2$Ph	70% EtOH + KHCO$_3$	37	10	7	3647
Cl, Br, I	H	Ph	Ph	67% Me$_2$CO	30	—	0	641, 644
F	H	Et	CH$_2$-1-C$_{10}$H$_7$	67% Me$_2$CO	30	—	0	641, 644
Cl	H	Et	CH$_2$-1-C$_{10}$H$_7$	67% Me$_2$CO	30	—	34	641, 644
Cl	H	Et	CH$_2$-1-C$_{10}$H$_7$	67% Me$_2$CO	30	—	86	642
Br	H	Et	CH$_2$-1-C$_{10}$H$_7$	67% Me$_2$CO	30	—	86	641, 644
I	H	Et	CH$_2$-1-C$_{10}$H$_7$	67% Me$_2$CO	30	—	100	644
F	H	Me	CH$_2$-1-C$_{10}$H$_7$	67% Me$_2$CO	30	—	0	641, 644
Cl	H	Me	CH$_2$-1-C$_{10}$H$_7$	67% Me$_2$CO	30	—	18	641, 644
Br	H	Me	CH$_2$-1-C$_{10}$H$_7$	67% Me$_2$CO	30	—	100	644
I	H	Me	CH$_2$-1-C$_{10}$H$_7$	67% Me$_2$CO	30	—	47	641, 644
F	H	Et	CH$_2$-2-C$_{10}$H$_7$	67% Me$_2$CO	30	—	0	644
Cl	H	Et	CH$_2$-2-C$_{10}$H$_7$	67% Me$_2$CO	30	—	47	641, 644
Br	H	Et	CH$_2$-2-C$_{10}$H$_7$	67% Me$_2$CO	30	—	96	641, 644
I	H	Et	CH$_2$-2-C$_{10}$H$_7$	67% Me$_2$CO	30	—	79	644
F	H	Me	CH$_2$-2-C$_{10}$H$_7$	67% Me$_2$CO	30	—	0	644
Cl	H	Me	CH$_2$-2-C$_{10}$H$_7$	67% Me$_2$CO	30	—	15	641, 644
Br	H	Me	CH$_2$-2-C$_{10}$H$_7$	67% Me$_2$CO	30	—	72	641, 644
I	H	Me	CH$_2$-2-C$_{10}$H$_7$	67% Me$_2$CO	30	—	52	644
Cl	H	Et	CH$_2$C$_6$H$_4$Cl-p	67% Me$_2$CO	30	30	36	65, 1517
Br	H	Et	CH$_2$C$_6$H$_4$Cl-p	67% Me$_2$CO	30	—	81	65
I	H	Et	CH$_2$C$_6$H$_4$Cl-p	67% Me$_2$CO	30	30	60	65
Cl	H	Et	CH$_2$C$_6$H$_4$Cl-m	67% Me$_2$CO	30	—	26	65, 1517
Br	H	Et	CH$_2$C$_6$H$_4$Cl-m	67% Me$_2$CO	30	—	75	65
I	H	Et	CH$_2$C$_6$H$_4$Cl-m	67% Me$_2$CO	30	—	52	65
Cl	H	Et	CH$_2$C$_6$H$_4$Cl-o	67% Me$_2$CO	30	—	22–23	65, 1517
Br	H	Et	CH$_2$C$_6$H$_4$Cl-o	67% Me$_2$CO	30	—	75	65
I	H	Et	CH$_2$C$_6$H$_4$Cl-o	67% Me$_2$CO	30	—	52	65
Cl	H	CH$_2$CH$_2$Cl	CH$_2$Ph	50% EtOH	25	20	61[b]	2851a

Table 1-I

MAXIMUM CONCENTRATIONS OF AZIRIDINIUM IONS FROM 2-HALOALKYLAMINES, $XCHR^1CH_2NR^2R^3$—*continued*

X	R¹	R²	R³	Solvent	Temp. (°C)	Time (min)	Ion formed (% of theory)[a]	References
Cl	H	CH₂CH₂Cl	CH₂C₆H₄Me-p	50% EtOH	25	20	67[b]	2851a
Cl	H	CH₂CH₂Cl	CH₂C₆H₄-iso-Pr-p	50% EtOH	25	20	71[b]	2851a
Cl	H	CH₂CH₂Cl	CH₂C₆H₄OMe-o	50% EtOH	25	20	92[b]	2851a
Cl	H	CH₂CH₂Cl	CH₂C₆H₄OMe-m	50% EtOH	25	20	52[b]	2851a
Cl	H	CH₂CH₂Cl	CH₂C₆H₄OMe-p	50% EtOH	25	20	77[b]	2851a
Cl	H	CH₂CH₂Cl	CH₂C₆H₄OEt-p	50% EtOH	25	20	70[b]	2851a
Cl	H	CH₂CH₂Cl	CH₂C₆H₄OPr-p	50% EtOH	25	20	79[b]	2851a
Cl	H	CH₂CH₂Cl	CH₂C₆H₄OBu-p	50% EtOH	25	20	73[b]	2851a
Cl	H	CH₂CH₂Cl	CH₂C₆H₃(OMe)₂-3,4	50% EtOH	25	20	74[b]	2851a
Cl	H	CH₂CH₂Cl	CH₂C₆H₃-3-NO₂-4-OMe	50% EtOH	25	20	31[b]	2851a
Cl	H	CH₂CH₂Cl	5,6,7,8-H₄-2-C₁₀H₇	50% EtOH	25	20	63[b]	2851a
Cl	H	CH₂CH₂Cl	CH₂C₆H₃[(CH₂)₅]-3,4	50% EtOH	25	20	59[b]	2851a
Cl	H	CH₂CH₂Cl	CH₂-5-indanyl	50% EtOH	25	20	62[b]	2851a
Cl	H	Et	9-Fluorenyl	67% Me₂CO	30	15	7	642, 1517
Br	H	Et	9-Fluorenyl	67% Me₂CO	30	15	36-40	642, 1517
I	H	Et	9-Fluorenyl	67% Me₂CO	30	15	14	642
Cl	H	Et	9-Fluorenyl	67% Me₂CO	30	15	7	642, 1517
Br	H	Et	9-Fluorenyl	67% Me₂CO	30	0.5	36-40	642, 1517
I	H	Et	9-Fluorenyl	67% Me₂CO	30	—	14	642
Cl	H	CH₂Ph	9-Fluorenyl	67% Me₂CO	30	—	1	642
Br	H	CH₂Ph	9-Fluorenyl	67% Me₂CO	30	—	4	642
Cl	Me	Et	9-Fluorenyl	67% Me₂CO	30	—	4	642
Br	Me	Et	9-Fluorenyl	67% Me₂CO	30	—	31	642
Cl	H	Et	Benzo[b]then-3-ylmethyl	67% Me₂CO	30	—	22	642

X	R_1	R_2	R_3	Conditions	Temp (°C)	Time (hr)	Yield (%)	Ref.
Br	H	Et	Benzo[b]thenyl-3-ylmethyl	67% Me$_2$CO	30	—	72	642, 1518
I	H	Et	Benzo[b]thenyl-3-ylmethyl	67% Me$_2$CO	30	—	56	642
Cl	H	Et	2-Thenyl	67% Me$_2$CO	30	—	1.5	642
Br	H	Et	2-Thenyl	67% Me$_2$CO	30	—	10	642
I	H	Et	2-Thenyl	67% Me$_2$CO	30	—	4	642
			($R_2 + R_3$ =)					
Cl	H		o-C$_6$H$_4$(—CH$_2$—/—CH$_2$—)	67% Me$_2$CO + KHCO$_3$	37	—	0	318
Cl	H		o-C$_6$H$_4$(—CH$_2$—/—CH$_2$CH$_2$—)	67% Me$_2$CO + KHCO$_3$	37	≈15	1	318
Cl	H		o-C$_6$H$_4$(—CH$_2$—/—CH$_2$CH$_2$CH$_2$—)	67% Me$_2$CO + K$_2$CO$_2$	37	8.5	60	318
Cl	H	CH$_2$Ph	CH$_2$CH$_2$OPh	67% Me$_2$CO	30	—	6	64
Br	H	CH$_2$Ph	CH$_2$CH$_2$OPh	67% Me$_2$CO	30	—	33	64
I	H	CH$_2$Ph	CH$_2$CH$_2$OPh	67% Me$_2$CO	30	—	7	64
Cl	H	CH$_2$Ph	CH$_2$CH$_2$OC$_6$H$_4$Me-o	67% Me$_2$CO	30	—	4	64
Br	H	CH$_2$Ph	CH$_2$CH$_2$OC$_6$H$_4$Me-o	67% Me$_2$CO	30	—	21	64
I	H	CH$_2$Ph	CH$_2$CH$_2$OC$_6$H$_4$Me-o	67% Me$_2$CO	30	—	3	64
Cl	H	CH$_2$Ph	CH$_2$CH$_2$OC$_6$H$_4$Me-p	67% Me$_2$CO	30	—	6	64
Br	H	CH$_2$Ph	CH$_2$CH$_2$OC$_6$H$_4$Me-p	67% Me$_2$CO	30	—	27	64
Cl	H	CH$_2$Ph	CHMeCH$_2$OPh	70% EtOH + KHCO$_3$	37	5	21	3647
Cl	H	Et	CHMeCH$_2$OPh	70% EtOH + K$_2$CO$_3$	37	3	83	3647
Br	p-MeC$_6$H$_4$	Me	Me	40% Me$_2$CO	37	5	67	640
Br	p-ClC$_6$H$_4$	Me	Me	40% Me$_2$CO	37	5	83	640
Cl	p-ClC$_6$H$_4$	Me	Me	40% Me$_2$CO	37	5	83	640
Br	3,4-Br$_2$C$_6$H$_3$	Me	Me	40% Me$_2$CO	37	5	88	640
Br	3,4-Cl$_2$C$_6$H$_3$	Me	Me	40% Me$_2$CO	37	5	87	640
Cl	3,4-Cl$_2$C$_6$H$_3$	Me	Me	40% Me$_2$CO	37	5	79	640

Table 1-I

MAXIMUM CONCENTRATIONS OF AZIRIDINIUM IONS FROM 2-HALOALKYLAMINES, $XCHR^1CH_2NR^2R^3$ —*continued*

X	Amine R^1	R^2	R^3	Solvent	Temp. (°C)	Time (min)	Ion formed (% of theory)[a]	References
Cl	3,4-Me$_2$C$_6$H$_3$	Me	Me	40% Me$_2$CO	37	5	78	*640*
Cl	H	Me	CH$_2$CH$_2$O$_2$CCPh$_2$OH	0.01M phosphate buffer, pH 7.3	23	20	82	*1470*
Cl	H	Me	CH$_2$CH$_2$O$_2$CCPh$_2$OH	0.01M phosphate buffer, pH 7.3	37	10	83	*1470*
Cl	H	Me	CH$_2$CH$_2$O$_2$CCPh$_2$OH	67% Me$_2$CO	30	≈ 60	< 30	*1470*

For a few 2-haloethylamines of type BrCRArCH$_2$NMe$_2$

X	Ar	R	R^3	Solvent	Temp. (°C)	Time (min)	Ion formed (% of theory)[a]	References
	Ph	Me		50% Me$_2$CO	31	—	0	*645*
	Ph	Et		50% Me$_2$CO	31	—	0	*645*
	Ph	Pr		50% Me$_2$CO	31	—	0	*645*
	1-C$_{10}$H$_7$	Me		50% Me$_2$CO	31	—	0	*645*

[a] On the basis of reaction of only one haloalkyl group.
[b] Not necessarily the maximum yield.

been measured. In some instances values have also been obtained for the frequency factor and the energy of activation for the cyclization. Such data are presented in Table 1-II, which considerably extends the compilation now available (*2677*).

Factors Affecting Rate of Cyclization. 1. Solvent. Since initially neutral parts of the molecule must come into a transition state which involves some separation of charge, solvents of high dielectric constant favor the reaction. There has been no systematic comparison of many solvents in the cyclization, but the higher rates of 2-haloalkylamines in water compared to methanol (Table 1-II, entries for 2-bromoethylamine hydrobromide) and acetone [entries for $(ClCH_2CH_2)_2NHEt^+Cl^-$] illustrate the effect. While both E, the energy of activation, and A, the frequency factor, are decreased in nonaqueous solvents, the effect of the change in A is the greater and the cyclization is retarded.

2. Nature of L. The most familiar leaving groups are seen here, and the rates of leaving are in the order to be expected: O_3SR (*1056, 1442, 1764*) > Br > Cl > F, OSO_3^- (*896*). Similar displacement occurs spontaneously in 2-aminoethyl diethyl phosphate (**10**) and 2-aminoethyl diphenyl phosphate (*498*) and in 2-dimethylaminoethyl diphenyl phosphate (*1013*).

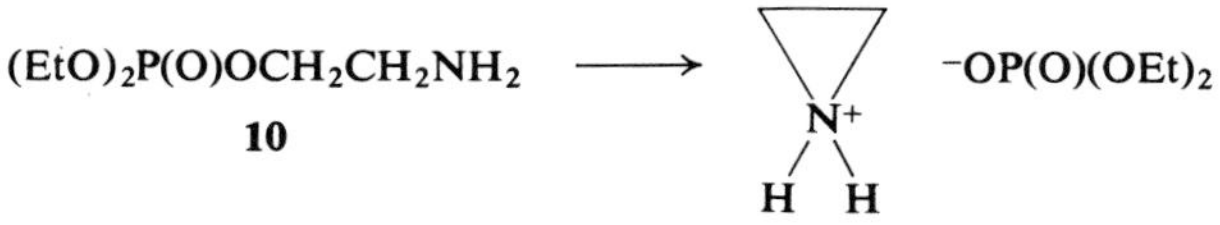

$$(EtO)_2P(O)OCH_2CH_2NH_2 \longrightarrow \underset{\underset{H \quad H}{N^+}}{\bigtriangledown} \quad {}^-OP(O)(OEt)_2 \quad (498)$$
10

Phosphatidylethanolamines, $RCO_2CH_2CH(O_2CR)CH_2OP(O)(OH)OCH_2$-$CH_2NH_2$, upon exhaustive treatment with diazomethane lose their nitrogen (*243*), probably as EI (*498*), and it is likely that merely treating a phosphatidylethanolamine with strong base, to which it is reported very sensitive (*1540*), will cause such elimination. However, 2-aminoethyl dihydrogen phosphate is undecomposed by boiling for 24 hours with 1N NaOH (*2895*); evidently the displacement of the highly charged phosphate ion is virtually impossible. 2-Aminoalkyl nitrates would probably cyclize to form aziridinium ions. This path has been suggested for the dimerization of the trinitric ester of triethanolamine, $N(CH_2CH_2ONO_2)_3$, to 1,1,4,4-tetrakis-(nitroxyethyl)piperazinium dinitrate (*1010*). The mechanism of the conversion of 2-(dialkylamino)alkyl halides by silver perchlorate to aziridinium perchlorates (*1306a, 2294, 2295*) has not been directly investigated. The path might

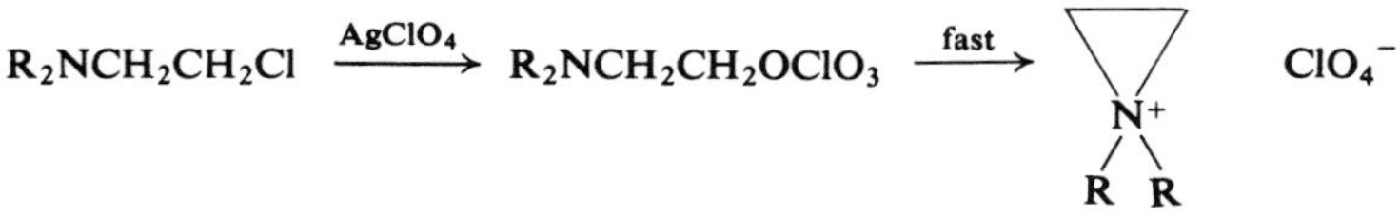

$$R_2NCH_2CH_2Cl \xrightarrow{AgClO_4} R_2NCH_2CH_2OClO_3 \xrightarrow{fast} \underset{\underset{R \quad R}{N^+}}{\bigtriangledown} \quad ClO_4^- \quad (3)$$

Table 1-II

RATES OF CYCLIZATION OF 2-SUBSTITUTED AMINES TO AZIRIDINIUM SALTS

Amine salt or free base	Solvent	Addend	Analytical method[a]	Temp. (°C)	k (= $10^{-n}k°$, sec^{-1}) $k°$	n	E (kcal)	A (= $10^{a}A°$, sec^{-1}) $A°$	n	References
$FCH_2CH_2NH_2$	D_2O	0.2M NaOH	I	90	1.6	5	—	—	—	2310
$(FCH_2CH_2)_2NH$	D_2O	0.2M NaOH	I	80	7.5	5	—	—	—	2310
$ClCH_2CH_2NH_3^+$ Cl$^-$	H_2O	NaOH	II	0	2	7	—	—	—	1344
$ClCH_2CH_2NH_3^+$ Cl$^-$	H_2O	NaOH	II	25	8	6	27.5	9	14	3095
$ClCH_2CH_2NH_3^+$ Cl$^-$	H_2O	NaOH	II	31	1.56	5	—	—	—	620
$ClCH_2CH_2NH_3^+$ Cl$^-$	D_2O	0.3M NaOH	I	50	1.3	5	—	—	—	2310
$ClCH_2CHMeNH_3^+$ picrate$^-$	H_2O	Ba(OH)$_2$	II	25	8.2	3	(But considered 2nd order)	—	—	3301
$ClCH_2CHMeNH_3^+$ Cl$^-$	H_2O	NaOH	II	25	2.5	4	—	—	—	1341
$MeCHClCH_2NH_3^+$ picrate$^-$	H_2O	Ba(OH)$_2$	II	25	1.13	3	(But considered 2nd order)	—	—	3301
$MeCHClCH_2NH_3^+$ Cl$^-$	H_2O	NaOH	II	25	3	5	—	—	—	1341
$MeCHClCH_2NH_3^+$ Cl$^-$	H_2O	NaOH	II	31	3.44	5	—	—	—	620
$ClCH_2CHPhNH_3^+$ Cl$^-$	H_2O	NaOH	II	25	≈ 5	6	≈ 27	—	—	1341
$PhCHClCH_2NH_3^+$ Cl$^-$	H_2O	NaOH	II	0	3.0	4	—	—	—	1341
$PhCHClCH_2NH_3^+$ Cl$^-$	H_2O	NaOH	II	25	7.0	3	—	—	—	1341
$PhCHClCH_2NH_3^+$ Cl$^-$	H_2O	NaOH	II	37	2.0	2	19.1	6	11	1341
$PhCHClCH_2NH_3^+$ Cl$^-$	H_2O	NaOH	II	—	—	—	20.6	1	13	3095
$PhCHClCH_2NH_3^+$ Cl$^-$	H_2O	None	II	82	≈ 1	3	—	—	—	3095
$PhCHClCH_2NH_3^+$ Cl$^-$	H_2O	None	II	100	≈ 5	3	—	—	—	3095
$MeCHClCH_2NHMe_2^+$ Cl$^-$	H_2O	KClO$_4$, μ ≈ 0.07, + AcOH or KH$_2$PO$_4$ + NaOH	II	25	1.63	3	—	—	—	1605

Compound	Solvent	Conditions	Products							
ClCH₂CHMeNHMe₂⁺ Cl⁻	H₂O	KClO₄, μ ≈ 0.07, + AcOH or KH₂PO₄ + NaOH	II	25	1.6	2	—	—	—	1605
ClCH₂CH₂NHMe₂⁺ Cl⁻	H₂O	NaOH	II + III	18	1.1	4	—	—	—	1605
ClCH₂CH₂NHMe₂⁺ Cl⁻	H₂O	NaOH	II + III	25	3	3	—	—	—	1605
ClCH₂CH₂NHMe₂⁺ Cl⁻	H₂O	NaOH	II + III	35	1	2	—	—	—	3269
ClCH₂CH₂NH₂(CH₂CH₂OH)⁺ Cl⁻	H₂O	NaOH, pH 7.2	II	37	1.01	4	≈22	—	—	2985
ClCH₂CH₂NH₂(CH₂CH₂OH)⁺ Cl⁻	H₂O	NaOH, pH 6.0	II	37	1.06	5	32.1	—	—	2985
ClCH₂CH₂NHMe(CH₂CH₂OH)⁺ Cl⁻	H₂O	NaOH, pH 7.9	II, IV, V	0	4.50	5	—	—	—	726
ClCH₂CH₂NHMe(CH₂CH₂OH)⁺ Cl⁻	H₂O	NaOH, pH 7.9	II, IV, V	15	3.84	4	22	1.6	13	726
ClCH₂CH₂NHEt₂⁺ Cl⁻	H₂O	NaOH, pH 8	II, IV?, V?	0	2.64	4	—	—	—	726
ClCH₂CH₂NHEt₂⁺ Cl⁻	H₂O	NaOH, pH 8	II, IV?, V?	15	2.42	3	23	8	14	726
ClCH₂CH₂NHEt₂⁺ Cl⁻	H₂O	KClO₄, μ ≈ 0.07, + AcOH or KH₂PO₄ + NaOH	III	25	9.3	3	—	—	—	1605
ClCH₂CH₂NHEt₂⁺ Cl⁻	H₂O	NaHCO₃ + Na₂CO₃, pH 10.7	II	25	4.17	3	—	—	—	2919
ClCH₂CH₂NHEt₂⁺ Cl⁻	67% Me₂CO	None	II	25	3.4	3	—	—	—	279
(ClCH₂CH₂)₂NH₂⁺ Cl⁻	H₂O	Borate buffer, pH 7.36	VI	25	5.5	5	—	—	—	3869
(ClCH₂CH₂)₂NH₂⁺ Cl⁻	D₂O	NaOH, 0.2M	I	37	6.2	5	—	—	—	2310
(ClCH₂CH₂)₂NH₂⁺ Cl⁻	H₂O	NaOH, pH 7.2	II	37	5.00	4	28.7	—	—	2985, 2986
(ClCH₂CH₂)₂NH₂⁺ Cl⁻	H₂O	NaOH, pH 6.0	II	37	7.01	5	28.9	—	—	2985, 2986
(ClCH₂CH₂)₂NHMe⁺ Cl⁻	H₂O	NaOH, pH 8.0	II, IV?, V?	0	3.84	5	—	—	—	726
(ClCH₂CH₂)₂NHMe⁺ Cl⁻	H₂O	NaOH, pH 8.0	II, IV?, V?	15	4.00	4	—	—	—	726
(ClCH₂CH₂)₂NHMe⁺ Cl⁻	H₂O	NaOH, pH 8.0	II, IV?, V?	30	3.25	3	—	—	—	726
(ClCH₂CH₂)₂NHMe⁺ Cl⁻	H₂O	Ba(OH)₂	II, V	10	1.87	4	—	—	—	1602
(ClCH₂CH₂)₂NHMe⁺ Cl⁻	H₂O	Ba(OH)₂	II, V	25	1.61	3	24	8	14	1602
(ClCH₂CH₂)₂NHMe⁺ Cl⁻	H₂O	Ba(OH)₂	II	15	3.7	4	—	—	—	3270
(ClCH₂CH₂)₂NHMe⁺ Cl⁻	H₂O	Ba(OH)₂	II	25	1.3	3	—	—	—	3270
(ClCH₂CH₂)₂NHMe⁺ Cl⁻	H₂O	Ba(OH)₂	II	35	3.7	3	—	—	—	3270

Table 1-II—*continued*

Amine salt or free base	Solvent	Addend	Analytical method[a]	Temp. (°C)	k ($= 10^{-n}k^o$, sec^{-1}) k^o	n	E (kcal)	A ($= 10^n A^o$, sec^{-1}) A^o	n	References
$(ClCH_2CH_2)_2NHMe^+$ Cl^-	H_2O	NaOH, pH 7.2	II	37	6.91	3	24.8	—	—	2985
$(ClCH_2CH_2)_2NHMe^+$ Cl^-	H_2O	NaOH, pH 6.0	II	37	1.78	3	—	—	—	2985
$(ClCH_2CH_2)_2NHMe^+$ Cl^-	50% Me_2CO	None	II	25	4.7	5	17.9	5	11	3540
$(ClCH_2CH_2)_2NHMe^+$ Cl^-	67% Me_2CO	None	II	25	≈ 3	4	—	—	—	279
$(ClCH_2CH_2)_2NHMe^+$ Cl^-	MeOH	None	II	0	≈ 2.3	6	—	—	—	1639
$(ClCH_2CH_2)_2NHMe^+$ Cl^-	MeOH	None	II	25	6.1	5	19.6	4	13	1639
$(ClCH_2CH_2)_2NHEt^+$ Cl^-	H_2O	NaOH, pH 9.1	II, IV?, V?	0	1.95	4	—	—	—	726
$(ClCH_2CH_2)_2NHEt^+$ Cl^-	H_2O	NaOH, pH 9.1	II, IV?, V?	15	2.14	3	25	2	16	726
$(ClCH_2CH_2)_2NHEt^+$ Cl^-	H_2O	None	II, V	25	1.37	5	—	—	—	1602
$(ClCH_2CH_2)_2NHEt^+$ Cl^-	25% Me_2CO	None	II, III	25	4	3	—	—	—	279
$(ClCH_2CH_2)_2NHEt^+$ Cl^-	67% Me_2CO	None	II, III	25	1.42	3	—	—	—	279
$(ClCH_2CH_2)_2NHPr^+$ Cl^-	H_2O	NaOH, pH≈ 8	II, IV?, V?	0	3.37	4	—	—	—	726
$(ClCH_2CH_2)_2NHPr^+$ Cl^-	H_2O	NaOH, pH≈ 8	II, IV?, V?	15	3.62	3	25	2	16	726
$(ClCH_2CH_2)_2NHPr^+$ Cl^-	H_2O	None	II, V	25	1.81	5	—	—	—	1602
$(ClCH_2CH_2)_2NH\text{-}iso\text{-}Pr^+$ Cl^-	H_2O	NaOH, pH 7.4	II, IV?, V?	0	9.20	4	—	—	—	726
$(ClCH_2CH_2)_2NH\text{-}iso\text{-}Pr^+$ Cl^-	H_2O	NaOH, pH 7.4	II, IV?, V?	15	8.16	3	23	2	15	726
$(ClCH_2CH_2)_2NH\text{-}iso\text{-}Pr^+$ Cl^-	H_2O	None	II, V	25	2.61	5	—	—	—	1602
$(ClCH_2CH_2)_2NHBu^+$ Cl^-	H_2O	NaOH, pH ~ 8	II, IV?, V?	0	2.57	4	—	—	—	726
$(ClCH_2CH_2)_2NHBu^+$ Cl^-	H_2O	NaOH, pH ~ 8	II, IV?, V?	15	2.57	3	24	4	15	726
$(ClCH_2CH_2)_2NHCH_2CH_2O$ Me^+ Cl^-	H_2O	NaOH, pH ~ 8	II, IV?, V?	0	8.16	5	—	—	—	726
$(ClCH_2CH_2)_2NHCH_2CH_2O$ Me^+ Cl^-	H_2O	NaOH, pH ~ 8	II, IV?, V?	15	8.67	4	25	4	15	726
$(ClCH_2CH_2)_3NH^+$ Cl^-	H_2O	NaOH, pH ~ 8	II, IV?, V?	0	1.15	4	—	—	—	726

Compound	Solvent	Conditions	II, IV?, V?	15			25	7	15	Ref
$(ClCH_2CH_2)_3NH^+ Cl^-$	H_2O	NaOH, pH ~ 8	II	15	1.22	3	—	—	15	726
$(ClCH_2CH_2)_3NH^+ Cl^-$	67% Me_2CO	None	II	25	9.2	5	—	—	—	279
$(ClCH_2CH_2)_3NH^+ Cl^-$	H_2O	Borate buffer, pH 7.3	VI	25	5.2	3	—	—	—	2427
$ClCH_2CH_2NH(CH_2Ph)_2^+ Cl^-$	50% EtOH	Acetate buffer, pH ~ 7	IV	25	1.55	4	—	—	—	2426
$ClCH_2CH_2NH(CH_2Ph)_2^+ Cl^-$	70% EtOH	0.1M in $KHCO_3$	II + IV	37	2.8	4	—	—	—	318
$MeCHClCH_2NH(CH_2Ph)_2^+ Cl^-$	60% EtOH	Acetate buffer, pH 7	IV	25	8.8	5	—	—	—	2426
$ClCH_2CH_2NHEt(CH_2\text{-}1\text{-}C_{10}H_7)^+ Cl^-$	70% EtOH	$NaHCO_3$	IV	37	2	3	—	—	—	1442
$ClCH_2CH_2NHEt(CH_2\text{-}1\text{-}C_{10}H_7)^+ Cl^-$	60% EtOH	Acetate buffer, pH 7	IV	25	2.4	4	—	—	—	2426
$ClCH_2CH_2NHEt(CH_2\text{-}1\text{-}C_{10}H_7)^+ Cl^-$	H_2O	Phosphate buffer, pH 5.9	IV	25	2.4	5	—	—	—	2343
$ClCH_2CH_2NHEt(CH_2\text{-}1\text{-}C_{10}H_7)^+ Cl^-$	H_2O	Phosphate buffer, pH 7.4	IV	25	5.56	5	—	—	—	2343
$ClCH_2CH_2NHEt(CH_2\text{-}1\text{-}C_{10}H_7)^+ Cl^-$	H_2O	Phosphate buffer, pH 9.3	IV	25	9.43	5	—	—	—	2343
$ClCH_2CH_2NHEt(CH_2CH_2 OPh)^+ Cl^-$	70% EtOH	0.1M in $KHCO_3$	II	37	2.7	3	—	—	—	317
$ClCH_2CH_2NHEt(CH_2CH_2 OC_6H_4NO_2\text{-}p)^+ Cl^-$	70% EtOH	0.1M in K_2CO_3	II	37	2.0	3	—	—	—	317
$ClCH_2CH_2NHEt(CH_2CH_2 OC_6H_4OMe\text{-}p)^+ Cl^-$	70% EtOH	0.1M in K_2CO_3	II	37	3.1	3	—	—	—	317
$ClCH_2CH_2NHEt(CH_2CH_2 OC_6H_4Cl\text{-}p)^+ Cl^-$	70% EtOH	0.1M in K_2CO_3	II	37	2.9	3	—	—	—	317
$ClCH_2CH_2NHEt(CH_2CH_2 CH_2Ph)^+ Cl^-$	70% EtOH	0.1M in K_2CO_3	II	37	5.8	3	—	—	—	317
$ClCH_2CH_2NHEt(CH_2 CH_2SPh)^+ Cl^-$	70% EtOH	0.1M in K_2CO_3	II	37	3.7	3	—	—	—	317
$ClCH_2CH_2NHEt(CH_2CH_2 OCH_2Ph)^+ Cl^-$	70% EtOH	0.1M in K_2CO_3	II	37	3.5	3	—	—	—	317

Table 1-II—*continued*

Amine, salt or free base	Solvent	Addend	Analytical method[a]	Temp. (°C)	k ($= 10^{-n} k^o$, sec^{-1}) k^o	n	E (kcal)	A ($= 10^n A^o$, sec^{-1}) A^o	n	References
ClCH₂CH₂NH(CH₂Ph)(CHMeCH₂OPh)⁺ Cl⁻	H₂O	Buffer	IV	25	3.6	4	—	—	—	2426
(structure)	H₂O?	KHCO₃	II + IV	37	6.8	5	—	—	—	318
(structure)	H₂O	KHCO₃	II + IV	37	2.5	4	—	—	—	318
(structure)	H₂O	KHCO₃	II + IV	37	3.4	3	—	—	—	318
(ClCH₂CH₂)₂N(CH₂CO₂H)₂⁺ Cl⁻	H₂O	Borate buffer, pH 7.36	VI	25	9.7	3	—	—	—	3869
(ClCH₂CH₂)₂NHCH₂— *(structure)*	H₂O	Borate buffer, pH 7.36	VI	25	4.0	3	—	—	—	3869

Compound	Solvent	Conditions							Ref.
ClCH₂CH₂NH₂CH(CH₂Cl)CH₂CH₂CH₂CH₂Cl⁺ Cl⁻	H₂O	Borate buffer, pH 7.36	VI	25	1.5	4	—	—	3869
(ClCH₂CH₂)₂NP(O)(O⁻)(OCH₂CH₂CH₂NH₃)⁺	H₂O	Borate buffer, pH 7.2	II	37	2.21	5	25.8	—	2985
(ClCH₂CH₂)₂NP(O)(O⁻)(OCH₂CH₂CH₂NH₃)⁺	H₂O	Borate buffer, pH 6.0	II	37	2.03	5	25.8	—	2985
ClCH₂CH₂-NH(CH(CH₂CH₂)₂O⁺ Cl⁻	H₂O	pH 7.0	II	17.5	1.42	4	—	—	2919
ClCH₂CH₂-NH(CH(CH₂CH₂)₂O⁺ Cl⁻	H₂O	pH 7.0	II	30.0	2.48	4	—	—	2919
ClCH₂CH₂-NH(CH(CH₂CH₂)₂O⁺ Cl⁻	H₂O	pH 7.0	II	45.0	7.6	4	—	—	2919
ClCH₂CH₂—N(piperazine)N—(C₆H₃(NO₂)₂)	MeCN	1,4-Diazabicyclo[2.2.2]octane	II	50.8	2.3	5	—	—	3066
ClCH₂CH₂—N(piperazine)—(cyclohexyl)—N—CH₂CH₂Cl	H₂O	pH 9	?	≈25	≈8	4	—	—	3079; cf. 2919
ClCH(CO₂H)CH₂NH₂	H₂O	0.03–0.05M in NaOH	II	35.5	1.29	−2	—	—	1553
(ClCH₂CH₂)₂NHCH₂CH₂O₂C C₆H₄NO₂-x⁺ Cl⁻	80% Me₂CO	Various R₃N	II	20	0.96	3	—	—	689
(ClCH₂CH₂)₂NHCH₂CH₂O₂C C₆H₄NO₂-x⁺ Cl⁻	80% Me₂CO	Various R₃N	II	20	1.38	3	—	—	689
(ClCH₂CH₂)₂NHCH₂CH₂O₂C C₆H₄NO₂-x⁺ Cl⁻	80% Me₂CO	Various R₃N	II	20	1.28	3	—	—	689
ClCH₂CH₂(CO₂H)NH₂	H₂O	0.03–0.05M in NaOH	II	35.5	4.28	−1	—	—	1553
ClCH(CO₂Et)CH₂NH₂	EtOH	N(CH₂CH₂OH)₃	II	25?	≈2	6	—	—	1553
BrCH₂CH₂NH₃⁺ Br⁻	H₂O	0.12M in NaOH	II	0	1.5	5	—	—	1338
BrCH₂CH₂NH₃⁺ Br⁻	H₂O	0.12M in NaOH	II	9.7	6.0	5	—	—	1338

Table 1-II—continued

Amine salt or free base	Solvent	Addend	Analytical method[a]	Temp. (°C)	k ($= 10^{-n}k°$) (sec^{-1}) $k°$	n	E (kcal)	A ($= 10^n A°$) (sec^{-1}) $A°$	n	References
BrCH$_2$CH$_2$NH$_3^+$ Br$^-$	H$_2$O	0.12M in NaOH	II	25.1	6.0	4	—	—	—	1338
BrCH$_2$CH$_2$NH$_3^+$ Br$^-$	H$_2$O	0.12M in NaOH	II	30	1.1	3	24	2	14	1338
BrCH$_2$CH$_2$NH$_3^+$ Br$^-$	H$_2$O	NaOH	II	0	0.96	5	—	—	—	620
BrCH$_2$CH$_2$NH$_3^+$ Br$^-$	MeOH	0.12M in NaOH	II	0	3	6	—	—	—	1338
BrCH$_2$CH$_2$NH$_3^+$ Br$^-$	MeOH	0.12M in NaOH	II	25	1.2	4	—	—	—	1338
BrCH$_2$CH$_2$NH$_3^+$ Br$^-$	MeOH	0.12M in NaOH	II	30	2	4	23	9	12	1338
BrCH$_2$CH$_2$NH$_3^+$ Br$^-$	MeOH	0.12M in NaOH	II	30	—	—	20.2	—	—	3095
BrCH$_2$CH$_2$NH$_3^+$ Br$^-$	H$_2$O	KClO$_4$, $\mu \approx 0.07$, + AcOH or KH$_2$PO$_4$ +NaOH	III	25	5.6	4	—	—	—	1607
BrCH$_2$CH$_2$NH$_3^+$ Br$^-$	H$_2$O	$\mu \approx 0.3$, buffer to pH 8	II	35	3.7	4	—	—	—	27
BrCH$_2$CH$_2$NH$_3^+$ Br$^-$	25% HCONMe$_2$	$\mu \approx 0.3$, buffer to pH 8	II	35	8.3	4	—	—	—	27
BrCH$_2$CH$_2$NH$_2$Me$^+$ Br$^-$	H$_2$O	$\mu \approx 0.3$, buffer to pH 8	II	35	1.4	3	—	—	—	27
BrCH$_2$CH$_2$NH$_2$Me$^+$ Br$^-$	25% HCONMe$_2$	$\mu \approx 0.3$, buffer to pH 8	II	35	3.4	3	—	—	—	27
MeCHBrCH$_2$NH$_3^+$ Br$^-$	H$_2$O	Na$_2$S$_2$O$_3$, 1 equiv. (2M)	I	36.5	1.14	5	—	—	—	2109
BrCH$_2$CH$_2$NHMe$_2^+$ Br$^-$	H$_2$O	KClO$_4$, $\mu \approx 0.07$, + AcOH or KH$_2$PO$_4$ + NaOH	III	25	1	2	—	—	—	1607

Compound	Solvent	Conditions							
BrCH$_2$CH$_2$NHMe$_2$$^+$ Br$^-$	H$_2$O	$\mu \approx 0.3$, buffer to pH 8	II	35	9.6	3	—	—	27
BrCH$_2$CH$_2$NHMe$_2$$^+$ Br$^-$	25% HCONMe$_2$	$\mu \approx 0.3$, buffer to pH 8	II	35	3.8	2	—	—	27
BrCH$_2$CH$_2$NHMe(iso-Pr)$^+$ Br$^-$	H$_2$O	KClO$_4$, $\mu \approx 0.07$, + AcOH or KH$_2$PO$_4$ + NaOH	III	25	4	1	—	—	1607
BrCH$_2$CH$_2$NH(iso-Pr)$^+$ Br$^-$	H$_2$O	KClO$_4$, $\mu \approx 0.07$, etc.	III	25	3	1	—	—	1607
MeCHBrCH$_2$NHMe$_2$$^+$ Br$^-$	H$_2$O	KClO$_4$, $\mu \approx 0.07$, etc.	III	25	8	2	—	—	1607
BrCH$_2$CH$_2$NHEt$_2$$^+$ Br$^-$	H$_2$O	KClO$_4$, $\mu \approx 0.07$, etc.	III	25	4	1	—	—	1607
BrCH$_2$CH$_2$NH$_2$Ph$^+$ Br$^-$	70% EtOH	NaOH	II	30	9.4	3	—	—	1668
PhCHBrCH$_2$NH$_3$$^+$ Br$^-$	H$_2$O	NaOH	II	≈ 25	1.7	1	—	—	1341
PhCHBrCH$_2$NH$_3$$^+$ Br$^-$	H$_2$O	NaOH	II	25	≈ 6	0	—	—	3095
BrCH$_2$CH$_2$NHCH$_2$CH$_2$Cl	H$_2$O	pH 6.2	II	37	≈ 6	0	—	—	3095
(ClCH$_2$CH$_2$)(BrCH$_2$CH$_2$)NH	H$_2$O	pH 6.0	II	37	2.5	3	26.8	—	2984
(ClCH$_2$CH$_2$)(BrCH$_2$CH$_2$)NH	H$_2$O	pH 7.2	II	37	1.28	2	26.5	—	2984
(BrCH$_2$CH$_2$)$_2$NH	H$_2$O	pH 6.0	II	37	6.46	3	28.4	—	2984
(BrCH$_2$CH$_2$)$_2$NH	H$_2$O	pH 7.2	II	37	3.90	2	28.0	—	2984
BrCH$_2$CH$_2$–[N$^+$H pyrrolidinium ring] Br$^-$	H$_2$O	KClO$_4$, $\mu \approx 0.07$, + AcOH or KH$_2$PO$_4$ + NaOH	III	25	2	2	—	—	1607
BrCH$_2$CH$_2$–[N$^+$H piperidinium ring] Br$^-$	H$_2$O	KClO$_4$, $\mu \approx 0.07$, etc.	III	25	8	2	—	—	1607

Table 1-II—*continued*

Amine salt or free base	Solvent	Addend	Analytical method[a]	Temp. (°C)	k ($= 10^{-n}k^o$), (sec^{-1}) k^o	n	E (kcal)	A ($= 10^n A^o$) (sec^{-1}) A^o	n	References
dl-BzCHBr / N—CHPh (morpholine)										
threo	EtOH	NaOH	VII	25	7	4	—	—	—	3345
erythro	EtOH	NaOH	VII	25	1.5	3	—	—	—	3345
dl-PhCHBr / N—CHBz (morpholine)										
threo	EtOH	NaOH	VII	25	3.53	3	—	—	—	3345
erythro	EtOH	NaOH	VII	25	1.26	4	—	—	—	3345
BrCH$_2$CH(NH$_3$)$^+$ 2 ClO$_4^-$ HN $\oplus$ NH	H$_2$O	$\mu \approx 0.10$, pH 10.85	III	25	4.83[b]	3	—	—	—	3670
BrCH$_2$CH(NH$_3$)$^+$ 2 ClO$_4^-$ HN $\oplus$ NH	H$_2$O	$\mu \approx 0.13$, pH 4.80	III	25	1.93–1.98[b,c]	5	—	—	—	3670
$^-$OSO$_3$CH$_2$CH$_2$NH$_3^+$	H$_2$O	0.5N in NaOH	V	75	8.0	6	—	—	—	896, 897

Compound	Solvent									Ref.
$^-OSO_3CH_2CHMeNH_3^+$	H_2O	0.5N in NaOH	V	75	5.2	5	—	—	—	896, 897
$^-OSO_3CHMeCH_2NH_3^+$	H_2O	0.5N in NaOH	V	75	1.6	5	—	—	—	896, 897
$^-OSO_3CH_2CMe_2NH_3^+$	H_2O	0.5N in NaOH	V	75	3.3	4	—	—	—	896, 897
$^-OSO_3CHMeCHMeNH_3^+$ (threo)	H_2O	0.5N in NaOH	V	75	1.07	4	—	—	—	896, 897
$^-OSO_3CHMeCHMeNH_3^+$ (erythro)	H_2O	0.5N in NaOH	V	75	1.36	4	—	—	—	896, 897
$^-OSO_3CH_2CHEtNH_3^+$	H_2O	0.5N in NaOH	V	75	7.4	5	—	—	—	896, 897
$^-OSO_3CHEtCH_2NH_3^+$	H_2O	0.5N in NaOH	V	75	1.6	5	—	—	—	897
$^-OSO_3CH_2CH(iso\text{-}Pr)NH_3^+$	H_2O	0.5N in NaOH	V	75	9.2	5	—	—	—	897
$^-OSO_3CH(iso\text{-}Pr)CH_2NH_3^+$	H_2O	0.5N in NaOH	V	75	8.3	6	—	—	—	896, 897
$^-OSO_3CH(tert\text{-}Bu)CH_2NH_3^+$	H_2O	0.5N in NaOH	V	75	5.7	7	—	—	—	897
$^-OSO_3CH_2CHPhNH_3^+$	H_2O	0.5N in NaOH	V	75	9.8	6	—	—	—	897
$^-OSO_3CHPhCH_2NH_3^+$	H_2O	0.5N in NaOH	V	75	4.8	4	—	—	—	897
$^-OSO_3CH(CH_2Ph)CH_2NH_3^+$	H_2O	0.5N in NaOH	V	75	4.0	6	—	—	—	896, 897

$$H_3\overset{+}{N}-CH \diagdown (CH_2)_n \diagup HC-OSO_3^-$$

	Solvent									Ref.
$n = 3$	H_2O	0.5N in NaOH	V	75	1.75	4	—	—	—	896, 897
$n = 4$	H_2O	0.5N in NaOH	V	75	1.9	5	—	—	—	897
$n = 5$	H_2O	0.5N in NaOH	V	75	6.8	5	—	—	—	897
$n = 6$	H_2O	0.5N in NaOH	V	75	2.2	5	—	—	—	897
$^-OSO_3CH_2CH_2NH_3^+$	H_2O	1N in NaOH	II	100	7.1	5	—	—	—	668, 4022
$^-OSO_3CH_2CH_2NH_2Me^+$	H_2O	1N in NaOH	II	100	3.7	4	—	—	—	668
$^-OSO_3CH_2CH_2NHMe_2^+$	H_2O	1N in NaOH	II	100	1.1	3	—	—	—	668
$^-OSO_3CH_2CH_2NHEt_2^+$	H_2O	1N in NaOH	II	100	5	3	—	—	—	668
$^-OSO_3CH_2CH_2^+NH(CH_2CH_2OH)_2$	H_2O	1N in NaOH	II	100	1.9	3	—	—	—	668
$^-OSO_3CH_2CH_2-\overset{+}{N}(\text{morpholine})H$	H_2O	1N in NaOH	II	100	3.9	4	—	—	—	668

Table 1-II—*continued*

Amine salt or free base	Solvent	Addend	Analytical method[a]	Temp. (°C)	k (= $10^{-n}k^o$), (sec^{-1}) k^o	n	E (kcal)	A (= $10^n A^o$), (sec^{-1}) A^o	n	References
$^-OSO_3CH_2CH_2NH(CH_2Ph)_2^+$	70% EtOH	NaHCO$_3$	IV	37	3.2	6	—	—	—	1442
$PhSO_2OCH_2CH_2NH(CH_2Ph)_2^+$ ^-O_3SPh	70% EtOH	NaHCO$_3$	IV	37	2	2	—	—	—	1442
p-CH$_3$C$_6$H$_4$SO$_2$OCH$_2$CH$_2$NH (CH$_2$Ph)$_2^+$ $^-O_3SC_6H_4$Me-p	70% EtOH	NaHCO$_3$	IV	37	1.5	2	—	—	—	1442
p-CH$_3$C$_6$H$_4$SO$_2$OCH$_2$CH$_2$NHEt (CH$_2$CH$_2$-1-C$_{10}$H$_7$)$^+$ $^-O_3SC_6H_4$Me-p	70% EtOH	NaHCO$_3$	IV	37	2	2	—	—	—	1442
2-C$_{10}$H$_7$SO$_2$OCH$_2$CH$_2$NH (CH$_2$Ph)$_2^+$ ^-O_3S-2-C$_{10}$H$_7$	70% EtOH	NaHCO$_3$	IV	37	2	2	—	—	—	1442
(EtO)$_2$P(S)OCH$_2$CH$_2$NEt$_2$	25% EtOH	None	IV	37.1	2	4	—	—	—	1375
(EtO)$_2$P(S)OCH$_2$CH$_2$NEt$_2$	25% EtOH	None	IV	37.1	2.7	7	—	—	—	1375

[a] I: determination of aziridinium ions by nuclear magnetic resonance. II: determination of X formed. III: determination of hydrogen ions formed. IV: determination of aziridinium ions with thiosulfate. V: determination of residual amine by titration with acid. VI: polarographic determination of aziridinium ions. VII: determination of aziridinium ions by ultraviolet spectrophotometry.

[b] Additional values of k at intermediate pH values are also reported (3670).

[c] These and other values of k for this system at low pH values are in fact composite rate constants for the cyclization of the imidazolium and the unprotonated form.

conceivably involve mainly metathesis first, then cyclization (Eq 3) (rather than these steps in reverse order), but this is unlikely.

The path by which N-(2-fluoroethyl)-β,β-difluoroborazane, $FCH_2CH_2NHBF_2$, is converted to EI by aqueous alkali (3712) is not clear, but in any case is of theoretical interest only. Benzoate ion is not displaced thus from 2-aminoalkyl benzoates (1442, 1606) but in the sterically favorable case of $L(+)$-2-tropanol acetate (**11**), the acetate ion and an unstable intermediate aziridinium ion are believed formed (Eq 4) (128).

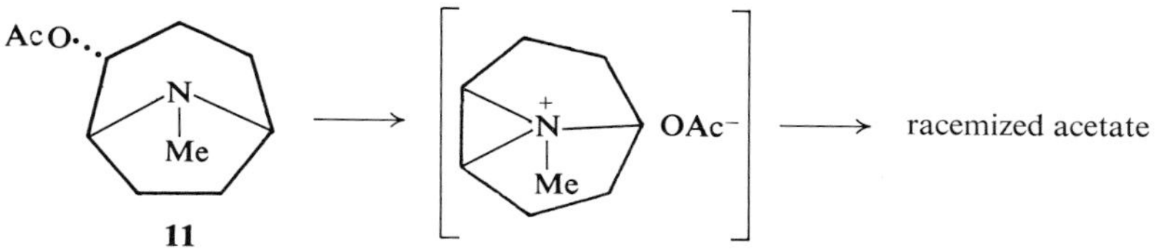

$$\text{(4)}$$

11

Perhaps formulation of the process via a more symmetrical transition state (**12**), similar to that suggested for the thermal ring expansion of 2-(chloromethyl)pyrrolidines (**13**) (476), would be preferable. The ready dimerization

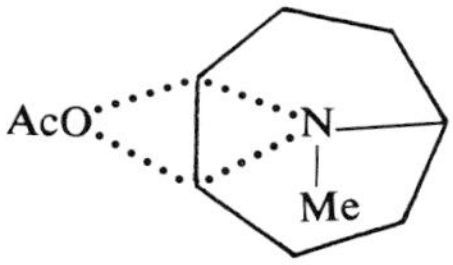

12 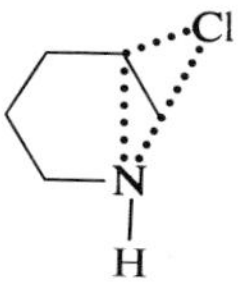   **13**

of 2-dialkylaminoalkyl perfluoroalkanoates to piperazine salts (Eq 5) indicates that the perfluorinated anion is a good leaving group (1637) and the reaction involves an aziridinium ion.

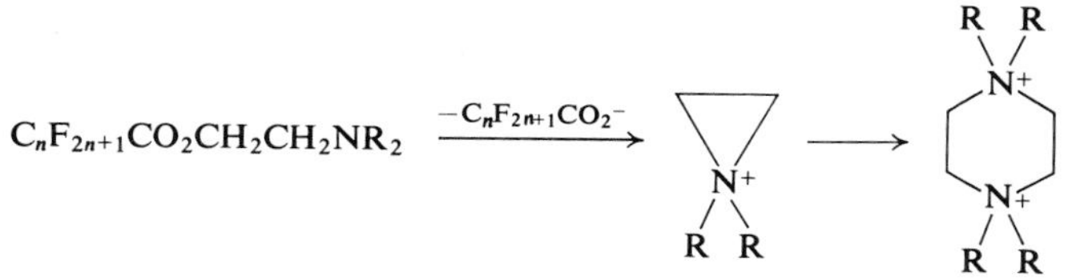

$$\text{(5)}$$

The possibility of cyclization of allylamines to aziridinium dipolar ions has been mentioned (3627) but there is at present no evidence that such a reaction as shown in Eq 6 occurs.

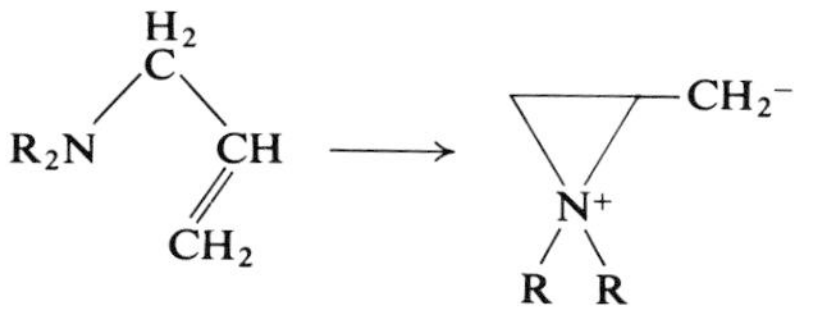

$$\text{(6)}$$

The same comment applies to the hypothetical tautomerization of α-amino ketones (Eq 7) (2813).

$$\tag{7}$$

There are two examples only of an aziridine-forming reaction in which the leaving group is trimethylamine (but compare the preparation of azirines, p. 63). The quaternary hydrazonium salts **14** when heated with alcoholic sodium methoxide gave 2-substituted aziridines as shown in Eq 8 (4071).

$$\tag{8}$$

R = Me, 35% yield
R = iso-Pr, 57% yield

Ordinarily, 2-amino alcohols cannot be dehydrated to aziridines, the reaction giving almost entirely acyclic imines and other products. Ethylenimine was suggested as an intermediate in the catalytic dehydration of 2-amino-ethanol (2271) and heterogeneous catalysts, such as silica gel, were reported to convert this alcohol mainly into EI and derived products (256); it is tempting to postulate esterification at the acid surface, displacement to give EI, and immediate polymerization at the surface. 1-Amino-1-cyclohexane-methanol over hot alumina does yield a little of the spiro aziridine **15** (202) and 2-hydrazinoethanol gives 1-aminoaziridine (1513). The mechanism of such processes is obscure.

3. The effect of pH on the rate of cyclization is easily stated. Since the amino group must be free, and not protonated, to accomplish the internal displacement the pH must be high enough to establish this condition. Buffers at pH 7–8 are often used in studies of such rates. Higher alkalinity has essentially no effect on the cyclization, but tends to stabilize the aziridine formed by deprotonating the aziridinium ion. The ring closure may be retarded by lowering the pH (345). The same effect is produced by cupric ions, which also combine with and reduce the reactivity of the amino groups; the retardation has been measured and interpreted (3671).

4. Clearly the nucleophilicity of the amino nitrogen atom is a major factor in fixing the rate of cyclization. However, there is close correspondence of base strength and rate of cyclization (proportionality of pK_a to $\log k$) only when compounds of very similar structure are compared, e.g., $EtN(CH_2CH_2Cl)_2$, $PrN(CH_2CH_2Cl)_2$, and $BuN(CH_2CH_2Cl)_2$ (726), and compounds of structure $p\text{-}XC_6H_4YCH_2CH_2NEt(CH_2CH_2Cl)$, where X and Y are various groups (317). Qualitatively the picture is better: as would be expected, rates of cyclization are in the order $Me_2NCH_2CH_2Br > MeNHCH_2CH_2Br > H_2NCH_2CH_2Br$ (27); $Me_2NCH_2CHBrMe > H_2NCH_2CHBrMe$ (643); and $Et_2NCH_2CH_2Cl > EtN(CH_2CH_2Cl)_2 > N(CH_2CH_2Cl)_3$ (280, 726). The failure of arylbis(2-chloroethyl)amines to hydrolyze via aziridinium intermediates (3067) must be due to their low basicity.

5. The rate of cyclization involved in neighboring group effects depends on ring size (573, 3397). For three-membered rings, the entropy decrease required to achieve the transition state is less than for larger ones, but the ring strain is greater and the mutual effects of the leaving group and the nucleophile are more detrimental. For two classes of compounds, the balance of these factors yields the relative rates of ring closure shown in Table 1-III.

Table 1-III

RELATIVE RATES OF RING CLOSURE OF $L(CH_2)_nNH_2$

n	L = Br (in H_2O, 25°C) (3093, 3095)	L = $^-OSO_3$ (in 0.5N NaOH, 75°C) (897)	L = $^-OSO_3$ (in 1N NaOH, 100°C) (668)
2	1.0	1.0	1.0
3	0.014	0.08	0.028
4	≈ 800	443	> 27
5	14	—	8.2
6	0.02	—	0.03

6. As for many ring closures, the reaction is facilitated by the presence of small alkyl groups on the ring-forming atoms. Some relative rates are $ClCH_2CH_2NH_2$, 0.8; $ClCH_2CHMeNH_2$, 25; $ClCH_2CMe_2NH_2$, 750 (573); $^-OSO_3CH_2CHEtNH_2$, 7.6; $^-OSO_3CH_2CHMeNH_2$, 5.2; $^-OSO_3CH_2CH_2NH_2$, 0.8 (896, 897); and $MeN(CH_2CH_2Cl)CH_2CHClMe > MeN(CH_2CH_2Cl)_2$ (2966). While some of these differences may be due to different nucleophilicities of the nitrogen atoms, most of them are attributable to steric effects (897, 1605, 1607). These are most likely the improvement of the driving force of the reaction, $-\Delta G$, by the alkyl substituent (72, 573) but the alteration of bond angles in favor of cyclization may also play a part (1605, 1607). A sufficiently bulky group, as in $^-OSO_3CH(\text{tert-}Bu)CH_2NH_3^+$, depresses the

rate of cyclization (*897*). The small but recurrent difference in rates between amines with primary and secondary leaving groups (L) [$ClCH_2CHMeNH_2$, 25; $ClCHMeCH_2NH_2$, 3 (*1341*); $ClCH_2CHMeNMe_2$, 1600; $ClCHMeCH_2NMe_2$, 163 (*1605*)] is consistent with the idea that these cyclizations are of S_N2 type (albeit intramolecular), in which primary halides react faster than secondary ones. This order is decisively reversed by the presence of the phenyl group [$ClCH_2CHPhNH_2$, 0.5; $ClCHPhCH_2NH_2$, 700 (*1344, 1387*); and $^-OSO_3CH_2CHPhNH_3{}^+$, 1.22; $^-OSO_3CHPhCH_2NH_3{}^+$, 59.2 (*897*)] and barely so by that of the carboxyl group [$ClCH_2CH(CO_2H)NH_2$, 4.28; $ClCH=(CO_2H)CH_2NH_2$, 12.9 (*1554*)] or when L is sulfate [$^-OSO_3CH_2CHMeNH_2$, 5.2; $^-OSO_3CHMeCH_2NH_2$, 1.6 (*896*)].

Equilibrium constants for processes of the type of Eq 9

$$-\underset{\underset{/\diagdown}{\overset{|}{N}}}{\overset{\overset{L}{|}}{C}}-\overset{\overset{|}{|}}{C}- \quad \rightleftharpoons \quad \underset{\underset{/\diagdown}{N^+}}{\diagup\diagdown} \quad L^- \tag{9}$$

are rarely measurable because too many other nucleophiles compete with L^- to open the ring (*1339*). Nevertheless the rate of reaction of the cyclic ion with L^- can be measured, and the equilibrium constant K calculated as the ratio of the rate constants. Thus for cyclization of $PhCHClCH_2NH_2$, $K = 16.7$ at 0°C and 4 at 24.6°C (*1341*). For $BrCH_2CH_2NH_2$, K is shifted from about 9 in aqueous solution to about 2 in presence of blood charcoal, presumably because of preferential absorption and stabilization of the bromo amine on the charcoal surface (*1343*). A similar shift was observed for $PhCHClCH_2NH_2$ (*1340, 1342*). For $MeN(CH_2CH_2Cl)_2$ in dilute aqueous solution at 37°C, K was calculated as 3.68, whence the amine was 99.86 % cyclized at equilbrium (*728*).

STEREOCHEMISTRY OF RING CLOSURE

It was early shown (*3763*) that (+)- and (−)-$PhCHClCHPhNH_2$ of m.p. 127°C give (+)- and (−)-*trans*-2,3-diphenylaziridine, and that the corresponding *dl* isomer of m.p. 59°C gives the *cis*-2,3-diphenylaziridine; but no conclusions could be drawn about the steric course of the reaction. The trans closing of the aziridine ring (which helped classify the reaction as an internal nucleophilic displacement) was firmly established (*910*) by the demonstration that pairs of Walden inversions are involved in converting *meso*-2,3-epoxybutane via *threo*-3-amino-2-butanol to *meso*-2,3-dimethylaziridine, and D(+)-2,3-epoxybutane (**16**) via the L(+) *erythro*-amino alcohol (**17**) to L(−)-2,3-dimethylaziridine (**18**).

16   **17**   **18**

This inversion during the cyclization was immediately confirmed when cyclohexenimine was obtained from *dl-trans*-2-aminocyclohexyl hydrogen sulfate but not from *dl-cis*-2-chlorocyclohexylamine, in which intramolecular displacement of the chlorine with inversion would generate only the sterically impossible *trans*-cyclohexenimine (*2813, 2820, 3456, 3463, 3817*). Still further verification came from similar preparations of *N*-methylcyclohexenimine (*2627, 3457, 3814*), cyclopentenimine (*1098*), cycloheptenimine (*3483*), cyclooctenimine (*2047*), and cyclodecenimine [from the *trans*- but not the *cis*-amino alcohol (*1101*)]. Only when the cyclododecenimines are reached are both the *cis*- and *trans*-aziridines capable of isolation (*1102*). The fact of inversion on closure of the aziridinium ring is now so well established that it is used to deduce the configuration of the parent chloro amine as trans (*2517*). When inversion is not possible because the amino group and leaving group are cis (*128*) or otherwise constrained from interaction (*1321, 2296, 3026*), the cyclization fails.

Interest in the stereochemistry of the long-known interconversion of ephedrine and pseudoephedrine has led to detailed examination of the related chloro compounds and aziridines. Piecing together the evidence shows once more that each cyclization of the chloro amine or sulfuric ester corresponding to a normal (*threo*) ephedrine or ephedrine analog proceeds with inversion to yield a cis (*erythro*) 2,3-disubstituted aziridine. This upon ring opening undergoes inversion again to give the normal (*threo*) alcohol or its derivative. Pseudoephedrine types in the same steps go via a *trans*-aziridine to pseudoephedrine (*erythro*) analogs (*1572, 2130, 2131, 2636, 2708, 3464, 3479, 3489, 3490*). Contrary to earlier belief (*1048*), the conversion of L(−)-ephedrine and D(+)-pseudoephedrine to the alkyl hydrogen sulfates occurs with retention of configuration if minimum temperatures are used (*443, 493, 1015*).

A series of papers, mostly by Cromwell and his students, has dealt with the cyclization of α,β-dibromo ketones upon treatment with primary or secondary amines (Eq 10).

RCHBrCHBrCOR′ + R″NH₂ $\longrightarrow$

R″NHCHRCHBrCOR′ $\longrightarrow$ Br⁻   (10)

usually both *cis* and *trans*

This was independently shown to proceed with a Walden inversion at the carbon atom from which the amino group displaces bromide (804). The ratios of isomers produced have been reported in a number of these papers (784, 790, 792, 793, 795, 796, 800, 802, 803, 805, 806, 2087, 2088, 3344), but of course these cis–trans ratios merely reflect the *threo–erythro* ratios in the bromo amines undergoing cyclization (795). The *threo–erythro* ratios are explained in terms of either steric factors (803, 3886) or chelation in the transition state (3344, 3346). The configurations of the stereoisomeric aziridinium salts have been verified by the NMR spectra of the isolated perchlorates (2299).

REARRANGEMENTS PROCEEDING THROUGH AZIRIDINIUM IONS

Some reactions of 2-aminoalkyl halides, especially alkylations, do not produce the products to be expected by direct replacement of the halogen. Since 1947 it has been recognized that this is well explained on the basis of intermediate cyclization. In every case of rearrangement the intermediate aziridinium ion is an unsymmetrical one, in which the ring may be opened in two ways (Eq 11) or at least in the way that gives the product not derivable by simple displacement.

$$(11)$$

Thus alkylation of diphenylacetonitrile carbanion (401, 3175–3177) with (2-chloropropyl)dimethylamine was observed to yield a mixture of isomers, and (2-chloro-1-methylethyl)dimethylamine gives the same mixture (Eq 12) (491).

$$(12)$$

Further instances of such rearrangements are shown in Table 1-IV.

The anomalous alkaline hydrolysis of 1-(2-chloroethyl)-2,2,5,5-tetramethyl-piperazine (**19**), while not involving a rearrangement, gives mostly polymers by way of an aziridinium ion (Eq 13) (*2501*).

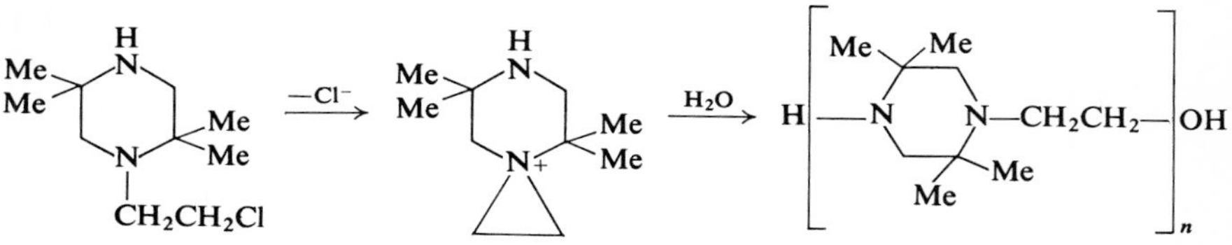

(13)

The formation of polymers from $(PhO)_2P(O)OCH_2CH_2N(CH_2CH_2OH)_2$ (*1296*) is attributable to a similar intermediate aziridinium ion. Involving the same principles, but more complex, is the set of transformations shown in Eq 14 (*1993, 2699, 2700*); some difference of opinion exists about the mechanism.

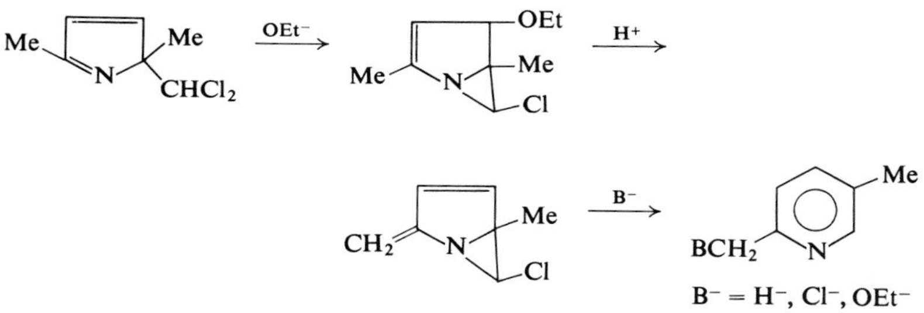

$$B^- = H^-, Cl^-, OEt^-$$

(14)

In reactions of **19A** and **19B**, which may be interconvertible, stabilized carbonium ions appear to be more probable intermediates than the bicyclic aziridinium ion **19C** (*903a, 1395a*).

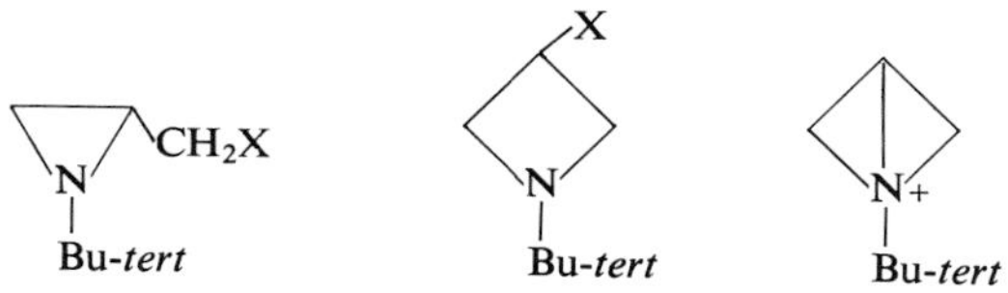

X = Cl or tosyloxy

A similar bicyclic aziridinium ion was a useful participant in the recent synthesis of a β-benzomorphan (*1359*). No comparable reaction occurs for 8-(chloromethyl)pyrrolizidine (**20**) because formation of the aziridinium ion is sterically impossible (*2296*), and no rearrangement (and hence no aziridinium intermediate) was observed upon treatment of 1-methyl-3-halo-4-phenyl-1,2,3,6-tetrahydropyridine (**21**) with base, presumably because of conformational preferences (*2374*).

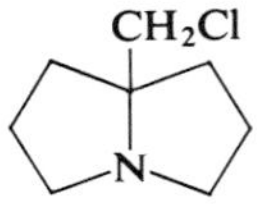

20   21

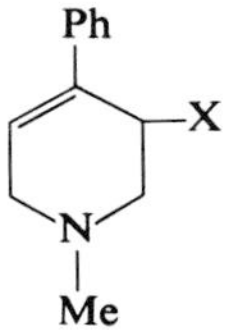

Table 1-IV

REARRANGEMENTS VIA AZIRIDINIUM IONS

Original halo amine	Nucleophile	References
ClCH$_2$CHMeNEt$_2$	Cl$^-$	*2074*
HOCH$_2$CMe$_2$NMe$_2$ + a carbodiimide	p-O$_2$NC$_6$H$_4$O$^-$	*164b*
ClCH$_2$CHMeN(CH$_2$Ph)$_2$	Cl$^-$	*2074*
ClCH$_2$CHEtN(CH$_2$Ph)$_2$	Cl$^-$	*2074*
BrCHMeCH$_2$NH$_2$	SO$_3$$^{--}$	*3074a*
ClCHMeCH$_2$NEt$_2$	H$_2$O/OH$^-$	*3065*
ClCHEtCH$_2$NEt$_2$	AlH$_4$$^{-a}$	*2683*
ClCH$_2$CHNH$_2$CO$_2$H	H$_2$O^a	*1551, 1553*
ClCH(CO$_2$H)CH$_2$NH$_2$	H$_2$O^a	*1551, 1553*
ClCHMeCH$_2$NMe$_2$	Ph$_2$CH^{-a}	*401*
ClCHMeCH$_2$NMe$_2$	3-Indolyl carbanion	*1404*
ClCHMeCH$_2$NMe$_2$	Phenothiazine anion	*646*
ClCHMeCH$_2$NHR	6-MeO-8-H$_2$N-quinoline	*757*
(R = c-C$_6$H$_{11}$ or iso-Pr)		
ClCHEtCH$_2$NHR	6-MeO-8-H$_2$N-quinoline	*757*
(R = c-C$_6$H$_{11}$ or iso-Pr)		
ClCH$_2$CHClCH$_2$NMe$_2$	RS$^-$	*2724a*
N,N-Me$_2$-1-ClCH$_2$-cyclohexylamine	Ph$_2$C(CN)$^{-a}$	*401*
N,N-Me$_2$-4-Br-cyclopent-2-enylamine	Me$_2$NH^b	*758*
(*cis* or *trans*)		
2-ClCH$_2$-1-Et-PY^c	Cl$^-$	*1379*
2-ClCH$_2$, or 2-RCO$_2$CH$_2$-1-Me-PY^c	Cl$^-$	*460a*
1-ClCHMeCH$_2$-PP^d	Ph$_2$C(CN)$^{-a}$	*401*
3-Cl-1-Me- or -1-Et-PP^d	NH$_3$ or amines	*3024a*
3-Cl-1-Me-PP^d	N$_2$H$_4$, Me$_2$N(CH$_2$)$_3$NH$_2$	*369*
2-BCH$_2$-1-R-PY^c[L(−)]^e	B$^-$(?)^a	*1601*
3-B-1-R-PP^d[D(+)]^e	B$^-$(?)^a	*1601*
1-Et-2-HOCH$_2$-PY^{c,f}	RCO$_2$$^-$	*3288*

Table 1-IV—*continued*

Original halo amine	Nucleophile	References
3-X-1-R-PP[d]	X[−a]	1601
3-Cl-1-Me-PP[d]	HO[−], PhCH$_2$O[−], NC[−]	460a
3-Cl-1-Et-PP[d]	EtO[−a]	2834
3-Cl-1-Et-PP[d]	NC[−]	2834
2-ClCH$_2$-1-Me-PY[c]	RCO$_2$[−a]	460a, 2834
3-Cl-1-Me-PP[d]	RCO$_2$[−a]	460a, 2834
3-Cl-1-Et-PP[d]	AcO[−a]	3288
3-Cl-1-Et-PP[d]	PhCH(CN)[−a]	2852
3-Cl-1-Me-PP[d]	Ph$_2$C(CN)[−a]	368
1-Et-3-tosyl-O-PP[d, g]	H$_2$O	3288
4-(BzOCH$_2$CHICH$_2$)-morpholine	BzO[−]	1287
1-ClCMe$_2$CH$_2$-2,2,4-Me$_3$-piperazine	H$_2$O/HO[−a]	2500
3,7-Cl$_2$-1,5-(p-MeC$_6$H$_4$SO$_2$)$_2$-1,5-diazocine	Cl[−]	2808
(EtO)$_2$P(S)OCH$_2$CH$_2$NR$_2$	—	1375, 3484
Mesylate of a *vic*-amino alcohol derived from thebaine	AlH$_4$[−]	2586

[a] Unrearranged amine also found.
[b] Allylic rearrangement involved.
[c] PY = pyrrolidine.
[d] PP = piperidine.
[e] B is undefined; R is alkyl.
[f] No halide involved; ester exchange gave 1-Et-3-HO-PP.
[g] No halide involved; product was 1-Et-2-HOCH$_2$-PY.

Pyrolysis of the hydrochlorides of sterically crowded amines and hydrolysis of the reaction products yield a mixture of allylamines, ketones, and saturated amines in varying proportions (Eq 15). An aziridinium ion (**22**) is probably intermediate (*1695*).

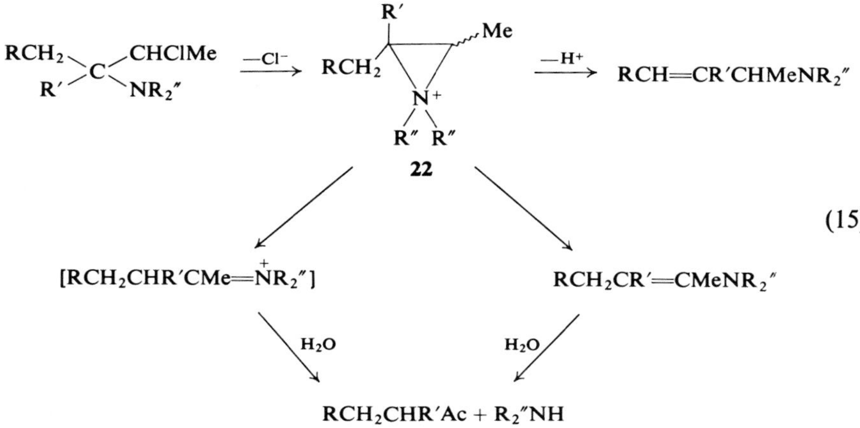

$$RCH_2\text{–}C(R')\text{–}CHClMe(NR_2'') \xrightarrow{-Cl^-} \underset{\substack{| \\ N^+ \\ R'' \; R''}}{RCH_2 \triangle (R', Me)} \xrightarrow{-H^+} RCH=CR'CHMeNR_2''$$

22

$$[RCH_2CHR'CMe{=}\overset{+}{N}R_2''] \qquad\qquad RCH_2CR'{=}CMeNR_2''$$

$$\xrightarrow{H_2O} \qquad\qquad \xleftarrow{H_2O}$$

$$RCH_2CHR'Ac + R_2''NH$$

(15)

PREPARATIVE METHODS

By far the commonest type of organic intermediates for the preparation of aziridines are the vicinal amino alcohols. These in turn are usually prepared by the well-known addition of ammonia or primary or secondary amines to epoxides (Eq 16) (*3063*).

$$
\triangle\!\!\!\!\triangle_{O} + H\!-\!N\!\!\!< \quad \longrightarrow \quad \underset{\substack{| \\ OH}}{-C}\!-\!\underset{\substack{| \\ N \\ \diagdown}}{C}- \tag{16}
$$

Alternative routes to the amino alcohols are the reduction of esters of α-amino acids with lithium aluminum hydride (*447, 2576, 3471, 3632*) and the hydrolysis of oxazolines (*1430*). Conversion of a protonated amino alcohol to a corresponding protonated halo amine is also a familiar operation in synthesis. Thionyl chloride is the most used for the conversion, but occasionally recourse is had to phosphorus pentachloride; direct esterification with hydrogen chloride or hydrogen bromide is feasible but requires forcing conditions (Eq 17).

$$
\underset{\substack{| \\ OH}}{-C}\!-\!\underset{\substack{| \\ N \\ \diagup\diagdown}}{C}- \quad \xrightarrow{\text{SOCl}_2,\ \text{PCl}_5,\ \text{HX}} \quad \underset{\substack{| \\ X}}{-C}\!-\!\underset{\substack{| \\ N \\ \diagup\diagdown}}{C}-, \text{ etc.} \tag{17}
$$

Handling of the 2-chloroethylammonium chloride thus formed is facilitated by using chlorobenzene as a diluent, etc. (*1180*). Amino alcohols of the type $R_2C(OH)CH_2NH_2$ can be converted to the desired chlorides $R_2CClCH_2NH_2$ only with great difficulty if at all (*724, 2101, 2519*); the reaction also fails for 3α-amino-2β-cholestanol (*1622*) and for 2-hydrazinoethanol (*1085*).

It was pointed out by Wenker (*3769*) that conversion of 2-aminoethanol to 2-aminoethyl hydrogen sulfate offers some advantage in preparing EI. The esterification step is very simple, requiring only heating an equimolar mixture of the amino alcohol and concentrated sulfuric acid to about 250°C. Moreover, since the ester is nonvolatile, unlike the halo amine, there is no danger of distilling unreacted starting material along with the EI and exposing the latter to the considerable hazard of polymerization catalyzed by the halo amine. Hence the method has been used frequently. An important improvement was effecting the esterification–dehydration under reduced pressure to minimize charring (*492, 1484, 2255, 2290, 3422, 4022*); other variations in this step are also claimed (*214, 237, 1308, 1313, 2890, 3052, 3229*) and even sulfur trioxide (*321a, 1432*) also has some advantages.

The Wenker esterification step, like conversion to a halo amine, usually fails when the alcohol is tertiary, dehydration to an olefinic compound (sometimes an enamine) then taking precedence (*12, 2170*); but 2-amino-1-methylcyclo-hexanol did give some of an aziridine along with the unsaturated amine (*3814*). 3α-Amino-2β-cholestanol, a secondary alcohol, was not esterified by sulfuric acid (*1622*), and 2-amino-2-methyl-1-tridecanol was merely charred (*2883*). Failure of the method applied to 2-anilinoethanol was attributed to sulfona-tion of the ring instead of esterification of the alcohol function (*1377*), but later work met no such difficulty (*492*).

A quite different synthesis of 2-aminoalkyl hydrogen sulfates involves the Ritter reaction; an allylic halide such as methallyl chloride treated with hydrogen cyanide or acetonitrile and concentrated sulfuric acid, then with water, yields a 2-aminopropyl ester such as $^-OSO_3CH_2CMe_2NH_3{}^+$ (*1430*). The process may be formulated, somewhat speculatively, as in Eq 18.

$$CH_2{=}CMeCH_2Cl \xrightarrow{-Cl^-} CH_2{=}CMeCH_2{}^+ \xrightarrow{H_2SO_4} CH_2{=}CMeCH_2OSO_3H$$

$$\Big\downarrow H^+ \qquad (18)$$

$$^+H_3NCMe_2CH_2OSO_3{}^- \xleftarrow{H_2O} HC{\equiv}\overset{+}{N}CMe_2CH_2OSO_3H \xleftarrow{HCN} Me_2\overset{+}{C}CH_2OSO_3H$$
$$+ HCO_2H$$

To return to the preparation of vicinal halo amines: most of the routes not yet discussed depend in principle upon addition to an olefinic bond at one stage. Thus the product of addition of bromine to ethylene, 1,2-dibromo-ethane, can be caused to react in excess with a primary (or secondary) aromatic amine to yield the "one-ended" displacement product, $ArNHCH_2CH_2Br$ (*461, 462*); some advantage is claimed in having the halogen atoms dissimilar, and a tertiary amine present to serve as acid acceptor (*1290*). Although no intermediate is claimed or isolated, this one-ended displacement must operate in the recent process (*119, 731, 921, 2561*) for producing aziridines from vicinal dihalides or alkylene sulfates or disulfonates and ammonia or primary amines (Eq 19). The acid acceptor may be either calcium hydroxide, excess nitro-genous base, or an ion-exchange resin (*3563a*). The process is improved by

$$XCH_2CH_2X \xrightarrow{NH_3} XCH_2CH_2NH_3{}^+ \xrightarrow{base} XCH_2CH_2NH_2$$

$$(19)$$

$$AzH \xleftarrow{base} \underset{H \quad H}{\overset{\diagup}{N}{}^+ \diagdown} \; X^-$$

operation at high pressures (*119*). A more laborious path is the one-ended reaction of a 1,2-dihaloethane in the Gabriel synthesis using phthalimide, then hydrolysis to the halo amine (*3353*). It has been suggested that one of the unidentified products of reaction of 1,2-dibromoethane and hydrazine is 1-aminoaziridine, isolated as the benzal derivative (*3391*), but no indication of formation of that aziridine from 1,2-dichloroethane in ethanol could be obtained (*1084*). It *has* been obtained by the Wenker method (*202, 1513, 1765*), as has 1-amino-2-phenylaziridine in 60–70% yield from the dimesyl ester of 1-phenyl-1,2-ethanediol and hydrazine (*1284c*).

An old observation that dibromides of 2-bromoanethole and 2,*x*-dibromo-anethole with excess aniline yield products that probably have the aziridine structure is also to be cited (*1676*), but should be confirmed. Less acceptable are the aziridine structures attributed to the products of reaction of potassium anilide with the dibromides of oleic and ricinoleic acids (*1757a*), which are not classified as aziridines in Beilstein and need reinvestigation.

The reaction of dibromides derived from α,β-unsaturated ketones (**23**) with ammonia and primary and secondary amines has already been mentioned (p. 27); secondary amines can of course yield only quaternary aziridinium compounds. While the process was at first formulated as yielding piperazine dimers (*3784*) or enamines (*46, 2622, 3073*), the assignment of aziridine structures to the products (*786*) has been amply confirmed. However, the reaction proceeds not by displacement, but by elimination to give the α-bromo-α,β-unsaturated ketone (**24**). Michael addition of a molecule of the nitrogenous base then yields the α-amino-β-bromo ketone (**25**), which cyclizes. The similar

reaction of dibromides of α,β-unsaturated acids and their derivatives takes the same course (*1364*). The nature of the amine can be influential: 2,3-dibromopropionitrile with most primary amines yields aziridines but benzyl-amine produces enamines also (*1553*), and aziridine-2-carbonitrile could not be isolated as a product (*1552*). In **23**, when R is aroyl and R′ is aryl, the product of reaction with ammonia is more often an enamine than an aziridine (*2360*). The concurrent reaction of iodine and amines with α,β-unsaturated ketones is a convenient route to substituted aziridines (*795, 802, 806, 2799, 3343*), but it involves addition of an iodine–amine complex to the olefinic bond and then elimination, and not the formation of a diiodide (*3343*).

Dibromides from allylic amines present difficulties in this reaction, because aziridine ring closure must yield a 2-(α-bromoalkyl)aziridine, in which the bromine function will tend to quaternize and activate the ring (intermolecularly) toward polymerization. 2,3-Dibromo-1-methylpropylamine thus gave a rapidly polymerizing aziridine (*3702*), and 2,3-dibromopropylamine has been found not to yield an aziridine at all by reaction with ammonia (*3071*) or aqueous sodium hydroxide (*1449*).

The well-known addition of hypochlorous acid to olefins for chlorohydrin preparation suggests an analogous preparation of chloro amines. Passing nitrogen-diluted chlorine into liquid ammonia containing styrene causes only oxidation of the ammonia, and no involvement of the olefin (*963*). However, the preparation of 2-chloroalkylamines by addition of *N*-chloro amines to olefins is well authenticated (*2564–2566, 2680–2684*). The process is believed to involve aminium radicals (*2683*) in which each of the nitrogen atoms bears either a proton or a transition metal chloride; a chain reaction may prevail (Eq 20).

$$R_2\overset{\bullet}{N}H^+ + \hspace{1em} \begin{matrix} \diagdown \\ \diagup \end{matrix}C\!\!=\!\!C\begin{matrix} \diagup \\ \diagdown \end{matrix} \hspace{1em} \longrightarrow \hspace{1em} R_2\overset{+}{N}H\!-\!\overset{|}{\underset{|}{C}}\!-\!\overset{|}{\underset{|}{C}}\!\cdot$$

$$R_2\overset{+}{N}H\!-\!\overset{|}{\underset{|}{C}}\!-\!\overset{|}{\underset{|}{C}}\!\cdot + R_2\overset{+}{N}H\!-\!Cl \hspace{1em} \longrightarrow \hspace{1em} R_2\overset{+}{N}H\!-\!\overset{|}{\underset{|}{C}}\!-\!\overset{|}{\underset{|}{C}}\!-\!Cl + R_2\overset{+}{N}H^+ \tag{20}$$

In a different reaction, *N*-bromo secondary amines have been shown to add to α,β-unsaturated ketones and thus lead to aziridinium ions (*3342, 3344, 3346*). The addition of nitrogen trichloride to olefins succeeds and the hydrolysis of the resultant β,*N*,*N*-trichloro amines yields β-chloro amines (*735*), but this is not an attractive route to these intermediates.

The addition of iodine isocyanate, INCO, to olefins stereospecifically yields 2-iodoalkyl isocyanates (**26**) hydrolyzable to 2-iodoalkylamines, which may spontaneously cyclize to aziridines (Eq 21) (*984, 1622, 1623*); the reaction is useful in laboratory application to complex olefins, such as unsaturated steroids.

$$INCO + \hspace{1em} \begin{matrix} \diagdown \\ \diagup \end{matrix}C\!\!=\!\!C\begin{matrix} \diagup \\ \diagdown \end{matrix} \hspace{1em} \longrightarrow \hspace{1em} \overset{NCO}{\underset{I}{-\!\overset{|}{\underset{|}{C}}\!-\!\overset{|}{\underset{|}{C}}\!-}} \hspace{1em} \overset{H_2O}{\longrightarrow} \hspace{1em} \overset{NH_2}{\underset{I}{-\!\overset{|}{\underset{|}{C}}\!-\!\overset{|}{\underset{|}{C}}\!-}} \tag{21}$$

$$\mathbf{26}$$

A somewhat similar route involves reducing a vicinal chloronitrosoalkane, $\begin{matrix} \diagup \\ \diagdown \end{matrix}CClC(NO)\begin{matrix} \diagdown \\ \diagup \end{matrix}$, to the vicinal chloro amine; stannous chloride is preferred as the reducing agent (*1006, 2517, 3703*). Whereas highly substituted aziridines are probably best made by this route, simple ones cannot be so made. Just the reverse situation sometimes prevails for the amino alcohol route to aziridines. Another predictable reduction, this one of α-chloro nitriles with lithium aluminum hydride, produces chloro amines cyclizable to aziridines. The following aziridines have been so prepared in the yields shown: 2-Pr, 82%; 2-iso-Pr, 72%; 2-n-C$_6$H$_{13}$, 62%; 2-Ph, 46%; and 2-PhCH$_2$, 58% (*1883*); **27**, 89%, and **28**, 86% (*2175*). For the preparation of 2-fluoroethylamines from fluoroacetamides (*2811*) or 2-iodoalkylamines from 2-azidoalkyl iodides (*1310, 1626*), reduction with diborane is particularly recommended.

27   28   29

A different reduction—that of a 2-azidoalkyl methanesulfonate (**30**), with hydrazine and Raney nickel—forms an amino ester that immediately undergoes ring closure by expulsion of the mesylate ion (Eq 22).

$$\qquad\qquad (22)$$

The reaction was used first for sugars and then for steroids (*1561, 2908*). Lithium aluminum hydride can also serve similarly as the reducing agent (*2907*), and 2-azido-3-cycloocten-1-yl iodide as the substrate for reduction and cyclization (*1310*).

Some failures of the conversion of vicinal haloalkyl amines may be noted. 2-Anilino-1-chloro-1,1,2-triphenylethane could not be made to yield an aziridine (*3506*), nor could triphenylmethylamine and methyl 2,3-dibromopropionate (*3310*); steric factors are surely implicated. A failure to obtain 1-phenylaziridine from *N*-(2-bromoethyl)aniline (*1378*) is unaccountable since the preparation in fact succeeds very well (see Table I-V). 1-Anilino-2-chloro-*N*-phenylsuccinimide (**29**) yields only the enamine and not the aziridine (*162*), probably because elimination in this case is faster than displacement by the weakly basic anilino nitrogen atom. Somewhat similarly, 1-(aminomethyl)-cycloheptyl hydrogen sulfate gives only 1-(aminomethyl)cycloheptene (*4064*). *N*-(2-Bromoethyl)-1,5-pentanediamine has been reported (*463*) to be dehydrobrominated to the *N*-vinyl diamine (Eq 23), but the product may in fact have been 1-(5-aminopentyl)aziridine (**31**) (*2002*).

Table 1-V

Aziridine made, or substituents therein	Method[a]	% Yield[b]	References
Aziridines Containing No Functional Groups			
No substituents	I	—	*57, 325, 464, 1182, 1385, 1391, 1392, 2091, 2117, 2125, 2440, 4034*
	I	>70–75	*325*
	I	>62	*1480*
	I	51.7	*2440*
	I	62	*470*
	I	up to 85	*1199*
	I	71.6	*1180*
	II	26.5	*3769*
	II	≈ 70–80	*3651*
	II	—	*525,1011,1083, 1430, 1742, 2177, 2254, 3052,3546*
	II	30–32	*1996, 1997*
	II	up to 85	*1199*
	II	70–76	*3841*
	II	34–37	*61*
	II	83	*3007*
	II	81–83	*1252, 2090*
	II	80–84	*1501*
	II	50–91	*1308*
	II	77	*176*
	III	—	*921*
1-Me	I	—	*2117, 2428*
	II	—	*1742, 3185*
	II	47	*3500*
	II	40	*3044*
	II	26	*333*
2-Me	I	—	*406,1383,1388, 1723, 3302*
	I	80	*3128*
	I	19	*2576*
	II	65	*1996, 1997*
	II	60–63	*321a, 447, 2576*
	II	—	*525*
	II	50	*4022*

Table 1-V—*continued*

Aziridine made, or substituents therein	Method[a]	% Yield[b]	Reference
Aziridines Containing No Functional Groups—continued			
1-Et	I	7	2269
	I	35	885
	II	—	525
	II	≈ 70	1043
	II	34	333
	II	55	2793
	—[c]	—	2662
2-Et	II	46	1997
	II	50	1466
	II	—	525, 3651
	II	68	2793
	II	65	270
	II	55–89	3629
1,2-Me$_2$	I	20	2576
1,2-Me$_2$	II	30–35	2576
2,2-Me$_2$	II	—	518, 525, 560, 1431, 1432, 2043
	II	68	1997
	II	45–51	565
2,3-Me$_2$	I	—	3166
	II	47	1997
	II	48–95	910, 1466
	II	82	333
	II	—	288
2-CH$_2$=CH	II	49	3389
1-iso-Pr	II	40–43	469
	II	34	2883
2-Et-1-Me	II	38	2883
1,2,2-Me$_3$	II	—	1976b, 2337
1,2,3-Me$_3$	II	—	1680
2,2,3-Me$_3$	II	19	1997
	II	45	333
	II	65	270
	II	> 50	443
1-iso-Pr-2-CH$_2$=	I, III	—	963
1-Bu	II	≈ 70–80	3651
	II	74	1043
	II	54	3796
1-*sec*-Bu	I	72	470
	II	35–40	469, 470
1-*tert*-Bu	II	27	453
2-iso-Bu	II	45	3471, 3631, 3632

Table 1-V—*continued*

Aziridine made, or substituents therein	Method[a]	% Yield[b]	References
Aziridines Containing No Functional Groups—continued			
1,2-Et$_2$	II	60	*1466*
2-Me-2-Pr	II	47	*2883*
2-iso-Pr-2-Me	II	39	*2883*
1-Et-2,3-Me$_2$	II	—	*1680*
	II	72–73	*1466*
	II	> 50	*443*
2,2,3,3-Me$_4$	I	79	*724*
2,3-(CH$_2$=CH)$_2$ (*trans*)	II	28.6	*3389*
1-(PrCHMe)	II	33–39	*469*
2-Bu-2-Me	II	53	*2883*
2(*S*)-iso-Bu-1-Me	II	40	*3631*
2-iso-Bu-2-Me	II	31	*2883*
1-iso-Pr-2,3-Me$_2$	II	—	*446, 1680*
	II	> 50	*443*
1-Et-2,2,3-Me$_3$	I	69	*1694*
1-Ethyl-2(*S*)-iso-Bu	II	48	*3631*
2,2-Me$_2$-3-Pr	II	57	*1997*
3-Et-2,2,3-Me$_3$	I	71	*724*
2,2,3-Me$_3$-3-Pr	I	84	*724*
1-Bu-2-Et	II	70	*1043*
1-Bu-2,2-Me$_2$	II	80	*1043*
1-*tert*-Bu-2,3-Me$_2$	II	> 50	*443*
1-iso-Pr-2,2,3-Me$_3$	I	73	*1694*
1-*c*-C$_6$H$_{11}$	II	32	*453*
1-Et-2,3-(CH$_2$=CH)$_2$ (*trans*)	II	≈ 21	*3388*
2-*n*-C$_6$H$_{13}$-2-Me	II	51	*2883*
1-*tert*-Bu-2,2,3-Me$_3$	I	69	*1694*
2-Et-1-iso-Pr-2,3-Me$_2$	I	73	*1694*
1-*tert*-C$_8$H$_{17}$	II	41	*435*
2-Me-1-*tert*-C$_8$H$_{17}$	II	76	*435*
1-Ph	I	≈ 40	*80*
	I	68	*1658*
	I	85	*1668*
	I	61	*1290*
	I	60	*453*
	I	—	*2745*
	I	56	*4018*
	II	High	*3651*
	II	81	*492*
2-Ph	I	—	*1387, 3824*
	I	66	*3889*
	I	80	*2564*
	II	90	*492*
1-*o*-MeC$_6$H$_4$	I	57	*1661*

Table 1-V—*continued*

Aziridine made, or substituents therein	Method[a]	% Yield[b]	References
Aziridines Containing No Functional Groups—continued			
1-*m*-MeC$_6$H$_4$	I	71	*1661*
1-*p*-MeC$_6$H$_4$	I	65	*1661*
1-*o*-ClC$_6$H$_4$	I	52	*1661*
1-*m*-ClC$_6$H$_4$	I	62	*1661*
1-*m*-FC$_6$H$_4$	I	59.5	*558*
1-*p*-FC$_6$H$_4$	I	57.5	*558*
1-PhCH$_2$	I	—	*1389*
	I	24	*1550*
	II	65	*453*
2-PhCH$_2$	II	76	*2046*
1-Me-2-Ph	II	32	*3765*
2-Me-1-Ph	I	—	*1290*
2-Me-2-Ph	I	—	*2564*
3-Me-2-Ph	I	—	*2130*
	II	84	*492*
1-PhCH$_2$-2-Me	I	—	*3390*
2-PhCH$_2$-3-Me	II	60	*3601*
1-Et-2-Ph	II	32	*3765*
2-Et-2-Ph	I	Poor	*568*
3-Et-2-Ph	II	88	*492*
1-PhCH$_2$CH$_2$	II	28	*3765*
1,3-Me$_2$-2-Ph	I	—	*2636, 2637 2708, 3464, 3479, 3489*
	II	—	*493, 1015, 1572*
2,2-Me$_2$-3-Ph	II	83	*492*
1-iso-Pr-2-Ph	II	52	*3765*
1-PhCH$_2$-2-(*S*)-iso-Bu	II	46	*3631*
1-(*p*-PhC$_6$H$_4$)	I	93	*302*
2,3-Ph$_2$	I	—	*853, 3762*
	I	80–96	*3763*
2,3-(*p*-ClC$_6$H$_4$)$_2$	I	—	*1630*
1,2-Ph$_2$-3-Me	I	—	*903*
2,3-Ph$_2$-1-Me	I	—	*3490*
2,2-Ph$_2$-3-Me	I	Low	*566*
3,3-Me$_2$-2,2-Ph$_2$	II	Low	*2101*
1-PhCH$_2$CH$_2$-2-Ph	II	34	*3765*
1,2,3-Ph$_3$	II	—	*3506*
1-(1-C$_{10}$H$_7$)	II	75	*3770*
1-iso-Pr-2-(2-C$_{10}$H$_7$)	I	—	*1773*
1-iso-Pr-2-(1-C$_{10}$H$_7$OCH$_2$)	I	—	*1773*
1,2-[(CH$_2$)$_3$]	I	20–25	*552*
	II	Trace to 40[d]	*1419*
2,3-[(CH$_2$)$_3$]	II	61–75	*1098, 1104*

Table 1-V—*continued*

Aziridine made, or substituents therein	Method[a]	% Yield[b]	Reference
Aziridines Containing No Functional Groups—continued			
2,3-Me$_2$-2,3-[(CH$_2$)$_3$]	I	73	724
1,2-[(CH$_2$)$_4$]	II	—	3458, 3854
2,2-[(CH$_2$)$_4$]	—[e]	—	202
2,2-[(CH$_2$)$_4$]	II	66	3482
	II	63	2883
2,3-[(CH$_2$)$_4$]	I	—	3456
	II	—	1435, 3463, 3814
	II	82.5	3151a
	II	28	2820
	II	70	3456
1-Me-2,3-[(CH$_2$)$_4$]	II	—	2627, 3457, 3814
	II	77.5	3151
2,3-(CH$_2$CHMeCH$_2$CH$_2$)	II	—	1436, 3151
2-Me-2,3-[(CH$_2$)$_4$]	II	—	3814
1-Et-2,3-[(CH$_2$)$_4$]	II	—	2131
2,3-Me$_2$-2,3-[(CH$_2$)$_4$]	I	76	724
1-Pr-2,3-[(CH$_2$)$_4$]	II	63.5	3151
1-C$_6$H$_{11}$-2,3-[(CH$_2$)$_4$]	II	73	3151
1-C$_8$H$_{17}$-2,3-[(CH$_2$)$_4$]	II	65	3151
1-Ph-2,3-[(CH$_2$)$_4$]	II	—	1685, 3151
1-PhCH$_2$-2,3-[(CH$_2$)$_4$]	II	72	3151
2,2-[(CH$_2$)$_5$]	II	57	1099
	II	68	2883
2,3-[(CH$_2$)$_5$]	II	78	3483
1-iso-Pr-2,2-[(CH$_2$)$_5$]-3-Me	I	59	1694
1-tert-Bu-2,2-[(CH$_2$)$_5$]-3-Me	I	56	1694
2,3-[(CH$_2$)$_6$]	II	33	2047
2,3-[(CH$_2$)$_8$]	II	13	1101
2,3-[(CH$_2$)$_{10}$]	II	30–50	1102
2,3-(CH=CHCH$_2$CH$_2$CH$_2$CH$_2$)	—[f]	—	1310
1-(7-Cl-4-quinolyl)	II	38	2837
1-(6-Cl-2-MeO-9-acridinyl)	II	15	2837
1-Adamantyl	II	—	991, 994
2,3-Epimino-1,2,3,4-H$_4$-naphthalene	I	—	984
1,2; 3,4-Diepimino-1,2,3,4-H$_4$-naphthalene (*trans*)	I	—	1021
4a,8a-Epimino-1,4,4a,5,8,8a-H$_6$-naphthalene	I	—	3703
4a,8a-Epimino-H$_{10}$-naphthalene	I	78	2517
2,3-Epimino-7,7-Me$_2$-norbornane[g]	I	42	1006
27 (see p. 36)	I	89	2175
28 (see p. 36)	I	86	2175
9,10-Epimino-1,5-cyclododecadiene	I	—	1623

Table 1-V—*continued*

Aziridine made, or substituents therein	Method[a]	% Yield[b]	References
Aziridines Containing No Functional Groups—continued			
5,6-Epiminodibenzo[*a,c*]cycloheptane	I	—	*3240*
2,3-Epiminosqualene	—[h]	—	*759*
2α, 3α-Epiminocholestane	—[i]	≈ 100	*2907*
2β, 3β-Epiminocholestane	I	75	*1622*
2β, 3β-Epiminocholestane	I	≈ 70	*2906*
2β, 3β-Epiminocholestane	—[i]	≈ 100	*2907*
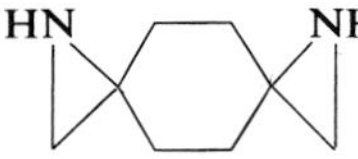	II	46	*2883*
Aziridinyl Ketones			
2-Bz-1-Me	III	30	*1905*
2-Bz-1,3-Me$_2$	III	68	*1905*
2-Ac-1-Me-3-Ph	III	36	*1905*
2-Bz-3-Ph	III	—	*46, 789, 2622, 3073*
	III	57	*3343*
2-Bz-1-*c*-C$_6$H$_{11}$	III	80	*796*
2-Bz-1-*c*-C$_6$H$_{11}$-3-Me	III	—	*3184*
2-Bz-1-Me-3-Ph	III	57	*1905*
	III	26	*798*
3-Ph-2-(*p*-MeC$_6$H$_4$CO)	III	61	*796*
2-Bz-3-(*p*-O$_2$NC$_6$H$_4$)	III	—	*3784*
	III	78	*801*
2-(*p*-O$_2$NC$_6$H$_4$CO)-3-Ph	III	—	*4075*
1,3-Me$_2$-2-(*p*-PhC$_6$H$_4$CO)	III	84.6	*795*
2,3-Bz$_2$-1-Me	III	43	*2360*
	III	50	*3638*
1-Me-3-Ph-2-(*p*-MeC$_6$H$_4$CO)	III	40	*796*
	III	High	*803*
2,3-Bz$_2$-1-Et	III	—	*2360*
1-*c*-C$_6$H$_{11}$-2-(*p*-PhC$_6$H$_4$CO)	III	80	*796*
2-Bz-1-*c*-C$_6$H$_{11}$-3-Ph	III	—	*789*
	III	78	*796*
	III	46	*3343*
	III	50–54	*788*
	III	—	*2799*
	III	97–100	*3344*
2-Bz-1-*c*-C$_6$H$_{11}$-3-(*p*-MeOC$_6$H$_4$)	III	—	*802*
2-Bz-1-*c*-C$_6$H$_{11}$-3-(*p*-O$_2$NC$_6$H$_4$)	III	89	*800*
2-Bz-1-*c*-C$_6$H$_{11}$-3-(*p*-O$_2$NC$_6$H$_4$)	III	60–90	*3344*
2-Ac-3-(*p*-PhC$_6$H$_2$)-1-*c*-C$_6$H$_{11}$	III	≈ 68	*805*
1-*c*-C$_6$H$_{11}$-2,3-Bz$_2$	III	65	*3638*

Table 1-V—*continued*

Aziridine made, or substituents therein	Method[a]	% Yield[b]	References
Aziridines Containing No Functional Groups—continued			
2-Bz-1-PhCH$_2$-3-Ph	III	—	789
	III	35	796
	III	73	3343
	III	52	788
	III	46	793
2-Bz-1-PhCH$_2$-3-(m-O$_2$NC$_6$H$_4$)	III	20	785
1-c-C$_6$H$_{11}$-3-Me-2-(p-PhC$_6$H$_4$CO)	III	92	806
1-c-C$_6$H$_{11}$-3-Ph-2-(p-MeC$_6$H$_4$CO)	III	77	796
2,3-Bz$_2$-1-Ph	III	31	2360
1-Me-3-Ph-2-(p-PhC$_6$H$_2$CO)	III	74	795
	III	92	803
1-PhCH$_2$-2,3-Bz$_2$	III	71	3638
1-PhCH$_2$-3-Ph-2-(p-MeC$_6$H$_4$CO)	III	74	796
	III	20	785
1-c-C$_6$H$_{11}$-3-Ph-2-(p-PhC$_6$H$_4$CO)	III	91	790
	III	94	795
2-(p-BrC$_6$H$_4$CO)-1-c-C$_6$H$_{11}$-3-Ph	III	89	2898
8,9-(N-Cyclohexylepimino)perinaphthan- 7-one	III	—	4031
Aziridines Containing Other Functional Groups			
1-H$_2$N	II	35	202, 1513, 1765
2-H$_2$NCH$_2$	II	42.7	3354
1-H$_2$NCH$_2$CH$_2$	II	16	1996
2-H$_2$NCH$_2$-2-Me	II	29	3354
1-R-2-Ph-2,3-(o-C$_6$H$_4$C-) $\parallel$ NR (R = Me or c-C$_6$H$_{11}$)	III	—	4116
1-(2-ClCH$_2$CH$_2$)	I	—	161b, 2987a
2-ClCH$_2$-3-Me (or 2-MeCHCl?)	—^{j}	—	891
2-BrCH$_2$-3-Me	I	—	3702
1-p-(4-H$_2$NC$_6$H$_4$SO$_2$C$_6$H$_4$)	I	$\approx$ 80	1942
2-MeO$_2$C	III	7.6	1364, 2215
2-EtO$_2$C	I	20	1551
	I	50	1553
	III	38	1364, 2215
	III	55	433
2-PrO$_2$C	III	25	2215
2-iso-PrO$_2$C	III	76	1364, 2215
2-BuO$_2$C	III	44	1364, 2215
1-Me-2-MeO$_2$C	III	49	124

Table 1-V—*continued*

Aziridine made, or substituents therein	Method[a]	% Yield[b]	References
Aziridines Containing Other Functional Groups—continued			
1,3-Me$_2$-2-MeO$_2$C	III	33.8	*3720*
2-EtO$_2$C-3-Me	III	44	*2215*
1-Bu-2-MeO$_2$C	III	76.9	*3720*
1-Et-2-MeO$_2$C-3-Me	III	40.4	*3720*
1-CH$_2$=CHCH$_2$-2-MeO$_2$C-3-Me	III	61.3	*3720*
1-EtOCH$_2$CH$_2$-2-MeO$_2$C-3-Me	III	49.2	*3720*
1-(3-HOCH$_2$CH$_2$CH$_2$)-2-MeO$_2$C-3-Me	III	26.3	*3720*
1-(3-Me$_2$NCH$_2$CH$_2$CH$_2$)-2-MeO$_2$C-3-Me	III	24.5	*3720*
1-Bu-2-MeO$_2$C-3-Me	III	73.0	*3720*
1-*n*-C$_6$H$_{13}$-2-MeO$_2$C-3-Me	III	71.4	*3720*
1-Bu-2-MeO$_2$C-3-Pr	III	41.5	*3720*
1-C$_6$H$_{11}$-2-MeO$_2$C	III	85	*572*
1-C$_6$H$_{11}$-2-MeO$_2$C-3-Me	III	78.4	*3720*
PhCH$_2$O$_2$C	III	34	*1684*
1-PhCH$_2$-2-MeO$_2$C	III	74	*572, 3390*
	III	—	*2078, 3310*
1-PhCH$_2$-2-MeO$_2$C-3-Me	III	50	*572, 3390*
	III	71.2	*3720*
1-(*p*-ClC$_6$H$_4$CH$_2$)-2-MeO$_2$C-3-Me	III	91.2	*3720*
1-(*p*-MeOC$_6$H$_4$CH$_2$)-2-MeO$_2$C-3-Me	III	62.8	*3720*
2-MeO$_2$C-1-PhCH$_2$CH$_2$	III	21	*572, 2078*
2-MeO$_2$C-1-(*p*-MeOC$_6$H$_4$)	III	36	*572*
2-EtO$_2$C-1-PhCH$_2$-3-Me	III	20	*572*
2-MeO$_2$C-3-Me-1-PhCH$_2$CH$_2$	III	51.9	*3720*
1-PhCH$_2$-2-iso-PrO$_2$C-3-Me	III	64	*572*
	III	65–85	*2928*
1-(*c*-C$_6$H$_{11}$NHCH$_2$CH$_2$)-2-MeO$_2$C	III	13	*572*
1-(2-Furylmethyl)-2-MeO$_2$C	III	68	*572*
1-(2-Furylmethyl)-2-EtO$_2$C-3-Me	III	Poor	*572*
2-MeO$_2$C-3-Me-1-(1-methylpiperid-4-yl)	III	17.2	*3720*
3-AcO-1-PhCH$_2$-2-MeO$_2$C	III	Poor	*572*
2-EtO$_2$C-1-Et-3-Ph	III	62	*2624*
1-C$_6$H$_{11}$-2-EtO$_2$C-3-Ph	III	99	*2624*
1-PhCH$_2$-2-EtO$_2$C-3-Ph	III	19	*2624*
1-Ph$_2$CH-2-MeO$_2$C	III	78–94	*3310*
1-(Ph$_2$CHCH$_2$)-2-MeO$_2$C	III	≈ 30	*572*
2-MeO$_2$C-1-Ph$_3$C	—[k]	80	*3310, 3311, 3315*
1,2,2-(*o*-MeC$_6$H$_4$NH)$_3$	III	—	*2656*
1,2,2-(*p*-MeC$_6$H$_4$NH)$_3$	III	—	*2656*
2-NC-1-Me	III	34.5	*125*
2-NC-1-Pr	III	—	*3721*
2-NC-1-iso-Pr	III	59	*125*
1-Bu-2-NC	III	77	*1553*

Table 1-V—*continued*

Aziridine made, or substituents therein	Method[a]	% Yield[b]	References
Aziridines Containing Other Functional Groups—continued			
2-NC-1-Me$_3$CCH$_2$	III	67	*1553*
2-NC-1-*c*-C$_6$H$_{11}$	III	51	*125*
	III	59	*3721*
1-PhCH$_2$-2-NC	III	—	*1553, 3721*
	III	39.5	*125*
1-(*p*-ClC$_6$H$_4$CH$_2$)-2-NC	III	66	*1553*
2-NC-1-(*p*-MeOC$_6$H$_4$CH$_2$)	III	—	*1553*
1-PhCH$_2$-2-NC-3-Me	III	—	*1553*
2-NC-1-*c*-C$_6$H$_{11}$-3-Ph	III	99	*2856a*
2,3-(MeO$_2$C)$_2$	III	≈ 28	*3798*
2,3-(EtO$_2$C)$_2$	III	30–45	*3798*
2,3-(PrO$_2$C)$_2$	III	≈ 50	*3798*
1-(R-MeOC$_6$H$_4$)-2,3-(MeO$_2$C)$_2$	III	< 5	*3798*
2-H$_2$NCO	III	—	*2215*
2-EtO$_2$C-3-H$_2$NCO	III	—	*1677, 2287*
2-H$_2$NCO-3-Ph	III	—	*3862*
2-H$_2$NCO-3-(*p*-O$_2$NC$_6$H$_4$)	III	56–80	*2087, 2088*
2,3-(H$_2$NCO)$_2$	III	—	*1677*
2,3-(EtO$_2$CCH$_2$CH$_2$)$_2$-2-Me	I	—	*1065*
1-Bz-2-NC	III	—	*150*
1,2-(CMe$_2$N=CPh)-3-(*p*-O$_2$NC$_6$H$_4$)	III	72	*4074*
2,3-(CH$_2$OCH$_2$)	II	49	*1095*
1-Me-2,3-(CH$_2$OCH$_2$)	II	58	*1095*
1,2-(CH$_2$CH$_2$NHCO)-3-Ph	III	16	*2623*
1,2-(CMe=CHCHOEt)-2-Me-3-Cl	I	—	*2699*
1,2-[C(*tert*-Bu)=CHCHOEt]-2-Me-3-Cl	I	—	*2700*
2,5-Az$_2$-hydroquinone[l]	I	—	*2453*
2-AzCH$_2$CH$_2$NH-quinoline	I	55	*2921*
N,N'-Methylenebis(1-R-aziridine-2-carboxamide) (R = Me, Et, Bu, or PhCH$_2$)	III	—	*152*
4-(MeN=)-1-Ph-1,2-(*N*-Me-epimino)-1,2,3,4-H$_4$-naphthalene	III	70–77	*797*
4-(PhN=)-1-Ph-1,2-(*N*-Ph-epimino)-1,2,3,4-H$_4$-naphthalene	III	73–81	*797*
Various dyes containing the CH$_2$Az[l] group	II	—	*2970*
TEM [2,4,6-tris(1-aziridinyl)-*s*-triazine]	II	—	*4210*
Methyl 4,6-*O*-benzylidene-2,3-dideoxy-2,3-epimino-α-D-mannoside	—[l]	83	*1561*
Methyl 4,6-*O*-benzylidene-2,3-dideoxy-2,3-epimino-α-D-alloside	—[l]	48–100	*1561*
1-(H or PhCH$_2$)-2-EtO$_2$C-3-(tetra-*O*-acetyl-L-*arabino*butyl)	III	up to 25	*924a*

Table 1-V—*continued*

Aziridine made, or substituents therein	Method[a]	% Yield[b]	References
Aziridines Containing Other Functional Groups—continued			
5-Cl-1a-R-1,1a-H$_2$-3-Ph-azirino[1,2-*a*]-			
quinazoline 2-oxide (R = H or ClCH$_2$)	I	—	1287b, 1744
6α, 7α-Epiminocholestanol-(3β) 3-acetate	—[i]	$\approx$ 80	2908
6β, 7β-Epiminocholestanol-(3β) 3-acetate	—[i]	$\approx$ 80	2908
5α, 6α-Epiminocholestanol-(3β) 3-acetate	—[i]	$\approx$ 85	2908
4α, 5α-Epiminoandrostanediol-(3β,17β)	—[f]	—	979a
4α, 5α-Epiminoandrostanediol-(3β,17β)			
17-propionate	—[i]	90	979a
Aziridinium Salts			
1,1-Et$_2$ (perchlorate)	—	94	2294
1,1,2,2-Me$_4$ (perchlorate)	—	98	2294
2,2-[(CH$_2$)$_5$]-1,1-[(CH$_2$)$_4$] (perchlorate)	—	40	2295
2-Bz-1,1-Me$_2$ (bromide)	—	42	1905
2-Bz-1,1,3-Me$_3$ (bromide)	—	24	1905
2-HO$_2$C-1,1-(CH$_2$CH$_2$CH$_2$CH$_2$CO)[m]			
(bromide)	—	64	13
2-Ac-1,1-[(CH$_2$)$_5$]-3-Ph (*dl-cis*)			
(perchlorate)	—	61	2299
2-Bz-1,1-(CH$_2$CH$_2$OCH$_2$CH$_2$)-3-Ph			
(perchlorate)			
dl-cis form	—	79	2299
dl-trans form	—	> 50	2299
(1-Et-1-azoniabicyclo[3.1.0]hexane)			
(perchlorate)	—	—	1601
(6-PhCH$_2$-4-Br-1,4,5-Me$_3$-1-azoniabi-			
cyclo[3.1.0]hexane) (perchlorate)	—	14	1359
(1-Azoniatetracyclo[7.3.2.0^{1,13}.0^{5,13}]-			
tetradecane) (perchlorate)	—	39	2295
1,1-(CH$_2$CH$_2$N$^+$HMeCH$_2$CH$_2$) (dipicrate)	—	—	825

[a] I = halo amine + strong base; II = aminoalkyl hydrogen sulfate + strong base; III = halo amine + NH$_3$ or amine, or olefinic compound + halogen + excess amine.

[b] When a patent claims a general process but gives no yields, only the simplest aziridine mentioned is tabulated here.

[c] By pyrolysis of HOCH$_2$CH$_2$NHEt$_2$$^+$ Cl$^-$.

[d] Trace from 3-piperidinol but 40% from 3-pyrrolidinemethanol.

[e] By dehydration of the amino alcohol over hot alumina.

[f] From the vicinal azido halide by reduction with LiAlH$_4$ and displacement of halide.

[g] Structure uncertain; formulated as an enamine in the literature.

[h] From the vicinal azido tosylate by reduction with LiAlH$_4$ and concomitant displacement of the tosylate group.

[i] From the vicinal azido mesylate as in *h*.

$$BrCH_2CH_2NH(CH_2)_5NH_2 \rightarrow CH_2{=}CHNH(CH_2)_5NH_2 \quad \text{or} \quad Az(CH_2)_5NH_2 \quad (23)$$
$$\textbf{31}$$

The actual cyclization step has been most studied preparatively for EI, partly because among all the aziridines it is most important commercially and at the same time one of those most easily destroyed in the preparation and isolation. Wenker's suggestion for use of 2-aminoethyl hydrogen sulfate (*3769*) appeared at nearly the same time that a general method was patented (*3651*). The major advances since then have been the realization that rapid removal of alkylenimine from the hot alkaline reaction mixture is essential to good yields, and development of ways to accomplish this.

The halo amine salt or sodium aminoalkyl sulfate solution is dropped into boiling aqueous alkali, whence the imine is immediately steam-distilled out (*304, 325, 1011, 1199, 3007, 3008, 3841*). In continuous processes operated at 50–80 atmospheres and 220°–250°C, all EI may be produced in 4–10 seconds in 80% yield (*176, 1252, 2090*). Ethylenimine is separable from mixtures by distillation as an azeotrope, preferably with hexane (*725*). Table 1-V presents results of preparations on aziridines and aziridinium salts by intramolecular displacements. A discussion of quaternary aziridinium salts, including review of their preparation, is given by Leonard (*2292*). The structures assigned to those derived from 2-pyridone (*13*) appear very improbable in view of the reactivity of activated aziridines in the presence of acid (see p. 248). If valid, these structures represent the only known stable activated aziridines containing tetracovalent nitrogen. In a good many instances of preparative work a 2-haloalkylamine or 2-aminoethyl hydrogen sulfate has been treated with aqueous alkali and a nucleophilic reagent simultaneously. Whether such reactions proceed by way of aziridines that undergo ring opening, or whether direct displacement occurs, is not usually clear, and can only be surmised for each individual reaction mixture. Since, as has been noted, 2-bromoethylamine cyclizes much faster than 2-chloroethylamine or 2-aminoethyl hydrogen sulfate (see p. 11 and Table 1-II), the arbitrary decision has been made for present purposes to regard use of a 2-bromoalkylamine in alkaline solution as an *in situ* preparation of an aziridine, whereas such reactions of the others are considered not to proceed via aziridines and are not reviewed here.

2-Bromoethylamine has thus been used to make methyl *N*-(2-mercapto-ethyl)dithiocarbamate (*2943*), 2-aminothiazolines, 2-aminooxazolines, and

---

[j] Claimed formed (but as a distillable product, which appears extremely unlikely) from 1,2,3-trichlorobutane and ammonia autoclaved together.

[k] By intramolecular displacement of a sulfonate group.

[l] From the vicinal azido halide, mesylate, or tosylate by reduction with Raney nickel and hydrazine and concomitant displacement.

[m] Structure is in doubt; see above.

2-mercaptothiazolines (*1386*), substituted thiazolidines from xanthates (*2395*), $H_3N^+CH_2CH_2SCS_2^-$ (*4153*), 2-aminoethanethiol (*3622*), 2-(alkylthio)ethylamines (*166, 723, 3622*), 2-(arylthio)ethylamines (*2205*), polyamines (*2752*), and aminated dextran (*3695*). 2-Bromobutylamine similarly gave a mercaptothiazoline (*418*) and an aminated dextrin (*3695*).

A curiosity of some biological interest is the detection of 1-(2-chloroethyl)-aziridine in the air exhaled by rats to which Endoxan had been administered; evidently hydrolysis and cyclization are involved (*4157*).

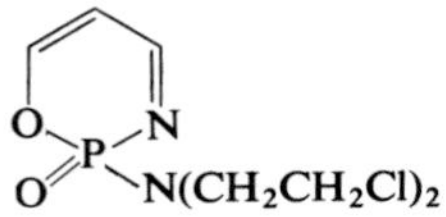

Endoxan

Intramolecular Displacement by Amide Anions

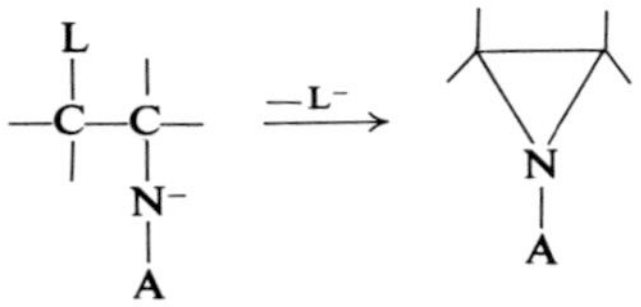

L = leaving group;
A = acyl or like group

This method of obtaining aziridines is very like the one already discussed, in stereochemistry, variability of L, order of reaction, etc. However, it succeeds only in solution alkaline enough to produce the requisite concentration of amide anions; the statement (*1444*) that it can proceed with elimination of HL appears unfounded. Sulfonamides are more readily converted to such anions than are carboxamides; their cyclization is reviewed first, in Tables 1-VI and 1-VII. No doubt diethyl *N*-(2-chloroalkyl)phosphoramidates (*3902*) can be cyclized similarly.

Table 1-VI

PREPARATION OF 1-ARYLSULFONYLAZIRIDINES BY CYCLIZATION

L	Aziridine substituents	% Yield	References
Cl	1-PhSO$_2$	90	*1848*
		94	*3183*
		70	*1979*
Cl	1-(p-FC$_6$H$_4$SO$_2$)	92	*3183*

Table 1-VI —*continued*

L	Aziridine substituents	% Yield	References
Cl	1-(m-H$_2$NC$_6$H$_4$SO$_2$)	64	*1979*
Cl	1-(p-H$_2$NC$_6$H$_4$SO$_2$)	65	*1979*
Cl	1-(p-MeC$_6$H$_4$SO$_2$)	94	*3183*
Cl	1-(m-O$_2$NC$_6$H$_4$SO$_2$)	81	*3183*
Cl	1-(p-O$_2$NC$_6$H$_4$SO$_2$)	75	*3183*
Cl	1-(p-MeOC$_6$H$_4$SO$_2$)	98	*3183*
Cl	1-(3-H$_2$N-4-MeOC$_6$H$_3$SO$_2$)	82	*1979*
Cl	1-PhSO$_2$-2-ClCH$_2$	65	*2058*
Br	1-PhSO$_2$-2-ClCH$_2$	85	*1453*
Cl	1-(p-ClC$_6$H$_4$SO$_2$)-2-ClCH$_2$	50	*2058*
Cl	1-(p-BrC$_6$H$_4$SO$_2$)-2-ClCH$_2$	70	*2058*
Cl	1-(p-MeC$_6$H$_4$SO$_2$)-2-ClCH$_2$	61	*2058*
Cl	1-PhSO$_2$-2-BrCH$_2$	—	*1453*
Br	1-PhSO$_2$-2-BrCH$_2$	70–81	*1, 1449, 1450, 2124*
Cl	1-PhSO$_2$-2-Et	—	*2322*
Cl	1-ArSO$_2$-2,2-Me$_2$	—	*2439*
Cl	1-PhSO$_2$-2,3-Me$_2$ (*cis* and *trans*)	82–93	*852a, 2322*
Br	1-PhSO$_2$-2,3-Me$_2$	—	*2323*
Br	1-PhSO$_2$-2-BrCH$_2$-2-Me	96	*541*
Br	1-(p-ClC$_6$H$_4$SO$_2$)-2-BrCH$_2$-2-Me	95	*541*
Cl	1-(p-BrC$_6$H$_4$SO$_2$)-2,2-Me$_2$	46	*12*
Br	1-(p-BrC$_6$H$_4$SO$_2$)-2-BrCH$_2$-2-Me	97	*541*
Br	1-(p-MeC$_6$H$_4$SO$_2$)-2-BrCH$_2$-2-Me	83	*541*
Br	1-(p-AcNHC$_6$H$_4$SO$_2$)	—	*1480*
Cl	1-PhSO$_2$-2-Ph	—	*3185a*
Br	1-PhSO$_2$-2-Ph	—	*519, 3479a*
Cl	1-(p-MeC$_6$H$_4$SO$_2$)-2-Ph	—	*3185a*
Br	1-(p-MeC$_6$H$_4$SO$_2$)-2-Ph	> 95	*2077*
Br	1-PhSO$_2$-2-PhCH$_2$	81	*1454*
Cl	1-PhSO$_2$-2-Bz	60–80	*2551*
Cl	1-ArSO$_2$-2-Me-2-Cl$_3$C	0	*2059*
Cl	1-(p-MeC$_6$H$_4$SO$_2$)-2,3-Ph$_2$ (*cis* and *trans*)	—	*3185a*
Br	1-PhSO$_2$-2,3-[(CH$_2$)$_4$] (CH$_2$CMe)n	56	*4185*
Cl	1-p-O$_2$SC$_6$H$_4$CONH	—	*2660*
Cl	1-[3-(1-Hydroxy-2-naphthoylamino)-4-methoxyphenylsulfonyl)]	—	*1366*
Cl	1-[4-(p-Anisoylacetylamino)phenylsulfonyl]	—	*1366*
Cl	1-[4-(5-Oxo-1-phenyl-2-pyrazoline-3-carboxamido)phenylsulfonyl]	—	*1366*
Cl	1-(p-MeC$_6$H$_4$SO$_2$)-2,3-(CH$_2$C$_6$H$_4$-o)	—	*3185a*
Br	1-PhSO$_2$-2-NC	—	*542a*

Table 1-VII

RATE OF CYCLIZATION OF SUBSTITUTED BENZENESULFONAMIDES TO AZIRIDINES[a]

Benzenesulfonamide	Solvent	Addend, $M \times 10^2$	Temp. (°C)	k ($= k^o \times 10^{-n}$) (sec^{-1})		E (kcal)	A ($= A^o \times 10^n$) (sec^{-1})		References
				k^o	n		A^o	n	
ClCH$_2$CHMeNHSO$_2$Ph	95% EtOH	NaOH, 2	0.04	3.74	4	—	—	—	1448
	95% EtOH	NaOH, 2	10.30	11.09	4	—	—	—	1448
	95% EtOH	NaOH, 2	15.10	25.03	4	—	—	—	1448
	95% EtOH	NaOH, 2	21.0	61.17	4	21.42	1.88	13	1448
(ClCH$_2$)$_2$CHNHSO$_2$Ph	95% EtOH	NaOH, 2	0.04	2.75	4	—	—	—	1448
	95% EtOH	NaOH, 2	10.30	10.26	4	—	—	—	1448
	95% EtOH	NaOH, 2	15.10	23.18	4	—	—	—	1448
	95% EtOH	NaOH, 2	21.0	43.03	4	21.65	7.4	12	1448
ClCH$_2$CH$_2$NHSO$_2$Ph	95% EtOH	Alkali,[b] 1–2	0.04	2.46–2.56	5	—	—	—	1448
	95% EtOH	NaOH, 2	10.30	10.79	5	—	—	—	1448
	95% EtOH	NaOH, 2	15.10	22.54	5	—	—	—	1448
	95% EtOH	NaOH, 2	21.0	40.23	5	21.54	1.59	12	1448

Compound	Solvent	Base							Ref.
ClCH₂CH₂NHSO₂Ph	47.5% EtOH	NaOH, 2	0.04	5.61	5	—	—	—	*1448*
ClCH₂CH₂NHSO₂Ph	47.5% EtOH	NaOH, 2	10.30	20.2	5	—	—	—	*1448*
ClCH₂CH₂NHSO₂Ph	47.5% EtOH	NaOH, 2	15.10	49.4	5	—	—	—	*1448*
ClCH₂CH₂NHSO₂Ph	47.5% EtOH	NaOH, 2	21.0	95.1	5	22.01	8.3	12	*1448*
(BrCH₂)₂CHNHSO₂Ph	95% EtOH	NaOH, 2	0.04	≈5	2	—	—	—	*1448*
ClCH₂CH₂NHSO₂Ph	EtOH	NaOEt, 0.8–6.2	25.0	5.6–4.5	4	—	—	—	*3183*
ClCH₂CH₂NHSO₂C₆H₄Me-*p*	EtOH	NaOEt, 0.9–6.7	25.0	6.8–5.9	4	—	—	—	*3183*
ClCH₂CH₂NHSO₂C₆H₄OMe-*p*	EtOH	NaOEt, 1.8–6.7	25.0	8.1–7.2	4	—	—	—	*3183*
ClCH₂CH₂NHSO₂C₆H₄F-*p*	EtOH	NaOEt, 1.5–6.7	25.0	3.8–3.1	4	—	—	—	*3183*
ClCH₂CH₂NHSO₂C₆H₄NO₂-*p*	EtOH	NaOEt, 1.1–6.7	25.0	0.97–0.81	4	—	—	—	*3183*
ClCH₂CH₂NHSO₂C₆H₄NO₂-*m*	EtOH	NaOEt, 1.0–6.7	25.0	0.88–0.80	4	—	—	—	*3183*
HO₃SOCH₂CHMeNHSO₂C₆H₄Cl-*p*	70% MeOH	NaOH, excess	60	6.24	4	—	—	—	*2111*
HO₃SOCHMeCH₂NHSO₂C₆H₄Cl-*p*	70% MeOH	NaOH, excess	60	8.37	5	—	—	—	*2111*

[a] Excepting for the last two sulfonamides, all rates were followed by determination of chloride.
[b] LiOH, NaOH, KOH, CsOH; added NaClO₄ had little effect.

What has been called "methylenation" of Schiff bases by sulfonium ylides, though only a few examples are known, may be classified here mechanistically. Trimethylsulfonium methylide (**32**) adds to the $\searrow$C=N– group and then intromolecular displacement of dimethyl sulfide closes the ring (Eq 24) (*760, 1326*).

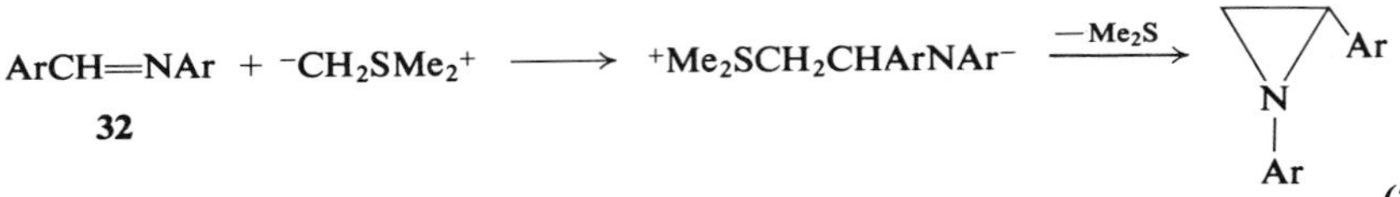

$$ArCH{=}NAr \; + \; ^-CH_2SMe_2{}^+ \; \longrightarrow \; ^+Me_2SCH_2CHArNAr^- \xrightarrow{-Me_2S}$$

32

(24)

Similar reactions occur, although more slowly, with dimethyloxosulfonium methylide, $^-CH_2S(O)Me_2{}^+$ (*760, 1800, 2126, 2536*), dimethyl sulfoxide being eliminated; the most striking example is the conversion of 3-phenyl-2*H*-azirine to the bicyclic compound **33** (*1763*). Carbonyl-stabilized sulfonium ylides, $^-RCOCHSMe_2{}^+$, ultimately yield not the aziridine **34** but its isomer RCOCH=CArNHAr (*3352*).

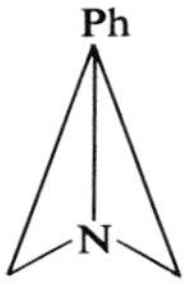

33 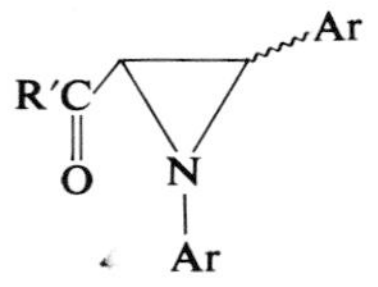   **34**

It might be supposed that cyclization of *N*-(2-substituted alkyl)carboxamides would yield 1-acylaziridines (Eq 25), but it has long been known and

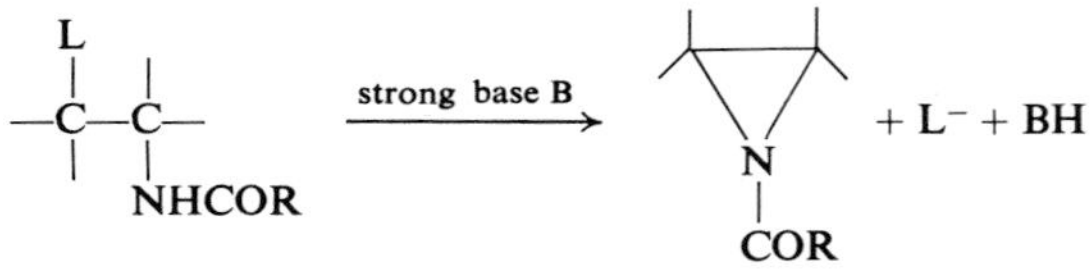

$$\text{(25)} \quad + \; L^- + BH$$

often redemonstrated that the usual course of the reaction (Eq 26) leads to an oxazoline (**35**).

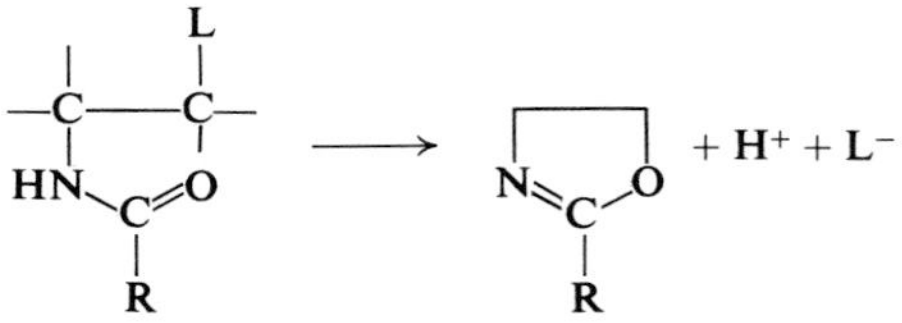

$$\text{(26)} \quad + \; H^+ + L^-$$

35

While 1-acylaziridines can be rearranged to oxazolines (*1656*), it is not likely that oxazoline formation proceeds by way of aziridine intermediates as a rule (*1667*). Those few instances in which aziridines are formed rather than oxazolines will now be discussed.

Possibly because of decreased resonance stabilization of the anion **36** resulting from removal of a proton from a mono-*N*-substituted urethan (Eq 27),

$$\text{RNHCO}_2\text{R}' \xrightarrow{\text{strong base}} \text{R}\overset{-}{\text{N}}\text{CO}_2\text{R}' \tag{27}$$
$$\mathbf{36}$$

which is apparently less than for other carboxamide anions, internal displacement of halide by the amide nitrogen atom to give aziridines occurs (Eq 28) instead of the displacement by amide oxygen to give oxazolines (Table 1-VIII).

$$\tag{28}$$

Since the iodo urethans can be made readily, and stereospecifically trans, by the addition of iodine isocyanate to olefins (see p. 35) and addition of alcohol to the product, the synthesis is an attractive one for laboratory use. In one example only, a mesylate anion, MeSO_2O^-, is displaced instead of halide, to produce a biaziridine (*1275*). Occasionally a competing elimination leads to the enamides, $>\text{C}=\text{CR}-\text{NHCO}_2\text{R}$, which tautomerize and hydrolyze to ketones (*1624*). The 1-(alkoxycarbonyl)aziridines, however, are as unusually susceptible to hydrolysis as a urethan is resistant, and normally the final product is an aziridine without the 1-substituents (Eq 29) (see p. 253).

$$+ \, 2\text{OH}^- \longrightarrow \qquad + \, \text{ROH} + \text{CO}_3^{2-} \tag{29}$$

Threo iodo carbamates yield aziridines (*cis*) more smoothly than the *erythro* forms do (to give *trans*-aziridines) (*1433*). This is attributed to steric impedance of formation of the transition state yielding the trans form; moreover, also for steric reasons, the hydrolysis of methyl *trans*-2,3-dialkyl-1-aziridine-carboxylates is much slower than that of the cis isomers.

Nearly all examples of this kind of aziridine formation remaining for discussion are facilitated by the presence of very effective leaving groups, tosylate or mesylate. They also all involve trans groups on six-membered rings. Thus

DL-*trans*-2-benzamidocyclohexyl tosylate (*3459*) and DL-*trans*-2-benzamido-cyclohexyl-*S*,*S*-dimethylsulfonium iodide (**37**) (*3465*) with hot alcoholic sodium ethoxide each yield an aziridine and an oxazoline in about 4:1 ratio (Eq 30).

Table 1-VIII

PREPARATION OF AZIRIDINES FROM *N*-(2-HALOETHYL)CARBAMIC ESTERS[a]

Aziridine, or substituents therein				% Yield	References
2-*tert*-Bu				60	*4056*
2,3-Et$_2$ (*trans*)				45	*3448*
3-Me-2-iso-Pr (*trans*)				33	*3448*
3-Me-2-iso-Pr (*cis*)				32	*3448*
2-(*n*-C$_8$H$_{17}$)				75[b]	*1305*
2-(*n*-C$_{10}$H$_{21}$)				65[b]	*1305*
2-(*n*-C$_{16}$H$_{33}$)				70[b]	*1305*
3-(*n*-C$_x$H$_{2x+1}$)-2-[R(CH$_2$)$_y$]					
x	R	*y*	Configuration		
5–8	Me	7–11	*cis*	30–43	*4115*
8	Me	7	*cis*	47	*1433*
5–8	HO	7–11	*cis*	35–50	*4115*
8	HO	8	*cis*	70	*1433*
5–8	Me	7–11	*trans*	49–65	*4115*
8	Me	7	*trans*	19	*1433*
5–8	HO	7–11	*trans*	30–58	*4115*
8	HO	8	*trans*	53–58	*1433*
8	MeO$_2$C	7	*cis*	51–97	*1433*
2-Ac				0	*4056*
2-Cl$_3$CCH$_2$				0	*4056*
2-Ph				60[b]	*1305*
2-Ph				61–88	*1624*
2-Ph-3-*d*				—	*1625*
2,3-Ph$_2$ (*cis*)				45	*1305*
2,3-[(CH$_2$)$_4$]				55	*1305*
2,3-[(CH$_2$)$_4$]				52[c]	*1624, 1627*

Table 1-VIII —*continued*

Aziridine, or substituents therein	% Yield	References
2,3-[(CH$_2$)$_4$]	70[b]	3167
2,3-[(CH$_2$)$_4$]	60	3448
2,3-[(CH$_2$)$_4$]	65[d]	1623
2,2-[(CH$_2$)$_5$]	64[e]	1623
2,3-[(CH$_2$)$_5$]	56[d]	1623
1,2-Epiminoindan	65	1624
2,3-(CH$_2$CMe=CHCH$_2$)	—	4140
2,3-(CH$_2$CH=CHCH$_2$)-2-Me	—	4140
1,2-Epimino-1,2,3,4-H$_4$-naphthalene	56–70[f]	1624, 1627
2,3-Epiminonorbornane	—	3165
Cholesten(2β,3β)imine[g,h]	88–90	1624, 1627, 3167
3,4-Epiminotetrahydrofuran	54	433
5,6-Epiminodibenzo[a,c]cycloheptadiene	Good	2837

[a] Halogen = iodine except as noted.

[b] Halogen = chlorine.

[c] In aqueous solution 0.01–0.001M in carbamate and 0.01–0.15M in KOH, at 24° ± 0.5°C; rate of cyclization, k, = 2.69–3.78 × 10^{-5} sec^{-1}.

[d] Via the sodium bisulfite adduct of the isocyanate instead of the alcohol adduct.

[e] Product isolated as the phenyl isocyanate adduct.

[f] For the methyl ester, for which rate (as before) = 12.1 × 10^{-5} sec^{-1}. Other rates: ethyl ester, 10.05 × 10^{-5} sec^{-1}; isopropyl ester, 7.32 × 10^{-5} sec^{-1}.

[g] By mild treatment the methoxycarbonyl derivative could be isolated in 64% yield (*1627*).

[h] Rate of cyclization for the methyl ester = 16.9 × 10^{-5} sec^{-1}.

In contrast, BzNHCHMeCHPhSMe$_2$$^+$ I$^-$ gives only the oxazoline (*3465*).

The products of acetolysis of either 2-benzyl-3-oxo-2-azabicyclo[2.2.2]-octan-*endo*-6-ol tosylate or 2-benzyl-3-oxo-2-azabicyclo[3.2.1]octan-*endo*-7-ol tosylate are best explained by postulating the acylaziridinium ion **38** as an intermediate (*1792*).

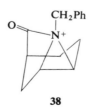

38

Desire for possible antitumor drugs and intermediates for synthesis of various amino sugars has motivated related research. Various methylpyranosides, but not furanosides (*549*), having appropriate groups in the 2- and 3-

Table 1-IX

PREPARATION OF 2,3-EPIMINO SUGAR DERIVATIVES

Parent sugar (as Me glucoside)[a]	Substituents[b]		Reaction conditions					Refer-ences
	2-	3-	Solvent	Base	Temp. (°C)	Time (min.)	Yield (%)	
D-Altrose	OMs	NHCS₂Me	Mixed alcs.	NaOMe, 1.1 eq.	60	4–5	65	685
D-Altrose	OMs	NHBz	EtOH	NaOEt	25	90	29	551
D-Altrose	OMs	NHBz	EtOH	NaOEt, 0.27N	B.p.	30	72c	551
D-Altrose	OMs	NHBz	THF[d]	LiAlH₄	B.p.	180	53c	551
D-Altrose	OMs	NHAc	EtOH	NaOEt	B.p.	20	53c	551
D-Altrose	OMs	NHC(=NNO₂)NH₂	EtOH	NaOMe, 0.13N	25	1080	76	246
D-Altrose	OMs	NHCSNH₂	EtOH	NaOMe, 0.3N	B.p.	10	85	247
D-Altrose[e]	OMs	NHCSNH₂	EtOH	NaOMe, 0.1N	40	Few	—	247
D-Altrose	OMs	NHCN	EtOH or H₂O	NaOMe or NaOH, resp.	25 or b.p., resp.	—	88–90	248
D-Altrose	OMs	NHCN	EtOH or H₂O	NH₃	—	—	61	249
D-Altrose	OMs	NHCONH₂	EtOH	NaOMe	B.p.	60	68–73	248
D-Altrose	OMs	NHC(=NOH)NH₂	EtOH	NaOMe, 0.1N	50	Few	—	249
D-Altrose	OMs	N=CHPh	H₂O	NaOH, 0.2N	B.p.	120	32f	248
D-Altrose	NHBz	OMs	EtOH	NaOEt	25	45	38	551, 1562
D-Altrose	NHBz	OMs	EtOH	NaOEt, 0.27N	B.p.	30	56c,g	551
D-Altrose	NHBz	OMs	HCONMe₂	KCN	100	120	49g	2539
D-Altrose	NHTos	OTos	MeOH	NaOMe, 0.6N	25	60	78	252

Sugar			Reagent	Solvent	Temp.	Time	Yield	Ref.
D-Altrose	NHTos	OTos	LiAlH$_4$	THF^d	B.p.	—	60–66^c	551
D-Altrose	OTos	NHTos	NaOMe, 0.1N	MeOH	B.p.	45	79	252
D-Altrose	NHAc	OMs	NaOEt, 0.14N	EtOH	B.p.	40	—^{c,h}	551
D-Altrose	NHCONH$_2$	OTos	NaOMe, 0.1N	MeOH	B.p.	120	100	250
D-Altrose (β)	NHCONH$_2$	OMs	NaOMe	EtOH	Warm	—	0^h	247
D-Glucose	OMs	NHCSNH$_2$	NaOMe, 0.2N	MeOH	B.p.	240	0	251
D-Glucose	OMs	NHCN	NaOMe, 0.2N	MeOH	B.p.	120	92^c	251
D-Glucose	NHBz	OMs	LiAlH$_4$	THF^d	B.p.	270	44	1467
D-Glucose	NHBz	OMs	NaOMe, 0.3N	EtOH	B.p.	10	85	1467
D-Glucose	NHAc	OMs	LiAlH$_4$	THF^d	B.p.	60	—	47a, 1467
D-Glucose (β)^i	NHBz	OMs	KCN	HCONMe$_2$	100	300	17^h	2538a
D-Arabinose (β)^j	OMs	NHMs	NaOH, 1N	H$_2$O	25	(3 days)	90	253
D-Arabinose (β)^j	OMs	NHMs	BzONa	HCONMe$_2$	90–100	540	56^k	253
D-Xylose (β)^l	OTs	N$_3$	LiAlH$_4$	THF?	—	—	61	722b

^{a} The α-glucoside was used unless otherwise noted.

^{b} The acylamino substituent is understood to be on a deoxy carbon atom, and a 4,6-benzylidene group present unless otherwise noted.

^{c} As the free epimine.

^{d} THF = tetrahydrofuran.

^{e} No benzylidene group present.

^{f} Of the benzylidenebis(aziridine).

^{g} Along with 25% of the oxazoline.

^{h} Oxazoline also formed.

^{i} In other cases, not cited here, the β-hexose derivative gave only the oxazoline, etc.

^{j} No benzylidene group present, but a 5-mesyl was.

^{k} The 5-Ms group was displaced by the 5-Bz group in the product.

^{l} No benzylidene group present, but a 5-azido group was. The product was isolated as the dibenzoyl derivative.

positions have been found to yield epimino sugar derivatives (aziridines) with bases (Eq 31).

(31)

The reaction requires careful choice of base and conditions. Results are given in Table 1-IX. A 3,4-epimino sugar derivative was suggested as an intermediate (3741) and subsequently one was prepared by similar reactions (273). Still more recently, reduction of trans-(4S-azido-3S-tosyloxy)-2S-benzoyl-oxymethyltetrahydrofuran with either lithium aluminum hydride or hydrogen and catalyst has produced the aziridine **39A** (4027) (see p. 36); **39B** was made

39A, R = CH$_2$OBz
39B, R = CHO

very similarly (722a). 3-O-Benzyl-1,2-O-isopropylidene-5,6-di-O-mesyl-D-glucofuranose (**40**) with hydrazine, by displacement of the primary mesyloxy group and ring closure, yields the N-aminoaziridine **41** (4145). The reaction succeeds for other similar furanoses, but not for pyranoses in which the vicinal mesyloxy groups are attached to the ring. Other 5,6-epimino sugar derivatives have been made from the 5-O-tosyl-6-azido-6-deoxy derivatives by treatment with lithium aluminum hydride (3088a).

40   41

The formation of an N-diazonium aziridine intermediate has been suggested to explain the steric course of the acetolysis of trans-2-azidocyclohexyl tosylate (Eq 32)·(3396), but an alternative rationalization by way of 1-azidocyclohexene (Eq 33) may be preferable (3448).

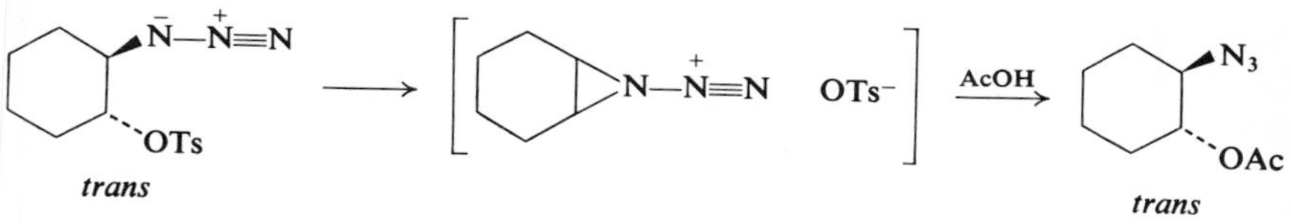

(32)

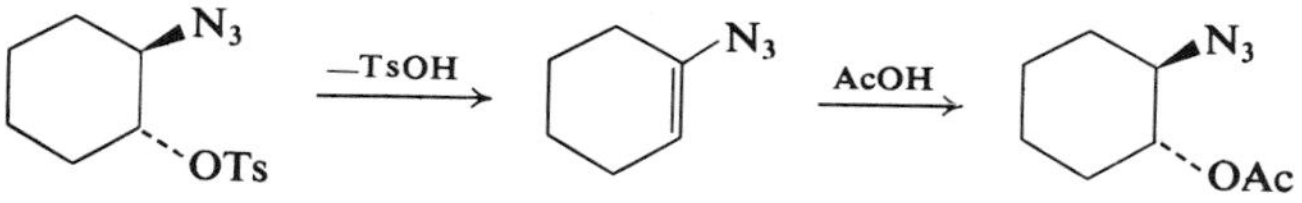

(33)

A recent claim that N-(2-chloroethyl)-β-ethoxyacrylamide (**42**) is converted by strong alkali to the aziridine derivative (*2135*) is of doubtful validity; the

$$\text{EtOCH}=\text{CHCONHCH}_2\text{CH}_2\text{Cl} \xrightarrow{\text{OH}^-} \text{EtOCH}=\text{CHCOAz} \ (?)$$
42

product was probably the oxazoline. The brief statement (*732*) that N-(2-chloro-1,2-diphenylethyl)benzamide, BzNHCHPhCHClPh (the original name α,β-diphenyl-β-chloroethylamine is a misprint), yields 1-benzoyl-2,3-diphenyl-aziridine when heated with alcoholic sodium ethoxide has been verified (*1670*).

Intramolecular Displacement by Carbanions

This class of reactions may be represented by Eq 34.

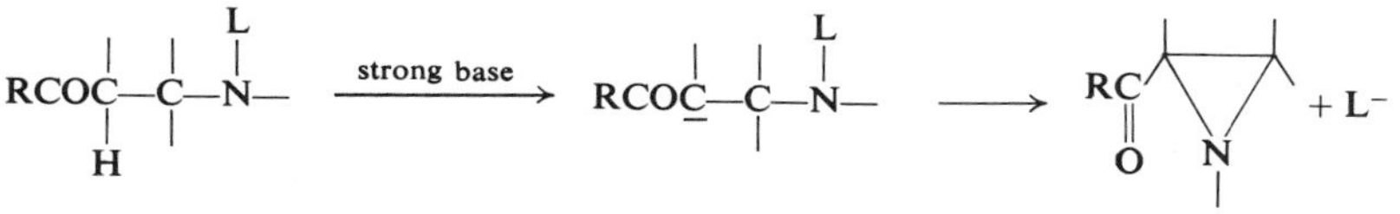

It is, of course, also possible that some such reactions proceed by a concerted mechanism instead of by the steps shown.

The reaction has been reported only once for an ordinary value of L, the leaving group, which in this case was chloride (Eq 35) (*2527*).

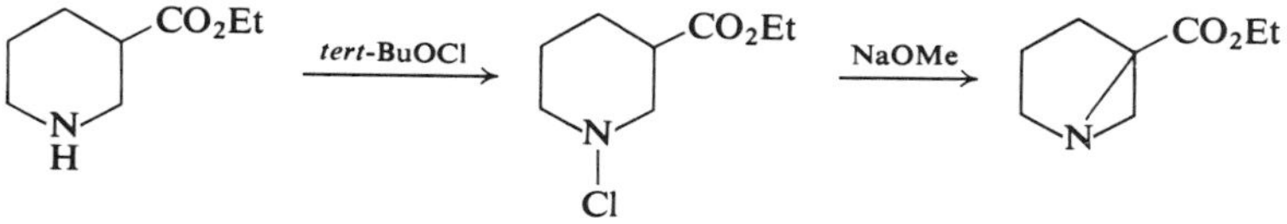

(35)

Nevertheless it appears to be the best mechanism (*784*) for explaining the formation of aziridines from N-alkoxyamino ketones in alkaline solution. The first examples (*381*) of the reaction (Eq 36) are represented by the equation shown although the products were not then so formulated.

$$\text{ArCOCH}_2\underset{\underset{\text{NHOMe}}{|}}{\text{CHPh}} \quad + \text{ base, B} \quad \longrightarrow \quad \text{ArC} \overset{\overset{\displaystyle \diagup\hspace{-0.3em}\diagdown\raise1ex{\,}\text{Ph}}{}}{\underset{\underset{\underset{\text{H}}{|}}{\text{N}}}{\underset{\parallel}{}}} \quad + \text{ OMe}^- \quad (36)$$

Applications of the synthesis are shown in Table 1-X.

Table 1-X

PREPARATION OF AZIRIDINES FROM 2-(ALKOXYAMINO)ETHYL KETONES

Aziridine made, or substituents therein	% Yield	References
2-Bz-3-Ph	94	*381, 980*
3-Ph-2-(p-MeC$_6$H$_4$CO)	64	*381*
3-Ph-2-(p-MeC$_6$H$_4$CO)	61	*796*
2-(p-ClC$_6$H$_4$CO)-3-Ph	66	*381*
2-Bz-3-(p-ClC$_6$H$_4$)	80	*381*
2-(p-BrC$_6$H$_4$CO)-3-Ph	83	*381, 980*
2-Bz-3-(p-BrC$_6$H$_4$CO)	90	*381*
2-(p-MeOC$_6$H$_4$CO)-3-Ph	65	*980*
3β-Hydroxy-16α,17α-epimino-5-pregnen-20-one	78–82	*985*

Intramolecular displacement reactions similar to the Favorskii rearrangement can also lead to the formation of aziridinones (α-lactams) (*4110*) (**43**), sometimes only as reactive intermediates but capable of isolation under favorable circumstances. Two routes have been used (Eqs 37 and 38).

$$\underset{\underset{\text{NHR}}{|}}{\overset{\overset{\text{Cl}}{|}}{-\text{C}}}-\text{C}{=}\text{O} \quad \xrightarrow{\text{strong base}} \quad \left[\underset{\underset{\underset{\text{R}}{|}}{\underset{\text{N}^-}{|}}}{\overset{\overset{\text{Cl}}{|}}{-\text{C}}}-\text{C}{=}\text{O} \right] \quad \xrightarrow{-\text{Cl}^-} \quad \underset{\underset{\text{R}}{|}}{\diagup\hspace{-0.6em}\diagdown}\overset{\displaystyle {=}\text{O}}{\text{N}} \quad (37)$$

$$\textbf{43}$$

$$\Big\uparrow {\scriptstyle -\text{Cl}^-}$$

$$\underset{\underset{\text{H}}{|}}{\overset{\overset{\text{O}}{\parallel}}{-\text{C}}}\underset{\underset{\text{H}}{|}}{\overset{}{-\text{C}}}-\text{NR} \quad \xrightarrow{\text{ROCl}} \quad \underset{\underset{\text{H}}{|}}{\overset{\overset{\text{O}}{\parallel}}{-\text{C}}}\underset{\underset{\text{Cl}}{|}}{\overset{}{-\text{C}}}-\text{NR} \quad \xrightarrow{\text{strong base}} \quad \overset{}{-\text{C}}\overset{\overset{\text{O}}{\parallel}}{-\text{C}}-\text{N}{\diagdown\hspace{-0.6em}\diagup}\overset{\text{R}}{\underset{\text{Cl}}{}} \quad (38)$$

Cyclizations of type 37 have been suggested and discussed for PhCHCl CONHPh (*3116, 3118*) and $Ph_2CClCONHPh$ (*3117, 3225*) but demonstrated for $Me_2CBrCONH$-*tert*-Bu (*3224*), *tert*-BuCHBrCONH-*tert*-Bu (*3222*), $Ph_2CClCONH$-*tert*-Bu (*2650*), several 1-(1-adamantyl)aziridinones (*440a, 3481*), and several ring compounds (*2651, 3223*). Those of type 38 were indicated by infrared spectra for *N-tert*-butylphenylacetamide, *N-tert*-butylacetamide, and *N-tert*-butylpropionamide (*298*), and products that pretty surely have the 1-*tert*-butyl-3-phenylaziridinone structure have been isolated and examined (*296, 300, 1362*). Products of the reaction of $Ph_2CClCONH_2$ with primary and secondary amines indicate that even with these weak bases the aziridinone is an intermediate (*3119*).

A reaction noted here in the absence of more information on mechanism is the conversion of *erythro*-1-azido-2-iodo-1,2-diphenylethane (**44**) (but not the *threo* isomer) by alcoholic base to 2-ethoxy-2,3-diphenylaziridine (Eq 39) (*1628*) (compare the Neber rearrangement, p. 63).

$$ (39) $$

44

Elimination–Addition Reactions

This very small class of reactions, discovered recently, is given only by 2-bromoallylamines, which are converted by alkali amides in liquid ammonia to 2-methyleneaziridines (= allenimines) (Eq 40) (Table 1-XI).

$$ (40) $$

Of the several paths that can be conceived, only that one is acceptable that involves formation of an allenamine, its conversion to an anion, cyclization, and protonation (Eq 41) (*444*).

$$ (41) $$

An unfailing side reaction, and indeed the only one that occurs with 2-chloro-allylamines, is formation of the isomeric propargylamines, $HC{\equiv}CCH_2$ NHR. Proof of structure of these aziridines, which were first regarded as allylidenamines (2905), was supplied by infrared (1081) and NMR (449) data.

Table 1-XI

PREPARATION OF 2-METHYLENEAZIRIDINES

$CH_2{=}CBrCH_2NHR$, % Yield of R =	$CH_2{=}\underset{\underset{R}{N}}{\overset{}{\triangle}}$	References
Me	≈ 50	450
Et	—	449
	≈ 45	450
	48–55	441
iso-Pr	68	2905
	—	450
Propyl-3-t	≈ 40	444
Bu	74.5	2905
tert-Bu	≈ 25	450
C_6H_{13}	≈ 50	450
tert-$BuCH_2CHMeCH_2CH_2$	45	2905
(+)-$CH_2{=}CHCHOHCH_2$	40–50	448
(−)-$CH_2{=}CHCHOHCH_2$	≈ 45	448

Preparation via Azirines

In all intramolecular displacements discussed up to this point, a saturated (aziridine) ring is formed. There is a small class of reactions, however, in which internal displacement yields an unsaturated (2H-azirine) ring. Inasmuch as the azirine often undergoes reduction to an aziridine, this family of reactions is reviewed here.

In one subfamily, aziridines are formed by the action of excess Grignard reagent on α-chloro nitriles. While a somewhat different mechanism has been written (1094), the one in Eq 42, involving intramolecular displacement of chloride by imine anion, seems preferable.

The last step, addition of the Grignard reagent to an azirine, is known separately (1025, 4057). It would be desirable to effect the reaction of an α-chloro alkanenitrile with a Grignard reagent in 1:1 ratio, to see whether an azirine intermediate could be isolated. The reaction with excess Grignard reagent is known to produce 2,2,3-triethylaziridine (*863*), 3,3-diethyl-2-propyl-aziridine (*3525*), and 2-isobutyl-3,3-diethylaziridine (*3525*). Chloroacetonitrile gave no aziridine (*2471*). α-Chloro nitriles with lithium aluminum hydride also produce aziridines (see p. 36) (*1883, 2175*); the mechanism is doubtless similar to that when Grignard reagents are used.

$$(42)$$

Another class of reactions yielding azirines by intramolecular displacement is the Neber rearrangement (Eq 43) (*1769, 2739, 3027*).

$$(43)$$

Reduction of the unstable intermediate azirine to an aziridine with lithium aluminum hydride (*777, 1630*) helped establish the course of the reaction.

In a closely related process, *N,N*-dichloro *sec*-alkylamines with alkali yield azirines and then, by acid hydrolysis, α-amino ketones (Eq 44) (*73, 294, 297, 299, 2736*).

$$(44)$$

The azirine was again reducible to an aziridine (*294*), as was the one made from the isolated *N*-chloro imine (*295*).

Another variation is the generation of the azirine from a quaternized hydrazone (**45**) (*1919, 2616, 2818, 3304*). In the reaction illustrated by Eq 45

$$\text{Me}_2\text{CHCPh}{=}\text{NNMe}_3{}^+ \xrightarrow{\text{iso-PrO}^-} \underset{\substack{\text{N}}}{\overset{\substack{\text{Me}}}{\text{Me}}}{\diagup}\!\!\!{-}\text{Ph} + \text{Me}_3\text{N}$$

45

it was possible to isolate an alkoxyaziridine adduct (**46**) in high yield, and to convert it either back to the azirine or, by hydrolysis, to the amino ketone (*1768, 2818, 4072*).

$$\underset{\substack{\text{N}}}{\overset{\substack{\text{Me}}}{\text{Me}}}{\diagup}\!\!\!{-}\text{Ph} + \text{iso-PrOH} \xrightarrow{\text{iso-PrO}^-} \underset{\substack{\text{N}\\\text{H}}}{\overset{\substack{\text{Me}\quad\text{Ph}}}{\text{Me}}}\text{O-iso-Pr} \qquad (45)$$

46

In contrast, 2-aryl-2-anilinoaziridines could not be isolated though they were postulated as intermediates in reactions of azirines (*3307*). Azirines add alcohols to form 2-alkoxyaziridines in the presence of acids also, preferably perchloric acid, though the aziridine ring does not then survive; but pyridine and perchloric acid with 3,3-dimethyl-2-phenyl-1-azirine gave the crystalline adduct **47** (*2302*), and the reaction of this azirine with primary aromatic amines is believed to involve similar aziridines as intermediates (*4112*).

$$\underset{\substack{\text{N}}}{\overset{\substack{\text{Me}}}{\text{Me}}}{\diagup}\!\!\!{-}\text{Ph} + \text{C}_5\text{H}_5\text{NH}^+ \text{ClO}_4{}^- \longrightarrow \underset{\substack{\text{N}\\\text{H}}}{\overset{\substack{\text{Me}\quad\text{Ph}}}{\text{Me}}}\overset{+}{\text{N}}\text{C}_5\text{H}_5 \quad \text{ClO}_4{}^-$$

47

The rearrangement of 2-acylcoumarone oxime *p*-toluenesulfonates is more complex but probably involves azirine and aziridine intermediates (*1441*). Presumably by reason of steric effects, neither the Neber nor the quaternized hydrazone route could be made to yield the fused aziridine ring system characteristic of mitomycins (*3026*). An isolable azirine proved to be intermediate in the photochemical rearrangement of a substituted isoxazole to an oxazole (*3272*), and several azirines have been shown to add arenesulfinic acids to produce *C*-arylsulfonylaziridines (*2510a*).

The reactions just discussed would scarcely be chosen as preparative routes to aziridines. The action of 3 moles of a Grignard reagent on a ketoxime, however, does have utility for laboratory synthesis (Eq 46).

The recorded examples of application of the ketoxime–Grignard and the ketoxime–lithium aluminum hydride reactions are listed in Table 1-XII, excepting some in very recent papers (*2103, 2165, 2165a*). That the reaction is thus related to the Neber reaction has been well established (*1025, 1619, 1697, 1917*), the evidence again including trapping of the azirine intermediate with lithium aluminum hydride to form the less alkylated aziridine (*1025*), and also such reduction of the authentic azirine otherwise prepared. The reduction gives *cis*-aziridines stereospecifically (*1626*). Catalytic reduction of azirine-carboxylic esters, however, yields acyclic enamines and not aziridines (*1619*).

$$RCH_2CR'=NOH \xrightarrow{2R''MgX} [RCH(MgX)CR'=NOMgX]$$

(46)

For preparative use the oxime–Grignard reaction works best when the ket-oxime is not wholly aliphatic. It occurs when cyclooctanone oxime tosylate is treated with phenyllithium (*1382*), but methyllithium gives a different kind of product (*1382*), as does a Grignard reagent with the tosylate of at least 4-*tert*-butylcyclohexanone oxime (*2841*). Evidently similar is the production of aziridines by reduction of ketoximes with lithium aluminum hydride (*2103, 3211*), although, unlike the Neber rearrangement, the reaction is stereochemically sensitive to the configuration of the oximes used (*2165, 4091*). It is applicable to a variety of ketoximes and aldoximes (*2165a, 2165b*).

Azirines in general yield rather unstable but isolable adducts, 1-benzoyl-2-chloroaziridines (e.g., **48** and **49**), with benzoyl chloride in benzene; the isomer **49** predominates (*4072*).

The remarkable change in reactivity of organic compounds effected by perfluorination extends to azirines. Perfluoro-3-methylazirine (**50**) and per-fluoro-2-methylazirine (**51**) are polymerized by catalytic amounts of bases to polyaziridines. Similarly, hydrogen fluoride causes isomerization of the

Table 1-XII

PREPARATION OF AZIRIDINES FROM KETOXIMES AND
GRIGNARD REAGENTS OR METAL HYDRIDES

From Grignard Reagents

Groups in ketoxime	Groups in Grignard reagent	Aziridine produced, or substituents therein	% Yield	References
Me, Me	Bu	2-Bu-2-Me	17	*1697*
Et, Et	Et	2,2-Et$_2$-3-Me	14	*1697*
Me, Me	*n*-C$_5$H$_{11}$	2-(*n*-C$_5$H$_{11}$)-2-Me	—	*1697*
Pr, Pr	Pr	3-Et-2,2-Pr$_2$	37	*1697*
Me, EtO$_2$CCH$_2$CH$_2$CH$_2$	Me	2,2-Me$_2$-3-HOCMe$_2$CH$_2$CH$_2$ and/or 2-Me-2-HOCMe$_2$CH$_2$CH$_2$CH$_2$	40	*3487a*
Ph, Me	Et	2-Et-2-Ph	20–60	*568*
Ph, Me	Et	2-Et-2-Ph	40–64	*1025, 1917*
Ph, Et	Me	2,3-Me$_2$-2-Ph	64	*1025, 1917*
Ph, Me	Pr	2-Ph-2-Pr	25–35	*568*
Ph, Et	Et	2-Et-3-Me-2-Ph	—	*1697, 1725*
Ph, Et	Et	2-Et-3-Me-2-Ph	50	*568*
Ph, Et	Pr	3-Me-2-Ph-2-Pr	—	*1697*
Ph, Pr	Pr	3-Et-2-Ph-2-Pr	43	*1697*
Ph, Et	Ph	3-Me-2,2-Ph$_2$	—	*1725*
Ph, iso-Pr	Ph	3,3-Me$_2$-2,2-Ph$_2$	—	*1773*
Ph, iso-Pr	—[a]	3,3-Me$_2$-2,2-Ph$_2$	24	*1773*

From Lithium Aluminum Hydride

Oxime	Aziridine produced, or substituents therein	% Yield	References
PhC(=NOH)Et or PhCH$_2$C(=NOH)Me	3-Me-2-Ph	—	*3245*
PhC(=NOH)Me or PhCH$_2$CH=NOH	2-Ph	—	*3245*
p-ClC$_6$H$_4$C(=NOH)Me or *p*-ClC$_6$H$_4$CH$_2$CH=NOH	2-(*p*-ClC$_6$H$_4$)	—	*3245*
p-MeOC$_6$H$_4$C(=NOH)Me or *p*-MeOC$_6$H$_4$CH$_2$CH=NOH	2-(*p*-MeOC$_6$H$_4$)	—	*3245*
PhC(=NOH)Et	3-Me-2-Ph	—	*3245*
PhCH$_2$C(=NOH)Me	3-Me-2-Ph	34	*2103, 3245*
PhC(=NOH)CH=CH$_2$	3-Me-2-Ph	50	*3211*

Table 1-XII —*continued*

From Lithium Aluminum Hydride

Oxime	Aziridine produced, or substituents therein	% Yield	References
PhCH$_2$($=$NOH)Ph	2,3-Ph$_2$	—	*1630*
PhCH$_2$($=$NOH)Ph	2,3-Ph$_2$	25–33	*2103, 3245*
p-ClC$_6$H$_4$C($=$NOH)CH$_2$C$_6$H$_4$Cl-p	2,3-(p-ClC$_6$H$_4$)$_2$	—	*1630*
2,4-(O$_2$N)$_2$C$_6$H$_3$CH$_2$C($=$NOH)Me	3,Me-2-[2,4-(O$_2$N)$_2$C$_6$H$_3$]	—	*777*
(PhCH$_2$)$_2$C$=$NOH, or its acetate, tosylate, or methyl ether	2-PhCH$_2$-3-Ph	36–94	*2103, 3245*
PhCH$=$CHC($=$NOH)Ph	2-PhCH$_2$-3-Ph	—	*2103, 3245*
1-C$_{10}$H$_7$C($=$NOH)Me	2-(1-C$_{10}$H$_7$)	64	*3245*
2-C$_{10}$H$_7$C($=$NOH)Me	2-(2-C$_{10}$H$_7$)	16	*3245*
PhCHMeC($=$NOH)Me	2-[Ph(Me)CH]	47	*3245*
PhCHEtC($=$NOH)Me	2-[Ph(Et)CH]	43	*3245*
Ph$_2$CHC($=$NOH)Me	2-Ph$_2$CH	41	*3245*
9-Phenanthryl-C($=$NOH)Me	2-(9-Phenanthryl)	—	*3245*
1-C$_{10}$H$_7$CH$_2$C($=$NOH)Me	3-Me-2-(1-C$_{10}$H$_7$)	32	*3245*
1-Tetralone oxime	1,2-Epiminotetralin	100?	*3245*
2-Tetralone oxime	1,2-Epiminotetralin	41	*3245*
2-C$_5$H$_4$NCH$_2$C($=$NOH)Ph	3-Ph-2-(2-C$_5$H$_4$N)	—	*3245*
2-(HON$=$)-1,2,3,4-H$_4$-1,4-methanonaphthalene	2,3-Epimino-1,2,3,4-H$_4$-1,3-methanonaphthalene	—	*3245*
2-(HON$=$)-1,2,3,4-H$_4$-1,4-ethanonaphthalene	2,3-Epimino-1,2,3,4-H$_4$-1,4-ethanonaphthalene	50 (*cis* + *trans*)	*2103, 3245*
1,4-Ethano-2-cyclohexanone oxime	2,3-Epimino-1,4-ethanocyclohexane	—	*2103, 3245*
1-Me-1,4-isopropylidene-2-cyclohexanone oxime	2,3-Epimino-1-methyl-1,4-isopropylidenecyclohexane	—	*3245*
2-*syn*, 3-*syn*-(MeO$_2$C)$_2$-9-(HON$=$)-1,2,3,4-H$_4$-1,4-ethanonaphthalene	2-*syn*, 3-*syn*-(HOCH$_2$)$_2$-9,10-*anti*-epimino-1,2,3,4-H$_4$-1,4-ethanonaphthalene	14	*3245*
11-(HON$=$)-9,10-H$_2$-9,10-ethanoanthracene	11,12-Epimino-9,10-H$_2$-9,10-ethanoanthracene	32–46	*2103, 3245*
6-(HON$=$)-dibenzo[a,c]cycloheptadiene	5,6-Epimino-dibenzo[a,c]-cycloheptadiene	70–96	*3245, 4097*
10-*syn*-(MeONHCO)-7-(HON$=$)-5,6,7,8-H$_4$-6,9-methano-9H-benzocycloheptene	10-*syn*-(HOCH$_2$)-7,8-*syn*- and *anti*-epimino-5,6,7,8-H$_4$-6,9-methano-9H-benzocycloheptene	58	*3245*
1-(HON$=$)-dibenzo[c,e]cyclooctane	1,2-Epiminodibenzo[c,e]-cyclooctane	70	*2103*

[a] Phenyllithium was used.

3-trifluoromethyl- to the 2-trifluoromethylazirine by way of the unstable aziridine **52** (*262, 721, 722*).

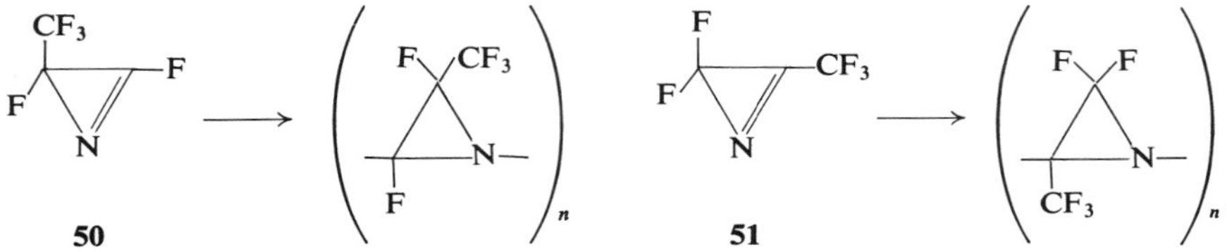

50   **51**

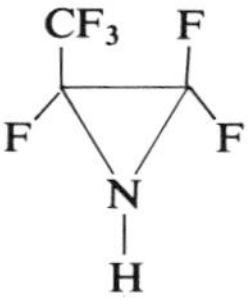

52

Additions to Olefinic Bonds

The direct "epimination" of carbon–carbon double bonds is by no means so easy and useful as epoxidation of such structures, but it is of theoretical interest and perhaps occasionally of preparative value. Recent reviews (*2373, 2634a, 3367a, 4103*) deal in part with many such reactions.

With only two exceptions (*2365, 2460*), the nitrogen which thus becomes part of an aziridine ring is the substituted one in an azide, $-N{=}N^+{=}N^-$. The formation of the aziridine may be by way of a Δ^1-1,2,3-triazoline adduct (**53**) which is pyrolyzed or photolyzed;

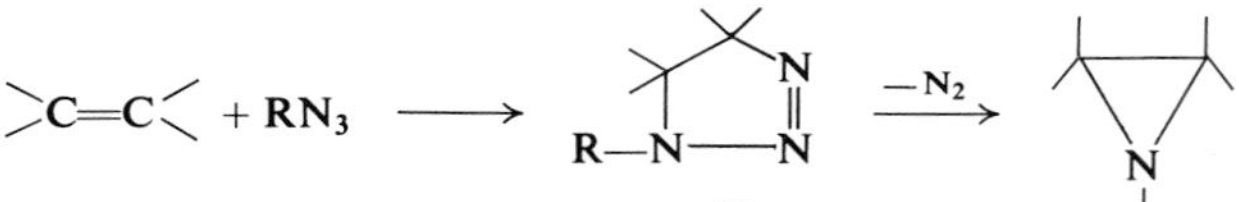

$$>C{=}C< + RN_3 \longrightarrow \underset{\textbf{53}}{\text{R—N—N}} \overset{-N_2}{\longrightarrow} \text{(aziridine)} \tag{47}$$

the pyrolysis may proceed via a dipolar-ion intermediate

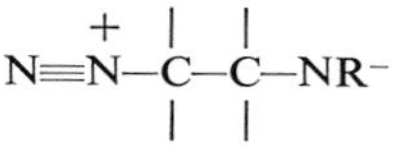

$$\overset{+}{N}{\equiv}N{-}\overset{|}{\underset{|}{C}}{-}\overset{|}{\underset{|}{C}}{-}NR^-$$

(*2340, 2747, 2748*), or a nitrene (*6, 1761*), which adds to the double bond (Eq 48).

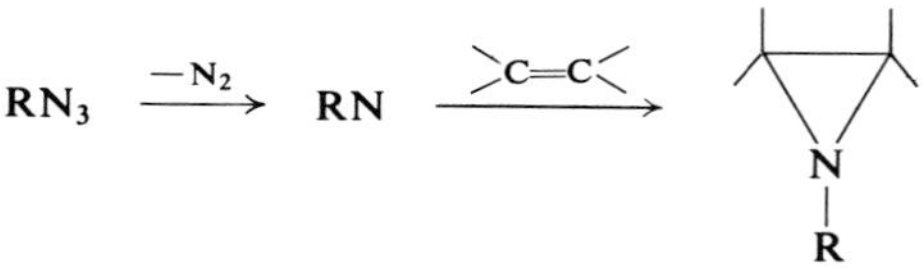

$$RN_3 \xrightarrow{-N_2} RN \xrightarrow{>C{=}C<} \text{(aziridine)} \tag{48}$$

Besides these paths, there is possible a concerted mechanism, in which the aziridine is formed as the nitrogen escapes from a complex (54).

54

Both the direct and the sensitized photolysis of triazolines show high efficiency, insensitivity to nature of the solvent, and much retention of configuration. These results suggest participation of an excited singlet state and a short-lived 1,3-diradical in the reaction (*3132*).

It is known that the formation of an isolable triazoline is favored by mild conditions, by absence of strongly electronegative groups in the azide, and by strain or other activation of the double bond. Indeed phenyl azide has often been used to establish the reactivity of olefins by their tendency to form adducts of triazoline structure. Olefinic azides can undergo the process intramolecularly (Eq 49) (*2340, 4209*).

$$(49)$$

However, the pyrolysis of the phenyltriazolines usually gives some anil along with the aziridine, and sometimes *only* anil (Eq 50) (*3133*). Photolysis

$$(50)$$

instead of pyrolysis gives clean conversions of the triazolines to aziridines (*3133, 3135*). The preparation of aziridines by decomposition of 1,2,3-triazolines is summarized here, Table 1-XIII presenting preparations from isolated triazolines, and Table 1-XIV those without isolation of the intermediate. That cyanogen azide reacts by the triazoline path rather than the nitrene path at 0°C has been proved by use of the ^{15}N-labeled form, $N^*{=}N{=}N^*{-}CN$, in which the nitrene becomes symmetrical, $\cdot N^*{=}C{=}N\cdot$, and must therefore give some unlabeled nitrogen in the aziridine ring; none is found (*95*). On the other hand, reactions of this azide with olefins above about 40°C go by way of cyanonitrene; thus cyclooctatetraene and cyanogen azide

Table 1-XIII

PREPARATION OF AZIRIDINES BY DECOMPOSITION OF ISOLATED TRIAZOLINES

Aziridine made, or substituents therein	% Yield	References
By Pyrolysis		
1-(m-ClC$_6$H$_4$)	—	*1659*
1,2-Ph$_2$	0^a	*2014*
1-(p-BrC$_6$H$_4$)-2,2,3-Me$_3$	69	*4163*
1-(p-BrC$_6$H$_4$)-2-Bu	64	*4163*
1-PhCH$_2$-2,2,3-F$_3$-2-F$_3$C	74	*587*
1-PhCH$_2$-2,3-F$_2$-2,3-(F$_3$C)$_2$	80	*587*
2-MeO$_2$C-1-(p-RC$_6$H$_4$)	—	*1795, 3451*
(R = H, Me, MeO, Cl, Bz, O$_2$N)		
1-PhCH$_2$-2,3-(MeO$_2$C)$_2$	—	*1795, 3451*
2,3-(MeO$_2$C)$_2$-1-(p-MeOC$_6$H$_4$)	81	*1795, 3451*
1-(p-BrC$_6$H$_4$)-2-MeC(=CH$_2$)	—	*3137a*
2-H$_2$NCO-1-Ph	—	*3137a*
2-NC-1-Ph	—	*1795, 3451,*
		4163
1-(p-BrC$_6$H$_4$)-2-(2-pyridyl)	—	*3137a*
1,2-[(CH$_2$)$_3$]	—	*2340*
1,2-(CHMeCH$_2$CH$_2$)	100	*2340*
1,2-(CMe$_2$CH$_2$CH$_2$)	100	*2340*
1,2-(CHMeCH$_2$CHMe)	—	*2340*
1-(p-BrC$_6$H$_4$)-2,3-[(CH$_2$)$_3$]	21	*4163*
1-(p-BrC$_6$H$_4$)-2,3-(CH$_2$OCH$_2$)	47	*4163*
1-(p-BrC$_6$H$_4$)-2,3-(CH$_2$NHCH$_2$)	61	*4163*
1-(p-BrC$_6$H$_4$)-2,3-(CH=CHCH$_2$CH$_2$)	—	*4163*
1-(p-BrC$_6$H$_4$)-2,3-[(CH$_2$)$_5$]	54	*4163*
1-(p-BrC$_6$H$_4$)-2,3-[(CH$_2$)$_6$]	64	*4163*
1-(p-BrC$_6$H$_4$)-2,2-[(CH$_2$)$_5$]	—	*4163*
1-PhSO$_2$-2,3-(OCH$_2$CH$_2$CH$_2$)	0	*2998*; cf. *1323,*
		3135
1,2-Epiminoindane	0	*1978*
2,3-Epiminonorbornane,^{b} substituents in:		
N-Ph	—^{c}	*38, 1797, 1798*
N-Bz	—	*1794*
N-CO$_2$Me	40	*1795, 2747*
N-CO$_2$Et	87	*3243, 3491*
Δ^5-N-CO$_2$Et	60	*3243, 3491*
5,6-Benzo-N-CO$_2$Et	97	*3243, 3491*
N-(p-BrC$_6$H$_4$)	53	*3133*
N-P(O)R$_2$ (R = Ph or OEt)	—	*341, 2496a*
5,6-[(CH$_2$)$_3$]-N-Ph (*cis* and *trans*)	—	*38*
5,6-(MeO$_2$C)$_2$-N-Ph (*cis* and *trans*)	—	*38*
5-NC-N-Ph	78	*3134*
5,6-(NC)$_2$-N-Ph	75.5	*3134*
1,5,6-(MeO$_2$C)$_3$-N-Ph	—	*39*
7-Oxa-5,6-(MeO$_2$C)$_2$-N-Ph	71	*3872*

Table 1-XIII—*continued*

Aziridine made, or substituents therein	% Yield	References
By Pyrolysis		
7-Oxa-5,6-(MeO$_2$C)$_2$-N-CH$_2$Ph	0	3872a
5,6-[C(O)OC(O)]-N-Ph (*cis*)	38	38
7-Oxa-5,6-[C(O)OC(O)]-N-Ph	93	3872
2,3-[Epiminobicyclo(2.2.2)octane], *endo* and *exo*	—	3578
N-(p-MeC$_6$H$_4$SO$_2$)-epiminoisodrin[d]	48	3370, 4175
N-(*tert* BuO$_2$C)-epiminoisodrin[d]	—	3370, 4175

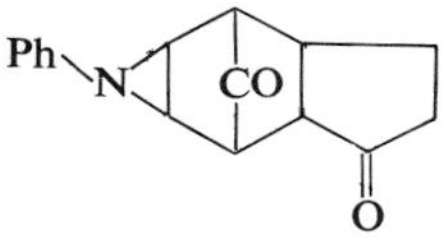

	40	1573b

R—N⟨...⟩N—Ar as follows:

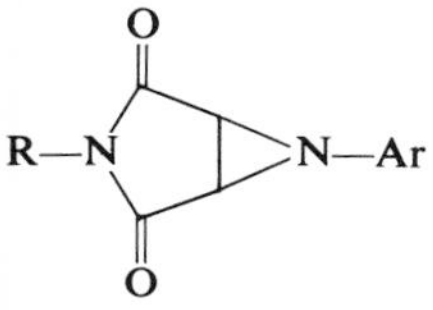

R	Ar		
H	Ph	—	861
H	p-O$_2$NC$_6$H$_4$	—	861
Ph	Ph	91	162, 2647, 2754
p-ClC$_6$H$_4$	Ph	77–94	162, 2647
p-O$_2$NC$_6$H$_4$	Ph	58	2647
p-MeC$_6$H$_4$	Ph	80	162
p-MeOC$_6$H$_4$	Ph	83	162
Ph	p-O$_2$NC$_6$H$_4$	73	162
p-ClC$_6$H$_4$	p-O$_2$NC$_6$H$_4$	90	162
p-MeC$_6$H$_4$	p-O$_2$NC$_6$H$_4$	90	162
p-MeOC$_6$H$_4$	p-O$_2$NC$_6$H$_4$	91	162
Ph	p-MeC$_6$H$_4$	86	2647
p-ClC$_6$H$_4$	p-MeC$_6$H$_4$	84	2647
p-O$_2$NC$_6$H$_4$	p-MeC$_6$H$_4$	81	2647
Ph	p-MeOC$_6$H$_4$	71	2647
p-ClC$_6$H$_4$	p-MeOC$_6$H$_4$	65	2647
p-O$_2$NC$_6$H$_4$	p-MeOC$_6$H$_4$	58	2647
Ph	p-EtOC$_6$H$_4$	61	2647
p-ClC$_6$H$_4$	p-EtOC$_6$H$_4$	64	2647
p-O$_2$NC$_6$H$_4$	p-EtOC$_6$H$_4$	65	2647
Ph	2,4-Me$_2$C$_6$H$_3$	92	2647
By Photolysis			
2,2-(F$_3$C)$_2$		84	2121
2,2,3-Me$_3$		83	4163
2,3-Et$_2$ (*trans*)		84	4163
2-Bu		88	4163

Table 1-XIII —*continued*

Aziridine made, or substituents therein	% Yield	References
By Photolysis		
1-(*p*-BrC₆H₄)-2-CH₂=CMe	100	*3137*
2,3-Ph₂	—	*3133*
3-Me-1,2-Ph₂ (*cis* and *trans*)	Various	*3132, 3136*
2-H₂NCO-1-Ph	—	*4163*
2-NC-1-Ph	—	*3133*
1-(*p*-BrC₆H₄)-2,3-[(CH₂)₃]	86–94	*3133, 4163*
1-(*p*-BrC₆H₄)-2,3-(CH₂OCH₂)	96	*4163*
1-(*p*-BrC₆H₄)-2,3-(CH=CHCH₂CH₂)	—	*4163*
1-(*p*-BrC₆H₄)-2,3-(OCH₂CH₂CH₂)	67	*3135*
1-(*p*-BrC₆H₄)-2,3-[(CH₂)₅]	89	*4163*
1-(*p*-BrC₆H₄)-2,3-[(CH₂)₆]	88	*4163*
1-Bu-2,3-(CONPhCO)	—	*3133*
2-(Me₂C=)-3,3-Me₂-1-picryl	0	*4013*
A steroidal aziridinium salt[e]	—	*3644*
2,3-Epiminonorbornane,[b] substituents in:		
N-Ph	94	*1798*
N-C₆H₄Me-*m*	90	*4163*
N-C₆H₄Me-*p*	92	*1798, 4163*
N-C₆H₄Cl-*m*	90	*3137a, 4163*
N-C₆H₄Cl-*p*	92	*1798*
N-C₆H₄Br-*m*	90	*3137a, 4163*
N-C₆H₄Br-*p*	100	*3133*
N-C₆H₄OMe-*m*	90	*4163*
N-C₆H₄OMe-*p*	90	*4163*
N-C₆H₄NO₂-*m*	0	*4163*
N-C₆H₄NO₂-*p*	18	*4163*
N-CH₂Ph	53	*558a, 3866*
N-CPh=CH₂	—	*4163*
N-P(O)(OEt)₂	> 90	*2496a*
N-CO₂Et	95	*3133, 4163*
N-SiMe₃	—	*4163*
N-Ph-2,3-[C(O)OC(O)]	—	*3133*
2,3;5,6-(*N*-EtO₂C-epimino)₂-norbornane	—	*4163*

[a] In spite of the suggestions of earlier workers (*38, 3822*).

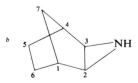

[c] Sometimes not isolated but hydrolyzed to the anilino alcohol.
[d] Isodrin = the adduct of hexachlorocyclopentadiene and norbornadiene.
[e] Not isolated but postulated as an intermediate.

Table 1-XIV

PREPARATION OF AZIRIDINES FROM OLEFINIC COMPOUNDS AND AZIDES VIA UNISOLATED TRIAZOLINES

Olefinic compound	Azide, RN_3 $R =$	% Yield of aziridine	References
Cyclohexene	H	1.5	2926
Cycloalkenes (C_5, C_7)	Ph	Low or zero	717, 1685
Cyclohexene	Ph	79	717, 1685
1-Octene	Ph	63	717, 1685
Cyclooctene (cis)	Ph	0	1685
Cyclooctene (trans)	Ph	85	1685
Indene	Ph	0	1685
2-Norbornene	Ph	64	1322, 1324. 3867
2,5-Norbornadiene	Ph	—	2749
Methyl methacrylate	Ph	70	1796
Methyl crotonate	Ph	—	3451
CH_2=CHSiMe(OSiMe_3)_2	Ph	10.6	101
Vinylheptamethylcyclotetrasiloxane	Ph	10	101
Allylheptamethylcyclotetrasiloxane	Ph	0	101
5-Norbornene-2,3-dicarboxylic anhydride (exo or endo)	Ph	—	1325, 3868
7-tert-Butoxy-2,5-norbornadiene	Ph	—	2114
7-PhNH-2,3-(CH=CHCH_2)-5-norbornane[c]	Ph	—	1375a
CH_2=CHSiMe(OSiMe_3)_2	PhCH_2	—	100
p-Benzoquinone	Ar, various	—	648
5-Norbornene-2,3-dicarboxylic anhydride	p-MeC_6H_4	64.6	1322
p-Benzoquinone and its 2-methyl derivative	p-O_2NC_6H_4	—	584
Indene	p-MeOC_6H_4	—	3728
Cyclopentene	2,4,6-(O_2N)_3C_6H_2	70	245
Cyclohexene	2,4,6-(O_2N)_3C_6H_2	20	245
Cycloheptene	2,4,6-(O_2N)_3C_6H_2	58	245
Cyclooctene	2,4,6-(O_2N)_3C_6H_2	68	245
1-Methylcyclopentene	2,4,6-(O_2N)_3C_6H_2	70	245
Indene	2,4,6-(O_2N)_3C_6H_2	60	245
2-Norbornene	2,4,6-(O_2N)_3C_6H_2	90	245
α-Pinene	2,4,6-(O_2N)_3C_6H_2	—	245
Dicyclopentadiene	2,4,6-(O_2N)_3C_6H_2	—	245
3a,4,7,7a-Tetrahydro-4,7-methanoindene	2,4,6-(O_2N)_3C_6H_3	—	245
endo-cis-Bicyclo[2.2.1]hept-5-ene-2,3-dicarboxylic anhydride	2,4,6-(O_2N)_3C_6H_3	—	245
Benzo-2,5-norbornadiene	2,4,6-(O_2N)_3C_6H_3	70 (exo)	2443b
Dimethyl 5-norbornene-2,3-dicarboxylate	4,6-Me_2-2-C_5H_2N	—	1794

Table 1-XIV —*continued*

Olefinic compound	Azide, RN$_3$ R =	% Yield of aziridine	References
Ethylene	NC	15	998
Propylene	NC	19–57	998
Isobutylene	NC	33	998, 2442
1-Butene, 2-butene, 2-methylbutene, 1-hexene	NC	0	998
3,3-Dimethyl-1-butene	NC	20	998
Methylenecyclohexane	NC	18	998
Cyclooctatetraene	NC	48	96
2-Norbornene	NC	80	93, 95, 397, 997, 998
2,5-Norbornadiene	NC	—[a]	92
3-Methyl-A-nor-3-cholestene	NC	—	4168
3β-Chloro-5-cholestene	NC	41	998
Norcholesteryl acetate	NC	—	4169
Cholesteryl acetate	NC	37	998
Cholesterol	NC	35	998, 2442
Various steroid alcohols	NC	—	440
Diethyl fumarate	H$_2$NCO	24–40	821
Diethyl maleate	H$_2$NCO	10–15	821
Cyclohexene	EtO$_2$C	—	2060, 2365, 2366, 2371
Cyclooctene	EtO$_2$C	—	4064
Anthracene	EtO$_2$C	—[a]	305
2-Norbornene	EtO$_2$C	—	344
Δ^2-Dihydropyran	EtO$_2$C	—	506
Cyclohexene	*tert*-BuO$_2$C	45	3554
2-Norbornene	Bz	63–79	558a, 1798
2-Norbornene	p-O$_2$NC$_6$H$_4$CO	100	1325, 1798
Diethyl fumarate	p-O$_2$NC$_6$H$_4$CO	0	3798
2-Norbornene	MeSO$_2$	—	1325
2-Norbornene	Et$_2$NSO$_2$	—	1325
Cyclohexene	PhSO$_2$	15–17	2214
2-Norbornene	PhSO$_2$	—	1325, 2748
Dicyclopentadiene	PhSO$_2$	—	1325, 2748, 3866
2,5-Norbornadiene	PhSO$_2$	—[a]	2749
7-Oxa-5-norbornene-2,3-dicarboxylic anhydride	PhSO$_2$	—	1325
cis-endo-5-Norbornene-2,3-dicarboxylic anhydride	PhSO$_2$	60 *endo*, 19 *exo*	2750
cis-exo-5-Norbornene-2,3-dicarboxylic anhydride	PhSO$_2$	74 *endo*, 22 *exo*	2750

Table 1-XIV—*continued*

Olefinic compound	Azide, RN_3 R =	% Yield of aziridine	References
Me 5,6-benzonorborn-2-ene-1-carboxylate	$PhSO_2$	83	*4205*
Dicyclopentadiene	$p\text{-}MeC_6H_4SO_2$	—	*1325*
2-Norbornene	$p\text{-}MeC_6H_4SO_2$	100	*1325, 1798*
Diethyl 2,3-diazabicyclo[2.2.1]-5-heptene-2,3-dicarboxylate	$p\text{-}MeC_6H_4SO_2$	74	*1798*
Benzo-2,5-norbornadiene	$p\text{-}MeC_6H_4SO_2$	45 (*exo*)	*2443b*
2-Norbornene	$p\text{-}BrC_6H_4SO_2$	83	*558a*
2-Norbornene	$p\text{-}MeOC_6H_4SO_2$	79	*558a*
2-Norbornene	$p\text{-}O_2NC_6H_4SO_2$	75	*558a*
2-Norbornene	$O(C_6H_4SO_2\text{-}p)_2$	—	*1325*
2,5-Norbornadiene	$p\text{-}N_3O_2SC_6H_4C_6H_4SO_2$	—	*1325*
2-Norbornene	$PhN(CHO)SO_2$	39	*3255*
Isodrin[b]	$p\text{-}MeC_6H_4SO_2$	48	*3370*
Dicyclopentadiene	$p\text{-}MeC_6H_4N{=}PPh_2$	Small	*398*
Cyclohexene	Me_3Si	13	*4049*
Trimethylvinylsilane	Me_3Si	20	*4049*

[a] Immediately rearranges with ring expansion or destruction.
[b] Adduct of hexachlorocyclopentadiene and 2,5-norbornadiene.
[c] Reacting at the olefinic bond on the 5-ring.

in boiling ethyl acetate yield **56** (p. 76) among other products, although the aziridine does not then survive long (*4003*).

It seems likely that photolysis of an azide–olefin mixture always bypasses triazoline formation, and indeed this has been proved in some cases. Thus either ethyl azidoformate or *N*-(*p*-nitrobenzenesulfonyloxy)urethan, the latter incapable of reacting via a triazoline, photolyzed in liquid cyclohexene yields the cyclohexenimine derivative ethyl 7-azabicyclo[4.1.0]heptane-7-carboxylate (**55**) via a nitrene (Eq 51) (*2365, 2366, 2371*).

$$N_3CO_2Et \longrightarrow$$
$$p\text{-}O_2NC_6H_4SO_2ONHCO_2Et \longrightarrow NCO_2Et \xrightarrow{\text{cyclohexene}} \underset{\textbf{55}}{\boxed{\quad}}N\text{—}CO_2Et$$

$$(51)$$

The vapor-phase reaction gives the same product (*344, 762*), and so does the base-induced decomposition of the urethan (*2367*; cf. *2493, 3088b*).

Photolysis of methyl azidoformate in *cis*- or *trans*-2-butene followed by saponification of the products yields mainly *cis*- and *trans*-2,3-dimethylaziridine, respectively, showing that the nitrene adds stereospecifically cis (*1576*). Similar selectivity has been observed for the addition of ethoxycarbonylnitrene to pure 4-methyl-2-pentenes and to isoprene, but the selectivity decreases with dilution of the olefins, and with temperature. This probably means that the nitrene *as generated* reacts in the singlet state, but has time to change to the triplet when dilution has slowed the reaction (*94, 305, 2369, 2370, 2493, 4010, 4128*). Ethoxycarbonylnitrene from photolysis of ethyl azidoformate is exceptional in giving about 30% nonstereospecific addition even (by extrapolation) at infinite olefin concentration; this and other evidence indicate that about one-third of such nitrene production yields the triplet form directly (*2494*). The multiplicity of cyanonitrene, NCN, is dependent on concentration in the same way, and on the nature of the solvent. Singlet NCN, favored in acetonitrile or cyclohexane and in concentrated solution, yields more 1,2-adduct **56** with cyclooctatetraene; triplet NCN, formed in dilute solutions in ethyl acetate or methylene bromide, undergoes 1,4-addition to the polyene (*4003*). The high (>95%) stereospecificity of the addition of the complex nitrene **57** to olefins indicates that it reacts exclusively in the singlet state (*4006*).

56   **57**

Except for cyanonitrene, addition of substituted nitrenes to conjugated dienes has proved to be exclusively 1,2- (*1576, 4006, 4128*); sometimes the aziridines produced are partly rearranged (*4128*). Photolysis of acyl azides in the presence of olefinic compounds has produced 2-acetyl-1-ethoxycarbonyl-2-methylaziridine and a cyclic analog **58** (*2060*), *N*-(trimethylacetyl)cyclohexenimine (*2368*), and other complex aziridines **59** (*506*) and **60** (*3866*).

58   **59**   **60**

Carbethoxynitrene from *N*-(*p*-nitrobenzenesulfonyloxy)urethan added to cyclopentadiene and 1,3-cyclohexadiene to give the expected aziridines and their rearrangement products (*4128*).

The products of photolyzing 2,3-diphenyl-2-cyclopropenylcarbonyl azide (**61**) (or the isocyanate formed from it by pyrolysis) are consistent with the suggestion that the reaction proceeds by an intramolecular addition to yield **62** as an intermediate (*603*). Pyrolysis of the vinylic azides $PhC(N_3)=CH_2$

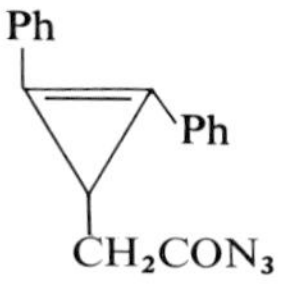

61

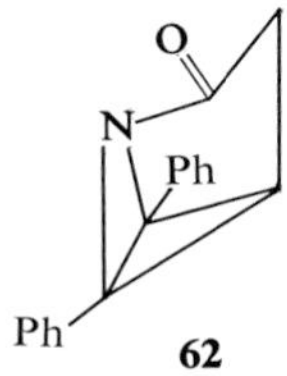

62

(*3308*), $PhC(N_3)=CHPh$ (*1310*), and $FC(N_3)=CFCF_3$ (*262*), the latter two at room temperature, yields azirines; photolysis is also effective (*1626*). However, the photolysis, at least for $PhC(N_3)=CH_2$, also gives some dimer **63** that has an aziridine structure (*4207*).

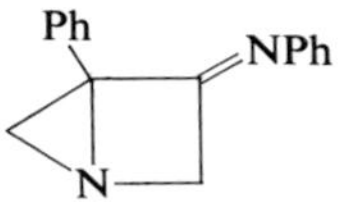

63

Also a bit difficult to classify is the photolytic rearrangement of **64** to **56**, presumably by a C_1-C_5 bridge migration (*97*).

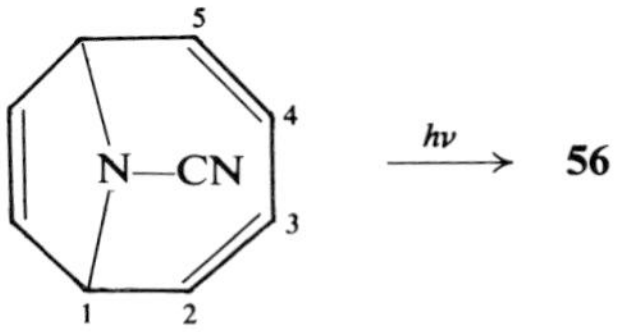

64

Photoisomerization of 3*H*-pyrazoles **64A** at low temperatures yields the tricyclic aziridines **64B**, but these upon warming revert very readily to the 3*H*-pyrazoles (*724a*).

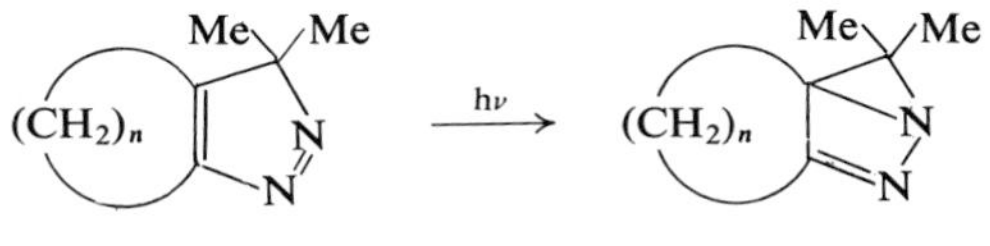

$n = 4$ or 5

64A

64B

It has even been possible to trap imidogen, NH, generated by photolysis of hydrazoic acid at 4°K in an argon matrix, by reaction with ethylene to give recognizable EI (*1956*). However, there was no sign, even for microseconds, of aziridines produced from imidogen and olefin vapors (*761*). Thus the suggestion that **65** may be an intermediate in the reaction of active nitrogen with propylene is admittedly only speculation (*3609*).

The oxidation of δ,ε-unsaturated primary amines **66** to highly strained bridged aziridines **67** is a recent novelty; the oxidation may be effected with *N*-chlorosuccinimide, lead tetraacetate, or mercuric oxide (*2655*). The preliminary report available does not establish whether the reaction proceeds by a nitrene or a radical mechanism.

This section will be closed by citation of those references that have postulated nitrene addition to aromatic nuclei to produce intermediates such as **68** (Eqs 52 and 53). In the beginning the suggestion of such structures was purely speculative, to help account for formation of nitrogenous bases from arenes and sulfuryl azide or carbonyl azide (*346, 822, 823, 3156*). More recent proposals are based on the known tendency of analogous norcaradienes to undergo ring expansion. It is probably only the singlet ethoxycarbonylnitrene that gives this reaction (*2372*).

Aromatic substitution by nitrenes is also still regarded as involving the bicyclic aziridines **68** as intermediates (*257, 305, 1575, 2367, 3285, 3551*).

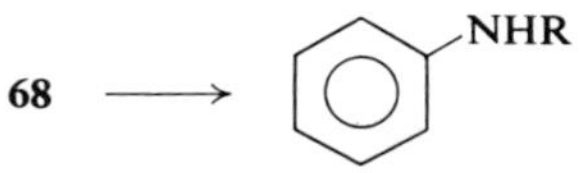

$$68 \longrightarrow$$

The reactions of 2-phenylazirine with anilines have been interpreted as proceeding by way of the adduct **69**, although formation of the observed product benzanilide thence (after hydrolysis), like the ring expansion noted above, requires an unusual but not unprecedented rupture of the carbon–carbon bond in the aziridine ring (*3307*).

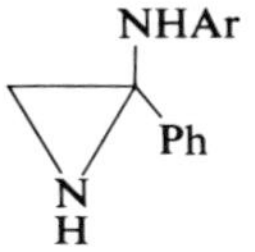

69

Additions to Carbon–Nitrogen Double Bonds

This small group of additions, usually to acyclic imines (Schiff bases), is of theoretical rather than preparative interest. Analogy with addition to carbon–carbon double bonds suggests that an alkylidenimine might yield an aziridine either by way of a triazoline (Eq 54)

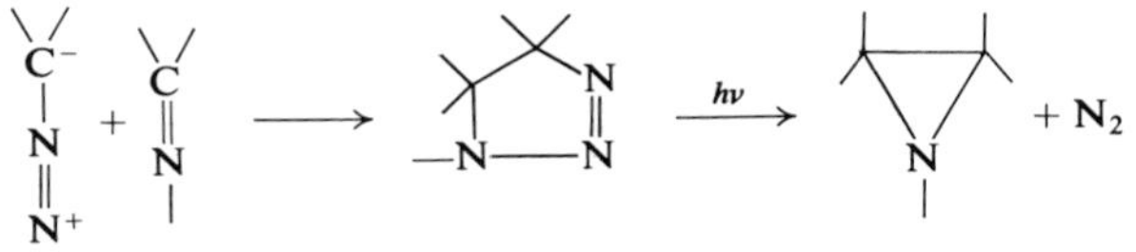

(54)

or by direct bridging of the Schiff base by a carbene (Eq 55).

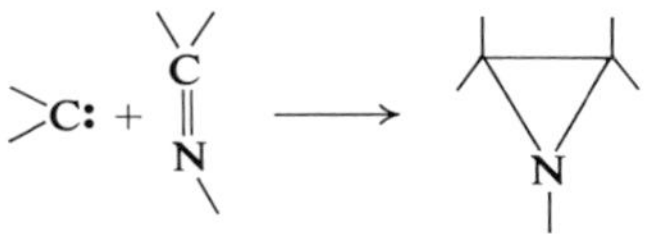

(55)

The second step of Eq 54 is not observable for triazolines made from diazomethane and ordinary Schiff bases (*2014*), but Eq 54 *is* followed by diazomethane and (methoxyimino)bis(methylsulfonyl)methane (**69**) (Eq 56) (*165*).

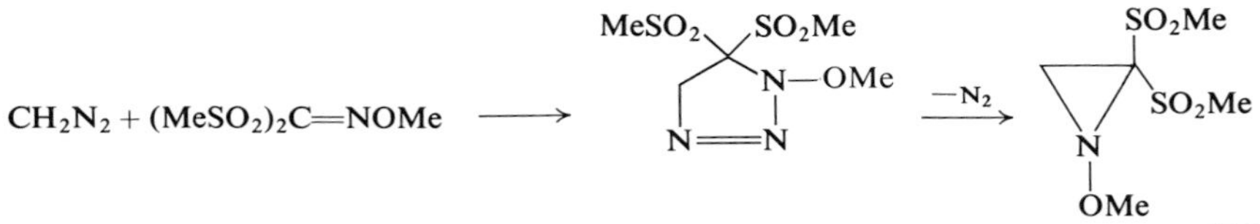

$$CH_2N_2 + (MeSO_2)_2C{=}NOMe \longrightarrow$$

                                                                              (56)

The initial $\diagup C{=}N{-}$ compound without the O-methyl group also yields an aziridine, probably by way of a less stable triazoline (165).

There is no evidence of triazoline intermediates in the preparation of aziridines from diazomethane and polyfluorinated Schiff bases (2339, 3775) or N-arenesulfonyl imines, $Cl_3CCH{=}NSO_2Ar$ (2439a) or from various diazoalkanes and ternary iminium perchlorates (70) or fluoroborates in the cold (Eq 57) (2062, 2292, 2300, 2301, 4165).

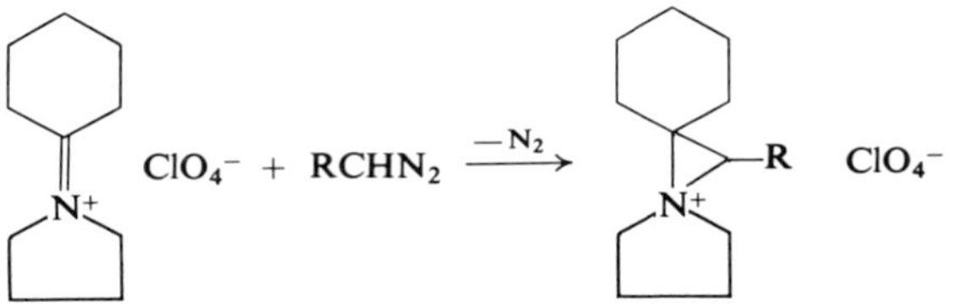

$$ \mathbf{70} \qquad ClO_4^- + RCHN_2 \xrightarrow{-N_2} \mathbf{71} \quad ClO_4^- \qquad (57) $$

The cyclopentylidene iminium salt homologous with 70 gives not only 72 in this reaction but also 71; by homocyclic ring enlargement and then formation of the aziridinium ion (2062).

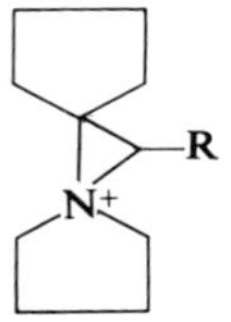

72

Table 1-XV

PREPARATION OF AZIRIDINES FROM DICHLOROCARBENE

Source of carbene[a]	PhCR = NR'		% Yield of aziridine	References
	R =	R' =		
A	H	Ph	55	1288, 3104
B	H	Ph	61	2013
C	H	Ph	—	1655
D	H	p-ClC$_6$H$_4$	68	753, 3104
D	H	p-MeOC$_6$H$_4$	91	753, 3104
D	Ph	Ph	63	902, 4079
D	Ph	p-MeC$_6$H$_4$	66	4079
D	Ph	p-ClC$_6$H$_4$	77	4079
D	Ph	m-MeC$_6$H$_4$	—	4079
D	Ph	m-ClC$_6$H$_4$	—	4079

[a] $A = CHCl_3 + NaOMe$; $B = (Cl_3C)_2CO + NaOMe$; $C =$ unspecified; $D = CHCl_3 +$ KO-*tert*-Bu.

Formation of the aziridine ring in such reactions occurs essentially with retention of configuration at the nitrogen atom (*3865a*).

Clear-cut examples of the addition of dichlorocarbene to Schiff bases, mostly benzalanilines, are available (Table 1-XV). The fact that $Ph_2C(CCl_3)$ NHPh yields an aziridine with potassium *tert*-butoxide alone but not with the strong base in the presence of 2,3-dimethyl-2-butene indicates that the starting material does not react by way of $Ph_2C(CCl_3)NPh^-$ and internal displacement, but by dissociation and dichlorocarbene formation (*902*). At low temperatures chlorocarbene (from $LiCHCl_2$) is stereospecifically trapped by benzalaniline to give *cis*-1,2-diphenyl-3-chloroaziridine in high yield (*902, 903*); *cis*-3-chloro-3-methyl-1,2-diphenylaziridine is formed similarly (*903*). The reaction of dichlorocarbene from sodium trichloroacetate with **70** probably yields an aziridine, but the ring does not survive nucleophilic attack by the trichloroacetate anion (Eq 58) (*753*).

$$\textbf{70} + :CCl_2 \longrightarrow \quad \xrightarrow{Cl_3CCO_2^-,\ H_2O} \quad \tag{58}$$

Similar difficulty is encountered with dichlorocarbene generated with ethylene oxide as acid acceptor; the intermediate dichloroaziridine **73** from benzophenone anil ends up as 1-(2-chloroethyl)-3,3-diphenyloxindole (**74**) (*2106*).

73   **74**

Difluorocarbene is considered to be the intermediate whereby pyrolysis of difluorodiazirine yields complex aziridines (Eq 59) (*2579*).

$$F_2C \underset{N}{\overset{N}{<}} \quad \xrightarrow{heat,\ -N_2} \quad \left[F_2C: \right] \quad \xrightarrow{F_2CN_2} \quad \left[F_2C=N-N=CF_2 \right]$$

$$\tag{59}$$

$$F_2C=N-N=CF_2 \quad \xrightarrow{:CF_2} \quad \xrightarrow{:CF_2}$$

By similar dissociation and recombination, fluorodifluoroaminoazirine gives fluorodifluoraminocarbene and thence **75**.

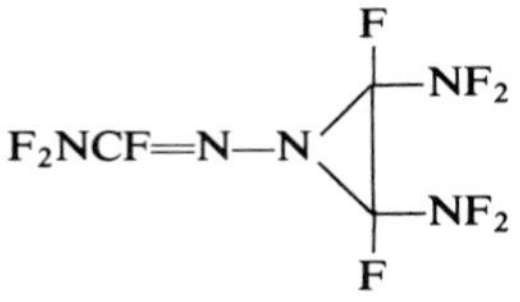

$$F_2NCF=N-N \begin{array}{c} F \\ -NF_2 \\ \\ -NF_2 \\ F \end{array}$$

75

A reaction in atisine chemistry is supposed to yield an aziridine ring in an unprecedented way, presumably because of the unusual rigidity of the molecule. Heating polycyclic Schiff bases with acetic anhydride is believed to produce complex *N*-acetylaziridines (Eq 60) (*1024, 2839*).

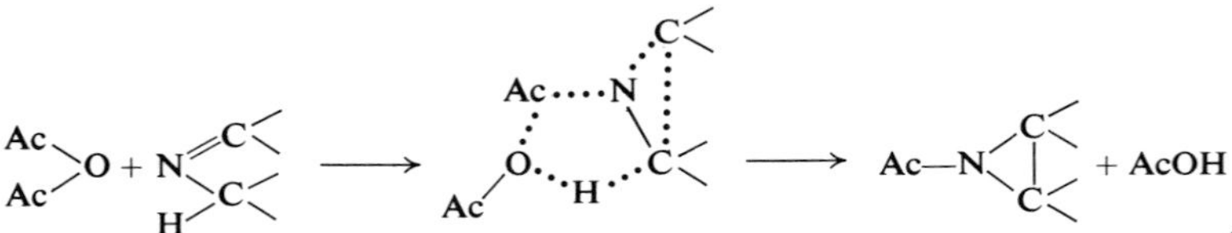

$$\begin{array}{c} Ac \\ Ac \end{array}\!\!O + N\begin{array}{c} C< \\ \\ C< \\ H \end{array} \longrightarrow \begin{array}{c} Ac\cdots N \\ O\cdots \\ Ac \end{array} \longrightarrow Ac-N\begin{array}{c} C< \\ | \\ C< \end{array} + AcOH$$

(60)

In a very different addition to Schiff bases, carbon vapor at −196°C yields new aziridines (**76**) of remarkable structure (Eq 61) (*878b*).

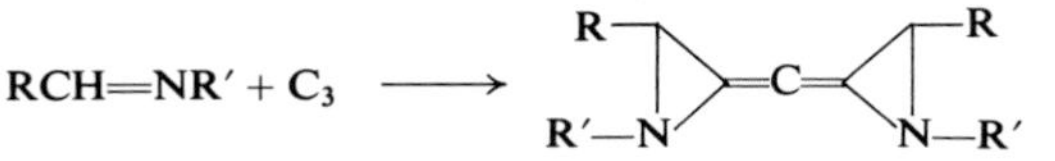

$$RCH=NR' + C_3 \longrightarrow \begin{array}{c} R \\ \triangleright=C=\triangleleft \\ R'-N \qquad N-R' \end{array}$$

(61)

76

A related reaction is that of benzophenone azine with diphenylmethyl radicals from pyrolysis of $Ph_2CHN=NCHPh_2$ to give 2,2,3,3-tetraphenylaziridine (Eq 62) (*3737*); the addition could be extended to only two analogous compounds (*3739*).

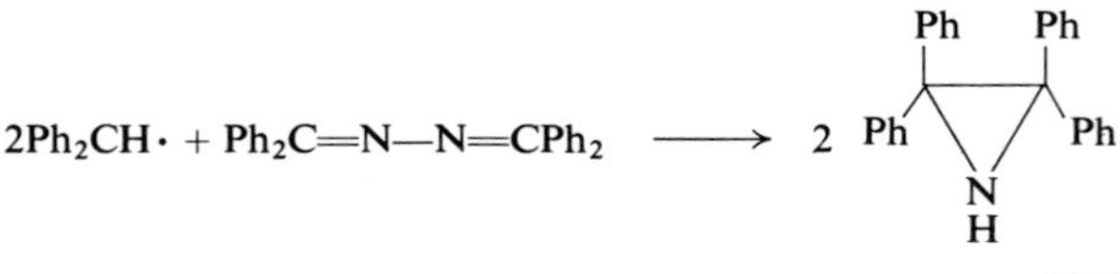

$$2Ph_2CH\cdot + Ph_2C=N-N=CPh_2 \longrightarrow 2\ \begin{array}{c} Ph \qquad Ph \\ Ph \qquad Ph \\ N \\ H \end{array}$$

(62)

50% yield

An isocyanide is capable of adding a complexed carbene **77** to give the complexed aziridine (*4008*).

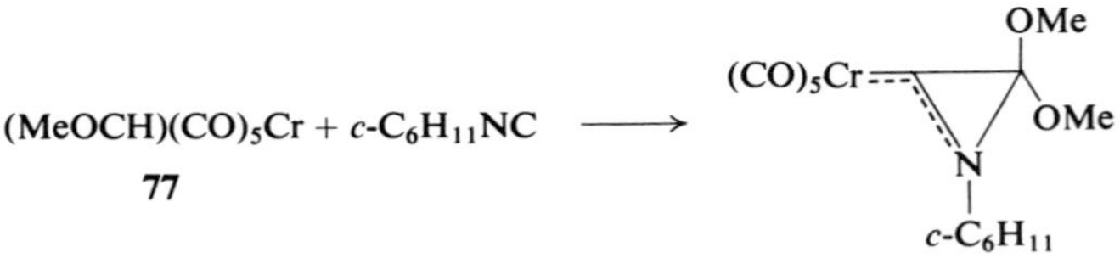

$$(MeOCH)(CO)_5Cr + c\text{-}C_6H_{11}NC \longrightarrow \begin{array}{c} (CO)_5Cr \\ OMe \\ OMe \\ N \\ c\text{-}C_6H_{11} \end{array}$$

(63)

77

Recently reported are additions of nitronic esters (78, $R^5 = $ OMe) and nitrones (78, $R^5 = $ alkyl or aryl) to acetylenes to yield aziridines; isoxazolines 79 were first postulated (3501) and then demonstrated ($257a$) to be intermediates (Eq 64).

$$R^1C{\equiv}CR^2 + \underset{R^4}{\overset{R^3}{>}}C{=}N{\overset{\nearrow O}{\underset{\searrow R^5}{}}} \longrightarrow \longrightarrow$$

78   **79** R^5

R^1, R^3, and $R^4 = $ alkyl groups, $R^2 = $ H, $R^5 = $ OMe   (3501)   (64)

$R^1 = R^2 = CO_2Me$, $R^3 = R^4 = $ H, $R^5 = $ mesityl; or $R^1 = CMe_2OH$,

$R^2 = R^3 = R^4 = $ H, $R^5 = $ *tert*-Bu ($257a$)

Intramolecular Insertion Reactions

This class of aziridine ring formation is very little known. It was surmised (2283) and later confirmed (1438, 2926) that the vapor-phase pyrolysis of ethyl azide yields some EI; isobutyl and *tert*-butyl azides likewise give 2,2-dimethylaziridine, but in even lower yield (2926). Photolysis of liquid *tert*-butyl azide is similar (Eq 65) (282).

$$Me_3CN_3 \xrightarrow{h\nu,\,-N_2} [Me_3CN] \longrightarrow \text{(12\% yield)}\qquad (65)$$

It has been suggested that the decomposition of 4-azido-2-butanone in acid solution goes by way of an aziridinium salt (Eq 66) (931).

$$AcCH_2CH_2N_3 \xrightarrow{H^+,\,-N_2} \left[\right] \longrightarrow AcCMe{=}NH_2^+ \xrightarrow{H_2O} Ac_2 + NH_4^+ \qquad (66)$$

Degradative Routes

Some reactions that might be reviewed here have already been discussed, e.g., the decomposition of 1,2,3-triazolines. The principal pyrolysis yet needing attention is that of 2-oxazolidinones (Eq 67) (3387).

$$\text{(structure)} \longrightarrow \text{AzH} + \text{CO}_2 \qquad (67)$$

Ordinarily this is a source of polyethylenimine (PEI) instead of the monomer shown, because the carbon dioxide concurrently produced catalyzes the polymerization (*808, 2002, 3336, 3561*). In the absence of additives, the polymer chain has 2-imidazolidinone end groups, and indeed a little 1-[2-(1-aziridinyl)-ethyl]-2-imidazolidinone (**80**) can be isolated from the product mixture (*2744*).

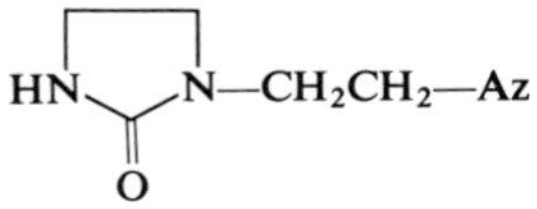

$$\text{HN} \quad \text{N—CH}_2\text{CH}_2\text{—Az}$$

80

The process is catalyzed by both the EI and PEI produced (autocatalysis) and by added amines (*2745*) as well as by imidazolidinones (*3734*). The claim (*3387*) that monomeric EI can be obtained if a stronger base, such as triethanolamine, is present to remove the carbon dioxide seems reasonable.

The pyrolysis of 3-amino-2-oxazolidinone in the same way gives polymeric poly(1-aminoaziridine), useful in rocket fuels (Eq 68) (*1085, 1711*).

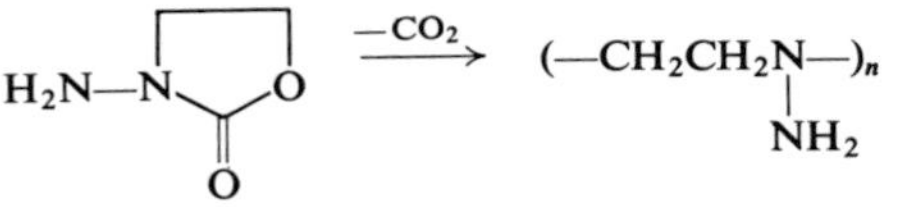

$$\text{H}_2\text{N—N} \quad \text{O} \xrightarrow{-\text{CO}_2} (\text{—CH}_2\text{CH}_2\text{N—})_n \qquad (68)$$
$$\qquad\qquad\qquad\qquad\qquad\qquad\quad \overset{|}{\text{NH}_2}$$

Three unrelated pyrolyses remain to be cited. The pyrolysis of some 2-oxazolines (*3753*) did not yield the 1-acylaziridines sought, but these may possibly have been intermediates (Eq 69).

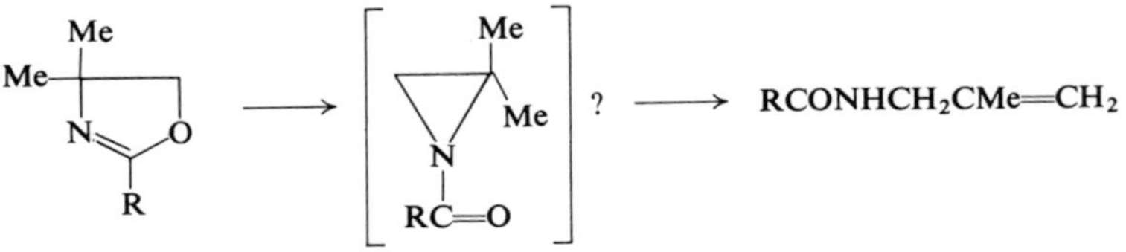

$$\text{(structure)} \longrightarrow \left[\text{(structure)}\right] ? \longrightarrow \text{RCONHCH}_2\text{CMe}{=}\text{CH}_2 \qquad (69)$$

Heating *N*-vinylphthalamide produces a little EI and phthalimide (Eq 70) (*2051*), most likely by way of the intermediate **81**.

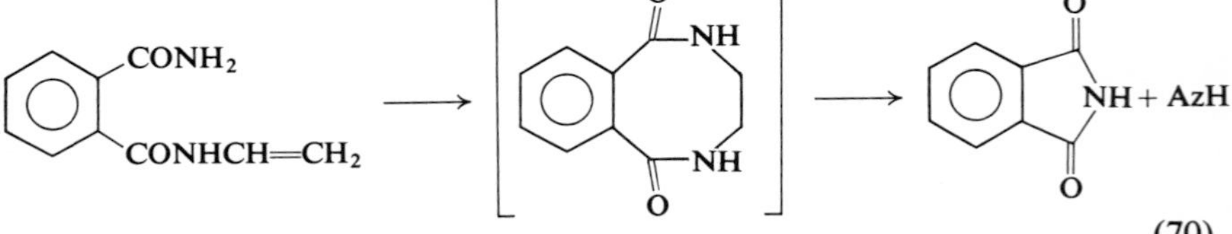

$$\text{(structure with CONH}_2 \text{ and CONHCH}{=}\text{CH}_2) \longrightarrow \left[\text{(structure 81)}\right] \longrightarrow \text{(structure)} \text{NH} + \text{AzH}$$

81

$$(70)$$

Diphenylketene and N,α-diphenylnitrone yield a cyclic adduct which upon pyrolysis gives carbon dioxide and 1,2,2,3-tetraphenylaziridine (Eq 71) (*3506*),

$$Ph_2C\!=\!C\!=\!O + PhCH\!=\!N(O)Ph \longrightarrow \underset{O}{\overset{Ph}{\underset{N\!-\!Ph}{\overset{O}{\underset{Ph}{\overset{Ph}{\fbox{}}}}}}} \xrightarrow{-CO_2} \underset{\underset{Ph}{N}}{\overset{Ph}{\underset{Ph}{\triangle}}} Ph$$

$$(71)$$

but the reaction could not be extended even to closely related ketenes and nitrones (Eq 71).

Ethylenimine has been observed among the products of photolysis (*2542*) and pyrolysis (*98*) of methylamine, and is in fact initially the major product of decomposition of dimethylamine in a hydrogen atmosphere at low pressure and high temperature on an evaporated tungsten film (*98*). 1,2,2-Trifluoro-aziridine is formed during fluorination of the acetonitrile–boron trifluoride adduct (*1057*). Intermediates with aziridine structure have been suggested to explain the course of alkaline cleavage of 2,2-dithiobis(ethylamine) (*2134*) and the hydrogenation of dimethyl 1,2,7-trimethylazepine-3,6-dicarboxylate (**82**) (which gave dimethyl 2,3-dimethylterephthalate) (*675*).

$$\underset{\overset{|}{Me}}{\underset{Me\diagdown\overset{N}{\diagup}Me}{MeO_2C\!-\!\fbox{}\!-\!CO_2Me}}$$

82

2,2,5,5-Tetramethyl-3,6-dipropylpiperazine partly decomposes upon distillation at 252°–256°C and 1 atmosphere, yielding a lower-boiling product which was supposed to be 2,2-dimethyl-3-propylaziridine (*3525*); but so extraordinary a dissociation should be verified before it is believed.

Long ago several authors (*1319, 1320, 3200*) surmised that the compounds obtained by the intramolecular dehydration of 2-(hydroxyamino)alkyl ketones in the presence of hot concentrated acids were aziridine derivatives (Eq 72).

$$\underset{RCOCHR'CNHOH}{} \overset{}{\cancel{\longrightarrow}} \underset{\underset{O}{\overset{}{\parallel}}\ \underset{H}{\overset{}{N}}}{RC}\overset{R'}{\triangle} \qquad (72)$$

In fact, the products were surely isoxazolines (**83**); the mode of preparation and reported properties are consistent with this interpretation.

Similarly, a few workers have written the outdated aziridinone structures (**84**) for the products of reaction of acetic anhydride and an amino acid, etc. (*1408, 1678, 2245, 3764*). These compounds are in fact the well-known azlactones (oxazolinones) (**85**) (*589*).

83   84   85

PHYSICAL PROPERTIES OF AZIRIDINES

Numerical values of physical constants of aziridinyl compounds may be required in establishing structure, in planning and executing preparations, or in detection and determination of such compounds. Nevertheless this chapter is devoted not to tabulation of all the hundreds of values, but to general review and comparison. For discussion of the analytical applications of such measurements, Chapter 7 should be consulted.

Thermal Properties

MELTING POINTS

The melting point of EI has been given as $-78°C$ (*3552*), but the more recent value $-74.1° \pm 0.03°C$ (*964*) is better, and $-73.96°C$ is better still (*1494a*).

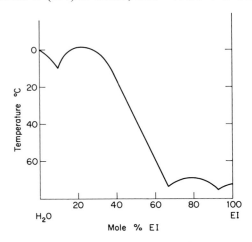

Fig. 1. Freezing point–composition diagram for EI–water mixtures.

Because of the notorious lack of a simple relationship between melting points and structure of organic compounds, no tabulation of values for aziridines has been made. Two studies of freezing points for the binary system EI–water have been recorded. The one (*2827*) obtained a maximum on the curve corresponding to a compound EI·2H$_2$O, but the other (*964*), from which

Table 2-I

BOILING POINTS AND REFRACTIVE INDICES OF SELECTED AZIRIDINES[a]

Aziridine substituents	B.p. (°C)/mm	Refractive index n_D/T (°C)	References
None	56.7/760	1.4123/25	*964*
1-Me	23.5/739	1.3885/19	*333, 1742, 2398, 3185*
2-Me	66.0/760	1.4084/25	*447, 668, 1997, 2576, 3128, 4082*
1-Et	52/746	1.392/25	*333, 453, 963, 2269, 2793*
2-Et	89	1.417/25	*270, 1997, 2793, 3629, 4155*
1,2-Me$_2$	43	—	*2576*
2,2-Me$_2$	70	1.405/25	*560, 1997, 2043*
2,3-Me$_2$, *cis*	83	1.4175/25	*270, 910, 3166*
2,3-Me$_2$, *trans*	75	1.407/25	*910, 1997*
1-Ph	73/18	1.500/25	*453, 492, 1658, 2745, 4019*
1-PhCH$_2$	86/12	1.530/20	*453, 1550*
1-HOCH$_2$CH$_2$	154–156	1.453/25	*963, 1376, 3625*
1-H$_2$NCH$_2$CH$_2$	126–127.5	1.451/25	*963, 1996*
1-NCCH$_2$CH$_2$	187	1.444/25	*963*
APO	90–100/0.3 (m.p. 43.5)	—	*350, 963*
APS	(m.p. ≈ 54)	—	*3415*
TEM	(m.p. dec. 139)	—	*343a, 3841*

[a] All references citing values for one or both physical constants (except for EI) are given, but a single value considered to be the best one is given for each. This is sometimes rounded off to one less significant figure for the refractive index.

the results have been replotted and reproduced in Fig. 1, indicated two complexes, corresponding to EI·5H$_2$O and about 4EI·H$_2$O.

BOILING POINTS AND VAPOR PRESSURE

Boiling points of the simplest aziridines and a few others are presented in Table 2-I. The effect of intermolecular hydrogen bonding in raising the boiling point is shown by comparing the values for 2-methylaziridine and 1-methylaziridine; it may further be noted that ethylene oxide boils at 13.5°C. The effect of ring closure in promoting hydrogen bonding is similarly evident: dimethylamine boils at 7.4°C, EI at 56.7°C.

The vapor pressure of EI varies with temperature as follows −10°C, 37 mm Hg; 0°, 63; 20°, 70; 14°, 130; 25°, 214; 39°, 390; 56.7°, 760 (*964*). Another set of data gives −51°, 1.2; −32°, 6.6; 0°, 58.5; 4°, 73.2; 9.65°, 99.5; 16.05°, 137.2; 20.55°, 171.5; 45.6°, 519 (*540*). More precise measurements at lower temperatures yielded results as follows: −60.011°, 0.549; −55.189°, 0.894; −50.354°, 1.420; −45.509°, 2.204; −40.661°, 3.361; −35.801°, 5.014; −30.933°, 7.358; −26.058°, 10.610; −21.176°, 15.050 (*1494a*). The first two sets of values lead in each case to a value of 7.9 kcal/mole for the heat of vaporization in this range. A better value is 8.148 kcal/mole, derived from the last set of vapor pressures above, and in good agreement with 8.14 kcal/mole determined by an unspecified method (*3713*). Corresponding values for 2-methylaziridine are as follows: vapor pressure at 20.0°C, 112 mm Hg; 30.0°, 179; 39.0°, 269; 51.0°, 436; 66.0°, 760; heat of vaporization, 7.94 kcal/mole (*4082*). Vapor-liquid equilibria for the EI–water (*964*) and 2-methylaziridine–water (*4082*) systems have been studied at several subatmospheric pressures; the curves have the expected shape, i.e., the EI is much more volatile than would be predicted from Raoult's law. An azeotrope consisting of 36.8% EI and 63.2% hexane is useful in purifying the imine (*725*).

Heats of mixing for the EI–water system, expressed as kcal/mole EI for solutions finally containing the weight percent of EI specified, are as follows: 20%, 3.3; 40%, 2.7; 80%, 1.2; 90%, 0.66. A single and apparently less reliable value from a different source is 54.4%, 4.05 (*2827*); one for 2-methylaziridine is 5%, 4.5 kcal/mole (*4082*).

THERMOCHEMICAL DATA

The heat of combustion of liquid EI at 25° ($\Delta H_c°$) has been determined to be −380.86 ± 0.14 kcal/mole (*2690*), and more recently as 381.14 ± 0.06 kcal/mole (*1494a*). From the heat of vaporization already given, it follows that the heat of formation of gaseous EI, $\Delta H_f°$ (25°C), is 30.40 kcal/mole. While an estimate of $\Delta H_f°$(g) based solely on bond energies was 12 kcal/mole (*2690*), the value 3.5 is more recent and probable (*772*). Thence the strain energy of the EI ring is to be assessed at about 26.9 kcal/mole. No more direct measurement of this value, as by heat of hydrogenation, is available. Corresponding values of strain energies for cyclopropane, ethylene oxide, and ethylene sulfide are 27.5, ≈ 28, and 18.6 kcal/mole, respectively (*772*).

Thermodynamic functions of EI have been computed from spectroscopic data independently by three groups (*964, 1494a, 3713*). Since one set of results (964) was based on a value now obsolete for the heat of vaporization, and another (3713) used the symmetry number $\sigma = 2$ instead of $\sigma = 1$ for the C_s symmetry of EI, only the most recent and best (1494a) is summarized here (Table 2-II). The experimental value of the entropy $S°$, 59.66 ± 0.20 cal deg^{-1}

Table 2-II

THERMODYNAMIC PROPERTIES OF ETHYLENIMINE IN THE IDEAL GAS STATE

T (°K)	$-(G° - H°_0)/T$ (cal/°K)	$(H° - H°_0)/T$ (cal/°K)	$S°$ (cal/°K)	$C_p°$ (cal/°K)
200	47.5481	8.1036	55.6518	8.9548
250	49.3858	8.4102	57.7961	10.4155
298.15	50.9049	8.8779	59.7828	12.2436
300	50.9598	8.8989	59.8587	12.3186
400	53.6983	10.2721	63.9704	16.4539
500	56.1623	11.8906	68.0529	20.1682
600	58.4761	13.5345	72.0106	23.2376
700	60.6817	15.1068	75.7886	25.7661
800	62.7961	16.5754	79.3715	27.8855
900	64.8279	17.9349	82.7629	29.6903
1000	66.7834	19.1900	85.9734	31.2427
1100	68.6675	20.3482	89.0157	32.5856
1200	70.4875	21.4177	91.9022	33.7511
1300	72.2383	22.4063	94.6447	34.7649
1400	73.9328	23.3213	97.2541	35.4389
1500	73.5711	24.1695	99.7406	36.4211

mole^{-1} at 298.15°K, and the spectroscopically calculated value 59.78 cal deg^{-1} mole^{-1} agree within experimental accuracy. The heat capacity of liquid EI is a linear function of temperature ranging from 0.57 kcal/gm at 0°C to 0.62 kcal/gm at about 42°C (964).

Mechanical Properties

DENSITY

The effect of ring closure in permitting closer molecular packing is shown by comparison of the densities of EI and dimethylamine: at 20°C, these are 0.837 and 0.680 gm/ml, respectively. The density of EI at various temperatures is as follows: −10°C, 0.865 gm/ml; 0°, 0.856; 10°, 0.846; 20°, 0.837; 25°, 0.831 ± 0.001; 65°, 0.789; 100°, 0.752 (264, 964, 1392, 1996). Corresponding values for 2-methylaziridine are 25°, 0.802; 35°, 0.791; 45°, 0.781 (4082). The densities of other aziridines have been reported only irregularly and none are reproduced here. The density of aqueous solutions of EI also shows the effect of molecular interactions by departure from linearity: this is shown in Table 2-III (964). The maximum deviation occurs at about 50 mole % EI; this has

Table 2-III

DENSITY OF MIXTURES OF ETHYLENIMINE AND WATER

Ethylenimine content		Density (gm/ml) at 26°C	
Wt %	Mole %	Observed	Calculated[a]
0	0	0.996	0.996
18.0	33.2	0.978	0.966
33.3	54.4	0.961	0.940
57.0	76.0	0.929	0.901
80.7	91.0	0.877	0.861
99.6	99.6	0.829	0.829

[a] On the basis of linearity.

been interpreted as signifying the formation of a 1:1 hydrate (264). Such deviations in density and refractive index in other hands (2827) produced the conclusion that a dihydrate, $EI \cdot 2H_2O$, is formed, but this appears unjustified.

cis-2,3-Dialkylaziridines have higher density and higher refractive index than the trans isomers, but for 3-alkyl-1,2-dimethylaziridines the isomer with the methyl groups trans has the higher values, presumably because of non-bonded interactions. These observations are believed to show applicability of the von Auwers-Skita rule, that the isomer with the higher density and refractive index has the higher heat content (443).

SURFACE TENSION

The surface tension of EI has been reported as 31.05 (2827) and 32.8 dyne/cm (964) at 25°C. If the parachor is calculated including the regular increment for a three-membered ring, the value is 124.3; the magnitudes quoted for surface tension produce the values of 121.8 and 123.7, respectively.

VISCOSITY

The viscosity of EI is 0.638 cP at $-10°C$; 0.585 at 0°; 0.506 at 10°; and 0.418 at 25° (964). By way of comparison, the viscosity of dimethylamine is about 0.44 cP at −33.5°C, and that of water, 0.89 cP at 25°C. The viscosity of aqueous EI exhibits a broad maximum in the neighborhood of 25 mole % EI, more marked at 5°C than at 20°C (964). The viscosity of 2-methylaziridine at 25°C is 0.491 cP (4082).

SOLUBILITY

Ethylenimine and 2-methylaziridine are miscible with water and virtually all organic liquids [including ethyl acetate, despite a report (2827) to the contrary]. Quantitative data on their behavior as solutes or solvents are rare, however. The ternary system EI–H₂O–NaOH has been studied (964, 2827), partly to ensure that NaOH is sufficiently soluble in essentially anhydrous EI (800–10,000 ppm water) to function as a stabilizer. Such solubility is about 250 ppm at room temperature (964). The partition of EI between water and immiscible organic solvents is ordinarily much in favor of the water because of the possibility of hydrogen bonding. At low temperatures EI dissolves enough sodium or lithium to produce a blue solution like that formed in liquid ammonia and some other amines, but the color disappears on warming the solution to room temperature (264, 963).

Properties Involving Interaction with Radiation

REFRACTIVE INDICES

The refractive index for EI is reported as 1.4123 at 20° (2827), 1.4100 at 25° (2097), or 1.4123 at 25°C (964). These lead to observed molecular refractions of 12.97, 12.83, or 12.90 ml, respectively. The calculated value is 12.78, 12.84, or 12.90, depending on which atomic or bond refractions are used (2097). For 1-phenylaziridine, the observed MR_D is 37.82 ml and the calculated one 37.39 ml; 1-alkylaziridines show similar agreement of observed and calculated values (4019). Evidently the strain of the aziridine ring causes little or no exaltation of the molecular refraction. Refractive indices of some common liquid aziridines are recorded in Table 2-I.

INFRARED ABSORPTION SPECTRA

Assignment of the 18 fundamental vibration frequencies of EI has been undertaken in whole or in part by a number of investigators (2128a, 2332, 2578, 2915, 3509, 3539, 3543, 3713). The most recent and reliable assignment (2578) is shown in Table 2-IV.

Comparison of the infrared spectra of 1-unsubstituted aziridines in the vapor state or in dilute solution with those for the pure liquids shows a shift of the NH bands to lower wave numbers in the latter; this is caused by the considerable intermolecular hydrogen bonding (*2272, 2332, 3228, 3542*). Doublets for the NH stretch in *C*-alkylated aziridines represent the cis and trans configurations of these molecules (*2272, 4124*).

Systematic comparative studies of Raman and infrared absorption spectra for various aziridines have been made by several groups (*40, 3227, 3349, 3509,*

Table 2-IV

FUNDAMENTAL VIBRATIONS OF ETHYLENIMINE[a]

Group	Type of vibration (A′ or A″)[b]	Frequency (cm^{-1})
NH	Stretching (A′)	3346
CH$_2$	Symmetrical stretching (A′)	3015
CH$_2$	Symmetrical deformation (A′)	1483
—	Ring breathing (A′)	1210
CH$_2$	Deformation (wagging) (A′)	998
—	Symmetrical ring deformation (A′)	856
NH	Deformation (A′)	1096
CH$_2$	Asymmetrical stretching (A′)	3079
CH$_2$	Twisting (A′)	1090
CH$_2$	Rocking (A′)	772
CH$_2$	Symmetrical stretching (A″)	3003
CH$_2$	Asymmetrical deformation (A″)	1462
CH$_2$	Wagging (A″)	1131
—	Asymmetrical ring deformation (A″)	1268
NH	Deformation (A″)	904
CH$_2$	Asymmetrical stretching (A″)	3079
CH$_2$	Twisting (A″)	1237
CH$_2$	Rocking (A″, solid phase)	820

[a] Mitchell *et al.* (*2578*).
[b] Symmetry species.

4170). In 1-substituted aziridines, which have been the ones most examined, the most characteristic infrared absorptions and their assignments are as follows: 3050–3080 cm^{-1}, asymmetrical CH$_2$ stretch; 2979–3005 cm^{-1}, symmetrical CH$_2$ stretch; 1250–1330 cm^{-1}, symmetrical ring breathing; and 1150–1170 cm^{-1}, CH$_2$ wag (*3349*; cf. *3509*). These apply well to aziridinylphosphorus compounds, which have been separately examined (*677b, 3207, 3207a, 3208, 3208a*). In general, activated aziridines have C–H stretching bands at slightly higher frequencies but with much lower intensities than basic aziridines do (*3349*); this, like other evidence (*4171*), shows the effect of greater delocalization of the electrons on nitrogen in activated aziridines. The ring CH stretching frequencies show reasonable correlation with Taft's σ_I constants for 1-substituents in basic aziridines, wherein such delocalization is at a minimum (*3349*). As oscillators the NH or ND groups are virtually independent of the rest of the molecule (*4124*). In 2-phenylaziridine, conjugation of the benzene ring is mainly with the π-electron system of the aziridine ring, but in 1-phenylaziridine such conjugation is with the extra pair of electrons on nitrogen (*40*).

From infrared evidence as well as its complexing tendency with phenol, EI is a better proton *donor* (acid) than the higher cyclic imines such as azetidine and pyrrolidine, but a poorer proton *acceptor* than these, because of the diminished availability of the electron pair in EI (*2332*).

ELECTRONIC SPECTRA

Simple aziridines do not absorb in the medium ultraviolet, and their spectra at lower wavelengths have not been reported. The 1-aziridinyl group, however, does have a different effect than other $-NR_2$ groups on the locations and intensities of the absorption maxima for substituted benzenes and benzoquinones. For 1-phenylaziridine $\lambda_{max} = 229.0–235.3$ mμ ($\epsilon = 9840–11,900$) and 272.0–278.0 ($\epsilon = 720–1160$), depending on solvent; these constants are lower than for dimethylaniline, 1-phenylazetidine, 1-phenylpyrrolidine, and 1-phenylpiperidine (*4018*). Similarly the values for aziridinylbenzoquinones (Table 2-V) are lower than for other aminobenzoquinones (*3733*). Evidently the resonance interaction between the nitrogen atom and the 1-substituent, which can be visualized as increase in the bond order, is at a minimum for the aziridines (cf. *2811a*).

In *trans*-2-aroyl-3-arylaziridines, but not the cis forms or those lacking the 3-aryl group, there is an interaction of the substituents by way of the aziridine ring. This manifests itself in absorption maxima at higher wavelength and greater extinction coefficient for the trans forms. The difference is useful in distinguishing geometric isomers. It is shown by absorptions corresponding to both $\pi–\pi^*$ and $n–\pi^*$ transitions, and is much greater for aziridines than for cyclopropanes or oxiranes (Table 2-VI) (*802*). The interaction is considered due to orbital overlap of bent bonds of the small ring with the π-orbital of the carbonyl group, a situation which is favored when the plane of the aziridine ring is parallel to this orbital, as it is in the trans isomer only (*784, 802*).

OPTICAL ISOMERISM

In 1939 and 1940 it was suggested that 1-substituted aziridines might well exceed all other nitrogen compounds in stability of configuration at

Table 2-V

ULTRAVIOLET ABSORPTION MAXIMA FOR AZIRIDINYL-p-BENZOQUINONES

Substituents in p-benzoquinone	Maximum (mμ)	Molar absorptivity ($\epsilon \times 10^{-2}$)	Maximum (mμ)	Molar absorptivity ($\epsilon \times 10^{-2}$)	Maximum (mμ)	Molar absorptivity ($\epsilon \times 10^{-2}$)	References
2,5-Az$_2$	415–417	6.2–6.4	328–330	1.60–1.75	209	2.42	827, 3733
2,5-Az$_2$-3,6-F$_2$	467	3.5	333.7	1.55	223	1.5	3733
2,5-Az$_2$-3,6-Cl$_2$	489	3.5	348	1.68	226	1.53	3733
2,3,5,6-Az$_4$	559	2.92	359	1.19	221, 246	4.22, 4.10	3733
2,5-Az$_2$-3,6-dipiperidino	604	4.37	464	0.56	233	1.71	3733
2,5-Az$_2$-3,6-(PhCH$_2$NH)$_2$	632	3.24	379	1.12	228, 256	1.66, 1.32	3733

the nitrogen atom, so that the long-sought optical isomers with trivalent nitrogen as an asymmetric center might be obtained (*12, 2089, 2396, 2519, 2588*). None of the investigators succeeded in preparing and resolving such an aziridine; nor did later ones (*2102*). The separation of diastereoisomeric forms of 1-chloro-2-methylaziridines by gas–liquid chromatography (*4016*) and of *N*-chlorocyclohexenimines by column chromatography on silica gel (*4055*), however, gives much promise that some 1-haloaziridines will prove resolvable at room temperature.

Table 2-VI

ULTRAVIOLET ABSORPTION MAXIMA FOR 1-ALKYL-2-AROYL-3-ARYLAZIRIDINES

	Cis isomer		Trans isomer		
Transition	λ_{max} (mμ)	Molar absorptivity $\times 10^{-3}$	λ_{max} (mμ)	Molar absorptivity $\times 10^{-3}$	References
$\pi-\pi^*$	243–253[a]	9.8–15.9	246–258[a]	14.4–18.5	*802*
$n-\pi^*$	323–331	0.14–0.26	344–351	0.26–0.73	*2804*

[a] The values are about 280 when the aroyl group is 4-phenylbenzoyl.

The measurement of NMR spectra of 1-substituted aziridines has showed that below some temperature characteristic of the aziridine, the protons on the ring carbon atoms appear as two triplets because the molecular configuration is then relatively stable and one pair of protons is closer to the N-substituent than the other one is. As the temperature is raised these signals broaden and finally coalesce; this coalescence marks the point at which the inversion frequency of the nitrogen atom—the rate at which the substituent and the lone pair of electrons exchange places—is much greater than the scanning frequency (*453, 455*). While the coalescence temperature T_c cannot be determined very precisely, it is of interest, partly because at this temperature the time for one inversion, t, can be simply calculated. The results appear in Table 2-VII.

It has been pointed out (*105*) that comparison of inversion times to seek relationships with structure should be made all at one temperature. However, it is qualitatively evident that compounds containing 1-substituents that can conjugate with the nitrogen and cause electron delocalization—activated aziridines—have much higher inversion rates (*104, 105, 453, 455, 557, 2157, 3603*). 1-(Perfluoroalkyl)aziridines also undergo rapid inversion (*2152c*). The reason for the dramatic decrease in inversion rates for 1-haloaziridines (*2152d, 4015, 4109*) and certain others (*158a*; cf. *495b*) is not yet clear.

The coalescence temperature is raised and the rate of inversion lowered by solvents that can hydrogen-bond with and thus increase the configurational stability of the nitrogen atom (453). By determination of the rate of inversion at various temperatures (by a related NMR technique), the results shown in Table 2-VIII were obtained.

Table 2-VII

RATES OF INVERSION OF NITROGEN IN 1-SUBSTITUTED AZIRIDINES

Aziridine substituents	T_c (°C)	$10^2 t$ (sec)	References
1-Ac (in CH_2=CHCl)	<− 160	—	104
1-MeO$_2$C (in CH_2=CHCl)	− 138	10	104
1-Ph$_2$P(O) (in CH_2Cl_2)	− 108	20	105
1-Me$_2$NCO (in CH_2=CHCl)	− 86	10	104
1-Et-2-CH$_2$	− 65	15	453
1-Ph	<− 77	—	453
1-Ph[a]	− 60	24	453
1-Alkyl-2,3-Bz$_2$	<− 50?	—	3638
TEM	<− 40	—	453
2,5-Az$_2$-p-benzoquinone	<− 40	—	826
1-Ph (in CS$_2$)	− 40	2	104
1-MeSO$_2$	<− 37	—	3603
1-p-MeC$_6$H$_4$SO$_2$	<− 37	—	3603
1-CF$_2$CH(CF$_3$)$_2$-2,2-Me$_2$	− 31	—	2152c
1-p-MeC$_6$H$_4$SO$_2$	− 30	2.8	105
1-PhSO$_2$	− 30	2.8	105
1-Et-2-CH$_2$[a]	− 25	1.5	453
1-MeSO$_2$	− 25	4	104
1-[2,4-(O$_2$N)$_2$C$_6$H$_3$S]	− 18	1.6	105
1-CF$_2$CHFCF$_3$-2,2-Me$_2$	− 13	—	2152c
1-PhS	− 11	1.4	105
1-PhSO	0	1.3	105
1-CF$_2$CH(CF$_3$)$_2$	9	—	2152c
1-CF$_2$CHFCF$_3$	11	—	2152c
1,2-Me$_2$-3-iso-Pr (trans)	< 30	—	446
1,2-Me$_2$-3-iso-Pr (trans) in CDCl$_3$	40	—	446
2,2,3,3-Me$_4$ (in CCl$_4$)	52	4	272
1-HOCH$_2$CH$_2$-2-Me	55	11	453
1-EtO$_2$CCH$_2$CH$_2$-2-Me	55	7.5	453
1-AzCOCH$_2$CH$_2$	57	6.1	557
1,2,2-Me$_3$	57	≈ 11	1776b
1-(CH$_2$=CHCH$_2$)$_2$NCH$_2$	58	3.5	557
1-Et-2,3-Me$_2$ (trans)	58	6.4?	453
1-Piperidino-CH$_2$	60	4.3	557
1-Morpholino-CH$_2$	63	3.6	557
1-Me$_2$NCH$_2$	65	3.5	557

Table 2-VII—*continued*

Aziridine substituents	T_c (°C)	$10^2 t$ (sec)	References
1-D-2,2,3,3-Me$_4$ (in CCl$_4$)	68	—	*272*
1-(AzCH$_2$)$_2$NCH$_2$CH$_2$	75	4.0	*557*
1-MeO$_2$CCH$_2$CH$_2$	≈ 80	—	*4159*
1-NCCH$_2$CH$_2$	≈ 80	—	*4159*
1-HOCH$_2$CH$_2$	83	4.7	*557*
1-*c*-C$_6$H$_{11}$	95	2.0	*453*
1-PhCH$_2$CH$_2$	96	1.4	*453*
1-PhCH$_2$	105	1.7	*453*
1-Et	108	1.7	*453*
1-Cl-2,2-Me$_2$	> 120	—	*4015*
1-Cl-2,2-Me$_2$	> 180	—	*4146*
1-Cl-2,2,3,3-Me$_4$	> 120	—	*4015*
1-Br-2,2-Me$_2$	> 140	—	*4146*
1,2-Et$_2$	> 140	—	*453*
1-Et-2,3-Me$_2$ (*cis*)	> 140	—	*453*

[a] In 0.01N methanolic NaOH.

Table 2-VIII

PARAMETERS FOR RATE OF NITROGEN INVERSION

Aziridine substituents	Solvent	ΔE^a (kcal/mole)	$\nu_0{}^b$ (sec^{-1})	References
1-Me	—	19	10^{11}	*1567, 1653*
1,2,2-Me$_3$	None	23.5–24.1	—	*1976b, 2337*
1,2,2-Me$_3$	C$_6$H$_6$	23.4	—	*1976b*
1,2,2-Me$_3$	CDCl$_3$	32.5	—	*1976b*
1-Me-2-CH$_2$	None	6.4	1×10^9	*2337*
1-H-2,2,3,3-Me$_4$	CCl$_4$	11.0–11.9	—	*272*
1-D-2,2,3,3-Me$_4$	CCl$_4$	14.3–15.0	—	*272*
1-F$_3$C-2,2-F$_2$[c]	None	5.5	5×10^8	*2339*
1-CF$_2$CHFCF$_3$	None	9.1	4×10^9	*2152c*
1-CF$_2$CHFCF$_3$-2,2-Me$_2$	None	6.9	2×10^8	*2152c*
1-CF$_2$CH(CF$_3$)$_2$	None	6.8	7×10^7	*2152c*
1-CF$_2$CH(CF$_3$)$_2$-2,2-Me$_2$	None	5.8	6×10^7	*2152c*
1-PhSO$_2$	CDCl$_3$	$\Delta H^{\ddagger} = 10.9$ kcal/mole, $\Delta G^{\ddagger} =$ 10.0 kcal/mole, $\Delta S^{\ddagger} = 3.6$ e.u.		*105*
1-Cl-2,2-Me$_2$	*o*-Xylene	$\Delta G^{\ddagger} = > 21$ kcal/mole		*4015*
1-Cl-2,2-Me$_2$	Hexachloro-butadiene	$\Delta G^{\ddagger} = > 23.5$ kcal/mole		*4109*

[a] Activation energy.   [c] ^{19}F nuclear magnetic resonance used.
[b] Frequency factor.

NUCLEAR MAGNETIC RESONANCE SPECTRA

Proton Magnetic Resonance. The chemical shifts that have been reported for EI are given in Table 2-IX. The several hundred corresponding values for substituted aziridines are not tabulated here, partly because they are so numerous and partly because they have been determined under too diverse conditions to be properly comparable.

Table 2-IX

PROTON CHEMICAL SHIFTS IN ETHYLENIMINE[a]

Proton	Solvent	Concentration	τ	References
N—H	None	—	8.8	*556*
	None	—	9.12	*2333, 2616a*
	None	—	9.37	*1468*
	None	—	9.63?	*1569*
	Pyridine	→ 0	8.5	*556*
	CCl$_4$	→ 0	10.22	*556*; cf. *4159*
C—H	None	—	8.61	*556*
	None	—	8.63	*4159*
	None	—	8.64	*2333, 2616*
	D$_2$O	10%	8.0	*2865*
	?	—	8.38	*826*
	CDCl$_3$	→ 0	8.39	*4159*
	CDCl$_3$	10%	8.48	*2865*
	CCl$_4$	3.0, 6.0%	8.52	*3547a*
	CCl$_4$	→ 0	8.52	*4159*

[a] At room temperature.

Absorption peaks for protons on nitrogen atoms in aziridines are difficult to interpret because of molecular association and other factors; and very few have been measured by extrapolation to infinite dilution to minimize inter-molecular effects. They tend to be at very high τ-values, even higher than those for acyclic amines and for other cyclic imines. This is taken to connote a greater tendency for the proton on nitrogen in EI to cause self-association; a trimer has been considered to exist in neat EI (*556*).

Protons on aziridine-ring carbon atoms are represented by peaks ranging all the way from $\tau = 5.0$ (for *trans*-2,3-dibenzoyl-1-alkylaziridines) (*3638*) to 9.19 [for one pair of protons, presumably those trans to the N substituent, in 1-(3-oxobutyl)aziridine] (*557*). Even lower values, $\tau = 4.42$ and 4.75, have been observed for complex aziridinium salts (*2299*). These lower limits exemplify the generalization that the presence of electron-withdrawing groups decreases the τ-values (shielding). Such values are also decreased for C protons cis to an

N-alkyl group (relative to those trans to such a group, or those in the
1-unsubstituted aziridine) (*495, 4014, 4159*) and for C protons trans, rather
than cis, to each other (*457a, 2898, 3638*).

The application of coalescence of peaks with temperature rise to estimation
of rate of inversion of the nitrogen atom is discussed on p. 96.

Some spin–spin splitting constants (J values) are tabulated in Table 2-X.
They resemble those for other three-membered ring compounds; but no
systematic measurement of J values for correlation with structure in a series
of related aziridines has been made, and little such correlation is evident. The
order $J_{cis} > J_{trans} > J_{gem}$ is obviously valid for all aziridines in Table 2-X
except $MeO_2CCH_2CH_2Az$ and $NCCH_2CH_2Az$, for which J_{gem} is unusually
high. The sum $J_{cis} + J_{trans}$ decreases by half in the series cyclopropane,
ethylene sulfide, EI, and ethylene oxide, owing to variations in electronega-
tivity of the hetero atom and in hybridization (*5*). Long-range coupling has
been observed in some complex aziridines (*2748, 3578, 3579*).

Table 2-X
PROTON COUPLING CONSTANTS FOR AZIRIDINES

Aziridine, or substituents therein	J_{cis} (Hz)	J_{trans} (Hz)	J_{gem} (Hz)	References
2-MeO-2-Ph	—	—	0	493
2-Cl-1-F₅S-2-F₃C	—	—	0	2339
1-MeO₂CCH₂CH₂	3.4	1.0	6	4159
1-NCCH₂CH₂	3.5	1.3	6	4159
1,2-(CHPrN=CPh)-3-*p*-O₂NC₆H₄	—	1.4	—	4075
1,3-(CHMeN=CPh)-3-*p*-O₂NC₆H₄	—	1.6	—	4075
1,2-(CMe₂N=CPh)-3-*p*-O₂NC₆H₄	—	1.8	—	4075
1,2-(CHPhN=CPh)-3-*p*-O₂NC₆H₄	—	2.0	—	4075
1,2-[CHPhN=C(C₆H₄NO₂-*p*)]-3-Ph	—	2.2	—	4075
1-[(2,4,6-(O₂N)₃C₆H₂]-2-MeO₂C-2-MeO₂CCO	—	—	2.3	257a
(*cis*-3-Cl-2-Ph)-1-Ph	5	—	—	902
1-(*p*-MeC₆H₄SO₂)-2,3-(CH₂C₆H₄-*o*)	5.0	—	—	3185a
2-iso-PrO₂C	5.2	2.8	2.1	2215
(*trans*-3-MeO-2-Ph)-1-Ph	—	2.0	—	902
(*trans*-2,3-Bz₂)-1-PhCH₂	—	2.3	—	3638
(*trans*-2-PhS-3-Ph)-1-Ph	—	2.5	—	902
(*trans*-2,3-Bz₂)-1-cyclohexyl	—	2.5	—	3638
(*trans*-2,3-Bz₂)-1-Me	—	2.6	—	3638
(*trans*-3-Me-2-Ph)-1-Ph	—	2.7	—	902
2-(2-C₁₀H₇CH₂)-1-(*p*-O₂NC₆H₄CO)	6.0	2.7	—	2165a
2-MeO₂C-2-Me-1-Ph	—	2.9	1.25	3451
1,2-D₂-3-Ph	6	3	—	1625
2-PhCH₂-3-Ph-1-PhNHCO	6	—	—	2103
(*cis*-3-Me-2-Ph)-1-Ph	6.0	—	—	902
2-Ph	5.96	3.32	0.76	2754a

Table 2-X—*continued*

Aziridine, or substituents therein	J_{cis} (Hz)	J_{trans} (Hz)	J_{gem} (Hz)	References
2-Ph	6.0	3.1	0.6	492, 3451
(cis-2-PhCHOH-3-Ph)-1-c-C$_6$H$_{11}$ (erythro)	6.0	—	—	4200
2-Ph	6.1	3.3	0.9	493, 2422
2-(2-C$_{10}$H$_7$)	5.99	3.30	0.76	2754a
2-NC-1-Ph	6.08	3.10	1.07	3451
2-MeO$_2$C-1-p-O$_2$NC$_6$H$_4$	6.19	3.12	1.55	3451
1-(p-O$_2$NC$_6$H$_4$CO)-2-Ph	6.24	3.57	< 0.2	2754a
2-MeO$_2$C-1-p-BzC$_6$H$_4$	6.22	3.01	1.57	3451
1-EtO$_2$C-2-(2-C$_{10}$H$_7$)	6.24	3.52	0.75	2754a
1-Me-2-Ph	6.30	3.14	1.23	2754a
1,2-Ph$_2$	6.30	3.31	1.49	2754a
No substituents	6.3	3.4–3.8	1.5	1568, 2616a
(cis-2-PhCDOH-3-Ph)-1-c-C$_6$H$_{11}$	6.3	—	—	4200
2-MeO$_2$C-1-Ph	6.34	3.06	1.70	3451
1-MeO$_2$C-2-Ph	6.33	3.51	0.80	2754a
MeN(CH$_2$Az)$_2$	—	3.3	1.5	557
2-MeO$_2$C-1-p-MeC$_6$H$_4$	6.39	3.26	1.96	3451
1-Me-2-(2-C$_{10}$H$_7$)	6.34	3.12	1.3	2754a
2-MeO$_2$C-1-p-ClC$_6$H$_4$	6.39	3.21	1.65	3451
2-MeO$_2$C-1-p-MeOC$_6$H$_4$	6.45	3.27	1.83	3451
(trans-2-PhCHOH-3-Ph)-1-c-C$_6$H$_{11}$ (threo)	—	3.5	—	4200
(cis-2-PhCHOH-3-Ph)-1-c-C$_6$H$_{11}$ (threo)	6.5	—	—	4200
(trans-2-PhCHOH-3-Ph)-1-c-C$_6$H$_{11}$ (erythro)	—	4.0	—	4200
cis-3-Me-2-Ph	6.5	—	—	2165
1-R-2-^{13}C	7.0^a	3.8	1.0	3851b
(R = Me, Et, or MeO$_2$CCH$_2$CH$_2$)	5.3^b	—	—	3851b
cis-2-(2-C$_{10}$H$_7$)-3-Me	6.7	—	—	2165a
cis-1-Cl-2-Me	6.7	5.4	2.3	4016
1-PhNHCO-2-Ph	6.73	4.00	0.66	2754a
1-(2 Oxo-3-benzoxazolinyl-2,3-Me$_2$	—	5.6	—	158a
N—C$_6$H$_2$(NO$_2$)$_3$	7.36	—	—	245
2-Ph-1-PhCH=N	7.4	4.6	—	1800
trans-1-Cl-2-Me	7.7	5.7	2.4	4016
1-Cl-2-Ph	8.5	6.3	—	3640
1-Cl-2,2-Me$_2$	—	—	2.6	4109
1-Br-2,2-Me$_2$	—	—	3.1	4109
dl-cis-1-Bz-2-Ph-6-oxa-3-azoniaspiro[2.5]-octane (perchlorate)	9.6	—	—	2299
dl-trans isomer of preceding compound	—	8.2	—	2299
dl-cis-1-Ac analog of preceding compounds	9.7	—	—	2299

^{a} For protons both *cis* to the R group.
^{b} For protons both *trans* to the R group.

Other Nuclear Magnetic Resonances. The ^{13}C chemical shifts (compared to benzene standard) for 1-phenylaziridine have been recorded (*2675*) as C_1, −27.4 ppm; C_o, 7.3; C_m, −0.1; C_p, 7.3; C_2 (the aziridine ring carbon), 103.0. For 1-methylaziridine (*2384*), $C_{CH_3} = 79.9$, and $C_2 = 100.0$. These values accord reasonably well with those for related nonaziridinyl compounds. In EI itself, the coupling constant for ^{13}C and an attached proton is 168.1 Hz (*2616a*). By the inclusion of a small amount (6.93 %) of ionic character in each C—N bond and identical hybridization of the N—H and lone-pair orbitals, maximum overlap orbital functions give a calculated value of 163.0 for J_{13C-H}, agreeing with the measured value (*613*; cf. *2952a*). In some alkylaziridines, the coupling constant for ^{13}C and the proton cis to the alkyl group is 161 ± 1; the corresponding $J_{13C-H(trans)}$ is 171 ± 1 (*3851b*).

Table 2-XI

DATA FROM MICROWAVE SPECTROSCOPY OF AZIRIDINES

	EI	1-MeAz	2-MeAzH (*trans*)
Ground-state rotational constants (MHz):			
A	22,736.1	16,443.15	16,892.59
B	21,192.3	7,219.84	6,533.63
C	13,383	3,152.69	5,761.37
Ground-state rotational constants for the 1-D form (MHz):			
A	0.5(A + C) = 16,757	—	16,082.31
B	—	—	6,338.70
C	0.5(A − C) = 3940.05	—	5,537.81
Dipole moments (D)			
μ_a	—	0.07	0.13
μ_b	1.67	—	0.83
μ_c	0.89	1.23	1.33
μ_{total}	1.89	1.24	1.57
Quadrupole coupling constants of ^{14}N (MHz)			
χ_{aa}	0.69	3.35	0.67
χ_{bb}	2.17	0.63	2.24
χ_{cc}	− 2.86	− 3.98	− 2.91
References	1713, 1992, 2064a, 3570, 3639, 3640, 3788	1612	2312

The ^{19}F NMR spectra of highly fluorinated aziridines (262, 2339) and of four other substituted aziridines [1-(m-FC$_6$H$_4$)Az, 2-(m-FC$_6$H$_4$)Az, 1-(p-FC$_6$H$_4$)Az, and 2-(p-FC$_6$H$_4$Az] have been measured along with those of related compounds. The derived Taft inductive and resonance substituent constants for arylated aziridines are $\sigma_I = 0.07$ for 1-(m-FC$_6$H$_4$)Az and −0.02 for 2-(m-FC$_6$H$_4$)Az; $\sigma_{R^\circ} = -0.29$ for 1-(p-FC$_6$H$_4$)Az and −0.085 for 2-(p-FC$_6$H$_4$)Az. These values harmonize well with other such constants; the change in sign for σ_I reflects the greater effect of the nitrogen atom, compared to carbon, when bound to the aromatic ring (558, 2866, 3864).

MICROWAVE SPECTRA AND ELECTRON DIFFRACTION DATA

Data from microwave spectroscopy of aziridines are reproduced in Table 2-XI, and the deduced molecular dimensions are in Table 2-XII. These results

Table 2-XII

STRUCTURAL PARAMETERS OF AZIRIDINES

	EI	1-MeAz	2-MeAzH (trans)	1-ClAz	1-PhAz
Interatomic distances (Å)					
C—C, ring	1.480	1.479[a]	1.480[a]	1.481	1.54
C—H, ring	1.083	1.083[a]	1.083[a]	1.074	1.08
C—N, ring	1.488	1.488[a]	1.488[a]	1.489	1.46
N—substituent	1.000[a]	1.470	1.01	1.754	1.41
C—C of Me	—	—	1.517	—	—
C—H in Me	—	1.090[a]	1.090[a]	—	—
Bond angles (deg)					
C—N—C, ring	—	59.6[a]	—	—	—
H—C—H, ring	116.68	116.7[a]	116.68[a]	112.9	—
H—C—H in Me	—	109.4[a]	109.4[a]	—	—
Ring plane–N-substituent	112	116.85	112[a]	114.1	125.5
C—C $\perp$[b]	—	—	33.0	—	—
H$_2$C—N[c]	159.4	159.6[a]	—	—	—
H$_2$C—C[d]	—	—	—	155.3	—
C—C—C	—	—	120.50	—	—
References	1884, 3639	1612	1612	2195	2679

[a] Assumed.

[b] Angle between the C—Me bond and a line perpendicular to the ring plane.

[c] Angle between the ring C—N bond and the line that bisects the H—C—H angle and lies in the H—C—H plane.

[d] Angle between the ring C—C bond and the line that bisects the H—C—H angle and lies in the H—C—H plane.

Table 2-XIII

CRYSTAL STRUCTURE OF AZIRIDINES

Aziridine, or substituents therein	Crystal class	Space group	Unit cell dimensions[a]			References
			a (Å)	b (Å)	c (Å)	
None	Triclinic	—	4.83	8.15	11.30	3209
1-(Cl$_3$CCHOH)	—	P2$_1$2$_1$2$_1$	10.50	9.25	7.75	102, 3234
1-(Br$_3$CCHOH)	—	P2$_1$2$_1$2$_1$	11.07	9.36	7.98	102
2,3-[(CH$_2$)$_3$]-1-(p-BrC$_6$H$_4$CO)	Monoclinic	P2$_1$/c	8.83	10.15	12.63	3864a
2,3-(CH$_2$OCH$_2$)-1-(p-IC$_6$H$_4$SO$_2$)	Monoclinic	C2/c	19.76	8.17	15.72	3605a, 4192
2,3-[(CH$_2$)$_4$]-1-(p-IC$_6$H$_4$SO$_2$)	Monoclinic	P2$_1$/n	10.35	16.33	8.22	3606
2,3-[(CH$_2$)$_5$]-1,1-Me$_2$, iodide	—	Pna2$_1$	17.31	8.58	7.56	3608
2,3-[(CH$_2$)$_5$]-1,1-Me$_2$, iodide	—	Pmn2$_1$	7.58	9.02	8.98	3604
2,3-[(CH$_2$)$_{10}$]-1,1-Me$_2$, iodide (trans)	—	Pmn2$_1$	8.26	11.00	8.70	3607
2,3-[(CH$_2$)$_{10}$]-1,1-Me$_2$, iodide (cis)	Orthorhombic	Pnam	21.36	9.07	8.29	3605
N-(BrC$_6$H$_4$SO$_2$)-mitomycin A · 0.5C$_6$H$_6$	Monoclinic	C2	19.70	8.24	16.05	3635, 3636
Cu(AzH)$_4$(NO$_3$)$_2$	Tetragonal	I$\bar{4}$	10.29	10.29	7.09	261

[a] Data on molecular structure given for all except 1-(Br$_3$CCHOH)Az.

largely speak for themselves. The quadrupole coupling constant measurements confirm that the barrier to nitrogen inversion in EI is much higher than in ammonia and other amines (*3570*). This inversion barrier has been treated theoretically by crystal field–LCAO–MO methods (*4196*). From an experimentally deduced inversion frequency of <15 kHz, the lower limit of the inversion barrier height is 11.6 kcal (*2064a*). The same work found the principal field gradient axis system coupling constants as χ_{aa}, 0.685 ± 0.005, $\chi_{\beta\beta}$, 3.004 ± 0.09, and $\chi_{\gamma\gamma}$, −3.689 ± 0.09 MHz; the Walsh model of bonding is more appropriate than the Coulson-Moffitt scheme.

CRYSTAL STRUCTURES

X-Ray diffraction has been applied to determination of crystal and molecular structures of some aziridines and aziridinium salts. The results are given in Table 2-XIII; no interpretation will be attempted here.

Electrical and Magnetic Properties

The dielectric constant of liquid EI is 21.9 at 0°C, 19.6 at 15°C, and 18.3 at 25°C; these lead to calculated dipole moments, respectively, of 2.44–2.46, 2.37–2.39, and 2.32–2.35 D (*2054, 2055*). The limiting dipole moment in benzene at infinite dilution is 1.73 D (*2097*) or 1.77 D (*2054*), and that for gaseous EI was reported as 1.89 D on the basis of microwave measurements (*1992*). Thus considerable association occurs in the pure liquid. The limiting molar polarization is 70.6 ($\times 10^{-25}$ cm³) (*2054*), in reasonable agreement with the value 63.87 previously calculated on the basis of the δ-function potential model via derived bond polarizabilities (*2333a*). The value of ≈ 80 (*2097*) is probably less good.

Only a very few other dipole moments of aziridinyl compounds have been measured; one such is 2-(1-aziridinyl)-2,4,4,6,6-pentachloro-2,2,4,4,6,6-hexahydro-1,3,5-triazatriphosphorine, for which $\mu = 3.07$ D (*2133*).

The specific conductance of EI was found to be rather high, $\kappa_0 = 8 \times 10^{-6}$ ohm^{-1} cm^{-1} (*2054*).

The measured magnetic susceptibilities ($\chi \times 10^6$) of EI picrate (−0.58) and TEM (−0.74) are higher than the values calculated from atomic and bond susceptibilities (−0.40 and −0.61, respectively); this is probably because of delocalization of electrons in the aziridine ring (*2486, 2946*).

3

REACTIONS OF AZIRIDINES

Introduction

There are two principal properties that account for all reactions of aziridines which involve the aziridine ring. These are the reactivity of the ring nitrogen atom and that of the strained three-membered ring. The reactive properties of the ring nitrogen atom may be attributed to the unshared pair of electrons on the nitrogen and thus closely resemble such properties of other nonaromatic amines. Reactions due to the strained three-membered ring all involve ring destruction or ring opening, forming either acyclic or ultimately ring-expanded compounds.

Nitrogen-substituted aziridines may be broadly divided into two groups of compounds. These are Group A (*activated* aziridines), compounds in which the substituent is capable of conjugating with the unshared pair of electrons on the aziridine nitrogen (e.g., the carbonyl group, making the aziridine nitrogen a tertiary amide nitrogen) and Group B (*basic* aziridines), compounds in which there is no such substituent (e.g., EI). Because of such conjugation in activated aziridines, reactions involving only the aziridine nitrogen are exhibited chiefly by compounds of Group B. Thus these reactions closely resemble those of typical secondary and tertiary amines. Such reactions may also be conveniently classified as ring-preserving reactions.

Ring-Preserving Reactions

One major difference exists between reactions of Group B aziridines and those of other secondary or tertiary amines. Reactions designed to produce nitrogen-substituted products containing the aziridine ring intact must be carried out under special conditions wherein the reactant aziridine and the product aziridine are both stable with respect to ring opening.

Most ring-opening reactions may be formulated as substitutions involving attack of a nucleophile at an aziridine carbon atom. With basic aziridines, ring-opening reactions may be ascribed to the reactivity of the protonated or quaternized aziridine or the Lewis acid–aziridine adduct.

These species are in some cases very reactive while in others they are reasonably stable. When very reactive aziridinium ions may be formed, often only catalytic amounts of relatively weak acids are necessary to promote a ring-opening reaction beyond realization of any other. In the absence of acidic reagents the basic aziridines do not undergo ring-opening reactions except under unusual conditions. Thus the one precaution usually necessary in amine-type reactions is to prevent formation, in even catalytic amounts, of one of the reactive species illustrated above.

An activated aziridine not only is still sensitive to acidic reagents but also undergoes ring opening with nucleophilic reagents even in the absence of acid. Fortunately many reactions producing such aziridines may be carried out at temperatures low enough to yield the desired aziridines without serious losses to competitive ring-opening reactions. Maintenance of low temperatures and use of nonpolar solvents are the usual precautions taken when this type of aziridine is prepared from a basic aziridine.

FORMATION OF SALTS AND COMPLEXES OF BASIC AZIRIDINES

Protonic Acid Salts. The simplest reaction involving only the nitrogen of basic aziridines is reaction with a protonic acid to form the aziridinium salt.

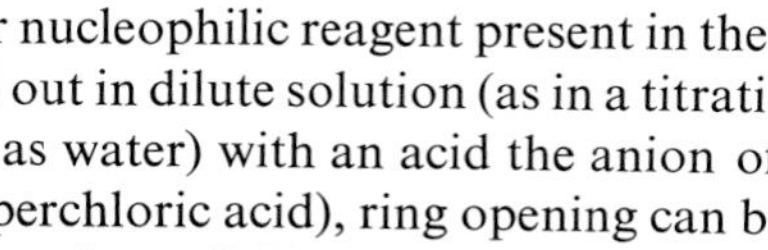

As mentioned previously, the protonated aziridine is a reactive species capable of undergoing a ring-opening reaction with X^-, solvent, basic aziridine nitrogen, or any other nucleophilic reagent present in the medium. If, however, the reaction is carried out in dilute solution (as in a titration) in a solvent of low nucleophilicity (such as water) with an acid the anion of which is also of low nucleophilicity (e.g., perchloric acid), ring opening can be completely avoided.

Apparently because of possibilities for ring opening, no report appeared before 1955 of the determination of base strengths in aqueous solutions for aziridines (*2767a*). Since that time a number of such values have been determined and these are shown in Table 3-I.

Table 3-I

BASICITY CONSTANTS FOR BASIC AZIRIDINES

$$\underset{\underset{R}{N}}{\overset{R^2 \quad R^3}{\underset{R^1}{\bigtriangleup}R^4}} + H_2O \rightleftharpoons \underset{\underset{R \; H}{N^+}}{\overset{R^2 \quad R^3}{\underset{R^1}{\bigtriangleup}R^4}} \; OH^-$$

R	R¹	R²	R³	R⁴	T (°C)	$10^6 k_B$	References
H	H	H	H	H	25	1.0	2767a, 3228
H	H	H	H	H	22	0.78	525
H	H	H	H	H	25	0.792	963
H	H	H	H	H	25	1.1	3185
H	H	H	H	H	25	0.7–0.9	264
H	Et	H	H	H	25	2.0	2767a
H	Et	H	H	H	25	1.99	525
H	Et	H	Ph	H	20	4.8	1026
H	Me	Me	H	H	25	4.3	2767a
H	Me	Me	H	H	23	4.2	525
H	Me	Me	Me (cis)	H	23	4.6	525
H	Me	Me	Me (trans)	H	24	4.7	525
Me	H	H	H	H	25	0.72	3185
Me	H	H	H	H	25	1.03	963
Et	H	H	H	H	24	0.81	525
Bu	H	H	H	H	25	0.65–0.8	264
Bu	H	H	H	H	25	0.80	907
Et	Et	H	H	H	24–25	1.55	525
Et	Me	H	Me (cis)	H	24–25	3.7	525
Et	Me	H	Me (trans)	H	23	26.7	525
PhCH₂CH₂	H	H	H	H	25	0.229	907
HOCHEtCH₂	H	H	H	H	25	0.196	963
CH₂=CHCH₂	H	H	H	H	25	0.164	963
HOCH₂CH₂	H	H	H	H	25	0.132	907
Me₃SnCH₂	H	H	H	H	—	0.0186[a]	2161
NCCH₂CH₂	H	H	H	H	25	0.0028	907

[a] In aqueous dioxane.

Although no basicity constant of an aziridine was reported until 1955, Gabriel (*1385*) prepared stable crystalline salts of EI with acids as derivatives of his new compound in 1888. The picrate was obtained simply by mixing aqueous solutions of picric acid and EI. Reaction of $PtCl_4$ with an aqueous mixture of HCl and EI or BiI_3 with HI and EI gave salts, presumably $(AzH_2)_2PtCl_6$ and $(AzH_2)_3(BI_4)_2I$. Even though protonated EI has long been recognized as a very reactive species, several relatively stable salts involving its association with such unwieldy anions as those of the acids just mentioned or 2,4,6-trinitrobenzenesulfonate anion (*719*) and simpler anions of low nucleophilicity such as BF_4^- (*1610*) and HSO_4^- (*2093*) have been prepared.

In general the stability of the salts of aziridines appears to depend to some extent on the base strength of the aziridine and the acid strength of the acid, to a much greater extent on the nucleophilicity of the acid anion and the crystal structure of the solid salt, and especially on the steric features (i.e., substituents on carbon and nitrogen) of the aziridine. Thus the hydrochlorides of EI, 2-methylaziridine, 2-ethylaziridine, and 2,3-dimethylaziridine were all easily isolated as crystalline solids at −78°C and appeared to be stable indefinitely at this temperature. On warming to room temperature, however, they all polymerized or at least underwent reaction exothermically (*719, 1996*). The hydrochloride of 2,2-dimethylaziridine was found to be stable in dry air for several days at room temperature (*719*) and aziridines containing a greater number of carbon substitutents or larger substituents form crystalline hydrochlorides which are apparently much more stable (*566, 568, 719, 1698, 2101, 3487*).

In one instance a stable crystalline hydrochloride of an aziridine containing only a nitrogen substituent, methyl p-(1-aziridinylmethyl)hydrocinnamate (**1**), has been reported (*3277*). However, tests suitable for distinguishing the aziridine hydrochloride from the dihydrochloride of the piperazine (**2**) which could have formed were not given and the method of preparation appears to be capable of producing the piperazine derivative (*963*).

$$p\text{-AzCH}_2\text{C}_6\text{H}_4\text{CH}_2\text{CH}_2\text{CO}_2\text{Me}$$
1

2

In reading reports of aziridine hydrohalides which do not specify such discriminatory characterization data (e.g., several examples in Table 3-II) consideration should be given to the dimeric piperazine derivatives as alternatives.

While aziridinium hydrogen sulfate, $AzH \cdot H_2SO_4$, is quite stable at room temperature (*2093*), attempts to prepare aziridinium sulfate, $(AzH)_2 \cdot H_2SO_4$, by the same procedure gave a product which decomposed within 2 hours at room temperature (*963*). In a similar manner the dihydrogen phosphate $AzH \cdot H_3PO_4$ was found to be completely decomposed after 15 days at room temperature and the p-toluenesulfonate after about 17 days; the nitric acid salt exploded shortly after preparation. Ethylenimine salts were obviously formed at low temperatures from salicylic acid, glycolic acid, formic acid, acetic acid,

benzoic acid, and dichloroacetic acid but decomposed within a very short time
(*963*). *N*-Alkyl- and even *N*-acylaziridinium salts have been made and their
NMR spectra recorded, but details are not yet available (*4182*); low temperatures were probably used.

Salts have been obtained from 1,1-dinitroethane and 2,2-dimethylaziridine
or 2-ethylaziridine (*313*). However, no characterization data or indication of
their stability is given.

Also reported but not properly characterized are heparin salts of 2,5-
bis(1-aziridinyl)hydroquinone and a bis(1-aziridinyl)-*p*-benzoquinone (*1027*).

The aziridine derivative **3** has been represented by the zwitterion structure **4**
(*3097*).

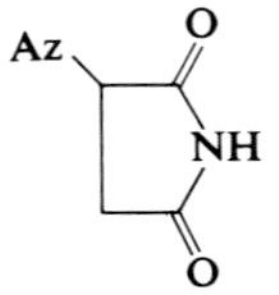

3 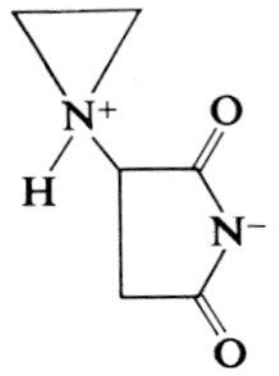   4

The only evidence given for the improbable structure **4**, however, was that the
compound is neutral in aqueous solution. A similar presumed "inner-salt"
structure was assigned (*2448, 2451*) for the aziridine **5**. On the basis of melting
point, solubility, reactivity compared with analogous compounds, and the
infrared spectrum this derivative was depicted as structure **6**.

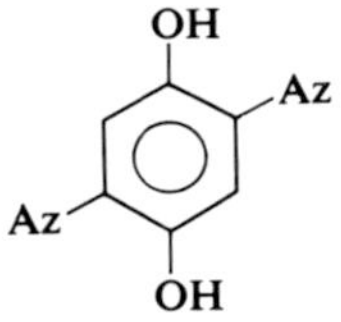

5

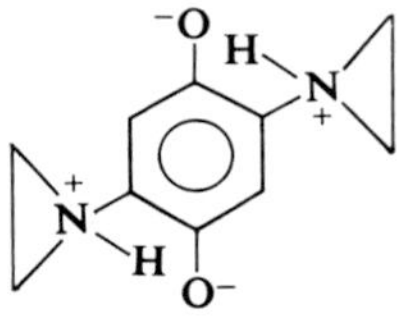

6

Assignment of **6** as the correct structure was challenged by other workers
(*1422*) and indeed the infrared data presented are best interpreted in terms of
a nonionic but strongly hydrogen-bonded structure **7** (*3348*). Similarly

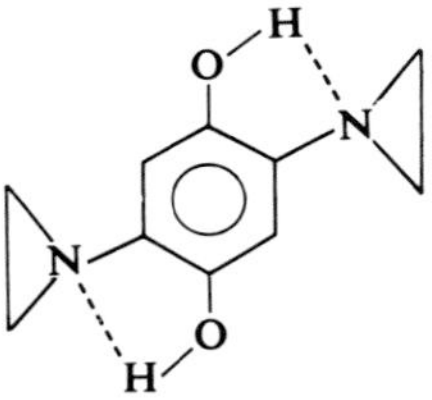

7

2,5-bis(1-aziridinyl)-*p*-benzoquinone, unlike other diamino-*p*-benzoquinones, probably has the quinone structure (corresponding to **5**) and not the dipolarion structure (corresponding to **6**) (*826*).

The products most often reported from decomposition of aziridine salts are water-soluble polymers. Ethylenimine hydrochloride polymerized at room temperature within about 10 minutes after preparation but treatment of the freshly isolated salt with aqueous alkali allowed the isolation of EI and 1-(2-aminoethyl)aziridine in about equal proportions (*1996*). The decomposition of aziridinium sulfate, $(AzH_2)_2SO_4$, yielded EI as a volatile product and 2-aminoethyl hydrogen sulfate in addition to polymer (*963*). 2,2-Dimethyl-aziridinium picrate rearranges on heating to 1-picrylamino-2-methyl-2-propanol (*715*).

A number of aziridinium salts of protonic acids which have been isolated as solids are shown in Table 3-II.

Table 3-II

AZIRIDINIUM SALTS FROM PROTONIC ACIDS

Aziridine, or substituents therein	Acid	M.p., (°C)	References
No substituents	HCl	Unstable at room temp.	*719, 1996*
No substituents	H_2SO_4 (hydrogen sulfate)	90.5–91	*2093*
No substituents	H_2SO_4 (sulfate)	61–65 dec within 2 hr at room temp.	*963, 2093*
No substituents	HBF_4	166–169	*1610*
No substituents	$HClO_4$	—	*1999*
No substituents	$(O_2N)_3C_6H_2SO_3H$	189 dec	*719*
No substituents	Oxalic acid	115 dec	*1392*
No substituents	Various polyhalophenols	—	*4099*
No substituents	Picric acid	125–127	*715*
		142	*1385*
No substituents	Polynitrophenols	—	*4100*
No substituents	$F_2P(O)OH$	98	*629*
1-Me	$HAuCl_4$	95	*2117*
2-Me	HCl	Unstable at room temp.	*719*
2-Me	H_2SO_4 (hydrogen sulfate)	—	*2093*
2-Me	$(O_2N)_3C_6H_2SO_3H$	173–174 dec	*719*

Table 3-II—*continued*

Aziridine, or substituents therein	Acid	M.p., (°C)	References
2-Me	Picric acid	110	*2519*
1-Et	Picric acid	111	*2662, 2269*
1-Et	HBF$_4$	—	*2758*
2-Et	HCl	Unstable at room temp.	*719*
2-Et	Picric acid	103–104	*715*
2,2-Me$_2$	HCl	54–56	*719, 3130*
2,2-Me$_2$	Picric acid	124–126	*283, 3131*
		128–128.5	*1431*
2,3-Me$_2$ (*meso* and *dl*)	HCl	Unstable at room temp.	*719*
2,2,3,3-Me$_4$	HCl	—	*719*
1-iso-Pr-2,3-Me$_2$ (*trans*)	(O$_2$N)$_3$C$_6$H$_2$SO$_3$H	211.5–212.5	*1680*
2,2-Et$_2$-3-Me	HCl	94–95	*1698*
1-iso-Pr-2,2,3-Me$_2$	HCl	131–133 dec	*1694*
2,2-Pr$_2$-3-Et	HCl	152–155	*1698*
2-Et-2-Ph	HCl	191–191.5	*568*
1,3-Me$_2$-2-Ph	Picric acid		
dl-threo		142–144	*2708, 3479*
erythro		97.5–98.5	*2636, 3464*
2-Ph-2-Pr	HCl	68–69	*568*
2-Et-3-Me-2-Ph	HCl	158–159	*578*
	HCl	180–185	*1725*
	Picric acid	135–136	*1725*
3-Et-2-Ph-2-Pr	HCl	140–141	*1698*
3-Me-2,2-Ph$_2$	HCl	139–140	*566*
	HCl	170–175	*1725*
	Picric acid	199–200	*566*
3,3-Me$_2$-2,2-Ph$_2$	HCl	227–228	*2101*
3-Et-2,2-Ph$_2$	HCl	144.5–145	*566*
2,3-Epimino-1,7,7-Me$_2$-norbornane	HCl	250 dec	*1007*
2,3-Epimino-1,7,7-Me$_2$-norbornane	H$_2$SO$_4$	272 dec	*1007*
2,3-Epimino-1,7,7-Me$_2$-norbornane	HNO$_3$	198–199 dec	*1007*
2,3-Epimino-1,7,7-Me$_2$-norbornane	Picric acid	214–215 dec	*1007*
1,2-[(CH$_2$)$_3$]	Picric acid	152	*552*
1,2-[(CH$_2$)$_3$]	Picric acid	115	*3458*
2,3-[(CH$_2$)$_4$]	Picric acid	120–122	*3456*
1-Me-2,3-[(CH$_2$)$_4$]	Picric acid	128	*3457*
1-[p-(MeO$_2$CCH$_2$CH$_2$)C$_6$H$_4$CH$_2$]	HCl	220–225	*2741*
1-Et-2,3-[(CH$_2$)$_4$]	Picric acid	118–120	*2131*
1-Bu-2,3-[(CH$_2$)$_4$]	Picric acid	140–141	*2820*
2,3-[(CH$_2$)$_6$]	Picric acid	190–195 dec	*2047*
1-Et-2,2-[(CH$_2$)$_5$]	HCl	—	*1418*
2,3-[(CH$_2$)$_{10}$] (*trans*)	Picrolonic acid	235 dec	*1102*

Table 3-II—*continued*

Aziridine, or substituents therein	Acid	M.p., (°C)	References
1-PhCH$_2$-2,2-[(CH$_2$)$_5$]	HCl	209	*1418*
(2,2-[(CH$_2$)$_5$]AzCH$_2$)$_2$	HCl	212	*1418*
2,3-(CH$_2$OCH$_2$)	Picric acid	161	*1095*
1-Me-2,3-(CH$_2$OCH$_2$)	Picric acid	156–158	*1095*
2-(H$_2$NCH$_2$)	Picric acid (dipicrate)	170–172	*3721*
2-(EtO$_2$C)	Picric acid	90–91	*1364, 2215*
2-HOCMe$_2$CH$_2$CH$_2$-3,3-Me$_2$	HCl	230	*3487*
2-Bz-1-PhCH$_2$-3-Ph	HCl	129-131 dec	*788, 793*
1-(NCCH$_2$CH$_2$)-2,2-Me$_2$	Picric acid	109–110	*3498*
1-(NCCH$_2$CH$_2$)-2,3-[(CH$_2$)$_4$]	Picrolonic acid	136	*2820*
1-(H$_2$NCH$_2$CH$_2$)-2,2-Me$_2$	Picric acid	163.5–164.5 dec	*3498*
1,2-(CH$_2$CH$_2$CMe$_2$)	Picric acid	187.5–189 dec	*2340*
1,2-(CH$_2$CH$_2$CHMe)	Picric acid	149–150 dec	*2340*
1,2-(CH$_2$CH$_2$CHMe)-2-Me	Picric acid	162.5–164	*2340*

	HCl	—	*2538a*
3β-HO-16α,17α-epimino-Δ^5-pregnenone-20	HCl	247–249	*982*
AzCH$_2$(CHOH)$_4$CH$_2$Az	HClO$_4$	152–156	*676, 1569a*

Complexes. As typical amines, aziridines readily form coordination compounds by donation of the unshared pair of electrons on the nitrogen atom to molecules or metal ions capable of accepting such electron pairs.

Of particular interest is the apparent wide variation in the stability of the aziridine ring when complexed in this manner. The proton may be treated as such an electron acceptor and it is well known that the protonated aziridine is very reactive in ring-opening reactions. Aluminum chloride, presumably through formation of an EI–aluminum chloride adduct, has been used to catalyze ring-opening reactions of EI (*468, 734, 1714*). A complex of EI and aluminum hydride has been suggested as an intermediate in a ring-opening polymerization (*1032*). The reaction of EI with BF$_3$ in ether at −80° to −60°C was reported to give a ring-opened product (*3711*) although undoubtedly the initial product was an adduct.

In contrast to these results the EI–trimethylboron complex could be heated for several hours at 100° to 140°C without causing any ring opening (*505*). At these temperatures the complex was partially dissociated into EI and BMe_3. Thus, if the complexed EI were very susceptible to ring opening, it should have undergone such reaction with the noncomplexed EI. Similarly, the BH_3–EI adduct has been reported to be quite stable at 100°C although some polymerization and/or other ring opening (<33%) occurred within about 45 minutes at this temperature (*540*).

Several adducts between aziridines and boron compounds are shown in Table 3-III.

Table 3-III

ADDUCTS OF AZIRIDINES AND BORON COMPOUNDS

R	BX_3	M.p., (°C)	References
H	BMe_3	10–12	*505*
Me	BMe_3	94.2–94.4	*2507*
H	BH_3	≈40	*540*
H	$B(OMe)_3$	2–3	*1272*
H	$B(OPh)_3$	63–65	*1272*

Treatment of AlH_3 : NMe_3 in toluene at −60°C with EI, followed by evaporation of the solvent, was reported to yield the AlH_3–EI complex (*2430*). However, the product obtained in this manner decomposed explosively.

Addition of EI to a kerosene solution of decaborane gave a yellow precipitate from which decaborane could be recovered by treatment with acid (*2421*). Although not fully characterized the yellow solid was apparently the $B_{10}H_{14} \cdot AzH$ complex.

A 2:1 complex was formed from EI and SiF_4, $SiF_4 \cdot 2AzH$ (*1566*). Treatment of the adduct with ammonia caused displacement of EI, forming the ammonia complex $SiF_4 \cdot 2NH_3$. An addition compound between a uranium(V) alkoxide and EI, $U(OCH_2CF_3)_5 \cdot 3AzH$, has been reported (*2005*).

A montmorillonite–triethylammonium complex with EI has been reported wherein the sorbed EI molecules are retained in the interlayer spaces (*1565*).

The first detailed study of coordination compounds formed from EI and metal ions was reported in 1961 (*1954*). Labile complexes with divalent copper, nickel, cobalt, manganese, and mercury were isolated and identified. Complexes from silver, zinc, cadmium, and lead salts all readily lost EI on exposure to vacuum or air. Stable inert complexes of cobalt(III), chromium(III), palladium(II), and platinum(IV) were also prepared (*1955*). It was concluded that EI behaves as a typical amine ligand with bonding similar to that in ammonia and other amine complexes. The maximum coordination number was found to be the same as in the ammonia complexes but the steric effect of the aziridine ring prevented the attainment of such a number in some cases. From the data obtained the steric properties of EI appeared to fall between those of methylamine and ethylamine. Studies of the formation constants showed that the metal-to-nitrogen bond was in all cases weaker than that of corresponding ammonia complexes. The rate for dissociation, in an excess of acid, of the nickel(II)–EI complex has been measured and found comparable to that of the ammonia complex (*2526*).

The complex of 1,1,6,6-tetraphenyl-2,4-hexadiyne-1,6-diol with EI (1:2) (*3557*) may be an inclusion compound.

It is reported that the EI ring is quite stable when bonded to a metal in a solid complex. Although some such complexes gradually lost EI after several months of storage, this apparently occurred without ring opening.

Similarly the presence of metal ions in EI solutions did not appear to cause a significantly more rapid ring opening. However, silver and copper salts have been reported as catalysts for polymerization of EI (*3094*).

The absorption spectra of the octahedral EI complexes $[\text{Ni}(\text{AzH})_6](\text{NO}_3)_2$ and $[\text{Co}(\text{AzH})_6](\text{NO}_3)_2$ (*2097*) have been studied. From these data and measurements of the dipole moment and polarizability of EI, calculations of bond energies were made using the electrostatic theory. The values appeared to agree with calculated bond energies of comparable complexes [e.g., $M(\text{NH}_3)_6{}^{2+}$].

A number of rhodium–EI complexes have been reported (*3142*). Of special interest is the reaction of $\text{Rh}(\text{AzH})_3\text{Cl}_3$ with HI or of $[\text{Rh}(\text{AzH})_3(\text{H}_2\text{O})_3]\text{Cl}_3$ with KI to produce the Rh(I) complex $\text{Rh}(\text{AzH})_3\text{I}$. The ease of such reduction by iodide ions indicates that the redox potential of the Rh(I)/Rh(III) couple is close to that of the I^-/I_2 couple, reported as surprising because EI would not be expected to act as a π-bonding ligand [e.g., a phosphine, which stabilizes Rh(I)].

Treatment of $\text{Rh}(\text{AzH})_3\text{Cl}_3$ with hot (about 95°C) HBr solution gave $\text{Rh}(\text{AzH})_3\text{Br}_3$. Also treatment with HCl solution was shown not to result in ring opening of the coordinated EI. Apparently coordinate saturation of the nitrogen atom precludes addition of a proton, and the coordinated rhodium ion does not exert a labilizing effect on the ring to any extent comparable to that of an attached hydrogen ion.

In Table 3-IV a number of metal ion–EI complexes are shown.

1-(2-Aminoethyl)aziridine has been shown to form complexes with Ni(II), Co(II), Pd(II), and Cu(II) (*963, 3057a*).

Inasmuch as the hydrogen bond may be considered to connote complex formation, even though weak, several hydrogen bond studies involving aziridines are appropriately mentioned here.

Infrared absorption spectra for solutions of EI in carbon tetrachloride clearly show the occurrence of association through N—H—N bonds (3542).

Table 3-IV

METAL ION–ETHYLENIMINE COORDINATION COMPOUNDS

Labile complexes		Inert complexes	
$[M(AzH)_x]X_y$	References	$[M(AzH)_x]X_y$	References
$[Cu(AzH)_4](NO_3)_2$	1954	$[Cr(AzH)_4Cl_2]Cl$	1955
$[Cu(AzH)_4]SO_4 \cdot 1.5H_2O$	1954	$[Cr(AzH)_5(H_2O)]Cl_3$	1955
$[Cu(AzH)_4]I_2$	1954	$[Co(en)_2(AzH)Cl]Cl_2 \cdot H_2O(cis)$	1955
$[Cu(AzH)_4]Cl_2$	1954	$[Co(AzH)_4(NO_2)_2]Br$	1955
$[Hg(AzH)_2](NO_3)_2$	1954	$Pd(AzH)_2Cl_2(trans)$	1955
$Hg(AzH)Br_2$	1954	$[Pt(AzH)_4]Cl_2$	1955
$Hg(AzH)Cl_2$	1954	$Pt(AzH)_2Cl_2$	1955
$[Mn(AzH)_5]I_2$	1954	$[Pt(AzH)_4Cl_2]Cl_2$	1955
$[Mn(AzH)_4]Cl_2$	1954	$[Pt(AzH)_4Cl_2]PtCl_6$	1955
$[Co(AzH)_6]I_2$	1954	$[Rh(AzH)_{6-n}X_n]X_{3-n}$	
$[Co(AzH)_4]Cl_2$	1954	$(X = Cl, Br, or I;$	
$[Co(AzH)_6][Co(CO)_4]_2{}^a$	1715	9 examples)	3142
$[Ni(AzH)_6](NO_3)_2$	1954	$[Rh(AzH)_5Cl][HgI_4]$	3142
$Ni(AzH)_6]Cl_2$	3057a	$[Rh(AzH)_3(H_2O)_2(OH)][HgI_4]$	3142
$[Ni(AzH)_6]I_2$	1954	$[Rh(NH_3)_5(AzH)]Cl_3$	3142
$[Ni(AzH)_6]Br_2$	1954	$Rh(AzH)_3I$	3142
$[Ni(AzH)_4]SO_4$	1954		
$[Ni(AzH)_4]Cl_2$	1954		
$Ni(AzH)_4Cl_2$ (trans)	3057a		
$Ni(AzH)_2Cl_2$	3057a		
$[Co(AzH)_4NO]Cl_2 \cdot H_2O$	1955a		
$[Co(AzH)_4NO](NO_3)_2$	1955a		

[a] An infrared spectral study of this complex has been made (3705).

NMR studies in this solvent indicated that EI (as well as azetidine and pyrrolidine) tends to form trimeric aggregates (556). Other secondary amines (piperidine, hexamethylenimine, dimethylamine, and diethylamine) were found to be tetrameric. On dilution the aggregates dissociate and in chloroform they do not exist, owing to complexing with the solvent. The equilibrium constant for formation of the 1:1 EI—chloroform complex has been reported as 1.70 at 22°C (556) and 3 ± 1 at 38°C (4159).

The nitrogen inversion rate in *pure* 1-phenylaziridine is so high that a single aziridine ring hydrogen signal was observed in the NMR spectrum at a temperature as low as $-77°C$ (*453*). In methanol, however, two signals due to the individual stereoisomers appeared at only about $-60°C$. Stabilization of the inverse forms by hydrogen bonding was suggested.

The extent of association between phenol and EI or 2,2-dimethylaziridine in carbon tetrachloride (*2331*) and between MeOD and EI or 1-methylaziridine (*3185*) has been determined. The data show that the aziridines form weaker hydrogen bonds than other alkylamines. At low concentrations, water in $(2\text{-MeAz})_3PO$ is monomeric because of hydrogen bonding with the solvent but the proportion of dimers and higher polymers (as shown by NMR) increases with water concentration (*4190*).

Infrared studies on gaseous mixtures of EI and MeOH indicate hydrogen-bonded complexes (*2558, 2559*).

Alkylation of 1-Alkylaziridines. The preparation of quaternary aziridinium salts from acyclic compounds (e.g., treatment of the perchlorate of an enamine with diazomethane) has been discussed elsewhere (p. 80). This section is concerned only with the alkylation of 1-alkylaziridines to give stable quaternary salts.

Formally such alkylation is similar to the reaction of a 1-alkylaziridine with a protonic acid.

$$\text{(1)}$$

$$\text{(2)}$$

An obvious difference in the two reactions is in their rates. Reaction 1, a simple neutralization, is virtually instantaneous and much, much faster than any ring-opening reaction which might take place with the product. Reaction 2, a typical S_N2 process, has a much lower rate and one which encounters competition, in many cases, with ring-opening reactions which may destroy the salt. The principal ring-opening reactions involved are as follows:

$$\text{Solvent} + \quad \longrightarrow \quad \text{Solvent—CH}_2\text{CH}_2\text{NRR}' \qquad \text{(3)}$$

$$X^- + \underset{\underset{R \quad R'}{N^+}}{\triangle} \longrightarrow XCH_2CH_2NRR' \xrightarrow{R'X} XCH_2CH_2\overset{+}{N}RR'_2 \; X^- \quad (4)$$

$$\underset{\underset{R}{N}}{\triangle} + \underset{\underset{R \quad R'}{N^+}}{\triangle} \longrightarrow \underset{\underset{R \quad CH_2CH_2NRR'}{N^+}}{\triangle} \longrightarrow \begin{array}{l} \text{polymeric or} \\ \text{other products} \end{array} \quad (5)$$

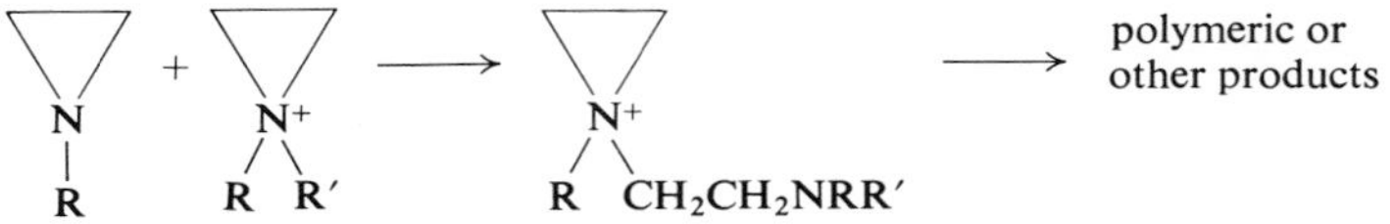

While the successful preparation of a salt from a protonic acid usually depends only on the inherent stability of the isolated salt **8**, the success of reaction 2 in preparative work depends also on the rates of the above side reactions relative to that of 2. Thus far, the only successful preparations of quaternary aziridinium salts by alkylation reactions have involved aziridines containing substituents in the 2,2- or 2,3-positions. With such carbon-substituted aziridines the side reactions (3, 4, and 5 reactions relative to reaction 2) are considerably slower than for carbon-unsubstituted aziridines. Several obvious methods for decreasing the rates of reactions 3 or 4 relative to 2 include the use of a nonnucleophilic solvent, a very reactive alkylating agent, and an alkylating agent which produces an anion (X^-) of low nucleophilicity.

Treatment of 1-benzylaziridine with benzyl chloride (*1550*) or of 1-methylaziridine with methyl iodide (*2428*) failed to produce the quaternary aziridinium salts because of reaction 4. Similarly when *N*-methylcyclohexenimine was treated with methyl iodide in ether the major product isolated was *trans*-2-iodo-*N*,*N*-dimethylcyclohexylamine (*1100, 3457, 3814*); cyclopentenimine also underwent ring opening (*1104*). Although higher cycloalkenimines, including cycloheptenimine, have been exhaustively alkylated with methyl iodide to give stable aziridinium salts (*1101, 1102*) the six-membered ring of cyclohexenimine is very nearly planar (*3606*) and presumably no axial hydrogens exist to obstruct nucleophilic attack by iodide ion (*1100*).

Reaction 4 as simply shown above does not accurately represent the effects of this reaction in alkylation of 1-alkylaziridines. Quaternization of *trans*-1,2-dimethyl-3-isopropylaziridine in benzene with trideuteriomethyl iodide gives the aziridinium salt but an equilibrium exists during the reaction (*451,452*).

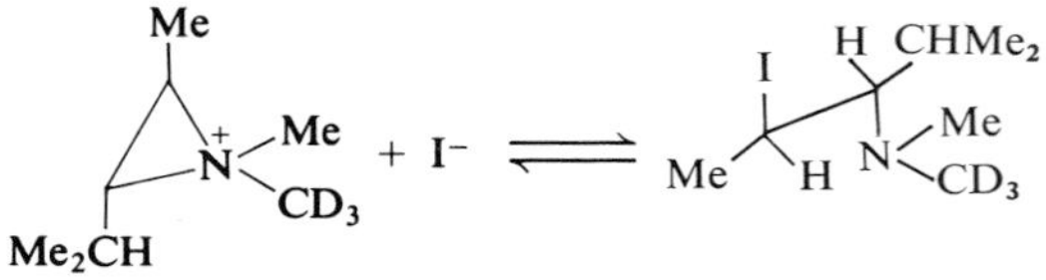

Although the aziridinium salt was isolated in high yield it was thus shown that the ring opening by iodide ion is competitive with the alkylation. It appears that the ability to produce a quaternary aziridinium salt by alkylation of a 1-alkylaziridine depends not only on the kinetic control exerted by the various side reactions but in some cases also on the position of equilibrium in reaction 4 and/or the ability to shift this equilibrium position (e.g., by formation of an insoluble aziridinium salt).

As a class, the quaternary aziridinium salts appear inherently more stable than the protonic acid salts. A reasonably stable quaternary salt (**10**) was prepared from 1,2,3-trimethylaziridine and methyl iodide (*1680*) but an exothermic reaction of 2,3-dimethylaziridinium chloride (**11**) was reported to occur at room temperature (*719*). The protonic acid salts such as **11** may dissociate to some small extent and thus provide a free basic aziridine capable of acting as the nucleophile in a ring-opening reaction. No such mechanistic path is available for decomposition of the quaternary aziridinium salts such as **10**. Remarks made previously regarding the stability of aziridinium salts from protonic acids (other than those pertaining to base and acid strengths) apply also to the quaternary aziridinium salts. Thus, whereas **10** was unstable to recrystallization the corresponding 2,4,6-trinitrobenzenesulfonate was found to be quite stable (*1680*).

Several unique properties of basic aziridines have provided a basis for elucidation of the stereochemistry of amines in general (*452*). *trans*-1,2-Dimethyl-3-isopropylaziridine (**12**) exists as a mixture of the conformers **12a** and **12b**, interconverting very rapidly but at a rate such that their equilibrium concentrations are observable from NMR spectra. Quaternization of **12** with trideuteriomethyl benzenesulfonate (ring opening by reaction of benzene-sulfonate ion with quaternized aziridine is not competitive with alkylation) was shown to give a mixture of diastereomeric aziridinium salts (**13a** and **13b**) in a ratio which is a fairly good estimate of the position of the conformational equilibrium for **12**.

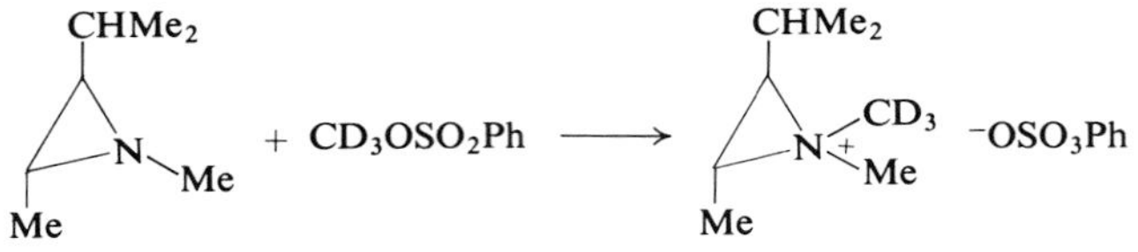

The **12a/12b** ratio is 4.1 at −60°, but is lowered to 3.5 by raising the temperature to 20°, or by the presence of phenols (which are considered to form hydrogen bonds preferentially with **12b**) to 2.1 or less (*446, 452, 452a*).

A number of quaternary aziridinium salts prepared by alkylation of 1-alkyl-aziridines are shown in Table 3-V.

Table 3-V

QUATERNARY AZIRIDINIUM SALTS

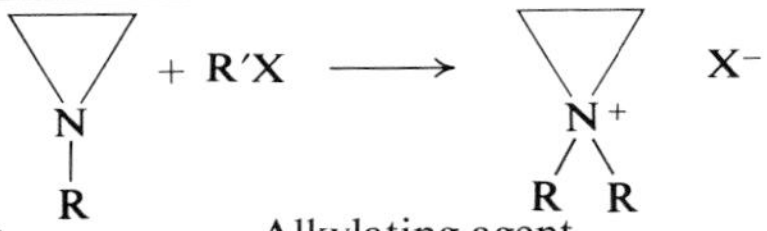

Aziridine substituents	Alkylating agent	% Yield	References
1,2,3-Me₃ (*trans*)	MeI	96	*1680*
1,2,3-Me₃ (*trans*)	$(Me_3O)^+ [2,4,6-(O_2N)_3C_6H_2SO_3]^-$	≈ 100	*1680*
1-Et-2,3-Me₂ (*cis*)	MeI	—	*1680*
1-Et-2,3-Me₂ (*cis*)	MeBr	—	*1680*
1-Et-2,3-Me₂ (*trans*)	MeI	—	*1680*
1-Et-2,3-Me₂ (*trans*)	$(Me_3O)^+ [2,4,6-(O_2N)_3C_6H_2SO_3]^-$	≈ 100	*1680*
2-iso-Pr-1,3-Me₂ (*cis* or *trans*)	MeI	94 (from *cis*)	*445*
2-iso-Pr-1,3-Me₂ (*cis* or *trans*)	CD₃I	—	*445*
2-iso-Pr-1,3-Me₂ (*trans*)	PhCH₂Br	—	*451*
2-iso-Pr-1,3-Me₂ (*trans*)	PhCH₂OSO₂Ph	—	*452*
1-Et-2,2-[(CH₂)₅]	PhCH₂Cl	72–81	*1418*
1-Ph-2,2-[(CH₂)₅]	CH₃(CH₂)₁₁Br	80	*1418*
(2,2-[(CH₂)₅]AzCH₂)₂	PhCH₂Cl	71	*1418*
2,3-[(CH₂)₅]	MeI	—	*1102*
2,3-[(CH₂)₆]	MeI	—	*1101*
2,3-[(CH₂)₆]	I(CH₂)₄I	—	*1101*
2,3-[(CH₂)₈]	MeI	—	*1101*
2,3-[(CH₂)₁₀] (*cis* or *trans*)	MeI	—	*1101*
1,2-[(CH₂)₃]	EtClO₄	—	*1601*
A complex bridged aziridine	MeI	—	*2655a*

REPLACEMENT OF HYDROGEN ON AZIRIDINE NITROGEN

Reaction with Alkyl Halides. This reaction may be formulated as a nucleophilic attack of the aziridine nitrogen on the halogen-bearing carbon.

As with other "amine-type" reactions, precautions are necessary to avoid formation of aziridinium ions which are susceptible to ring opening. Thus, in Eq 6 a base is used which is capable of essentially irreversible removal of the HX formed. Such bases which have been used include sodium or potassium carbonate, sodium hydroxide, calcium oxide, and triethylamine. When an inorganic base is used the reaction mixture is frequently heterogeneous. A tertiary amine (e.g., triethylamine) is usually employed either in large excess or in a diluent at such temperature that the amine hydrohalide precipitates.

$$(6)$$

The aziridine reactant itself has been used for removal of the acid formed in the reaction as illustrated in Eq 6a (*2798*). Use of an aziridine for this purpose should be done with caution, however, especially if a large excess of it is employed, since an exothermic polymerization of the aziridine could result.

$$(6a)$$

In one instance the 1-substituted aziridine product was apparently very insoluble in the reaction mixture, which contributed to its successful separation from the acid formed in the reaction (*2402*).

Formation of a quaternary aziridinium ion **14** as the result of a competition between the 1-alkylaziridine product and the aziridine reactant for the remaining alkyl halide may lead to side products.

$$(7)$$

$$(8)$$

14

Although the rate of reaction 7 is inherently considerably greater than that of reaction 8, even very small amounts of **14** cannot be tolerated towards the end of the reaction. At such stage of the reaction one of the nucleophilic reagents present in high concentration will be the 1-alkylaziridine product. Ring opening of **14** by 1-alkylaziridine simply produces another aziridinium ion, a process which may be repeated a number of times and lead to polymeric 1-alkylaziridine (Eq 9).

$$(9)$$

Problems associated with formation of **14** are reduced or avoided by using an excess of aziridine reactant over alkyl halide. In addition to increasing the rate of reaction 7 over that of reaction 8, the higher concentrations of 1-unsubstituted aziridine favor destruction of **14** by reaction 10 before the polymerization results in greatly decreased yields of 1-alkylaziridine.

$$(10)$$

A reaction which conveniently illustrates the various side reactions mentioned is that between bis-(2-chloroethyl) ether and EI in the presence of potassium carbonate. The product was initially reported to be bis-[2-(1-aziridinyl)ethyl]ether (*2417*). *N*-[2-(1-Aziridinyl)ethyl]morpholine (*932*) (Eq 11) was later found to be the correct structure for the product.

$$(ClCH_2CH_2)_2O + AzH \longrightarrow$$

$$(11)$$

In this case the side reaction 8 is greatly facilitated by ring closure to form a morpholine ring.

The data for the reaction of allyl chloride with EI demonstrate the effect of mole ratio on the yield of 1-allylaziridine (919).

$$AzH + CH_2\!\!=\!\!CHCH_2Cl + NaOH \xrightarrow[\substack{nitrobenzene,\\40°-50°C}]{} AzCH_2CH\!\!=\!\!CH_2 + NaCl + H_2O$$

Mole ratio $AzH/CH_2\!\!=\!\!CHCH_2Cl$	% Yield of 1-allylaziridine at 94% conversion
1.0	43
2.0	71
3.0	79

If the alkyl halide used in reaction 6 contains a strongly electronegative group near the reaction center, the problems associated with formation of **14** are considerably reduced. In such a case the rate of the desired reaction is inherently much greater than that of reaction 8.

Oxonium salts such as the trialkyloxonium fluoroborates have been used for alkylation of EI. The products are the stable HBF_4 salts of the 1-alkyl-aziridines (2758).

Another method for alkylating 1-unsubstituted aziridines with alkyl halides involves conversion of the aziridine to its alkali metal salt and subsequent reaction with the alkyl halide. The alkali metal salt of EI, for example, is readily formed by treatment with an alkyllithium (1474) or potassium metal (2148). This method virtually eliminates any problems associated with formation of **14** (although other side reactions such as dehydrohalogenation may become important) since the aziridine anion is many times more reactive towards alkyl halides than is the 1-alkylaziridine. The method has been applied to a variety of alkyl halides, 1,1-dihaloalkanes (2152), and halomethyl ethers (2148). The possibility of α-elimination leading to a carbene intermediate should not be overlooked for these latter reactions.

The alkylation of aziridines with alkyl halides is summarized in Table 3-VI.

Reaction with Epoxides. This reaction may be depicted as a nucleophilic attack of the aziridine nitrogen on a carbon atom of the oxirane ring (Eq 12).

$$\longrightarrow \quad AzCHRCHOHR' \qquad (12)$$

Table 3-VI

ALKYLATION OF 1-UNSUBSTITUTED AZIRIDINES WITH ALKYL OR SUBSTITUTED
ALKYL HALIDES

Halide displaced	Aziridine produced	Method[a]	% Yield	References
	(A) From Alkyl, Alkenyl, or Haloalkyl Halides			
Br	Az-iso-Bu	—	52.2	2158
Cl	Az-n-$C_{10}H_{21}$	C	59	963
Cl	Az-n-$C_{12}H_{25}$	C	—	3512
Cl	Az-n-$C_{18}H_{37}$	C	—	3512
Br	Az-n-$C_{18}H_{37}$	C	86.5	3512
Cl	$AzCH_2CH_2$=CH_2	C	48	963
Cl	$AzCH_2CH_2$=CH_2	D	77.0	919
Br	2,3-[$(CH_2)_4$]Az-n-$C_{12}H_{25}$ or -n-$C_{18}H_{37}$ or -n-C_4H_9	C	—	871, 2820
Cl	2,3-(Benzylepimino)norbornane	A	—	3866
Cl	$AzCH_2CH_2Cl^b$	B	83	2562
I	6-Me-6-aza-5,7-cyclocholestanol	—	—	4169
I	2β,3β-(Methylepimino)cholestane	C	99	1621
I	3,4-Me_2-4-aza-3,5-cyclocholestane	—	—	4168
I	Methylmitomycin C	C	—	2530, 3716
I	Methylmitomycin A	C	—	2218, 2233, 2540, 2541, 4102
I	Ethylmitomycin A	C	—	2540, 2541
	(B) From α-Halo Acids and Derivatives			
Cl	$AzCH_2CO_2Me$	A	72	350
Cl	$AzCH_2CO_2Me$	A	65	1532
Cl	$AzCH_2CO_2Et$	A	—	3437
Br	$AzCH_2CO_2$-n-C_6H_{13}	A	60	3279
Cl	$AzCH_2CO_2Et$	C	60	193, 2413
Br	$AzCH_2CONH$-n-C_8H_{17}	—	66	3278
Cl	2-Me$AzCH_2CONEt_2$	C	65	193
Br	$AzCH(CH_2Ph)CO_2H$	A	—	3437
Br	$AzCH(CH_2Ph)CO_2Et$	A	—	3437
Cl	$AzCH(CO_2H)CH_2CO_2H$	A	—	3437
Cl	$AzCH_2CO_2CH_2CH(NH_2)CO_2H$	A	—	3437
Cl	$AzCH_2CO_2CH_2CH(CO_2H)$-$NHCO_2CH_2Ph$	A	—	3437
Cl	$AzCH_2CONHCH(CH_2OH)CO_2H$	A	—	3437
Cl	2,2-[$(CH_2)_5$]$AzCH_2CN$	C	—	3324
Br	$AzCH(CO_2Me)_2$	A	—	2418
	(C) From α-Halo Ketones			
Br	AzCHPhAc	A	—	1299
—	$AzCH_2CONHPh$	C	—	3280

Table 3-VI—*continued*

Halide displaced	Aziridine produced	Method[a]	% Yield	References
Br	p-AzCH$_2$COC$_6$H$_4$CH$_2$CH$_2$CO$_2$Me	A	52	*3281*
Cl	7-(AzCH$_2$CONH)-1-HO-2-(PhN=N)- 3,6-(KO$_3$S)$_2$C$_{10}$H$_3$	C	—	*693*
	2-Az-2-R-1,3-indandiones, R =			
Br	Me	E	—	*2798*
Br	Ph	A	80	*129*
Br	p-MeOC$_6$H$_4$	A	73	*131*
Br	3,4-(OCH$_2$O)C$_6$H$_3$	A	60	*130*
Br	Ph	E	—[c]	*2518*

(D) From Halomethyl Aromatics

Cl	AzCH$_2$Ph	C	—	*3512*
Cl	AzCH$_2$Ph	D	75.9	*2158*
Br	4-AzCH$_2$-2,6-(*tert*-Bu)$_2$C$_6$H$_2$OH	E	97	*511, 4198*
Cl	p-AzCH$_2$C$_6$H$_4$CH$_2$CH$_2$CO$_2$Me	C	69	*2741*
Cl	p-AzCH$_2$C$_6$H$_4$(CH$_2$)$_{11}$Me	C	61	*963*
Br	5-Az-2,4-Me$_2$-3-pyridinol	E	—	*1531a*
Cl	2-AzCH$_2$-4-R-quinoline N-oxide; R = H or NO$_2$	E	—	*2741*
Br	8-AzCH$_2$-benzo[b]quinoline	E	85–90	*3083*
Cl	2-AzCH$_2$-benzimidazole	C	71	*3282*
Cl		E	—[d]	*688*

(E) From Other Substituted Alkyl Halides

F	AzCF(OR)CHF(CF$_2$)$_n$F	—[e]	—	*312a*
Cl	AzCH$_2$CH$_2$NEt$_2$	D	68	*3575*
Cl	1-AzCH$_2$CH$_2$-piperidine	F	67.5	*350*
Cl	AzCH$_2$CH$_2$SCH$_2$Ph	C	—	*612*
Cl	AzCH$_2$SnEt$_3$	D	89	*2148*
Cl	AzCH$_2$OR; R = Me, Et, or Ph	F	20–30	*2153, 4084*
Cl	AzCHMeOEt	A	61.5	*2949*
Cl	5-Az-3,4-Cl$_2$-2,5-H$_2$-2-furanone	A	—	*3813b*
Cl	AzCH$_2$CH$_2$P(O)(OEt)$_2$	Me$_4$NOH	28	*1119*
Br	AzCH$_2$CH$_2$P(O)(OEt)$_2$	A	—	*1119*
Cl	Az(CH$_2$)$_3$SiMe$_3$	C	53.5	*4189*

Table 3-VI—*continued*

Halide displaced	Aziridine produced	Method[a]	% Yield	References
	(*F*) *Bisaziridines from Dihalides*			
Cl	Az_2CH_2	F	38.9	*2152*
Cl	Az_2CHPh	F	34	*2152*
Cl	$AzCH_2CH=CHCH_2Az$	C	41	*963*
Cl	$p\text{-}(AzCH_2)_2C_6H_4$	C	36	*963*
Cl	$p\text{-}(AzCH_2)_2C_6H_4$	D	34	*963*
Cl	$1,4\text{-}(AzCH_2)_2\text{-}2,3,5,6\text{-}Me_4\text{-benzene}$	C	91[e]	*3512*
Cl	$3,5\text{-}(AzCH_2)_2\text{-}2,6\text{-}Me_2C_5HN$	—	31	*2550*
Cl	$(AzCH_2CH_2)_2S$	C	80	*350*
Cl	$AzCH_2CH_2(OCH_2CH_2)_nAz$ $n = 2, 3, 8, 12, 22,$ or 35	C	84–87	*3512*
Cl	$2\text{-}MeAzCH_2CH_2(OCH_2CH_2)_2AzMe\text{-}2$	C	87	*3512*
Cl	$2,5\text{-}(AzCH_2CONH)_2\text{-}p\text{-benzoquinone}$	E	89.3	*2402*
—	$m\text{-}$ or $p\text{-}(AzCH_2CONEtCH_2)_2C_6H_4$	C	—	*3280*
—	$(AzCH_2CONH)_2(CH_2)_8$	C	—	*3280*
—	$o\text{-}$ or $p\text{-}(AzCH_2CONH)_2C_6H_4$	—	—	*3276*
Br	$AzCH_2CO_2CH_2CH_2CH_2\text{-}$ groups in a silicone	E?	—	*1068*

[a] Bases used to take up the hydrogen halide are designated as A, a tertiary amine; B, CaO; C, other inorganic base; D, alkali metal salt of the aziridine; E, the aziridine reactant itself.

[b] Unstable at room temperature.

[c] A 1,3-perinaphthindandione derivative.

[d] A rearrangement was also involved.

[e] No acid acceptor was used; product isolated was $AzC(OR)=CF(CF_2)_nF$.

The reaction was found to be significantly affected by the mole ratio of aziridine to epoxide in the case of EI and epoxides containing only one or no substituent on the oxirane ring (*963*). The higher the mole ratio of aziridine to epoxide, the greater was the yield of 1-(2-hydroxyalkyl)aziridine product. For example, the reaction of diglycidyl ether or the diglycidyl ether of hydroquinone with essentially stoichiometric amounts of EI was reported to give the bis(aziridinyl) products (*1817*). Attempts to repeat this work, however, produced only polymer and the desired products were obtained only when an excess of EI was used (*963*). Modest to low yields of aziridinyl products have often been reported from this reaction as well as the formation of polymers (*1376, 2314, 3024*). These observations may be rationalized in terms of the following as an important side reaction (Eq 13).

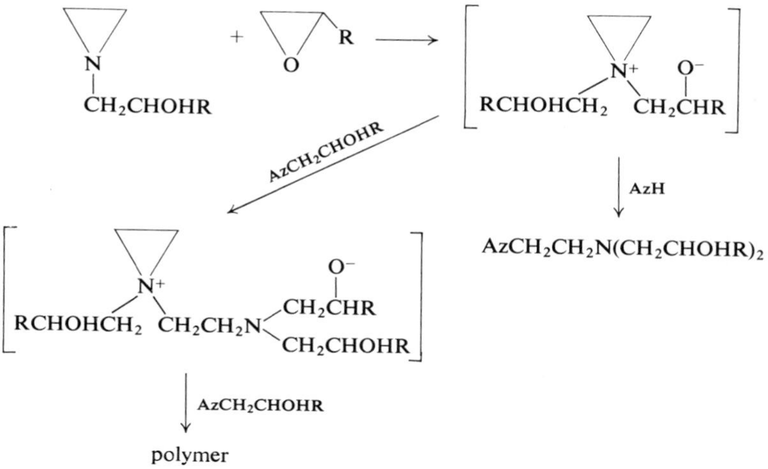

$$\text{(diagram of aziridine + epoxide reaction)}$$

Aziridine structure with N–CH$_2$CHOHR + oxirane with R → bracketed intermediate with N$^+$, RCHOHCH$_2$, CH$_2$CHR, O$^-$

(13)

↓ AzH

AzCH$_2$CH$_2$N(CH$_2$CHOHR)$_2$

AzCH$_2$CHOHR (arrow pointing to bracketed structure)

Bracketed structure: N$^+$, RCHOHCH$_2$, CH$_2$CH$_2$N, with O$^-$, CH$_2$CHR, CH$_2$CHOHR

↓ AzCH$_2$CHOHR

polymer

This polymer representation is in conflict with a report of reaction 14 (*182*). The products were not completely characterized, however, and the same reaction applied to 1-(2-hydroxyethyl)aziridine produced polymers resulting from ring opening of the aziridine (*963*).

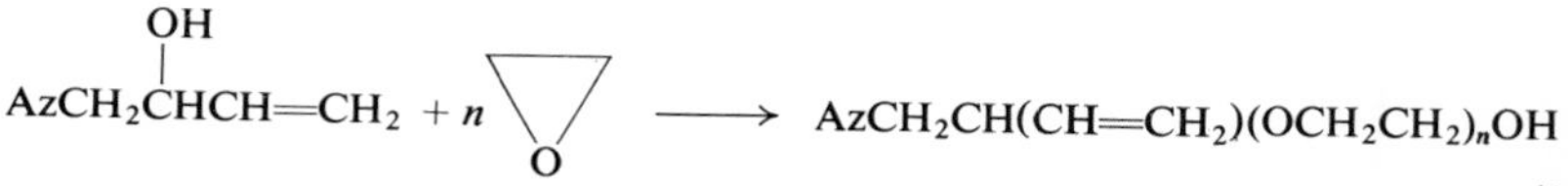

$$\overset{\text{OH}}{\underset{|}{\text{AzCH}_2\text{CHCH}}}=\text{CH}_2 + n \; \underset{O}{\triangle} \longrightarrow \text{AzCH}_2\text{CH(CH}=\text{CH}_2)(\text{OCH}_2\text{CH}_2)_n\text{OH}$$

(14)

Epoxides prepared from halohydrins often contain traces of the halohydrin as an impurity. Use of such epoxides in reaction 12 may produce polymeric products or products which are unstable towards distillation because of trace amounts of acid introduced in this manner. Addition of small amounts of sodium hydroxide or strong base has been claimed advantageous (*198, 1817, 3024*).

In general the addition of an aziridine to unsymmetrical epoxides will produce as major products compounds in which the aziridinyl group is attached to the less-substituted carbon atom of the oxirane ring (*3023*). In reading records of reaction 12, however, attention should be directed to the possibility of isomeric mixtures. Early reports of reaction of EI with 3,4-epoxy-1-butene indicated the product to correspond to structure 15 (*182, 255, 2314*).

AzCH$_2$CHOHCH=CH$_2$ AzCHCH$_2$OH
                                              |
                                         CH=CH$_2$

15   16

Later papers showed the product from either EI or 2-methylaziridine to be an isomeric mixture consisting of approximately 70% 15 and 30% 16 (*447, 3371*).

Table 3-VII

REACTION OF 1-UNSUBSTITUTED AZIRIDINES WITH EPOXIDES

Epoxide (Oxirane substituents or whole epoxide shown)	Aziridine produced	% Yield	References
No substituents	$AzCH_2CH_2OH$	28	3625, 3628, 3802
		50	1376
No substituents	$2\text{-}MeAzCH_2CH_2OH$	53	3802
No substituents	$2\text{-}(H_2NCH_2CH_2)AzCH_2CH_2OH$	—	3354
2-Me	$AzCH_2CHMeOH$	28	2779, 3802, 4135
		50	3023
2-Et	$AzCH_2CHEtOH$	45	3023
2,3-Me$_2$	$AzCHMeCHMeOH$	15	1376
2-Et-2-Me	$AzCH_2CMeEtOH$	48–60	1376, 4080[a], 4178
2-Ph	$AzCH_2CHPhOH$	15	1376
2-Me-2-Ph	$AzCH_2CMePhOH$	—	1376
3-Me-2-Ph	$AzCHPhCHMeOH$	65	1299
3-Me-2-Ph		60	1299
cis	$AzCHMeCHPhOH\text{-}(threo)$	61	3096
trans	$AzCHPhCHMeOH\text{-}(erythro)$	53	3096
1,2-Epoxyindan	1-Az-2-indanol	—	182, 3700
1,2-Epoxyindan	1-(2-MeAz)-2-indanol	38	255
2-CH$_2$=CH	$AzCH_2CHOHCH{=}CH_2$	60	2314, 2930
2-CH$_2$=CH	$AzCH_2CHOHCH{=}CH_2$	58.2	3371
2-CH$_2$=CH	$AzCH_2CHOHCH{=}CH_2$	—	3700
2-CH$_2$=CH	$AzCH_2CHOHCH{=}CH_2 + AzCH(CH_2OH)CH{=}CH_2$	—	447
2-CH$_2$=CH	$2\text{-}MeAzCH_2CHOHCH{=}CH_2$	—	3700
2-CH$_2$=CH	$2\text{-}MeAzCH_2CHOHCH{=}CH_2 + 2\text{-}MeAzCH(CH_2OH)CH{=}CH_2$	—	447
2-CH$_2$=CH	$2\text{-}BuAzCH_2CHOHCH{=}CH_2$	—	3700
2-CH$_2$=CH	$2,2\text{-}Me_2AzCH_2CHOHCH{=}CH_2$	70	255, 3023
2-CH$_2$=CH	$2,2\text{-}[(CH_2)_5]AzCH_2CHOHCH{=}CH_2$	50	2314, 2930
2-Me-2-CH$_2$=CH	$AzCH_2CMeOHCH{=}CH_2$	—	3700
2-Me-2-CH$_2$=CH	$AzCH_2CMeOHCH{=}CH_2$		
2-Me-2-CH$_2$=CH	$AzCH_2CMeOHCH{=}CH_2$		

		Yield	References
2-Me-2-CH₂=CH	2-MeAzCH₂CMeOHCH=CH₂	—	*3700*
2-MeCH=CH	AzCH₂CHOHCH=CHMe	20	*2314, 2930*
2-CH₂=CCl	AzCH₂CHOHCCl=CH₂	44	*255*
2,3-[(CH₂)₄]-2-CH₂=CH	2-Az-1-CH₂=CH-c-C₆H₉OH	—	*3700*
2,3-[(CH₂)₄]-2-CH₂=CH	2-(2-MeAz)-1-CH₂=CH-c-C₆H₉OH	—	*3700*
1,2-Epoxy-3-cyclohexene	2-Az-cyclohex-5-en-1-ol	—	*3700*
1,2-Epoxy-4-(2-propenyl)-1-methylcyclohexane	2-Az-4-(CMe=CH₂)-1-Me-c-C₆H₉OH + 2-Az-5-(CMe=CH₂)-2-Me-c-C₆H₉OH	73	*188*
2-(CH=C)-2-Me	AzCH₂CMe(OH)C=CH	—	*194*
2-(CH=C)-2-Me	2-MeAzCH₂CMe(OH)C=CH	—	*194*
2-(CH=C)-2-Me	2,2-[(CH₂)₅AzCH₂CMe(OH)]C=CH	—	*194*
2,3-[(CH₂)₄]-2-CH=C	2-Az-1-CH=C-c-C₆H₉OH	—	*194*
2,3-[(CH₂)₄]-2-CH=C	2-MeAz-1-CH=C-c-C₆H₉OH	—	*194*
2-(CH₂=CHCH₂OCH₂)	AzCH₂CHOHCH₂OCH₂CH=CH₂	47	*198*
2-(CH₂=CHCH₂SCH₂)	AzCH₂CHOHCH₂SCH₂CH=CH₂	55	*198*
2-(CH₂=CHCH₂NRCH₂)	AzCH₂CHOHCH₂NRCH₂CH=CH₂ (R = Me or Pr)	—	*198*
2-(CH₂=CHCHMeOCH₂)	2-MeAzCH₂CHOHCH₂OCHMeCH=CH₂	—	*198*
2-(RR′NCH₂)	AzCH₂CHOHCH₂NRR′ •		
	R = R′ = Et	70	*322*
	R = Me, R′ = Ph	68	*322*
	R = Me, R′ = PhCH₂	55	*322*
	RR′N = Piperidino	50	*322*
	RR′N = Morpholino	56	*322*

		Yield	References
	AzCH₂CROH(CH₂)ₙCHOHCH₂Az		
	R = H, n = 0	38	*1495, 3024*
	Meso isomer	—	*1276*
	D or L isomer	—	*3024*
	Racemic form	—	*1817*
	Unspecified isomer	—	*3024*
	R = Me, n = 0	—	*3024*
	R = H, n = 1	—	*3024*
	R = H, n = 2	—	*3024*

Table 3-VII—*continued*

Epoxide (Oxirane substituents or whole epoxide shown)	Aziridine produced	% Yield	References
Butadiene dioxide (*meso*)	(2-MeAz)CH$_2$CHOHCHOHCH$_2$(AzMe-2)		
	Meso isomer A	18	1495, 1755
	Meso isomer B	14	1495, 1755
	DL-racemate	—	1495, 1755
	Product from D(+)-2-MeAzH	43	1755
Diglycidyl ether	(AzCH$_2$CHOHCH$_2$)$_2$O	100	941, 963, 1817
p-C$_6$H$_4$(O-glycidyl)$_2$	p-C$_6$H$_4$(OCH$_2$CHOHCH$_2$Az)$_2$	100	963, 1817
Me$_2$C(C$_6$H$_4$-O-glycidyl-p)$_2$	Me$_2$C(C$_6$H$_4$OCH$_2$CHOHCH$_2$Az)$_2$	100	941, 963
2-MeO-3,3-Me$_2$-2-Ph	AzCMe$_2$Bz	89	3379
3-Et-2-MeO-2-Ph-3-Me	AzCMeEtBz	78	3379
	AzCH$_2$CHOH	—	1569, 2392a, 3683, 3685, 3686
	AzCH$_2$CHOHCHOHCH$_2$Az	—	1569, 2392a, 3683–3686
Various polyepoxides	Various	—	526

^{a} This patent also describes preparation of a number of homologous and analogous aziridines.

The reaction of aziridines with 2-alkoxy-2-phenyloxiranes gives β-(1-aziridinyl) ketones in high yields (Eq 15) (*3379*).

$$\underset{O}{\overset{\underset{\displaystyle MeO \quad Me}{\displaystyle Ph \diagdown \diagup Me}}{\triangle}} + AzH \longrightarrow AzCMe_2Bz \qquad (15)$$

Of interest is the reaction of aziridines with epichlorohydrin. Such reactions have been reported (*3299*) to produce 1-(2,3-epoxypropyl)-2-alkylaziridines (Eq 16).

$$\overset{R}{\underset{\underset{H}{N}}{\triangle}} R' + \overset{CH_2Cl}{\underset{O}{\triangle}} \longrightarrow \overset{R}{\underset{\underset{CH_2CHOHCH_2Cl}{N}}{\triangle}} R' \xrightarrow{NaOH} \overset{R}{\underset{\underset{CH_2CH-CH_2}{\underset{O}{\diagdown\diagup}}}{\underset{N}{\triangle}}} R' \qquad (16)$$

It is noteworthy that although the 2-methyl-, 2-ethyl-, and 2,2-dimethyl-1-aziridinyl derivatives were successfully prepared no mention was made of the EI derivative. The derivative without C substituent should be quite susceptible to homopolymerization because of reaction 13. In another study (*2387*) the reaction of aziridines (in excess and including EI) with epichlorohydrin in the presence of sodium hydroxide was found to proceed as follows (Eq 17):

$$2AzH + \underset{O}{\overset{}{CH_2-CHCH_2Cl}} + NaOH \longrightarrow AzCH_2CHOHCH_2Az + NaCl + H_2O \qquad (17)$$

In reaction 17, 1,3-dichloro-2-propanol may be substituted for epichlorohydrin and in general it is safe to assume that reaction of aziridines with halohydrins in the presence of caustic involves initial formation of the epoxide.

A summary of recorded hydroxyalkylations of aziridines with epoxides is presented in Table 3-VII.

Reaction with Alkylene Sulfides. Formally this reaction resembles the reaction of aziridines with epoxides (Eq 18). Several side reactions (Eqs 19, 20, and 21), are important for this system, however, which do not exist for the epoxide reaction.

$$\overset{}{\underset{\underset{H}{N}}{\triangle}} \dashrightarrow \overset{}{\underset{S}{\triangle}} R \longrightarrow AzCH_2CHRSH \qquad (18)$$

$$2AzCH_2CHRSH \xrightarrow{[O]} (AzCH_2CHRS)_2 \qquad (19)$$

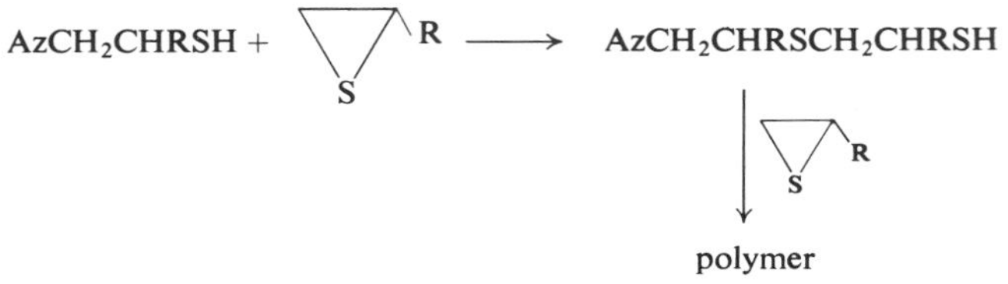

$$AzCH_2CHRSH + \underset{S}{\triangle}R \longrightarrow AzCH_2CHRSCH_2CHRSH \qquad (20)$$

$$\underset{S}{\triangle}R$$

polymer

$$AzCH_2CHRSH + AzH \longrightarrow AzCH_2CHRSCH_2CH_2NH_3 \qquad (21)$$

Apparently the extent to which these side reactions are important depends to a large degree on the structures of the aziridine and alkylene sulfide. Thus the various products shown in Table 3-VIII (as well as polymers) were obtained for several reactants although the reactions were carried out under approximately the same conditions (*195, 1020a, 3061*).

Table 3-VIII

REACTIONS OF AZIRIDINES WITH ALKYLENE SULFIDES

Aziridine	Alkylene sulfide	Products	% Yield
AzH, 2-MeAzH	Thiiran, 2-methylthiiran	1-(2-Mercaptoalkyl)aziridines	—
AzH	2-Phenylthiiran	$AzCH_2CHPhSH$	30
		$AzCH_2CHPhSCH_2CH_2NH_2$	25
		$(AzCH_2CHPhS)_2$	38
2-MeAzH	2-Vinylthiiran	$2\text{-MeAzCH}_2CH(CH{=}CH_2)SCH_2CHMeNH_2$	25
		$[2\text{-MeAzCH}_2CH(CH{=}CH_2)S]_2$	32
$2,2\text{-}[(CH_2)_5]AzH$	2-Vinylthiiran	$2,2\text{-}[(CH_2)_5]AzCH_2CH(CH{=}CH_2)SH$	10
		$\{2,2\text{-}[(CH_2)_5]AzCH_2CH(CH{=}CH_2)S\}_2$	34

Reactions with Aziridines. As mentioned previously, a protonated or quaternized aziridine is a reactive ring species capable of undergoing a ring-opening reaction involving nucleophilic substitution at an aziridine carbon. Thus isolation of a 23% yield of 1-(2-aminoethyl)aziridine from freshly prepared EI hydrochloride was presumed to be the result of reaction 22 (*1996*).

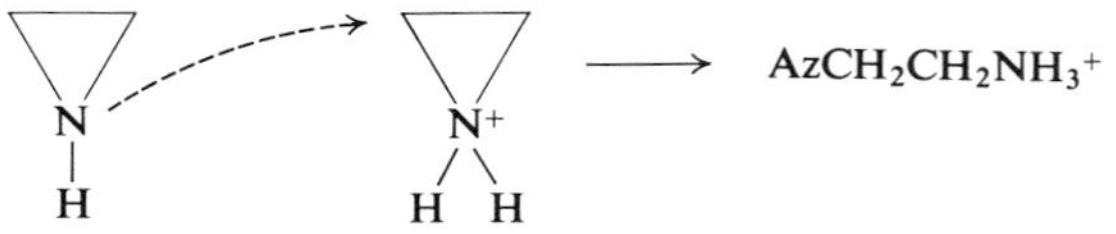

$$\underset{\underset{H}{|}}{\underset{N}{\triangle}} \dashrightarrow \underset{\underset{H\ \ H}{/\backslash}}{\underset{N^+}{\triangle}} \longrightarrow AzCH_2CH_2NH_3{}^+ \qquad (22)$$

Similarly, the dimerization of EI in low yield in dilute aqueous solutions (*3803a*) may be attributed to this reaction, wherein the water serves as a proton source. The reaction actually represents the initial stage of polymerization.

A 10% conversion of EI to the dimer was obtained simply by refluxing the pure compound for 28 days (*350*). It is very probable that trace amounts of some acidic reagent were responsible for this amount of conversion since highly purified EI is very stable to heat.

Although basic aziridines are extremely stable in the absence of any acidic material towards ring opening by nucleophilic substitution at the aziridine carbon, this stability apparently depends on the strength of the nucleophile. About 50% conversion of EI to 1-(2-aminoethyl)aziridine with a very high efficiency has been obtained by first treating dry EI with catalytic amounts of potassium and then heating at 100°C (*963*). The reaction may be formulated as involving nucleophilic substitution by ethylenimide ion (Eq 23).

$$\text{N}^- \quad \dashrightarrow \quad \text{N}^- \quad \longrightarrow \quad AzCH_2CH_2NH^- \xrightarrow{\ AzH\ } AzCH_2CH_2NH_2 + Az^-$$

$$\text{(23)}$$

Activated aziridines undergo ring-opening reactions with nucleophiles in the absence of acidic catalysts. Thus treatment of ethyl 1-aziridinecarboxylate with an excess of EI gives excellent yields of ring-opened derivative (see Table 3-IX) (*963*). When EI is the basic aziridine involved the yield is significantly affected by mole ratio of EI to the 1-substituted aziridine, being raised by an excess of EI.

Table 3-IX

RING OPENINGS OF ACTIVATED AZIRIDINES BY BASIC AZIRIDINES

$$AzH + AzA \ \rightarrow\ Az\text{-}CH_2CH_2NHA$$

Product	% Yield	References
$(CONHCH_2CH_2Az)_2{}^a$	—	*196, 350*
iso-$PrOCMe_2CONHCH_2CH_2Az$	19.7	*4069*
$RO_2CNHCH_2CH_2Az$		
$\quad R = Et$	94	*963*
$\quad\quad n\text{-}C_{13}H_{27}$	92	*963*
$\quad\quad \text{-}CH_2CH_2\text{-}$	99	*963*
$P(O)(NHCH_2CH_2Az)_3$	100	*963*
$1\text{-}(2\text{-}BzNH\text{-}c\text{-}C_6H_{10})\text{-}2,3\text{-}[(CH_2)_4]AzH$	55	*3459*
$\quad (trans)$		
$ClzCCONHCH_2CH_2Az$	—	*3850*
$4\text{-}AzCH_2CH_2NH\text{-}3,6\text{-}Cl_2\text{-}pyridazine$	—	*3414*
$2,4\text{-}(AzCH_2CH_2NH)_2 6\text{-}Cl_3C\text{-}s\text{-}triazine^a$	—	*350*

^{a} This reaction was presumed to account for the products.

Reaction with Aldehydes and Ketones. Most secondary amines add to simple aldehydes to form aminohydrins which are very unstable and may exist only as reactive intermediates. Aziridines, however, form reasonably stable amino-hydrins with aliphatic aldehydes (*934, 1717, 2152b, 2315, 2318a, 2783, 2947, 3356, 3625*). This reaction (Eq 24) is reported to yield either merely a complex between the aldehyde and aziridine or the aminohydrin, depending on pH (*1717*).

$$AzH + RCHO \rightarrow RCHOHAz \qquad (24)$$

17

Early work indicated that in reaction 24 formaldehyde gave methylene-bis(1-aziridine), CH_2Az_2, in addition to the aminohydrin (**17**, R = H) (*2154, 2417, 3625*). Later, however, it was shown that the secondary product was actually $(AzCH_2)_2NCH_2CH_2Az$ (**18**) (*2159*); **18** may result ultimately from an initial ring-opening reaction of the very reactive aziridinium ion **19**.

Aromatic aldehydes (including furfural) undergo reaction at $-60°C$ according to Eq 24 in quantitative yield (*2147*). Under more ordinary conditions, however, the reaction takes a different course. Arylidenebis(1-aziridines) were reported as the products (*934*) but later it was shown that the process actually involved a ring opening (Eq 25) (*351, 1717, 2315, 2783*).

$$ArCHO + 2 AzH \rightarrow ArCH=NCH_2CH_2Az \qquad (25)$$

The explanation shown for formation of **18** may also be applied to this reaction of aromatic aldehydes.

Of interest is the fact that *p*-nitrobenzaldehyde and 5-nitrofurfural form only 1:1 molecular complexes with EI (*1717, 2315*).

Addition of EI to aldehydes containing conjugated double bonds (e.g., cinnamaldehyde) gives either the products of 3,4-addition or the diadducts (Eq 26) (*1717, 2317*).

$$PhCH=CHCHO + AzH \xrightarrow{\hspace{1.5cm}} PhCHAzCH_2CHO \xrightarrow{AzH}$$

$$PhCHAzCH_2CHOHAz \qquad (26)$$

An older claim that initial addition occurs at the aldehyde group (*173*) is probably less reliable.

Aziridines also add readily to ketones, forming aminohydrins that are relatively stable when compared with those from ordinary secondary amines (Eq 27).

$$AzH + R_2CO \rightarrow R_2C(OH)Az \tag{27}$$

As would be expected, the adducts are much less stable than the corresponding aziridine–aldehyde adducts, and on distillation a dissociation may occur (Eq 28) (*350*).

$$AzCH_2CH_2CMe(OH)Az \rightarrow AzCH_2CH_2Ac + AzH \tag{28}$$

If the ketone used in reaction 27 is one in which the R groups are electronegative (e.g., $-CF_3$), quite stable aminohydrins are obtained (*2155*).

Reaction of EI with β-diketones or β-keto esters occurs with ring opening (Eq 29) (*2156*).

$$MeCOCH_2COMe + 2AzH \rightarrow AzCH_2CH_2NHCMe\!=\!CHCOMe \tag{29}$$

An earlier report erroneously suggested $MeCAz_2CH_2CHCOMe$ as the product from this reaction (*171*). It seems reasonable again to invoke the explanation used in the case of formaldehyde for formation of **18**. The active aziridinium ion can also be represented as the hybrid **20**.

20

Treatment of an α-halo ketone with lithium ethylenimide gave a 1-aziridinyl-substituted epoxide (Eq 30) (*3380*).

In what also appears to be addition of EI, displacement, and cyclization, ethyl 2,3-dichloro-4-oxo-2-butenoate yields 4,5-bis(1-aziridinyl)-3-chloro-2,5-dihydro-2-furanone (Eq 30a) (*3813b*).

Of interest is the report that refluxing equimolar amounts of EI and aldehydes or ketones in ether for 24 hours or longer produces oxazolidines (Eq 31) (*938*). In a later study by other workers, no conversion into oxazolidines was observed (*1717, 2315, 2318a*).

$$AzH + R_2CO \longrightarrow \underset{\underset{R}{\diagdown}\overset{}{\diagup}\underset{R}{}}{HN\diagdown\diagup O} \qquad (31)$$

A solution of glucose and EI in methanol when heated to reflux temperature yields mixed α- and β-(1-aziridinyl)-D-glucosides (*2392a*).

Properly mentioned here are Mannich reactions involving 1-unsubstituted aziridines. In addition ιo the reaction illustrated for 2-hydroxy-1,4-naphtho-quinone (Eq 32) (*3690*), 1-aziridinylmethyl derivatives of estrone (*1403*) and 3-oxocyclopentanecarboxylic acid (*3416*) have been obtained. Inasmuch as aryl hydroxymethyl sulfones are formaldehyde derivatives (derived from reaction of the arylsulfinic acid with formaldehyde), the reaction is also represented here (Eq 33) (*1280*). The concomitant deacetylation is noteworthy.

$$(32)$$

$$p\text{-}AcNHC_6H_4SO_2CH_2OH + AzH \rightarrow p\text{-}H_2NC_6H_4SO_2CH_2Az \qquad (33)$$

Unlike other amines tested, EI does not yield any phenolic product, but only tars, upon reaction with 2-acetoxy-2-methyl-3,5-cyclohexadienone (*2264*) ; and with 2,2-dinitropropanol it gives only polymers (*3658*).

In Table 3-X are shown a number of aldehyde and ketone adducts.

Reaction with Olefinic and Acetylenic Compounds. Aziridines add readily to a variety of olefinic compounds forming 1-alkylaziridines. The most familiar of these reactions is the Michael-type addition to α,β-unsaturated esters, nitriles, ketones, and the like. The reaction may be viewed as a nucleophilic attack by the aziridine nitrogen at the β-olefinic carbon (Eq 34; A, activating group).

$$(34)$$

The proton shown on the aziridine nitrogen of the carbanion intermediate (21) is very probably transferred in the transition state (3060). Thus the reaction is especially useful for preparation of 1-alkylaziridines wherein the alkyl contains such A substituents since the reaction may be carried out in the absence of any

Table 3-X

ADDUCTS OF AZIRIDINES WITH CARBONYL COMPOUNDS

(A) $R^1R^2CO + AzH \rightarrow AzCR^1R^2OH$

R^1	R^2	% Yield	References
H	H	40–97	2154, 2159, 2160, 2783, 3626
H	Me	57–92	1717, 2783, 2947
H	Et	73–83	2137a, 2160, 2783, 2947; cf. 3356
H	Pr	58	934, 1717, 2783, 2947
H	iso-Pr	—	1717
H	iso-Bu	—	1717
H	Me(CH$_2$)$_5$	—	934, 1717
H	Me(CH$_2$)$_6$	—	934, 2783; cf. 2137a
H	CCl$_3$	85	2155
H	H(CF$_2$)$_6$	100	459
CF$_3$	CF$_3$	59	2155
CO$_2$Et	CO$_2$Et	81	2155
H	CH=CH-2-furyl[a]	81	1717, 2317
H	CH=CHPh[a]	40	1717, 2317
$R^1 + R^2 = (CH_2)_5$		—	934, 1717

(B) 2-RAzH + (CHO)$_2$ → (2-RAzCHOH)$_2$

R	% Yield	References
H	97	3099
Me	94	3099
Et	79	3099

[a] The product was of form ArCHAzCH$_2$CHOHAz.

acid or in the presence of basic catalysts and there is no danger of generating aziridinium ions.

The ease of addition to such unsaturated compounds depends on the ability of the A group to stabilize the transient partial negative charge which develops on the α-carbon in the transition state. Thus with EI the following order of reactivity was observed (3060): CH$_2$=CClCN > CH$_2$=CHCN $\approx$ CH$_2$=CHCOMe > CH$_2$=CHCO$_2$Et > CH$_2$=CHCONH$_2$ > CH$_2$=CHCO

NH-iso-Pr > CH_2=CHCONMe$_2$. The reaction is also subject to various steric effects, one such effect being exemplified by the fact that methyl crotonate is much more reactive than ethyl crotonate (*3060*). In another study, the most reactive class consisted of CH_2=CHCO$_2$R, CH_2=CHCN, CH_2=CHAc, and MeCH=CHCO$_2$Me; an intermediate group contained styrenes and vinyl acetate; and least reactive were CH_2=CMeCO$_2$Me, Me$_2$C=CHAc, CH_2=CHCH$_2$O$_2$CR, CH_2=CHOR, and CH_2=CHR (*2780*).

Vinylogs of CH_2=CHA also participate to give the expected product (Eq 35) (*3386*) and when such an A group is present in an allene, addition readily occurs (Eq 36) (*2209, 3813a*).

$$AzH + CH_2=CHCH=CHCN \rightarrow AzCH_2CH=CHCH_2CN \qquad (35)$$

$$AzH + CH_2=C=CHCN \rightarrow AzCMe=CHCN \qquad (36)$$

Ethylenimine has been added to a number of acetylenes containing such A groups attached to the acetylenic carbon (Eq 37) (*927, 1537, 2510, 2914, 3615*).

$$AzH + HC\equiv CCO_2Et \rightarrow AzCH=CHCO_2Et \qquad (37)$$

Whereas ordinary secondary aliphatic amines produce only trans adducts in this reaction, EI gives a mixture of cis and trans products. The stereospecificity depends partly on the solvent. With acetylenic sulfones only cis product was observed in several solvents (*3615*). Various explanations have been offered for these stereochemical results (*927, 3615, 3812, 3813*). Acetylenic–olefinic esters such as MeO$_2$CCH=CHC≡CCO$_2$Me have also been employed in this reaction (*3812*). The vinylation of EI by autoclaving it with acetylene and catalysts has not been successful (*353*) and has led to explosions (*963*).

The primary product formed from addition of EI to acetylenic esters or nitriles may add a second mole of EI and form the saturated bis(aziridinyl) derivative (Eq 38) (*2156*).

$$AzCH=CHCO_2Et + AzH \rightarrow Az_2CHCH_2CO_2Et \qquad (38)$$

Compounds which contain alkoxy, halogen, or alkylthio groups on a β-olefinic carbon, (i.e., XCH=CHA, where A has the same meaning as above) may undergo reaction with aziridines wherein the net result is replacement of the X group by an aziridinyl group (*126, 216, 935, 1113*). Such reactions may be formulated as addition–elimination reactions (Eq 39) (*935*) and are highly stereospecific (*3616*).

$$PhC(OMe)=C(CN)_2 + AzH \rightarrow [PhCAz(OMe)CH(CN)_2] \rightarrow PhCAz=C(CN)_2 + MeOH$$
$$(39)$$

Table 3-XI

ADDITION OF AZIRIDINES[a] TO UNSATURATED COMPOUNDS

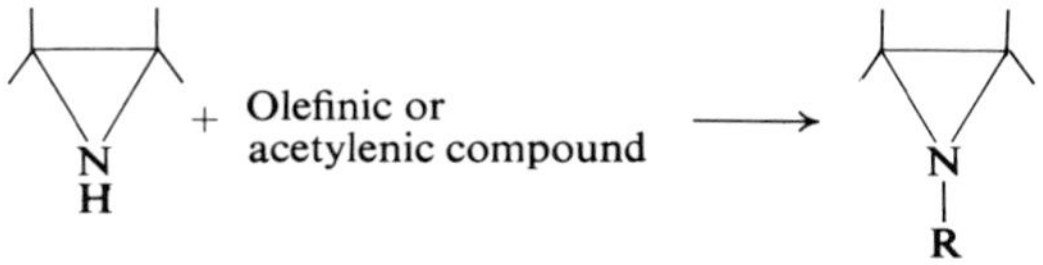

R	% Yield	References
$CH_2CH_2CO_2Me$	80–90	164, 350, 1080, 1203, 1471, 3060, 3625, 3852
$CH_2CH_2CO_2Me$	—[b]	2102
$CH_2CH_2CO_2Et$	88–90	164, 3060, 3351, 3625
$CH_2CH_2CO_2Bu$	88	3351
$CH_2CH_2CO_2C_{10}H_{21}$	78	3060
$CH_2CH_2CO_2CH_2CH_2OMe$	89	3351
$CH_2CHMeCO_2Me$	30	3060, 3852
$CH_2CHMeCO_2(CH_2)_2NMe_2$	75	3060
$CH_2CHMeCO_2(CH_2)_2NH$-tert-Bu	74	3060
$CH_2CHMeCO_2$-iso-Pr	40	3060
$CH_2CHMeCO_2(CH_2)_3Si(OMe)_3$	94	1586
$CHMeCH_2CO_2Me$	84–85	350, 1471, 3060
$CHMeCH_2CO_2Et$	69	3060
$CH(CO_2Et)CH_2CO_2Et$	94	350, 1203, 1495, 2413
$CH_2CH(CO_2Et)_2$	4	928
$CH_2CHBrCO_2Me$	32	126
$CH_2CHClCO_2Me$	72	170
$CH_2CH_2CONH_2$	55–70	350, 1203, 3060
CH_2CH_2CONH-iso-Pr	90	3060
CH_2CH_2CONH-tert-Bu	51	3060
CH_2CH_2COAz	81	2150
$CH_2CHMeCONH_2$	21	3060, 3852
$CHMeCH_2CONH_2$	60	350
CH_2CH_2CN	90	350, 1203, 3852
CH_2CH_2CN	66[b]	3498
CH_2CH_2CN	82[c]	2820, 3814
$CH_2CHMeCN$	73	3060
$CH_2CHMeCN$	41	620a
$CHMeCH_2CN$	83	3060
$CHMeCH_2CN$	48.8	620a
$CHPhCH_2CN$	57	3060
$CHPhCH_2CN$	63	620a
$CH_2CH=CHCH_2CN$	90	3386
$CH_2CHCNCH_2CH_2CN$	88.6	620a
CH_2CH_2Ac	61–80	350, 928, 1080a, 2147, 3060

Table 3-XI—*continued*

R	% Yield	References
3-(3-Indenyl)-3-oxopropyl	99.5	*3452*
2,5-Dioxopyrrolidin-3-yl	83	*3097, 3325*
3-Oxocyclopentyl	84	*2147*
3-Oxocyclohexyl	65	*928*
16β-AzCH$_2$-3β-HO-Δ^5-androsten-17-one	90	*510, 2531, 3161*
16α-Az-3β-HO-5-pregnen-20-one	—	*3321*
16α-Az-4-pregnene-3,20-dione	—	*3321*
CHAzCH$_2$CO$_2$Me	—	*2156*
CHAzCH$_2$CN	—	*2156*
CHTsCH$_2$Ts	19–70	*4125*
CF$_2$CHFCF$_3$	60	*2152c*
CF$_2$CHFCF$_3$	55[b]	*2152c*
CF$_2$CH(CF$_3$)$_2$	37	*2152c*
CF$_2$CH(CF$_3$)$_2$	45[b]	*2152c*
C$_n$F$_{2n+1}$ (n = 3–18) or *c*-C$_6$F$_{11}$	—	*702a*
CMe=CHCN	72	*2209*
CH=CHCO$_2$Me	73–78	*2157, 3812*
CH=CHCO$_2$Et	51–81	*927, 1537, 2914, 3615*
CH=CHCN	—	*2157*
CH=CHSO$_2$C$_6$H$_4$Me-*p*	64–84	*3615*
CMe=CHSO$_2$Et	73–80	*3615*
CMe=CHCO$_2$Et	59	*616a, 1537, 2914*
CMe=CHCN	72	*616a, 2209*
CPh=CHCO$_2$Et	71	*1537, 2914*
C(CO$_2$Me)=CHCO$_2$Me	16–91	*927, 1467b, 1537,*
		2914, 3812, 3813
C(CO$_2$Me)=CHCO$_2$Me	85[d]	*2800*
C(CH$_2$CO$_2$Me)=CHCO$_2$Me	—	*3813a*
C(CO$_2$Et)=CHCO$_2$Et	—[d]	*2800*
C(CO$_2$Me)=CHCH=CHCO$_2$Me	—	*3812*
C(CF$_3$)=CHCF$_3$	90[e]	*3389*
C(CF$_3$)=CHCF$_3$	—[f]	*3389*
2(CPh=CH)-1-Me-quinolinium	78	*2094*
CH$_2$CH$_2$P(O)(OEt)$_2$	55–70	*1157, 2413*
CH$_2$CH$_2$P(O)(OPr)$_2$	—	*1157*
CH$_2$CH$_2$P(S)Az$_2$	—	*2862*
CH$_2$CH$_2$SO$_2$CH=CH$_2$	81	*1238*
CH$_2$CH$_2$SiMe$_3$	—	*2668*
CH$_2$CH$_2$SiMe$_2$Ph	—	*2668*
CH$_2$CH$_2$SiMePh$_2$	—	*2668*
CH$_2$CH$_2$SiEt$_3$	28–90	*2668*
CH$_2$CH$_2$Si(OEt)$_3$	69	*2668*
CH$_2$CH$_2$SiMePh(CH=CH$_2$)	—	*2672*
CH$_2$CH$_2$SiPh$_2$(CH=CH$_2$)	—	*2672*
CH$_2$CH$_2$Ph	89	*350, 1063, 3852*
CH$_2$CH$_2$C$_6$H$_4$CH=CH$_2$-*p*	—	*2413*
CH$_2$CH$_2$Ph	—[g]	*1063*

Table 3-XI—*continued*

R	% Yield	References
$CH_2CH_2C_6H_4SiMe_3$-p	—	2668
$CH_2CH_2C_6H_4Cl$-p	—	2668
CH_2CH_2-2-furyl	70	2721
CH_2CH_2-2-C_5H_4N	—	59
$CH_2CH=CHMe$ and $CHMeCH=CH_2$	—	1063
$CH_2CH_2CH_2OH$	42	2102
$CH_2CH_2CH_2SiEt_3$	35	2671
Et	100	963
Et	100^g	963
iso-Pr	—	963
CHMeOAc	—	3852
$CHMeNMe_2$	71	2950
$CHMeNEt_2$	68	2950
$C(OEt)=CH_2$	27	963
CMe(Az)OEt	45	963
CH_2CH_2CONH-1-anthraquinonyl	—	2891
$CH_2CH_2SCH_2OMe$	60	328a, 328b

Addition–Elimination Reactions

Unsaturated compound	Product	% Yield	References
$BzCH=CHCl$	$BzCH=CHAz$	Quant.	216
$BzCH=CHCl$	$BzCH_2CHAz_2$	99	216
$BzCH=CHCl$	$BzCH=CH(2\text{-}MeAz)$	—	216
$BzCH=CHCl$	$BzCH_2CH(2\text{-}MeAz)_2$	—	216
n-$C_{11}H_{23}COCH=CHCl$	n-$C_{11}H_{23}COCH=CHAz$	42	216
n-$C_{11}H_{23}COCH=CHCl$	n-$C_{11}H_{23}COCH_2CHAz_2$	95	216
n-$C_{18}H_{37}COCH=CHCl$	n-$C_{18}H_{37}COCH=CHAz$	95	216
$EtO_2CCH=CHCl$	$EtO_2CCH=CHAz$	—	3616
$EtO_2CCH=CMeCl$	$EtO_2CCH=CMeAz$	77	3782
$PhC(OMe)=C(CN)_2$	$PhCAz=C(CN)_2$	83	935
3-Cl-2-Ph-2-cyclohexen-1-one	3-Az-2-Ph-2-cyclohexen-1-one	80	3782
4-Cl-coumarin	4-Az-coumarin	—	1437
4-Cl-7-MeO-coumarin	4-Az-7-MeO-coumarin	—	1437
4-Cl-7,8-$(MeO)_2$-coumarin	4-Az-7,8-$(MeO)_2$-coumarin	—	1437
$TsCH=CHCl$	$TsCH=CHAz$	—	3616
$TsCH=CHTs$ (*cis*)	$TsCH=CHAz$ (*cis*)	59	4125
$TsCH=CHTs$ (*trans*)	$TsCH=CHAz$ (*trans*)	<14	4125

| | | — | 3642 |

Table 3-XI—*continued*

Addition to Di-, Tri-, or Polyfunctional Unsaturates

$$\text{Product,} \quad Q\left(N\overset{\displaystyle\triangle}{}\right)_n$$

Q	% Yield	References
-CH$_2$CH$_2$CO$_2$CH$_2$CH$_2$O$_2$CCH$_2$CH$_2$-	—	*154*
-CH$_2$CH$_2$CO$_2$CH$_2$CH$_2$CHMeO$_2$CCH$_2$CH$_2$-	100	*361*
-CHMeCH$_2$CO$_2$CH$_2$CH$_2$O$_2$CCH$_2$CHMe-	—	*361*
-CHMeCH$_2$CO$_2$(CH$_2$)$_4$O$_2$CCH$_2$CHMe-	100	*361*
(-CHMeCH$_2$CO$_2$)$_3$ glyceryl	—	*361*
-CHMeCH$_2$CO$_2$(CH$_2$)$_2$O$_2$CCH$_2$CHMe-	—^{g}	*361*
-CHMeCH$_2$CO$_2$(CH$_2$)$_2$O(CH$_2$)$_2$O$_2$CCH$_2$CHMe-	—	*361*
-CH$_2$CH$_2$CO$_2$(CH$_2$)$_6$O$_2$CCH$_2$CH$_2$	90	*3279*
-CH$_2$CH$_2$CONHCH$_2$NHCOCH$_2$CH$_2$-	72	*3426*
-CH$_2$CH$_2$CONHCHBuNHCOCH$_2$CH$_2$-	—	*3426*
-CH$_2$CH$_2$CONHCH$_2$CH$_2$NHCOCH$_2$CH$_2$-	—	*3426*
-CH$_2$CH$_2$CONH(CH$_2$)$_3$NHCOCH$_2$CH$_2$-	—	*3426*
-CH$_2$CH$_2$CONH(CH$_2$)$_6$NHCOCH$_2$CH$_2$-	—	*3426*
-CH$_2$CH$_2$CON(CH$_2$CH$_2$)$_2$NCOCH$_2$CH$_2$-	—	*1901*
-CH$_2$CH$_2$CON(CH$_2$CH$_2$)$_2$NCOCH$_2$CH$_2$-	—^{g}	*1901*
-CH$_2$CH$_2$CON(CH$_2$CH$_2$)$_2$NCOCH$_2$CH$_2$-	—^{b}	*1901*

	—	*1790*

	—	*834*

| -CH$_2$CH$_2$SO$_2$CH$_2$CH$_2$- | 88 | *350* |
| -CH$_2$CH$_2$SO$_2$CH$_2$CH$_2$- | —^{g} | *682* |

	84	*830, 1203, 3878*

	96	*1545*

Y = (CH$_2$)$_6$ or p-C$_6$H$_4$CH$_2$C$_6$H$_4$-p

Table 3-XI—*continued*

Q	% Yield	References
$(x\text{-})\text{-}CH_2CH_2C_6H_4CH_2CH_2\text{-}$	65	*2413*
Product[h] is $\left[\begin{array}{c} \text{—YO}_2\text{CCHCH}_2\text{CO}_2 \\ \vert \\ \text{Az} \end{array}\right]_n$	—	*164, 1786–1788, 2491*
$\text{-}CH_2CH_2CH(CH_2CN)\text{-}$	94	*1245*
$\text{-}CH_2CH_2CH(CH_2CN)\text{-}$	85[g]	*1245*
$\text{-}CH(CH_2CO_2Me)C_6H_4CH(CH_2CO_2Me)\text{-}$	65–70	*2418*

[a] The aziridine was EI unless otherwise noted.
[b] $2,2\text{-Me}_2\text{AzH}$.
[c] Cyclohexenimine.
[d] *cis*-$2,3\text{-Ph}_2\text{AzH}$.
[e] $2\text{-CH}_2\!\!=\!\!CHAzH$.
[f] $2,3\text{-}(CH_2\!\!=\!\!CH)_2AzH$.
[g] 2-MeAzH.
[h] EI was added to polymeric esters from maleic anhydride and diols.

When X is halogen it is, of course, necessary to have an acid acceptor present for irreversible removal of the HX formed.

Reaction of aziridines with olefins which do not contain A groups as defined above but which do contain conjugated double bonds may be promoted by catalytic amounts of an alkali metal. Presumably the alkali metal forms the metal ethylenimide, which is the active species. Thus 1-phenethylaziridine in 89% yield was obtained under mild conditions (Eq 40) (*350, 1063*).

$$PhCH\!\!=\!\!CH_2 + AzH \xrightarrow{\text{Na}} PhCH_2CH_2Az \qquad (40)$$

Other such conjugated olefins which have been thus treated with aziridines include 2-vinylfuran (*2721*), 2-vinylpyridine (*59*), and 1,3-butadiene (*1063*). A similar addition occurs during the reduction of naphthalene with sodium in EI as solvent. The products were 1-(1-aziridinyl)-1,2,3,4-tetrahydronaphthalene (28%) and tetralin (54%) (*262a*).

Of special interest is the fact that aziridines may be added to simple olefins such as ethylene and propylene in the presence of sodium under conditions only somewhat more rigorous than those required for conjugated olefins (Eq 41) (*959*). Essentially quantitative yields were obtained. The product from propylene was 1-isopropylaziridine.

$$CH_2\!\!=\!\!CH_2 + AzH \xrightarrow{\text{Na}} AzEt \qquad (41)$$

Also of interest is the sodium-catalyzed addition of 2,2-dimethylaziridine to allyl alcohol, yielding 1-(3-hydroxypropyl)-2,2-dimethylaziridine (*2102*).

Reactions which do not involve an alkali metal catalyst or otherwise resemble the Michael type are the addition of EI to vinyl acetate (*3852*), N,N-dimethylvinylamine (Eq 42) (*2948, 2950*), and ethoxyacetylene (*963*). In these cases the aziridinyl group becomes attached to the α-olefinic carbon.

$$CH_2{=}CHNMe_2 + AzH \rightarrow MeCHAzNMe_2 \tag{42}$$

From ethoxyacetylene either the mono- or diaddition product was obtained, depending on reaction conditions.

Reaction with Quinones. This reaction may be viewed as simply a special case of addition of aziridines to α,β-unsaturated ketones. The reaction has received considerable attention due to the pharmacological activity (see Chapter 6) of the products. Many examples are presented in Table 3-XII.

Treatment of *p*-benzoquinone with EI may produce either the 2,5-bis(1-aziridinyl)-substituted benzoquinone or the similarly substituted hydroquinone depending on the presence or absence of an oxidizing agent. Excess benzoquinone may serve as the oxidizing agent. Thus when equimolar amounts of benzoquinone and EI were allowed to react, only the hydroquinone derivative was obtained (Eq 43) (*2448, 2451, 2453*).

$$\tag{43}$$

Although 2-methylaziridine acted analogously (*2448, 2455*), the addition of 2,2-dimethylaziridine produced only the substituted benzoquinone derivative (*2448, 2451*). The use of a suitable excess of benzoquinone (or other oxidizing agent) results in good yields of the benzoquinone derivative. Thus Eq 44 was followed with EI (*2448, 2451, 2453*).

$$\tag{44}$$

These reactions may, of course, occur as successive additions and oxidations (Eq 45).

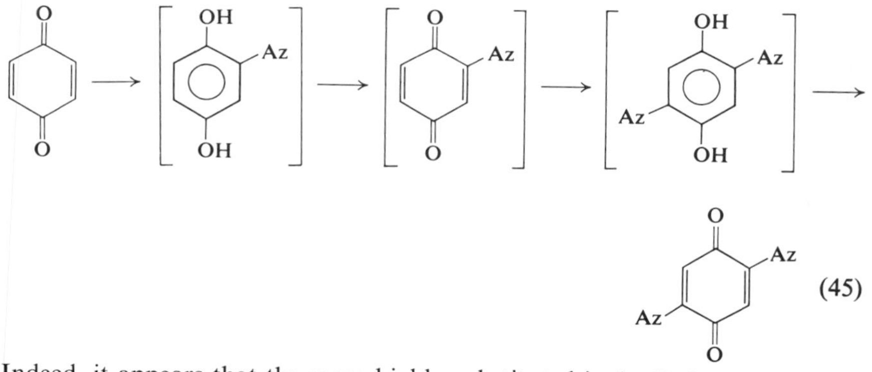

(45)

Indeed, it appears that the more highly substituted is the hydroquinone, the more easily it is oxidized. For example, reaction of 2,6-dimethoxy-*p*-benzo-quinone with EI under nitrogen proceeded as shown in Eq 46 (*1137, 1425*).

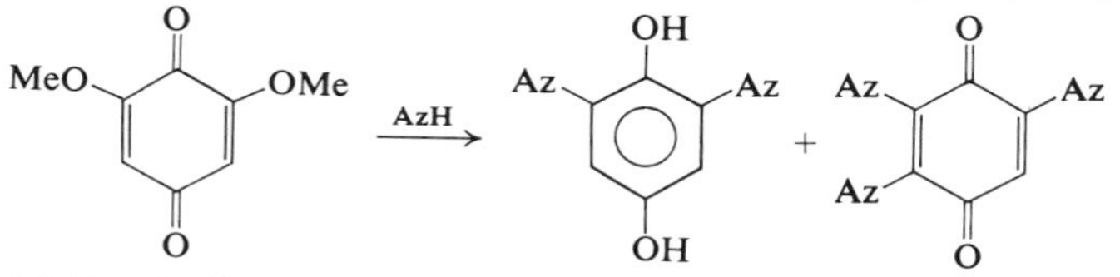

(46)

The 2,6-bis(1-aziridinyl)hydroquinone was readily oxidized to the benzo-quinone derivative with benzoquinone.

In one instance, an *ortho*-benzoquinone was generated *in situ* and the addition performed (Eq 47) (*1760*).

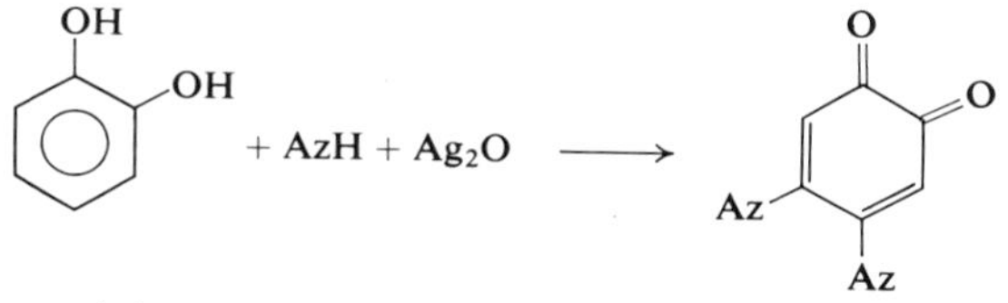

(47)

Quinones containing substituents (e.g., alkoxy, alkylthio, and halogen) on the quinone ring may undergo reaction with aziridines with replacement of the substituent by a 1-aziridinyl group. In the manner mentioned in the previous section, these reactions may be pictured as addition–elimination reactions. The ease of such replacement depends on the ring positions of the substituents and on the nature of the substituent. For example, alkoxy groups are more readily displaced than halogen (*2403*), as shown in Eq 48 (*339*; but cf. *2406a*).

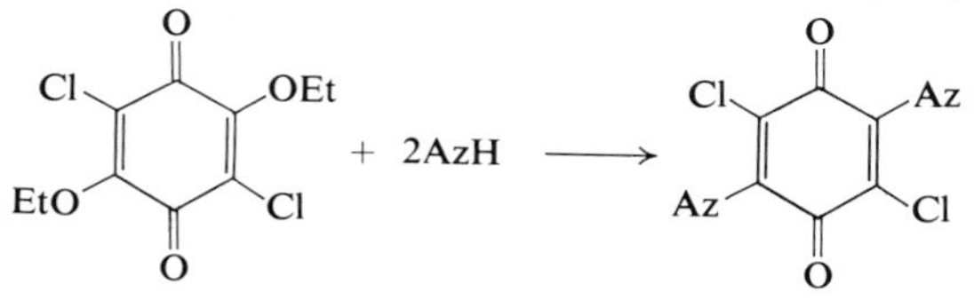

(48)

Table 3-XII

REACTION OF 1-UNSUBSTITUTED AZIRIDINES WITH QUINONES

p-Benzoquinone Derivatives

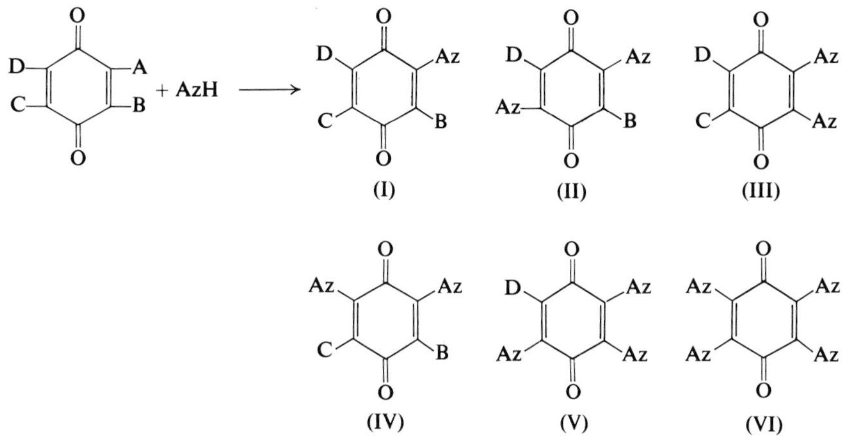

A	B	C	D	Product type	% Yield	References
H	H	H	H	II	77–83	1117, 2400, 2448, 2451, 2453
H	H	H	H	II	—[a]	1117, 2455
H	H	H	H	II	53[b]	2448, 2451
H	H	H	H	II	—[c]	2215
H	H	H	H	II	—[d]	2215
H	Me	H	H	I	—	2127

H	H	OMe	H	I	57	1425
H	H	OPh	H	I	—	1117
H	H	Br	H	I	—	2127, 2446a
H	H	Me	Me	I	45	2127
H	Me	H	Me	II	—	563
OMe	OMe	CO₂Me	OR?	II	—	4162
OMe	H	OMe	H	V	—	2127
OEt	H	H	OMe	II	—	2127
H	Cl	OEt	H	II	—	1155
Cl	Cl	Cl	H	II	—	1137, 1425
OMe	H	H	H	II	—	1155
H	H	Az	H	II	—	1117, 1154
H	H	CH₂CH(CO₂Et)NHAc	H	I, IV	—	2446a
H	H	CH₂C(CO₂Et)₂NHAc	H	II	—	2446a
OPh	H	OPh	H	II	—	1151
OPh	H	OPh	H	II	—[a]	1151
OMe	OMe	OMe	OMe	II	80	1425
F	F	F	F	II	73–78	2404, 2446, 3732
F	F	F	F	IV	13	2446
F	F	F	F	VI	74	1231, 3731, 3732
Cl	Cl	Cl	Cl	II	—[a]	1111, 1117, 1151, 1421
Cl	Cl	Cl	Cl	II	—	1117, 1154
Br	Br	Br	Br	II	93	1117, 1151, 1154, 2318
OMe	OMe	OMe	OMe	II	—	1111, 1132, 1421
OMe	OMe	OMe	OMe	VI	—	1169
OPh	OPh	OPh	OPh	II	—	1151
SEt	SEt	SEt	SEt	II	—	1111, 1132, 1421
SPh	SPh	SPh	SPh	II	—	1421
SAr[e]	SAr[e]	SAr[e]	SAr[e]	II	—	1421
F	Az	F	Az	V	—	2445
Az	F	F	F	V	73	2446

Table 3-XII—*continued*

p-Benzoquinone Derivatives

A	B	C	D	Product type	% Yield	References
Cl	NHAc	NHAc	NHAc	II	—	1133, 1421, 2450, 2454
Cl	NHAc	NHAc	NHAc	II	—[a]	2450, 2454
Cl	NHCOEt	NHCOEt	NHCOEt	II	—[a]	2450, 2454
Cl	NHCOEt	NHCOEt	NHCOEt	II	—[a]	2450, 2454
Cl	NHCOPr	NHCOPr	NHCOPr	II	—	2450, 2454
Cl	NHCO(CH$_2$)$_4$Me	NHCO(CH$_2$)$_4$Me	NHCO(CH$_2$)$_4$Me	II		698, 699
Cl	NHCO(CH$_2$)$_5$Me	NHCO(CH$_2$)$_5$Me	NHCO(CH$_2$)$_5$Me	II		698, 699
Cl	NHCO-c-C$_6$H$_{11}$	NHCO-c-C$_6$H$_{11}$	NHCO-c-C$_6$H$_{11}$	II		2458
Cl	NHCOCH$_2$NH$_2$	NHCOCH$_2$NH$_2$	NHCOCH$_2$NH$_2$	II		2402
Cl	NHCOCH$_2$Az	NHCOCH$_2$Az	NHCOCH$_2$Az	II		2402
Cl	NHCO$_2$Et	NHCO$_2$Et	NHCO$_2$Et	II		1143, 2856
OMe	Br	OMe	OMe	IV		2450, 2456
OMe	Br	OMe	OMe	IV		2456
OMe	OPh	OMe	OPh	II		1151, 1421
OEt	Cl	Cl	OEt	IV	80	339
OEt	Cl	OEt	Cl	II	93	339
OEt	Cl	Cl	Cl	L	70	340
OEt	Cl	Cl	Cl	II		340
Az	OEt	OEt	Az	V		930, 1425
OEt	Az	OEt	Az	IV	69	1169
OEt	Az	OEt	Az	II		1169
OMe	Az	Az	Az	I		1169
OEt	Piperidino	OEt	Piperidino	II		1173
OEt	Morpholino	OEt	Morpholino	II		1173
OPr	Az	OPr	Az	II	68–75	1169, 1424
OCH$_2$CH$_2$OMe	Az	OCH$_2$CH$_2$OMe	Az	II		1169
OPh	Cl	OPh	Cl	II		1421

OBz	OAc	OBz^{b,f}	OAc^{b,f}	Cl	Cl	Cl	Cl	I	I	45	40	2403	2403

1,4-Naphthoquinone Derivatives

A	B	Product type	% Yield	References
H	H	I	—	1117
H	Me	I	—	1117
F	F	II	—	1231
Cl	Cl	I	—	413, 1117, 1132, 1154
OMe	OMe	II	—	1171, 1424
OMe	OMe	I	93	1111, 1421
OPh	OPh	I	—	1151, 1421
OC$_6$H$_4$Me-p	OC$_6$H$_4$Me-p	I	—	1151, 1421
SMe	SMe	I	77	1111
NHSO$_2$Me	NHSO$_2$Me	I	—	1165
Br	SPh	I	92	3111, 3124
Br	SC$_6$H$_4$Cl-p	I	—	3111, 3124
Br	SC$_6$H$_4$Me-p	I	—	3111, 3124
Cl	NHAc	I	—	1133, 1421
Cl	N(Me)Ac	I	—	1133, 1421
Cl	N(Et)Ac	I	—	1133, 1421
Cl	NHCO$_2$Me	I	—	1143, 2856

Table 3-XII—*continued*

1,4-Naphthoquinone Derivatives

A	B	Product type	% Yield	References
Cl	NHCO$_2$Et	I	—	1143, 2856
Cl	NHCO$_2$Et	I	—[a]	1143, 2856
Cl	N(COEt)$_2$	I	—	1143, 2856
Cl	NHSO$_2$Me	I	—	1165
Cl	NMeSO$_2$Me	I	—	1109, 1421
N(CH$_2$CH=CH$_2$)SO$_2$Me	N(CH$_2$CH=CH$_2$)SO$_2$Me	I	—	1109
Cl	N(NO)CH$_2$CO$_2$Et	I	47	413
Cl	NAcCH$_2$CO$_2$Et	I	69	413
H	H	I	—	1135, 1427

(in 5,6,7,8-tetrahydronaphthoquinone)

1,2-Naphthoquinone Derivatives

Y	A	B	Z	% Yield	References
O	Cl	Cl	H	—	1162, 1421, 1424, 3138
O	Cl	Cl	H	—[a]	1162, 1421, 1424, 3138
O	Cl	Cl	H	—[b]	1162, 1421, 1424, 3138
O	OMe	H	H	—	1162, 1421, 1424, 3138

				% Yield	References
O	OMe	Cl	H	—	1162, 1424, 3138
O	H	SO_3K	H	—	1421, 1424, 1428
O	H	SO_3K	H	—[a]	1421, 1424, 1428
	H	SO_3K	H	—[b]	1421, 1424, 1428
N_2	H	SO_3Na	$6\text{-}NO_2$	58	2030
N_2	H	SO_3Na	x-Cl	44	2030
N_2	H	SO_3Na	H	15	2030
O	H	OMe	H	—	1162
O	H	H	H	—	1162

Other Quinones

Quinone reactant	Product	% Yield	References
5,8-Isoquinolinequinone	6-Az or 7-Az derivative	64	2008
5,8-Quinolinequinone	6-Az derivative	—	1130
2-Me-5,8-quinolinequinone	6-Az derivative	—	1130
$6,7\text{-}(MeO)_2\text{-}5,8$-quinolinequinone	$6,7\text{-}Az_2$ derivative	—	1171, 1424
$2,3\text{-}Me_2\text{-}5,8$-quinoxalinequinone	6-Az derivative	—	1306b, 1554
1,4:5,8-Anthradiquinone	$2,7\text{-}Az_2$ derivative	—	412
1,4:5,8-Anthradiquinone	$2,3,6\text{-}Az_3$ derivative	—	412
1-F-anthraquinone	1-Az derivative	85	1306, 1909, 3103
1-F-4-Me-anthraquinone	1-Az-4-Me derivative	87	1306, 1909
2-F-anthraquinone	2-Az derivative	73	1306, 1909
2-F-3-Cl-anthraquinone	2-Az-3-Cl derivative	88	1306, 1909
$1,5\text{-}F_2$-anthraquinone	$1,5\text{-}Az_2$ derivative	76	1306, 1909

[a] 2-MeAz derivative.
[b] $2,2\text{-}Me_2Az$ derivative.
[c] $2\text{-}EtO_2CAz$ derivative.
[d] $2\text{-}iso\text{-}PrO_2CAz$ derivative.
[e] $Ar = p\text{-}MeOC_6H_4$.
[f] The C group in the product was OH.

Substituents in the 2,5-positions of benzoquinone are very easily displaced. If the benzoquinone contains additional substituents, these may also be displaced, but under more rigorous conditions (Eq 49) (*2400a*).

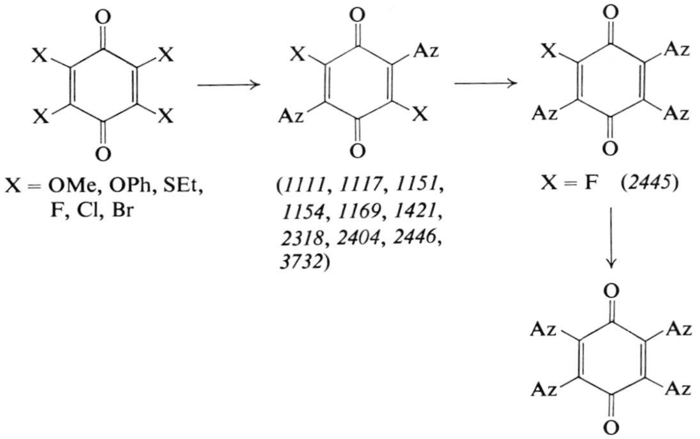

X = OMe, OPh, SEt,
F, Cl, Br

(*1111, 1117, 1151,
1154, 1169, 1421,
2318, 2404, 2446,
3732*)

X = F (*2445*)

(49)

X = OMe, F
(*1169, 1231, 2215, 3731*)

Disubstituted benzoquinones containing the substituents in the 2,3- or 2,6-positions undergo reaction with EI with more difficulty; the process apparently involves simple addition as well as addition–elimination (Eq 50) (*1117, 1154*).

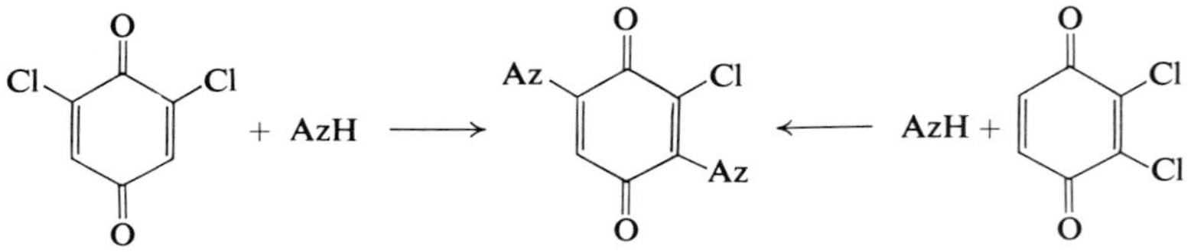

$$+ \text{AzH} \longrightarrow \longleftarrow \text{AzH} +$$

(50)

From the manner in which EI reacts with monosubstituted benzoquinones (as shown in Eq 51) it appears that the addition reaction occurs before the addition–elimination. It is probable, however, that many of these reactions are thermodynamically controlled.

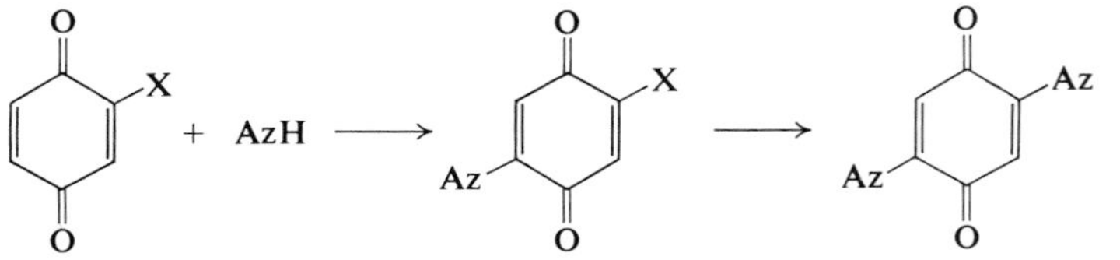

$$+ \text{AzH} \longrightarrow \longrightarrow$$

(51)

X = OMe, Br

(*2127, 2402*)

(*1425*)

Replacements of quinone substituents which would result in formation of acid (HCl, HBr, etc.) are usually done in the presence of an additional tertiary base such as triethylamine or pyridine.

Naphthoquinones, both 1,2- and 1,4-, and other quinones (2233) undergo reactions with aziridines like those described above for p-benzoquinones.

Nucleophilic Aromatic Substitution by 1-Unsubstituted Aziridines. The reaction of amines, including aziridines, with such compounds as aromatic halides formally resembles bimolecular nucleophilic substitution at saturated carbon atoms (Eq 52).

$$ArX + AzH \xrightarrow{\text{base}} Ar\text{---}Az \tag{52}$$

While the mechanism is different, involving the formation of an adduct between the aryl halide and the aziridine which then eliminates halide ion, the major consideration when an aziridine is the amine is the same as for S_N2 displacements on aliphatic halides (see p. 121). Precautions are necessary to avoid formation of aziridinium ions, which are susceptible to ring opening. Thus, a base which is capable of essentially irreversible removal of acid formed in the reaction is necessary.

Nucleophilic aromatic substitution by amines generally involves aromatic compounds containing activating groups (e.g., nitro) in the aryl moiety. Only a few such examples involving homoaromatic systems exist for aziridines. The rate of such displacement by aziridines is lower than for ordinary aliphatic amines, as might be expected from the lower base strengths for aziridines. Thus the following second-order rate constants were obtained for the reaction of amines with 4-nitrofluorobenzene (3411):

Amine	$10^6 k$ (liter sec^{-1} mole^{-1})
Me$_2$NH	12000
Et$_2$NH	163
Pyrrolidine	14600
Piperidine	8900
EI	77

If the aromatic compound contains no activating group, reaction 52 may still be achieved by first converting the aziridine to its alkali metal salt. Thus, dissolving a potassium–sodium alloy in excess EI and subsequent treatment with bromobenzene produced N-phenylaziridine in 67% yield (2158). Such a reaction may be viewed as an elimination–addition involving formation of a benzyne intermediate.

Included in this section is a discussion of displacements by aziridines on heteroaromatic nitrogen compounds (e.g., *s*-triazines and pyrimidines) (Eq 53) (Table 3-XIII). While reaction of amines with such halo-substituted heterocyclic nitrogen compounds formally resembles nucleophilic aromatic substitution, the resemblance to an acylation reaction is just as close if not more so.

$$\text{(pyrimidine-Cl)} + \text{AzH} \xrightarrow{\text{K}_2\text{CO}_3} \text{(pyrimidine-Az)} \tag{53}$$

For example, in reaction 53 the structural part of the chloropyrimidine involved closely resembles an imidyl chloride (Eq 54).

$$\underset{\text{C—Cl}}{\overset{\text{N—}}{\|}} + \text{AzH} \longrightarrow \underset{\text{C—Az}}{\overset{\text{N—}}{\|}} \tag{54}$$

Not only is the chlorine in the chloropyrimidine of comparable reactivity to that of an acid chloride, but the 1-substituted aziridine so formed is also analogous to 1-acylated aziridines in properties. As mentioned previously, such activated aziridines undergo ring-opening reactions with nucleophiles in the absence of acidic catalysts (see p. 107). Thus in reaction 52, performed with such heterocyclic nitrogen compounds, it is necessary not only to avoid the presence of acid, but also to maintain reaction conditions (generally low temperatures) such that ring opening of the product aziridine by the 1-unsubstituted aziridine reactant does not occur (other secondary reactions are also possible; see p. 162). For example, the reaction of 2,4,6-tris(trichloromethyl)-*s*-triazine with EI produces such a secondary reaction (Eq 55) (*350*).

$$\tag{55}$$

Similarly, treatment of 3,6-dichloropyridazine with excess EI yields 3-[2-(1-aziridinyl)ethylamino]-6-chloropyridazine (*2731*, *3414*) instead of 3-(1-aziridinyl)-6-chloropyridazine. The latter compound was reported earlier as the product from this reaction (*3424*).

With di-, tri-, or polyhalo heterocyclic nitrogen compounds, replacement of the halogen atoms by amines occurs stepwise, each successive halogen being replaced with more difficulty. In 2,4,6-trichloro-s-triazine the third chlorine is replaced only under more vigorous conditions when the amine is dimethylamine. If the amine is EI, however, all three chlorines are readily replaced even under mild conditions. With 3,5-dichloro-as-triazine the monoaziridinyl product 3-(1-aziridinyl)-5-chloro-as-triazine was obtained in 38% yield (1542a). Also in dihaloquinoxalines, dihalopyridazines, dihalopurines, and trihalopyrimidines the presence of the aziridinyl group in the initial product so reduces the reactivity of the remaining halogen atoms that monoaziridinyl products may be obtained (2139, 3424, 3667, 3689). 2,4,6-Trichloropyrimidine undergoes successive replacement of chlorine atoms by EI under progressively more rigorous conditions (Eq 56).

(2139)

(1723a, 2139)   (3645)   (56)

In 2,4,6-trichloropyrimidine the chloro group at the 4-position is replaced first (2139) and not according to suggestions made in an earlier report (1682).

In a tetrachloro-s-triazine derivative **22** the chloro groups could be successively replaced with aziridinyl groups by changing the conditions (3091).

The feasibility of successively replacing halogens on 2,4,6-trihalo-s-triazines has allowed preparation of a number of complicated dyes containing aziridinyl

Table 3-XIII

NUCLEOPHILIC AROMATIC SUBSTITUTION BY AZIRIDINES[a]

ArX	Position(s) of Az group	% Yield	References
Benzenes and Naphthalenes			
PhBr	1	67.6[b]	2158
4-$O_2NC_6H_4F$	1	47[c]	3411
2,4-$(O_2N)_2C_6H_3F$	1	—[d]	1672a
2,4,6-$(O_2N)_3C_6H_2OMe$	1	—[e]	1672a
2,4-$(O_2N)_2C_6H_3Cl$	1	95	3375
2,4,6-$(O_2N)_3C_6H_2Cl$	1	41	3375
2,4,6-$(O_2N)_3C_6H_2OMe$	1	—	2723
2,6-$(O_2N)_2$-4-$F_3CC_6H_2Cl$	1	—	2203
$Cl_3F_3C_6$	? (F replaced)	—	455
2,4,6-Cl_3-1,3,5-F_3C_6	1,3	57	4000
C_6F_6	1	52	4000
2,3-$(O_2N)_2C_{10}H_6$	—	68	2615
Pyridines and Quinolines			
2-Cl-3-$O_2NC_5H_3N$	—	—	3286
2-Cl_3C-4,6-$Cl_2C_5H_2N$	4,6	—	1474
2-ClC_9H_6N	2	73[b]	299
Pyridazines (substituents shown)			
3-$MeSO_2$-6-Cl	6	60	2731
3,6-Cl_2-4-Me	6	—[f]	3418
3,6-Cl_2-4-MeO	6	—[f]	3418
3,6-Cl_2-4-EtO	6	—[f]	3414
Pyrimidines (substituents shown)			
2,4,6-F_3	2,4	91	3172
2-Cl	2	—[f]	81
2,4-Cl_2	2	—[f]	81
2,4,6-Cl_3	2,4	—[f]	1723a
2,4,6-Cl_3	4	—	2139
2,4-Cl_2-6-MeO_2C	4	—	2139
2,4-Cl_2-5-Me	4	—	2139
2,4-Cl_2-5-F	2,4	67	2933
2,4-Cl_2-5-F	4	50	2933
2,4-Cl_2-6-Me	2	46	553
2,4,6-Cl_3-5-F	2,4,6	—	409
2,4,5,6-Cl_4	2,4,6	—	409
2,4,5-Cl_3-6-Me	4	78	1042
2,4-Cl_2-5-Br-6-Me	4	—	1042
2,4-Cl_2-5-O_2N	2,4	46	1682
2,4-Cl_2-5-O_2N-6-Me	2,4	20–27	553, 1042, 1914
2,4,6-Cl_3-5-Ph	2,4	—	1682

Table 3-XIII—*continued*

ArX	Position(s) of Az group	% Yield	References
Pyrimidines (substituents shown)			
2-Cl-4-Me-5-O$_2$N-6-H$_2$N	2	45	*1682*
2-Cl-4-*p*-FC$_6$H$_4$NH-5-O$_2$N-6-Me	2	69	*1042*
2-Me-4,6-Cl$_2$-5-O$_2$N	4,6	62	*1682*
2-MeO-4,6-Cl$_2$-5-O$_2$N	4,6	—	*408, 2942*
2-H$_2$N-4-Cl-5-O$_2$N-6-Me	4	45	*2139*
2-Et$_2$N-4,6-Cl$_2$-5-O$_2$N	4,6	—	*408, 2942*
2-MeS-4-Cl-5-F	4	—	*410*
2-MeS-4-Cl-5-EtO$_2$C	4	—	*2139*
2-MeS-4-Cl-5-Br-6-Me	4	—	*2139*
2-MeS-4,5,6-Cl$_3$	4	—	*410*
2-MeS-4,6-Cl$_2$	4	—	*2139*
2-MeS-4,6-Cl$_2$	4	—^{g}	*2139*
2-MeS-4,6-Cl$_2$-5-F	4	—	*410*
2-MeS-4,6-Cl$_2$-5-Ph	4	—	*2139*
2-MeS-4-Cl-6-MeO$_2$C	4	—	*2139*
2-MeSO$_2$-4,6-Cl$_2$	2	—	*2139*
2-EtSO$_2$-4-H$_2$N-5-MeO$_2$C	2	44	*2139a*
2-MeSO$_2$-4,6-Cl$_2$-5-Br	2,4	—	*2139*
2-Ph-4,6-Cl$_2$	4	56	*1682*
2-Ph-4,6-Cl$_2$	4,6	38^b	*1682*
2-Ph-4,6-Cl$_2$-5-O$_2$N	4,6	42	*1682*
2-*p*-ClC$_6$H$_4$-4,6-Cl$_2$-5-O$_2$N	4,6	44.5	*1682*
2-*p*-MeOC$_6$H$_4$-4,6-Cl$_2$	4	61	*1682*
2-*p*-EtOC$_6$H$_4$-4,6-Cl$_2$	4	66	*1682*
2-*p*-ClC$_6$H$_4$CH$_2$S-4-Cl-5-Br	4	—	*2139*
2-*p*-ClC$_6$H$_4$CH$_2$S-4-Cl-5-Br-6-Me	4	—	*2139*
2-*p*-ClC$_6$H$_4$NH-4,6-Cl$_2$	4	46	*1682*
2-(4-Me-*x*-O$_2$NC$_6$H$_3$)-4,6-Cl$_2$-5-O$_2$N	4,6	71	*1682*
2-(4-MeO-3-O$_2$NC$_6$H$_4$)-4,6-Cl$_2$-5-O$_2$N	4,6	78	*1862*
2-(4-EtO-3-O$_2$NC$_6$H$_4$)-4,6-Cl$_2$-5-O$_2$N	4,6	57	*1682*
2-(2-C$_{10}$H$_7$)-4,6-Cl$_2$	4	84	*1682*
2-(2-C$_{10}$H$_7$)-4,6-Cl$_2$	4,6	41	*1682*
2-(2-C$_{10}$H$_7$)-4,6-Cl$_2$-5-O$_2$N	4,6	41	*1682*
2,6-Cl$_2$-4-Az	2	—	*2139*
2,6-Az$_2$-4-Cl	4	—	*3645*
4,6-Cl$_2$	4	—	*410*
4-Cl-6-MeSO$_2$	4	39	*2731*
4,6-Cl$_2$-5-O$_2$N	4,6	69	*1682*
s-Triazines (substituents shown)			
2,4-Cl$_2$	2,4	59^f	*1889, 2027, 3126*
2,4,6-Cl$_3$	2,4	47^f	*1889, 2027, 3126*

Table 3-XIII—*continued*

ArX	Position(s) of Az group	% Yield	References
s-Triazines (substituents shown)			
2,4,6-Cl$_3$	2,4,6	73–85[c, f]	472, 1889, 1910, 2649a, 2878, 3128, 4035
2,4,6-Cl$_3$	2,4,6	33–98[g]	350, 839, 1209, 1221, 3841, 3842
2,4-Cl$_2$-6-Me	2,4	—	1889
2,4-Cl$_2$-6-Et	2,4	64.2[c]	472
2,4-Cl$_2$-6-MeO	2,4	44[c, f]	472, 1889, 2027, 3126
2,4-Cl$_2$-6-EtO	2,4	50.3[c]	472, 1889
2,4-Cl$_2$-6-iso-Pr	2,4	—	1889
2,4-Cl$_2$-6-H$_2$N	2,4	65[f]	1889, 2027, 3126
2,4-Cl$_2$-6-MeNH	2,4	12[c, f]	473, 1889
2,4-Cl$_2$-6-Me$_2$N	4	—	1894
2,4-Cl$_2$-6-Me$_2$N	2,4	—[f]	1894
2,4-Cl$_2$-6-iso-PrNH	2,4	—[f]	1889
2,4-Cl$_2$-6-N$_2$CH	2,4	53	1542, 1543, 1544, 1683
2,4-Cl$_2$-6-Ph	2,4	40	1889, 2027, 3126
2,4-Cl$_2$-6-*p*-MeC$_6$H$_4$	2,4	—	1889
2,4-Cl$_2$-6-PhO	2,4	—[c]	472, 1889
2,4-Cl$_2$-6-PhCH$_2$NH	2,4	23[c]	474
2,4-Cl$_2$-6-piperidino	2,4	34[c]	465, 474, 3442
2,4-Cl$_2$-6-morpholino	2,4	40[c]	474
2,4-Cl$_2$-6-EtO$_2$CCH$_2$NH	2,4	—	3442
2,4-Cl$_2$-6-MeO$_2$CCHMeNH (D,L)	2,4	—	3442
2,4-Cl$_2$-6-MeO$_2$CCH$_2$CH$_2$NH	2,4	—	3442
2,4-Cl$_2$-6-EtO$_2$CCHMeNH (D,L)	2,4	—	3442
2,4-Cl$_2$-6-EtO$_2$CCH$_2$CH$_2$NH	2,4	—	3442
2,4-Cl$_2$-6-EtO$_2$CCH(iso-Bu)NH (D,L)	2,4	—	3442
2,4-Cl$_2$-6-PhCH$_2$O$_2$CCHMeNH (D,L)	2,4	—	3442
2,4-Cl$_2$-6-*p*-MeO$_2$CC$_6$H$_4$NH	2,4	68	1297
2,4-Cl$_2$-6-*p*-EtO$_2$CC$_6$H$_4$NH	2,4	70	1297
2,4-Cl$_2$-6-EtO$_2$CCH$_2$CH$_2$CH(CO$_2$Et)NH (D,L)	2,4	—	3442
2,4-Cl$_2$-6-MeO$_2$CCH(NHAc)C$_6$H$_4$NH-*p* (D,L)	2,4	40.5	336
2-Cl-4,6-Me$_2$	2	81	3171
2-Cl-4,6-(MeO)$_2$	2	69–76[c, f]	472, 2027, 3126
2-Cl-4,6-(ClCH$_2$)$_2$	2	83	3171
2-Cl-4,6-(Cl$_3$C)$_2$	2	86	3171
2-Cl-4-*c*-C$_6$H$_{11}$NH-6-Me	2	—	3668
2-Cl-4,6-Ph$_2$	2	96.7[c]	472
2,4,6-(Cl$_3$C)$_3$	2,4	—	350

Table 3-XIII—*continued*

ArX	Position(s) of Az group	% Yield	References
Phthalazines (substituent shown)			
1-Cl	1	Small	*4020*
Quinazolines (substituent shown)			
4-Cl	4	63	*4020*
Quinoxalines (substituents shown)			
2,3-Cl$_2$	2	73	*1664, 3689*
2-Cl-3-MeO	2	—	*1664*
2,3-Cl$_2$-6-O$_2$N	2	—	*3419*
Pyrimido(5,4-d)pyrimidines (substituent shown)			
4,6,8-Cl$_3$	4,8	—	*3538*
Purines (substituents shown)			
2,6,Cl$_2$-7-Me	6	49[f]	*3667*
2,6-Cl$_2$-9-Me	6	—[c]	*2792*
2-H$_2$N-6-Cl-9-Me	6	33.8[c]	*2792*
6-Cl-9-(H$_4$-2-pyranyl)	6	—	*3044a*
s-Tetrazines (substituents shown)			
3-Br-6-Ph	3	—	*1518a*
3-Br-6-(*p*-ClC$_6$H$_4$)	3	43	*1518a*

[a] The aziridine was EI, and an amine was used as acid acceptor, except as otherwise noted.
[b] The alkali metal salt of EI was used.
[c] Excess AzH was used as acid acceptor.
[d] The product was the 2-Bz-3-PhAz derivative.
[e] The product was the *cis*-2,3-Ph$_2$Az derivative.
[f] An inorganic base such as NaOH or K$_2$CO$_3$ was used as acid acceptor.
[g] The product was the 2-MeAz derivative.

groups (*695, 2105, 2477*). Thus **23** was prepared from the appropriate dye, cyanuric chloride, and EI.

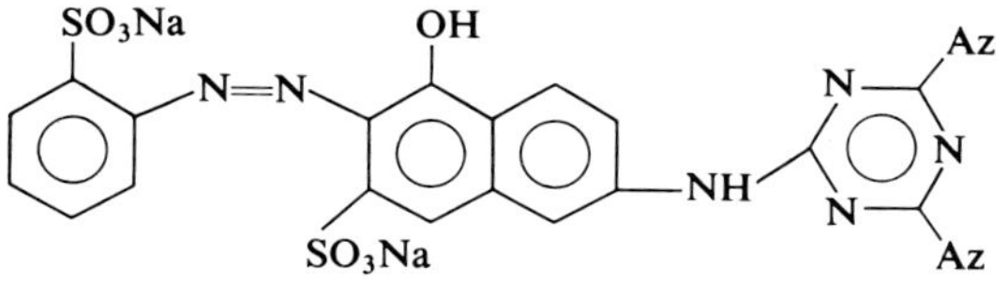

23

Acylation of 1-Unsubstituted Aziridines. Included in this section are the reactions of aziridines with any compound containing a carbon atom doubly bound to a hetero atom and singly bound to a replaceable group (Eq 57).

$$R-\overset{\overset{\displaystyle Y}{\|}}{C}-X + AzH \xrightarrow{\text{Base}} R-\overset{\overset{\displaystyle Y}{\|}}{C}-Az \tag{57}$$

Thus included are acid halides, acid anhydrides, esters, carbamoyl halides, haloformates, halothioformates, imidyl halides, and the like.

The reaction of aziridines with such reagents does not appear to be different in mechanism from that of typical amines. However, EI appears to be more nucleophilic than would be predicted from its base strength (*1271*). Use of the reaction for preparation of 1-acylated aziridines requires special precautions, primarily because the product can undergo a variety of ring-opening reactions.

This same problem has been emphasized for "amine-type" reactions of aziridines. In alkylation by alkyl halides, all such problems may be attributed to the formation of protonated or quaternized aziridines (see p. 121). When the reaction is acylation by acyl halides, the 1-acylated aziridine is very weakly basic and quaternization or formation of high concentrations of protonated aziridine product is generally impossible. Because 1-acylated aziridines contain N-substituents capable of conjugation with the unshared pair of electrons on the aziridine nitrogen, these derivatives undergo ring-opening reactions with nucleophiles even though the aziridine nitrogen is not protonated or quaternized. Thus, in contrast to alkylations, acylations are complicated primarily by the inherent reactivity of the 1-acylated aziridine. Acidic reagents are very strong catalysts for nucleophilic ring-opening reactions with 1-acylated aziridines, however, and it is necessary to maintain basic conditions for reaction 57.

The major precaution usually taken (other than maintaining basic conditions) is to carry out the reaction at low temperatures.

$$RCOX + AzH \xrightarrow{\text{base}} RCOAz \tag{58}$$

$$RCOAz + Nu^- \longrightarrow RCON CH_2CH_2-Nu \tag{59}$$

When X is a group which is easily displaced (Cl^-, AcO^-, etc.) reaction 58 may occur readily at temperatures much lower than are necessary for reaction 59, wherein Nu is some nucleophilic reagent present (including the 1-unsubstituted aziridine). When X is a group not so easily replaced (e.g., OEt), reaction 59 becomes important. For example, the reaction of EI with diethyl oxalate or ethyl trichloroacetate (X = OEt) gave 2-(1-aziridinyl)ethyl amide derivative (*197, 350, 3850*; see Table 3-IX). Evidently under conditions which were necessary to obtain a reaction, the secondary reaction of EI with the 1-acylaziridine occurred; there was not sufficient difference in rate between reactions 58 and 59 to permit only reaction 58. The reaction of ethyl perfluoroheptanoate with EI is reported to give the 1-acylated aziridine in essentially quantitative yield (24). The product was not properly characterized, however, and it was very probably that corresponding to the secondary reaction.

It is sometimes possible to alter the relative rates of reaction 58 and 59 by choice of solvent. Thus in reaction 60 an 80% yield of the desired acylated aziridine (corresponding to reaction 58) was obtained when the solvent was a mixture of ether and methanol whereas the only product isolated when methanol alone was the solvent was the ring-opened product shown (2348).

$$H_2NC \overset{NNO_2}{\underset{SMe}{{<}}} + AzH \xrightarrow{Et_2O-MeOH} H_2NC \overset{NNO_2}{\underset{Az}{{<}}}$$

(60)

$$\xrightarrow{MeOH} H_2NC \overset{NNO_2}{\underset{NHCH_2CH_2SMe}{{<}}}$$

Generally the solvent chosen for reaction 57 is a nonpolar solvent such as ether or benzene. This is particularly appropriate when the acylating agent is an acyl halide and a tertiary amine is used to take up the hydrogen halide, which is precipitated as the amine salt.

A different secondary reaction which may occur during acylation of aziridines with arylthiocarbonyl halides, aryl haloformates, or thiophosgene is rearrangement to an isocyanate or isothiocyanate (Eq 61).

$$Az-\overset{\overset{Y}{\|}}{C}-X \longrightarrow XCH_2CH_2N{=}C{=}Y$$

(61)

This rearrangement is discussed in detail on p. 291. The reaction between EI and thiophosgene has been reported (3038) to occur as shown (Eq 62).

$$AzH + CSCl_2 \rightarrow AzCSCl$$

(62)

24

The product was characterized only by nitrogen analysis, however, and it was later found that **24** was unstable in the reaction mixture at temperatures above about $-10°C$ (963). The actual product formed when this reaction is performed at temperatures above about $-10°C$ is 2-chloroethyl isothiocyanate or its derivatives (e.g., trimer). This same rearrangement has been observed to occur during attempts to prepare **25** and **26** (963).

$$2,4\text{-}Cl_2C_6H_3O_2CAz$$

25

$$PhSCOAz$$

26

Another rearrangement (also discussed in detail later, p. 280) may be depicted as follows (Eq 63).

$$\text{(aziridine with COR on N, CH}_2\text{—)} \longrightarrow RCONHCH_2CH{=}CH{-} \tag{63}$$

Attempted benzoylation of cyclodecenimine or cyclooctenimine thus gave the following products (Eq 64).

$$(CH_2)_n \underset{CH}{\overset{CH}{\diagdown}} NH + BzCl \xrightarrow{Et_3N} (CH_2)_{n-1} \underset{CH}{\overset{CH}{\diagdown}} \overset{CH}{\underset{NHBz}{}} \tag{64}$$

Acetylation of cyclodecenimine with acetic anhydride under otherwise the same conditions was successful.

Two other secondary reactions which are troublesome in preparation of 1-acylated aziridines are rearrangement to ring-expanded compounds, particularly oxazolines (Eq 65), and polymerization.

$$\underset{R\overset{|}{C}Az}{\overset{Y}{\|}} \longrightarrow \underset{R}{\overset{}{N{=}}}{\diagup}Y \tag{65}$$

These secondary reactions are frequently observed during the workup of an acylation mixture or distillation of a 1-acylated aziridine (*350, 963*). For example, distillation of 1-benzoylaziridine resulted in the formation of 2-phenyl-2-oxazoline and polymer (*1392*). The preferred method of purification for 1-acylated aziridines is recrystallization at as low a temperature as possible. Where such recrystallization is impossible, vacuum distillation at the lowest possible temperature is often satisfactory.

The occurrence of these secondary reactions is highly dependent on the structure of the 1-acylated aziridine. They also appear to be promoted by the presence of certain impurities in the crude 1-acylated aziridine. For example, 1-acetylaziridine prepared from acetyl chloride with triethylamine as the acid acceptor changed to polymer after several months at room temperature whereas the same compound prepared from ketene was essentially unchanged under the same conditions (*963*).

The most widely used general procedure for effecting reaction 57 is the addition of acyl halide to a solution of the aziridine and a tertiary amine (e.g., triethylamine) in a nonpolar solvent such as ether or benzene at about 0°C. The precipitate of tertiary amine hydrohalide is removed by filtration, the solvent removed from the filtrate under vacuum and the residual crude 1-

acylated aziridine purified by some suitable technique. Pyridine has been used as both an acid acceptor and solvent, particularly when acetic anhydride was the acylating agent.

The aziridine itself has been used as an acid acceptor. In one report, however, it was noted that the amine hydrochloride (presumably aziridine hydrochloride) which precipitated from a reaction mixture in ether at $-5°C$ had to be immediately dissolved in water to avoid an exothermic polymerization (471).

The major problem encountered with this general procedure is that the 1-acylaziridine products are sometimes unstable with respect to polymerization (especially the most reactive of the 1-acylaziridines) when stored at room temperature for extended periods (e.g., 3 months). This problem is partly overcome for water-insoluble 1-acylaziridines (3297) by adding a solution of the acyl halide in a water-insoluble solvent (e.g., ether, benzene, chloroform) to a water solution of the aziridine and inorganic base (e.g., sodium hydroxide, potassium carbonate), separating the organic layer, drying, and removing the solvent under vacuum. The procedure is especially useful for preparation of high molecular weight 1-acylaziridines which cannot be purified by recrystallization or distillation. Modifications of this procedure have included the use of ammonium hydroxide as an acid acceptor (3559) and the use of nonionic surfactants (833, 3559).

The stability of 1-acylated aziridines on storage depends on the structure, the purity of product, and the temperature. Solutions (20–40 wt %) in unreactive solvents such as benzene are usually much more stable than the isolated products (963, 3295, 3297). Indeed the claimed stabilization of other activated aziridines by various materials (832, 1198, 2659) probably results from dilution rather than any specific stabilizing action.

A special case of an acylation of EI is shown in Eq 66 (1148).

$$+ \text{AzH} \longrightarrow \quad + \text{CO}_2 \qquad (66)$$

Another example is provided by the reaction of ketene dimer with aziridines (1923, 1937, 2001) (Eq 67)

$$+ \text{AzH} \longrightarrow \text{AcCH}_2\text{COAz} \qquad (67)$$

and still another by the use of $ArC(S)SCH_2CO_2H$ as an acylating agent (1921, 1927c).

Although the carbodiimide-promoted acylation has not been widely used, it appears to be potentially general (Eq 68) (*717, 878, 1684, 3256*; cf. *2863*). The method does not require conversion of the acid into the acid chloride and is particularly convenient when it is necessary or desirable to avoid the use of an alkaline medium.

$$ArCO_2H + AzH + RN{=}C{=}NR \rightarrow ArCOAz + (RNH)_2CO$$

$$R = c\text{-}C_6H_{11} \tag{68}$$

The reaction of carbon disulfide with an aziridine in the presence of base may be regarded as a special type of acylation. An example is shown in Eq 69 (*685*). Treatment of simple aziridines (e.g., EI or 2,2-dimethylaziridine) with carbon disulfide in aqueous base has been claimed as a method for preparation of salts of the dithiocarbonates (*2469, 3797*), but this appears unlikely.

$$\tag{69}$$

The remarkable tendency of 5-carboxydehydroacetic acid to form amides under ordinary conditions extends to EI, which is acylated in a few hours at room temperature (*3789*).

Aziridines have been acylated with compounds containing both an acid chloride group and some other reactive group. In the case of acryloyl chloride the acylation could be accomplished at $-30°C$ without appreciable addition of EI to the double bond (Eq 70) (*2150*).

$$CH_2{=}CHCOCl + AzH \xrightarrow{Et_3N} CH_2{=}CHCOAz \tag{70}$$

With compounds containing an isocyanate and a carbamoyl chloride group (*191, 1204*) or a phosphonyl chloride and a formamidoyl chloride group (*881*) (as shown in Eq 71), reaction occurred at both functional groups.

$$\underset{\overset{\|}{PhNH{-}C{-}Cl}}{\overset{NPOCl_2}{}} + AzH \xrightarrow{Et_3N} \underset{\overset{\|}{PhNH{-}C{-}Az}}{\overset{NPOAz_2}{}} \tag{71}$$

In several instances mixtures of acid chlorides have been treated with aziridines. For example, a "half ester" was prepared *in situ* by reaction of a 1:3:3 molar proportion of $EtC(CH_2OH)_3$, terephthaloyl chloride, and triethylamine and the product treated directly with 2-methylaziridine (*3537*).

In Table 3-XIV are shown many acylation reactions performed on aziridines.

Table 3-XIV[a]

REACTION OF 1-UNSUBSTITUTED AZIRIDINES WITH ACYL HALIDES, ANHYDRIDES,
HALOFORMATES, CARBAMOYL HALIDES, AND IMIDYL HALIDES

Aliphatic Acyl Halides

$$RCOX + AzH \xrightarrow{\text{base}} RCOAz$$

R	Aziridine or substituents therein	% Yield[b]	References
Me	No substituents	30	3284, 3430; cf. 510a
CH$_2$=CH	No substituents	63.7	2150
CH$_2$=CMe	No substituents	77	239, 2305
Bu	No substituents	55	3375
Bu	2-Me	60	3375
Bu	2,2-Me$_2$	70	3375
Bu	2-Bu	70	3375
Me[c]	2,3-(CH$_2$)$_8$	—	1101
Et	2-Et-2-Ph	—	3516
n-C$_{11}$H$_{23}$	No substituents	94[d]	833
Me	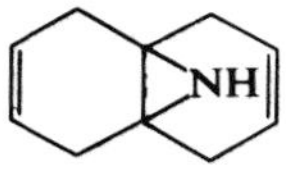	—	3703
n-C$_{11}$H$_{23}$	2-NH$_2$CH$_2$	—	3354
Pr$_2$CH	No substituents	38	323
7,7-Me$_2$-1-norbornyl	No substituents	96[e]	843
n-C$_{15}$H$_{31}$	No substituents	92[d]	833, 3901
1-Adamantyl	No substituents	—	2674
Me(CH$_2$)$_7$CH=CH(CH$_2$)$_7$	2-Et	—	3274
Me	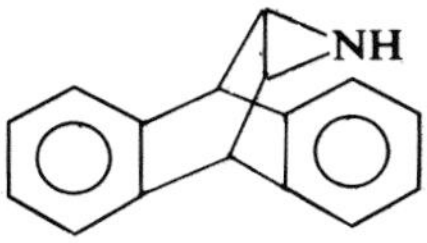	—	2103
Me[c]	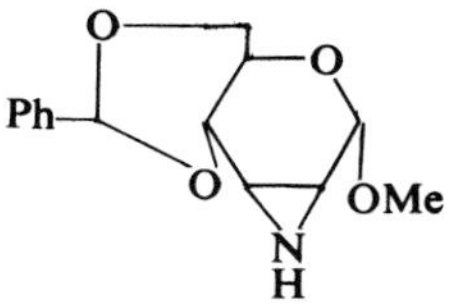	85–100	1561, 2538a, 3172
Me[c]	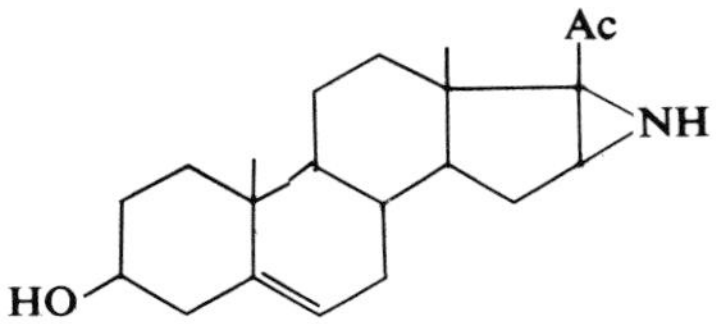	80	982
Me[c]	Mitomycin C	—	2227

Table 3-XIV[a]*—continued*

Substituted Aliphatic Acyl Halides		
R	% Yield[b, f]	References
CF_3	39.5	2150
$CF_3(CF_2)_2$	63[e, g]	24, 69, 2886
$CF_3(CF_2)_6$	—	24,69,2885,2886
$CF_3(CF_2)_6(CH_2)_{10}$	—	69
Various 3-oxocyclopentyl	—	4048
$Ph_2CHCHPh$	—	415
$F_3COCF_2CF_2$	—[e, g]	24
$PhCH=CPh$	—	4038
$MeO_2CCH_2CH_2$	62.5	3201
$MeO_2CCH_2CH_2$	39[e]	3097
$PhNHCH_2$	69[h]	1234
$AzCONH(CH_2)_5$	—	191
2-Furyl-CH=CH-	18–66[d]	2319
Various 5-R^1-2-furyl-CH=CR^2	—	4161
6-Oxo-2-(6H)pyranyl	60	3790
2,4-Me_2-6-oxo-3-(6H)pyranyl	80	3790
2-Me-1,4-oxathien-3-yl	59	3659
$HOCH_2CMe_2CHOHCONHCH_2CH_2$	—[i]	3181, 4184
p-$(ClCH_2CH_2)_2NC_6H_4CH_2$	88.5[j]	878, 3256
p-$(ClCH_2CH_2)_2NC_6H_4CH_2CH_2$	88.5[j]	878, 3256
3,4,5-$(MeO)_3C_6H_2CH_2CH_2$	75[d]	2864
o-$C_6H_4(CO)_2NCH_2CH_2$	—	1302
o-$C_6H_4(CO)_2NCH_2CH_2$	—[k]	2225
o-$C_6H_4(CO)_2NCH_2$	—	1302
o-$C_6H_4(CO)_2NCH(CH_2OMe)$	—	1302
$(MeO)_2P(S)CH_2$	82.5[e, l]	3193
p-$(ClCH_2CH_2)_2NC_6H_4CH_2CH_2CH_2$	96[j]	878, 3256
$Az_2P(O)CH_2$	—	2860
$Az_2P(O)CH_2CH_2$[h]	—	2860

Aromatic Acyl Halides			
R	AzH substituents	% Yield[b]	References
Ph	None	27–74[d]	1480, 1555, 1801, 2319
Ph	2-Me	79–85[d]	1801, 1910
Ph	2-NH_2CH_2	—[d]	3354
Ph	2-Et	72	4155
Ph	2-EtO_2C	75[d]	2215
Ph	2,3-Ph_2	—	732
Ph	2,3-$[(CH_2)_4]$	90[d]	3443, 3814
Ph	2,3-Epiminonorbornane	—	3866

Table 3-XIV^a—continued

R	Aromatic Acyl Halides AzH substituents	% Yield^b	References
Ph	Ph— (structure: bicyclic with N, O, H, OMe)	100	2538a
Ph	Ph— (structure: bicyclic with O, N, H, OMe)	70–84^l	551, 685
Ph	Mitomycin C	—^{l}	2227, 4102
o-MeC$_6$H$_4$CO	Mitomycin C	—	2222
3-Pyridyl	None	82$^{e, i}$	471, 3182
2-Indolyl	None	—	2794a
1,4-Naphthoquinon-2-yl	None	—$^{e, m}$	3036

R	Substituted Aromatic Acyl Halides % Yield^b	References
o-MeC$_6$H$_4$	81–85^d	1801, 3834
o-MeC$_6$H$_4$	72–84$^{d, n}$	1801, 3834
m-MeC$_6$H$_4$	62–91^d	1801, 3834
m-MeC$_6$H$_4$	72–92$^{d, n}$	1801, 3834
p-MeC$_6$H$_4$	62–74^d	1810, 3834
p-MeC$_6$H$_4$	69–91$^{d, n}$	1801, 3834
3,5-Me$_2$C$_6$H$_3$	60	2864
p-FC$_6$H$_4$	35^d	2864
o-ClC$_6$H$_4$	90^d	3834
m-ClC$_6$H$_4$	50^d	3834
p-ClC$_6$H$_4$	58^d	1660, 3834
3,4-Cl$_2$C$_6$H$_3$	80^d	1234, 2864
o-H$_2$NC$_6$H$_4$	77^h	3834
o-MeOC$_6$H$_4$	71–80^d	1801, 3834
o-MeOC$_6$H$_4$	90$^{d, n}$	1801
m-MeOC$_6$H$_4$	95^d	3834
m-MeOC$_6$H$_4$	59$^{e, n}$	41
p-MeOC$_6$H$_4$	84$^{d, n}$	1801
p-MeOC$_6$H$_4$	79–85^d	1801, 2864, 3834
3,4-(MeO)$_2$C$_6$H$_3$	72	2864
3,4-(OCH$_2$O)C$_6$H$_3$	75	2864
m-O$_2$NC$_6$H$_4$	75^d	1801
m-O$_2$NC$_6$H$_4$	73$^{d, n}$	1801
p-O$_2$NC$_6$H$_4$	—	2175, 3375

Table 3-XIV—*continued*

Substituted Aromatic Acyl Halides		
R	% Yield[b]	References
$p\text{-}O_2NC_6H_4$	59[e, n]	*1660*
$p\text{-}O_2NC_6H_4$	33–84[o, d]	*1660, 1801, 2319*
$p\text{-}O_2NC_6H_4$	98 (crude)[o]	*1670*
$p\text{-}O_2NC_6H_4$	82[p]	*2046*
$p\text{-}O_2NC_6H_4$	79[q]	*2047*
$p\text{-}O_2NC_6H_4$	—[r]	*3601*
$p\text{-}O_2NC_6H_4$	67–98[d, n]	*1662, 1801, 3375*
$p\text{-}O_2NC_6H_4$	91[d, s]	*1662*
$p\text{-}EtOC_6H_4$	—[d]	*1659*
$o\text{-}ClCH_2C_6H_4$	—	*1663*
$m\text{-}(ClCH_2CH_2)_2NC_6H_4$	—[e]	*3701*
$p\text{-}(ClCH_2CH_2)_2NC_6H_4$	86[j]	*710, 878, 3256*
$2\text{-}H_2N\text{-}5\text{-}BrC_6H_3$	60[h]	*1234*
$2\text{-}H_2N\text{-}3,5\text{-}Cl_2C_6H_2$	—[h]	*1234*
$2\text{-}H_2N\text{-}5\text{-}NO_2C_6H_3$	82[h]	*1234*
$2\text{-}H_2N\text{-}5\text{-}NO_2C_6H_3$	—[h, n]	*1234*
$2\text{-}H_2N\text{-}5\text{-}NO_2C_6H_3$	—[h, t]	*1234*
$3,5\text{-}(O_2N)_2C_6H_3$	—[d]	*1660*
$3,4,5\text{-}(MeO)_3C_6H_2$	90–93	*2864, 3152*
$(MeO)_5C_6$	78[e]	*844*
$2\text{-}H_2N\text{-}1\text{-}C_{10}H_6$	53[h]	*1234*
2-Furyl	—	*4161*
$3,4,5\text{-}Cl_3\text{-}2\text{-furyl}$	—[e]	*2291*
$RCOX = p\text{-}MeC_6H_4CSX$	79	*1921*
5-Br-2-furyl	22–38[d]	*2319*
$5\text{-}O_2N\text{-}2\text{-furyl}$	45–65[d]	*2319*
$3,5\text{-}(O_2N)\text{-}2\text{-furyl}$	11–17[d]	*2319*
Various	—[k]	*2217*

Aliphatic Di- or Triacyl Halides

$$Q(COCl)_n + AzH' \xrightarrow{\text{base}} Q(COAz)_n$$

Q	% Yield[b]	References
$-CH=CHCH=CH-$	71	*1303*
$-CH_2C_6H_4OC_6H_4CH_2-$	67	*1303*
$-CH_2CH=CHCH_2-$	—	*1303*
$-(CF_2)_3-$	—[d]	*69, 2885, 2886*
$-CH_2-$	—[d]	*3834*
$-(CH_2)_2-$	21–60[d]	*1994, 3625, 3834*
$-(CH_2)_4-$	30–87[d]	*1994, 3296, 3297, 3834*
$-(CH_2)_5-$	55[d]	*3834*

Table 3-XIV—*continued*

Aliphatic Di- or Triacyl Halides

Q	% Yield[b]	References
$-(CH_2)_6-$	30^d	3834
$-(CH_2)_7-$	38–50	3834
$-(CH_2)_8-$	$30–71^d$	1994, 2569, 3834
$-CH=CH-$ (*trans*)	43^d	3834
1,2-Cyclobutanediyl	$—^d$	3834
$-(CH_2)_4CHEtCH_2-$	$79–93^d$	1315, 2569, 3296, 3297, 3743
$-(CH_2)_4CHEtCH_2-$	$90^{d,\,s}$	2569, 3296, 3743
$EtC(CH_2OCH_2CH_2-)_3$	$—^n$	3385
$-(CH_2)_2S(CH_2)_2-$	79^d	3296
$-(CH_2)_{17}-$	90^d	3296
$Q(COCl)_n = COCl_2$	29–73	350, 1211, 1936
$Q(COCl)_n = COCl_2$	$43^{d,\,n}$	1910

Aromatic Di- or Triacyl Halides

$$Q(COCl)_n + AzH^f + \xrightarrow{\text{base}} Q(COAz)_n$$

Q	% Yield[b]	References
$m\text{-}C_6H_4$	$80–98^d$	2569, 3295, 3834
$m\text{-}C_6H_4$	$98^{d,\,n}$	2569, 3295, 3297
$m\text{-}C_6H_4$	$89^{d,\,s}$	3295
$p\text{-}C_6H_4$	$30–98^d$	1994, 3294, 3834
$p\text{-}C_6H_4$	$—^{d,\,s}$	2569
$p\text{-}C_6H_4$	$41–98^{d,\,n}$	2569, 3297, 3834
$1,3,5\text{-}C_6H_3$	67^d	3295, 3834
$1,3,5\text{-}C_6H_3$	$97.5^{d,\,s}$	3182a, 3295
$1,3,5\text{-}C_6H_3$	$92^{d,\,t}$	1910, 3295
$1,3,5\text{-}C_6H_3$	$87^{d,\,n}$	1910
$-C_6H_4OC_6H_4-$	89	1303

Derivatives from Alkyl Chloroformates

$$RO_2CCl + AzH^f \xrightarrow{\text{base}} RO_2CAz$$

R	% Yield[b]	References
Me	$—^d$	1811
Et	60–74	350, 1933, 4184
Et	$—^k$	2227
Bu	76	1933, 3375
$Me(CH_2)_{11}$	98	3559
$Me(CH_2)_{17}$	88	3559

Table 3-XIV—*continued*

Derivatives from Alkyl Chloroformates

R	% Yield[b]	References
$CH_2{=}CH$	—	962
$CH_2{=}CHCH_2$	74	3625
FCH_2CH_2	90[d]	2757
$c\text{-}C_6H_{11}$	71	1933
Ph	—	1933
$p\text{-}MeC_6H_4$	72	1933
$p\text{-}AcC_6H_4$	78	1933
$p\text{-}O_2NC_6H_4$	65	1933
$RO_2CCl = p\text{-}ClC_6H_4CH_2SCOCl$	—[e]	2732
$RO_2CCl = p\text{-}MeC_6H_4OCSCl$	69	1921
$RO_2CCl = PhSCOCl$	—	1663
$RO_2CCl = p\text{-}ClC_6H_4CS_2Cl$	59	1921
$RO_2CCl =$ mitomycin analog in which $-CH_2O_2COPh \rightarrow -CH_2O_2CAz$	—	62

Derivatives from Bis Chloroformates

$$Q(O_2CCl)_n + AzH^f \xrightarrow{\text{base}} Q(O_2CAz)_n$$

Q	% Yield[b]	References
$-CH_2CH_2-$	56–70	1693, 1928, 1931, 1994, 2571, 3625
$-CH_2CH_2-$	88–91[d]	1931
$-CH_2CH_2-$	93[d, n]	1910
$-(CH_2)_4-$	50–79[d]	2570, 2886
$-CH_2CMe_2CH_2-$	82.6	3625
$-CH_2CH_2OCH_2CH_2-$	56–80	1931, 1994, 3625
$-CH_2CH_2OCH_2CH_2-$	88–91[d]	1931
$-CH_2CH_2OCH_2CH_2-$	94[d, n]	1910
$-CH(CH_2CH_2)_2CH_2-$	53	1928
$-(CH_2)_{10}-$	77	1928
$-(CH_2CH_2O)_2CH_2CH_2-$	90–99[c, d]	1315, 1994, 2571, 3297, 3298
$-(CH_2CH_2O)_{13}CH_2CH_2-$	56–70	1931
$-(CH_2CH_2O)_{13}CH_2CH_2-$	88–91[d]	1931
$m\text{-}C_6H_4$	90[d]	2570, 2571
$p\text{-}C_6H_4$	58	1928
$p\text{-}C_6H_4CMe_2C_6H_4-$	55–95[c, d]	1693, 2570, 2571, 3298, 3625

Table 3-XIV—*continued*

Urea Derivatives

$$R^1R^2NCOCl + AzH^f \xrightarrow{\text{base}} R^1R^2NCOAz$$

R^1	R^2	% Yield[b]	References
Me	Me	75	350, 1208
Et	Et	—[n]	1208
iso-Bu	iso-Bu	—	1208
Me(CH$_2$)$_{17}$	Me	—	1208
Ph	Me	—	350, 1208
Ph	Ph	—	350, 1208
p-AzCONHC$_6$H$_4$[u]	Me	77[d]	1204
p-AzCONHC$_6$H$_4$[u]	Me	—[d, n]	1204
AzCONHCH$_2$CH$_2$[u]	Bu	—[d]	1204
$R^1 + R^2$ = -(CH$_2$)$_5$-		—	1208
R^1R^2N = EtO$_2$C—N(CH$_2$CH$_2$)$_2$N–		—	2614
R^1R^2N = EtO$_2$CCH$_2$—N(CH$_2$CH$_2$)$_2$N–		—	2614
R^1R^2NCOCl = ClCO—N(CH$_2$CH$_2$)$_2$N—COCl		—	350
R^1R^2NCOCl = dye-NHCO$_2$Ph		—	3101

Imidyl Derivatives

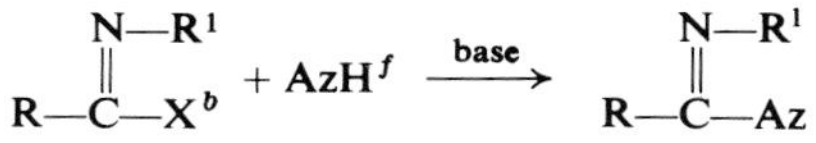

$$\underset{R—C—X^b}{\overset{N—R^1}{\|}} + AzH^f \xrightarrow{\text{base}} \underset{R—C—Az}{\overset{N—R^1}{\|}}$$

R	R^1	% Yield[b]	References
H$_2$N	O$_2$N	80.2[e, v]	2348
H$_2$N	O$_2$N	83[e, n, v]	2348
H$_2$N	O$_2$N	—[w]	246
Ph	Ph	—	1654
Ph	p-O$_2$NC$_6$H$_4$	—	1654
p-O$_2$NC$_6$H$_4$	Ph	—	1654
Ph	p-PhCH$_2$OC$_6$H$_4$	—	382
Ph	Az$_2$P(O)	—	2190
PrS	(EtO)$_2$P(O)[x]	—	56
PhNH	Az$_2$P(O)[x]	30	881, 2095
p-MeC$_6$H$_4$NH	Az$_2$P(O)[x]	—	881, 2095
p-ClC$_6$H$_4$NH	Az$_2$P(O)[x]	—	881, 2095
Ac	ArNH (various)	—	999a
Bz	o-EtOC$_6$H$_4$NH	51[e]	1000
Bz	o-O$_2$NC$_6$H$_4$NH	50[e]	1000
Bz	m-O$_2$NC$_6$H$_4$NH	59[e]	1000
Bz	2-MeO-5-O$_2$NC$_6$H$_3$NH	58[e]	1000
p-O$_2$NC$_6$H$_4$CO	o-O$_2$NC$_6$H$_4$NH	47[e]	1001
p-O$_2$NC$_6$H$_4$CO	2-MeO-5-O$_2$NC$_6$H$_3$NH	69[e]	1001
$R + R^1$ = CH$_2$CH=CHCH=CH		—[g]	2815

Table 3-XIV—*continued*

Imidocarbonyl Derivatives

$$RN{=}CX_2{}^b \;+\; AzH \;\xrightarrow{\text{base}}\; RN{=}CAz_2$$

R	% Yield[b]	References
p-$O_2NC_6H_4$	66	*1159*
Ph	51	*1159, 1719*
m-$AzCOC_6H_4{}^y$	38	*1159*
RSO_2	—[v]	*1494*
$RN{=}CX_2 = p\text{-}C_6H_4(N{=}CCl_2)_2$	61	*1159, 2788*
$RN{=}CX_2 = Br_2C{=}N{-}N{=}CBr_2$	68[d]	*2686*

[a] Since a very large number of such acylations have been performed, only representatives from many of the references are cited here.

[b] X was chlorine except as otherwise noted and an amine was used as acid acceptor.

[c] $X = OAc$.

[d] An inorganic base was used as acid acceptor.

[e] Excess AzH was used as acid acceptor.

[f] AzH was EI except as otherwise specified.

[g] X sometimes was OEt or OMe

[h] No acid acceptor was necessary.

[i] $X = OCO_2Et$.

[j] $X = OH$, and a carbodimide was used.

[k] Product was a derivative of mitomycin C.

[l] $X = OBz$.

[m] $X = I$.

[n] Product was a 2-MeAz derivative.

[o] Product was a 2,3-Me_2Az derivative.

[p] Product was a 2-$PhCH_2Az$ derivative.

[q] Product was a 2,3-$[(CH_2)_6]Az$ derivative.

[r] Product was a 2-$PhCH_2$-3-MeAz derivative.

[s] Product was a 2-EtAz derivative.

[t] Product was a 2,2-Me_2Az derivative.

[u] The starting material was $R^1 = {-}C_6H_4NCO$ or ${-}CH_2CH_2NCO$.

[v] $X = SMe$ or other SR.

[w] $X = NMeNO$.

[x] The starting material was $ArNHCCl{=}NP(O)Cl_2$.

[y] The starting material was m-$ClCOC_6H_4N{=}CCl_2$.

Reaction with Derivatives of Acids of Tetrasubstituted Phosphorus. This reaction with aziridines appears to have the same mechanism as reaction of such reagents with typical amines (Eq 72).

$$R_{3-n}P(Y)X_n + nAzH \;\xrightarrow{\text{base}}\; R_{3-n}P(Y)Az_n \tag{72}$$

The reaction is, of course, very similar to acylation of aziridines and precautions to be observed are maintenance of low temperatures and basic conditions. The aziridine product is similar to 1-acylated aziridines in that the substituent on nitrogen is capable of conjugation with the unshared pair of electrons on that atom; the product will thus undergo ring-opening reactions with nucleophiles in the absence of an acid catalyst. The phosphorylated aziridines are much less reactive in ring-opening reactions than acylated aziridines, however, and such side reactions are seldom competitive with reaction 72. Also in contrast to the situation in acylations, there are no reports of rearrangements fast enough to compete with reaction 72.

Reaction 72 may be used to prepare derivatives containing a variety of groups attached to the phosphorus atom and a multiplicity of aziridine rings. Examples are as follows:

$$(MeO)_2P(O)Cl + AzH \xrightarrow{Et_3N} (MeO)_2P(O)Az$$

$$MeP(O)Cl_2 + AzH \xrightarrow{Et_3N} MeP(O)Az_2$$

$$\underset{\underset{NEt_2}{|}}{PhP(S)Cl} + AzH \xrightarrow{Et_3N} \underset{\underset{NEt_2}{|}}{PhP(S)Az}$$

$$PhSO_2N{=}PCl_3 + AzH \xrightarrow{Et_3N} PhSO_2N{=}PAz_3$$

$$POCl_3 + AzH \xrightarrow{Et_3N} P(O)Az_3$$

Other amines which have been used as the acid acceptor include pyridine, N,N-dimethylaniline, trimethylamine, and the aziridine reactant. Cautions indicated in previous sections (see pp. 154 and 160) should be observed if the aziridine reactant is used for this purpose (*2444*). The reactions are effected in solvents such as benzene or ether at room temperature or below.

In preparing the phosphorylated aziridines, anhydrous ammonia has also been used as an acid acceptor (*1206, 1212, 1220*). The reaction is carried out in a solvent such as benzene and gaseous ammonia bubbled through the aziridine solution as the phosphorus halide is added. Under these conditions no appreciable reaction between the phosphorus acid halide and ammonia is observed.

Although the procedure most frequently used for reaction 72 employs a nonpolar solvent and a tertiary amine, solvents such as water (*516*) or ethanol (*1136*) have been used with inorganic bases such as sodium hydroxide or sodium carbonate. The technique of employing a water-immiscible solvent such as benzene, chloroform, or methylene chloride along with an aqueous solution of an inorganic base has also been applied for reaction 72 (*320a, 320b, 1224, 1910, 3297*).

The phosphorus derivative which has been used in practically all cases is the acid chloride. One example of the use of an anhydride is shown here (Eq 73)

(*629*); another was very similar (*2862a*). The aziridinium salt was sufficiently stable in this case to be isolated.

$$F_2P(O)OP(O)F_2 + 2AzH \rightarrow F_2P(O)Az + AzH_2{}^+ [OP(O)F_2)^- \qquad (73)$$

The reaction just cited (Eq 73) illustrates the isolation of an aziridine derivative containing both a halogen and a 1-aziridinyl group attached to a phosphorus atom. Other examples exist in which the halogen is fluorine (*4051*). Where the halogen is chlorine the product has been described as unstable. In the reaction represented by Eq 74 (*134, 269, 271, 820*) the stoichiometric amount of EI was used to prepare the product *in situ*.

$$P(Y)Cl_3 + 2AzH \xrightarrow{\text{R}_3\text{N}} Az_2P(Y)Cl \qquad (74)$$
$$Y = O \text{ or } S$$

This was then treated with another reagent to replace the third remaining chlorine atom and form a relatively stable product. This reaction (Eq 74) also illustrates the difference which must exist in the relative rates for replacement of each subsequent halogen.

The reaction of secondary phosphites with amines in the presence of a polyhalo compound has been applied to EI with excellent results. Thus the phosphorylated aziridine from diethyl hydrogenphosphonate was obtained in 96 % yield (Eq 75) (*2701*).

$$(EtO)_2P(O)H + CCl_4 + AzH \xrightarrow{\text{Et}_3\text{N}} (EtO)_2P(O)Az \qquad (75)$$

The reaction is also applicable to phosphorus derivatives which contain dialkylamino or alkyl groups in place of ethoxy groups.

Of interest is the report of a reaction (*2796*) yielding a product which contains both an acid group and an aziridinyl group (Eq 76).

$$\underset{\underset{OH}{|}}{PhSO_2NHP(O)Cl} + AzH \xrightarrow{\text{Et}_3\text{N}} \underset{\underset{OH}{|}}{PhSO_2NHP(O)Az} \qquad (76)$$

It is also possible to displace an aryloxy group instead of a halogen atom on phosphorus (Eq 76a) (*2977a*).

$$(ClCH_2CH_2)_2NP(O)(OAr)_2 + AzH \longrightarrow (ClCH_2CH_2)_2NP(O)(OAr)Az \quad (76a)$$

The preparation of phosphorylated aziridine derivatives by reaction 72 may usually be accomplished with very good yields. The major problem with these derivatives is the tendency towards polymerization on distillation. As with the 1-acylaziridines, this tendency appears to be (at least in part) dependent on the presence of small amounts of specific impurities. Purification by either distillation or recrystallization should be done at the lowest possible temperature.

In Table 3-XV are shown a number of examples of reaction 72.

Table 3-XV[a]

REACTION OF ACID CHLORIDES OF TETRASUBSTITUTED-PHOSPHORUS ACIDS
WITH 1-UNSUBSTITUTED AZIRIDINES

RR'P(O)Cl + AzH[b] $\xrightarrow{\text{base}}$ RR'P(O)Az			
R	R'	% Yield[c]	References
Bu	Bu	44	3375
Ph	Ph	53	3375
Ph	Ph	89[d]	3375
Ph	CH$_2$=CH	—	2727
Ph	ClCH$_2$CH$_2$	—	2727
Me	EtO	95[e]	1920, 2701, 4132
Et	EtO	60[f]	2992, 2993
Various	HOCH$_2$CH$_2$O	—[e]	4170
Me	CH$_2$=CHCH$_2$NH	81	2859
Ph	Et$_2$N	—	1136
MeO	MeO	74–82[e]	615, 1523, 4132
EtO	EtO	79–96[e]	615, 1136, 1523, 1526, 2701, 4132
EtS	EtS	54	2795
ClCH$_2$CH$_2$O	ClCH$_2$CH$_2$O	92[g, e]	3208, 4132
PrO	PrO	—[g]	320a
iso-PrO	iso-PrO	74	1523, 1728, 3724
BuO	BuO	88	320a, 1136, 1523, 1728
iso-BuO	iso-BuO	82[g, e]	320a, 4132
PhO	PhO	100	3375
EtO	Et$_2$N	—	1136
EtO	MeO$_2$C	98	2860
EtO	EtO$_2$CCH$_2$	82	2860
iso-PrS	MeO$_2$CCH$_2$CH$_2$	57	2860
EtO$_2$CCH$_2$	CH$_2$=CHCH$_2$NH	67	2860
HO	PhSO$_2$NH	—	2796
HO	p-MeC$_6$H$_4$SO$_2$NH	—	2796
PhO	(ClCH$_2$CH$_2$)$_2$N	98	1348, 2212, 3646
m-MeC$_6$H$_4$O	(ClCH$_2$CH$_2$)$_2$N	84	2212, 3646
p-IC$_6$H$_4$O	(ClCH$_2$CH$_2$)$_2$N	71	2212, 3646
½(OCH$_2$CH$_2$O)	EtO	93[e]	4132
EtO$_2$CCH$_2$O	CH$_2$=CHCH$_2$NH	65	2860
Me$_2$N	Me$_2$N	80[e]	433, 2701, 3339
Me$_2$N	Me$_2$N	87[d]	3339, 4132
Me$_2$N	Me$_2$N	81[h]	3339
CH$_2$=CHCH$_2$NH	CH$_2$=CHCH$_2$NH	60	2859
Et$_2$N	Et$_2$N	—	1136
PhNH	PhNEt	—	1136
EtO$_2$CCH$_2$NH	(ClCH$_2$CH$_2$)$_2$N	65	4101

Table 3-XV^a—*continued*

R	R'	% Yield^c	References
1-Piperidyl	1-Piperidyl	—	*1136*
1-Piperidyl	4-Morpholinyl	—	*1136*
4-Morpholinyl	4-Morpholinyl	—	*1136*
H$_6$-1-azepinyl	H$_6$-1-azepinyl	—	*3624*
Et 5'-[2',3'-O-(EtOCH)-6-azauridyl		—^{e}	*2608a*
R + R' = OCH$_2$CH$_2$O		—	*4062*
R + R' = OCH$_2$CH$_2$CH$_2$O		77	*4062*
R + R' = o-OC$_6$H$_4$O		—	*3107, 3438*

$$\text{RP(O)Cl}_2 + \text{AzH}^b \xrightarrow{\text{base}} \text{RP(O)Az}_2$$

R	% Yield^c	References
Me	83	*615*
ClCH$_2$	90	*2692, 4146, 4147*
Et	—	*2282a*
ClCH$_2$CH$_2$	72	*4147*
CH$_2$=CH	71	*4147*
CH$_2$=CHCH$_2$	83	*1525*
Me$_2$C=CH	—	*2282a*
c-C$_6$H$_{11}$	92	*2282a, 3900*
F$_3$C(CF$_2$)$_9$CH$_2$CH$_2$	—	*390a*
Ph	—	*1136, 2282a*
p-ClC$_6$H$_4$	—	*2282a*
p-O$_2$NC$_6$H$_4$	90^f	*1328*
p-MeC$_6$H$_4$	—	*2282a*
PhCH=CH	70	*1525*
2-C$_{10}$H$_7$	—	*2282a*
MeO	72	*615, 2582*
EtO	70–85	*350, 615, 1207, 1220, 1461, 2582, 2795*
ClCH$_2$CH$_2$O	—	*2795*
EtOCH=CH	76	*1525*
EtSCH=C(CCl=CH$_2$)	—	*3688*
n-C$_5$H$_{11}$O	52–76	*831, 2582*
n-C$_8$H$_{17}$O	69	*2582, 2824*
n-C$_{12}$H$_{25}$O	63	*831, 2582*
PhO	80–96	*1207, 2187, 2692, 3438*
1-C$_{10}$H$_7$O	—^{d}	*3109*
2-C$_{10}$H$_7$O	93	*1207, 3113, 3438*
EtO$_2$CCH$_2$	87	*2860*
EtO$_2$CCH$_2$O	68	*2860*

Table 3-XV[a]—*continued*

R	% Yield[c]	References
n-$C_{17}H_{35}CO_2CH_2CH_2O$	—	292
AzCOCH$_2$CH$_2$	—[i]	2860
4-H$_2$N-2-MeS-5-pyrimidinyl-CH$_2$O	61[f]	1726
Me$_2$N	—	433, 638, 1145, 2823
MeNH	62–85	638, 1212, 2581
Cl	—	820
Az (RPOCl$_2$ = POCl$_3$)	76–92[j]	350, 774[j], 1211, 1220, 1461, 3900
2-MeAz (RPOCl$_2$ = POCl$_3$)	94[d, g]	1910
2,2-Me$_2$Az (RPOCl$_2$ = POCl$_3$)	—[h]	2825, 4130
2-(iso-PrCO$_2$)Az (RPOCl$_2$ = POCl$_3$)	—	2215
Et$_2$N	92	350, 1207, 1220
(ClCH$_2$CH$_2$)$_2$N	—	157, 851
CH$_2$=CHCH$_2$NH	77–90[j]	1224, 2859
BuNH	38–93	838, 1212, 2581, 3297
MeCH=CHCH$_2$NH	—	1224
CH$_2$=CHCH$_2$NEt	—	1224
(CH$_2$=CHCH$_2$)$_2$N	74	1224, 1525
n-C_7H_{15}NH	57	933, 2581
n-C_8H_{17}NH	27–90	638, 838, 1212, 2581
n-$C_{12}H_{25}$NH	53	933, 2581
n-$C_{14}H_{29}$NH	56–76	838, 2581
n-$C_{16}H_{33}$NH	55	2581
n-$C_{19}H_{39}$NH	—	1238
PhNH	51–95[j]	350, 1211, 1220, 1461, 2140[k], 3900
p-FC$_6$H$_4$NH	—	2930, 2931
p-IC$_6$H$_4$NH	77	2187
2,4-Cl$_2$C$_6$H$_3$NH	—	2141, 3724
p-O$_2$NC$_6$H$_4$NH	—	2141
p-MeC$_6$H$_4$NH	68	2141, 2795
p-F$_3$CC$_6$H$_4$NH	—	2930, 2931
PhCF$_2$NH	—	2930, 2931
p-MeOC$_6$H$_4$NH	55	2187
PhNEt	85	1207
PhN(CH$_2$CH=CH$_2$)	—	1224
PhCH$_2$N(CH$_2$CH=CH$_2$)	—	1224
1-$C_{10}H_7$NH	—	17
2-$C_{10}H_7$NH	38	17, 2187
3-Indole-CH$_2$NH	—	58
Various alkylindole-3-(CH$_2$)$_n$NH	—	2613a

Table 3-XV^a—continued

R	% Yield^c	References
m-AzCOC$_6$H$_4$NH^l	—	2187
1-Piperidyl	94	933, 1207, 2826, 3202
1-Piperidyl	—^{d}	2826
1-Piperidyl	—^{h}	2826
1-Piperidyl-CH$_2$CH$_2$	81	4147
4-Morpholinyl	—	2826
4-Thiamorpholinyl	—	2312a
MeO$_2$C—N(CH$_2$CH$_2$)$_2$N	71	2614, 4147
EtO$_2$C—N(CH$_2$CH$_2$)$_2$N	—^{d}	2614
H$_6$-1-azepinyl	—	3624
2-Me-1-thiazolidinyl	54	1906, 2312a
PhNHCAz=N	30	881, 2095
AzSO$_2$C$_6$H$_4$NH	76	2796
p-EtO$_2$CCH$_2$C$_6$H$_4$NH	65	2120
p-PhCH$_2$O$_2$CCH$_2$C$_6$H$_4$NH	70^f	3900
p-(EtO)$_2$P(O)CH$_2$C$_6$H$_4$NH	—	2120
p-MeO$_2$CCH$_2$CH$_2$C$_6$H$_4$NH	70^f	2444
p-MeO$_2$C(CH$_2$)$_3$C$_6$H$_4$NH	49	3900
p-EtO$_2$CCH(NHAc)CH$_2$C$_6$H$_4$NH	—	2120
p-PhCH$_2$O$_2$CCH$_2$CH$_2$C$_6$H$_4$NH	96^f	2444
p-EtO$_2$CCH(iso-Bu)NHCOCH$_2$C$_6$H$_4$NH	50	3900
p-PhCH$_2$O$_2$CCH(NHCO$_2$Et)CH$_2$C$_6$H$_4$NH	25^f	2444
p-EtO$_2$CCH(CH$_2$Ph)NHCO(CH$_2$)$_3$C$_6$H$_4$NH	52	3900
Phthalimido-CH(CO$_2$Me)CH$_2$C$_6$H$_4$NH-(*m*)	44^f	2444
2-Pyridyl-NH	—	3187, 4133
6-Cl-3-pyridazinyl-NH	—	3420
2-Pyrimidinyl-NH	78	2192
2-Pyrimidinyl-NH	60^d	4133
5-Cl-2-pyrimidinyl-NH	83	2192
Various 2-R′-6-R″-4-pyrimidinyl-NH	—	3125a
4,6-Me$_2$-2-pyrimidinyl-NH	81	2192
4-Az-2-pyrimidinyl-NH	22	2192
4-MeO-6-Cl-2-pyrimidinyl-NH	84	2193
4-Me-5-Br-2-pyrimidinyl-NH	96	2193
4-Piperidino-2-pyrimidinyl-NH	89	337, 2193
4,6-Cl$_2$-5-pyrimidinyl-NH	69	2410a
5-Me-2-(1,3,4-benzothiazolyl)-NH	—	3428
5-Pr-2-(1,3,4-benzothiazolyl)-NH	—	3428
5-Ph-2-(1,3,4-benzothiazolyl)-NH	—	3428
2-(1,3,4-Thiadiazolyl-NH)	—	3429
2-(1,3,4-Thiadiazolyl)-NEt	—	82, 3186, 3187
5-Cl-2-(1,3,4-Thiadiazolyl)-NEt	—	3187
5-Me-2-(1,3,4-Thiadiazolyl)-NEt	—	3187

Table 3-XV^a—*continued*

R	% Yield^c	References
2-(1,3,4-Thiadiazolyl)-NBu	—	*3187*
2-(1,3,4-Thiadiazolyl)-NPh	68	*3187*
BzNH	26	*2929^k, 2934*
p-FC$_6$H$_4$CONH	—	*2930, 2931, 2934*
o-ClC$_6$H$_4$CONH	—	*4150*
3,4,5-Cl$_3$C$_6$H$_2$CONH	—	*4150*
o-BrC$_6$H$_4$CONH	61	*2932*
2,5-Br$_2$C$_6$H$_3$CONH	—	*2932*
2,3,5-Br$_3$C$_6$H$_2$CONH	—	*2932*
m-IC$_6$H$_4$CONH	58–74	*2935*
2,4-I$_2$C$_6$H$_3$CONH	58–74	*2935*
2,3,5-I$_3$C$_6$H$_2$CONH	58–74	*2935*
m-F$_3$CC$_6$H$_4$CONH	—	*2930, 2931*
PhCF$_2$CONH	—	*2930, 2931*
PhCH=CHCONH	—	*2934*
PhSO$_2$NH	—	*2796*
p-ClC$_6$H$_4$SO$_2$NH	—	*2796*
MeO$_2$CNH	76	*134, 188, 267, 271, 2304, 2810, 4152*
EtO$_2$CNH	—^{d}	*134, 188, 270, 271*
EtO$_2$CNH	40^h	*270*
EtO$_2$CNH	30^m	*270, 678*
EtO$_2$CNH	25^n	*270*
EtO$_2$CNH	—^{o}	*270*
EtO$_2$CNH	20^p	*268*
PhCH$_2$O$_2$CNH	55	*134, 188, 271, 2304, 2810, 4152*
iso-BuNHCONH	—^{d}	*1193*
iso-BuNHCONH	—^{j}	*1193*
c-C$_6$H$_{11}$NHCONH	30	*134, 271, 1193*
PhNHCONH	20–92	*271, 1193, 2189*
PhNHCONH	—^{d}	*2956*
o-ClC$_6$H$_4$NHCONH	87	*2189*
p-MeC$_6$H$_4$NHCONH	90	*2189, 2934*
p-MeOC$_6$H$_4$NHCONH	82	*2189*
1-C$_{10}$H$_7$NHCONH	90	*2189*
EtO$_2$CCHMeNHCONH	80	*2189*
ROCSNH	—	*134*
Cholesteryl-O–	80	*2858*
Estrone-O–	84	*2858*

Table 3-XV[a]—*continued*

	RR'P(S)X[q] + AzH[b] $\xrightarrow{\text{base}}$ RR'P(S)Az		
R	R'	% Yield[c]	References
F	F	—[f, r]	629
F	Me	27[s]	4051
F	Et	37[s]	4051
F	PhNH	77	4173
F	p-FC$_6$H$_4$NH	47	4173
F	p-ClC$_6$H$_4$NH	54	4173
F	p-IC$_6$H$_4$NH	17	4173
F	(ClCH$_2$CH$_2$)$_2$N	35	4173
Cl	H$_6$-1-azepinyl	—	3624
Me	Me	—	1168
Et	Et	—	1168
Me	EtO	—	1920
Me	BuO	—	1920
Ph	EtO	—	1136
Me	CH$_2$=CHCH$_2$NH	97	2859
Ph	Et$_2$N	—	1136
MeO	MeO	95	516, 819a
EtO	EtO	89	516, 1136
EtS	EtS	—	3110
MeO	2,4,5-Cl$_3$C$_6$H$_2$O	—[f]	3568
PhO	PhO	80–88	1224
Me$_2$N	Me$_2$N	—	1136
CH$_2$=CHCH$_2$NH	CH$_2$=CHCH$_2$NH	85	2859
H$_6$-1-azepinyl	H$_6$-1-azepinyl	—	3624
R + R' = OCH$_2$CH$_2$O		80	2795, 3110
R + R' = CMe$_2$CH=CMeO		75	3168

RP(S)X$_2$[q] + AzH[b] $\xrightarrow{\text{base}}$ RP(S)Az$_2$		
R	% Yield[c]	References
Cl	—	134, 269, 271
Me	78	4146
c-C$_6$H$_{11}$	100	3900
Ph	86	516, 629, 2198
Ph	92[d]	1910
EtO	70–92[j]	516, 1206, 2795
EtO	79[d]	516
EtO	58[h]	516
EtS	78	2795
iso-BuO	90	1206
iso-C$_5$H$_{11}$	—	819a
c-C$_6$H$_{11}$O	—	1206
n-C$_{10}$H$_{21}$O	100	2197

Table 3-XV^a—*continued*

R	% Yield^c	References
PhO	—	*1206*
PhO	81$^{d,\,g}$	*516*
p-BrC$_6$H$_4$O	80	*2938*
2,4,5-Cl$_3$C$_6$H$_2$O	—^{f}	*3569*
Az [RP(S)X$_2$ = PSCl$_3$]	98^d	*2197*
MeNH	94	*3368*
CH$_2$=CHCH$_2$NH	82	*1224, 2859*
(CH$_2$=CHCH$_2$)$_2$N	—	*1224*
PhNH	35	*2936*
p-ClC$_6$H$_4$NH	65	*2936*
p-MeC$_6$H$_4$NH	52	*2936*
p-MeOC$_6$H$_4$NH	62	*2936*
p-O$_2$NC$_6$H$_4$O	95	*2938*
o-MeC$_6$H$_4$O	79	*2938*
p-MeC$_6$H$_4$O	95^g	*516*
p-MeOC$_6$H$_4$O	96	*516*
2-Br-4-*tert*-BuC$_6$H$_3$O	—^{f}	*3569*
2-C$_{10}$H$_7$O	—	*3113, 3438*
2-Pyrazinyl-O	—	*2560, 2560a*
4-H$_2$N-3-MeS-5-pyrimidinyl-CH$_2$O	52^f	*1726*
Et$_2$N	—	*2197*
(ClCH$_2$CH$_2$)$_2$N	—	*157*
Az [RP(S)X$_2$ = PSCl$_3$]	100^j	*1910, 2179, 2313, 2318, 2821, 3715*
Az [RP(S)X$_2$ = PSBr$_3$]	—^{t}	*3265*
p-EtO$_2$CCH$_2$C$_6$H$_4$NH	—	*2120*
p-PhCH$_2$O$_2$CCH$_2$CH$_2$C$_6$H$_4$NH	35^f	*2444*
m-[Phthalimido-CH(CO$_2$Me)CH$_2$]C$_6$H$_4$NH	33^f	*2444*
3-Indole-CH$_2$NH	—	*58*
Various alkylindole-3-(CH$_2$)$_n$NH	—	*2613a*
H$_6$-1-azepinyl	82	*629, 3624*
2-(1,3,4-Thiadiazolyl)-NEt	—	*1161*
Me-N(CH$_2$CH$_2$)$_2$N	—	*3187*
MeO$_2$C-N(CH$_2$CH$_2$)$_2$N	70	*4908*
Et$_2$NCO-N(CH$_2$CH$_2$)$_2$N	73	*4098*

$$Y[P(O)Cl_2]_2 + AzH\,^b \xrightarrow{\text{base}} Y[P(O)Az_2]_2$$

Y	% Yield^c	References
–CHMeCH$_2$–	67	*2861*
–(CH$_2$)$_4$–	80	*4147*
–O(CH$_2$)$_6$O–	—	*1902*
4-Me-1,3-HNC$_6$H$_4$NH–	56	*2187*
p-(-HNCOC$_6$H$_4$CONH-)	—	*4151*

Table 3-XV[a]—*continued*

Y	% Yield[c]	References
–OCH$_2$CH$_2$OCH$_2$CH$_2$O–	—	*682a, 1902*
m-(-OC$_6$H$_4$O-)	—	*4151*
p-(-OC$_6$H$_4$O-)	—	*3105, 3125,[k] 3438, 4151*
2-Cl-1,4-OC$_6$H$_4$O–	—	*4151*
2-Me-1,4-OC$_{10}$H$_6$O–	—	*3108*
–N(CH$_2$CH$_2$)$_2$N–	75[g]	*57, 83, 4098*
–N(CH$_2$CH$_2$)$_2$N–	—[d]	*83*
p-(-N═CAzC$_6$H$_4$CAz═N-)	47–69	*2940*
BuN$<$	—	*3188*
PhN$<$	—	*3189*
p-ClC$_6$H$_4$N$<$	—	*3189*
3,5-(MeO)$_2$C$_6$H$_3$N$<$	—	*3189*
p-PhN═NC$_6$H$_4$N$<$	—	*3189*
2-C$_{10}$H$_7$N$<$	—	*3189*

$$Y[P(S)Cl_2]_2 + AzH^b \xrightarrow{\text{base}} Y[P(S)Az_2]_2$$

Y	% Yield[c]	References
–O(CH$_2$)$_4$O–	—[g]	*1728*
–OCH$_2$CH$_2$OCH$_2$CH$_2$O–	—[g]	*1728*
–OCH$_2$CH$_2$OCH$_2$CH$_2$O–	—[d, g]	*1728*
–OCH$_2$CH$_2$SCH$_2$CH$_2$O–	—	*1739*
p-(-OC$_6$H$_4$O-)	87	*3106, 3438*
–N(CH$_2$CH$_2$)$_2$N–	83	*83, 4098*

$$Q[P(O)Cl_2]_4 + AzH^b \xrightarrow{\text{base}} Q[P(O)Az_2]_4$$

Q	% Yield[c]	References
C(CH$_2$O-)$_4$	67	*2955, 2959*
C(CH$_2$O-)$_4$	79[d]	*2955, 2959*

$$RN═PCl_3 + AzH^b \xrightarrow{\text{base}} RN═PAz_3$$

R	% Yield[c]	References
Cl$_3$CCO	—	*515*
Bz	—	*2190*
o-BrC$_6$H$_4$CO	—	*2190*
p-O$_2$NC$_6$H$_4$CO	—	*2190*
MeSO$_2$	—[d, j]	*3030*
PhSO$_2$	83	*2190, 2796, 3112*
PhSO$_2$	84–99[d, j]	*3030*
p-ClC$_6$H$_4$SO$_2$	82	*2190, 2796, 3112*

Table 3-XV^a—*continued*

R	% Yield^c	References
p-MeC$_6$H$_4$SO$_2$	77$^{d, j}$	2190, 3030
3-O$_2$N-4-PhNHC$_6$H$_3$SO$_2$	—^{g}	3030
p-AzSO$_2$C$_6$H$_4$	81^u	2796

$$RN{=}PR_2'Cl + AzH^b \xrightarrow{\text{base}} RN{=}PR_2'Az$$

R	R'	% Yield^c	Reference
p-MeC$_6$H$_4$SO$_2$N$\diagdown$	Ph	91	398

$$Y[N{=}PCl_3]_2 + AzH^b \xrightarrow{\text{base}} Y[N{=}PAz_3]_2$$

Y	% Yield^c	References
m-C$_6$H$_4$(CO)$_2$	—	2940
p-C$_6$H$_4$(CO)$_2$	—	2940
–SO$_2$–	—	2940
m-C$_6$H$_4$(SO$_2$)$_2$	—	2940
p-(-C$_6$H$_4$SO$_2$-)	54	2796, 3114

^{a} Since a very large number of such products have been prepared, only representatives from many of the references are reported here.

^{b} AzH was EI except as otherwise noted.

^{c} An amine was used as acid acceptor except as otherwise noted.

^{d} Product was the 2-MeAz derivative.

^{e} Product was sometimes made from RR′P(O)H + CCl$_4$.

^{f} Excess AzH was used as the acid acceptor.

^{g} An inorganic base was used as acid acceptor.

^{h} Product was the 2,2-Me$_2$Az derivative.

^{i} The reactant was ClCOCH$_2$CH$_2$P(O)Cl$_2$.

^{j} Either an amine or an inorganic base was used as acid acceptor.

^{k} The tagged ^{32}P derivative was prepared.

^{l} The reactant was ClCOC$_6$H$_4$NHP(O)Cl$_2$.

^{m} Products were the *meso-cis-* and DL-*trans*-2,3-Me$_2$Az derivatives.

^{n} Product was the 2,2,3-Me$_3$Az derivative.

^{o} Product was the 2-EtAz derivative.

^{p} Product was the 2,2,3,3-Me$_4$Az derivative.

^{q} X was chlorine except as noted.

^{r} X = OP(O)F$_2$.

^{s} X = F.

^{t} The alkali metal salt of EI was used.

^{u} The reactant was p-ClSO$_2$C$_6$H$_4$N{=}PCl$_3$.

Reaction with Trivalent Phosphorus Derivatives. The preparation of 1-aziridinyl derivatives of trivalent phosphorus has been accomplished by procedures exactly analogous to those used with tetrasubstituted phosphorus (Eq 77) (with one exception). At this time, only a relatively few such derivatives have been reported and little is known regarding the reactive characteristics of the aziridine ring when so linked. One precaution sometimes taken, which is unnecessary for the tetrasubstituted-phosphorus derivatives, is to perform the reaction in an inert atmosphere. In reaction 77, R has been phenyl, alkoxy, alkylthio, alkylamino, and dialkylamino.

$$R_{3-n}PX_n + nAzH \xrightarrow{\text{base}} R_{3-n}PAz_n \qquad (77)$$

Table 3-XVI presents a summary of the preparative use of such reactions.

Table 3-XVI

REACTION OF DERIVATIVES OF TRIVALENT PHOSPHORUS WITH
1-UNSUBSTITUTED AZIRIDINES

$$RR'PX^a + AzH \xrightarrow{\text{base}} RR'PAz$$

R	R'	% Yield[b]	References
Ph	Ph	26[c]	1508, 3303
C_6F_5	C_6F_5	—[d]	2391
EtO	EtO	63.5	1523, 1526
$ClCH_2CH_2O$	$ClCH_2CH_2O$	—[e]	2795
EtO	MeS	>50	1120
EtO	EtS	—	1120
EtO	iso-PrS	>51	1120
EtO	sec-BuS	>40	1120
iso-PrO	iso-PrO	—	1529
PhO	PhO	—	524a
EtS	EtS	60[e]	2795
Me_2N	Me_2N	62.7	2725, 2728[f]
Et_2N	Et_2N	69.2	2725, 2728[f]
R + R' = $-OCH_2CH_2O-$		43–55	1530, 2795
R + R' = $-OCH_2CH_2CH_2O-$		50[e]	1530
R + R' = $-OCHMeCH_2O-$		45[e]	1530
R + R' = $-OCHMeCHMeO-$		55[e]	1530
R + R' = $-OCHMeCH_2CH_2O-$		55[e]	1530
$RR'PX = Cl-P\big\langle{}^{O-}_{O-}\big\rangle{}_{O-}^{-O}\big\rangle P-Cl$		53	2955, 2959
R + R' = $-NMeCH_2CH_2NMe-$		52	4164

Table 3-XVI—*continued*

$$RPX_2^a + AzH \xrightarrow{\text{base}} RPAz_2$$

R	% Yield[b]	References
Et	59	2729
Ph	53	2729
C_6F_5	—[d]	2391
EtO	—	1461
$ClCH_2CH_2O$	—[e]	2795
EtO	—[f]	2728a
PrO	—	1529
iso-PrO	—	1529
$CH_2=CHCH_2O$	—	1529
BuO	58	1529, 2795
EtS	29[e]	2795
Me_2N	59.3	2725, 2728[f]
Me_2N	—[g]	2701
Az ($RPX_2 = PCl_3$)	56.1	2725
Et_2N	67.4	1461, 2725, 2728[f]
$CH_2=CHCH_2NH$	71	2859

[a] X was chlorine except as noted.
[b] An amine was used as acid acceptor except as otherwise noted.
[c] Excess AzH was used as acid acceptor.
[d] 2-Methylaziridine derivative.
[e] Unspecified base used as acid acceptor.
[f] 2,2-Dimethylaziridine derivative.
[g] X = Me_2N; transamidation reaction.

The reaction of PCl_3 with EI or 2,2-dimethylaziridine in the presence of triethylamine to give the tris(1-aziridinyl) derivative has been reported (Eq 78) (*2725, 2728*).

$$PCl_3 + 3AzH \xrightarrow{\text{Et}_3\text{N}} PAz_3 \qquad (78)$$

However, other workers found that attempts to isolate products from this reaction with EI invariably led to explosions (*963, 2031*).

Of interest is the reaction of the adduct chlorodiphenylphosphine–decaborane with EI (Eq 79) (*3169, 3170*). The reaction was performed in ethanol and the reaction occurred as shown for primary amines ($MeNH_2$) and EI but with other secondary amines (Me_2NH) the product obtained was that resulting from reaction with solvent.

$$B_{10}H_{12}(Ph_2PCl)_2 + \text{excess AzH} \rightarrow B_{10}H_{12}(Ph_2PAz)_2 \qquad (79)$$

The relative similarity in base strengths for methylamine and dimethylamine makes it inappropriate to attribute the difference in reactivity of EI and dimethylamine to differences in this factor.

The single example, at this time, of preparation of a trivalent phosphorus derivative by a method other than Eq 77 is a transamidation (Eq 80) (2701). This transamidation, occurring at 40°–50°C, was reported to be very facile for displacement of the R_2N group.

$$(Me_2N)_3P + 2AzH \rightarrow Me_2NPAz_2 + 2Me_2NH \tag{80}$$

Reaction with Trimeric Phosphonitrilic Chlorides. The techniques that have been used for performing this reaction are closely analogous to those used for other acid halides (Eq 81) (e.g., acyl halides and other phosphorus acid halides).

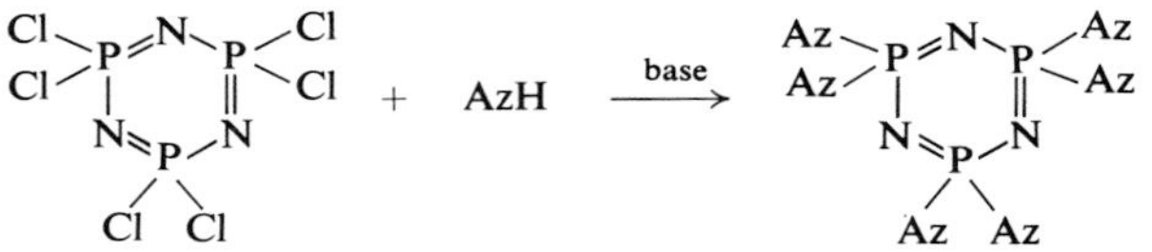

$$\tag{81}$$

The acid acceptors used in the above reaction have included tertiary amines, ammonia, the aziridine reactant employed in excess, and inorganic bases such as sodium hydroxide or sodium carbonate. The technique of performing the reaction in mixed solvent systems of aqueous base and a water-immiscible organic solvent has also been employed with good results. Although low temperatures (0°C to room temperature) have, as a rule, been used for reaction 81 and similar reactions involving phosphonitrilic derivatives, a number of such displacements with EI have been performed at higher temperatures (50°–60°C) or for extended periods (10 days) at room temperature. The results are presented in Table 3-XVII.

The chlorine atoms of trimeric phosphonitrilic chloride ($P_3N_3Cl_6$; 2,2,4,4,6,6-hexachlorocyclotriphosphaza-1,3,5-triene) may be successively displaced by treatment with aziridines (or other nucleophiles). With aziridines (or other amines) the replacement of remaining chlorines becomes more difficult as more of the chlorines are replaced. Thus a complete series of mono-, di-, tri-, tetra-, and pentasubstituted 1-aziridinyl derivatives of trimeric phosphonitrilic chloride has been prepared (2122, 2186, 2191, 2787). Preparation of the various partially substituted products was accomplished by choice of reaction conditions and ratio of EI to the starting hexachloride.

In di-, tri-, or tetrasubstituted derivatives positional isomers are possible. Ethylenimine replaces primarily geminal chlorines in formation of the di- and tetrasubstituted derivatives. This result is in contrast to that obtained with ammonia, methylamine, or dimethylamine (Eq 82) (2122).

$$
\begin{array}{ccc}
Cl{-}\underset{\underset{N\lesseqgtr P\diagdown N}{|}}{\overset{Cl\diagdown P\eqsim N\diagdown P\diagup Cl}{}}{-}Cl \\
\underset{Cl\quad Cl}{}
\end{array}
\quad + \quad Me_2NH \quad \xrightarrow{base} \quad
\begin{array}{c}
Me_2N\overset{Cl\diagdown P\eqsim N\diagdown P\diagup Cl}{\underset{\underset{N\lesseqgtr P\diagdown N}{|}}{}}NMe_2 \\
\underset{Cl\quad Cl}{}
\end{array}
$$

$$
+ \quad AzH \quad \xrightarrow{base} \quad
\begin{array}{c}
Cl\overset{Cl\diagdown P\eqsim N\diagdown P\diagup Az}{\underset{\underset{N\lesseqgtr P\diagdown N}{|}}{}}Az \\
\underset{Cl\quad Cl}{}
\end{array}
$$

$$(82)$$

The course of the reaction with EI parallels that of arylamines, which also give geminal substitution. From the knowledge of how EI acts, it was determined that the ethyl ester of glycine also gives geminal substitution (*2182*). Thus it would appear that the tendency towards geminal substitution is correlated roughly with the base strengths of the amines.

The fact that the several partially substituted aziridinyl derivatives may undergo reaction with other amines without affecting the aziridine ring has provided routes to different isomers and aided in structure assignment of isomers. Thus the structure of the tetrakis(1-aziridinyl)bis(dimethylamino) isomer formed from reaction of $P_3N_3Cl_6$ with first one amine and then the other depends on which amine is the first reactant (Eq 83) (*2122*).

$$
P_3N_3Cl_6 + Me_2NH \quad \xrightarrow{\quad} \xrightarrow{AzH} \quad
\begin{array}{c}
Me_2N\overset{Az\diagdown P\eqsim N\diagdown P\diagup Az}{\underset{\underset{N\lesseqgtr P\diagdown N}{|}}{}}NMe_2 \\
\underset{Az\quad Az}{}
\end{array}
$$

$$(83)$$

$$
P_3N_3Cl_6 + AzH \quad \xrightarrow{\quad} \xrightarrow{Me_2NH} \quad
\begin{array}{c}
Az\overset{Az\diagdown P\eqsim N\diagdown P\diagup Az}{\underset{\underset{N\lesseqgtr P\diagdown N}{|}}{}}Az \\
\underset{Me_2N\quad NMe_2}{}
\end{array}
$$

With the ethyl ester of glycine the same mixed derivative was formed regardless of the order of reaction (Eq 84) (*2182*).

The tetrakis(1-aziridinyl) product ($P_3N_3Cl_2Az_4$) has been reported to exist in three isomeric forms (*2191*). This fact suggests that geminal substitution by EI is not exclusive (although it is predominant) and that stereoisomers are formed.

Charge-transfer complexes between transition metal salts and hexakis(1-aziridinyl)cyclotriphosphaza-1,3,5-triene (apholate) have been obtained. The following compositions were reported (*4156*):

$$[P_3N_3Az_6]\cdot3AgNO_3 \qquad [P_3N_3Az_6]\cdot2CuSO_4 \qquad [P_3N_3Az_6]\cdot2ZnCl_2$$

Table 3-XVII

REACTION OF 1-UNSUBSTITUTED AZIRIDINES WITH TRIMERIC PHOSPHONITRILIC CHLORIDES

Reactant[a]	Product[a]	% Yield	References
$P_3N_3Cl_6$	$P_3N_3Cl_5Az$	81	2122, 2186, 2191, 2790
$P_3N_3Cl_6$	$2,2\text{-}P_3N_3Cl_4Az_2$	38–57	2122,[b] 2186, 2191,[b] 2789, 2790, 2958[c]
$P_3N_3Cl_6$	$2,2,4,4\text{-}P_3N_3Cl_2Az_4$	35	2122, 2186,[b] 2191,[b] 2789
$P_3N_3Cl_6$	$P_3N_3ClAz_5$	40	2122, 2186, 2191, 2790
$2,4\text{-}P_3N_3Cl_4(NMe_2)_2$	$2,4\text{-}(NMe_2)_2\text{-}2,4\text{-}Az_2P_3N_3Cl_2{}^{c}$	41	2122, 2789[b]
$2,4\text{-}P_3N_3Cl_4(NMe_2)_2$	$2,4\text{-}(NMe_2)\text{-}2,4,6,6\text{-}Az_4P_3N_3$	10	2122, 2790
$2,2,4,4\text{-}P_3N_3Cl_2(NHC_6H_4Me\text{-}p)_4{}^{c}$	$2,2,4,4\text{-}(NHC_6H_4Me\text{-}p)_4\text{-}6,6\text{-}Az_2P_3N_3{}^{c}$	95	2122
$2,2\text{-}P_3N_3Cl_4(NHC_6H_4Me\text{-}p)_2{}^{c}$	$2,2\text{-}(NHC_6H_4Me\text{-}p)_4\text{-}4,4,6,6\text{-}Az_4P_3N_3{}^{c}$	84	2122
$2,4,6\text{-}P_3N_3Cl_3(NMe_2)_3{}^{c}$	$2,4,6\text{-}(NMe_2)_3\text{-}2\text{-}AzP_3N_3Cl_2{}^{c}$	37	2122
$P_3N_3Cl_6$	$2,2,4\text{-}Az_3P_3N_3Cl_3$	15	2186,[b] 2191[b], 2787, 2790
$2,2\text{-}P_3N_3Cl_4Az_2$	$2,2,4\text{-}Az_3P_3N_3Cl_3$	—	2787
$P_3N_3Cl_5Az$	$2,2\text{-}Az_2P_3N_3Cl_4$	—	2787
$2,2,4\text{-}P_3N_3Cl_3Az_3$	$2,2,4,4\text{-}Az_4P_3N_3Cl_2$	39	2787
$2,4,6\text{-}P_3N_3Cl_3(NMe_2)_3$	$2,4,6\text{-}(NMe_2)_3\text{-}2,4,6\text{-}Az_3P_3N_3$	—	2787, 2790
$P_3N_3Cl_6$	$P_3N_3Az_6$	70–99	2186, 2191, 2489, 2786, 2953, 2957, 4156
$P_3N_3Cl_6$	$P_3N_3(2\text{-MeAz})_6$	90–93.3	1910, 2957, 4156
$P_3N_3Cl_6$	$P_3N_3(2,2\text{-Me}_2Az)_6$	95	2957, 4156
$P_3N_3Cl_6$	$P_3N_3(2\text{-anisyl-Az})_6$	70	4156
$P_3N_3Cl_5(NHCH_2CO_2Et)$	$P_3N_3Az_5(NHCH_2CO_2Et)$	—	2183

2,2-P$_3$N$_3$Cl$_4$(NHCH$_2$CO$_2$Et)$_2^d$	4,4,6-Az$_4$P$_3$N$_3$-2,2-(NHCH$_2$CO$_2$Et)$_2$	—	2183, 2186^b
2,2,4-P$_3$N$_3$Cl$_3$(NHCH$_2$CO$_2$Et)$_4^d$	6,6-Az$_2$P$_3$N$_3$-2,2,4,4-(NHCH$_2$CO$_2$Et)$_4^d$	—	2183
	Pip$_2$-Az$_4$P$_3$N$_3^b$	—	2186
	Pip-Az$_4$P$_3$N$_3$Cl^e	—	2186
	Pip-Az$_3$P$_3$N$_3$Cl$_2^{b,e}$	—	2186
	Pip$_2$-Az$_3$P$_3$N$_3$Cl$_2^{b,e}$	—	2186
	Pip$_4$-AzP$_3$N$_3$Cl^{b,e}	—	2186
	Mor$_2$-Az$_4$P$_3$N$_3^{b,f}$	—	2186
	Mor-Az$_4$P$_3$N$_3$Cl^{b,f}	—	2186
	Mor$_2$-Az$_2$P$_3$N$_3$Cl^{b,f}	—	2186
	Mor-Az$_3$P$_3$N$_3$Cl$_2^{b,f}$	—	2186
	Mor-Az$_2$P$_3$N$_3$Cl$_3^{b,f}$	—	2186
	Mor$_3$Az$_2$P$_3$N$_3$Cl^{b,f}	—	2633
	Mor$_4$Az$_2$P$_3$N$_3^{b,f}$	—	2633
	Az$_4$P$_3$N$_3$(NHCH$_2$CH$_2$CO$_2$Me)$_2^b$	—	2186
	Az$_5$P$_3$N$_3$(NHCHPhCH$_2$CO$_2$Me)	—	2186
2,2,4-(CF$_3$CH$_2$CF$_2$CH$_2$O)$_4$P$_3$N$_3$Cl$_2$	2,2,4-(CF$_3$CF$_2$CF$_2$CH$_2$O)$_4$-6,6-Az$_2$P$_3$N$_3$	98	2958
2,4,6-P$_3$N$_3$Cl$_3$(NMe$_2$)$_3$	2,4,6-(NMe$_2$)$_3$-AzP$_3$N$_3$Cl$_2$	—	2789
2,2-P$_3$N$_3$Cl$_4$Az$_2$	2,2,4-Az$_4$P$_3$N$_3$Cl$_2$	—	2790
Various	Various (pyrrolidino)$_n$Az$_{6-n}$P$_3$N$_3$	—	2185, 2188

^{a} The numbers refer to position of substituents other than chlorine on the P$_3$N$_3$ ring; e.g., 2,4-P$_3$N$_3$Cl$_4$(NMe$_2$)$_2$ is 2,4-bis(dimethylamino)-2,4,6-tetrachlorocyclotriphosphaza-1,3,5-triene.

^{b} Isomer assignment not made in reference.

^{c} Isomer assignment not clear from reference.

^{d} See ref. 2182 for isomer assignment.

^{e} Pip = 1-piperidyl.

^{f} Mor = 4-morpholinyl.

$$(84)$$

Also, a molecular addition compound has been obtained from a one-to-one mixture of trimeric phosphonitrilic chloride ($P_3N_3Cl_6$) and a bis(1-aziridinyl)-substituted product ($P_3N_3Cl_4Az_2$) (*2122*). Tetrameric phosphonitrilic chloride has been treated with EI to yield the octakis(1-aziridinyl) product, **27** (*2489, 2957, 4156*).

27

Reaction with Halides of Sulfur Acids. This reaction (e.g., Eq 85) is very similar to acylation of aziridines (cf. p. 160); precautions observed are low temperatures and basic conditions.

$$RSO_2X + AzH \xrightarrow{\text{base}} RSO_2Az \qquad (85)$$

The aziridine product, containing a substituent capable of conjugation with the unshared pair of electrons on the nitrogen, will readily undergo ring-opening reactions with nucleophiles in the absence of acid catalysts. As a group, the 1-sulfonyl aziridines are more reactive in such ring-opening reactions with nucleophiles than are other activated aziridines. Thus polymerization of the product aziridine sometimes occurs concomitantly with reaction 85 and it is frequently reported that specific 1-sulfonyl aziridines cannot be purified by distillation because of polymerization [see, for example, Bestian (*350*)]. The preparation of such 1-sulfonyl aziridines is described in Table 3-XVIII.

Although several workers found that the reaction of sulfuryl chloride with EI produced only polymeric products under the usual conditions (*426, 963*),

Table 3-XVIII

REACTION OF 1-UNSUBSTITUTED AZIRIDINES WITH SULFONYL HALIDES

Monofunctional Derivatives

$$RSO_2Cl + AzH \xrightarrow{\text{base}} RSO_2Az$$

R	Aziridine or substituents therein	Method[a]	% Yield	References
Me	No substituents	A	63	*350*
Bu	No substituents	A	56	*3375*
n-$C_{12}H_{25}$	No substituents	—	—	*2688*
Ph	No substituents	B	—	*1771*
p-MeC_6H_4	No substituents	B	—	*1771*
p-BrC_6H_4	No substituents	—	—	*1771*
m-$O_2NC_6H_4$	No substituents	B	69	*1662, 1801*
p-$O_2NC_6H_4$[b]	No substituents	—	54	*1801, 2285*
p-$H_2NC_6H_4$	No substituents	B	—	*324*
p-$AcNHC_6H_4$	No substituents	B	90	*2285[b], 2473, 2476*
4-Me-3-$NO_2C_6H_3$	No substituents	A	74	*1771*
2-H_2N-3-MeC_6H_3	No substituents	B	—	*2473*
5-H_2N-2-MeC_6H_3	No substituents	B	—	*2473*
2-Me-5-$O_2NC_6H_3$	No substituents	—	—	*1279*
3-H_2N-4-$MeOC_6H_3$	No substituents	B	—	*2473*
5-H_2N-2-$EtOC_6H_3$	No substituents	B	—	*2473*
3,4-$Cl_2C_6H_3$	No substituents	—	—	*2688*
3-KO_2C-4-HOC_6H_3	No substituents	—	—	*2688*
4-H_2N-2,5-$Cl_2C_6H_2$	No substituents	—	—	*2688*
$PhCH{=}CH$	No substituents	B	—	*1934*
p-$CH_2{=}CHC_6H_4$	No substituents	A	—	*1927a*
m-$AzCOC_6H_4$[c]	No substituents	A	—	*2688*
p-$Az_2P(O)NHC_6H_4$[d]	No substituents	A	75.6	*2796*
p-$Az_3P{=}NC_6H_4$[e]	No substituents	A	80.6	*2796*
4-$AcNH$-1-$C_{10}H_6$	No substituents	B	—	*2474*
6-HO-5-NaO_2C-2-$C_{10}H_5$	No substituents	—	—	*324*
Cu phthalocyanine	No substituents	—	—	*695*
Et_2N	No substituents	A	—	*190*
1-Piperidyl	No substituents	A	—	*190*
Bu	2-Me	A	83	*3375*
Ph	2-Me	A	90	*1448, 3375*
Bu_2N	2-Me	B	—	*190*
Ph	2-CH_2NHSO_2Ph[f]	B	—	*3354*
p-MeC_6H_4	AzH = mitomycin	A	—	*252*
Me	AzH = mitomycin C	A	—	*2227*

Table 3-XVIII—*continued*

Monofunctional Derivatives

R	Aziridine or substituents therein	Method[a]	% Yield	References
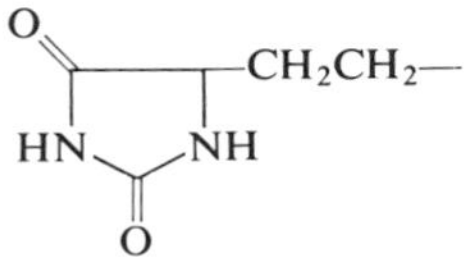	No substituents	—	—	2342
p-BrC$_6$H$_4$	2,3-[(CH$_2$)$_3$]	A	97	1104
p-MeC$_6$H$_4$	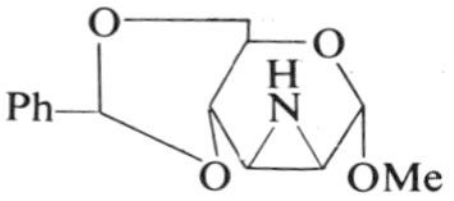	A	87	252
Ph	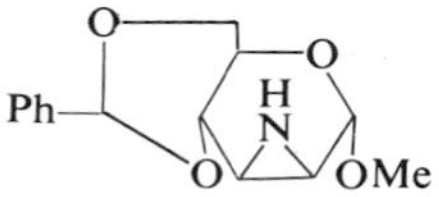	A	87	1095
p-BrC$_6$H$_4$	2,3-(CH$_2$OCH$_2$)	A	96	1095
p-IC$_6$H$_4$	2,3-(CH$_2$OCH$_2$)	A	81	1095
Ph	2,3-Epiminonorbornane	A	—	3866
p-MeC$_6$H$_4$	2,3-Epiminonorbornane	A	82	982

Difunctional Derivatives

$$Y(SO_2Cl)_2 + AzH + \xrightarrow{\text{base}} Y(SO_2Az)_2$$

Y	AzH substituents	Method	% Yield	References
$+CH_2+_3$	None	A	22	544, 1859
m-C$_6$H$_4$	None	—	—	1859, 2688
1-Me-2,4-C$_6$H$_3$	None	A,B	72	4127
1,5-C$_{10}$H$_6$	None	—	—	2688
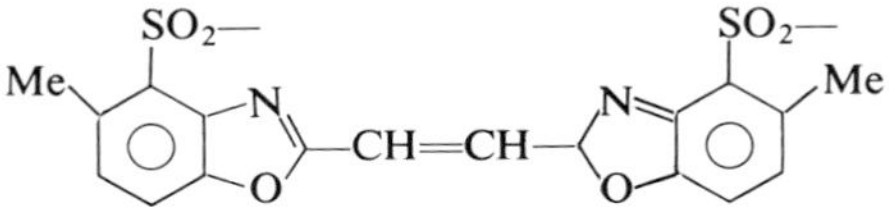	None	B	—	2447, 2715

[a] Denotes the use of the following acid acceptors: A, an amine; B, an inorganic base.
[b] The use of Ac$_2$O solvent as reported appears to be an error.
[c] The reactant was m-ClCOC$_6$H$_4$SO$_2$Cl.
[d] The reactant was p-Cl$_2$P(O)NHC$_6$H$_4$SO$_2$Cl.
[e] The reactant was p-Cl$_3$P=NC$_6$H$_4$SO$_2$Cl.
[f] The aziridine reactant was 2-(aminomethyl)aziridine.

isolation of the crude bis(1-aziridinyl) product was later reported (Eq 86) (*3708*). This product was found to be particularly unstable with respect to polymerization.

$$SO_2Cl_2 + 2AzH \xrightarrow[Et_2O, 0°C]{Et_3N} SO_2Az_2 \qquad (86)$$

The same degree of instability was not noted for the reaction products from thionyl chloride and EI or 2-methylaziridine (Eq 87) (*426, 1949, 3708, 3835, 3836*).

$$SOCl_2 + 2AzH \rightarrow SOAz_2 \qquad (87)$$

More detailed study showed that the product from one mole of EI and one mole of thionyl chloride, 1-aziridinesulfinyl chloride, can be observed at low temperature; on warming, a rearrangement occurs (see p. 291) (*3571*).

The reactivity of the 1-sulfonyl aziridine group towards materials such as cellulose has prompted the synthesis of a variety of dyes containing one or more such groups (*324, 1895, 2378, 2473, 2474, 2476, 2716, 2891*). Examples include such procedures as treating copper phthalocyanine with chlorosulfonic acid to prepare the tetrachlorosulfonylated product and subsequent reaction with EI in the presence of base (*1895*).

Addition of 1-Unsubstituted Aziridines to Compounds with Cumulated Double Bonds (Isocyanates, Isothiocyanates, Ketenes, Carbodiimides). This reaction is very useful for preparation of 1-acylated aziridines of the indicated types since it may be performed at low temperatures and does not result in liberation of an acid (Eq 88).

$$R—Q{=}C{=}Y + AzH \rightarrow RQH—C(Y)Az \qquad (88)$$

where Q is C—H or N and Y is O, S, or NR′. Simply mixing stoichiometric amounts of the aziridine and the compound containing cumulated double bonds frequently produces essentially a quantitative yield of product. The reaction is often exothermic and is usually performed in a solvent at room temperature or below. Solvents which have been employed include hexane, benzene, ether, acetone, and dichloromethane. In one instance where a water solution of the product was desired, an alkylene diisocyanate was added to an ice-cold aqueous solution of EI (*356*).

Side reactions or secondary reactions are usually insignificant. However, the products sometimes tend to homopolymerize on attempted distillation (cf. p. 162).

As mentioned previously (p. 162), 1-acetylaziridine prepared from ketene and EI was found to be more stable on storage than that from acetyl chloride. The reaction with ketene may be performed in solvents or simply by passing the gas directly into the pure aziridine.

Of interest is the reaction of EI with carbon suboxide to give a quantitative yield of the malonyl product (Eq 89) (*424, 855, 856*).

$$O{=}C{=}C{=}C{=}O + 2AzH \rightarrow CH_2(COAz)_2 \tag{89}$$

For the preparation of urea derivatives, the isocyanate may be generated *in situ* from the *N*-chloro amide (*1213, 2772*). Thus addition of an *N*-chloro amide to an aqueous solution of sodium hydroxide and EI gave the corresponding 1-aziridinyl derivative (Eq 90).

$$ClNHCO(CH_2)_6CONHCl + AzH \xrightarrow{\text{NaOH}} AzCONH(CH_2)_6NHCOAz \tag{90}$$

Reaction 88 has been used for the preparation of polymers containing 1-aziridinecarboxamide end groups. This has been accomplished by reaction of a polymer containing hydroxyl end groups, or a simpler di- or polyhydroxy compound, with a diisocyanate in such proportion as to provide unreacted isocyanate groups and then treatment with an aziridine (*177, 1736, 1737, 3592, 3811, 4050*). The same type of sequential addition was used to prepare a related 1-aziridinyl derivative (Eq 91) (*2711*).

$$4\text{-}MeC_6H_3\text{-}1,3\text{-}(NCO)_2 + AzH \longrightarrow 1\text{-}(OCN)\text{-}4\text{-}MeC_6H_3\text{-}3\text{-}NHCOAz$$
$$\downarrow \text{ArNH}_2 \tag{91}$$
$$ArNHCONHC_6H_3\text{-}4\text{-}Me\text{-}3\text{-}NHCOAz$$

Reaction of aziridines with nitrile oxides (Eq 92) occurs in a manner similar to Eq 88 (*2965*).

$$ArCNO + AzH \longrightarrow Ar{-}\overset{\overset{\displaystyle N{-}OH}{\|}}{C}{-}Az \tag{92}$$

Less predictably, phenyl cyanate, PhOCN, with EI undergoes first trimerization and then metathesis to give 2,4-diphenoxy-6-(1-aziridinyl)-*s*-triazine in 65% yield (*2443a*).

Table 3-XIX gives many examples of these reactions.

Preparation of Miscellaneous 1-Substituted Aziridines. Included in this section are preparations, from 1-unsubstituted aziridines, of derivatives which contain hetero elements (other than phosphorus or sulfur acid derivatives) directly bound to the aziridine nitrogen. The most frequently used reaction for such preparations is treatment of the aziridine with an active halogen compound in the presence of base (Eq 93).

$$M{-}X + AzH \xrightarrow{\text{base}} Az{-}M \tag{93}$$

In this reaction M—X represents NOCl (*719, 3076*), arenediazonium chlorides (*1657, 3057*), alkylarsenic chlorides (*2031*), various chlorosilicon compounds

Table 3-XIX

ADDITION OF 1-UNSUBSTITUTED AZIRIDINES TO ISOCYANATES,
ISOTHIOCYANATES, KETENES, AND CARBODIIMIDES

$$RNCO + AzH^a \rightarrow RNHCOAz$$

R	% Yield	References
H	Good	350, 1215
H	—[b]	1215
H	83[c]	250
Me	74	350, 1842
Me	—[b]	1842
Et	—	350
$CH_2=CH$	—	2766
iso-Pr	—	1949
$CH_2=CHCH_2$	—	2181
$CH_2=CMe$	—	2766
Pr	—	1582a
Bu	30–74	430, 1842, 3375
Bu	34–69[b]	430, 3375
iso-Bu	—	1922
$X(CF_2)_nCH_2$ (X = F or H, $n > 2$)	—	660a
$c\text{-}C_6H_{11}$	—[d]	350, 1213
iso-C_8H_{17}	—	1213, 1842
tert-C_8H_{17}	—[e]	434
$n\text{-}C_{11}H_{23}$	—[d]	1213
$n\text{-}C_{17}H_{35}$	—[d]	1213
$Me(CH_2)_4CH=CHCH_2CH_2CH=CH(CH_2)_8$	—	926
$n\text{-}C_{18}H_{37}$	—	1197, 1213, 1235, 2158
Ph	94	2657, 2658
Ph	91[b, d]	1213, 3375
Ph	—[e]	2043
Ph	—[f]	2101
Ph	47[g]	514
Ph	—[h]	1621
Ph	—[i]	2103
$o\text{-}MeC_6H_4$	78–95	430, 2657
$m\text{-}MeC_6H_4$	65–84	430, 2657, 2658
$p\text{-}MeC_6H_4$	70–94	430, 2657, 2658
$2,6\text{-}Me_2C_6H_3$	78	2657
$o\text{-}ClC_6H_4$	57	430, 2657, 2658
$m\text{-}ClC_6H_4$	82–89	430, 1295, 2657, 2658
$p\text{-}ClC_6H_4$	65–82	430, 1295, 2657, 2658
$2,5\text{-}Cl_2C_6H_3$	91	2657, 2658
$3,4\text{-}Cl_2C_6H_3$	89	1295, 2657, 2658
$p\text{-}BrC_6H_4$	—	1295
$p\text{-}O_2NC_6H_4$	92–95	430, 2657, 2658
$o\text{-}MeOC_6H_4$	73–92	430, 2657

Table 3-XIX—*continued*

RNCO + AzH^a → RNHCOAz		
R	% Yield	References
p-MeOC$_6$H$_4$	93	430, 2658
3-Cl-4-MeC$_6$H$_3$	—	1295
1-PhCHMe	—^{e}	560
p-CH$_2$=CMeC$_6$H$_4$	100	2181
1-C$_{10}$H$_7$	56–94	430, 2657, 2658
1-C$_{10}$H$_7$	68^b	430
1-C$_{10}$H$_7$	—^{j}	566
p-(c-C$_6$H$_{11}$)Ph	—	1197
CH$_2$=CHOCH$_2$CMe$_2$	—	2520
CH$_2$=CHOCHMeCMe$_2$	—	2520
CH$_2$=CHOCH$_2$CH$_2$CHMe(CH$_2$)$_3$CMe$_2$	—	2520
EtO$_2$CCH$_2$	—	1044
MeO$_2$CCH$_2$CH$_2$	—	1044
EtO$_2$CCHMe	—	1044
EtO$_2$CCH(CH$_2$Ph)	—	1044
EtO$_2$CCH$_2$CH(CO$_2$Et)	—	1044
CH$_2$=CMeCO$_2$CH$_2$CH$_2$	94	436
C$_{16}$H$_{33}$O$_2$CCH$_2$CH$_2$CH(CO$_2$C$_{16}$H$_{33}$)	—	2753
Tetraacetylglucosyl	—	933
(MeO)$_2$P(O)	90	880
(PhO)$_2$P(O)	62	880
AzCO(CH$_2$)$_5$	—^{k}	191
BuN(COAz)CH$_2$CH$_2$	—^{i}	1204
p-AzCONMeC$_6$H$_4$	77^m	1204
p-(2-MeAz)CONMeC$_6$H$_4$	77$^{b,\,m}$	1204

Q(NCO)$_n$ + AzH^a → Q(NHCOAz)$_n$		
Q, n = 2	% Yield	References
(CH$_2$)$_4$	90	350, 356, 1927, 2772
(CH$_2$)$_6$	89–100	350, 356, 1816, 1927, 2772, 3040
(CH$_2$)$_6$	—^{b}	470, 3040
(CH$_2$)$_6$	—^{e}	470
(CH$_2$)$_8$	100	350, 356
(CH$_2$)$_{10}$	95	3040
–CH=CH– (*trans*)	90	430
1,4-c-C$_6$H$_{10}$	—	356
p-C$_6$H$_4$	86	2772
MeC$_6$H$_3$-2,4	80–92	1994, 3202
MeC$_6$H$_3$-2,4	90^e	470
	88	430

Table 3-XIX—*continued*

$$Q(NCO)_n + AzH^a \rightarrow Q(NHCOAz)_n$$

Q, $n = 2$	% Yield	References
—CH$_2$CH$_2$—(ring with O)—CH$_2$CH$_2$—	—	1927
—CH$_2$CH$_2$—(benzene ring with O)—CH$_2$CH$_2$—	—	1927
—CH$_2$CH$_2$—(benzene ring with S)—CH$_2$CH$_2$—	—	1927
4,4'-C$_6$H$_4$CH$_2$C$_6$H$_4$	50–98	350, 1994, 2692
4,4'-(3-MeC$_6$H$_3$)CH$_2$(3-MeC$_6$H$_3$)	90–100	1994
2,2'-C$_6$H$_4$SO$_2$C$_6$H$_4$	94	1147
4,4'-C$_6$H$_4$CH$_2$CH$_2$C$_6$H$_4$	—	3477

$$Q = \text{(biphenyl with positions A and A')}$$

A	A'	% Yield	References
3-Me	3'-Me	90–100	430, 1147, 1994
3-Me	3'-Me	93[b]	430
3-MeO	3'-MeO	56–86	430, 1147, 1994
3-MeO	3'-MeO	26[b]	430
2-MeO	2'-MeO	90	1147
2,5-(MeO)$_2$	2',5'-(MeO)$_2$	61	1147
3-EtO	3'-EtO	82	1147
2-O$_2$N	H	93	1147
3-Cl	3'-Cl	96	1147
3-PhO	3'-PhO	—	1147

Q, $n = 3$	% Yield	References
C$_6$H$_3$-1,3,5	—	350
MeC$_6$H$_2$-2,4,6	90	350
1,3-Me$_2$C$_6$H-2,4,6	87	350
1,3,5-Me$_3$C$_6$-2,4,6	—	350

$$RNCS + AzH^a \rightarrow RNHCSAz$$

R	% Yield	References
CH$_2$=CHCH$_2$	100	2181
c-C$_6$H$_{11}$	—	3553
Ph	71–90	888, 1930

Table 3-XIX—*continued*

$RNCS + AzH^a \rightarrow RNHCSAz$		
R	% Yield	References
Ph	61^e	*888*
m-MeC_6H_4	—	*3553*
p-MeC_6H_4	—	*3553*
$2,3$-$Me_2C_6H_3$	—	*3553*
m-ClC_6H_4	—	*3553*
p-ClC_6H_4	—	*1295, 3553*
p-BrC_6H_4	—	*3553*
p-$MeOC_6H_4$	—	*3553*
p-IC_6H_4	$—^n$	*2181*
$3,4,5$-$Cl_3C_6H_2$	$—^b$	*2181*
o-$MeO_2CC_6H_4$	94	*1772*
1-$C_{10}H_7$	—	*3553*
Ph	$—^o$	*566*
Ph	$—^f$	*2101*
Ph	$—^p$	*1098*
Ph	88^g	*1095*
Ph	$—^q$	*2820*
Ph	$—^r$	*3483*
Ph	$—^s$	*3482*
Ph	$—^t$	*2047*
Tetraacetylglucosyl	—	*933*
$RNCS = (CH_2)_6(NCS)_2$	—	*1116*

$RCH{=}C{=}O + AzH^a \rightarrow RCH_2COAz$		
R	% Yield	References
H	93	*350, 360, 1856*
H	$Good^b$	*360*
H	$—^e$	*1103*
H	68^r	*3482*
$Me(CH_2)_{16}$	—	*1857*
Ac	Good	*1923, 2199*

$RN{=}C{=}NR' + AzH^a \rightarrow RNHC({=}NR')Az$			
R	R'	% Yield	References
Ph	Ph	—	*15*
o-$MeOC_6H_4$	o-$MeOC_6H_4$	—	*15*
Bu	$MeOCH_2$	$—^u$	*1142*
c-C_6H_{11}	$MeOCH_2$	$—^u$	*1142*

(*1200*), and various sulfenyl chlorides (*55, 375, 426, 1139, 1149, 2631, 3708, 3835, 3836*). In addition to the usual precautions against ring opening (a basic reaction medium and low temperatures) special considerations are necessary for certain of the derivatives. For example the 1-nitroso derivative was prepared at $-70°C$ by Eq 94 in essentially quantitative yield and was stable for days at $-60°C$ (*3076*).

$$\text{AzH} + \text{NOCl} \xrightarrow[\text{Et}_2\text{O, } -70°C]{\text{Et}_3\text{N}} \text{AzNO} \qquad (94)$$

At higher temperatures ($-20°$ to $-10°C$) the product decomposed to ethylene and nitrous oxide (*719, 3076*); thus very low temperatures are necessary for preparation of 1-nitroso derivatives (see p. 293 for additional details on the decomposition).

For preparation of 1-nitrosoaziridines, use of nitrosating agents other than nitrosyl chloride is possible (*1565*). Products resulting from decomposition of *cis*- or *trans*-2,3-dimethyl-1-nitrosoaziridine are also formed by treatment of the aziridine with 3-nitro-*N*-nitrosocarbazole or methyl nitrite (*719*).

The reaction of sulfur dichloride with EI was reported to give a poor yield of a product which consisted of about 50% 1,1'-dithiobiaziridine (*426*). The formation of this material was explained on the basis of the equilibrium existing between sulfur dichloride and sulfur monochloride.

---

[a] EI unless other aziridine is specified.

[b] The aziridine was 2-MeAzH.

[c] The aziridine was

[d] Isocyanate prepared *in situ* from the *N*-chloro amide.

[e] The aziridine was 2,2-Me$_2$AzH.

[f] The aziridine was 3,3-Me$_2$-2,2-Ph$_2$AzH.

[g] The aziridine was 2,3-(CH$_2$OCH$_2$)AzH.

[h] The aziridine was 2β,3β-epiminocholestane.

[i] The aziridine was 2-PhCH$_2$-3-PhAzH.

[j] The aziridine was 3-Et-2,2-Ph$_2$AzH.

[k] Reactant was ClCO(CH$_2$)$_5$NCO.

[l] Reactant was BuN(COCl)CH$_2$CH$_2$NCO.

[m] Reactant was *p*-ClCONMeC$_6$H$_4$NCO.

[n] The aziridine was 2-BuAzH.

[o] The aziridine was 3-Me-2,2-Ph$_2$AzH.

[p] The aziridine was 2,3-[(CH$_2$)$_3$]AzH.

[q] The aziridine was 2,3-[(CH$_2$)$_4$]AzH.

[r] The aziridine was 2,2-[(CH$_2$)$_5$]AzH.

[s] The aziridine was 2,3-[(CH$_2$)$_5$]AzH.

[t] The aziridine was 2,3-[(CH$_2$)$_6$]AzH.

[u] It is not clear which isomer was produced.

A number of 1-arylazoaziridines have been prepared but many of these derivatives are very heat-sensitive (*1657, 3057*). Two derivatives exploded violently after standing at room temperature for 20–30 minutes (*1657*). In the preparation from diazotized arylamines, sodium acetate was used to adjust the pH for the reaction of the aziridine with the diazonium chloride and very careful control of conditions was necessary (*1657*).

Treatment of an aziridine with aqueous sodium hypohalite produced the 1-haloaziridine in good yield (*1510–1512*). 1-Chloroaziridine was sufficiently stable for distillation at 38°C and 245 mm but underwent some change at higher temperatures. 1-Bromoaziridine could be distilled (48°C at 131 mm) but was too unstable for analysis. It exploded either during distillation or within a few hours thereafter. 1-Chloroaziridine which had been stored several months at 0°C exploded like nitroglycerine when dropped into a disposal pit (*1509*).

Table 3-XX

MISCELLANEOUS 1-SUBSTITUTED AZIRIDINES

Reactant	Aziridine product	% Yield	References
Li	AzLi	—	*213, 1474*
Na	AzNa	92	*213*
K	AzK	85	*213*
Cl_2 + NaOH	AzCl	80	*1510–1512*
Br_2 + NaOH	$AzBr^a$	—	*1510*
N-Bromosuccinimide	1-Br-2-MeAz (*trans*)	56	*2152d*
LiAz + NH_2Cl	$AzNH_2$	—	*495, 1513*
LiAz + ClAz	AzAz	11.1	*1510, 1512*
$EtO_2CNHOSO_2C_6H_4NO_2$-*o*	*N*-EtO_2CNH-cyclohexenimine	12	*1284c*
Et_2Zn	Az_2Zn	91	*3029*
Et_2Zn	$(2-MeAz)_2Zn$	—	*3029*
BCl_3	$(2-MeAz)_3B$	—	*1747a*
Et_3Al	$EtAlAz_2$ + Et_2AlAz	—	*3029*
NOCl	$AzNO^b$	—	*3076*
NOCl	$2,3-Me_2AzNO^b$	—	*719*
PhN_2Cl	PhN=NAz	—	*1657, 3057*
p-$MeC_6H_4N_2Cl$	*p*-$MeC_6H_4N_2Az$	—	*1657, 3057*
m-$ClC_6H_4N_2Cl$	*m*-$ClC_6H_4N_2Az$	—	*1657*
p-$ClC_6H_4N_2Cl$	*p*-$ClC_6H_4N_2Az$	—	*1657*
p-$BrC_6H_4N_2Cl$	*p*-$BrC_6H_4N_2Az$	33–74	*1657, 3057*
p-$IC_6H_4N_2Cl$	*p*-$IC_6H_4N_2Az$	—	*1657*
m-$O_2NC_6H_4N_2Cl$	*m*-$O_2NC_6H_4N_2Az$	—	*3057*
p-$O_2NC_6H_4N_2Cl$	*p*-$O_2NC_6H_4N_2Az$	95	*1657, 3057*
p-$O_2NC_6H_4N_2Cl$	1-(*p*-$O_2NC_6H_4N_2$)-2-MeAz	54	*1657*
$3-O_2N-4-MeC_6H_3N_2Cl$	$3-O_2N-4-MeC_6H_3N_2Az$	89	*1657*
$3,4-Cl_2C_6H_3N_2Cl$	$3,4-Cl_2C_6H_3N_2Az$	—	*1657*
$EtAsCl_2$	$EtAsAz_2$	17.4	*2031*

Table 3-XX—*continued*

Reactant	Aziridine product	% Yield	References
$PrAsCl_2$	$PrAsAz_2$	10	*2031*
$PhAsCl_2$	$PhAsAz_2$	76.4	*2031*
Et_2AsCl	Et_2AsAz	24	*2031*
Pr_2AsCl	Pr_2AsAz	55	*2031*
Bu_2AsCl	Bu_2AsAz	74.7	*2031*
H_3SiI	H_3SiAz	0	*4009*
Me_3SiCl	Me_3SiAz	44	*3139*
Et_3SiCl	Et_3SiAz	60	*4084*
Me_2SiCl_2	Me_2SiAz_2	42	*1200, 3139*
$(PhCH_2)_2SiCl_2$	$(PhCH_2)_2SiAz_2$	—	*1200*
$(PhCH_2)_2SiCl_2$	$(PhCH_2)_2Si(2\text{-}MeAz)_2$	—	*1200*
$(MeO)_2SiCl_2$	$(MeO)_2SiAz_2$	—	*1200*
$(BuO)_2SiCl_2$	$(BuO)_2SiAz_2$	—	*1200*
Et_2NSiCl_3	Et_2NSiAz_3	—	*1200*
Et_3SiH^c	Et_3SiAz	—	*2669, 3576*
Et_2MeSiH^c	$Et_2MeSiAz$	—	*2669, 3576*
$MePh_2SiH^c$	$MePh_2SiAz$	—	*2669, 3576*
Ph_3SiH^c	Ph_3SiAz	—	*2669, 3576*
$(PhCH_2)_2MeSiH^c$	$(PhCH_2)_2MeSiAz$	—	*2669, 3576*
$(EtO)_2EtSiH^c$	$(EtO)_2MeSiAz$	—	*2669, 3576*
$(EtO)_2MeSiH^c$	$(EtO)_2MeSiAz$	—	*2669, 3576*
$Me_2PhSiCH_2CH{=}CH_2^d$	$Me_2PhSiAz$	10	*2671, 3523b*
Et_2SiH_2	Et_2SiAz_2	—	*2669, 2672, 3576*
Me_3SiSCl	Me_3SiSAz	—	*3711a*
Cl_3CSCl	Cl_3CSAz	69	*375*
$EtSCl$	$EtSAz$	30	*1273a, 4084*
$c\text{-}C_6H_{11}SCl$	$c\text{-}C_6H_{11}SAz$	33	*2631*
$PhSCl$	$PhSAz$	66	*1105,1273,3711a*
Cl_5C_6SCl	Cl_5C_6SAz	—	*1139*
$Et_2NCH_2CH_2SCl$	$Et_2NCH_2CH_2SAz$	30	*1273, 4084*
$O(CH_2CH_2)NSCl$	$O(CH_2CH_2)_2NSAz$	55	*1149*
$S(CH_2CH_2)_2NSCl$	$S(CH_2CH_2)_2NSAz$	63.5	*1149*
$(EtO)_2P(O)NEtSCl$	$(EtO)_2P(O)NEtSAz$	30–50	*55*
S_2Cl_2	S_2Az_2	60–87	*1273a, 3708, 3835, 3836*
S_2Cl_2	$S_2(2\text{-}MeAz)_2$	42	*3835, 3836*
SCl_2	SAz_2	70.7	*3708*
SCl_2	$S(2\text{-}MeAz)_2$	—	*426*
$(1\text{-Imidazolyl})_2S_x$ $(x = 1,2,3,4,5)$	S_xAz_2	—	*1274*

^{a} Decomposed on attempted distillation or shortly after distillation.

^{b} Unstable at temperatures greater than about $-20°$ to $-10°C$.

^{c} Alkali metal catalyst.

^{d} Propylene was identified as byproduct.

Aziridines have also been 1-chlorinated and 1-brominated with *N*-halosuccinimides (*4015, 4016*).

The alkali metal salts of EI are readily prepared by treatment of EI with a metal alkyl or an alkali metal (*213, 1474*). Such preparations have been used in subsequent reactions without isolation (*963, 1474, 1682, 2148, 2152, 2153, 3094*). Lithium readily dissolves in excess EI at 0°C, displacing hydrogen (*963*). In an attempt to characterize dry lithium ethylenimide, the gel obtained by reaction of lithium with a tenfold excess of EI was dried to a powder by evaporating the excess EI with an equal volume of cyclohexane under reduced pressure; if the cyclohexane were omitted only an intractable gel could be obtained. The dry powder (presumably lithium ethylenimide) ignited spontaneously when exposed to air (*963*).

Exchange of the N—H in EI with D_2O vapor to give 1-deuterated EI is very rapid (*3639*). Exchange of protons is also rapid between EI and 2-propanethiol, but ring opening is a serious side reaction (*4118*).

In addition to the use of chlorosilicon compounds for preparation of the corresponding 1-substituted aziridines, reaction 95 has been reported (*2669, 2672, 3576*).

$$R_3SiH + AzH \xrightarrow[\text{catalyst}]{\text{alkali metal}} R_3SiAz + H_2 \qquad (95)$$

where R may be Me, Et, Ph, $PhCH_2$, or EtO.

This same reaction was not successful when the silane was replaced with triethylstannane. The tin derivative was prepared, however, by an exchange reaction (Eq 96) (*2163*).

$$Me_3SnNMe_2 + AzH \rightarrow Me_3SnAz + Me_2NH \qquad (96)$$

The preparation of various 1-substituted aziridines is described in Table 3-XX.

OTHER REACTIONS INVOLVING AZIRIDINE-RING ATOMS

Cis–Trans Isomerization. Geometric isomerization of 2,3-disubstituted aziridines has been only infrequently reported and then only for aziridines wherein one of the carbon substituents is an acyl group (Eq 97).

The reaction with R = $PhCH_2$, R′ = Ph, R″ = p-MeC_6H_4 was reported to occur to some extent when catalyzed by light or dry hydrogen chloride (*792, 793*). However, the efficacy of light was later questioned (*2714, 2802*). Base catalysis (brief treatment with hot sodium ethoxide solution) afforded excellent yields of the cis isomer from the trans (*999*). Recently equilibrium constants for the base-catalyzed cis–trans interconversion of the aziridines shown in

Eq 97 have been determined in a number of alcohols and dimethyl sulfoxide (*2361*; cf. *3638a*). For 2,3-dibenzoyl-1-benzylaziridine the variation for K(cis/trans) ranged from 5.24 in dimethyl sulfoxide to 0.32 in *tert*-butyl alcohol, and paralleled approximately the dielectric constant of the solvent.

$$R' = Ph, Bz; \quad R'' = Bz, p\text{-}MeC_6H_4;$$
$$R = Me, PhCH_2, c\text{-}C_6H_{11}$$

The base-catalyzed isomerization is presumed to involve formation of the intermediate enolate anion **28**. Of interest is the fact that *trans*-1-cyclohexyl-2-phenyl-3-benzoylaziridine is unchanged by *N*-methylanilinolithium in ether under conditions which caused a ring-opening isomerization of the cis isomer (*1256*).

28

Attack of Aziridines by Radicals. The characteristic and by far predominant effect of radicals on aziridines is to abstract the atom or group attached to nitrogen and form 1-aziridinyl radicals or their C-substituted homologs. Such is the behavior of EI in the mass spectrometer, where the principal peak is due to $C_2H_4N\cdot^+$; the ionization potential observed was 9.8–10.2 eV, the calculated one 9.04 eV (*1402, 2098*). More recent LCAO–MO calculations yielded the value 11.137 eV (*716*). In comparison, an estimate of the photoionization potential was 8.24 eV (*2052*). Fragmentation of R_2NCH_2Az types upon electron impact gives parent ions that preferentially lose $C_2H_4N\cdot$ radicals (*2151*), and compounds of type $RN(CH_2Az)_2$ behave similarly; when R is methyl, an ion of m/e 56, $AzCH_2^+$, is observed (*2809*). Decay of parent ions from $ROCH_2Az$, however, gives $ROCH_2^+$ and $AzCH_2^+$ about equally; thus the aziridinyl group is more like an alkoxy group than like a piperidino group (*2148*). 1-Acyl-aziridines often yield carbon monoxide in the mass spectrometer, but 1-acetyl-aziridine produces formaldehyde (*2811a*). The photolysis of EI and radiolysis of 1-unsubstituted aziridines also involves abstraction of the hydrogen on nitrogen by radicals (*4087, 4092, 4193*).

Treatment of EI with hydrogen atoms (*1964*) or methyl radicals from various sources (*477, 478, 1520, 1521, 2112a*; cf. *2614a*) produces the same 1-aziridinyl radical. Evidence was found that 1,1'-biaziridine was formed in such reactions (*477, 2112a*). Atomic hydrogen likewise preferentially abstracts the 1-hydrogen atom in 2-methylaziridine (*1965*), and the 1-methyl group in 1-methylaziridine (*1964*). The 1-aziridinyl radicals decay to products that will not be reviewed here. While EI is unsuitable for other reasons as a vapor for use in Geiger counter tubes, it is one of those showing good quenching (*507*), probably because of ease of removal of the 1-hydrogen.

Replacements on Carbon. Very facile reactions of 2-monochloroaziridines (**29**) occur wherein the chlorine atom is replaced with some other nucleophilic group (Eq 98) (*903*; see also p. 220).

$$\text{29} \qquad + \; X^- \quad \longrightarrow \quad + \; Cl^- \qquad (98)$$

Where **29** was the 3-methyl-1,2-diphenyl derivative, the reaction was successful for displacements by sodium cyanide, sodium thiophenoxide, and lithium aluminum hydride. With the 1,2-diphenyl derivative, sodium methoxide, sodium thiophenoxide, and methyllithium were used.

The reaction occurs with inversion of configuration, as indicated in Eq 98. However, it was also found to follow a first-order rate expression for both derivatives of **29**, with the 3-methyl-1,2-diphenyl derivative being the more reactive (*903*).

A mechanism was suggested for the reaction (Eq 99) which is consistent with the observed rate data and the greatly enhanced reactivity of haloaziridines over halocyclopropenes (*903*).

$$\text{29} \longrightarrow \left[\quad \longleftrightarrow \quad \right] \xrightarrow{X^-} \text{product} \qquad (99)$$

The stereochemistry observed is not necessarily inconsistent with this scheme; however, more data will be required to identify the origin of the stereospecificity (*903*).

Replacements on Nitrogen. Treatment of 1-chloroaziridine with lithium ethylenimide yields the hydrazine derivative, 1,1'-biaziridine (*1510, 1512*). This method is unsuitable for the preparation of acyclic alkylhydrazines owing to the ready dehydrohalogenation of *N*-chloroalkylamines by alkylamide anions, but it may be applied to the corresponding EI derivatives since dehydrohalogenation in this case would result in formation of the highly strained azirine ring (*1510*).

Other replacements of groups attached to the aziridine nitrogen atom include those shown in Eqs 100 (*1531*), 101 (*2148, 2151*), and 102 (*2817*). The deethylation of 1-ethylaziridine in 102 is not described experimentally, and appears improbable (see p. 226).

$$\underset{\text{Az}}{\underset{|}{O_{\diagdown P \diagup}O}} \quad + \quad \text{HOAc} \quad \longrightarrow \quad \text{AzAc} \quad + \quad \underset{\text{OH}}{\underset{|}{O_{\diagdown P \diagup}O}} \qquad (100)$$

$$\underset{(NR_2)}{AzCH_2OR} \quad + \quad Ac_2O \quad \longrightarrow \quad AzAc \quad + \quad \underset{(NR_2)}{AcOCH_2OR} \qquad (101)$$

$$AzEt \quad + \quad H_2O_2 \quad \longrightarrow \quad AzOH \quad + \quad CH_2{=}CH_2 \qquad (102)$$

Ring-Destroying Reactions of Aziridines

INTRODUCTION

Ring opening was referred to many times in the previous section, which dealt with reactions of aziridines as amines, i.e., with ring-preserving reactions. This was necessary in order to indicate precautions and techniques required to avoid ring opening. In this section, emphasis is directed toward the characteristics of various ring-opening reactions and to conditions necessary for realization of specific reactions.

As mentioned previously, most ring-opening reactions may be formulated as nucleophilic substitutions involving attack of a nucleophile at an aziridine carbon. The nature of the substituent on the aziridine nitrogen determines certain characteristics for such reaction. The broad classification of aziridines into two groups of compounds, activated aziridines and aziridines possessing a basic nitrogen, is based primarily on the reactivity of these compounds toward nucleophilic reagents. Activated aziridines have been defined as those derivatives possessing a nitrogen substituent capable of stabilizing a negative charge which is formed on the aziridine nitrogen in the transition state when the compound reacts with a nucleophile, e.g., 1-acetylaziridine (*1583*).

The ability of the substituent to conjugate with the partial negative charge on the aziridine nitrogen in **30** greatly reduces the activation energy needed to attain this state from that required to attain the transition state **31**. Also, such substituents conjugate more readily with nonaziridine than with aziridine nitrogen. Thus, for a basic aziridine to undergo ring opening with a nucleophile under ordinary conditions, the nitrogen must first be positively charged (e.g., by addition of acid) whereas the activated aziridines readily undergo such ring opening.

$$MeC(=O)-N\underset{CH_2}{\overset{CH_2}{\diagdown}} + X^- \longrightarrow \left[Me-C\overset{\delta^-}{\underset{}{\overset{O}{\diagdown}}}\cdots N\overset{..}{\underset{CH_2}{\overset{..CH_2\cdots X^{\delta^-}}{\diagup}}} \right]$$

30

$$H-N\underset{CH_2}{\overset{CH_2}{\diagdown}} + X^- \longrightarrow \left[H-N\overset{\delta^-}{\underset{CH_2}{\overset{..CH_2\cdots X^{\delta^-}}{\diagup}}} \right]$$

31

Ring-destroying reactions will be classified in this section as ring opening of basic, activated, and quaternary aziridines; isomerization of basic and activated aziridines; deamination of aziridines; hydrogenolysis of aziridines; and miscellaneous reactions.

RING-OPENING REACTIONS OF BASIC AZIRIDINES

With Halogen Acids or Water. The description of the first successful preparation of an aziridine (EI) also included its reaction with a halogen acid (*1385*), regenerating the 2-haloethylamine from which it was prepared (Eq 103).

$$XCH_2CH_2NH_2 \underset{HX}{\overset{NaOH}{\rightleftarrows}} AzH \tag{103}$$

Thus it was established early that both 1- and 2-substituted aziridines readily undergo ring opening with halogen acids (*1342, 1384, 1385, 1388, 1389, 2428, 3301*). Both the forward and the reverse reactions shown in Eq 103 have been shown to proceed quantitatively in the presence of base and of excess HX, respectively. Attempts to measure equilibrium constants for Eq 104 have generally been unsuccessful owing to competition of various reagents with X^- for the aziridinium ion (*1339, 1342, 1343*; see also pp. 5 and 26).

$$XCHRCH_2NH_2 \rightleftharpoons 2\text{-}RAzH_2^+ \ X^- \tag{104}$$

The kinetic expression for reaction of EI with HBr from early work is given in Eq 105 (*1339*).

$$\text{rate} = k[\text{AzH}][\text{Br}^-] \tag{105}$$

It is clear from later work (*1018, 3130, 3131*), that a more accurate expression and depiction is Eq 106.

$$rate = k[AzH_2^+][Br^-]$$

$$AzH + HBr \rightleftharpoons AzH_2^+ + Br^- \quad rapid \tag{106}$$

$$AzH_2^+ + Br^- \longrightarrow BrCH_2CH_2NH_2 \quad rate\text{-}determining$$

From kinetic, stereochemical, and product distribution studies and data reflecting the effect of nucleophilicity of the reagent on rate, the mechanism for ring opening of carbon-unsubstituted aziridines by nucleophiles has been established as an S_N2 displacement at the aziridine carbon atom.

$$\overset{\delta-}{X}\cdots CH_2\cdots\overset{\delta+}{NH_2}$$
$$| \quad \diagup$$
$$CH_2$$

Such reactions involving carbon-unsubstituted aziridines have sometimes been incorrectly represented as involving primary carbonium ions (most often in disciplines other than organic chemistry); such aziridinium ions should *not* be considered in equilibrium with primary carbonium ions (*791*). Indeed, the S_N2 course of reaction of protonated EI with water (a very weak nucleophile) is so well established that the reaction (along with other reactions of established mechanism) has been used as a criterion for defining parameters which would indicate the role of water in the rate-determining step (*536*). The claim that 1 mole of EI dissolves in 2 moles of water to form a "chelated ethanolamine hydrate" (*2827*) is completely untenable.

For aziridines which possess substituents on carbon, the mechanism for such ring-opening reactions is not clearly defined as an S_N1 or an S_N2 type. Treatment of 2,2-dimethylaziridine with aqueous HCl leads to 1-methyl-1-(chloromethyl)ethylamine (*1095*) and 1-amino-2-methyl-2-propanol (*3130, 3131*). The mechanism proposed to account for these products is shown in Eq 107 (*3131*).

$$\begin{array}{c} Me \\ \diagup \\ \diagdown Me \\ N+ \\ \diagup \diagdown \\ H \quad H \end{array} \quad \overset{S_N2}{\nearrow} \quad [Me_2\overset{+}{C}CH_2NH_2] \quad \overset{H_2O}{\longrightarrow} \quad Me_2C(OH)CH_2NH_2 \quad \mathbf{32}$$

$$\overset{Cl^-}{\underset{S_N2}{\searrow}} \quad Me_2C(NH_2)CH_2Cl \quad \mathbf{33} \tag{107}$$

Rough rate data obtained in the above work was consistent with Eq 108.

$$rate = (k_1 + k_2[X^-])[\text{aziridinium ion}] \tag{108}$$

where k_1 is the first-order rate constant for the S_N1 process (formation of **32**); k_2 is the second-order rate constant for the S_N2 process (formation of **33**); and X⁻ is a nucleophilic reagent (chloride ion). In this work the amount of **32** formed served as the quantitative measure of that portion of reaction which had occurred by an S_N1 process. Hydration of 2,2-dimethylaziridine with aqueous perchloric acid was found to yield 2-amino-2-methyl-1-propanol (about 20% of the distilled product) in addition to **32** ($\approx 80\%$) (*1018*). An S_N2 reaction involving water is thus indicated to occur to some extent in the absence of nucleophilic anions. Similar perchloric acid hydration of 2-ethyl-aziridine yielded about 22% 1-amino-2-butanol and 61% 2-amino-1-butanol. This was interpreted as indicating that with 2-ethylaziridine the hydrolysis of the ring is primarily S_N2 with possibly a small S_N1 contribution (*1018*).

It has been suggested that nucleophilic substitutions on aziridines involve competitive S_N1 and S_N2 processes, the latter being dominant for aziridines with primary carbon atoms, both being important for aziridines with secondary carbon atoms, and the former being the main path for aziridines with tertiary carbon atoms (*525, 1018, 3131*). It is noteworthy, however, that studies on the stereochemistry of ring opening by water or halogen acids with aziridines in which both carbon atoms are secondary have shown the reaction to occur with inversion at the reaction site (Eq 109).

$$R = R' = Me, R'' = H \ (910)$$
$$R = R' = Ph, R'' = H \ (3762, 3763)$$
$$R + R' = (CH_2)_n, \ n = 3, 4, 5; \ R'' = H \ (1098, 2820, 3483, 3814, 3853)$$
$$R = Me, R' = Bz \ or \ p\text{-}MeC_6H_4CO, \ R'' = PhCH_2 \ or \ c\text{-}C_6H_{11} \ (804)$$
$$R + R' = (CH_2)_4, \ R'' = Me \ (2627)$$
$$R + R' = \text{fused steroid ring}, R'' = H \ (1621)$$

One study (*804*) postulated that an S_N1 (along with an S_N2) mechanism was operative even though inversion had occurred. Also it has been suggested that such a steric result is not necessarily incompatible with an S_N1 mechanism because in the transition state the carbonium ion being formed is shielded by the departing nitrogen atom (525).

It is probable that an accurate representation of ring opening will not be found solely in the classical descriptions of S_N1 and S_N2 mechanism. Available data suggest that a transition from an S_N1 to an S_N2 mechanism occurs as aziridine carbon atoms are changed from tertiary to primary. These probably represent limiting cases, however. It is instructive to compare formulations put forth for epoxide ring-opening reactions wherein S_N processes approaching S_N1 or S_N2, differing in relative proportions of bond forming and bond breaking, are considered [2822, 3062; see also Streitweiser (3395) for a general discussion of nucleophilic displacement reactions].

In addition to evidence cited for the S_N1 mechanism for aziridines possessing tertiary carbon atoms (positional isomers formed, rate expression shown as Eq 108), thermodynamic activation parameters for hydrolysis of aziridines, shown in Table 3-XXI, have been considered to indicate existence of the S_N1 path (1018).

In accord with Eq 108, when X is a strong nucleophile (e.g., SCN⁻) virtually the only reaction realized for 2,2-dimethylaziridine is an S_N2 substitution at the primary carbon atom. The effect on the rate of changing the nucleophilicity of X has been measured for such substitution with EI, 1-butylaziridine, 2-ethylaziridine, and 2,2-dimethylaziridine (1018). The rings are opened at relative rates which are normal for displacements in rate-determining steps. These rate constants, as well as those for first-order hydrolysis rate constants, are shown in Table 3-XXI.

From the Table it may be noted that, in general, substitution of alkyl groups at one of the aziridine ring carbon atoms increases the rate for ring opening by nucleophiles if the fact that EI has two available reaction sites is taken into account. Alkyl groups on the aziridine nitrogen cause a decrease in rate compared with that for the unsubstituted compound, except that if the alkyl group contains an electronegative group (e.g., OAc or CN) the rate is increased.

The basicity of 1-alkylaziridines and the reactivity of their conjugate acids toward bromide ion are related. For five such compounds an excellent linear relationship was found between log K_B (basicity constant) and log k_2 (second-order rate constant) (963). As would be expected, the most basic 1-alkylaziridine is the least reactive.

A number of rate studies have been reported for the disappearance of aziridines in aqueous solutions of different pH established by buffers (106, 331, 343a, 1416, 1759, 3719). Such measurements do not necessarily reflect the rate of hydrolysis of the aziridine ring since the buffer anion (e.g., acetate, borate, or phosphate) may successfully compete with water for the protonated

Table 3-XXI

RATE CONSTANTS FOR RING OPENING OF BASIC AZIRIDINES BY NUCLEOPHILES

$$AzH_2^+ + X^- \text{ (or HX)} \rightarrow XCH_2CH_2NH_2$$

Aziridine substituents	Nucleophile, X⁻ or HX	T (°C)	$k = k^0 \times 10^{-n}$ (liter mole⁻¹ sec⁻¹)		$\Delta H^{\ddagger}$ (kcal mole⁻¹)	$\Delta S^{\ddagger}$ (e.u. mole⁻¹)	$\Delta V^{\ddagger}$ (cm³ mole⁻¹)	References
			k^0	n				
None	H_2O^a	21	4.61	7	—	—	—	1018
	H_2O^a	25	5.17	7	—	—	—	1018
	H_2O^a	45	9.76	6	—	—	—	1018
	H_2O^a	65	8.15	5	23.0	—	—	1018
	H_2O^a	65	1.05	4	—	−9.4	—	525
	H_2O^a	65	1.12	4	—	—	—	258
	H_2O^a	21	4.43[b]	7	—	—	1.8	1018
	H_2O^a	65	1.22[c]	6	—	—	—	258
	H_2O^a	65	1.33[d]	6	—	—	—	258
	H_2O^a	65	1.43[e]	6	—	—	−2.4	258
	D_2O	37	4.3	4	—	—	—	2310
	OAc⁻	25	5.18	6	—	—	—	1018
	Cl⁻	25	5.48	6	—	—	—	1018
	Br⁻	25	2.85	5	—	—	—	1018
	Br⁻	25	3.38	5	—	—	—	963
	SCN⁻	25	2.30	4	—	—	—	1018
	I⁻	25	4.36	4	—	—	—	1018
	$S_2O_3^{2-}$	25	5.36	3	—	—	—	1018
2-Me	H_2O^a	65	1.17	4	—	—	—	525
2-Et	H_2O^a	21	2.64	7	—	—	—	1018
	H_2O^a	25	4.58	7	—	—	—	1018
	H_2O^a	45	5.83	6	—	—	—	1018

	H_2O^a	65	5.33	5	23.1	-10.0	—	*1018*
	H_2O^a	65	7.00	5	—	—	—	*525*
	H_2O^a	21	2.79^b	7	—	—	-2.5	*1018*
	OAc⁻	25	2.96	6	—	—	—	*1018*
	Cl⁻	25	3.56	6	—	—	—	*1018*
	Br⁻	25	1.78	5	—	—	—	*1018*
	SCN⁻	25	1.45	4	—	—	—	*1018*
	I⁻	25	1.68	4	—	—	—	*1018*
	$S_2O_3^{2-}$	25	5.92	3	—	—	—	*1018*
2,3-Me₂ cis	H_2O^a	65	1.15	4	—	—	—	*525*
2,3-Me₂ trans	H_2O^a	65	8.17	5	—	—	—	*525*
2,2-Me₂	H_2O^a	21	2.10	6	—	—	—	*1018*
	H_2O^a	25	3.63	6	—	—	—	*1018*
	H_2O^a	40	2.90	5	—	—	—	*1018*
	H_2O^a	45	5.23	5	24.3	-1.9	—	*1018*
	H_2O^a	65	6.17	4	—	—	-4.4	*525*
	H_2O^a	21	2.32^b	6	—	—	—	*1018*
	OAc⁻	25	4.73	6	—	—	—	*1018*
	Cl⁻	25	7.56	6	—	—	—	*1018*
	Br⁻	25	3.3	5	—	—	—	*1018*
	SCN⁻	25	2.43	4	—	—	—	*1018*
	I⁻	25	2.97	4	—	—	—	*1018*
	SC(NH₂)₂	25	6.80	4	—	—	—	*1018*
	$S_2O_3^{2-}$	25	4.88	3	23.6	—	—	*1018*
2-Et-2-Ph	H_2O	25	—	—	—	—	—	*1026*
1-Me	Br⁻	25	1.35	5	—	—	—	*963*
1-Et	Br⁻	25	1.17	5	—	—	—	*963*
1-Bu	H_2O^a	25	3	6	—	—	—	*1018*
	OAc⁻	25	2.2	6	—	—	—	*1018*
	Cl⁻	25	1	6	—	—	—	*1018*
	Br⁻	25	8.3	6	—	—	—	*1018*
	Br⁻	25	1.23	5	—	—	—	*963*

Table 3-XXI—*continued*

Aziridine substituents	Nucleophile, X⁻ or HX	T (°C)	$k = k^0 \times 10^{-n}$ (liter mole⁻¹ sec⁻¹)		$\Delta H^{\ddagger}$ (kcal mole⁻¹)	$\Delta S^{\ddagger}$ (e.u. mole⁻¹)	$\Delta V^{\ddagger}$ (cm³ mole⁻¹)	References
			k^0	n				
1-Bu	SCN⁻	25	1.10	4	—	—	—	1018
	S₂O₃²⁻	25	3.50	3	—	—	—	1018
1-CH₂CH=CH₂	Br⁻	25	4.74	5	—	—	—	963
1-CH₂CH₂OH	Br⁻	25	5.97	5	—	—	—	963
1-CH₂CHNHCO₂Et	Br⁻	25	1.13	4	—	—	—	963
1-CH₂CH₂OAc	Br⁻	25	1.33	4	—	—	—	963
1-CH₂CH₂CN	Br⁻	25	8.24	4	—	—	—	963

[a] k is the measured first-order rate constant for hydration in units of sec⁻¹.

[b] Measured at 555 bar pressure.

[c] Measured at 1000 bar pressure.

[d] Measured at 2000 bar pressure.

[e] Measured at 3000 bar pressure.

aziridine. This is almost certainly true for the reported and otherwise un-accountable increase in rate of EI "degradation" with increased pH (*343a*).

The hydration of 1-aziridinylbenzoquinones has been reported to be very rapid in acid solutions [$t_{1/2} = 1.1$ second for 2,5-bis(1-aziridinyl)benzoquinone] (*293*) compared with that of 1-unsubstituted basic aziridines (*106, 293, 331, 1759, 3719*). Such substituents on an aziridine nitrogen would be expected to markedly increase reactivity of the protonated ring. Indeed, the 1-aziridinyl quinones may more closely resemble activated aziridines than basic aziridines in reactions (see p. 248).

Of interest is the low rate for hydration of 3,3-dimethyl-2,2-diphenylaziridine (*2101*). The compound was recovered unchanged after heating at reflux for 30 minutes in $3N$ sulfuric acid. Also remarkable is the observation that aziridine derivatives **34** could be recovered unchanged after treatment with alcoholic HCl at room temperature when Ar was *p*-nitrophenyl (*162*).

When Ar was phenyl, *p*-tolyl, or *p*-chlorophenyl the expected ring-opening reaction occurred. Lower basicity of the *p*-nitrophenyl derivative was suggested as the reason for its resistance to reaction.

When an unsymmetrically carbon-substituted aziridine undergoes ring opening, formation of two positional isomers is possible (Eq 110).

(110)

Knowledge and generalizations concerning the isomer distribution for such reactions would be of value for mechanistic considerations. However, in much of the work reported only one of the isomers was isolated (sometimes in low yield) and where both were isolated and the distribution determined, the combined yield was seldom nearly quantitative. The problem is fraught with other difficulties, shown in a series of papers on reactions of 3-aroyl-2-aryl-aziridines with halogen acids (*788, 792, 793, 798, 804*). It was found that isomer distribution was dependent on a number of factors, some of which are listed below:

    (a) The use of the cis or trans derivative.
    (b) The use of excess hydrogen halide.
    (c) The concentration of reactants.
    (d) The presence of excess halide ion.
    (e) The choice of solvent.

Table 3-XXII

POSITIONAL ISOMERS FROM RING OPENING OF BASIC AZIRIDINES WITH WATER OR HALOGEN ACIDS

$$R^2R^3C{-}CR^4R^5 \;(N^+{-}R^1H) + X^- \longrightarrow R^2R^3CXC(NHR^1)R^4R^5 \;(I) \quad \text{and/or} \quad R^2R^3C(NHR^1)CXR^4R^5 \;(II)$$

X	R^1	R^2	R^3	R^4	% Yield of I and II	Isomer composition		References
						% I	% II	
H_2O	H	Et	H	H	83	26	74	1018
H_2O	H	Ph	H	H	—	Only	—	3824
H_2O	Me	Ph	H	Me	—	Only	—	3489
H_2O	H	Me	Me	H	—	Only	—	560
H_2O	H	Me	Me	H	100	85	15	1018
H_2O	H	Me	Me	H	95	Only	—	3131
H_2O	$(CH_2)_3NH_3^+$	Me	Me	H	72	Only	—	3499
H_2O	H	Me	Bu	H	—	Only	—	1697
H_2O	H	Et	Ph	H	—	Only	—	568, 1026
H_2O	H	Pr	Ph	H	—	Only	—	568
H_2O	H	Et	Et	Me	—	Only	—	1697
H_2O	H	Pr	Pr	Et	—	Only	—	1697
H_2O	H	Et	Ph	Me	—	Only	—	568
H_2O	H	Pr	Ph	Me	—	Only	—	1697
H_2O	H	Pr	Ph	Et	—	Only	—	1697
H_2O	H	Ph	Ph	Me[a]	—	Only	—	566
H_2O	H	Ph	Ph	CO_2H	83	Only	—	2101
H_2O	H	H	H	CO_2H	90	92	8	1553
H_2O	H	H	H	CO_2-iso-Pr	86	Only	—	2215

HX	R^1	R^2	R^3	Yield (%)	Minor	Major	IR
H_2O	$PhCH_2$	H	Me	73	Only	—	2928
H_2O	H	Ph	$CO_2\text{-}iso\text{-}Pr$	—	Only	—	1382
H_2O	Aziridine = 1,2-epimino-1,2,3,4-H_4-naphthalene		$R^3 + R^4 = (CH_2)_6$	—	The 1-HO-2-H_2N compound only		984
H_2O	Aziridine = 5,6-epiminodibenzo[a,c]cycloheptane			—	The 5-HO-6-H_2N compound only		3242
Cl	H	Me	H		Only	—	1387, 3473
Cl	H	Ph	H		14	86	3824
Cl	H	Me	H		Only	—	3131
Cl	iso-Pr	Me	Me		69	31	1694
Cl	H	H	CO_2H	—	47	53	1553
Br	H	H	CO_2H	—	Only	—	1553
Cl	$c\text{-}C_6H_{11}$	H	CO_2H	86	62	38	3723
Cl	H	H	CO_2Et	77	42	58	1363
Cl	H	H	CO_2Et	83	63	37	1364, 1553
Cl	H	H	$CO_2\text{-}iso\text{-}Pr$	70	Only	—	1363
Cl	$PhCH_2$	H	CO_2Me	—	Only	—	3390
Cl	Et	Ph	CO_2Et	75	Only	—	2624
Cl	$PhCH_2$	Ph	CO_2Et	—	Only	—	2624
Cl	$c\text{-}C_6H_{11}$	Ph	CO_2Et	89	Only	—	2624
Cl	$c\text{-}C_6H_{11}$	H	$CONH_2$	96	Only	—	3723
Cl	H	H	CONHOH	86	Only	—	3311, 3314
Cl	$PhCH_2$	H	CONHOH	—	Only	—	3312
Cl	$PhCH_2CH_2$	H	CONHOH	—	Only	—	2078, 3314
Cl	Ph_2CH	H	CONHOH	—	Only	—	3312, 3314
Cl	Ph_3C	H	CONHOH	46	Only	—	3312
Cl	Et	Ph	CONHEt	—	Only	—	2624
Cl	$PhCH_2$	Ph	$CONHCH_2Ph$	75	Only	—	2624
Cl	$PhCH_2$	H	CN	96	Both formed		3723
Cl	$c\text{-}C_6H_{11}$	H	CN	95	Only	—	3723
Br	Me	H	CN	55	—	Only	125
Br	iso-Pr	H	CN	75	—	Only	125, 3723
Br	$PhCH_2$	H	CN	43	—	Only	125, 3723

Table 3-XXII—*continued*

X	R¹	R²	R³	R⁴	% Yield of I and II	% I	% II	References
Br	c-C₆H₁₁	H	CN		67	—	Only	125
Cl	Me	H	Bz		30	0	100	1904
Cl	Me	Me	Bz		68	29	71	1904
Cl	Me	Ph	Bz		57	67	33	1904
Cl	Me	Ph	Ac		36	83	17	1904
Cl	R¹ + R² = (CH₂CH₂CH₂)		CO₂Et	H	—	Only	—	2527
Cl	R¹ + R² = (CH₂CH₂NHCO)		Ph	H	—	—	Only	2623
Cl	Aziridine = 5,6-epiminodibenzo[a,c]cycloheptane				—	The 5-Cl-6-NH₂ only		3241
F	Aziridine = a mitomycin containing the [ring structure with N—Me] moiety				—	The [ring structure with F, NHMe] moiety only		2541

^{a} In this case the carbon atom bearing this group carried a methyl group instead of hydrogen.

Thus it is not surprising that discrepancies appear between reports for isomer distributions, as may be discerned for the ring-opening reactions with water or halogen acids shown in Table 3-XXII.

It has also been found that the isomer distribution depends on the nucleophilicity of the attacking species (X^-), as shown in Table 3-XXIII.

Table 3-XXIII

ORIENTATION OF RING OPENING OF AZIRIDINES BY VARIOUS NUCLEOPHILES

Aziridine $$R^2-\underset{\underset{N}{\underset{|}{\overset{|}{C}}}-\overset{\overset{R^3}{|}}{\underset{|}{C}}-$$ R^1	Nucleophile HX	% Product		
		C-substituted	C-substituted	References
$R^1 = H$, $R^2 = R^3 = Me$	H_2O	85	15	*1018*
	HSCN	0	100	*1018*
$R^1 = R^3 = H$	H_2O	8	92	*1553*
$R^2 = CO_2H$	HCl	31	69	*1553*
	HBr	53	47	*1553*
	AcSH	Only	—	*1553*
$R^1 = c\text{-}C_6H_{11}$	HCl aq.	Only	—	*3723*
$R^2 = CN$, $R^3 = H$	HBr aq.	—	Only	*3723*

It would appear that for every unsymmetrically carbon-substituted aziridine, reaction of a nucleophile occurs with more bond making in the transition state (or more S_N2 character) at one carbon atom than at the other. In other words, every such unsymmetrical aziridine may be considered to contain a more "S_N1-susceptible" carbon atom and a more "S_N2-susceptible" carbon atom. Thus, the greater the nucleophilicity of the attacking species, the greater will be the proportion of product derivable from reaction at the more "S_N2-susceptible" carbon atom. It would also appear that changes in reaction conditions which are expected to increase the rate of an S_N1 or else an S_N2 type reaction will alter the isomer distribution in a corresponding manner. For 3-aroyl-2-arylaziridines, the reaction with HCl produced a greater proportion of α-chloro ketone in the presence of excess chloride ion, added as tetraethylammonium chloride, than in HCl alone, even though it was shown that reaction at either aziridine carbon atom involved a Walden inversion (*804*).

Ring opening by halogen acids or water are among the oldest and most often reported reactions for aziridines. It would be of little value to attempt to list every example which has appeared in the literature, but the following references are cited since they would not otherwise be included in the bibliography (*187, 853, 1908, 2405, 2462, 3683, 4185, 4186*). These reactions are not usually of preparative value since the products, 2-haloethylamine hydrohalides or 2-aminoalkanols, are often starting materials for the aziridine preparations. In a few cases the reactions have found utility for preparation of an acyclic intermediate for subsequent ring closure to a different heterocyclic compound (*1594, 3379*), as shown in Eq 111 (*1363, 1364, 2078, 3312, 3314, 3521*).

$$\tag{111}$$

Spontaneous consecutive reactions after opening of the aziridine rings in **34a** by acid or base led to the polynuclear heterocyclic products shown (*4120*).

34a

The hydrolysis of substituted aziridine rings does not result in rearrangements as frequently as that of epoxides of similar structure. One such example of rearrangement, however, is the hydration of 8-azadibenzo[3.2.2.0^{7,9}]tricyclo-nonadiene in dilute sulfuric acid to yield *syn*-8-aminodibenzo[3.2.1]bicyclo-octadien-*exo*-2-ol (*2103*). Also of interest is the hydrolysis of 2,2,3,3-tetraphenylaziridine, yielding benzophenone, tetraphenylethylene, and tetraphenylethylene oxide (*3738*).

The hydrolytic ring opening of EI provides a good example of the major problem which must be overcome to achieve good yields of ring-opened products from aziridines and nucleophilic reagents. Water is sufficiently acidic to provide a very low concentration of aziridinium ion ($10^7 K_B = 7.92$).

$$AzH + H_2O \rightleftharpoons AzH_2^+ + OH^-$$

The aziridinium ion will then undergo reaction with the various nucleophilic reagents present at rates corresponding to the nucleophilicity of the reagents. Thus, for a solution of EI in water, the rate expression for the initial reaction of aziridinium ion can be represented as

$$rate = (k_I[H_2O] + k_{II}[OH^-] + k_{III}[AzH])[AzH_2^+]$$

Data have been reported (*2000*) which allow an estimation of the Swain nucleophilic constant n (*3445*) for EI as about 4.4 to 4.7 (compared to 4.20 for OH^- and 0.00 for water). Since k_{III} is very much greater than k_I and the concentration of EI is much, much greater than the concentration of hydroxide ion, it is clear that virtually the only initial reaction which will be realized is that represented by

$$rate = k_{III}[AzH_2^+][AzH]$$

The initial product is thus 1-(2-aminoethyl)aziridine, which contains an acyclic amino group that is even more nucleophilic than EI. Also, this product represents the first stage of polymerization of EI; and indeed polyethylenimine (PEI) is virtually the only product obtained from such a reaction mixture. In order to force the reaction to produce 2-aminoethanol, one may convert all the EI to aziridinium ion by adding a strong acid, HB.

$$AzH + HB \rightleftharpoons AzH_2^+ + B^-$$

The rate expression can then be represented by:

$$rate = (k_I[H_2O] + k_{III}[AzH] + k_{IV}[B^-])[AzH_2^+]$$

Obviously, the anion of the strong acid must be one of low nucleophilicity (the term $k_{IV}[B^-]$ must be negligible compared to $k_I[H_2O]$) and sufficient acid must be added to cause complete conversion of both the EI and the acyclic amine product (2-aminoethanol) into the protonated form.

Solvolysis of 2-Alkoxy-, 2-Halo-, and 2,2-Dihaloaziridines. The existence and hydrolysis of a 2-alkoxyaziridine (**35**) as an intermediate in the Neber rearrangement was postulated as early as 1926 (Eq 112) (*2685*).

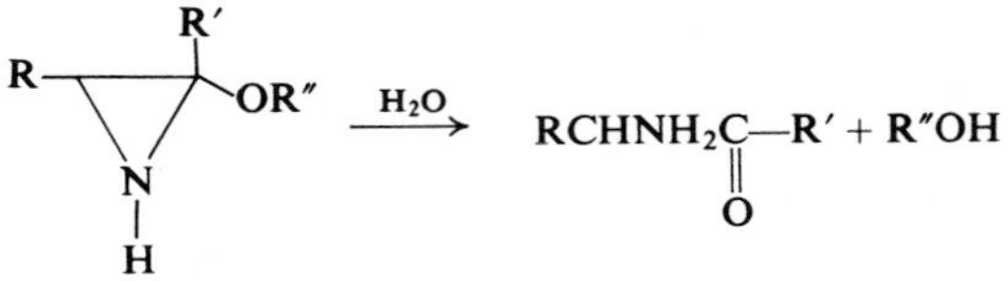

$$R-\overset{R'}{\underset{\underset{H}{\overset{|}{N}}}{\triangle}}OR'' \xrightarrow{H_2O} RCHNH_2C\overset{\overset{\displaystyle O}{\|}}{-}R' + R''OH \qquad (112)$$

35

Later work confirmed this suggestion (*777, 1630, 2235, 2739, 2818*); compare p. 63. The base-induced conversion of a 1-unsubstituted-2-alkoxyaziridine into an azirine is related (Eq 113) (*2818*).

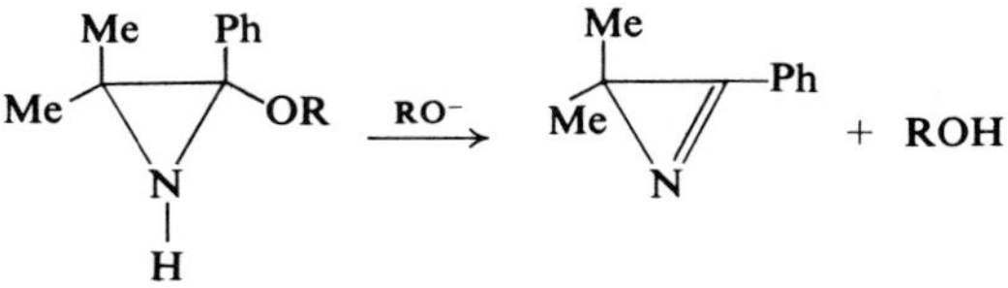

$$\overset{Me \quad Ph}{\underset{\underset{H}{\overset{|}{N}}}{Me\triangle}}OR \xrightarrow{RO^-} \overset{Me}{\underset{N}{Me\triangle}}Ph + ROH \qquad (113)$$

The alcoholysis of a 2-haloaziridine may produce a 2-alkoxyaziridine which is stable or one which undergoes further solvolysis, depending on the structure. Heating 1,2-diphenyl-2-chloro-2-methylaziridine in methanol in the presence of methoxide ion produced the dimethyl ketal of the amino ketone. Formation of a ketal under basic conditions was considered to preclude a carbonyl precursor and to indicate the intermediacy of the 2-alkoxyaziridine (Eq 114) (*903*).

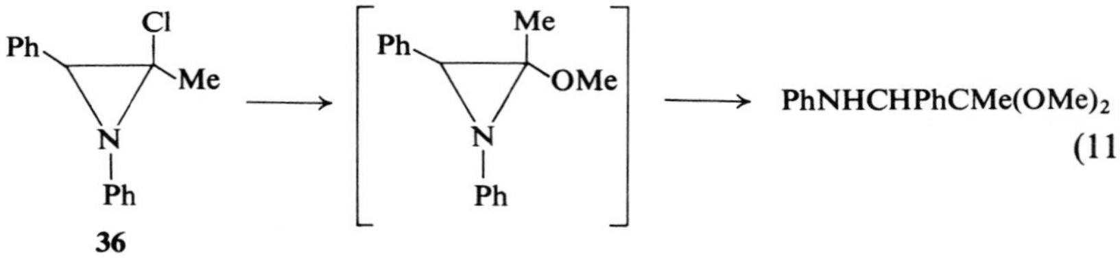

$$\overset{Cl}{\underset{\underset{Ph}{\overset{|}{N}}}{Ph\triangle}}Me \longrightarrow \left[\overset{Me}{\underset{\underset{Ph}{\overset{|}{N}}}{Ph\triangle}}OMe\right] \longrightarrow PhNHCHPhCMe(OMe)_2 \qquad (114)$$

36

The alcoholysis of 1,2-diphenyl-2-chloroaziridine under similar conditions gave the 2-alkoxyaziridine. The stability of this aziridine towards methoxide ion in methanol (along with other evidence) was considered to indicate that the mechanism for ring opening involved a unimolecular rupture of the bond between the aziridine nitrogen and the alkoxy-substituted carbon atoms (*903*).

Treating **36** with potassium *tert*-butoxide in *tert*-butyl alcohol gave 3-phenyl-propionanilide instead of the product to be expected from Eq 114. Intermediates resulting from initial dehydrohalogenation were suggested (Eq 115) (*904*).

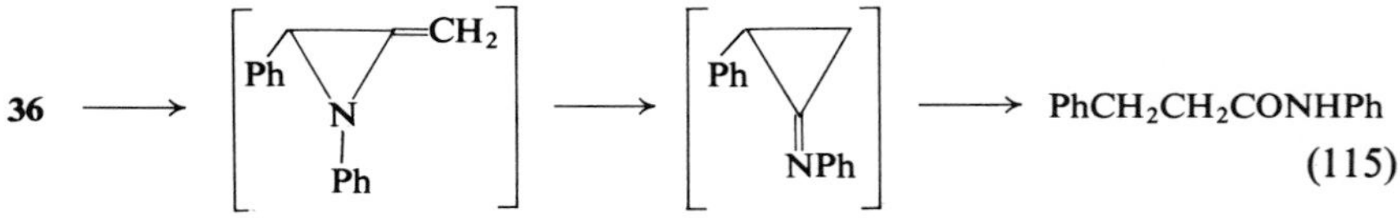

$$\mathbf{36} \longrightarrow \left[\overset{=CH_2}{\underset{\underset{Ph}{\overset{|}{N}}}{Ph\triangle}}\right] \longrightarrow \left[\underset{NPh}{\overset{Ph}{\triangle}}\right] \longrightarrow PhCH_2CH_2CONHPh \qquad (115)$$

However, 1-benzoyl-2-chloro-2-phenyl-3-methyl-(or phenyl)-aziridine with the same base in ether underwent dehydrochlorination only, forming the azirine (*4057*).

In Eq 116 a 2-chloroaziridine appears to undergo a typical ring opening by HCl; in Eq 117 a presumed 2-alkoxyaziridine intermediate undergoes extensive rearrangement in acid (*1441*, *2699*, *2700*).

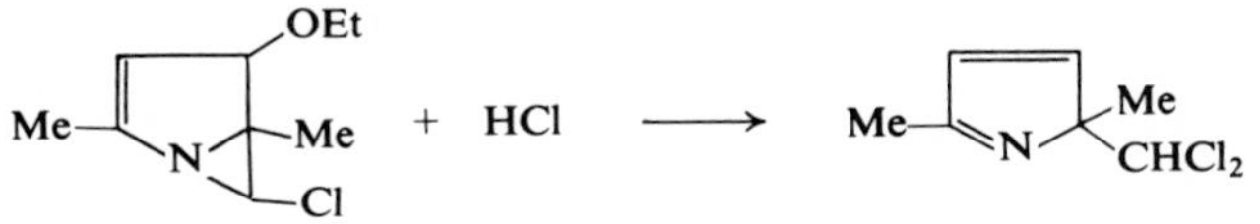
OEt
Me
Me
N
Cl
+ HCl
Me
N
Me
$CHCl_2$

(116)

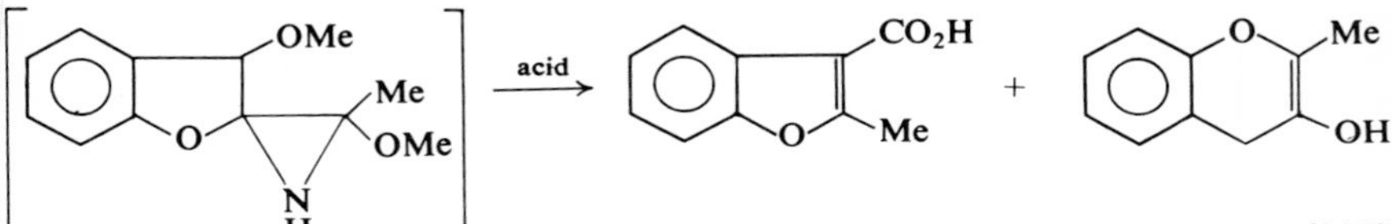
OMe
Me
OMe
O
N
H
acid
CO_2H
Me
O
+
O
Me
OH

(117)

The solvolysis of 2,2-dichloroaziridines (**37**) produces rearranged products (Eq 118) (*753*, *903*, *1288*, *1655*, *1882*, *2013*, *3104*).

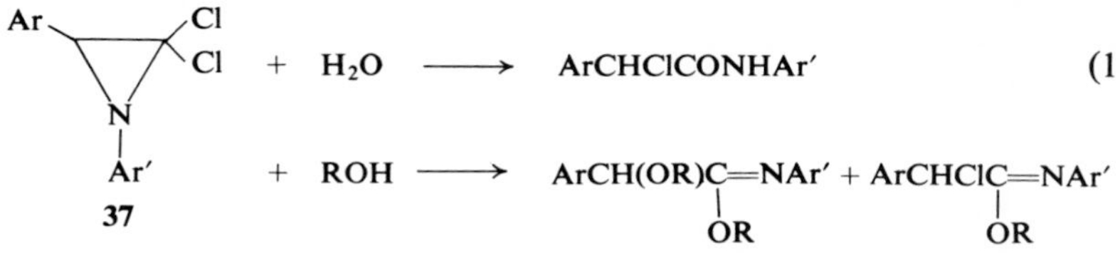
Ar
Cl
Cl
N
Ar′
+ H_2O
ArCHClCONHAr′
+ ROH
ArCH(OR)C=NAr′ + ArCHClC=NAr′
OR
OR

37

(118)

A mechanism suggested for this solvolysis (*496*, *502*) is consistent with S_N displacements on 2-monochloroaziridines (see p. 204) and also appears applicable to the pyrolytic rearrangement (*1655*, *1882*) shown (Eq 119).

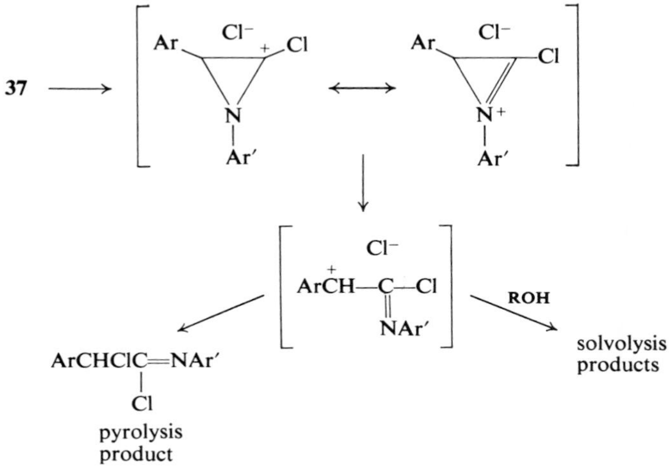
37
Ar
Cl^-
Cl
N
Ar′
Ar
Cl^-
Cl
N^+
Ar′
Cl^-
$Ar\overset{+}{C}H$—C—Cl
NAr′
ROH
solvolysis
products
ArCHClC=NAr′
Cl
pyrolysis
product

(119)

Formation of ketenimines by the action of iodide ion on 2,2-dichloro-aziridines (*4079*) is clearly interpretable in the same pattern.

$$\text{(aziridine)} \xrightarrow{\text{I}^-} Ph_2C=C=NAr$$

Other Acids. Included here are those acids which contain neither halogen nor carbonyl group. Ring openings by hydrogen sulfide, and thiols, and some thiolic acids are discussed elsewhere (p. 220). The acids cited here and references to their use are as follows.

Acid	References
$H_2S_2O_3$	*458, 2108, 2109, 3060, 3061, 3476, 4020, 4189*
H_2SO_3	*1384, 1388, 1391, 2109, 2428, 3075, 3467*
H_2SO_4	*963, 1391*
$MeSO_3H$	*677*
HSCN	*89, 1018, 1387, 1562, 2626, 4080, 4178*
HN_3	*722b, 1562, 3448*
H_2SeSO_3	*2110*
$RP(O)(OH)_2$	*4083*
$ROP(O)(OH)_2$	*3623*
$ArOP(O)(OH)_2$	*3623*
$ROP(O)(OH)OP(O)(OH)_2$	*3115, 3475*
$(RO)_2P(S)SH$	*2040a*
H_3PO_4	*9, 683*

The reactions with $H_2S_2O_3$, HSCN, and H_2SeSO_3 are carried out by addition of another strong acid to an aqueous mixture of the sodium or potassium salt and the aziridine. One modification uses ammonium thiosulfate (*2108*). Reactions with $H_2S_2O_3$ and HSCN (which yield very nucleophilic anions) are the basis for determining aziridines (p. 446) and proceed essentially quantitatively. Procedures for isolation of the ring-opened products may, however, result in substantially lower recovered yields (*2108, 3060*). The reaction with HSCN may produce either the ring-opened product (*1018*) or a product of subsequent ring closure, a 2-iminothiazolidine (Eq 120) (*1387, 2626*).

$$AzH_2^+ + SCN^- \longrightarrow H_2NCH_2CH_2SCN \longrightarrow \text{(iminothiazolidine)} \quad (120)$$

The reaction of HSCN or $H_2S_2O_3$ with aziridines has been shown to involve trans opening of the aziridine ring (*2626, 2708*).

Ring opening of a basic aziridine by sodium azide in aqueous 2-methoxyethanol has been reported (*1562*). However, it is reasonably clear that the aziridine nitrogen must first be protonated, and even though sodium hydroxide is generated in the reaction, the process in effect constitutes an example of ring opening by hydrazoic acid. In more predictable aziridine ring openings by azide ion, acids were present (*1065, 3448*).

Ring opening by sulfurous acid, one of the oldest known reactions of basic aziridines (*1391*), produces 2-aminoalkanesulfonic acids (Eq 121).

$$AzH_2^+ + HSO_3^- \ \rightarrow \ H_2NCH_2CH_2SO_3H \tag{121}$$

Although heating aqueous solutions of sulfuric acid (yielding the moderately weakly nucleophilic hydrogen sulfate anion) with basic aziridines causes ring opening by water, evaporation of an aqueous mixture of EI and H_2SO_4 gave 2-aminoethyl hydrogen sulfate (*1391*). Decomposition of the reasonably stable aziridinium hydrogen sulfate gives substantial amounts of the same product (*963*). Similarly, ring opening of a 1-substituted aziridine by methanesulfonic acid has been recorded (*677*).

Of interest is a comparison of nitric acid and sulfuric acid. Evaporation of an aqueous mixture of nitric acid and EI, under conditions apparently similar to those used for sulfuric acid, produced the nitric acid salt of 2-aminoethanol (*1391*).

The reaction between hydrogen cyanide and EI fails to give reasonable yields of 2-aminopropionitrile (*3144*). Although cyanide ion is a fairly strong nucleophile, it is also a strong base, and the inability of cyanide ions and aziridinium ions to coexist constitutes a major problem in this reaction (*963*).

The reaction of EI with acids of phosphorus is noteworthy. Treatment with phosphoric acid gives 2-aminoethyl dihydrogen phosphate in 67% yield (Eq 122) (*683*). Alkyl or aryl dihydrogen phosphates react with EI to give 2-aminoethyl alkyl or aryl hydrogen phosphates (Eq 123) (*3115, 3475, 3623*).

$$H_3PO_4 + AzH \ \rightarrow \ (HO)_2P(O)OCH_2CH_2NH_2 \tag{122}$$

$$ROP(O)(OH)_2 + AzH \ \rightarrow \ ROP(O)(OH)OCH_2CH_2NH_2 \tag{123}$$

However, attempts to form 2-aminoethyl dibenzyl phosphate by reaction of dibenzyl hydrogen phosphate with EI yielded only polymers of EI; even under a variety of conditions the dibenzyl hydrogen phosphate was always recovered (*498*). It was also shown that attempted preparation of 2-aminoethyl diethyl phosphate by an alternate route produced a similar product. The reaction sequence shown (Eq 124) appears to offer an adequate explanation (*498*; see also p. 11).

$(EtO)_2P(O)OH + AzH$ ⟶

$(EtO)_2P(O)O^-$ AzH_2^+ ⟶ salt of PEI

(124)

$PhCH_2O_2CNHCH_2CH_2OP(O)(OEt)_2$ $\xrightarrow{H_2/Pd}$ $H_2NCH_2CH_2OP(O)(OEt)_2$

The claimed preparation of tris(2-aminoethyl) phosphate from phosphoric acid and EI (*9*) appears questionable in view of Eq 124.

Alkyl Halides. As just reviewed, treatment of a basic aziridine with an excess of halogen acid gives essentially quantitative yields of a 2-haloethylamine hydrohalide, whereas treatment with catalytic amounts produces polymers (see p. 315). The same antithesis is true for reactive alkyl halides (*1095, 1392, 2428, 3287, 3457, 3461, 3814, 3872*), except that quaternary ammonium salts are formed. For example, treatment of EI or 1-methylaziridine with an excess of methyl iodide gives 2-iodoethyltrimethylammonium iodide, whereas catalytic amounts of such an alkylating agent cause polymerization. Dimerization to piperazines is sometimes possible by control of reaction conditions (p. 318).

With Alcohols. Ring opening of basic aziridines with alcohols to produce 2-alkoxyethylamines is very similar to the reaction with water. The aziridine is converted to its aziridinium ion with at least a stoichiometric amount of strong acid, yielding a very weakly nucleophilic anion, and heated with a large excess of alcohol. Results of such reactions are shown in Table 3-XXIV.

The reaction with unsymmetrically carbon-substituted aziridines may produce positional isomers. When the aziridine possesses a tertiary carbon atom, the product most often reported is that resulting from reaction of the alcohol at this site (*715, 3498, 3499*). Both isomers are formed, however (*1610*).

The reported failure of a fused steroidal aziridine to undergo reaction with methanol in the presence of perchloric acid is almost certainly due to the use of too mild conditions (*1621*).

Of interest is the reaction of EI with polysaccharides (polyglucose, cellulose, starch), reported to convert some hydroxyl groups to 2-aminoethoxy groups (*988, 1036, 1309, 1330, 1410, 1617, 2072, 2718, 2762, 3329, 3827*). The procedures used have not specified the required stoichiometric amounts of a proper strong acid, and it is difficult to reconcile such a product structure with what is known regarding the mechanism for ring-opening alcoholysis.

Work specifically addressed to this question (*1309*) found no aminoethylation at all under alkaline or acid conditions. In acid medium the cellulose is not swelled enough to react, and attempts to overcome this difficulty by using

Table 3-XXIV

RING OPENING OF BASIC AZIRIDINES WITH ALCOHOLS

$$AzH_2^+ + ROH \rightarrow ROCH_2CH_2NH_3^+$$

Aziridine substituents	Acid	R	% Yield	References
None	Picric acid	Me	91	715
None	Picric acid	Et	88	715
None	H_2SO_4	Me	52	1610
None	H_2SO_4	Et	70	1610
None	H_2SO_4	Pr	51	963
None	HBF_3OR	Me	91	1610
None	HBF_3OR	Et	87	1610
None	HBF_3OR	Pr	92	1610
None	HBF_3OR	iso-Pr	80	1610
None	HBF_3OR	Bu	75	1610
None	HBF_3OR	sec-Bu	85	1610
None	HBF_3OR	iso-Bu	73	1610
None	HBF_3OR	n-C_5H_{11}	85	1610
None	HBF_3OR	c-C_6H_{11}	75	1610
None	HBF_4	tert-Bu	48	1610
None	HBF_4	$PhCH_2$	51	1610
None	HBF_4	$PhCH_2CH_2$	55	1610
None	HBF_4	BuO_2CCH_2	—	2867
2-Me	HBF_3OR	Me	88	1610
2-Me	HBF_3OR	Et	86	1610
2-Et	Picric acid	Me	80	715
2-Et	Picric acid	Et	86	715
2-Et	HBF_3OR	Me	91	1610
2-Et	HBF_3OR	Et	95	1610
2,2-Me_2	Picric acid	Me	83	715
2,2-Me_2	HBF_3OR	Et	93	1610
2,2-Me_2	HBF_3OR	Pr	93	1610
2,2-Me_2	HBF_3OR	iso-Pr	82	1610
2,2-Me_2	HBF_3OR	Bu	95	1610
2,2-Me_2	HBF_3OR	sec-Bu	78	1610
2,2-Me_2	HBF_3OR	iso-Bu	75	1610
1-$H_2N(CH_2)_3$-2,2-Me_2	Picric acid	Me	—	1610, 3498

	Picric acid	Me or Et	≈ 30	2551a

hydroxyethylated cellulose (*2606, 2607*) failed. A polymer of EI was produced which could be removed by prolonged washing.

Indeed, the 2-aminoethyl ether structure has been questioned (*756, 3329*) and evidence presented (*756*) to demonstrate that at best the polysaccharides so aminated contain a few PEI chains grafted to a few sites in the polysaccharide chain. Reaction times and temperatures are sufficient for polymer formation in the presence of water, and definitive structure determination of the treated polysaccharides is difficult. Claims of the presence of 2-aminoethyl groups based on nitrosation (*1036*) are of doubtful validity since PEI chains may be degraded by this reagent (*963*). Although products are obtained containing nitrogen even after an acid (HCl) wash, it is well known that PEI is very substantive to cellulose or starch and the polymer adsorbed on cellulose or starch can not be completely removed with an acid wash (*963, 3121*).

Inasmuch as hydroperoxides may be considered to be like alcohols, mention is made here of the reaction of *tert*-butyl hydroperoxide with 2-methylaziridine to produce (apparently in low yield) a mixture of *tert*-butyl 2-aminopropyl peroxide and the isomeric *tert*-butyl 2-amino-1-methylethyl peroxide (*1049*).

Phenols. Phenol is a good example of a reagent which is acidic enough to protonate a reasonable proportion (but not all) of an aziridine when the two are mixed and which provides an anion (phenoxide ion) that is sufficiently nucleophilic to compete (but not very well) with the basic aziridine (or amine) for the protonated aziridine. Heating a chloroform solution of phenol and 2,2-dimethylaziridine gives a mixture of products as shown (Eq 125) (*714*).

$$2,2\text{-Me}_2\text{AzH} + \text{PhOH} \rightarrow \text{PhO}(\text{CH}_2\text{CMe}_2\text{NH})_n\text{H} \tag{125}$$

$$n = 1, 34\%; n = 2, 29\%; n = 3, 13\%$$
$$\text{Higher polymer } 17\%$$

The results may be rationalized by the scheme shown in Eq 126,

$$\text{AzH} + \text{PhOH} \rightleftharpoons \text{AzH}_2^+ + \text{PhO}^-$$

$$\text{PhO}^- + \text{AzH}_2^+ \rightarrow \text{PhOCH}_2\text{CH}_2\text{NH}_2$$

$$\text{PhOH} + \text{AzH}_2^+ \rightarrow \text{PhOCH}_2\text{CH}_2\text{NH}_2 + \text{H}^+$$

$$\text{PhOCH}_2\text{CH}_2\text{NH}_2 + \text{AzH}_2^+ \rightarrow \text{PhO}(\text{CH}_2\text{CH}_2\text{NH})_2\text{H} + \text{H}^+$$

$$\text{AzH} + \text{AzH}_2^+ \rightarrow \text{Az-CH}_2\text{CH}_2\text{NH}_2 + \text{H}^+$$

$$\text{Az-CH}_2\text{CH}_2\text{NH}_2 + \text{PhOH} \rightleftharpoons \text{AzH}^+\text{CH}_2\text{CH}_2\text{NH}_2 + \text{PhO}^-$$

$$\text{AzH}^+\text{CH}_2\text{CH}_2\text{NH}_2 + \text{PhO}^- \rightarrow \text{PhO}(\text{CH}_2\text{CH}_2\text{NH})_2\text{H} \tag{126}$$

for which, in the rate expression

$$-d[\text{AzH}_2^+]/dt = (k_\text{I}[\text{PhOH}] + k_\text{II}[\text{PhO}^-] + k_\text{III}[\text{PhOCH}_2\text{CH}_2\text{NH}_2] + k_\text{IV}[\text{AzH}])[\text{AzH}_2^+]$$

the terms $k_I[PhOH]$ and $k_{II}[PhO^-]$ must be comparable in magnitude to either $k_{III}[PhOCH_2CH_2NH_2]$ or $k_{IV}[AzH]$ or both. For a detailed consideration of the mechanism and kinetics, however, the existence of ion pairs should not be overlooked.

This picture is consistent with the fact that an increase in mole ratio of phenol to aziridine from 3 to 10 increases the yield of monoadduct ($n = 1$) from 34% to 51%. Also, heating phenol and the HBF_4 salt of EI in 2/1 mole ratio gave 2-phenoxyethylamine in 47% yield (*1610*) whereas heating a mixture of phenol and only EI in 3/1 mole ratio gave the product in only 33% yield.

A number of phenols have been treated with EI and other basic aziridines (*404, 714, 2236*), but the yields of 2-phenoxyethylamines are low for the alkyl-, alkoxy-, and especially 2,6-dialkyl-substituted phenols (*714*). High yields have been claimed for chlorinated phenols (*404*).

As mentioned previously, heating the picric acid salt of 2,2-dimethylaziridine in water or alcohol results in hydrolysis or alcoholysis. When the salt was heated in a nonhydroxylic solvent the product isolated was 2-methyl-1-picrylamino-2-propanol (*715*). A scheme involving ring opening by the picrate ion with subsequent rearrangement was proposed (Eq 127), but this could not be repeated for 2,4-dichlorophenol (*963*).

$$2,2\text{-}Me_2AzH_2^+ \ (NO_2)_3C_6H_2O^- \ \rightarrow \ [(NO_2)_3C_6H_2OCMe_2CH_2NH_2] \ \rightarrow$$

$$(NO_2)_3C_6H_2NHCH_2CMe_2OH \quad (127)$$

Carboxylic Acids. Essentially the same reaction scheme as previously shown for reaction with phenols may be applied to the reaction with carboxylic acids. In certain of the studies, very high yields of the ring-opened products have been reported; this may be explained in terms of higher concentrations of the aziridinium ion with correspondingly lower concentrations of basic amino species. For example, the reaction of 2,3-dimethylaziridine with a large excess of acetic acid gave an essentially quantitative yield of the acetic salt of 2-acetoxy-3-butanamine (*1465*). The corresponding reaction has been performed with EI and methacrylic acid (*2501a, 2502*). Benzoic acid and 2,2-dimethylaziridine in a 2:1 mole ratio in chloroform combine to form in quantitative yield the benzoic salt of the ring-opened product wherein the benzoyloxy group is attached to the less-substituted carbon atom (*963, 2916, 2917*). However, the reaction of EI with benzoic acid under the same conditions gives a significant yield of product corresponding to 2 or more moles of EI combined with 1 mole of acid (**38**) (*963*; cf. *328b*).

$$RCO_2(CH_2CH_2NH)_nH \qquad n = 2, 3, \text{ etc.}$$

38

Since EI is a weaker base than 2,2-dimethylaziridine, a smaller proportion of the EI would exist in the protonated form; moreover the reaction of nucleophiles with the protonated EI would be faster than with the protonated 2,2-dimethylaziridine, so that the competitive reaction of amines would become more significant.

The stereochemistry of ring opening, by carboxylic acids, of aziridines possessing only secondary carbon atoms has been demonstrated; in each case a Walden inversion (trans opening of the ring) was shown to occur (*1465, 1621, 1622, 2722a*). Racemization occurred, however, in aqueous acetic acid (*2722a*).

The kinetics have been determined for the reaction of 2,2-dimethylaziridine and 2-ethylaziridine with benzoic or substituted benzoic acids in dioxane (*2916, 2917*) and in chloroform (*963*). In dioxane as solvent, the reaction followed second-order kinetics, first order in acid and first order in aziridine, when acid:aziridine mole ratios of at least 2 were employed (*2916, 2917*), but the reaction was followed only to less than 50% completion and adequate variations in reactant concentrations were not employed (*2917*). It is probable that the reaction more closely approximates first-order kinetics (the rate being dependent only on the aziridine concentration when acid is in excess) as has been found when chloroform is the solvent (*963*). NMR studies in chloroform (ambient temperature, $0.2M$ concentration) permitted estimating that approximately 80% of the aziridine was protonated immediately after mixing with benzoic acid (1:1 mole ratio) (Eq 128) (*963*).

$$2,2\text{-Me}_2\text{AzH} + \text{BzOH} \rightleftharpoons 2,2\text{-Me}_2\text{AzH}_2{}^+ \text{BzO}^- \tag{128}$$

It was also shown that the measured first-order rate constant (for reaction involving a 2:1 mole ratio of acid to aziridine) became smaller as the reaction

Table 3-XXV

EFFECT OF CONCENTRATIONS ON RATE CONSTANT FOR REACTION OF 2,2-DIMETHYLAZIRIDINE WITH BENZOIC ACID IN CHLOROFORM AT $50.0°C^a$

Mole ratio BzOH/2,2-Me₂AzH	[BzOH] (moles-liter)	[2,2-Me₂AzH] (moles-liter)	$10^3 k$ (min⁻¹)
4/1	0.719	0.176	9.16[b]
2/1	0.719	0.353	9.34[b]
2/1	0.361	0.178	6.88
2/1	0.0809	0.0396	2.80
2/1	0.0427	0.0199	1.81

[a] From The Dow Chemical Co. (*963*).
[b] Reaction followed to greater than 90% completion.

mixture was made more dilute (963). This observation is consistent with involvement of an ion pair in reaction 128. At very low concentrations the position of equilibrium could conceivably be such (mostly free acid and aziridine) that the reaction would conform to approximately second-order kinetics. Thus an accurate representation of detailed kinetic expressions and mechanisms must take into account not only this ion pair but also the one formed with the ring-opened product; and at this time data sufficient for this interpretation have not been obtained. The effects of mole ratio and concentration on the measured first-order rate constants for the reaction of benzoic acid with 2,2-dimethylaziridine in chloroform are shown in Table 3-XXV.

The Hammett ρ constants for reaction of substituted benzoic acids with 2,2-dimethylaziridine and 2-ethylaziridine in dioxane have been found to be, respectively, 1.50 and 1.66 at 45°C. Such positive values indicate that an increased rate of reaction is favored by low electron density at the carboxylate anion, but the difficulties (already mentioned) inherent in applying kinetic measurements to mechanistic interpretations should be considered. The rate constants for the above reactions are shown in Table 3-XXVI (2916).

Table 3-XXVI

RATES OF REACTION OF AZIRIDINES WITH SUBSTITUTED BENZOIC
ACIDS IN DIOXANE

$$2,2\text{-RR'AzH} + 2p\text{-XC}_6\text{H}_4\text{CO}_2\text{H} \rightarrow p\text{-XC}_6\text{H}_4\text{CO}_2\text{CH}_2\text{CRR'NH}_3{}^+ \; {}^-\text{O}_2\text{CC}_6\text{H}_4\text{X-}p$$

R	R'	X	T (°C)	$k = 10^n k^{0a}$ (liter mole^{-1} min^{-1}) k^0	n	$\Delta H^{\ddagger}$ (kcal mole^{-1})	$\Delta S^{\ddagger}$ (cal mole^{-1} deg^{-1})
Et	H	MeO	45	2.93	3	—	—
Et	H	Me	45	3.74	3	—	—
Et	H	H	45	7.40	3	—	—
Et	H	Br	45	2.60	2	—	—
Et	H	O$_2$N	45	1.32	1	—	—
Et	H	H	35	3.92	3	—	—
Et	H	H	25	1.30	3	17.0	−25
Et	H	O$_2$N	35	3.75	2	—	—
Et	H	O$_2$N	25	2.23	2	16.8	−19
Me	Me	MeO	45	8.91	3	—	—
Me	Me	H	45	2.04	2	—	—
Me	Me	Br	45	5.17	2	—	—
Me	Me	O$_2$N	45	2.22	1	—	—

[a] Although it is possible, even probable, that the reaction follows first-order kinetics, the second-order rate constants which were reported (2916) are shown here.

In addition to formation of products such as **38** another secondary reaction may occur between carboxylic acids and aziridines: the rearrangement of the 2-aminoethyl ester product into a 2-hydroxyethyl amide (Eq 129).

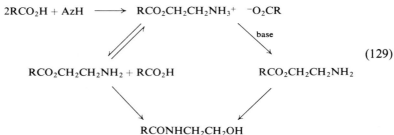

$$2RCO_2H + AzH \longrightarrow RCO_2CH_2CH_2NH_3^+ \quad {}^-O_2CR$$

(129)

$$RCO_2CH_2CH_2NH_2 + RCO_2H \qquad\qquad RCO_2CH_2CH_2NH_2$$

$$RCONHCH_2CH_2OH$$

The rate of rearrangement of the 2-aminoethyl ester is highly dependent on its structure, being very sensitive to steric effects and being increased by lack of alkyl substituents in either the acid or the aminoethyl moieties. In certain cases the rearrangement can occur concomitantly with the reaction between aziridine and acid (since the free aminoethyl ester is in equilibrium with its salt form). Such rearrangement is, of course, avoided by the use of a large excess of acid.

The ring opening of basic aziridines by carboxylic acids is very general and has included not only simple aziridines such as EI or others previously mentioned but also more complicated derivatives such as steroidal aziridines (*1621, 1998, 2773*). Moreover, the reaction of polymers containing carboxylic acid groups with basic aziridines (e.g., EI) has been described (*999, 1287a, 3266*; see also p. 384); however, an absolute proof of structure for these products is difficult to obtain and the presence of some groups corresponding to structure **38** is a possibility.

Mercaptans and Other Reagents Containing Mercapto Groups. Included in this section are reactions of basic aziridines with hydrogen sulfide, mercaptans, thiophenols, thiourea, xanthates, and carbon disulfide. Reaction with such sulfur nucleophiles represents one of the most important preparative methods for such ring-opened derivatives.

If a reaction scheme similar to that considered for phenol is applied to reaction with materials possessing –SH groups, it is readily seen that high yields of ring-opened products may be expected in most cases (Eq 130).

$$RSH + AzH \rightleftharpoons RS^-AzH_2^+$$

$$RS^- + AzH_2^+ \rightarrow RSCH_2CH_2NH_2$$

$$RSH + AzH_2^+ \rightarrow RSCH_2CH_2NH_3^+$$

(130)

The RS⁻ (and/or RSH) is sufficiently nucleophilic to compete successfully for the protonated aziridine with any free amino group (aziridine or ring-opened product) present in the medium, and thus it is unnecessary to employ large amounts of acid or a large excess of the RSH compound.

Treatment of EI with hydrogen sulfide produces good yields of either 2-aminoethanethiol or bis(2-aminoethyl) sulfide, depending primarily on the mole ratio of hydrogen sulfide to EI (*350, 363, 407, 1248, 1390, 1851a, 3306, 3544*). The reaction has been frequently used to obtain these ring-opened products for subsequent use (*275, 1045, 1312, 2521, 2548, 2563, 2676, 2693, 2761, 2836, 3160, 3785, 3815, 3828, 4188*) including some containing radioactive sulfur (^{35}S) (*342, 986, 1394, 3267*). Treatment of a mixture of EI and sulfur with hydrogen sulfide is reported to yield bis(2-aminoethyl) polysulfides (*1174*). Reaction of EI with ammonium disulfide at temperatures much higher than normally used to effect a simple ring opening (125°) causes its conversion to 1,2-ethanedithiol (*922*).

Ring opening by hydrogen sulfide gives equally good results with both nitrogen- and/or carbon-substituted basic aziridines (*333, 458, 512, 684, 922, 932, 1495, 2626, 2627, 2883, 3060, 3090, 3271a, 3456, 3500, 3814, 4107*). It was reported that 2,2,3-trimethylaziridine did not react under conditions suitable for 2,3-dimethylaziridine (*333*). However, such failure was probably due only to the choice of too mild conditions; the stability of highly carbon-substituted aziridinium ions to nucleophiles is well known. Although the reaction ordinarily gives excellent yields of 2-aminoethanethiols, care must be taken to avoid oxidation by air to the disulfide, especially during isolation of the product (*3060*). Many such ring openings are presented in Table 3-XXVII.

The stereochemistry for ring opening of cyclohexenimines by hydrogen sulfide has been demonstrated to involve a trans opening of the aziridine ring (*2626, 2627, 3456, 3814*).

Treatment of a basic aziridine with hydrogen sulfide in the presence of an aldehyde or ketone gives a thiazolidine (**39**) in good yield (Eq 131) (*350, 981, 1862, 2154, 2537, 2952, 3575, 4107*; cf. *155a*).

$$\text{AzH(R)} + \text{R}'\text{R}''\text{CO} + \text{H}_2\text{S} \longrightarrow \quad \text{(R)HN} \underset{\text{R}'\quad\text{R}''}{\diagup\diagdown}\text{S} \quad + \text{H}_2\text{O} \qquad (131)$$

39

The reaction may be viewed as involving ring opening of the aziridine–carbonyl adduct (*350, 2154*) and/or formation of the aminoethanethiol, which then reacts with the carbonyl compound (as would be necessary with 1-alkyl-aziridines) (*3575*). Treatment of *gem*-dithiols with EI also gives thiazolidines (*1983*). From an α,β-unsaturated aldehyde (e.g., crotonaldehyde) it is possible to obtain a product wherein addition of EI to the carbon–carbon double bond has occurred and one aziridine ring is retained (Eq 132) (*350*).

$$\text{MeCH=CHCHO} + 2\text{AzH} + \text{H}_2\text{S} \longrightarrow \underset{\text{N}}{\overset{\text{S}}{\square}}\text{-CH}_2\text{CHMeAz} + \text{H}_2\text{O} \quad (132)$$

Treatment of *o*-(2-bromoethyl)benzaldehyde with EI and hydrogen sulfide yields a fused thiazolidinoisoquinoline salt (Eq 133) (*3162*).

$$\text{(structure: benzaldehyde with CHO and CH}_2\text{CH}_2\text{Br)} + \text{AzH} + \text{H}_2\text{S} \longrightarrow \text{(fused thiazolidinoisoquinoline salt) NH}^+ \quad \text{Br}^- \quad (133)$$

As with hydrogen sulfide, the reaction with alkanethiols or thiophenols gives good to excellent yields of the 2-aminoethyl alkyl or aryl sulfides (*327, 690, 819, 963, 1474, 1679, 1782, 1932, 2344, 2425, 2489a, 2503, 2512, 2585, 2767, 2951, 2962, 3072, 3203, 3637, 3786*). With alkanethiols the reaction occurs more readily in polar (e.g., alcohols) than in nonpolar solvents (*963*). The more acidic the thiol, the more readily will reaction occur. For example, whereas thiophenols cause rapid ring opening in nonpolar solvents (e.g., carbon tetrachloride) the alkanethiols are only slightly affected under the same conditions, and conditions suitable for reaction of primary or secondary thiols caused no conversion of a tertiary thiol (*963*).

Reaction of aziridines with thiols which have the mercapto groups α or β to a functional group capable of reaction with an amine may lead either to acyclic ring-opened products or to five-, six-, or seven-membered ring compounds resulting from secondary ring closures (*155, 156, 350, 1481, 1493, 1679, 1958, 2286, 2962, 3069a*). Examples are shown in Eqs 134–137.

$$\text{MeO}_2\text{C(NC)C=C(SMe)SH} + \text{AzH} \longrightarrow \underset{\text{N}}{\overset{\text{S}}{\square}}\text{=C(CN)CO}_2\text{Me} \quad (1493) \quad (134)$$

$$\text{EtCOCHMeSH} + \text{AzH} \longrightarrow \text{(ring structure with N, Et, S, Me)} \quad (155) \quad (135)$$

$$\text{HSCH}_2\text{CO}_2\text{H} + \text{AzH} \longrightarrow \text{(ring structure S, N-H, O)} + \text{H}_2\text{O} \quad (350) \quad (136)$$

$$\text{HSCH}_2\text{CH}_2\text{CO}_2\text{Me} + \text{AzH} \longrightarrow \text{(seven-membered ring structure S, N-H, O)} + \text{MeOH} \quad (1958) \quad (137)$$

The product of reaction 135 is also formed in good yield from diethyl ketone, sulfur, and EI (*155a*); use of selenium instead of sulfur yields the selenazine derivative (*154a*). Treatment of cysteine with EI gave a product wherein practically

Table 3-XXVII

RING OPENING OF BASIC AZIRIDINES WITH H_2S, THIOLS, AND H_2S PLUS
CARBONYL COMPOUNDS

$$RSH + AzH \rightarrow RSCH_2CH_2NH_2$$

Aziridine substituents	R	% Yield	References
None	H	70–80	*164, 350*
2-Me	H	75	*963*
2,3-Me$_2$	H	75	*333*
2,3-[(CH$_2$)$_4$]	H	80	*3814*
1-Me	H	66	*333*
1-Et	H	46	*333*
1-Me-2,3[(CH$_2$)$_4$]	H	—	*2627, 3814*
1-EtO$_2$CCH$_2$	H	—	*458*
1-MeO$_2$CCHMeCH$_2$	H	80	*3060*
1-Me$_3$SiCH$_2$CH$_2$	H	76	*4189*
None	Me	69	*2503, 3622, 3786*
None	Et	74	*963, 3622, 3786*
None	Pr	78	*327*
None	iso-Pr	60	*963, 3622*
None	Bu	76	*963, 3072*
None	n-C$_8$H$_{17}$	60	*963*
None	n-C$_{12}$H$_{25}$	90	*963*
None	CH$_2$=CHCH$_2$	76	*963*
None	PhCH$_2$	87	*690, 2586*
None	HOCH$_2$CH$_2$	84	*2344*
None	Et$_2$NCH$_2$CH$_2$	92	*723*
2-Me	PhCH$_2$	55	*3637*
1-(2-Quinolyl)	Et$_2$NCH$_2$CH$_2$	61	*1474*
None	Ph	78–96	*963, 2303*
None	p-MeC$_6$H$_4$	78	*963*
None	p-ClC$_6$H$_4$	95	*963*
None	p-NO$_2$C$_6$H$_4$	91	*963*
None	p-HOC$_6$H$_4$	99	*963*
None	o-H$_2$NH$_6$H$_4$	86	*963*
2-Me	o-MeC$_6$H$_4$	87	*963*
2-Me	o-ClC$_6$H$_4$	89	*963*
2-Me	p-H$_2$NC$_6$H$_4$	77	*963*
2-Me	Ph	92	*963*
2-Et	Ph	92	*2512*
2,2-Me$_2$	Ph	86	*2512*
1-PhCH$_2$CH$_2$	Ph	42	*963*
2,3-[(CH$_2$)$_4$]	Ph	—	*3814*
None	(CH$_2$)$_n$, n = 2, 4, 5, or 6	—[a]	*1932*

Table 3-XXVII—*continued*

$$H_2S + RR'CO + AzH \longrightarrow \underset{\underset{R}{S} \diagdown \underset{R'}{NH}}{\boxed{}}$$

Aziridine substituents	R	R'	% Yield	References
None	H	H	—	*2154*
None	H	Me	51	*350*
None	H	$n\text{-}C_8H_{17}$	66	*3575*
None	H	$AzCHMeCH_2$	—	*350*
None	H	Ph	80	*3575*
None	H	2-Pyridyl	74	*3575*
None	Me	Me	90	*350*
None	Me	$n\text{-}C_9H_{19}$	—	*3575*
None	Me	MeO_2CCH_2	70	*350*
None	Me	$PhCH_2$	89	*3575*
None	Me	$PhCH_2CH_2$	84	*3575*
None	Et	$n\text{-}C_5H_{11}$	73	*3575*
None	iso-Bu	iso-Bu	2	*3575*
None	Me	Ph	—	*350*
None	Me	$p\text{-}ClC_6H_4$	35	*3575*
None	Me	$1\text{-}C_{10}H_7$	50	*3575*
None	$R+R' =(CH_2)_5$		83	*350*
None	$RR'CO = $ 3-Cholestanone		—	*981*
$1\text{-}PhCH_2CH_2$	H	H	—	*3575*
$1\text{-}PhCH_2CH_2$	H	$PhCH_2$	—	*3575*
$1\text{-}PhCH_2CH_2$	Me	Me	40	*3575*
$1\text{-}EtO_2CCH_2CH_2$	Me	Me	87	*3575*
$1\text{-}NCCH_2CH_2$	Me	Me	73	*3575*
$1\text{-}PhCH_2CH_2$	$R+R' = (CH_2)_4$		80	*3575*
$1\text{-}PhCH_2CH_2$	$R+R' = (CH_2)_5$		71	*3575*
$2,2\text{-}Me_2$	Me	H	—	*4107*

[a] Both $HS(CH_2)_nSCH_2CH_2NH_2$ and $(CH_2)_n(SCH_2CH_2NH_2)_2$ were formed.

all reaction occurred at the mercapto group (*909, 1679, 1702*). The second-order rate constant for this ring opening was found to be 0.6 mole⁻¹ min⁻¹ (25°C, 0.025M NaHCO₃, pH 7.3, reagents $\approx 0.01 M$) (*909*). The trapping of mercapto groups in proteins by treatment with EI prior to hydrolytic degradation has been useful (p. 393). In another instance of reaction of mercapto groups in polymers, reduction products of copolymers of sulfur and conjugated dienes are aminoalkylated at both ends of the chain by use of EI or 2-methylaziridine (*751a*).

Although thiophenols have, in general, been found to give simple ring-opened products (*963, 2512, 3203*), treatment of 1-cyclohexyl-2-benzoyl-3-

phenylaziridine with thiophenol gave a reductive cleavage product, 3-phenyl-3-(phenylthio)propiophenone (*2511*).

As is to be expected, ring opening by thiocarboxylic acids occurs very readily. The reaction resembles ring opening by carboxylic acids in that the initially formed (2-aminoethyl)thio ester readily rearranges to a 2-mercaptoethyl amide (Eq 138) (*222, 1553, 1579, 2201, 2202, 3443, 3457, 3463*).

$$AcSH + AzH \rightarrow [AcSCH_2CH_2NH_2] \rightarrow AcNHCH_2CH_2SH \qquad (138)$$

The stereochemistry has been demonstrated in cyclohexenimine derivatives (*2131, 3463*) and cis-2,3-diphenylaziridine (*3443*) to involve a trans opening of the aziridine ring.

The tautomerism which exists for compounds containing a H—Y—C=S group is well known, as is the tendency of many such compounds to undergo alkylation reactions at the sulfur atom. A number of such ring-opening alkylations are known for aziridines. These include reaction of EI with cyclohexanethione (Eq 139) (*963*) and thiourea (Eq 140) (*465, 495, 1755, 3460, 3462, 3474, 4080, 4178*) as well as 2-mercaptoimidazoles (*1782*), 2-mercapto-benzothiazoles (*2425, 2857*), 2-mercaptobenzoxazoles (*2425*), 2-mercapto-thiazolines (*2004*), and mercaptopurines (*2638*).

$$(139)$$

$$(H_2N)_2CS + AzH + 2HX \longrightarrow H_2NC(=NH)SCH_2CH_2NH_2 \cdot 2HX \qquad (140)$$

The reaction with thiourea, for which a trans opening of the aziridine ring has been demonstrated (*3458*), has most often been performed in the presence of an equivalent amount of a mineral acid. Yields are essentially quantitative. Partial neutralization of the 2-aminoethylisothiuronium salts results in a rearrangement, similar to that of 2-aminoethyl carboxylic esters, giving 1-(2-mercaptoethyl)guanidine salts (*3460*). N-Alkyl-substituted thioureas, when treated with 1-alkylaziridines, give 2-alkyliminothiazolidines in good yield (*1407*; cf. *89*). Likewise thio acids and thio amides with 1-unsubstituted aziridines give 2-alkylthiazolines in a trans ring opening (*2130, 2349*).

Treatment of EI with *O,O*-dialkyl hydrogenphosphonothioate gives *O,O*-dialkyl 2-aminoethyl thiophosphites (Eq 141) (*2213*).

$$(RO)_2P(S)H + AzH \rightarrow (RO)_2PSCH_2CH_2NH_2 \qquad (141)$$

The reaction of 1-unsubstituted aziridines with carbon disulfide proceeds readily to form 2-mercaptothiazolines (**40**) (*391, 392, 406, 713, 895, 896, 1384,*

1388, 1392, 1603, 3407). The reaction has the characteristics of a typical S_N2 ring-opening process in that 2-alkyl- or 2,2-dialkylaziridines give products wherein the aziridine ring has been opened at the primary carbon atom (*713, 896*) and the stereochemistry has been indicated to involve a trans opening of the aziridine ring (*895, 896, 2526*). In reaction media containing only carbon disulfide and an aziridine or these reactants in a solvent such as ether, the reaction is probably best explained in terms of an initial formation of the aziridine salt of the dithiocarbamic acid (Eq 142).

$$AzH + CS_2 \longrightarrow [AzCS_2^- \quad AzH_2^+] \longrightarrow [AzCS_2CH_2CH_2NH_2]$$

$$\qquad (142)$$

40

Very similar is the reaction of alkali metal xanthates, which may be conducted to yield 2-alkoxy-2-mercaptothiazolidines (**41**) (*978, 1827, 1836, 2395*); these on heating lose alcohol to give 2-mercaptothiazolines (*978*) or on treatment with excess aziridine yield 2-alkoxy-2-(2-aminoethylthio)thiazolidines (**42**) (Eq 143) (*1827*).

$$ROC(S)S^- + AzH_2^+ \longrightarrow$$

41   **40**   **42**

$$\qquad (143)$$

Ammonium trithiocarbonate with EI can be made to yield the 2-amino-ethyl ester of the acid as the dipolar ion, $^+H_3NCH_2CH_2SCS_2^-$ (*2943a*).

As would be expected, ring opening of carbon-substituted basic aziridines by all the sulfur nucleophiles listed in this section occurs at the less-substituted aziridine carbon atom. One report contrary to this (*1579*) appears to be in error.

Properly mentioned here is an example of ring opening by a selenophosphorus compound (Eq 144) (*29*).

$$(EtO)_2P(O)SeH + AzH \rightarrow (EtO)_2P(O)SeCH_2CH_2NH_2 \qquad (144)$$

Amines. Ring opening of basic aziridines by amines represents one of the most direct preparative methods for unsymmetrically nitrogen-substituted ethylenediamines (Eq 145).

$$RR'NH + AzR'' \xrightarrow{\text{acid}} RR'NCH_2CH_2NHR'' \tag{145}$$

It is readily apparent that the capability for producing high yields depends on the rate of reaction of starting amine relative to that of product amine with the protonated aziridine. Byproducts are, of course, polymeric materials of structure **43**, sometimes purposely prepared (*1255, 2722*).

$$RR'N(CH_2CH_2NR'')_nH \qquad n = 2, 3, 4, \text{etc.}$$

43

Since the product amine may be expected to have a nucleophilicity comparable to that of reactant amine, the yield from the reaction represented by Eq 145 depends primarily on the mole ratio of amine to aziridine. The differences in nucleophilicity for the two amines are of importance, however; for example, an 85 % yield of ring-opened product was obtained by use of 3 moles of morpholine to 1 of 2-ethylaziridine, whereas the same mole ratio of aniline to aziridine gave only a 19% yield (*712*). It has been suggested that the use of nonpolar solvents (e.g., benzene) results in lower yields of the desired ethylenediamine (*467*). Known examples of ring opening of basic aziridines by amines are presented in Table 3-XXVIII.

The overall rate of Eq 145 depends on the usual parameters: total concentrations, concentration of acid catalyst, solvent, temperature, structure of amine and aziridine, etc. It is sometimes difficult, however, to relate data on the rate with a given amine to that for a different amine. Important are two factors: concentration of aziridinium ion and the specific rate for ring opening of that aziridinium ion by the reactant amine. There is generally a rough parallel between amine basicity and nucleophilicity. Thus, with a very basic amine the concentration of aziridinium ion is very low but the reactivity of the amine is high, whereas with an amine which is much less basic, a higher concentration of aziridinium ion is present but the amine is less reactive.

It has been suggested that amines cause ring opening of basic aziridines in the absence of any acid or any other reagent which would provide an aziridinium ion, although at a very low rate (*350*). While this may be true, it is entirely possible that in the experiment used to demonstrate this (the reaction of piperidine with EI or EI with itself) minute traces of acidic material, such as carbon dioxide, were present and thus the rate may be very much lower than was indicated.

Any reagent capable of providing even very low concentration of aziridinium ion acts as a suitable catalyst. Successful ring-opening reactions between amines

Table 3-XXVIII

RING OPENING OF BASIC AZIRIDINES BY AMINES

$$RR'NH + AzH \rightarrow RR'NCH_2CH_2NH_2$$

Aziridine substituents	R	R'	% Yield	References
None	H	H	55	*712*
2-Et	H	H	55	*712, 3629*
(R)-(+)-2-Et	H	H	57	*1737*
2,2-Me$_2$	H	H	68	*712*
2,3-Me$_2$	H	H	30	*910*
2,3-[(CH$_2$)$_4$]	H	H	75	*2995*
2-KO$_2$C(CH$_2$)$_7$- 3-n-C$_8$H$_{17}$	H	H	—	*3449*
None	H	PhCH$_2$CHMe	22	*467*
None	H	HOCH$_2$CH$_2$	28	*467*
None	H	Ph	13	*467*
2-Et	H	Et	20–45	*712, 1466*
2-Et	H	Bu	68	*712*
2-Et	H	c-C$_6$H$_{11}$	55	*712*
2-Et	H	n-C$_{12}$H$_{25}$	19	*712*
2,2-Me$_2$	H	Et	42	*712*
2,2-Me$_2$	H	Bu	84	*712*
2,2-Me$_2$	H	c-C$_6$H$_{11}$	82	*712*
2,2-Me$_2$	H	Ph	40	*712*
2,3-Me$_2$	H	Et	60	*1466*
None	Me	Me	77	*963*
None	Et	Et	44	*466, 2504*
None	Pr	Pr	10	*466, 2504*
None	Bu	Bu	—	*466*
None	CH$_2$=CHCH$_2$	CH$_2$=CHCH$_2$	33	*467*
None	Me$_2$CHCH$_2$CH$_2$	Me$_2$CHCH$_2$CH$_2$	27	*467*
None	HOCH$_2$CH$_2$	HOCH$_2$CH$_2$	27	*2177*
None	R$_1$ + R$_2$ = O(CH$_2$CH$_2$)$_2$		48	*1646*
None	R$_1$ + R$_2$ = (CH$_2$)$_6$		79	*691*
2-Et	Et	Et	54	*712*
2-Et	Bu	Bu	20	*712*
2-Et	Me	Ph	14	*712*
2-Et	R$_1$ + R$_2$ = O(CH$_2$CH$_2$)$_2$		85	*712*
2,2-Me$_2$	R$_1$ + R$_2$ = O(CH$_2$CH$_2$)$_2$		85	*712*
1-HOCH$_2$CH$_2$	H	Et	65	*963*
1-Et-2,3-Me$_2$	H	Et	55	*1466*
(CH$_2$)$_4$	H	Me	—	*3814*
(CH$_2$)$_4$	Me	Me	—	*3814*

and basic aziridines have been performed in water and even alcohol without the addition of an acid catalyst (*466, 1646, 2177, 2995, 3046a, 3804, 3805*). A general claim to the reaction of the gaseous reagents on a heterogeneous catalyst has been made (*2885a*).

As with other ring-opening processes, the stereochemistry for reaction with amines has been shown to involve a trans opening of the aziridine ring (*910, 1466, 1737, 3814*).

Of special interest is the reaction of aziridines with amines in the presence of equimolar amounts of aluminum chloride (*734, 1714, 1745, 1752, 1777, 2609a, 3000, 3001, 3376, 3486, 3488*). Boron trifluoride may also be used (*1426*). The reaction appears to involve a different mechanism from that previously indicated, since quite high yields (77–89 %) of the ethylenediamines have been obtained and the absence of polymeric amines has been reported (*734*) even though only a 2:1 mole ratio of amine to aziridine was used.

The reaction of nicotinamide with 1-(2-hydroxy-3-butenyl)aziridine in the presence of HCl (*1012*) provides an example of ring cleavage wherein the amine is a pyridine. Since the reaction using a large excess of pyridine (Eq 146) is the basis of an analytical procedure for aziridines (p. 446), it may be considered quite general.

$$\text{(pyridine)} + \text{AzH} + \text{HCl} \longrightarrow \text{(pyridinium)} \quad Cl^- \qquad (146)$$

$$\underset{CH_2CH_2NH_2}{N^+}$$

Of interest is the use of Eq 145 for preparation of other heterocyclic compounds, as in Eqs 147 and 148.

$$\text{(structure)} + \text{AzH} \xrightarrow{HCl} \text{(structure)} \qquad (861a, 885a, \quad (147)$$
$$885b, 1327, 3412)$$

$$\text{(structure)} + \text{AzH} \xrightarrow{AlCl_3} \text{(structure)} \qquad (1745, 3002)$$

$$(148)$$

Ring opening of basic aziridines by hydrazine or substituted hydrazines occurs analogously to Eq 145 (*963, 1172, 1395*). The reaction of 2-acylaziri- dines with phenylhydrazine in the presence of acetic acid is of interest. The products may be 4-aminopyrazolines (**44**) or pyrazoles (**45**), presumed to be formed by condensation of the hydrazine with the oxo group and subsequent ring opening of the aziridine (Eq 149) (*796, 800, 805, 806, 807*).

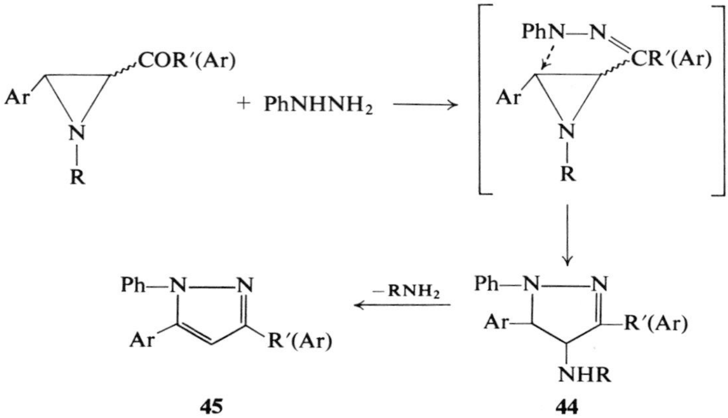

(149)

45   44

It was found that *cis*-aziridine derivatives produced only pyrazoles whereas the 4-aminopyrazolines could be formed from *trans*-aziridines. Thus, the reaction has been used as a diagnostic tool for structure assignment.

Treatment of 1-benzoyl-2-cyanoaziridine with ammonium carbonate to yield 2-phenylimidazole (*150*) is probably best interpreted as involving an initial ring opening of the aziridine by ammonia, occurring at the cyano-substituted carbon atom.

Amides. Certain amides and other nitrogen compounds contain an N—H group wherein the hydrogen is relatively acidic when compared to that in amines or even carboxamides. Examples include imides (e.g., phthalimide), sulfonamides, sulfonimides, hydantoins, and xanthines. These reagents are acidic enough to provide a reasonable concentration of protonated aziridine in such mixtures and at the same time provide a very nucleophilic amide anion. Thus, quite good yields of *N*-(2-aminoalkyl) derivatives of such compounds may be obtained by reaction with basic aziridines (Eq 150) (*144, 145, 147, 229, 2435, 2563a*).

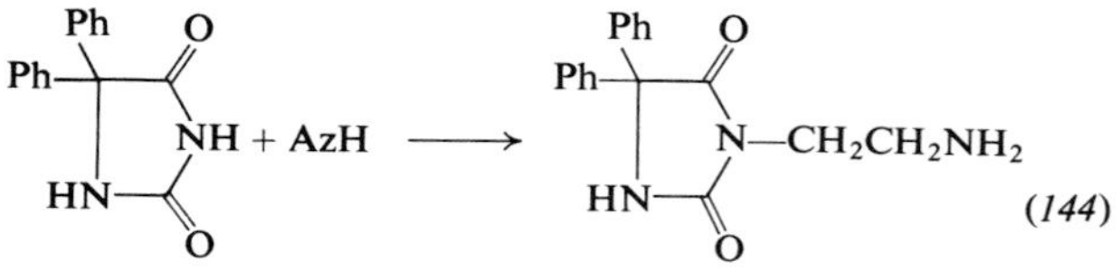

(150)

(*144*)

Similarly, the formation of a product from EI and phthalimide which can be hardened by subsequent heating may be interpreted in terms of this reaction (Eq 151) (*1687*).

$$\text{(151)}$$

Also of interest is the ring opening of EI by a 5-halobarbituric acid derivative (**46**) and subsequent ring closure (Eq 152) (*143*).

$$\text{(152)}$$

Acid Halides and Anhydrides. Ring opening by these reagents is somewhat different for 1-unsubstituted basic aziridines and for aziridines possessing nitrogen substituents.

In both cases the reaction involves the formation of an intermediate aziridinium ion (Eq 153).

$$AzR + R'COCl \longrightarrow \left[\begin{array}{c} \end{array} \right] \longrightarrow R'CONRCH_2CH_2Cl \quad \text{(153)}$$

When R is hydrogen (in 1-unsubstituted aziridines), excess aziridine will abstract this proton and produce the 1-acylaziridine (Eq 154); indeed excess aziridine is sometimes so used (p. 163).

$$\text{(154)}$$

Thus for ring opening the aziridine must be added to the acid halide (which is always maintained in excess) so that the second step of Eq 153, which occurs readily (p. 249), may proceed with minimum competition. When R is not hydrogen (in 1-alkylaziridines, etc.) no such competition with ring opening is possible, but excess acid halide is still desirable to minimize polymerization.

Although classified here as a ring-opening reaction of a basic aziridine, the reaction is thus actually a ring opening of an activated aziridine intermediate which has been prepared *in situ*. The products are usually obtained in excellent yield (sometimes quantitatively). The reaction is very general, being applicable to a wide variety of acid halides or anhydrides and aziridines. References mention the following acid halide or anhydride types:

Acid derivative	References
With 1-Unsubstituted Aziridines	
$RCOCl, Y(COCl)_2$	*289a, 350, 364, 1303, 3523a, 3625, 4048*
$COCl_2$	*350, 545, 1821*
$ArCOCl$	*350, 1555, 1819, 2417, 2428, 2907, 3261, 3814*
$ROCOCl$	*350, 1845, 3192*
Ar_2NCOCl	*824; cf. 1821*
$(RCO)_2O$	*2337a, 3516, 4199*
RSO_2Cl	*350, 364*
$ArSO_2Cl$	*350, 2428, 2714*
$(RO)_2P(O)Cl$	*1526*
$(RO)RP(O)Cl$	*2993*
BX_3	*1272a, 3711, 3712*
With 1-Alkylaziridines	
$RCOCl$	*926a, 3489, 3490*
$ArCOCl$	*2417, 3479, 3489*
$ROCOCl$	*928, 2794, 3272a*
$RSCOCl$	*2794*
$(RCO)_2O$	*219, 228, 2148, 2536, 2655a, 3609a, 3610, 3872*
RSO_2Cl	*2655a*

The reaction has been useful for preparation of intermediates, as in a pyrrolidine synthesis (Eq 155) (*928*).

$$AzCH_2CH_2Ac + EtO_2CCl \longrightarrow ClCH_2CH_2\underset{\underset{CO_2Et}{|}}{N}CH_2CH_2Ac$$

(155)

For the preparation of N-(2-chloroethyl)-p-vinylbenzenesulfonamide (*1927a*) and compounds of type $(RO)_2P(O)NHCH_2CH_2Cl$ (*819a*), however, ring opening of the isolated activated aziridine with HCl worked better than ring opening of EI with the acid chloride.

Halogens (or Halogenoids such as Cyanogen Bromide). This ring-opening reaction may be represented by Eq 156.

$$AzR + X_2 \rightarrow [AzRX^+ X^-] \rightarrow RNXCH_2CH_2X \qquad (156)$$

Treatment of EI with chlorine in the presence of aqueous caustic has already been mentioned (p. 200). In this case the group R in Eq 156 was hydrogen, and the HX from the reaction was neutralized, so that 1-chloroaziridine was formed. When R is an alkyl group, ring opening 156 occurs. However, the N-halo amine product may undergo subsequent reactions, as shown for 2,3-dibenzoyl-1-methylaziridine (Eq 157) (*2360*).

Cyanogen bromide causes ring opening in a similar manner (Eq 158) (*1043*).

$$Az\text{-}R + BrCN \rightarrow BrCH_2CH_2N(CN)R \qquad (158)$$

The fluorinolysis of EI at 100°–120°C is more severe, and gives a mixture of products including CF_4, $(CF_3)_2NF$, $(CF_3)_2N_2$, $(CF_3)_4N_2$, CF_3NF_2, and C_2F_6 (*1459*). A similar distribution of products was obtained from any one of the methylamines or ethylenediamine.

Aromatic Hydrocarbons in the Presence of Aluminum Chloride. Treatment of the EI–aluminum chloride complex (or a 1-alkylaziridine–aluminum chloride complex) with excess aromatic hydrocarbon at 120°–180°C for 7–8 hours is reported to give good yields (40–80%) of the 2-aminoethyl derivatives (Eq 159) (*468, 469*).

$$AzR + ArH \xrightarrow{\text{AlCl}_3} ArCH_2CH_2NHR \qquad (159)$$

In such reaction of 2-methylaziridine with substituted arenes, the ratio of $ArCHMeCH_2NH_2$ to $ArCHNH_2Et$ produced is increased by the presence of electron-releasing substituents on the ring but decreased by increase in temperature (*2563b*). 2-Methyl- or 2,2-dimethylaziridine gave predominantly that product resulting from ring opening at the more highly substituted aziridine carbon atom (*469*). A mixture was obtained from anisole, but 2-phenoxyethyl-amine could be isolated as the hydrochloride (*468*). In what appears to be contradictory work, it was found that under much milder conditions veratrole did not condense with EI (*3699*).

Somewhat analogous to such ring opening is the reaction of indole with aziridinium tetrafluoroborate (Eq 160) (*2867*).

$$\text{(indole)} + \text{AzH}_2{}^+ \text{ BF}_4{}^- \longrightarrow \text{(indole)}-\text{CH}_2\text{CH}_2\text{NH}_3{}^+ \text{ BF}_4{}^- \tag{160}$$

Nitriles, Alkylidenimines, Isocyanates, and Isothiocyanates. Ring opening of EI has been effected with these weak nucleophiles but naturally only when the EI was completely in the form of an aziridinium ion. Products from isocyanates and isothiocyanates are 2-aryl- or 2-alkylamino-2-oxazolines and -2-thiazolines, respectively (Eq 161) (*2869, 3273*).

$$\text{AzH}_2{}^+ \text{ BF}_4{}^- + \text{RN}{=}\text{C}{=}\text{Y} \xrightarrow{\text{base}} \underset{\text{NHR}}{\overset{\text{N}{=}\text{Y}}{\bigsqcup}} \tag{161}$$
$$\text{Y = O or S}$$

1-Alkylaziridines heated with organic isocyanates and metal halide catalysts yield 1,3-disubstituted 2-imidazolidinones (*663a*). From alkylidenimines are obtained imidazolidines (Eq 162). Similarly, nitriles yield imidazolines (Eq 163) (*2868*).

$$\text{AzH}_2{}^+ \text{ BF}_4{}^- + \text{PhCH}{=}\text{NPh} \longrightarrow \underset{\text{Ph}}{\overset{}{\text{Ph}-\text{N}\bigsqcup\text{NH}_2{}^+}} \text{ BF}_4{}^- \tag{162}$$

$$\text{AzH}_2{}^+ \text{ BF}_4{}^- + \text{RCN} \longrightarrow \underset{\text{R}}{\overset{\text{N}{=}}{\bigsqcup\text{NH}_2{}^+}} \text{ BF}_4{}^- \tag{163}$$

Anionic Reagents. The stability of basic aziridines with respect to ring opening when the aziridine nitrogen is not positively charged has been repeatedly emphasized. If the nucleophile is of sufficient strength, however, such ring opening can be effected.

Ring opening by amide ions (e.g., ethylenimide ion) has already been mentioned (Eq 164) (p. 133) (*963*).

$$(164)$$

Phosphines, as their alkali metal salts, behave in a similar manner (Eq 165) (*1918*).

$$R_2PK + AzH \xrightarrow{\quad\quad} \xrightarrow{\text{hydrolysis}} R_2PCH_2CH_2NH_2 \qquad (165)$$

$$R = Et \text{ or } Ph$$

Inasmuch as Grignard reactions may be considered to involve carbanions, several such ring cleavages of basic aziridines are properly mentioned here. Although treatment of EI with phenylmagnesium bromide only replaces the hydrogen atom on nitrogen, ring-opened product is obtained in good yield (46%) from indolemagnesium bromide (Eqs 166 and 167) (*521, 522*).

$$PhMgBr + AzH \xrightarrow{\quad\quad} PhH + AzMgBr \qquad (166)$$

$$(167)$$

Treatment of 1-methylaziridine with phenylmagnesium bromide gave the ring-opened product in only a 4% yield under the conditions chosen (*521*). The aziridine ring of **47** is apparently much more reactive towards aryl-magnesium halides, giving the indicated (Eq 168) ring-opened products in 83% to 94% yields (*163*).

PhNHCHCONHAr
Ar'CHCOAr'   (or isomer)

$$(168)$$

Similarly, the reaction of excess malonic esters or β-keto esters with 1-alkyl- or 1-arylaziridines in the presence of lithium ethoxide at 80°–145°C may be considered as an example of ring opening by a carbanion (*3361, 4179*). The same reaction has also been performed with the lithium salt of diethyl malonate in benzene (*3362, 3364*).

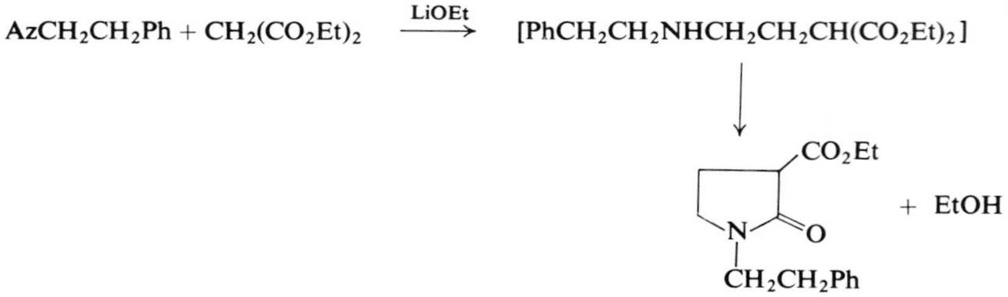

$$AzCH_2CH_2Ph + CH_2(CO_2Et)_2 \xrightarrow{\text{LiOEt}} [PhCH_2CH_2NHCH_2CH_2CH(CO_2Et)_2]$$

+ EtOH

In a 2,2-dimethylaziridine derivative the carbanion attacked the unsubstituted carbon atom (*4179*). The reaction can be stopped at the amino ester stage when 1-*tert*-butyl- or 1-*o*-tolylaziridine is used (*3364a*).

Although these ring-opening reactions are visualized here strictly as involving attack of the anionic species on the aziridine carbon, the possibility of assistance by the cationic species present should not be overlooked.

Alkenes and Alkynes (*Carbon–Carbon Bond Cleavage*). Recently it has been found that a ring-opening reaction, involving cleavage of aziridine carbon–carbon bonds, occurs between certain substituted aziridines and certain olefinic (Eq 169) or acetylenic compounds (Eq 170).

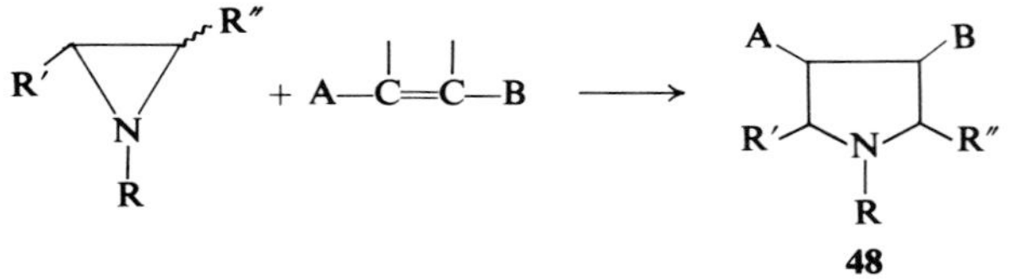

(169)

48

$R = PhCH_2$, Ph, p-BrC_6H_4, p-$MeOC_6H_4$ or c-C_6H_{11}; $R' = R'' =$ Ph, Bz, or CO_2Me with $A = B = Bz$, CO_2Me, or CO_2Et; and olefinic compound = maleic anhydride, maleimide, N-phenylmaleimide, methyl fumarate, or norbornene (*1665, 1672, 1795, 3824a*)

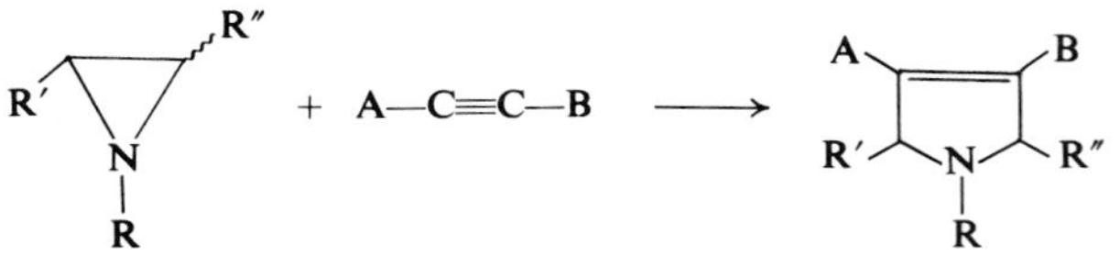

(170)

49

$R =$ Ph or p-BrC_6H_4; $R' = R'' =$ Ph or CO_2Me with $A = B = Bz$, CO_2Et or CF_3, and $A = CO_2Et$, $B = H$ (*1665, 1672, 1799, 4074*); or $R = PhCH_2$,

$$R' + R'' = -CON(C_6H_4OMe\text{-}p)CO-, \quad A = B = CO_2Me \qquad (2754b)$$

When the alkyne was acetylene ($R = p$-$MeOC_6H_4$; $R' = R'' = CO_2Me$) a mixture of 1:1 adducts, presumably the 2- (**50**) and 3-pyrrolines (**49**), was formed (*1795*). When the nitrogen substituent of the aziridine was hydrogen or cyclohexyl ($R' = Bz$; $R'' = Ph$; $A = B = CO_2Me$) the corresponding pyrrole (**51**) or a mixture of **50** and **51**, respectively, was formed (*2800, 2801*).

The products **50** and/or **51** are apparently derived from initially formed **49** (*2801*). The reaction with alkynes (Eq 170) has been shown to be quite stereo-specific, producing *trans*-**49** from *cis*-aziridine (*1799*).

More complex but fundamentally similar examples are presented by the addition of 1,2,3-triphenylaziridine to cyclohexene to form an isoindole system (*4134*) and by that of 2,2-dimethyl-4-phenyl-6-(*p*-nitrophenyl)-1,3-diazabicyclo[3.1.0]hex-3-ene (**51a**) with activated olefinic and acetylenic compounds and with diethyl azodicarboxylate (*4074*).

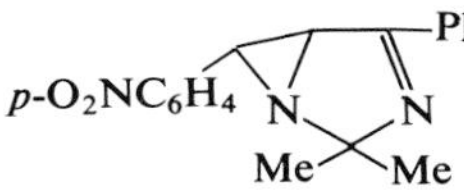

51a

Although data on reactions 169 and 170 are rather limited at this time, the mechanism has been described as a 1,3-dipolar addition involving intermediate **52** (*1795, 1799, 2801, 4074*).

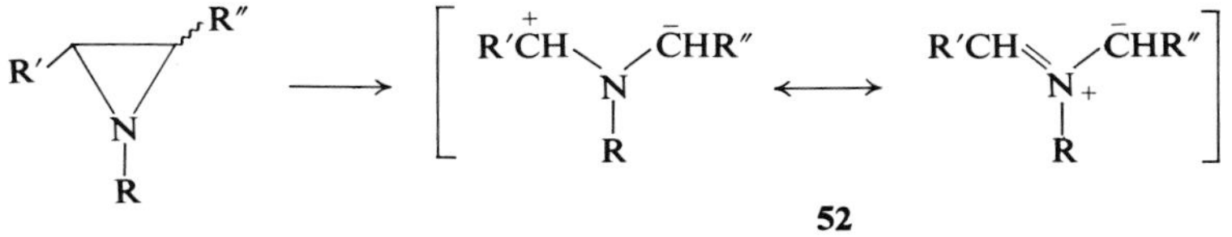

52

Contrary to Eq 169, it is reported that treatment of carbon-unsubstituted aziridines with olefins such as propylene or 1-hexene at high temperatures ($\approx 350°C$) gives 2-alkylpyrrolidines (Eq 171) (*1332*).

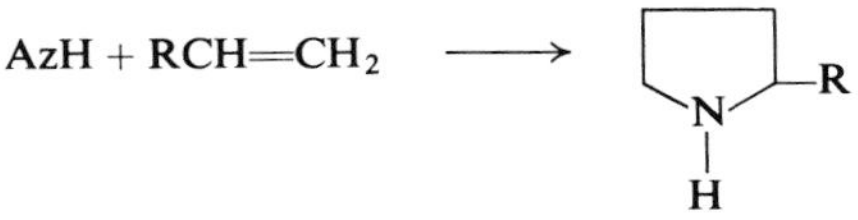

$$AzH + RCH{=}CH_2 \longrightarrow \qquad (171)$$

However, the same author also reports in subsequent patents the formation of 3-substituted pyrrolidines when the olefin was substituted with various electro-negative groups (*1334, 4058*) and 3-alkylpyrrolines from 1-alkynes (*1333*).

Thus, it appears that carbon–carbon bond cleavage also occurs with such simply substituted or nonsubstituted aziridines, but at much higher temperatures.

A most unusual ring opening of 1-ethyl-2-methyleneaziridine by dimethyl acetylenedicarboxylate has recently been reported (Eq 172) (755).

$$\tag{172}$$

RING OPENING OF ACTIVATED AZIRIDINES

Activated aziridines have already been defined; they include structures such as the following.

It will be quickly recognized that certain 1-substituted aziridines, such as 1-phenylaziridine, may be classified as either basic or activated aziridines. The sensitivity of such derivatives to nucleophilic reagents has been mentioned (pp. 107 and 206), and their reactions have been reviewed (1927b). The nature of the nitrogen substituent makes it unnecessary to further "activate" the aziridine ring by making the nitrogen positively charged (as with basic aziridines) in order to promote a ring-opening reaction.

Solvolysis or Ring Opening by Hydrogen Halides—Mechanism. In the presence of acid, an activated aziridine will undergo an extremely rapid ring opening. This is most dramatically illustrated by the acid-catalyzed alcoholysis of an activated aziridine (Eq 173) (963).

$$
EtO_2CAz + MeOH \quad \xrightarrow[\substack{50°C,\ 24\ hr}]{\text{no catalyst}} \quad <5\%\ \text{conversion}
$$

$$\tag{173}$$

$$
\xrightarrow[\substack{\text{room temperature,}\\ 10\ min}]{H_2SO_4} \quad \substack{100\%\ \text{conversion to}\\ MeOCH_2CH_2NHCO_2Et\\ +\ \text{other products}}
$$

This great difference in rates for the catalyzed and noncatalyzed reactions is interpreted as indicating the existence of an extremely reactive intermediate which, in this case, might be depicted as structure **53** or **54**.

53   **54**

Thus, when an activated aziridine is treated with a hydrogen halide, the reaction actually involves a nucleophilic substitution by halide ion at the ring carbon atom of a species analogous to **53** or **54** (Eq 174)

$$AzA + HX \rightleftharpoons AzAH^+ \ X^- \quad \text{rapid} \qquad (174)$$

$$\downarrow$$

$$XCH_2CH_2NHA \qquad \text{rate determining}$$

In Eq 174 A may be any group which satisfies the definition given for activated aziridines. It should also be noted that the ring-opened product contains an amide nitrogen atom (very weakly basic) and therefore the competing secondary reaction represented by Eq. 175 is not as important as in the case of basic aziridines (although it does exist, the more so in acid-catalyzed ring opening by weak nucleophiles).

$$XCH_2CH_2NHA + AzAH^+ \rightarrow X(CH_2CH_2NA)_2H \qquad (175)$$

Thus, in contrast to the reaction of hydrogen halides with basic aziridines, the same reaction with activated aziridines may give high yields of ring-opened products when performed with only stoichiometric amounts of reagents.

A very large number of activated aziridines have been treated with hydrogen halides and there is little value in attempting to cite every such example. Such ring opening is reported in many of the references to activated aziridines shown in Tables 3-XIII, 3-XIV, 3-XV, 3-XVII, 3-XIX, and 3-XX. Two references limited to the addition of hydrogen halides to activated aziridines are given here for completeness (*3248, 4005*).

Certain activated aziridines undergo isomerization when treated with a hydrogen halide (p. 289). An example is provided by various 1-aziridinyl-*s*-triazines (Eq 176) (*3127*).

(176)

Similarly, aziridines possessing a 1-thiocarbamyl substituent give 2-thiazolines with aqueous HCl (*258, 888, 1925, 1930, 3553*) and reaction 177 was presumed to involve such isomerization (*1772*).

$$\tag{177}$$

For carbon-substituted activated aziridines, ring opening may apparently occur by an S_N1 mechanism, especially in 2,2-dialkyl derivatives. Kinetic and stereochemical evidence (such as is available for basic aziridines) is lacking, however. The most frequently used criterion for such mechanism is the formation of product derived from cleavage of the carbon–nitrogen bond at the more highly substituted carbon atom in unsymmetrically carbon-substituted derivatives. Of course, the analogy to similar carbon-substituted basic aziridines is often cited and is indeed applicable in many cases. Since activated aziridines are sensitive to nucleophiles in the absence of acid, further support for an S_N1 ring opening is possible where the nature of the predominant isomer formed may be changed by changing from acidic or neutral to basic conditions, as in the alcoholysis of 1-benzenesulfonyl-2,2-dimethylaziridine (Eq 178) (*2436, 3032*).

$$\tag{178}$$

In such a case the rate of reaction by an S_N2 process at the unsubstituted aziridine carbon atom is markedly increased (presumably without affecting the rate of the S_N1 reaction) by increasing the nucleophilicity of the attacking species (ROH versus RO^-).

It might well be expected that highly carbon-substituted activated aziridines may undergo rearrangement during acid-catalyzed or neutral solvolysis. One example is provided by the acid treatment of a steroid aziridine (Eq 179) (*983*).

$$(179)$$

It has been suggested that activated aziridines have a greater tendency to undergo ring opening by an S_N1 process than the protonated forms of the corresponding basic aziridines (*3032*). The predominant products of Eq 180 are consistent with this view; where A = H, the main product is **55** (*3131*), but where A = PhNHCS (*888*) or PhSO$_2$ (*2436*), **56** predominates.

$$\text{Me}_2\text{C(CH}_2\text{Cl)NHA} \quad \text{or} \quad \text{Me}_2\text{CClCH}_2\text{NHA}$$
$$\text{55} \qquad\qquad\qquad \text{56}$$

$$(180)$$

Indeed, it seems reasonable to extend this concept to include a variation with different substituents on nitrogen; as the electron-withdrawing ability of the

Table 3-XXIX

POSITIONAL ISOMERS FROM RING OPENING OF ACTIVATED AZIRIDINES
BY HYDROHALIC ACIDS

				% Yield		
X	R'	R²	Ar	I	II	References
Cl	Me	H	Ph	—	Only	*1448*
Br	PhCH₂	H	Ph	—	65	*1452*
Cl	ClCH₂	H	Ph	—	86	*1448, 2058*
Cl	BrCH₂	H	Ph	—	68	*1453*
Br	BrCH₂	H	Ph	—	68	*1454*
Cl	Ph	H	p-MeC₆H₄	Only	—	*2077*
Br	Ph	H	p-MeC₆H₄	Only	—	*2077*
I	Ph	H	p-MeC₆H₄	Only	—	*2077*
Cl	Bz	H	Ph	—	91	*2551*
Cl	Me	Me	—ᵃ	55–80	—	*2045, 2436*
Cl	BrCH₂	Me	Ph	—	Only	*541*

ᵃ Ar = Ph, *o*- or *p*-MeC₆H₄, *m*-O₂NC₆H₄, *p*-Br.

nitrogen substituent is increased, the greater will be the tendency towards an S_N1 reaction.

Isomers resulting from ring opening of a number of unsymmetrically carbon-substituted activated aziridines (1-arylsulfonyl derivatives) by hydrogen halides are shown in Table 3-XXIX. The stereospecific ring opening of methyl 2,3-acetyl-4,6-O-benzylidene-2,3-dideoxy-α-D-allopyranoside by the same acids demonstrates not only selective formation of a positional isomer owing to the fused ring system but also the trans opening of the aziridine ring and the lability of the activated aziridine ring compared to the benzylidene acetal moiety in acid medium (550). Ring-opening solvolysis (or reaction with hydrogen halides) of carbon-unsubstituted activated aziridines may be considered as an S_N2 process under either acid, basic, or neutral conditions. The following transition states, illustrated with a 1-sulfonylaziridine, are presumably involved (Eqs 181, 182, and 183).

In reaction 181 the protonated activated aziridine, present in very low concentration, is the reactive aziridine species. In reaction 182 the reactive species is the activated aziridine itself, but alcoholysis is catalyzed by the alkoxide ion because of the high nucleophilicity of that ion. In both reactions 182 and 183 it is possible that proton transfer from the solvent to the sulfonamide anion may be involved in the transition state.

The side reaction (polymerization) analogous to Eq 175 is the result of successful competition by the amide group of the ring-opened product for the protonated activated aziridine in the case of acid catalysis or by the product amide ion in the case of base catalysis. Such side reaction can be significant in both acid (963) and base (3183) catalysis and is obviously dependent on the concentration of activated aziridine, as shown for the acid-catalyzed methanolysis of ethyl 1-aziridinecarboxylate (Eq 184) (963, 1598).

$$AzCO_2Et + MeOH \xrightarrow{H_2SO_4} MeOCH_2CH_2NHCO_2Et$$

57

$+$

$$MeO[CH_2CH_2N]_nH$$
$$| $$
$$CO_2Et$$

58

$n = 2, 3,$ etc.

(184)

[AzCO₂Et] (moles/liter)	Yield		
	57	**58** $n = 2$	**58** $n > 2$
1.0	84	small	—
2.0	41	17	7

When the activated aziridine has a carbonyl group attached to the aziridine nitrogen, base-catalyzed solvolysis may involve only reaction of the solvent at the carbonyl carbon atom (*963, 1660, 3032*) whereas solvolysis under neutral conditions may give a different result (*963, 1598*) as shown in Eqs 185 and 186 for ethyl 1-aziridinecarboxylate.

$$AzCO_2Et + EtOH \begin{cases} \xrightarrow{EtO^-} AzH + (EtO)_2CO & (185) \\ \xrightarrow{neutral} AzCH_2CH_2NHCO_2Et + (EtO)_2CO & (186) \end{cases}$$

59

This base-catalyzed solvolysis of a carboxylic amide to form an ester and an amine is unusually rapid when the amine moiety of the amide is an aziridine, as shown from a rough comparison of ethanolysis rates under the same conditions for 1-acetylaziridine and *N,N*-diethylacetamide (Eq 187) (*963*).

$$AcAz + EtOH \xrightarrow{EtO^-} AzH + EtOAc$$
100% in <10 min
at 25°C

$$AcNEt_2 + EtOH \xrightarrow{EtO^-} \text{No reaction in 30 min}$$
at 50°C

(187)

However, the rate is significantly dependent on the structure of the activated aziridine (and probably also that of the hydroxylic reagent) and for derivatives which contain sterically hindered carbonyl groups, both base-catalyzed and "neutral" solvolysis results in ring opening, as shown for 1-mesitoylaziridine (Eq 188) (*3032*).

$$2,4,6\text{-}Me_3C_6H_2COAz + EtOH \xrightarrow{EtO^-} 2,4,6\text{-}Me_3C_6H_2CONHCH_2CH_2OEt$$

$$(188)$$

The formation of **59** in reaction 186 is interpreted as the result of an initially small amount of product corresponding to reaction 185. As the free aziridine is generated, it produces some alkoxide ion and reaction 185 (becoming autocatalytic) then occurs but at a rate which is comparable to or lower than that of ring opening of the activated aziridine by the basic aziridine (see also pp. 133 and 266). Indeed, in cases where reaction 185 (base-catalyzed solvolysis) is slow for structural reasons, the result may be essentially that of reaction 186 (*3465*) and/or reaction 188. In one case, the production of only the ring-opened compound by solvolysis under neutral conditions of an ethyl 1-aziridine-carboxylate containing carbon substituents (nonhindered carbonyl) was apparently due to the high reactivity of the aziridine carbon atom (*506*). It is thus clear that the close interplay of relative rates at the two available reaction sites is of utmost importance in determining the products of solvolysis of activated aziridines possessing a 1-carbonyl substituent.

Rate constants for ethanolysis under neutral conditions of activated aziridines containing 1-arylsulfonyl and 1-aroyl substituents are shown in Table 3-XXX. Only those derivatives for which the *N*-(2-ethoxyethyl) amide product may be expected are included. Rate measurements have been reported for the hydrolysis of various 1-phosphorylated aziridines (*268, 343, 2930*) and the reactions shown to follow first-order kinetics. However, such hydrolysis is more complicated, apparently giving a variety of products including the free aziridine (*268*). Also, the use of buffers (*343, 2930*) makes it impossible to assess the contribution to the rate from reaction of the buffer anion.

It has been found, qualitatively, that the trans-diaxial ring opening of methyl 4,6-*O*-benzylidene-2,3-dideoxy-2,3-epimino-*N*-tosyl-α-D-manno-pyranoside by hydroxide or methoxide ions occurs at a rate considerably lower than that of the corresponding epoxide (*252*).

Alkyl Halides. Ring opening of activated aziridines with alkyl halides (Eqs 189 and 190) occurs in a manner analogous to ring opening of basic aziridines by these reagents (*1528, 3709, 3710*).

$$Az_2SO + MeI \xrightarrow[\text{overnight, 0°C}]{} (ICH_2CH_2NMe)_2SO \qquad (189)$$

$$(EtO)_2P(O)Az + PhCH_2Cl \xrightarrow[\text{6 hr, 135°–185°C}]{} ClCH_2CH_2N(CH_2Ph)P(O)(OEt_2)$$

$$(190)$$

Formation of the quaternized aziridines from basic aziridines was considered a prerequisite for reaction of the aziridine with the halide ion. It appears reasonable to invoke the same explanation for reaction of activated aziridines

Table 3-XXX

RATE CONSTANTS FOR ETHANOLYSIS[a] OF ACTIVATED AZIRIDINES[b]

$$AzA + EtOH \rightarrow EtOCH_2CH_2NHA$$

$$k = k^0 \times 10^{-n} \quad (sec^{-1})$$

Aziridine substituents	A	T (°C)	k^0	n	$\Delta H^{\ddagger}$ (kcal mole^{-1})	$\Delta S^{\ddagger}$ (e.u. mole^{-1})
None	$PhSO_2$	80	3.78	5	—	—
	$PhSO_2$	90	8.66	5	—	—
	$PhSO_2$	100	2.03	4	22.4	−15.6
	$2,4,6\text{-}Me_3C_6H_2CO$	80	2.0	5	—	—
	$2,6\text{-}Cl_2C_6H_3CO$	80	3.09	4	—	—
2-Me	$PhSO_2$	80	2.66	5	—	—
	$PhSO_2$	90	5.38	5	—	—
	$PhSO_2$	100	9.86	5	17.8	−29.8
cis-2,3-Me$_2$	$PhSO_2$	80	1.24	5	—	—
	$PhSO_2$	90	2.68	5	—	—
	$PhSO_2$	100	5.52	5	20.6	−20.6
trans-2,3-Me$_2$	$PhSO_2$	80	1.43	5	—	—
	$PhSO_2$	90	2.63	5	—	—
	$PhSO_2$	100	4.86	5	16.7	−34.2
2,2-Me$_2$	$PhSO_2$	70	7.1	5	—	—
	$PhSO_2$	80	1.48	4	—	—
	$PhSO_2$	90	2.80	4	—	—
	$PhSO_2$	100	5.80	4	17.0	−28.6
2,2-Me$_2$	$p\text{-}O_2NC_6H_4SO_2$	80	1.07	3	—	—

[a] Under neutral conditions.
[b] Resnick *et al.* (*3032*).

(Eq 191), even though these derivatives are much weaker bases (thus weaker nucleophiles) than the basic aziridines.

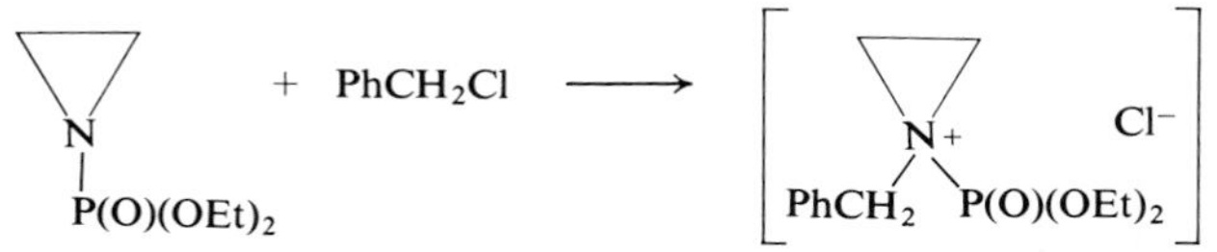

$$(191)$$

The wide variation in reaction conditions required, as shown above in reactions 189 and 190 (dependent to some extent on the 1-substituent), is apparently due primarily to the ease with which these derivatives enter into such nucleophilic displacements.

Phenols. Surprisingly, there are only a few reports describing preparative reactions between phenols and activated aziridines. The success of such reaction apparently depends to a large extent on the structure of the aziridine. Although 1-benzoylaziridine gave such a ring opening with phenol (Eq 192) (*2687*) the failure of the same reaction performed with an alkyl 1-aziridinecarboxylate (*1936*) and a 1-phosphorylated aziridine (*1526*) was given as evidence for the lack of reactivity of the aziridine ring in such derivatives.

$$AzBz + PhOH \rightarrow PhOCH_2CH_2NHBz \qquad (192)$$

Apparently phenols are insufficiently acidic to act as acid catalysts for this reaction (i.e., to protonate the activated aziridine) since ring opening of an alkyl 1-aziridinecarboxylate is readily effected in the presence of an added acid such as boron trifluoride (*1595*).

In practically every case, the major side reaction of basic aziridines can be attributed to the reaction of product amine with the protonated form of the aziridine (formation of polymeric products). However, activated aziridines can undergo not only this reaction but also a variety of isomerizations and/or reactions involving the 1-substituent. For example, the apparent conflict in the results shown in reactions 193, 194, and 195 may be attributed to the relative ease with which the various side reactions leading to isomerized products occur.

$$PhO_2CAz + PhOH \longrightarrow (PhOCH_2CH_2NH)_2CO \quad (1936) \qquad (196)$$

The reported formation of polymer in reactions 193 and 194 may actually represent only that of intractable residues and not necessarily reaction of ring-opened product with the aziridinyl derivative. The ring-opening reaction of phenyl 1-aziridinecarboxylate, shown as reaction 196, is probably best interpreted in terms of the isomerization leading to 2-substituted ethyl isocyanates (Eq 197) (p. 291).

$$AzCO_2Ar \xrightarrow{ArO^-} ArOCH_2CH_2NCO \qquad (197)$$

A number of examples exist, mentioned elsewhere in appropriate sections, wherein di- or polyphenolic compounds have been treated with di- or poly-activated aziridines to produce resinous materials.

Carboxylic Acids. A variety of activated aziridines have been treated with carboxylic acids. Structural types include the following:

Activated aziridines	References
$RCOAz$	*1923, 2687*
RO_2CAz	*1928, 1936*
$ArNHCOAz$	*1930, 3031*
$ArNHCSAz$	*1930*
$ArSO_2Az$	*1324, 2077*
$\overset{O}{\underset{\vert}{\overset{\uparrow}{-P-Az}}}$	*489, 736, 1524, 1525, 1990, 2115, 2228, 2939, 2939a*
(phosphazene structure)—Az	*4156*

Ring opening of all these derivatives occurs to give some of the expected product according to Eq 198.

$$AzA + RCO_2H \rightarrow RCO_2CH_2CH_2NHA \qquad (198)$$

However, the variety of side reactions common to activated aziridines and characteristic of the specific 1-substituent (isomerizations, etc.) is amply illustrated by reactions with carboxylic acids.

Ring opening of simple 1-acyl-, 1-aroyl-, and 1-arylsulfonylaziridines apparently occurs readily without problems (*1923, 2077, 2687*). For example, essentially a quantitative yield of the expected product was obtained from 1-tosyl-2-phenylaziridine and an excess of acetic acid (*2077*). The secondary reaction between the ring-opened product and the aziridine (yielding polymeric products) may occur, however, when equimolar amounts of activated aziridine and carboxylic acid are employed (*963, 1598, 1990*).

With 1-aziridinethiocarboxanilide the course of the reaction is dependent to some extent on reaction conditions (Eq 199) (*1930*).

$$\text{PhNHCSAz} + \text{HOAc} \xrightarrow{\text{refluxing HOAc}} \underset{\text{NHPh}}{\overset{\displaystyle \square}{N \diagdown S}} \qquad (199)$$

$$\xrightarrow{\text{EtOAc}} \text{AcOCH}_2\text{CH}_2\text{NHCSNHPh} + \text{polymer}$$

From 1-aziridinecarboxanilide, N,N'-diphenylurea and acetanilide are obtained in addition to ring-opened products (Eq 200) (*1930, 3031*).

$$\text{PhNHCOAz} + \text{HOAc} \rightarrow \text{AcOCH}_2\text{CH}_2\text{NHCONHPh} + (\text{PhNH})_2\text{CO} + \text{PhNHAc} \qquad (200)$$

A mixed-anhydride structure, formed from phenyl isocyanate and glacial acetic acid, was suggested as an intermediate in this reaction since it decomposed in such a manner (Eq 201) (*3031*).

$$\underset{\text{PhNHC}-\text{O}-\text{Ac}}{\overset{\displaystyle \text{O}}{\overset{\displaystyle \|}{}}} \xrightarrow{\text{heat}} (\text{PhNH})_2\text{CO} + \text{CO}_2 + \text{PhNHAc} \qquad (201)$$

Ring opening of phenyl 1-aziridinecarboxylate by benzoic acid gave both the expected ring-opened product and N,N'-bis(2-benzoyloxyethyl)urea (Eq 202) (*1936*).

$$\text{PhO}_2\text{CAz} + \text{BzOH} \rightarrow \text{BzOCH}_2\text{CH}_2\text{NHCO}_2\text{Ph} + (\text{BzOCH}_2\text{CH}_2\text{NH})_2\text{CO} \qquad (202)$$

Like other ring-opening reactions of aryl 1-aziridinecarboxylates, the formation of the bis(2-substituted ethyl)urea is best interpreted in terms of isomerization leading to 2-substituted ethyl isocyanates. This side reaction is not a problem with most alkyl 1-aziridinecarboxylates, a fact consistent with the presumed mechanism for the isomerization (see p. 291).

1-Phosphorylated aziridines upon treatment with carboxylic acids give quite respectable yields of ring-opened products (*1524, 1525, 2258, 3339, 4063*). Attention to reaction conditions is important, however, since the products may undergo secondary reactions under conditions not very dissimilar to those necessary to effect ring opening (*2258, 2356, 3541*) (e.g., Eq 203).

$$>P(O)Az + RCO_2H \xrightarrow[\text{toluene, 120°C, 4 hr}]{} >P(O)NHCH_2CH_2O_2CR \quad (203)$$

$$\overset{\text{excess } RCO_2H}{\underset{150°C, 3 hr}{\diagdown}} \qquad \overset{185°C}{\underset{30 min}{\diagup}}$$

$$RCONHCH_2CH_2O_2CR$$

The rearrangement shown by Eq 204 was shown to occur at room temperature in the presence of catalytic amounts of sodium methoxide (*2115*).

$$(EtO)_2P(O)NHCH_2CH_2OAc \rightarrow (EtO)_2P(O)OCH_2CH_2NHAc \quad (204)$$

Thus, the presence of basic impurities in the ring-opened products must be avoided. Such rearrangement is to be expected in the absence of catalyst but at a much higher temperature.

Attempts have been made to determine the kinetics for ring opening of tris(2-methyl-1-aziridinyl)phosphine oxide (MAPO) with carboxylic acids (Eq 205) (*489, 1990, 2258*).

$$(2\text{-MeAz})_3PO + RCO_2H \rightarrow (RCO_2CH_2CHMeNH)_3PO$$
$$+ \quad (205)$$
$$(RCO_2CHMeCH_2NH)_3PO$$

The reports give conflicting results, and it is clear that reaction 205 is complicated at least by homopolymerization of the aziridine (reaction of ring-opened product with aziridine derivative) (*1990, 3393*). It was shown, however, that the rate depends on the acid strength of the carboxylic acid (faster for stronger acids) and on the solvent. The rate was also significantly increased by addition of catalytic amounts of a very strong acid, such as *p*-toluenesulfonic acid (*1990*), which incidentally can itself open such rings (*2939*).

Of interest is a consideration of the stepwise reactions involved when a tris(1-aziridinyl)phosphine oxide such as APO (**60**) is treated with a carboxylic acid (Eq 206).

$$Az_3P(O) + HOAc \xrightarrow{(a)} Az_2P(O)NHCH_2CH_2OAc \xrightarrow{(b)}$$
$$\quad\text{60} \qquad\qquad\qquad\qquad \text{61}$$

$$AzP(O)(NHCH_2CH_2OAc)_2 \xrightarrow{(c)} P(O)(NHCH_2CH_2OAc)_3 \quad (206)$$
$$\qquad\quad \text{62} \qquad\qquad\qquad\qquad \text{63}$$

The relative rates for these three reactions have been indicated as (a) > (b) > (c) (*489*). This order is consistent with expectations, since an aziridine ring attached to a phosphorus atom bearing one or more acyclic amide groups would be less readily opened by a nucleophile in the rate-determining step (greater conjugation by acyclic amide nitrogen than by aziridinyl nitrogen; see p. 206).

$$>P(O)Az + RCO_2H \underset{\text{rapid}}{\rightleftarrows} \quad >P(O)AzH^+ \quad RCO_2^- \xrightarrow{\text{rate determining}}$$

$$>P(O)NHCH_2CH_2OAc \qquad (207)$$

However, the reverse order would not be unreasonable. The order of basicity of the various ring-opened products in reaction 206 is **63 > 62 > 61 > 60**. The concentration of protonated activated aziridine from the equilibrium in Eq 207 may be considered as significantly greater for **61** than for **60**, for **62** than for **61**, etc.

This latter explanation may be used to account for the relative rates of ring opening of **64** and **65** by acetic acid in toluene, wherein **65** reacts faster than **64** (*963*).

$$(EtO)_2P(O)Az \qquad\qquad (Me_2N)_2P(O)Az$$

64   **65**

The reverse order in rates is observed for ring opening for these derivatives by amines, a reaction which does not involve the protonated activated aziridine species (*963, 3338*).

Thiols and Other Compounds Containing Mercapto Groups. Included in this section are ring-opening reactions of activated aziridines with hydrogen sulfide, thiols, thiocarboxylic acids, *O,O*-dialkyl dithiophosphates, thioureas, and carbon disulfide. The activated aziridines studied have been various.

Activated aziridines	References
RCOAz and ArCOAz	*1174, 1302, 1480, 1798, 1923, 2199, 2200, 2202, 3443, 4184*
RO$_2$CAz and ArO$_2$CAz	*1928, 1931, 1932, 1936, 3181, 3369*
ArNHCOAz and ArNHCSAz	*1174, 1930, 1933, 1939*
RCSAz	*1921*
H$_2$NC(=NNO$_2$)Az	*2348*
ArSO$_2$Az	*1324, 2436, 2687, 2750*
>P(O)Az types	*244a, 1526, 1920, 3339*
>P–N=P–Az / N–P=N types	*4156*

As one might expect, ring opening of these derivatives by thiols, which are highly nucleophilic, gives the expected product (Eq 208) with only infrequent observation of side reaction leading to isomerized products.

$$RSH + AzA \rightarrow RSCH_2CH_2NHA \qquad (208)$$

For example, whereas other ring-opening reactions attempted with 1-aziridine-carboxanilide gave problems, an 81% yield of product corresponding to Eq 208 was obtained from thiophenol (*1930*). Similarly, good yields of ring-opened product could be obtained from thiophenol and aryl 1-aziridine-carboxylates. However, reaction leading to N,N-bis[2-(phenylthio)ethyl]urea did occur to some extent depending on reaction conditions (*1936*).

With hydrogen sulfide (*1480, 2199, 2200, 2202, 2436, 2687, 4156, 4184, 4185*) it is possible to produce good yields of either the corresponding thiol or the sulfide, depending primarily on the mole ratio of hydrogen sulfide to aziridine employed (Eq 209).

$$H_2S + AzA \longrightarrow HSCH_2CH_2NHA \xrightarrow{+AzA} (ANHCH_2CH_2)_2S \qquad (209)$$

Disulfides may be obtained by treatment of the aziridine derivative with hydrogen sulfide and sulfur (*1174*) or by air oxidation of thiols obtained in Eq 209 (*1302*).

Other sulfur nucleophiles which have been used in such ring-opening reactions include thiocarboxylic acids (*2650a, 2726, 3181, 3182, 3443*), for which a trans opening of the aziridine ring has been demonstrated (*3443*), O,O-dialkyl dithiophosphates (*3268a*), thiourea (Eq 210), and carbon disulfide (Eq 211).

$$ArSO_2Az + (H_2N)_2CS + HX \longrightarrow ArSO_2NHCH_2CH_2S\overset{\overset{\displaystyle NH_2^+ \ X^-}{\|}}{-C}NH_2 \qquad (210)$$
$$(244a, 1256)$$

$$2,2\text{-}MeAzSO_2Ar + CS_2 \xrightarrow{KOH} \qquad (542, 2438) \qquad (211)$$

Of interest in connection with positional isomers derived from unsymmetric-ally carbon-substituted activated aziridines, Eq 211 (in the presence of base) gave the product wherein the nucleophile was attached to the less-substituted aziridine carbon atom. The same aziridine treated with hydrogen sulfide also gave this isomer (*2436*); but treatment with potassium thiocyanate in acetic acid produced a quantitative yield of the other isomer (Eq 212) (*2438*).

$$2,2\text{-}Me_2AzSO_2Ar + KSCN \xrightarrow{HOAc \ solvent} ArSO_2NHCH_2CMe_2SCN \qquad (212)$$

It may be recalled that treatment of 2,2-dimethylaziridine with potassium thiocyanate in aqueous acid gave the isomer with the thiocyano group attached to the less substituted aziridine carbon atom (465). These data support the idea that activated aziridines have a greater tendency to undergo ring opening by an S_N1 process than the protonated forms of the corresponding basic aziridine.

Also pertinent in this connection is ring opening of the bicyclic aziridine **66** by thiophenol under acid conditions and by thiophenoxide ion (Eq 213) (1324).

$$(213)$$

Obviously, ring opening of activated aziridines by the alkali metal salts of thiols as well as the thiols themselves occurs readily (1324, 1798, 2687, 2750) and a base may thus act as a catalyst (1932). In certain derivatives (e.g., aryl 1-aziridinecarboxylates, simple 1-acylaziridines in aqueous medium), however, basic conditions may cause side reaction to occur more readily (1936).

Amines. The ready ring opening of activated aziridines by amines is in marked contrast to the same reaction with basic aziridines. In the latter, such ring opening occurs only in the presence of acidic catalysts and may be ascribed to the reactivity of the aziridinium ions (1583). It is unlikely that a truly acid-catalyzed ring opening of activated aziridines by amines (in the sense previously mentioned, p. 249) can be effected.

Variations in the 1-substituents for activated aziridines which have been treated with amines include the following structural types:

Activated aziridines	References
(Ar)RCOAz	1583, 1801, 1850, 2687, 2688, 3412, 3459, 3814
(Ar)RO₂CAz	1583, 1808, 1928, 1933
(ArNH)R₂NCOAz	350, 1808, 1930
ArSO₂Az	1426, 1801, 1847, 1850, 2045, 2437, 2447, 2476, 2687, 2688
>P(O)Az	963, 1524–1526, 1920, 4062
2-Triazinyl-Az	963

Ring opening of activated aziridines by amines may be pictured as a simple S_N2 process (Eq 214).

$$R_2NH \quad \triangleright\!\!-N\!\!-\!\!A \longrightarrow \left[\begin{array}{c} H^{\delta+} \\ | \\ R_2\overset{}{N}\cdots\cdots CH_2\cdots\cdots\overset{\delta-}{N}\!\!-\!\!A \\ | \\ CH_2 \end{array} \right] \qquad (214)$$

67

As might be anticipated from the structure of transition state **67**, the reaction occurs more readily in hydroxylic solvents and may indeed involve proton transfer in the transition state. The reaction has been shown to follow second-order kinetics, being first order in amine and first order in activated aziridine (*963, 1583, 3338*). The Hammett rho constants for reaction of *m*- and *p*-substituted anilines with 1-acetylaziridine and ethyl 1-aziridinecarboxylate in ethanol at 50°C were found to be −1.26 and −1.47, respectively (*963, 1583*). Rate constants used to derive these values are shown in Table 3-XXXI. These values are comparable to that obtained for the same reaction with methyl tosylate (−1.48) under the same conditions (*1583*).

The rates for reaction of various activated aziridines with piperidine (*963*) and pyrrolidine (*3338*) are also shown in Table 3-XXXI. These data appear to be consistent with the definition of activated aziridines and an S_N2 mechanism in that those derivatives which give the highest rate contain 1-substituents that for other reasons might be expected best to stabilize the partial negative charge formed on the aziridine nitrogen in the transition state.

Ring opening of unsymmetrically carbon-substituted activated aziridines by amines gives that isomer which is formed by substitution at the less-substituted aziridine carbon atom (*2045, 2437*). For cyclohexenimine containing an *N*-benzoyl substitutent, a trans opening of the aziridine ring has been demonstrated (*3459, 3814*).

Whereas reaction of equimolar amounts of aromatic primary amines and activated aziridines gives a quantitative yield of the single ring-opened product **68** (Eq 215) (*1583*), aliphatic primary amines give both mono- (**69**) and di-adducts (**70**) according to Eq 216 (*963, 1426, 1524, 3547, 4067*).

$$ArNH_2 + AzA \longrightarrow ArNHCH_2CH_2NHA \qquad (215)$$

68

$$RNH_2 + AzA \longrightarrow RNHCH_2CH_2NHA \qquad (216)$$

69

$\Big\downarrow + AzA$

$$RN(CH_2CH_2NHA)_2$$

70

Table 3-XXXI

REACTION RATES OF AMINES WITH ACTIVATED AZIRIDINES

$$ArNH_2 + AzA \xrightarrow[\text{EtOH, 50°}]{} ArNHCH_2CH_2NHA$$

A	Ar	$10^3 k$ (liters mole^{-1} min^{-1})
Ac	p-MeOC$_6$H$_4$	7.85
	p-MeC$_6$H$_4$	7.05
	m-MeC$_6$H$_4$	4.98
	Ph	4.30
	p-ClC$_6$H$_4$	1.94
EtOCO	p-MeOC$_6$H$_4$	7.67
	p-MeC$_6$H$_4$	6.33
	m-MeC$_6$H$_4$	4.11
	Ph	3.58
	p-ClC$_6$H$_4$	1.74

$$\text{NH} + AzA \xrightarrow[\text{MeCN, 50°}]{} \text{N—CH}_2\text{CH}_2\text{NHA}$$

A	$k = k^0 \times 10^{-n}$ (liters mole^{-1} min^{-1})	
	k^0	n
p-O$_2$NC$_6$H$_4$CO		
MeO—triazine—OMe	Too fast to measure accurately[a]	
	3.04	2
Ac	2.00	2
EtOCO	1.49	2
(EtO)$_2$P(O)	1.67	3
Me$_2$N—triazine—NMe$_2$	3.12	4
(Me$_2$N)$_2$P(O)	3.33	5
Me$_2$NCO	Too slow to measure accurately	

Table 3-XXXI—*continued*

AzA	T (°C)	$10^4 k$ (liters mole^{-1} min^{-1})	$\Delta H^{\ddagger}$ (kcal/mole)	$\Delta S^{\ddagger}$ (e.u./mole)
$(Me_2N)_2P(O)Az$	50	8.7		
	40	3.8		
	30	1.5	16.6	−21.2
$(Me_2N)_2P(O)$-2-MeAz	50	2.7		
	40	1.2		
	30	0.45	17.3	−23.2
$(EtO)_2P(O)Az$	30	22.5		

$^a k = 2.1 \times 10^{-1}$ at 26.5°C.

Apparently the nucleophilicity of the amino group in the aliphatic amine **69** is comparable to that of the original reactant amine. The tendency to form diadduct at a rate competitive with formation of monoadduct appears to be a function of the basicity or nucleophilicity of the reactant amine since a diadduct was produced in low yield during ring opening by the more basic substituted aniline *p*-phenetidine (*1933*). The relative amounts of **69** and **70** formed from reaction of equimolar amounts of primary aliphatic amine and ethyl 1-aziridine-carboxylate (Eq 216, A = CO$_2$Et) in acetonitrile solvent is as follows (*963, 4067*):

	% Yield	
R	69	70
n-Bu	48	49
iso-Bu	51	42
tert-Bu	64	29

Formation of isomerized products is not an important side reaction in ring opening of activated aziridines with amines. Polymerization in such reactions with 1-aziridinecarboxanilides and 1-aziridinethiocarboxanilides has been claimed (*1930*) but this needs reinvestigation.

Aryl 1-aziridinecarboxylates undergo a secondary reaction (Eq 217) at a rate which is comparable to that of ring opening (*1933*).

$$ArNH_2 + Ar'O_2CAz \longrightarrow ArNHCH_2CH_2NHCO_2Ar'$$

$$\text{(217)}$$

The reaction between 1-acylaziridines or alkyl 1-aziridinecarboxylates and amines, when conducted in water or primary alcohols as solvents, forms products wherein the solvent has undergone reaction at the carbonyl carbon atom and displaced the aziridine (Eq 218) (*963*).

$$\text{(218)}$$

$$\text{CH}_2\text{CH}_2\text{NHCO}_2\text{Et} + \text{AzH} + (\text{EtO})_2\text{CO}$$

(81%)

The extent of this side reaction is a function of the basicity of the amine reactant (*963*) (note that such side reaction is not observed with the weakly basic aromatic amines). The solvolysis part of reaction 218 does not take place in isopropyl or *tert*-butyl alcohol, a result which may be due to several factors including lower acidity and increased steric requirement of these alcohols. This side reaction is similar to the base-catalyzed solvolysis of 1-acylaziridines (see p. 253) and derivatives which contain sterically hindered carbonyl groups would not be expected to undergo it. It is noteworthy that in reaction 218 no product is obtained which corresponds to reaction of piperidine at the carboxylate group (**71**) or ethanol at an aziridine carbon atom (**72**).

$$\text{EtOCH}_2\text{CH}_2\text{NHCO}_2\text{Et}$$

71   **72**

Ring opening of activated aziridines by hydrazine occurs in the same manner as reaction with amines, as found for 1-aziridinecarboxanilide (*1172*).

In the aminolysis of the γ-oxo acylated aziridine **72a**, the ring-opened product, if formed, is recyclized (*4195*).

Few examples exist of ring opening of activated aziridines by tertiary amines in the presence of acid to form the quaternary ring-opened product.

72 a

A reaction of an α,α-dichloroperfluoroalkyl ester with EI and triethylamine to produce such a product (*460*) (Eq 219) may involve such ring opening.

$$Cl(CF_2)_6CO_2CCl_2(CF_2)_6Cl + 2AzH + 2Et_3N \longrightarrow [2Cl(CF_2)_6COAz + 2Et_3N \cdot HCl]$$

$$\downarrow \qquad\qquad (219)$$

$$2Cl(CF_2)_6CONHCH_2CH_2\overset{+}{N}Et_3 \quad Cl^-$$

Also, ring opening by pyridine in the presence of pyridine hydrochloride is the basis for an analytical procedure for activated aziridines (see p. 446).

Amides. Ring opening of activated aziridines by carboxylic amides and imides, sulfonamides, and sulfonimides has been reported. Examples are shown in reactions 220, 221, and 222.

$$ArSO_2NH_2 + 2,2\text{-}Me_2AzSO_2Ar' \xrightarrow{\text{base}} ArSO_2NHCH_2CMe_2NHSO_2Ar' \qquad (220)$$
$$(1801, 2437)$$

$$(221)$$

$$AcNH_2 + AzAc \longrightarrow AcNHCH_2CH_2NHAc \quad (963) \qquad (222)$$

Such reaction can cause instability of activated aziridines with respect to polymerization, since ring-opened products which may result from trace impurities (water, HX, etc.) are frequently amides.

Halogens (or Halogenoids Such as Cyanogen Halides). Such ring opening may be pictured as analogous to reaction of an activated aziridine with a hydrogen halide, forming very low concentrations of the extremely reactive intermediate analogous to a protonated activated aziridine, as indicated in Eq 223.

$$R_2P(O)Az + Cl_2 \longrightarrow \left[\begin{array}{c} \triangle \\ N-Cl^+ \ Cl^- \\ | \\ R_2P(O) \end{array} \right] \longrightarrow R_2P(O)\overset{\overset{\textstyle Cl}{|}}{N}CH_2CH_2Cl$$

R = RO, BzNH

$(1528, 2941)$

(223)

Similarly, reaction of 1-(nitroguanyl)aziridine with cyanogen bromide to form a five-membered heterocyclic compound was presumed to involve such ring opening (Eq 224) (*2348*).

$$H_2N-\overset{\overset{\textstyle N-NO_2}{\|}}{C}-Az + BrCN \longrightarrow \left[BrCH_2CH_2N(CN)\overset{\overset{\textstyle N-NO_2}{\|}}{C}-NH_2 \right]$$

(224)

$$O_2N-N \overset{\triangle}{\underset{NH}{\bigtriangledown}} N-CN + HBr$$

Aromatic Hydrocarbons in the Presence of Aluminum Chloride. Very few data exist in the literature concerning this reaction of activated aziridines. Of the two examples (Eqs 225 and 226), a multiple reaction with rearrangement was observed in one case and the products were not isolated in the other. Hence conclusions about the generality of the reaction are impossible.

$$\overset{*}{\underset{\underset{SO_2Ph}{|}}{\underset{N}{\triangle}}}{}^{CH_2Br} + 2PhH \xrightarrow{\text{AlCl}_3} Ph_2CHCH_2\overset{*}{C}H_2NHSO_2Ph \qquad (225)$$

$\qquad\qquad\qquad\qquad\qquad\qquad\qquad\qquad$ **74**

$\qquad\qquad\qquad\qquad\qquad\qquad\qquad\qquad\qquad (1451, 1452, 2124)$

73

$$\underset{\underset{SO_2Ph}{|}}{\underset{N}{\triangle}}{}^{CH_2Ph} + PhH \xrightarrow{\text{AlCl}_3} \begin{array}{l} \text{product which did not} \\ \text{crystallize from common} \\ \text{solvents} \quad (1452) \end{array} \qquad (226)$$

By using an aziridine containing ^{14}C at one position, it was shown that 100% of the labeled carbon atom occupied the position in the product as shown in Eq 225 (*1451, 2124*). To account for this fact and the structure of the product, a reaction path (Eq 227) was suggested (*1451*).

$$73 \longrightarrow \left[\begin{array}{c} {}^*\!\!\!\!\overset{CH_2^+}{\triangle} \\ N \\ | \\ SO_2Ph \end{array} \right] \longrightarrow \left[\begin{array}{c} {}^* \square \\ N \!\!-\!\!+ \\ | \\ SO_2Ph \end{array} \right] \longrightarrow \left[\begin{array}{c} {}^* \square \\ N \searrow Ph \\ | \\ SO_2Ph \end{array} \right] \longrightarrow 74$$

$$(227)$$

Although it was shown that 1-benzenesulfonyl-2-phenylazetidine gave the same product under the same conditions, this scheme does not take into account the extreme sensitivity of activated aziridines to acid conditions with respect to ring opening. It seems entirely possible that the observed facts may be accounted for by other reaction paths and other intermediates.

Carbanions and Other Anionic Reagents. The sensitivity of activated aziridines to various anionic reagents, such as alkoxide, sulfide, and amide ions, has already been mentioned. Included here are examples of ring opening by carbanions and less common anionic reagents.

Treatment of a telechelic polymer, prepared from a suitable olefin and a dilithioalkyl initiator, with a 1-phosphorylated aziridine containing two or more aziridinyl rings has been used to prepare such polymers containing 1-phosphorylated aziridine end groups (Eq 228) (*2877*).

$$LiCH_2 \Big[\!\!-\!\!polymer\!\!-\!\! \Big] CH_2Li + 2PhP(O)Az_2 \quad \xrightarrow{\;\;H_2O\;\;}$$

$$AzPPh(O)NH(CH_2)_3 \Big[\!\!-\!\!polymer\!\!-\!\! \Big] (CH_2)_3NHPPh(O)Az \qquad (228)$$

Similarly, ethyl 1-aziridinecarboxylate undergoes ring opening by Ph_3CNa and $Ph_2C(CN)Na$ (*3363*).

A somewhat different example, not involving a carbanion in the strictest sense, is ring opening of ethyl 1-aziridinecarboxylate by an enamine (Eq 229) (*929*).

$$\left[\begin{array}{c} \text{(structure with } CH_2-CH_2, -N-CO_2Et, N^+\text{)} \end{array} \right] \longrightarrow \text{(bicyclic structure with N, CO}_2Et, N\text{)} \qquad (229)$$

Ring-opening reactions with other anionic reagents include the reaction of triphenylplumbyllithium with 1-acylaziridines (*3796*) and the ring-opening reduction of a 1-benzenesulfonylaziridine by lithium aluminum hydride (Eq 230) (*1324*).

$$\text{(structure) } N{-}SO_2Ph \quad + \quad LiAlH_4 \quad \longrightarrow \quad \text{(structure) } NHSO_2Ph \tag{230}$$

Equation 230 should not be considered general, since treatment of many 1-acylaziridines with lithium aluminum hydride gives an entirely different result (see p. 314).

Isocyanates. Ring opening of activated aziridines by isocyanates has been effected in the presence of lithium chloride or lithium bromide (Eq 231) (*1549*). The reaction is competitive with trimerization of the isocyanate.

$$\begin{array}{l} AzA + PhNCO \quad \longrightarrow \\ A = Bz, CO_2Et \end{array} \qquad A{-}N{\underset{\underset{O}{\|}}{}}N{-}Ph \tag{231}$$

RING-OPENING REACTIONS OF QUATERNIZED AZIRIDINES

These reactions are very similar to ring-opening reactions of protonated basic aziridines. Slight differences exist, however, which deserve mention. Unlike a protonated aziridine, the quaternary aziridinium salt does not exist in equilibrium with the basic form of the aziridine and thus the aziridine does not represent a source of side reactions. Moreover, when a ring opening does occur with the quaternary aziridinium salts, the product is a tertiary amine (Eq 232) which participates in nucleophilic substitutions much more slowly than a primary or a secondary amine.

$$X^- \underset{\substack{N^+ \\ R\ \ R}}{\triangledown} \quad \longrightarrow \quad XCH_2CH_2NR_2 \tag{232}$$

75   **76**

The isolation of rearranged products from reactions of 2-haloalkyl tertiary amines proceeding through aziridinium ions has already been mentioned (p. 28) as well as ring-opening reactions which can occur during alkylation of 1-alkylaziridines (p. 117). The intermediacy of such aziridinium ions in solvolysis of 2-haloalkyl tertiary amines has been often postulated or demonstrated (*64, 65, 642–644, 727, 787, 1409, 1479, 1491, 1562, 2620, 2621, 2834, 3347*) and also in reactions with various anionic reagents (e.g., RCO_2^-, HCO_3^-, SPO_3^{3-}, $S_2O_3^{2-}$) (*28, 140, 476, 728, 3347*). Frequently formation of piperazine derivatives is observed in solvolysis (or other) reactions of **76** when X is halogen (Eq 233) (p. 317) (*279, 281, 825, 1492, 1602, 1639, 3347*).

$$2XCH_2CH_2NR_2 \longrightarrow \quad \underset{R}{\overset{R}{>}}\overset{+}{N}\underset{}{\boxed{}}\overset{+}{N}\underset{R}{\overset{R}{<}} \quad 2X^- \qquad (233)$$

The good yields of ring-opened products often reported from reactions of **75** testify to the inability of **76** to compete effectively with X or solvent in ring openings of **75**.

A number of stable aziridinium salts have been prepared and their reactions studied (*1680, 2062, 2293–2295, 2297, 2298, 2300, 2301, 2315*). Such salts characteristically contain very weakly nucleophilic anions such as perchlorate or fluoroborate (*2300*). They undergo ring-opening reactions typical of the protonated basic aziridines, such as solvolysis (*2295, 2297, 2298, 2300, 2301*) and ring opening by halide ions (*2294, 2295, 2315*) and amines (*1680*). Solvolysis of unsymmetrically carbon-substituted aziridinium ions may proceed by an S_N1 path or, in the presence of alkoxide ion (or hydroxide ion), by an S_N2 path (Eq 234) (*2295, 2297, 2298, 2300, 2301*).

$$\underset{\underset{R\;R}{\overset{|}{N^+}}}{\overset{R}{\triangle}}\overset{R}{\underset{}{}} \; + \; ROH \quad \underset{\overset{S_N2\;(RO^-)}{\longrightarrow}}{\overset{S_N1}{\longrightarrow}} \quad \begin{array}{l} R_2NCH_2CR_2OR \\[4pt] ROCH_2CR_2NR_2 \end{array} \qquad (234)$$

The generality of ring expansions resulting from solvolysis via an S_N1 path of bicyclic aziridinium ions has been suggested (e.g., Eq 235) (*2295, 4165*) and indeed bicyclic activated aziridines can behave similarly (*4140*).

$$\text{(bicyclic structure, Et, } +N, \text{Me)} \; + \; MeOH \; \longrightarrow \; \text{(ring-expanded structure, Et, OMe, } N^+, \text{Me H)} \qquad (235)$$

Treatment of unsymmetrically carbon-substituted aziridinium perchlorates with lithium halides in acetonitrile (with continuous extraction of product with pentane) gave 2-haloalkylamines wherein the halogen was attached to the more highly substituted carbon atom (*2294, 2295, 2315*). It has been suggested that displacement by halide ion should be reversible and should therefore yield the more stable isomer (*2294*). Shift of charge in the aziridinium ion with subsequent collapse of the ion pair was regarded as a possible mechanism (Eq 236).

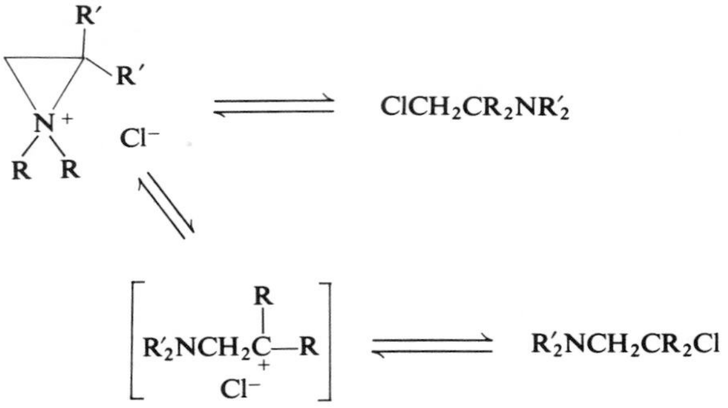

$$ClCH_2CR_2NR'_2$$

(236)

$$\left[R'_2NCH_2\overset{R}{\underset{Cl^-}{\overset{|}{C}}}-R \right] \rightleftharpoons R'_2NCH_2CR_2Cl$$

Very weakly nucleophilic reagents, such as aldehydes and ketones, cause ring opening of aziridinium perchlorates to give ring-expanded products (Eq 237) (*2297, 2298*).

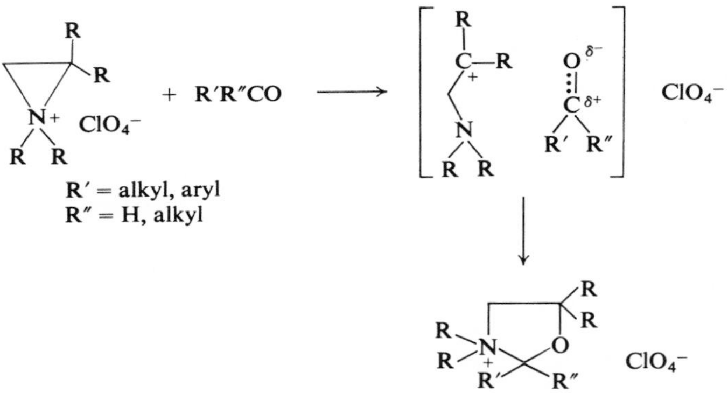

R′ = alkyl, aryl
R″ = H, alkyl

(237)

When performed with unsymmetrically carbon-substituted aziridinium salts, the reaction appears to proceed by attachment of the oxygen at the aziridine carbon atom which forms the more stable carbonium ion. Good yields are obtained and the reaction appears quite general. This same type of reaction has also been applied to nitriles, leading to formation of imidazolinium salts (Eq 238) (*2293, 2868*);

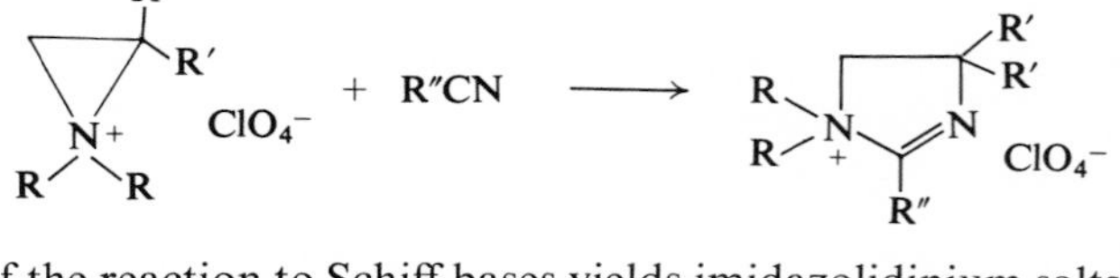

(238)

extension of the reaction to Schiff bases yields imidazolidinium salts, as would be expected (*2868*). Nitrones produce six-membered ring compounds (Eq 239) (*4111*).

$$
\underset{\substack{R \\ R}}{\overset{R}{\triangle}}\underset{N^+}{\overset{R}{}} + R^2-\overset{O}{\underset{}{N}}=CHR^1 \longrightarrow \underset{R^2-N}{\overset{R}{\underset{}{O}}}\overset{R}{\underset{R^1}{\underset{}{N^+-R}}} \tag{239}
$$

Of interest is the thermal isomerization of 1,1,2,2-tetramethylaziridinium perchlorate into N-isobutylidenedimethylammonium perchlorate (Eq 240) (*2298*).

$$
\underset{\substack{Me \\ N^+ \\ Me}}{\overset{Me}{\triangle}}\overset{Me}{}\ ClO_4^- \quad\xrightarrow[\text{45 min, 120°C}]{}\quad Me_2CHCH=\overset{+}{N}Me_2\ ClO_4^- \tag{240}
$$

Basic aziridines thus simply substituted (e.g., 1,2,2-Me$_3$Az) are not isomerized under such mild conditions (see p. 277). More complex aziridinium salts were isomerized into quaternary Schiff base salts or into complex protonated allylamines, rarely to both (*2062*).

ISOMERIZATION OF BASIC AZIRIDINES

Enamine and Alkylidenimine Structures. Isomerization to enamines or alkylidenimines has been promoted by light, by heat, by glacial acetic acid, and by basic reagents for a relatively few substituted aziridines. Treatment of 2,3-dibenzoylaziridines with glacial acetic acid (Eq 241) is of interest since the isomerization apparently occurs much faster than simple ring opening by acetic acid (*3638*).

$$
\underset{\substack{N \\ R}}{\overset{Bz\quad Bz}{\triangle}} \quad\xrightarrow{\text{HOAc}}\quad \underset{NHR}{\overset{BzC=CHBz}{}} \tag{241}
$$

$$
R = PhCH_2,\ c\text{-}C_6H_{11},\ Me
$$

Treatment of 2,3-dibromopropionitrile with benzylamine in the presence of triethylamine gave **77** and **77a** in addition to the expected aziridine (*1553*). It was suggested that triethylamine hydrobromide might have catalyzed formation of these isomerized products from the aziridine (*3638*), but it was also reported (*1553*) that the aziridine could be thermally isomerized (Eq 242).

$$
\underset{\substack{N \\ CH_2Ph}}{\overset{}{\triangle}}CN \quad\xrightarrow{\text{heat}}\quad MeC(CN)=NCH_2Ph + MeCH(CN)N=CHPh \tag{242}
$$

77   **77a**

Related is the electrophile-catalyzed isomerization of 2-aroyl-1-benzyl-3-phenylaziridines **78** (or the 1-cyclohexyl analogs), but the Schiff base is immediately hydrolyzed to a *trans*-benzalacetophenone, ammonia, and benzaldehyde (or cyclohexanone) (*4139*).

When Ar is *p*-tolyl, formation of the diaryloxazole **78a** is a significant competing reaction. Formation of **78a** by pyrolysis of **78**, or the *N*-Me, *N*-*tert*-Bu, or *N*-*c*-C_6H_{11} analogs, involves C—C bond scission (Eq 243) (*4138*).

(243)

Treatment of Schiff bases with sulfur ylids (prepared from sulfonium salts and sodium hydride in tetrahydrofuran) gave enamines, presumably via aziridines (*3352*). This reaction thus provides an example of such isomerization which may be presumed to be base-catalyzed.

The hydrazine-catalyzed rearrangement of **79** into the pyridazine **79a** (*4073*) is presumably favored by the aromatization that takes place.

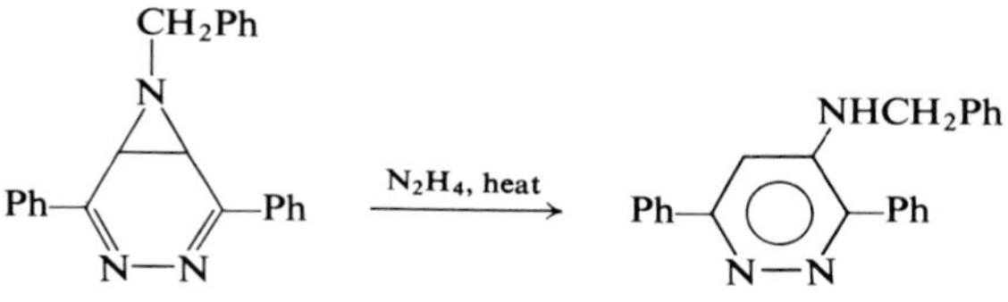

79 → **79a**

Also base-catalyzed, but more intricate and involving a ring expansion, is the reaction shown in Eq 244 (*2899*). It is noteworthy that the trans isomer was unaffected by similar conditions.

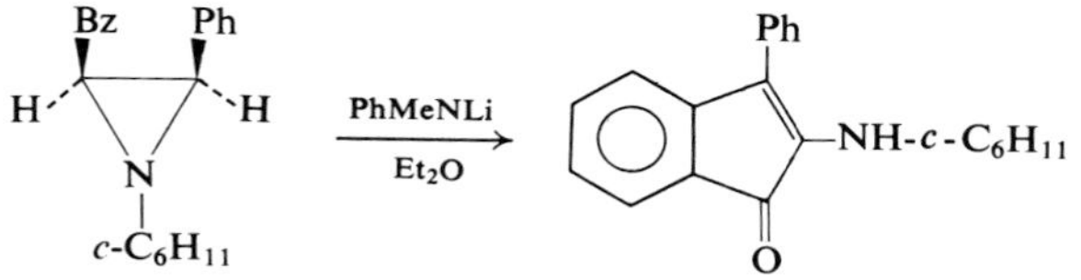

$$(244)$$

Examples of such thermal isomerization for rather esoteric aziridine structures are shown in Eqs 245, 246, and 246a.

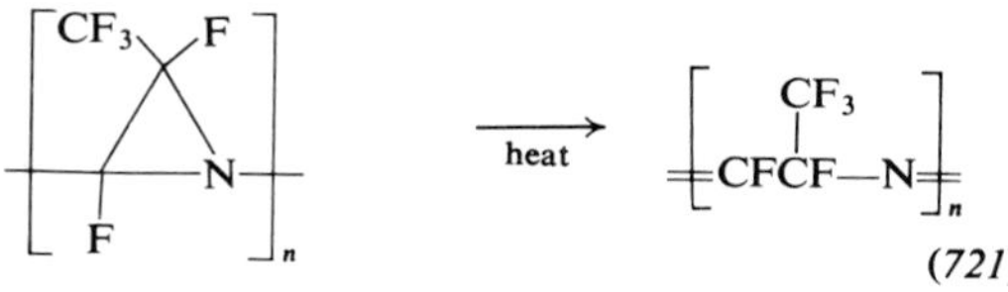

$$(245)$$

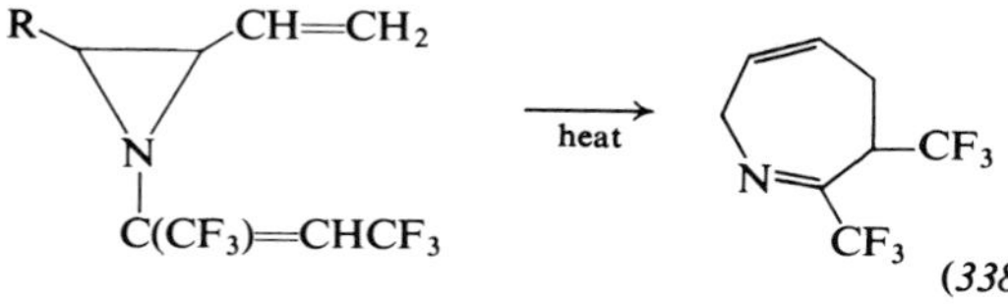

(*721*)

$$(246)$$

(*3389*)

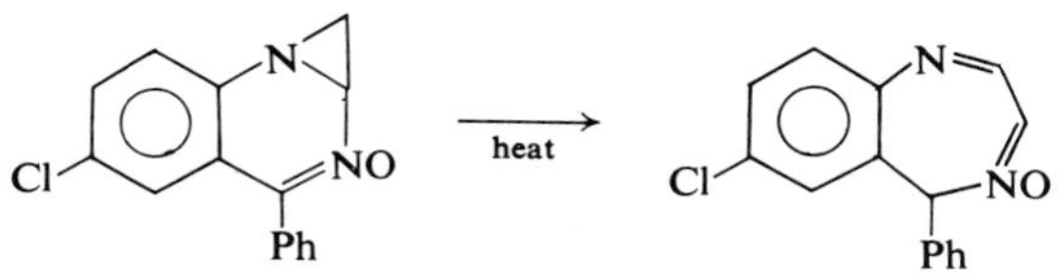

(*1287b, 1746a*)

$$(246a)$$

The isomerization shown in Eq 246, involving a ring expansion, is clearly dependent on a 1,2-divinylaziridine structure and may be pictured as involving only electron shifts (**80**).

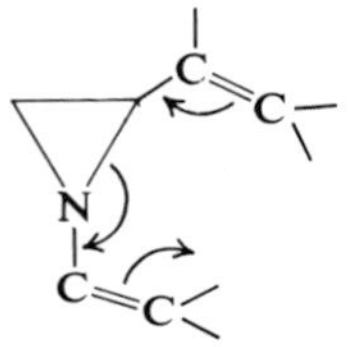

80

1-(*p*-Bromophenyl)-2-isopropenylaziridine upon thermal isomerization gave the amino Claisen rearrangement rather than simple ring expansion to a pyrroline (*3137*), but use of iodide catalyst produced the pyrroline (Eq 247).

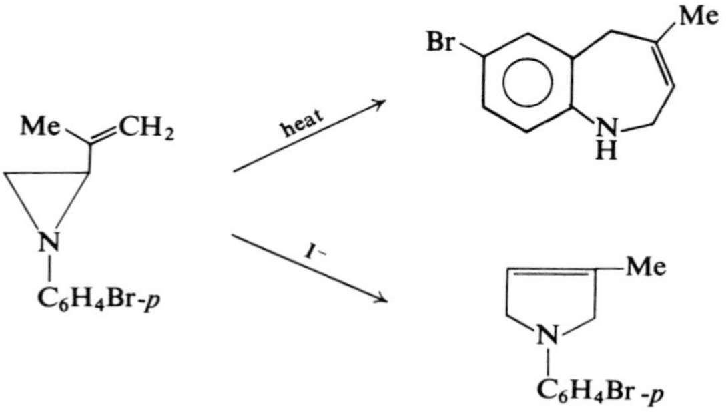

$$(247)$$

In contrast, when the 1-substituent was a 3-benzoxazinyl radical, thermal rearrangement very readily yielded a pyrroline and iodide ion catalyst gave almost none (*4007*). Still different is the pyrolysis of a similar 1-(benzoxazolin-2-on-3-yl)aziridine, which yielded no pyrroline, but only acyclic unsaturated amines (*158b*).

Another valence isomerization, but involving carbon–carbon cleavage, was presumed to occur in the attempted preparation of *cis*-1-ethyl-2,3-divinyl-aziridine from *threo*-4-ethylamino-1,5-hexadien-3-ol (Eq 248) (*3388*). The *trans*-aziridine could be so prepared from the *erythro* isomer.

$$CH_2=CHCHOHCH(NHEt)CH=CH_2 \xrightarrow[\text{method}]{\text{via sulfate}}$$

threo

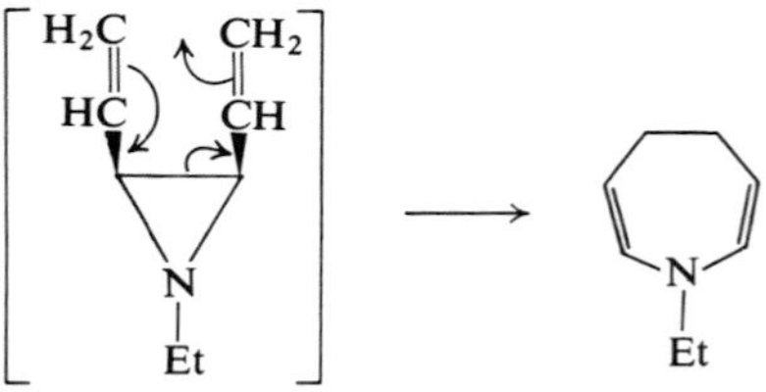

$$(248)$$

Still another example of reaction probably involving valence isomerization is the transformation of **79** to 1-benzyl-4-phenylimidazole and benzonitrile (*4073*).

The intermediacy of an aziridine and similar isomerization involved in decomposition of phenyl azide in aniline (*1793*) has already been mentioned (see p. 78).

Examples of isomerization, via aziridine carbon–carbon bond cleavage, to *acyclic* Schiff bases are provided by arylated aziridines: the pyrolysis of 2-phenylaziridine at 320°C (*3891*), 2,3-diphenylaziridine at about 165°C (*732, 733*), and 3-methyl-2,2-diphenylaziridine (Eq 249) at 175°–205°C (*564*).

$$Ph_2C{=\!=}NEt \qquad (249)$$

Isomerization to Other than Enamine or Imine Structures. There are three recorded examples of isomerization of a basic aziridine that affords a product which is neither an enamine or an alkylidenimine. Heating 1,2,3-triphenyl-aziridine with potassium *tert*-butoxide for 3 days at 180°C gave 1,2-diphenyl-isoindoline in 70% yield (Eq 250) (*1666*).

$$(250)$$

The reaction, involving an aziridine carbon–carbon bond cleavage, probably proceeds by formation of carbanion **81** and intramolecular attack on the

more remote *C*-phenyl group to give the intermediate **82**, which is protonated
and tautomerized to the isoindoline (*1666*).

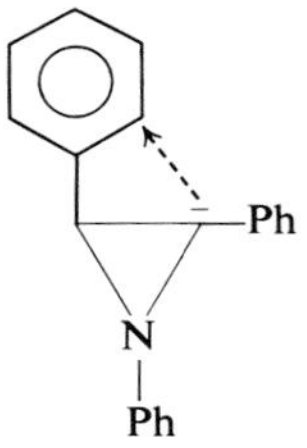

81 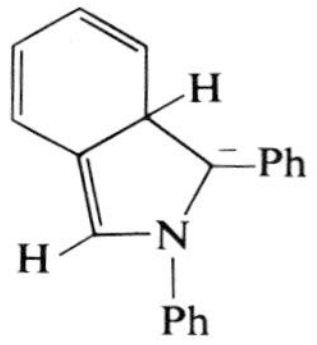   **82**

Also requiring an aziridine carbon–carbon bond cleavage, but hardly by the
same mechanism, is the thermal rearrangement of methyl 1-mesityl-2-
methoxalylaziridine-2-carboxylate to 3-mesityl-Δ^4-1,3-oxazoline-4,5-dicar-
boxylate (**82a**) (*257a*).

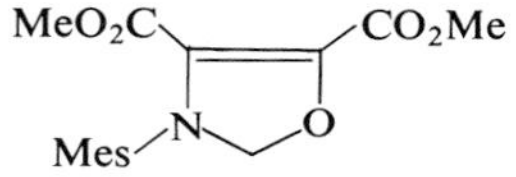

82a

In a remarkable rearrangement–cleavage on which more study is promised,
1-alkylaziridine-2-carbohydrazides are solvolyzed in water or methanol, via
an amino ketene and diimide, to 3-(alkylamino)propionic acids or esters
(*904a*).

ISOMERIZATION OF ACTIVATED AZIRIDINES

Enamine and Alkylidenimine Structures. *N*-Substituted azepines are formed
when solutions of acyl or sulfonyl azides in benzene are heated or subjected to
ultraviolet radiation (*346, 822, 823, 832, 3156, 3285, 3540*). The reaction (which
has already been mentioned on p. 78) presumably involves formation of the
activated aziridine intermediate, which then isomerizes, via carbon–carbon
bond cleavage, to an azepine. However, treatment of anthracene with benzenesulfonyl azide gives *N*-benzenesulfonyl-1-anthramine in 55% yield (Eq 251)
(*3551*).

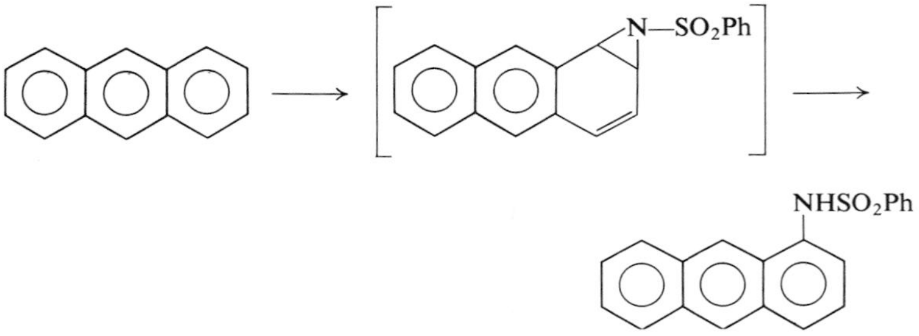

(251)

The high yield of 1-substituted product was attributed to the formation of the activated aziridine intermediate (3551) and if this occurs the reaction represents an isomerization to an enamine structure (although a special case).

Not involving *presumed* aziridine intermediates is the recent observation that 1,3-diaroyl-2-arylaziridines can be pyrolyzed to enamine derivatives (Eq 252) (1669).

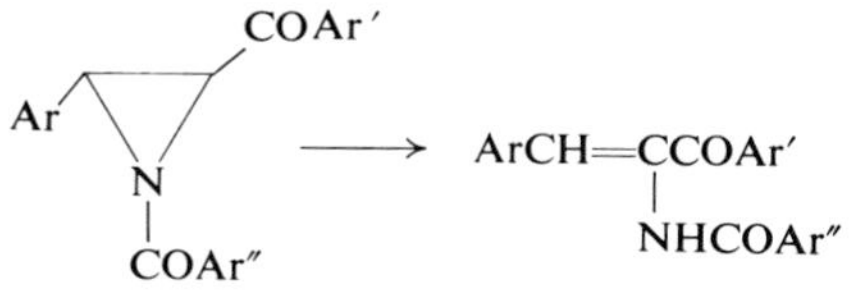

$$ArCH{=}CCOAr' \qquad (252)$$
$$\underset{NHCOAr''}{|}$$

Similarly, *N*-pivaloylcyclohexenimine is isomerized at 200°C into an alkyliden-imine structure (Eq 253) (2368).

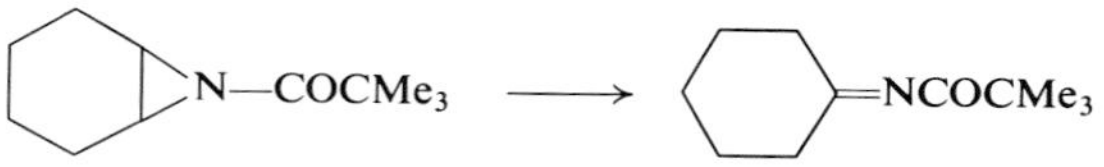

$$=NCOCMe_3 \qquad (253)$$

Aziridines derivable from norbornadiene isomerize spontaneously into enamine derivatives, presumably via the intermediate 83 (Eq 254) (92, 2748, 2749).

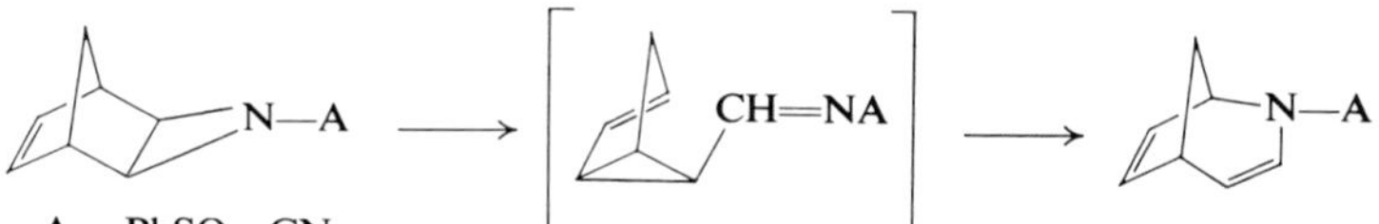

$$\qquad (254)$$

A = PhSO$_2$, CN

83

Treatment of a much more complicated aziridine (84) with formic or trifluoro-acetic acid caused formation of the ketimine structure 85 (Eq 255) with skeletal rearrangement (3370, 4175).

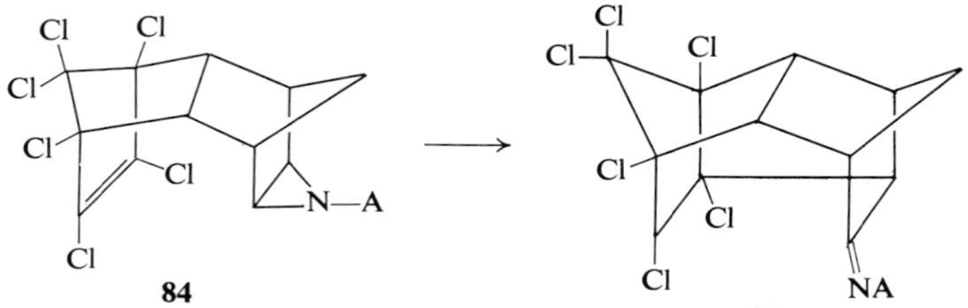

$$\qquad (255)$$

84

A = Me$_3$CO$_2$C, *p*-MeC$_6$H$_4$SO$_2$

84

Two interesting isomerizations to enamine structures, involving cleavage of the aziridine carbon–carbon bond, are shown in Eqs 256 and 257.

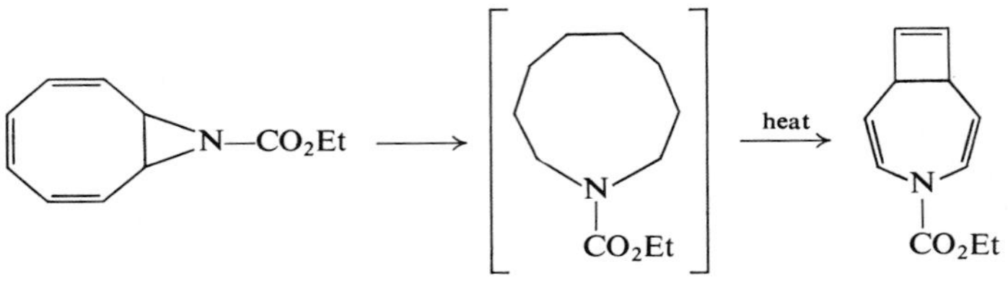

(256)

(2460, 4003)

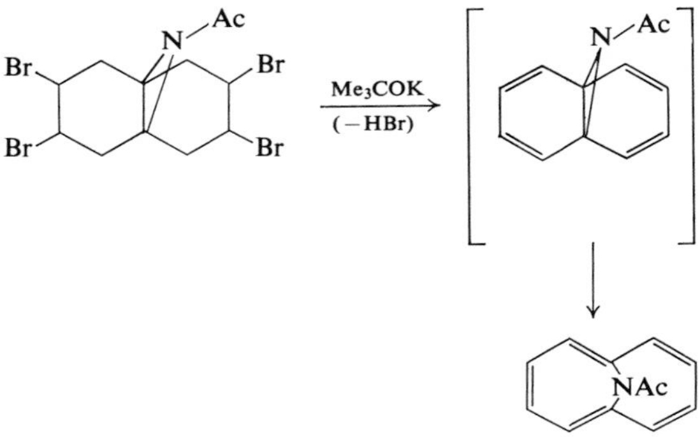

(257)

(405, 3703)

The light-catalyzed isomerization shown in Eq 258 may possibly involve formation of an unusual aziridinium ion followed by ring opening by chloride ion (1663).

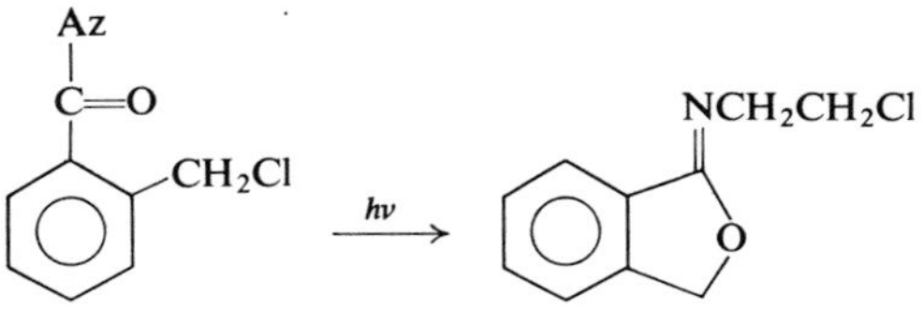

(258)

Isomerization to N-Allylcarboxamide Structures. Thermal isomerization of 1-acylaziridines bearing *C*-alkyl groups may be effected to produce substituted allylamides in high yield (Eq 259) (1097, 1100, 1103, 1105, 1660, 2046, 2047, 3184, 3287, 3482, 3601, 4057, 4064).

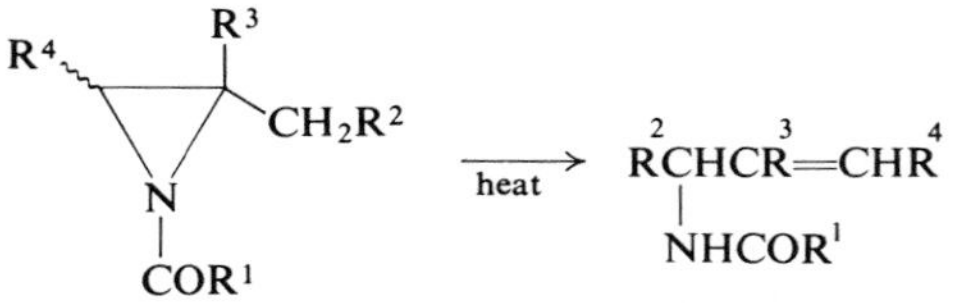

(259)

The temperature necessary for such isomerization is dependent on the structure of the aziridine. Thus 1-acetyl-2,2-dimethylaziridine requires temperatures in excess of 150°C (*1103*, *3184*), 2,2-dimethyl-1-(*p*-nitrobenzoyl)aziridine requires only about 75°–100°C (*1097*) and the *N*-benzoyl derivatives of cyclo-octenimine and cyclodecenimine evidently are isomerized at or below room temperature since the allyl amides are isolated upon attempted benzoylation of these 1-unsubstituted aziridines (*1101*). The attempted thermal isomerization of 1-acetyl-2-methylaziridine did not occur readily and under more forcing conditions gave predominantly a resin (*1096*). However, 2-benzyl-1-(*p*-nitro-benzoyl)aziridine was completely isomerized upon refluxing in toluene for 24 hours (*2046*).

This isomerization has been shown to be stereospecific (*1101*, *2046*, *2047*) and has been classified with the well-known group of pyrolytic cis eliminations involving, in this case, a transition state such as **86** (*1096*, *1097*, *2046*, *2047*, *3482*).

$$
\begin{array}{c}
-\overset{|}{C}\cdots\cdots\overset{|}{C}-\overset{|}{C}- \\
\\
H N \\
\\
\ddots O\cdots\cdots C \\
\backslash
\end{array}
$$

86

Kinetic evidence, wherein the reaction was shown to be first order and to have a large negative entropy of activation (−10.4 e.u.), is also consistent with this view (*1097*).

The isomerization has also been applied to a 1-arenesulfonylaziridine (Eq 260) (*1099*, *2045*, *3287*).

$$
\underset{\underset{SO_2Ar}{|}}{\underset{N}{\triangle}}\!\!\begin{array}{c}Me\\Me\end{array} \longrightarrow ArSO_2NHCH_2CMe\!\!=\!\!CH_2 \tag{260}
$$

The possibility that 1-acylaziridines are intermediates in the similar pyrolysis (at $T > 500°C$) of 2-alkyl-2-oxazolines (Eq 261) has been considered (*3753*).

$$
\underset{Et}{\overset{Me}{\boxed{N\!\!=\!\!O}}}\!\!-Me \longrightarrow \left[\underset{\underset{COEt}{|}}{\overset{Me}{\underset{N}{\triangle}}}\!\!Me\right] \longrightarrow EtCONHCH_2CMe\!\!=\!\!CH_2 \tag{261}
$$

It was also noted, however, that 1-acetyl-2-methylaziridine is not readily isomerized according to Eq 259 (*1096*) whereas 2,4-dimethyl-2-oxazoline was successfully pyrolyzed to give *N*-allylacetamide (*3753*).

The thermal rearrangement of 1-(*p*-nitrobenzoyl)-2-vinylaziridine to 2-(*p*-nitrophenyl)-4,7-dihydro-1,3-oxazepine (*2526a*) is classified here since the product is a cyclic imido ester containing an allylamino unit. However, it is more like the isomerizations of basic 2-vinylaziridines (p. 276).

Isomerization to Five-Membered Ring Structures. This isomerization (Eq 262) is by far the most general for activated aziridines which have a carbon atom (or certain other unsaturated groups such as ArN=N) attached to the aziridine nitrogen.

$$ \text{(structure)} \longrightarrow \text{(structure)} \tag{262} $$

Y = O, S, or NR
X = R, RO, R$_2$N, or RNH

Within certain structural limits, the reaction may be promoted by heat or acid. However, the most general method for obtaining it is catalysis by some nucleophilic ion (or nucleophile) which is also a good "leaving" group (see also p. 293 for structural limitations on this nucleophile-catalyzed isomerization).

1. *Thermal Isomerization.* Formation of 2-oxazolines may be effected simply by heating carbon-unsubstituted 1-acylaziridines (Eq 262, Y = O, X = alkyl or aryl group) (*1392, 1480, 2319, 3246, 3284*). Similarly, 2-amino- or 2-aryl-amino-2-thiazolines have been obtained from the corresponding aziridines (Eq 262, Y = S, X = H$_2$N or ArNH) (*1925, 1930*). The thermal isomerization of 1-[*o*-(chloromethyl)benzoyl]aziridine into *N*-(2-chloroethyl)phthalimidine may well involve an oxazoline as an intermediate (*1663*). It is frequently reported that heating carbon-unsubstituted activated aziridines produces resins or polymers. However, such polymer formation is probably due in part to the presence of impurities (see p. 162).

Pyrolysis of 1-acylaziridines with 2-alkyl substituents normally results in formation of *N*-allylcarboxamides, as previously mentioned. However, for structures in which formation of the transition state leading to such pyrolytic cis elimination is unfavorable, 2-oxazolines are formed (Eqs 263 and 264).

$$ \text{(structure)} \longrightarrow \text{(structure)} \qquad (1794, 1798) \tag{263} $$

$$ \text{(structure)} \longrightarrow \text{(structure)} \qquad (1095) \tag{264} $$

Certain structures can rearrange to oxazolines and allyl amides concomitantly; N-(p-nitrobenzoyl)cycloalkenimines (*1105, 2047*) are examples. 1-Benzoyl-2-chloro-2-phenyl-3-methylaziridine, however, produced no allylamide, the 2-substituents presumably stabilizing the ionic intermediate leading to oxazoline (*4057*).

The thermal isomerization of 1-acylaziridines to 2-oxazolines is stereospecific. Although an early report tells of formation of the *trans*-oxazoline in 20% yield from the *N*-benzoyl-*cis*-cyclohexenimine (*3814*), subsequent work with polycyclic structures less disposed to trans configurations has demonstrated isomerization of cis-fused aziridines to cis-fused oxazolines (Eqs 263 and 264) (*1095, 1798, 3287*) and recently it has been shown that isomerization of a *cis*- or *trans*-2,3-diphenylaziridine derivative occurs with retention of configuration (Eq 265) (*1669*).

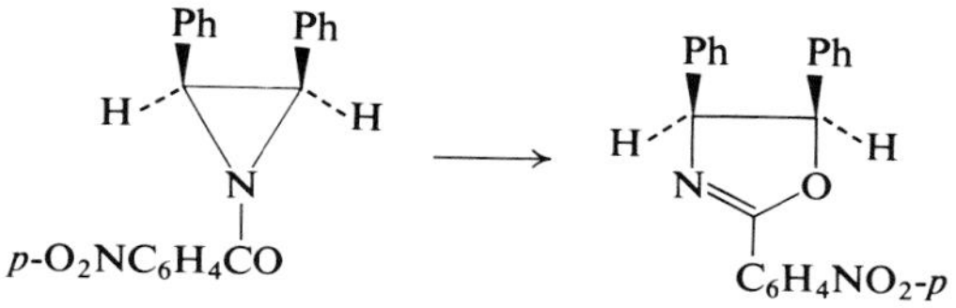

$$ \text{(265)} $$

This latter result (Eq 265) is especially pertinent to the mechanism for such thermal isomerizations since the same reaction catalyzed by iodide ion produces the *trans*-oxazoline (*1670*) (see p. 286). Mechanisms which have been proposed involve either a four-center transition state (**87**) (*1656, 1669*) or an intermediate tight ion pair (**88**) (*1095, 1669*).

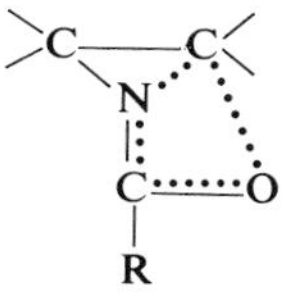

87

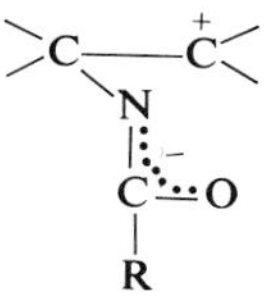

88

Of interest is the thermal isomerization of the carbon-unsubstituted activated aziridine **89**, which produces an imidazolidone instead of an oxazoline and also involves a shift of the trimethylsilyl group (Eq 266) (*3139*).

$$ \text{Me}_3\text{SiNEtCOAz} \longrightarrow \qquad \text{(266)} $$

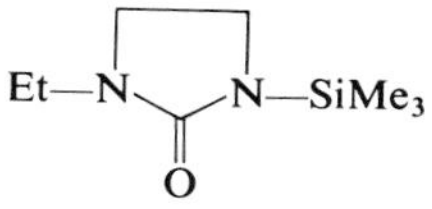

89

2. *Isomerization Catalyzed by Nucleophiles.* The sensitivity of all activated aziridines to ring opening by nucleophiles provides a path for realization of Eq 262, by which a wide variety of five-membered heterocyclic ring compounds

may be produced. The scope of the reaction is shown in Table 3-XXXII. It is generally performed simply by heating the activated aziridine with catalytic amounts of an alkali metal or quaternary ammonium salt containing a nucleophilic anion (e.g., NaI) in an inert solvent.

Table 3-XXXII

NUCLEOPHILE-CATALYZED ISOMERIZATION OF ACTIVATED AZIRIDINES TO
FIVE-MEMBERED RING COMPOUNDS

Activated aziridine	Isomerized product	References
N–COR	N=⟨O⟩ R (oxazoline)	150, 981a, 1095, 1100, 1563, 1593, 1656, 1660, 1662, 1669, 1670, 1717, 2017, 2526a, 2687, 2886, 3287, 3547, 4086, 4155, 4161
N–CSR [a]	N=⟨S⟩ R (thiazoline)	3032a
N–CO₂R	N=⟨O⟩ OR and/or RN⟨O⟩ O	818a, 1584, 1587, 1593
N–CONR₂	N=⟨O⟩ NR₂	1662
N–CONHR	N=⟨O⟩ NHR and/or HN⟨O⟩N—R	1662, 2657, 2658, 3121b
N–CSNHR	N=⟨S⟩ NHR	1662
N–C=NR, R	N=⟨N—R⟩ R	1654

Table 3-XXXII—*continued*

Activated aziridine	Isomerized product	References
		15
		1664
		1662
		1657
		3781, 3782
		3286
$R = NO_2$ or NH_2	(sought but not found)	

[a] Not isolated, but presumed intermediate in reaction of RC(S)OR and EI or 2-MeAzH.

The mechanism proposed to account for such catalyzed isomerizations is shown in Eq 267 (*1656, 1660, 1662, 1669, 1670, 4155*).

The reaction may be treated as a ring-opening reaction forming the intermediate ambident anion **90**, which undergoes ring closure to form a five-membered ring. Thus the nucleophile catalyst, Nu⁻, must also be a good leaving group. Nucleophiles which have been used include iodide ion (*15, 1095, 1584, 1587,*

$$(267)$$

1593, 1654, 1657, 1660, 1662, 1664, 1669, 1670, 2017, 2886, 4155), bromide ion (*2886, 4155*), thiocyanate ion (*1654, 1662, 2657, 2658*), azide ion (*1563*), and possibly cyanide ion (*2687*) (see p. 290). Neutral nucleophiles such as tributyl-amine (*3547*) and dimethyl sulfoxide (*1671*) are also effective; ambident dipolar ion intermediates **91** and **92**, respectively, may be presumed.

The stereochemistry for this isomerization is accounted for by the mechanism shown (Eq 267), the reaction occurring with overall retention (two inversions) of configuration (*981a, 1669, 1670, 3798*). An exception is the iodide ion-catalyzed isomerization of *cis*-1-aroyl-2,3-diphenylaziridines into the *trans*-4,5-diphenyl-2-oxazolines (Eq 268) (*1670*).

The explanation offered for this anomaly is that steric factors so inhibit ring closure of the *threo* ambident ion to an oxazoline that displacement of iodide from the ambident ion by another iodide ion is possible, three inversions occur, and overall inversion of configuration results (*1670*). Molecular models suggest such steric inhibition, and indeed it was shown that the ambident ion generated by alkaline ethanolysis of *threo*-*N*-(1,2-diphenyl-2-chloroethyl)-*p*-nitrobenz-amide underwent ring closure to form the cis activated *aziridine* whereas the corresponding *erythro* ambident ion formed only the *trans* oxazoline (*1670*).

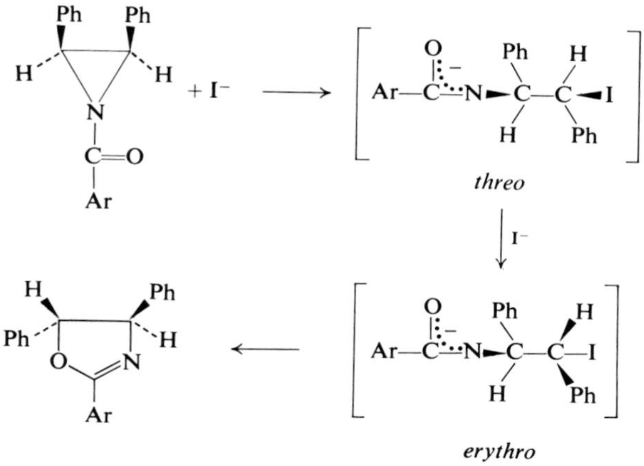

(268)

The nature of the positional isomers formed by treatment of unsymmetrically carbon-substituted activated aziridines with nucleophiles (Eqs 269, 270, 271) is not inconsistent with the mechanism shown. Although an S_N2 reaction of the nucleophilic ion at an aziridine carbon atom is involved, steric factors may not necessarily be dominant (Eq 270) (1669).

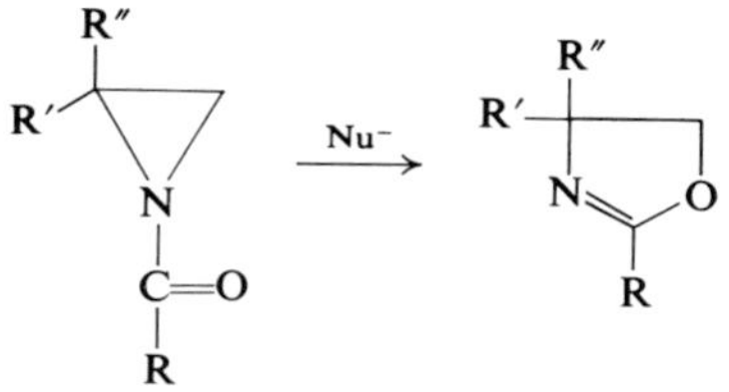

(1660, 1662)   (269)

R' = H or Me, R" = Me or Et

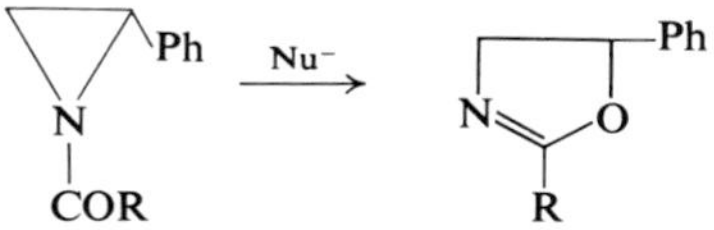

(1669, 1671)   (270)

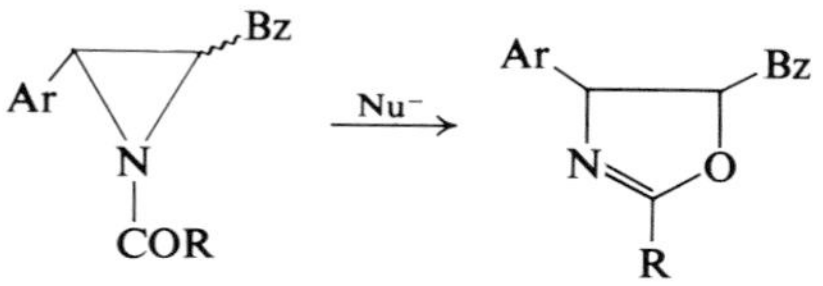

(1669)   (271)

The mechanism (Eq 267) adequately explains a variety of side reactions which may take place for activated aziridines. For example, one might expect polymerization to compete with isomerization, and in the case of 1-perfluoro-acylaziridines this is observed (2886) (see p. 321). Similarly, ring opening of the activated aziridine by the intermediate ambident ion could produce a "dimeric" intermediate ambident ion which could undergo ring closure to a 1,4-disubstituted piperazine. Such reaction has been observed to compete with oxazoline formation in the case of 1-aziridinecarboxanilides and is the observed course when ring closure to a five-membered ring is not possible (e.g., for 1-arenesulfonylaziridines) (see p. 321) (*1662*).

In the presence of relatively acidic hydroxy compounds such as water or methanol, the intermediate ambident ion may be neutralized and the products resulting may cause other side reactions. The rapid methanolysis of 1-(*p*-nitrobenzoyl)aziridine (*1600*) may be thus explained (Eq 272) (see also p. 253).

$$\triangle \underset{\substack{| \\ COAr}}{N} + I^- + MeOH \longrightarrow ArCONHCH_2CH_2I + MeO^- \qquad (272)$$

$$\xrightarrow{MeO^-, MeOH} ArCO_2Me + AzH$$

This presumption of neutralization of the intermediate ambident ion may also be invoked to explain the formation of 3-ethyl-2-oxazolidinone concomitantly with 2-ethoxy-2-oxazoline on treatment of ethyl 1-aziridinecarboxylate with sodium iodide (*1587, 1593*). In this case it was shown that the 2-ethoxy-2-oxazoline rearranged to the oxazolidinone in the presence of a primary alkyl iodide (EtI or $ICH_2CH_2NHCO_2Et$) (Eq 273) and that traces of water present in the sodium iodide were responsible for the oxazolidinone formation (*963*).

$$\underset{\substack{\| \\ OEt}}{N \diagdown O} \xrightarrow{RI} Et-\underset{\substack{\| \\ O}}{N \diagdown O} \qquad (273)$$

The formation of 2-iodocyclohexylurethan from *N*-(ethoxycarbonyl)cyclohexenimine may also be attributed to traces of water present in the sodium iodide and solvent (acetone) used (*3475*).

The intermediate ambident ion from 1-aziridinecarboxanilides may tautomerize and yield a five-membered ring compound from closure of the preferred form of the tautomeric ion (Eq 274) (*1662, 2657, 2658*).

$$\triangle \underset{\substack{| \\ COAr}}{N} + I^- \longrightarrow \left[\underset{\substack{\| \\ ArNHCNCH_2CH_2I}}{O^-} \right] \rightleftharpoons \left[\underset{\substack{\| \\ ArNCNHCH_2CH_2I}}{O} \right]$$

$$Ar-\underset{\substack{\| \\ O}}{N \diagdown NH} + I^- \qquad (274)$$

1-Aziridinecarboxanilides with thiocyanate ion form N-(2-thiazolinyl)-N'-arylureas in addition to the imidazolidones and 2-arylamino-2-oxazolines (*2657, 2658*). With excess thiocyanate ion the thiazolinyl urea is the major product (*2657*).

The iodide ion-catalyzed isomerization of 3-(1-aziridinyl)-2-phenyl-2-cyclohexenone represents the first such rearrangement of a 1-vinylaziridine (*3781, 3782*), but it is not surprising since the starting material is a vinylogue of a 1-acylaziridine.

Also of special interest is the iodide ion-catalyzed isomerization of a 1-aryl-vinylaziridine into a 1-aryl-3-pyrroline (Eq 275) (*3137*; cf. *4007*).

$$(275)$$

This reaction illustrates the behavior of a 1-arylaziridine as an activated aziridine (see p. 248) and also ring closure of the intermediate anilide anion involving an S_N2' reaction.

3. *Acid-Catalyzed Isomerizations.* Treatment of 2,2-dialkyl activated aziridines with concentrated acids produces five-membered ring compounds that are isomeric with those obtained by treatment with nucleophiles (Eq 276).

$$(276)$$

(*1656, 1660, 4086, 4155*)

Y = O; R = p-O$_2$NC$_6$H$_4$; R' = H, Me, Et; R'' = Me, Et
Y = S; R = PhNH; R' = R'' = Me (*888*)

The reaction may be pictured as occurring via protonation of the activated aziridine followed by ionization to a secondary or tertiary carbonium ion and subsequent ring closure (Eq 277) (*888, 1656, 1660, 4155*).

Such acid-catalyzed isomerization of carbon-unsubstituted activated aziridines is not so readily rationalized. In 1-aziridinyl-s-triazines, 1-aziridinethio-carboxanilides, and related compounds (*888, 1392, 1921, 1925, 1930, 3127,*

$$(277)$$

3553) treatment with concentrated hydrochloric acid or aqueous sulfuric or phosphoric acid possibly produces the respective ring-opened products which spontaneously cyclize under the reaction conditions (e.g., Eq 278).

$$\text{ArNH}\overset{\text{S}}{\overset{\|}{\text{C}}}\text{NHCH}_2\text{CH}_2\text{Cl} \quad \xrightarrow[\text{heat}]{\text{H}^+} \quad + \text{ HCl} \qquad (278)$$
$$(\text{OH}) \qquad\qquad\qquad\qquad\qquad\qquad\qquad (\text{H}_2\text{O})$$

However, such an explanation does not appear applicable to isomerizations under relatively mild conditions where the corresponding ring-opened products would presumably be stable, as indeed they sometimes are (*981a*). Examples include isomerization of 1-acetyl-aziridine into 2-methyl-2-oxazoline by picric acid (*3284*), 1-aziridinecarboxanilide into 2-anilino-2-oxazoline by picric acid (*821*), and ethyl 1-carbamylaziridine-2,3-dicarboxylate into ethyl 2-oxoimidazolidine-4,5-dicarboxylate by dilute hydrochloric acid (*821*). Somewhat the same difficulty obtains regarding an explanation for the aluminum bromide-catalyzed isomerization of 1-(*p*-ethoxybenzoyl)aziridine into 2-(*p*-ethoxyphenyl)-2-oxazoline (*1659*.) It has been suggested that the reaction involves electron shifts in the protonated or coordinated activated aziridine (*1659, 3127*), presumably leading to a transition state such as **93**.

93

Formula **93** involves a transition state different from that proposed for thermal isomerizations (see **87**, p. 283) only in that the activated aziridine is protonated. It is implied that pyrolytic isomerizations occur at a much lower temperature for protonated activated aziridines than for the nonprotonated species.

Treatment of 1-benzoylaziridine with HCN gives 2-phenyl-2-oxazoline (*2687*). It is probable that with so weak an acid the reaction is of the nucleophile (cyanide ion)-catalyzed type rather than acid-catalyzed.

Isomerization to Compounds with Cumulated Double Bonds (Isocyanates, Isothiocyanates, etc.). The first reported example of this type of isomerization appeared in 1962 (*1656*). 1-Phenylthiocarbonylaziridine was converted into 2-phenylthioethyl isocyanate in refluxing toluene or xylene (Eq 279) (*1656, 1663*).

Since then the reaction has been observed for a variety of similar activated aziridines (Eqs 280–283).

$$ArO_2CAz \longrightarrow [ArOCH_2CH_2NCO] \longrightarrow \text{isocyanate trimer} \quad (1595a)$$
$$Ar = 2,4\text{-}Cl_2C_6H_3, p\text{-}O_2NC_6H_4 \tag{280}$$

$$AzC(Y)Cl \longrightarrow ClCH_2CH_2N{=}C{=}Y \quad (1993, 3571, 3571a) \tag{281}$$
$$Y = O \text{ or } S$$

$$Az\overset{+}{C}ONR_3 \ Cl^- \longrightarrow ClCH_2CH_2NCO + R_3N \quad (3572) \tag{282}$$

$$AzS(O)Cl \longrightarrow ClCH_2CH_2N{=}S{=}O \quad (3573) \tag{283}$$

In Eq 281 (when $Y = O$) and in Eq 282 the aziridine derivatives were not actually observed, but there is little doubt that they existed as intermediates (*963, 1993, 3572*).

It was originally suggested that the thermal isomerization of 1-(phenyl-thiocarbonyl)aziridine (Eq 279) was analogous to such isomerization of 1-benzoylaziridine into 2-phenyl-2-oxazoline (*1663*). However, later work indicated that the temperature required for isomerization was dependent on the purity of the aziridine and established that triethylamine (frequently used in preparing such aziridine derivatives) acted as a catalyst (*963*). It was also noted that iodide (*1663*) or thiophenoxide ion (*963*) catalyzes the reaction. The isomerization (Eq 279) catalyzed by potassium thiophenoxide was found to follow a pseudo-first-order rate expression wherein the first-order rate constant was linearly dependent on the catalyst concentration (Eq 284) (*963*).

$$\text{rate} = k_1[\text{PhSCOAz}] \tag{284}$$
$$k_1 = k_2[\text{PhSK}]$$

Thus the reaction may be considered as a nucleophile-catalyzed isomerization. Consistent with this view is the fact that the predominant isomer formed from the 2-methylaziridine derivatives in reactions shown as Eqs 281 (Y = O), 282, and 283 is the one resulting from attachment of the chlorine atom at the less-substituted carbon atom (*963, 1993, 3572*). Furthermore, isomerization of the *N*-chlorocarbonyl derivative of cyclohexenimine occurred stereospecifically, producing only *trans*-2-chlorocyclohexyl isocyanate (*1989a*).

The mechanism may be formulated as a ring opening by a nucleophile, present in catalytic amounts, followed by a 1,2-elimination of a nucleophilic ion from the intermediate ambident ion (Eq 285).

$$NuCH_2CH_2N{=}C{=}Y + Nu'$$

$$Nu'CH_2CH_2N{=}C{=}Y + Nu'$$

Another equally acceptable interpretation may be depicted as an S_N2' reaction, involving transition state **94**.

For 2,2-dialkylaziridine derivatives, the predominant isomer from reactions shown in Eqs 281, 282, and 283 is that wherein the chlorine atom is attached at the tertiary carbon atom (*963, 1993, 3572*). A coproduct is methallyl isocyanate (*963, 1993, 3572*) or isothiocyanate (*963*). Thus, an S_N1 ring opening is indicated which may be preceded by ionization to a carbamoyl or thiocarbamoyl cation such as **95** (*1993, 3572*).

Indeed such ionization to **95** may be important for carbon-unsubstituted aziridine derivatives. Insufficient data are available to permit deciding on the mechanism.

It is noteworthy that for the nucleophile-catalyzed isomerization the conditions are quite similar to those for conversion of activated aziridines into five-membered ring compounds. The data obtained thus far indicate that formation of acyclic compounds containing cumulated double bonds is important when good leaving groups (Nu) are available (Eq 286).

$$\text{(286)}$$

where Nu = ArO, ArS, Cl → $NuCH_2CH_2N{=}C{=}Y$

where Nu = RO, R, R_2N

DEAMINATION OF AZIRIDINES

Although this reaction may be more aptly described as a special type of decomposition for activated aziridines, the importance of the reaction for structural definition makes a separate classification desirable.

It was recognized quite early (in 1903) that EI does not act like a typical secondary amine when treated with nitrous acid, but undergoes decomposition (*1082*). It was subsequently shown that an olefin was one of the products of such treatment [see, for example, Theunis (*3525*)] and still later that 1-nitrosoaziridine, the expected product, was formed at low temperatures but was unstable at room temperature (*719, 899, 3076*). Indeed any reagent which may undergo reaction with a 1-unsubstituted aziridine to produce the 1-nitroso derivative as an expected product will cause such decomposition. Such reagents are nitrosyl chloride in the presence of an acid acceptor (*345a, 719, 1065, 3076*), *N*-nitroso-3-nitrocarbazole (*534, 719*), methyl nitrite (*719*), and nitrous acid (*980, 982, 2908, 3525*) (Eq 287).

$$\text{(287)}$$

$$\to \quad {>}C{=}C{<} + N_2O$$

The reaction has been applied to a variety of carbon-substituted aziridines (*719, 759, 1065, 3525, 3798*), including steroid aziridines (*722a, 979a, 980, 982, 2907, 2908, 4148*) and epimino sugars (*1565, 2384*). It has been shown to be stereospecific, producing trans olefins from *trans*-2,3-disubstituted aziridines and cis olefins from *cis*-aziridines (Eq 288) (*718, 719*).

$$\text{(image of nitrosoaziridine structure)} \longrightarrow \underset{R}{\overset{H}{>}}C=C\underset{H}{\overset{R}{<}} + N_2O \qquad (288)$$

The decomposition of *trans*-2,3-dimethyl-1-nitrosoaziridine at $-15°C$ followed a first-order rate expression and was faster in ionizing solvents. Rate constants (min^{-1}) obtained in various solvents were as follows: pentane, 1.2×10^{-2}; ethyl ether, 1.8×10^{-2}; methanol, 6.3×10^{-2}; dimethylformamide, 1.3×10^{-1} (*719*). A transition state (**96**) which involves a concerted cleavage of the two aziridine carbon–nitrogen bonds was suggested (*719*).

96

The other activated aziridines which have been observed to decompose in this manner are the unstable intermediate formed from difluoroamine and EI (Eq 289) (*535*) and the 1-(arylazo)aziridines (Eq 290) (*1329, 1800, 3057*).

$$\text{(structure)} + HNF_2 \longrightarrow \left[\text{(structure)}\right] \longrightarrow \underset{H}{\overset{R}{>}}C=C\underset{H}{\overset{R}{<}} + N_2 \qquad (289)$$

$$\text{(structure)} \xrightarrow[60°-75°C]{} ArN_3 + RCH_2=CH_2 \qquad (290)$$

$$Ar = Ph \text{ or } p\text{-}MeC_6H_4, \ R = Ph \text{ or } H$$

The deamination by HNF_2 is also stereospecific (*1329*). Such a reaction as shown in Eq 290 cannot be expected to be very general since aryl azides and olefins often give triazolines (p. 68).

Also similar is the fragmentation that hydrazones derived from 1-amino-aziridines undergo upon heating [Eq 290a, 290b (Refs. *1801, 1284c*, resp.)].

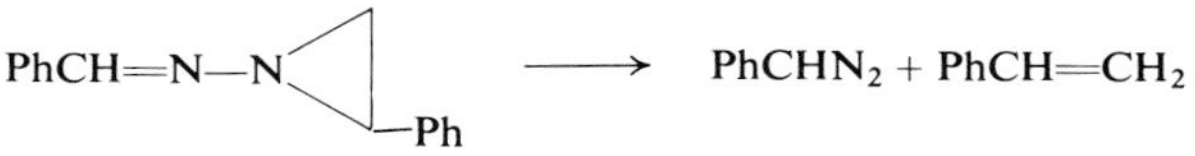

$$\text{PhCH}{=}\text{N}{-}\text{N}\!\!\triangleleft_{\text{Ph}} \longrightarrow \text{PhCHN}_2 + \text{PhCH}{=}\text{CH}_2 \qquad (290a)$$

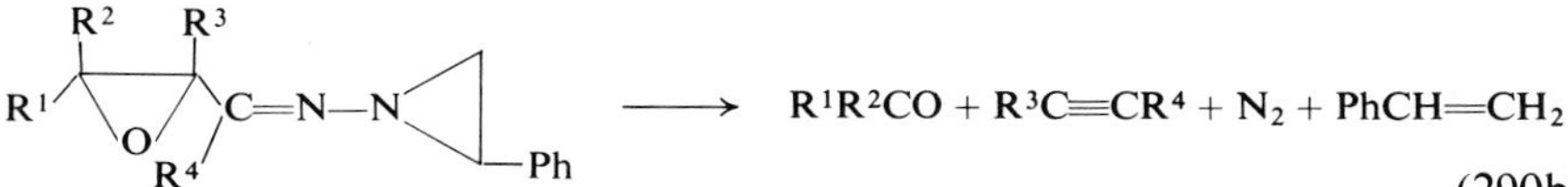

$$\underset{R^4}{\overset{R^2\ \ R^3}{R^1\diagdown\!\!\underset{O}{\triangle}\!\!\diagup}}\!\!C{=}\text{N}{-}\text{N}\!\!\triangleleft_{\text{Ph}} \longrightarrow R^1R^2\text{CO} + R^3\text{C}{\equiv}\text{CR}^4 + N_2 + \text{PhCH}{=}\text{CH}_2$$
$$(290b)$$

The formation of ethylene by reaction of diphenylcyclopropenone with EI, while not yet fully accountable, appears to belong in this class of ring openings; the other main product is 2,4-diphenylazetin-2-one (*4038*).

Of interest is the photochemical deamination of (*trans*-2-benzoyl-3-phenyl)-1-cyclohexylaziridines (Eq 291) (*2799, 2802*).

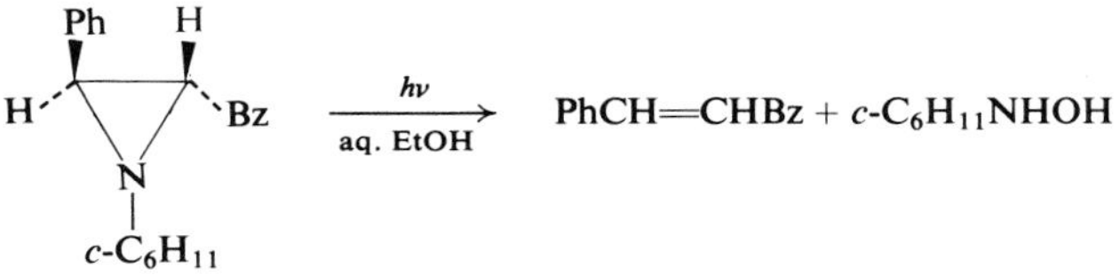

$$\underset{c\text{-}C_6H_{11}}{\overset{\overset{\displaystyle\text{Ph}\quad\text{H}}{H^{\cdot'}\!\!\triangle\!\!{}^{\cdot}\text{Bz}}}{N}} \xrightarrow[\text{aq. EtOH}]{h\nu} \text{PhCH}{=}\text{CHBz} + c\text{-}C_6H_{11}\text{NHOH} \qquad (291)$$

The reaction was found to be nonstereospecific. An entirely different result was obtained on irradiation of the *cis*-aziridine (see p. 302).

Also notable is the peracid oxidation of 1,2,3-triphenylaziridine. Stilbene and nitrosobenzene were formed in about equal amounts along with benzaldehyde and benzalaniline. The products may have resulted from decomposition of the intermediate aziridine *N*-oxide or rearrangement of the *N*-oxide to a 1,2-oxazetidine and decomposition of the latter (Eq 292) (*2803*).

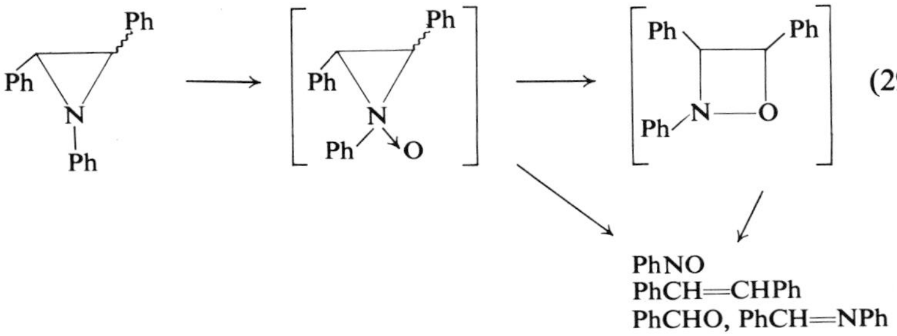

$$(292)$$

PhNO
PhCH=CHPh
PhCHO, PhCH=NPh

HYDROGENOLYSIS OF AZIRIDINES

Aziridines often undergo ring opening when catalytically hydrogenated (Eq 293).

$$\text{(aziridine structure)} + H_2 \xrightarrow{\text{catalyst}} -\overset{|}{\underset{|}{C}}-\overset{|}{\underset{|}{C}}-NH- \qquad (293)$$

However, present data are insufficient for broad generalizations regarding the reaction. A number of such hydrogenolyses are shown in Table 3-XXXIII. The examples indicate that for 2,2-dialkylaziridines or 2,2-dialkylaziridinium ions, cleavage of the aziridine ring occurs between the nitrogen atom and the less-substituted carbon atom. In 2-(or 3-)phenylaziridines, cleavage between the nitrogen and the phenyl-substituted carbon atom occurs.

Excepting hydrogenolysis of 1-alkyl carbon-unsubstituted aziridines, most of the reactions shown in Table 3-XXXIII take place under relatively mild conditions (such as room temperature and low hydrogen pressure). For 1-alkyl-aziridines, high temperatures (100°–170°C) were necessary (963). Thus, hydrogenation of easily reducible functions on the alkyl group may be effected without hydrogenolysis of the aziridine ring (see p. 304).

The selectivity for hydrogenation versus hydrogenolysis of 1-allylaziridine was affected by catalyst to some extent, the amount of hydrogenolysis increasing in the order Ru < Rh < Pt < Pd (1585).

Catalyst-dependent selectivity is also observed in the hydrogenation of 1-phenethylaziridine. Rhodium did not effect any conversion under the same conditions (1000 lb/sq inch hydrogen, 100°C, about 20 hours) at which hydrated ruthenium dioxide caused complete conversion. The products with the latter catalyst were 1-(2-cyclohexylethyl)aziridine (41%) and N-ethyl-2-cyclohexylethylamine (55%) (1596), whereas rhodium catalyst at the same hydrogen pressure but for 1.4 hours at 200°C gave N-ethyl-2-phenethylamine (54%), N-ethyl-2-cyclohexylethylamine (11%), ethylbenzene, and ethylamine (963).

On prolonged hydrogenation, the aziridine ring of the *erythro* isomer of **97** underwent hydrogenolysis while the *threo* isomer was unaffected (Eq 294) (1298).

$$\begin{array}{cc} & \textit{erythro} + H_2 \xrightarrow{\text{Ni}} \text{MeCHOHCH(NHEt)CH}_2\text{Ph} \\ \text{MeCHOHCHAzCH}_2\text{Ph} & \\ \textbf{97} & \textit{threo} \qquad \text{no reaction} \qquad (294) \end{array}$$

Hydrogenolysis of 1-alkyl-2-methyleneaziridine occurs under very mild conditions over Adams catalyst and results in cleavage of the aziridine ring between the nitrogen and methylene-substituted carbon atoms (Eq 295) (*442, 444, 2905*).

$$ \text{CH}_2 \diagup \underset{\underset{\text{R}}{\overset{|}{\text{N}}}}{\triangle} + \text{H}_2 \xrightarrow{\text{Pt}} \text{RNHPr} \qquad (295) $$

Hydrogenolysis of EI over evaporated metal films gave ethylamine when the catalyst was Pt and Pd; acetonitrile with Co, V, and Cu; and a mixture of both over Ni and W (*98*).

The gas-phase hydrogenolysis of EI at 210°C over platinum catalyst produces ethane as a principal product (*343*). Hydrogen atoms at 300°C also produce ethane (*1965*).

The ring opening which 3-benzoyl-1-cyclohexyl-2-(*o*-nitrophenyl)aziridine suffers during catalytic hydrogenation is probably best interpreted as an isomerization (Eq 296) (*800*).

$$ (296) $$

The reductive cleavage of 1-nitrosoaziridine by LiAlH$_4$ at -30°C to yield hydrazine (*3076*) is only distantly related to typical hydrogenolysis of aziridines; but reduction without ring opening is claimed to be possible, to produce 1-aminoaziridine (*1513*). Another reductive ring opening is that of EI in its complex with BH$_3$; reaction with B$_2$H$_6$ yields the ethylaminodiborane (Eq 297) (*540*).

$$ \text{AzH or AzH} \cdot \text{BH}_3 + \text{B}_2\text{H}_6 \;\rightarrow\; \text{EtNHB}_2\text{H}_5 \text{ (polymers)} \qquad (297) $$

In other examples, *N*-mesyl-2α,3α-epiminocholestane and lithium aluminum hydride give 3α-mesylaminocholestane (*2907*), a complex polycyclic aziridine undergoes ring expansion upon reduction with sodium borohydride (*1287b, 1744*), and a highly arylated one, 1,2,2,3-tetraphenylaziridine, is cleaved by aluminum amalgam and acid to *N*-(1,1,2-triphenylethyl)aniline (*3056*).

Table 3-XXXIII

CATALYTIC HYDROGENOLYSIS OF AZIRIDINES

Aziridine or substituents therein	Catalyst	Product	References
1-H	Ni	EtNH₂	350
	Pt (black)	EtNH₂	3890
	Pd (black)	EtNH₂	3890
1-Et	Pd (alumina)	Et₂NH	963
	Pt (alumina)	Et₂NH	963
1-Pr	Pt (alumina)	EtNHPr	963
1-PhCH₂CH₂	Rh (alumina)	PhCH₂CH₂NHEt	1298
1-MeCHOHCH(CH₂Ph)	Ni	MeCHOHCH(CH₂Ph)CH₂CH₂NH₂	
1-Ph	Pt (black)	PhNHEt	3890
	Pd (black)	PhNHEt	3890
	Pd (carbon)		2103
	Ni	+ isomer	550
2,2-Me₂	Ni	Me₂CNH₂	565, 567, 2043
2-(CH₂=)-1-(CH₂=CHCHOHCH₂)	Pt	PrNHCH₂CHOHEt	442
2-Ph	Pt (black)	PHCH₂CH₂NH₂	3889
	Pd (black)	PhCH₂CH₂NH₂	3889

	Catalyst	Product	Ref.
2-Me-1-Ph	Pd	PhCH₂CHMeNHMe	*1572*
3-Ph-2-CONH₂	Pt	PhCH₂CH(NH₂)CONH₂	*863*
1-Ph-2-CO₂Me	Ni	PhNHCH₂CH₂CO₂Me	*3451*
1-(2,4,6-Me₃C₆H₂)-2-CO₂Me-3-COCO₂Me	Pd/C	2,4,6-Me₃C₆H₂NH₂ and MeO₂CCHMeCOCO₂Me	*257a*
3-Ph-1-(p-MeC₆H₄SO₂)	Pd (BaSO₄)	PhCH₂CH₂NHSO₂C₆H₄Me-p	*2077*
1-CH₂=CHCMe(OH)CH₂	Pd	EtCMe(OH)CH₂NHEt	*255*
1-BuNHCHPhCMe₂	Pd	BuNHCHPhCMe₂NHEt	*3379*
1-AcCH(CH₂Ph)	Ni	MeCHOHCH(CH₂Ph)CH₂CH₂NH₂	*1298*
cis-2-Bz-1-c-C₆H₁₁-3-Ph	—	PhCH₂CH(NH-c-C₆H₁₁)CHOHPh and cis-1-c-C₆H₁₁-2-PhCHOH-3-PhAz	*167, 4200*
A complex 1-aminoaziridine of type 2-RAzNH₂	Ni	RCHMeNH₂	*4145*
2-Az-2-Ph-cycloheptanone	Pd/C	2-EtNH₂-2-Ph-cycloheptanone	*3380*

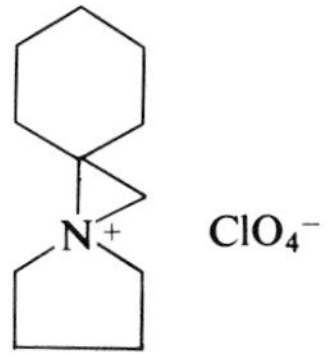

Pt — *2300, 2301*

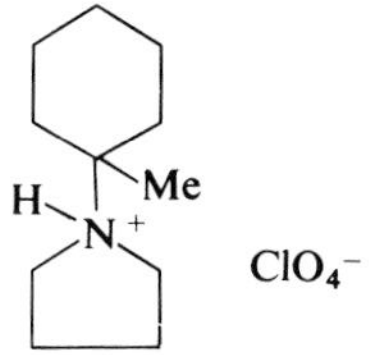

Pt — *2295*

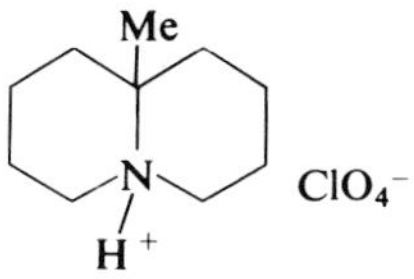

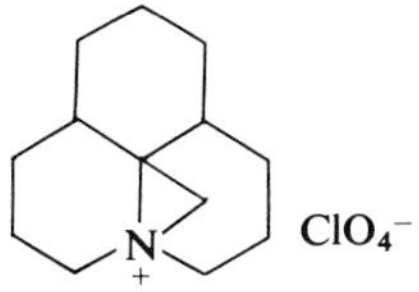

Pt — *2295*

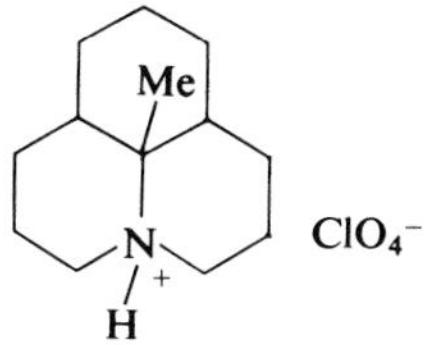

Table 3-XXXIII—*continued*

Aziridine or substituents therein	Catalyst	Product	References
	—		2655a
	Ni		1287b; cf. 1746
	Pd/C		3380

MISCELLANEOUS RING-DESTROYING REACTIONS

Included here are a variety of reactions which are not conveniently classified in other sections.

A most unusual reaction between EI and sodium borohydride has been recently reported (Eq 298) (30).

$$\text{AzH} + \text{NaBH}_4 \longrightarrow \underset{\text{H}_2\text{B}\text{---}\text{NH}_2{}^+}{\boxed{}} \tag{298}$$

Ring opening of basic or activated aziridines by alkyl halides is well documented. The same reaction with an N-arsenic-substituted aziridine (Eq 299) occurred with a curious elimination of arsenic (2031).

$$\text{R}_2\text{AsAz} + \text{MeI} \rightarrow \text{ICH}_2\text{CH}_2\text{NMe}_3{}^+ \text{ I}^- + \text{As} \tag{299}$$

Very little has been reported to date on the oxidation of aziridines. Of interest is the oxidation of 3-hydroxy-5,6-N-cyanoimino steroids by chromic oxide in pyridine (Eq 300) (440).

$$\text{HO---} \qquad + \text{CrO}_3\cdot\text{C}_5\text{H}_5\text{N} \longrightarrow \tag{300}$$

Treatment of EI with carbon dioxide in ether at −10°C is reported to give the EI salt of vinylcarbamic acid (3192). However, no precedent exists for such a reaction and additional structure proof for the product is needed.

Most appropriately mentioned here is the fact that the EI (or azetidine) derivative corresponding to 98 is not photochemically rearranged as are larger heterocyclic homologs (Eq 301) (563).

$$\tag{301}$$

98

Photolysis. The products of photolysis of EI (*2358*) and a series of 1-alkyl-2-methyleneaziridines (*479*) have been examined. Ethylenimine produced mainly hydrogen, nitrogen, and ethylene whereas the 2-methyleneaziridine derivatives gave ethylene, nitriles, and isonitriles. The scheme shown in Eq 302, involving two main paths, was suggested to account for the observations (*479*).

$$ RNC + C_2H_4 \quad \longleftarrow \qquad \qquad \qquad \tag{302} $$

$$ RCN + C_2H_4 $$

The products of photolysis of 1,2,3-triphenylaziridine depend in part upon the nature of the solvent, which traps or otherwise reacts with the intermediate initially formed by C—C cleavage. In alcohols the products are *N*-benzylidenebenzylamine and acetals of benzaldehyde; in benzene or cyclopentene, phenylbenzylamine and benzylideneaniline; and in cyclohexene, 1,2,3-triphenylisoindoline (*4134*). (*cis*-2-Benzoyl-3-phenyl)-1-cyclohexylaziridine similarly gives a Schiff base among other products (Eq 303) (*2799*), but photolysis of the trans isomer affords an entirely different result (see p. 295).

$$ \xrightarrow{h\nu} \quad PhCH{=}NC_6H_{11}\text{-}c \tag{303} $$

1-(2,4,6-Trinitrophenyl)-*cis*-2,3-diphenylaziridine in ethanol gave benzaldehyde and 2-phenyl-4,6-dinitrobenzimidazol-1-ol (**98a**) in 95% yield, with evident participation of a nitro group; 1-(2,4-dinitrophenyl)-2-benzoyl-3-phenylaziridine similarly produced 96% 2-phenyl-6-nitrobenzimidazol-1-ol (*1672a*).

98a

Pyrolysis. Except for thermal isomerizations, the alteration of aziridines by heat has received little attention. Among the few known examples are reactions shown in Eqs 304 and 305.

$$MeSO_2SO_2Me, MeSO_2H, \text{ and } MeSO_3H \quad (165) \quad (304)$$

$$B_{10}H_{12}(Ph_2PAz)_2 \xrightarrow[\text{heat}]{} H_2, C_2H_6 \quad (305)$$

The pyrolysis of either *cis-* or *trans* methyl 1-cyclohexyl-3-*p*-biphenylyl-aziridine-2-carboxylate resembles the photolyses just described in giving fewer products, the aromatic aldehyde *p*-PhC$_6$H$_4$CHO and RNHCH$_2$CO$_2$Me (R = cyclohexyl) in methanol at 60° or the aldehyde and H$_2$NCHRCO$_2$Me in boiling benzene (*3824a*).

Reactions of Aziridines Occurring at Sites Other than the Aziridine Ring

The aziridine ring is known to be susceptible to ring opening or other ring destruction under a variety of conditions. Thus it is significant that many reactions have been performed on aziridines wherein the ring has remained intact. These reactions are more or less consistent with the chemical properties of the aziridine undergoing reaction. For example, a basic aziridine is not ring-opened by basic reagents and thus the ring survives a reaction such as shown in Eq 306.

$$+ \text{ NaOH} \longrightarrow \qquad + \text{ ROH} \quad (306)$$

Such reactions may be broadly divided into two groups. These are (a) those wherein a functional group present in the aziridine derivative is *changed* and (b) those wherein a substituent is *removed* from an aziridine ring but the ring remains intact.

ALTERATION OF SUBSTITUENT GROUP

A number of aziridines containing unsaturated linkages ($C{=}C$, $C{\equiv}C$, $C{=}O$, $C{\equiv}N$, $C{=}N$) can be converted to saturated compounds without opening the aziridine ring. Catalytic hydrogenation as a means to this end has already been mentioned as a competitor of hydrogenolysis (p. 296). Table 3-XXXIV presents types of compounds that have been hydrogenated with

Table 3-XXXIV

CATALYTIC HYDROGENATION OF AZIRIDINYL COMPOUNDS WITHOUT RING
OPENING

Change effected by hydrogenation	Catalyst	References
$>C{=}C< \rightarrow >CH{-}CH<$	Pt	*982, 1266, 1585*
	Pd, Rh, Ru	*759, 1585*
$>C{=}O \rightarrow >CHOH$	Ni, Pd	*1266, 1298, 1299, 3641, 4200*
Quinone $\rightarrow$ hydroquinone	Ni	*705, 2829*
	Pd, Pt	*705*
$-CO_2CH_2Ph \rightarrow -CO_2H$	Pd	*1684, 3900*
$-CN \rightarrow -CH_2NH_2$	Ni	*350, 1266, 3386, 3498*
$-NO_2 \rightarrow -NH_2$	Ni	*2285[a], 2909, 3286*

[a] This result has been questioned (*1801*).

survival of the aziridine ring. Other reducing agents producing the same effect are set forth in Table 3-XXXV. Reduction of *cis-* and *trans-*2-phenyl-3-aroyl-1-cyclohexylaziridines with lithium aluminum hydride or lithium diisopropylamide gave the corresponding alcohols stereospecifically by attack from the less-hindered side, whereas the smaller borohydride ion as reducing agent gave both possible diastereoisomeric racemates (*4200*). However, both *cis-* and *trans-*2,3-dibenzoyl-1-benzylaziridines were stereospecifically reduced even with borohydride because of interaction of the carbonyl groups (*3641*).

Basic aziridines which have substituents containing a ketone functional group undergo reaction with Grignard reagents in a normal manner to give aziridines that have tertiary hydroxyl in the substituent group (Eq 307) (*785, 799*). Phenyllithium performs similarly (*3184*).

$$\text{(307)}$$

Perhaps more surprisingly, a 2-chloro activated aziridine with phenyl-magnesium bromide undergoes simply replacement of the chlorine by a phenyl group (*4057*). 1-*tert*-Butyl-2-(chloromethyl)aziridine undergoes solvolytic removal of the chlorine in water or acetic acid (*1395a*), and the methanolysis of (1-*tert*-butyl-2-aziridinyl)methyl tosylate is similar.

A substituted 1-phenacylaziridine has been found to behave as a normal ketone toward *n*-butylamine (Eq 308) (*3379*).

Table 3-XXXV

NONCATALYTIC REDUCTION OF AZIRIDINYL COMPOUNDS WITHOUT RING
OPENING

Change effected by reduction	Reducing agent	References
$>$C=O → $>$CHOH	LiAlH$_4$	*167, 4200*
$>$C=O → $>$CHOH	NaBH$_4$	*193, 982, 3281, 3379, 3645, 4200*
Quinone → hydroquinone	Na$_2$S$_2$O$_4$	*705, 1167, 2452, 4025*
Quinone → hydroquinone	Na + EtOH	*705*
Quinone → hydroquinone	PhNHNH$_2$	*1424*
—CO$_2$R → —CHO	LiAlH$_4$	*2673a*
—CO$_2$R → —CH$_2$OH	LiAlH$_4$	*453, 572, 2102*
—CONHR → —CH$_2$NHR	LiAlH$_4$	*3720*
—CN → —CH$_2$NH$_2$	LiAlH$_4$	*3090, 3723*
$>$C=NR → $>$CHNHR	NaBH$_4$	*3379*
—CS$_2$Me → [—CH(SH)SMe]?	NaBH$_4$	*685*

	NaBH$_4$	*3380*

	NaBH$_4$	*257a*

$$\text{BzCR}^1\text{R}^2\text{Az} + \text{BuNH}_2 \xrightarrow{-\text{H}_2\text{O}} \text{BuN}=\text{CPhCR}^1\text{R}^2\text{Az} \qquad (308)$$

and 1-(2-aminoethyl)aziridines to give the expected adducts, such as $\text{AzCH}_2\text{CH}_2\text{NHC}(\text{CF}_3)_2\text{OH}$, with hexafluoroacetone (451). 2-Acyl-1-benzyl-3-phenylaziridines with phenylhydrazine and acetic acid form isolable N-acetylphenylhydrazones in some cases (807) (cf. p. 239).

Treatment of 2,3-diaroylaziridines with hydrazine gives a triaza-2,4-nor-caradiene derivative (Eq 309) (3638).

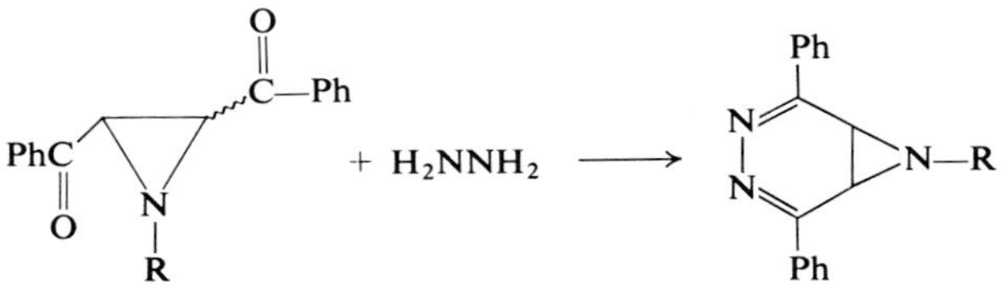

$$(309)$$

The aziridinyl group in **99** survives thermal rearrangement of the molecule to 2-(1-aziridinyl)-2-phenylcycloheptanone (3380).

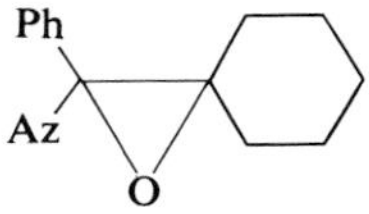

99

In a lately reported series of carbanion-mediated reactions, 1-alkyl-2,3-dibenzoylaziridines condense with acetone in alkaline medium to yield tricyclic ketones **99a** (3641).

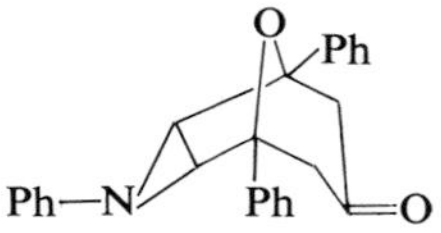

99a

Basic aziridines with substituents which contain a carboxylic ester group undergo a variety of reactions at this group without ring opening. In addition to basic hydrolysis (Eq 306) (124, 717, 821, 933, 1284c, 2215, 2527, 3723) alcoholysis (2304) and ammonolysis or aminolysis of the ester group (188, 904a, 1471, 2078, 2226, 2623, 2810, 3310–3312, 3314, 3720) may be performed. Similarly, basic hydrolysis may be accomplished on aziridines containing, instead of the ester group, a cyano (124), amide (124), imide (2754), or anhydride (2336) group. A complex N-cyanoaziridine with ammonia gives the N-guanido derivative (249). Treatment of a 1-(2-cyanoethyl)aziridine with butyllithium caused dimerization at the nitrile function (Eq 310) (3498).

$$(310)$$

Esterification of alcohols which also contain basic aziridinyl groups is possible. However, since acids, anhydrides, and acid halides readily cause ring opening of aziridines, the reaction is successful only when reagents such as N-acylimidazoles are used (*215, 218, 3357–3359*) or mixtures of the aziridinyl alcohol and esters are heated with a basic catalyst (Eq 311) (*730a, 3625*).

$$AzCH_2CH_2OH + RCO_2R' \rightarrow AzCH_2CH_2O_2CR + R'OH\uparrow \qquad (311)$$

A similar reaction has been performed on a mixed ester anhydride of boric acid (Eq 312) (*2303*).

$$(312)$$

Esterification of aziridinyl alcohols with dimethylcarbamoyl chloride, Me_2NCOCl, and triethylamine (*182*) as well as combination of the sodium derivatives of such alcohols with $(RO)_2P(O)Cl$ (*4043*) has been claimed. Acylation of such alcohols is possible also with ketene (*2529, 3371*), diketene (*182*), and dimethylketene dimer (*4069*), and not unexpectedly, these alcohols add readily to isocyanates and isothiocyanates to form, respectively, urethans and thiourethans (*2947, 3359, 3672a*). Similar aziridines containing amino groups instead of hydroxyl groups also add easily to α,β-unsaturated esters (*1080*), isocyanates (*1588*), and isothiocyanates (*3090*). 1-(2-Aminoethyl)aziridine attacks the Si—H bonds in $(-SiHMeO)_n$ to yield hydrogen and the polymer with $-NHCH_2CH_2Az$ groups attached to silicon (*1068*). If 1-hydroxyaziridines can indeed be prepared as claimed (*2817*), they probably do add to divinyl sulfone to give compounds of type $(AzOCH_2CH_2)_2SO_2$.

1-(1-Aziridinyl)alkanols, the adducts from aldehydes and aziridines, interact with ammonia to give small yields of tertiary amines such as $N(CH_2Az)_3$, better ones of $RN(CH_2Az)_2$ types from primary amines (*2162*), and still better yields from secondary amines (Eq 313) (*2146, 2149, 2152a, 2152b, 2160, 3765*).

$$RCHOHAz + R'_2NH \rightarrow RCHAzNR'_2 + H_2O \qquad (313)$$

100

Rather remarkably, treatment of such aziridines (**100**) with diazomethane results in insertion of a methylene group between the aziridinyl nitrogen and the hydroxylated carbon atom (*2160*).

Somewhat related is the reaction of a 2-acetylaziridine of steroid structure with acetone to form a cyclic hemiketal pattern (Eq 314) (*982*).

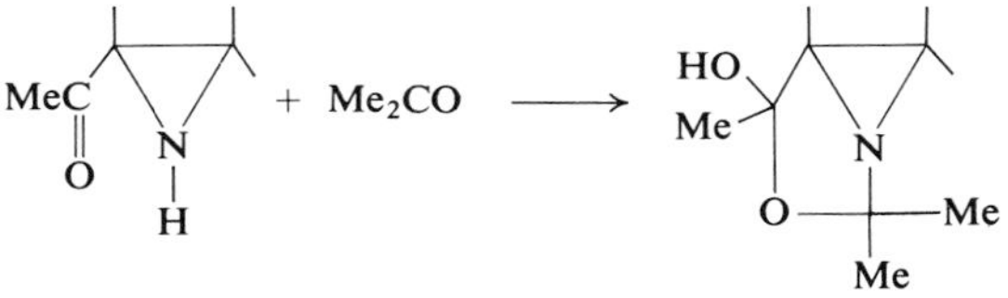

(314)

When ammonia is present also, an imidazoline ring is formed (Eq 315).

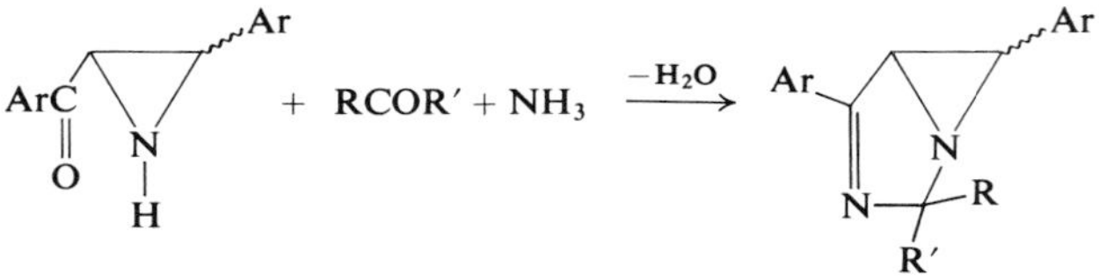

(315)

More striking is the survival of the aziridine ring when reaction 315 is reversed with moist acetic acid (*4075*).

1-(2-Aminoethyl)aziridine can be converted to $(Me_2N)_2P(O)NHCH_2CH_2Az$ by treatment with the appropriate acid chloride and sodium hydroxide as acid acceptor (*4068*). In another predictable reaction, 1-aminoaziridines give hydrazones with carbonyl compounds (*1284c, 4145*), as does 1-benzylaziridine-2-carbohydrazide with acetone (*904a*).

Another reaction that may be viewed as involving a net insertion occurs upon treatment of 1-(trialkylsilyl)aziridines with organic isocyanates (Eq 316) (*3139*) or aldehydes (*2673*).

$$R_3SiAz + R'NCO \rightarrow R_3SiNR'COAz \qquad (316)$$

$$+ R'CHO \rightarrow R_3SiOCHR'Az$$

All the examples thus far noted have involved basic aziridines under either basic or neutral conditions. Certain acid-catalyzed reactions may also be performed on such aziridines providing the acid is one with a weakly nucleophilic anion, it is used in stoichiometric amount, and there are only very weakly nucleophilic reagents present in the reaction medium. An example is the perchloric acid-catalyzed hydrolysis of an acetal which contains a basic aziridinyl group (676, 1569a). The very old claim that ethyl 3-carbamoyl-aziridine-2-carboxylate is hydrolyzed in hydrochloric acid to monoethyl aziridine-2,3-dicarboxylate (1677) should be verified before it is believed.

Reactions involving basic aziridines for which it would have been difficult to predict survival of the aziridine ring are shown in Eqs 317 (2949) and 318 (376).

$$AzCH(OR)CH_2Cl + Mg \rightarrow AzCH{=}CH_2 + MgCl(OR) \qquad (317)$$

$$AzSCCl_3 + (RO)_3P \rightarrow AzSC[P(O)(OR)_2]_3 + RCl \qquad (318)$$

Of interest is the reaction of 1-ethyl-2-methyleneaziridine with tetracyano-ethylene (Eq 319) (755).

$$(319)$$

Ring opening of activated aziridines occurs readily under acidic, basic, or neutral conditions. Where reaction at a functional group other than the aziridine ring is desired, the ability of the ring to survive depends primarily on the relative rates of the desired functional group reaction and potential ring-opening reactions. For example, for the aziridine 101, bromination of the double bonds occurs much faster than ring opening by bromine (405, 3703, 4140).

101

Pyrolysis of $Az_2P(O)NHCONH_2$ and $Az_2P(S)NHCONH_2$ is alleged to yield the respective isocyanates, $Az_2P(Y)NCO$, which add alcohols, thiols, and amines predictably at the isocyanato group (2810a).

2,6-Di-tert-butyl-4-R-phenols, where R is an α-(1-aziridino)alkyl group, can be oxidized with potassium ferricyanide to the corresponding p-benzo-quinone methides without loss of the aziridine ring (4198). Oxidation of aziridinylhydroquinones to aziridinylquinones is commonplace in that field.

1-Aziridinyl derivatives of trivalent phosphorus compounds may be oxidized by various reagents to form pentavalent phosphorus derivatives (Eq 320)

(*1120, 1528–1530, 2725, 2728, 2728a, 2729a, 2729b, 2859, 2954, 2955, 2959, 4039, 4164*).

$$
\text{Az—P}\Big<
\begin{array}{l}
\xrightarrow{\text{[O]}} \quad \text{Az—P(O)}\Big< \\
\xrightarrow{\text{S, Se}} \quad \text{Az—P(S)}\Big< \text{ or } \text{Az—P(Se)}\Big< \\
\xrightarrow[\text{—N}_2]{\text{RN}_3} \quad \text{Az—P(NR)}\Big<
\end{array}
\qquad (320)
$$

In a similar manner, bis(1-aziridinyl) sulfoxide can be so oxidized by potassium permanganate (Eq 321) (*426, 3835, 3836*).

$$
\text{Az}_2\text{SO} \xrightarrow{\text{[O]}} \text{Az}_2\text{SO}_2 \qquad (321)
$$

Of interest also is the reaction shown in Eq 322, which forms the indicated adduct instead of the dichlorovinyl compounds that might have been expected (*1529*).

$$
\text{CCl}_3\text{CHO} + \text{iso-PrOPAz}_2 \longrightarrow \underset{\underset{\text{O—Pr-iso}}{|}}{\text{CCl}_3\text{CHP(O)Az}_2} \qquad (322)
$$

However, dichlorovinyl compounds *are* formed from cyclic phosphorus esters (*1524a*).

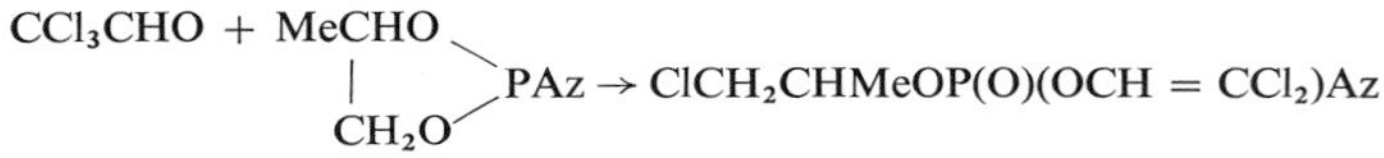

$$
\begin{array}{c}
\text{CCl}_3\text{CHO} + \text{MeCHO} \\
\underset{\text{CH}_2\text{O}}{|} \quad \Big\rangle\text{PAz} \rightarrow \text{ClCH}_2\text{CHMeOP(O)(OCH = CCl}_2)\text{Az}
\end{array}
$$

The most common reaction of the "substituent group alteration" type involving activated aziridines is displacement of an active halogen present in the molecule. Examples include displacements on aziridinyl halo-*s*-triazines (e.g., Eq 323) (*336, 465, 473, 1896, 2208, 3126, 3442*) and aziridinyl halo-1,4-benzoquinones (e.g., Eq 324) (*708, 1131, 1231, 2400a, 2404, 2405, 2418, 2445, 2452, 2456, 3732*).

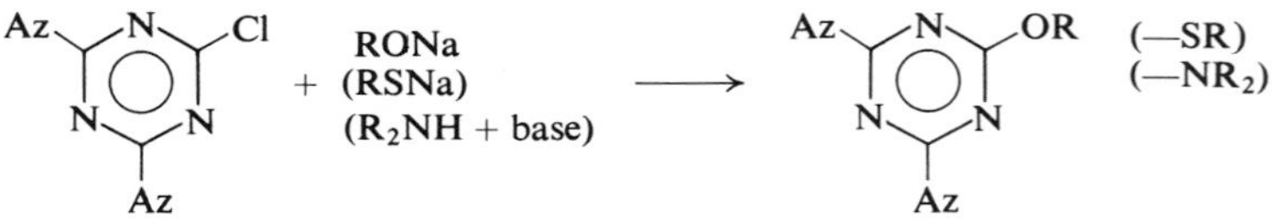

$$
(323)
$$

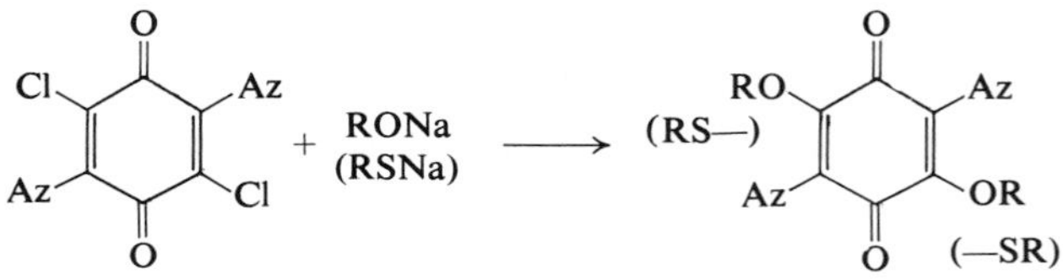

$$
(324)
$$

Such displacements have also been performed on aziridinyl haloquinoxalines (*3689*), aziridinyl halopyrimidines (*1682, 3125a*) and mixed aziridinyl halo derivatives obtained from the trimer of phosphonitrilic chloride (*2122, 2182, 2787, 2789, 2790*) (see p. 186). Bis(1-aziridinyl)phosphinyl chloride undergoes displacement of the chlorine by N,N'-dimethylethylenediamine to yield the tetrafunctional compound $Az_2P(O)NMeCH_2CH_2NMeP(O)Az_2$ (*628*).

In this type of reaction the ability of the aziridine ring to remain intact during treatment with such very nucleophilic reagents as alkylthio ions is surprising. Such displacement reactions provide a convenient route to derivatives which would otherwise be difficult or impossible to obtain. For example, in Eq 325 the dimethylamino groups so reduce the activity of the remaining chlorine that displacement by EI occurs only under conditions which do not allow survival of the product aziridine. The aziridinyl group does not exert this effect, so that the alternative sequence is successful (*963, 3126*).

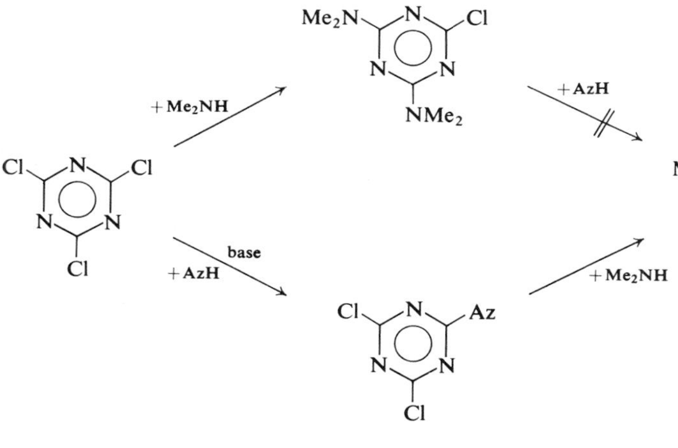

(325)

Aziridinylbenzoquinones containing acetylamino groups are hydrolyzed in alkaline solution with removal of the acetylamino groups (Eq 326) (*2457*).

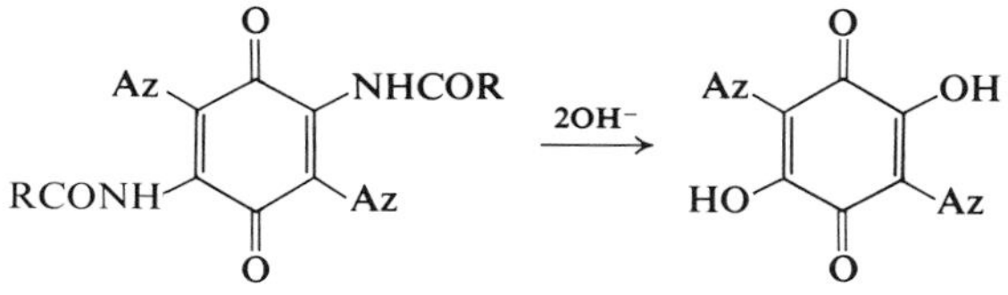

(326)

A related replacement of methoxy or amino groups while the aziridinyl ring is retained has repeatedly been observed for the mitomycins (see p. 403). One more example: 1-benzenesulfonyl-2-chloromethylaziridine with sodium iodide gives the iodomethyl derivative (*1448*).

Trivalent-phosphorus compounds containing both aziridinyl and dimethyl-amino groups undergo acid-catalyzed ethanolysis to yield products retaining the ring, Az_2POEt and $AzP(OEt)_2$ (*2701*). A reaction more similar to the displacements on triazine and quinone rings (Eq 327) gave only a low yield of **102** (*2861*), presumably because it involved conditions too vigorous for survival of the aziridine rings.

$$(EtO)_2P(O)Na + ClCH_2CH_2P(O)Az_2 \rightarrow (EtO)_2P(O)CH_2CH_2P(O)Az_2 \qquad (327)$$

102

However, the same product was obtained in high yield according to the reaction shown in Eq 328 (*2861*).

$$(EtO)_2P(O)H + CH_2{=}CHP(O)Az_2 \xrightarrow{\text{basic catalyst}} \textbf{102} \qquad (328)$$

Likewise vinylphosphinic acid derivatives **103** and their thio counterparts give adducts with alcohols and alkanethiols in 40–60% yields (Eq 329) (*4146*), as well as with dialkyl hydrogenphosphonates and hydrogenphosphono-thioates (*2861*) and piperidine (*4147*).

$$RSH + CH_2{=}CHP(O)Az_2 \xrightarrow{\text{base}} RSCH_2CH_2P(O)Az_2 \qquad (329)$$

103

It is claimed that a sulfonylaziridine group on an aromatic ring will persist through diazotization and azo coupling to yield reactive dyes (*1582, 1895*).

Neutron irradiation of thiotepa, Az_3PS, in CCl_4 (to provide ^{35}S atoms by nuclear reaction of ^{35}Cl) produced a compound labeled with both ^{35}S and ^{32}P (*1017*).

REMOVAL OF SUBSTITUENT GROUP

Reactions of this type might be more accurately regarded as removal of the aziridinyl group from the compound represented by the substituent group. All examples involve 1-substituted aziridines and all the substituents are such as would make the aziridines true or borderline examples of activated aziridines.

Treatment of 1-acylaziridines with hydroxylic solvents such as water in the presence of base (*251, 252, 551, 963, 1467, 1561, 1576, 1624, 1627, 2538a, 2907, 3243, 3370, 3449, 3491*) or even acid (*3370*) causes solvolysis to the 1-unsubsti-tuted aziridine (see p. 253). The reaction has also been applied to a 1-(tri-methylsilyl)aziridine and 1-aziridinyl-1,4-benzoquinone derivatives (Eq 330) (*2406*).

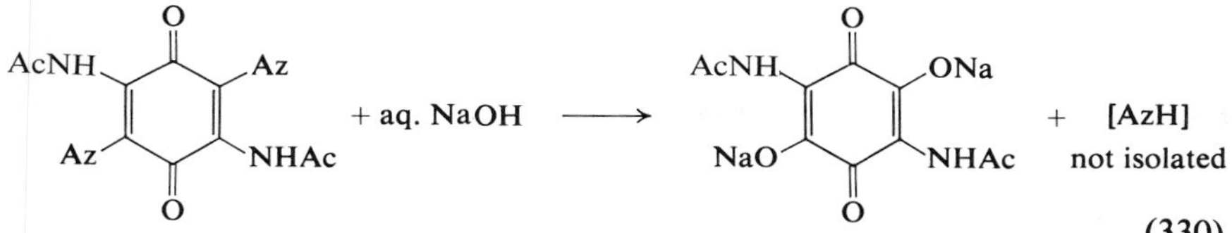

$$\text{(structure: AcNH and Az substituted 1,4-benzoquinone)} + \text{aq. NaOH} \longrightarrow \text{(structure: AcNH, ONa, NaO, NHAc substituted quinone)} + [AzH] \quad \text{not isolated} \tag{330}$$

Replacement of aziridinyl groups in such 1,4-benzoquinone derivatives is very frequently observed upon treatment with alkylamines (Eq 331) (*339, 2401, 2405, 2407*).

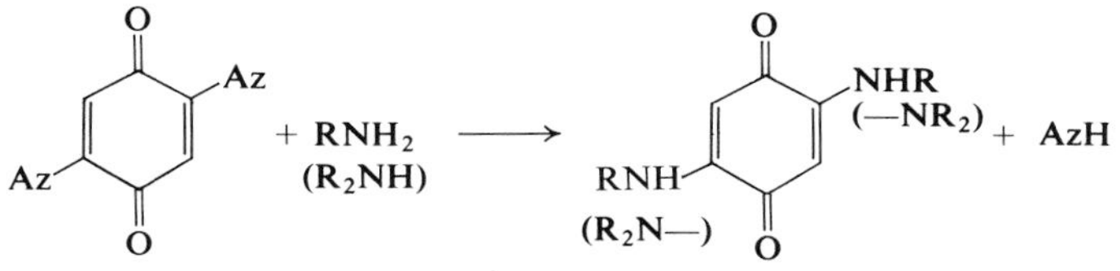

$$\text{(Az-substituted benzoquinone)} + \begin{matrix} RNH_2 \\ (R_2NH) \end{matrix} \longrightarrow \text{(product with NHR, (—NR}_2\text{), RNH, (R}_2N—\text{))} + AzH \tag{331}$$

The ease of replacement depends on the basicity of the amine and upon the nature of other substituents present in the quinone (*2404*). Under certain conditions either one or both aziridinyl groups could be replaced (*339, 2401, 2407*). 2,2-Dimethylaziridine can displace EI from a trivalent phosphorus atom (*2729b*).

Other examples of such displacement of the aziridinyl group by amines are shown in Eqs 332 (*2156*; cf. *2152b*), 333 (*1790*), and 334 (*1531*).

$$AzCH{=}CHCO_2Me + R_2NH \longrightarrow R_2NCH{=}CHCO_2Me + AzH \tag{332}$$
$$\text{(probably by addition and elimination)}$$

$$\begin{matrix} AzCHCO_2R \\ | \\ CH_2CO_2R \end{matrix} + (CH_2NH_2)_2 \longrightarrow AzH + [CH_2NHCH(CO_2R)CH_2CO_2R]_2 \tag{333}$$

$$Az{-}P\underset{O}{\overset{O}{\big[}}{-}Me + R_2NH \longrightarrow R_2N{-}P\underset{O}{\overset{O}{\big[}}{-}Me + AzH \tag{334}$$

Phenol can act as the R_2NH does in Eq 334 (*2728*).

It is of some theoretical interest that denitrosation of 1-nitrosoaziridine by HCl to give EI and NOCl proceeds at $-60°C$ (*3076*).

The elimination of a 1-unsubstituted aziridine from such compounds as are illustrated here is apparently due to decreased conjugation existing between the unshared pair of electrons on the aziridine nitrogen atom and the unsaturated group to which it is attached, compared to that in ordinary amides.

This effect was suggested as the basis for preparing aldehydes from 1-acylaziridines via reduction with lithium aluminum hydride (Eq 335) (*502, 504*); it has also been used to make the aziridine (*558a*).

$$RCOAz + LiAlH_4 \rightarrow RCHO + [AzH] \tag{335}$$

The reaction has been used for synthesis of a variety of aldehydes; for such purpose the aziridine is seldom isolated (*415, 502–504, 843, 2674, 3767, 3809, 3901, 4206*). 1-Cyanoaziridines also give 1-unsubstituted aziridines on treatment with lithium aluminum hydride (*93, 551, 4168, 4169*). In one instance the reaction resulted in reduction to an *N*-alkylaziridine (Eq 336) (*1798*).

$$\text{(bicyclic)} N-Bz + LiAlH_4 \longrightarrow \text{(bicyclic)} N-CH_2Ph \tag{336}$$

The susceptibility towards anionic reagents of a carbonyl group attached to an aziridinyl nitrogen atom also makes possible the conversion of ethyl 1-aziridinecarboxylate to higher-alkyl 1-aziridinecarboxylates through a base-catalyzed ester exchange reaction (Eq 337) (*1597*).

$$AzCO_2Et + BuOAc \xrightleftharpoons{NaOMe} AzCO_2Bu + EtOAc \uparrow \tag{337}$$

The 1-(1-hydroxyalkyl)aziridine adducts from carbonyl compounds and EI are dissociated upon distillation from aqueous alkali to regenerate EI and the carbonyl compounds (*2152b, 2318a*); sublimation also can cause the dissociation (*3356*).

POLYMERIZATION AND POLYMERS OF AZIRIDINES

Polymerization

The three-membered ring compounds all are thermodynamically less stable than their polymers (*840*), but differ considerably in polymerizability. Cyclopropane is apparently not known to polymerize as such; ethylene oxide and ethylene sulfide are readily polymerized by acids and especially by bases and coordination catalysts; and EI is polymerized readily only by acids. None of these monomers are effectively polymerized by radical catalysts.

The present discussion updates a number of more or less extensive reviews of the course and products of polymerization of aziridines (*365, 1094, 1598, 1999, 3751, 3820, 3881, 4037*). However, of the hundreds of references to the claimed applications of PEI and other aziridine polymers, the presentation here is intended to include only those in which the polymer or its reaction products were particularly characterized. Information on uses is given in Chapters 5 and 6.

Catalysts

Aziridines are polymerized by a wide variety of acidic reagents and quaternizing agents. The polymerization of EI is catalyzed by strong protonic acids (*265, 1996, 2071, 3519, 3650, 3820*), onium salts containing bulky anions (*1263*), carboxylic acids (*122, 265, 1057, 1182, 1996, 2288, 3820*), a dichlorophenol (*265*), Lewis acids (*3094, 3820*), alkyl and acyl halides and polyhalides (*350, 650, 1219, 2924, 3580, 3650, 3807, 4060*), esters of strong acids (*1264, 1996*), and hot acidic inorganic surfaces (*277, 284, 2196, 3398, 3400*). Even water can cause slow polymerization (*264, 3803*). In spite of the authors' claims to have produced poly(vinylamine) from EI and carbon dioxide by a series of special steps (*2169, 3192*), the product was in all probability PEI. The polymerization of EI by acids occurs only very slowly at $-78°C$, but warming causes initiation of an exothermic reaction that may be explosive and may even approximate a detonation. The heat of polymerization is about 23 kcal/mole; moreover the monomer is endothermic with respect to the elements $(\Delta H°_f = -22$ kcal/mole) (2690). It is therefore usual to effect the polymerization in 20–30% aqueous solution, with due regard to removal of the heat of reaction, which is then about -17.5 kcal/mole at 85°C (963). Commercial PEI is made thus, with carbon dioxide, a mineral acid, or 1,2-dichloroethane as initiator. The reaction can be stopped at will by raising the pH sufficiently with alkali (203). When EI is polymerized by the use of 2-ethoxy-4,5-dimethyl-1,3,2-dioxaphosphole 2-oxide, about one-third of the nitrogen atoms in the polymer become ethylated $(1507a)$.

Oligomers of EI have not been much studied. The dimer, $AzCH_2CH_2NH_2$, has been obtained by (a) cautious alkaline hydrolysis of the unstable hydrochloride of EI (1996), (b) prolonged refluxing of EI, preferably with addition of a trace of CO_2 or acid $(350, 365, 3806)$, and (c) similar refluxing of aqueous (3803) or alcoholic (963) EI. Methods (b) and (c) give also trimer, tetramer, etc. The same is true for the treatment of EI with potassium ethylenimide, but in this case the yield of higher oligomers is much lower (963).

It is of theoretical interest, but not preparatively useful, that 2-aminoethanol sorbed on fine-pore silica gel is converted to PEI $(3398–4000;$ cf. $256, 2271)$.

DECARBOXYLATIVE ROUTES TO POLYMERS

The pyrolysis of 2-oxazolidinone (1) and some of its derivatives yields aziridines and carbon dioxide

but the reaction is not clean and the aziridine does not survive unless the carbon dioxide is concurrently neutralized (3387). The reaction is discussed on p. 83. The pyrolysis of 2-oxazolidinone gives more 1-(2-hydroxyethyl-2-imidazolidinone than it does PEI, so that the process is of only theoretical interest. 3-Aryl-2-oxazolidinones do go completely to poly(1-arylaziridines) (2744) and 3-amino-2-oxazolidinone yields poly(1-aminoaziridine) $(1085, 1711)$, but 3-acetyl-2-oxazolidinone produces considerable 2-methyl-2-oxazoline (2744).

Very recently it has been claimed that pyrolysis of a 2-aminoethanol–carbon dioxide adduct in the presence of potassium carbonate or a similar base yields

PEI in which most of the nitrogen atoms are part of orthocarbamate anions, $\geq$N C(OH)$_2$O$^-$. Acidification and workup were believed to produce a PEI with essentially unbranched chains (226, 277). These results could not be duplicated and appear to be incorrect (963).

POLYMERIZATION OF BASIC AZIRIDINES

The polymerization of C-substituted aziridines and those in which a 1-substituent is not electron-withdrawing (nonactivated aziridines) is altogether like that of EI but less vigorous. Thus a diluent may not be necessary (362). Bicyclic aziridines such as cyclohexenimine are remarkably sluggish in polymerization. Besides the catalysts already mentioned, arenediazonium salts containing a bulky anion have been claimed (1230); they also polymerize activated aziridines.

Formation of Piperazines. There are many records in the literature—too many to cite here—of spontaneous or base-promoted transformation of 2-haloalkylamines to cyclic dimers, i.e., piperazines. Similar cyclizations are known for various 2-aminoalkyl or 2-dialkylaminoalkyl tosylates (559, 1916, 3058, 3548), diethyl (1375, 1916) and diphenyl (1013) phosphates, thiocyanates (3058), and perfluoroalkanoates (1916), and for 2-(benzenesulfonamido)ethyl benzenesulfonate (Eq 1) (3548).

$$2 \; \geq\!NCH_2CH_2L \quad \longrightarrow \quad \geq\!\overset{+}{N} \quad \overset{+}{N}\!\!< \; 2L^- \qquad (1)$$

It is also well known that primary amines and 1,2-dihaloethanes or 2-haloethyl tosylates heated together yield 1,4-disubstituted piperazines; these reactions may reasonably be assumed to proceed by way of 2-substituted ethylamines. Other examples are the formation of 2,3,5,6-tetraphenylpiperazine by reduction of 1,2-dinitro-1,2-diphenylethane (3157), and possibly the conversion of oxanilic acid to piperazine-2,3,5,6-tetrone (2) by thionyl chloride (Eq 2) (520).

$$PhNHCOCO_2H \xrightarrow{\text{SOCl}_2} \qquad (2)$$

2

In view of the demonstrated tendency of 2-substituted amines to isomerize to aziridinium salts (279, 281, 1602; see also p. 28) and thence to form piperazines, it is extremely probable that all these dimerizations involve participation of aziridinium ions (Eq 3).

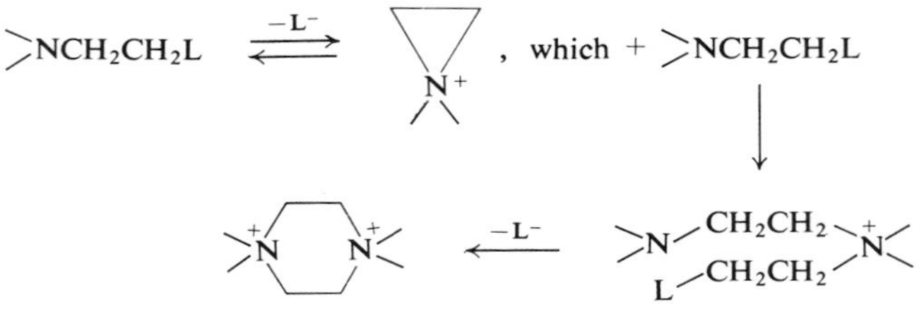

$$>NCH_2CH_2L \xrightleftharpoons{-L^-} \quad \text{, which} + >NCH_2CH_2L \tag{3}$$

Indeed, the original procedure (*2912*) for preparation of 1-(2-chloroethyl)-aziridine was soon shown (*747, 4149*) to have yielded the dimer (3) instead.

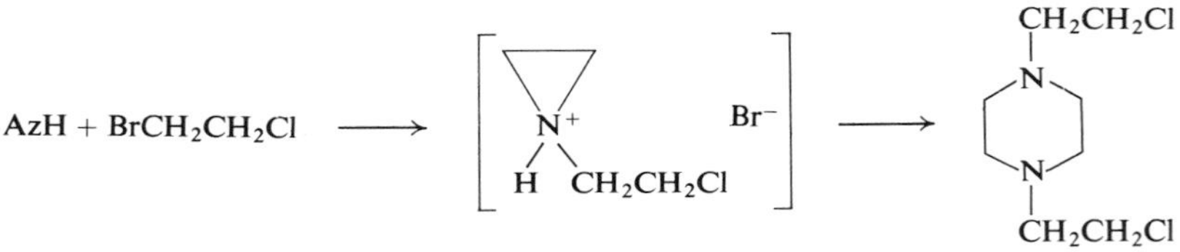

$$AzH + BrCH_2CH_2Cl \longrightarrow \left[\begin{array}{c} N^+ \\ / \backslash \\ H \quad CH_2CH_2Cl \end{array} \quad Br^- \right] \longrightarrow \begin{array}{c} CH_2CH_2Cl \\ | \\ N \\ \\ N \\ | \\ CH_2CH_2Cl \end{array}$$

3

While 2-dialkylaminoalkyl chlorides ordinarily only dimerize, when the free bases are heated to 80°–100°C in aqueous suspension (*1125*) or preferably in solution (*1126*) they are converted to water-soluble polymers which are presumably fully quaternized forms of PEI, e.g., $(CH_2CH_2N^+Et_2)_n$. Several related instances of polymer formation are cited on p. 29. The isomerization of 1-(2-aminoethyl)aziridine to piperazine requires predictable ring opening by hydrogen halide and cyclization by base (*1594, 1596a*). Formation of piperazines as well as diamines, etc., when EI or 2-ethylaziridine was autoclaved with liquid ammonia and ammonium chloride (*712*) probably occurred by way of the aziridinyl-containing dimer. However, the reported conversion of EI to piperazine in and by phenol (*714*) could not be duplicated (*963*).

Although polymers and/or ring-opened compounds are the usual products from treatment of 1-substituted basic aziridines with an acid or an alkylating agent, the reaction can be made to produce piperazines in high yields even though the aziridine is present in large excess (*906a, 907, 908, 3273*).

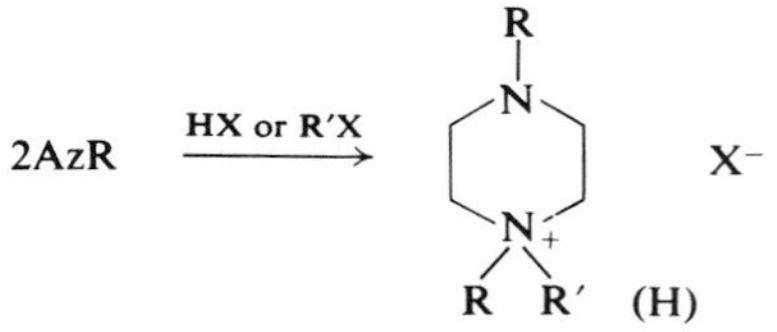

$$2AzR \xrightarrow{HX \text{ or } R'X} \begin{array}{c} R \\ | \\ N \\ \\ N^+ \\ / \backslash \\ R \quad R' \quad (H) \end{array} \quad X^-$$

4

Good yields of **4** were obtained only when X was halogen; alkyl tosylates gave only polymers. A solvent of moderate to low polarity is required, as shown for the reaction when R was ethyl and R′X was ethyl bromide.

Solvent	% Yield of **4**	% Yield of polymer
Acetone	99	< 1
Acetone: H_2O (9:1)	80	19
Acetone: H_2O (1:1)	< 1	99

The structure of the alkylating agent R′X (or choice of HX) appeared also to have an effect on product distribution, and the choice of aziridine had a marked effect; this is illustrated by data for the reaction when R′X was allyl bromide and the solvent was acetone.

R	% Yield of **4**	% Yield of polymer
Et	99	—
Bu	96	—
$PhCH_2CH_2$	90	10
$HOCH_2CH_2$	< 1	99
$NCCH_2CH_2$	0.2	99

Similarly, treatment of 1-(2-triethylsilylethyl)aziridine with catalytic amounts of aluminum chloride in heptane gave the 1,4-disubstituted piperazine in 90 % yield, whereas under the same conditions only polymer was produced from 1-phenethylaziridine (*2667*).

The scheme shown in Eq 4 was suggested to account for formation of piperazines and polymers (*907*).

(4)

It is readily apparent that the product distribution between a piperazine and a polymer for any given system will depend on the relative rates of the competitive reactions, and that these rates may be differently influenced by changes in reaction conditions.

Sometimes, most often with nitrogen-substituted aziridines, piperazines have been obtained from reaction mixtures wherein an aziridine was present and very possibly an acid or alkylating agent also. For example, 2-(1-aziridinyl)-2-methyl-1,3-indandione was found spontaneously to change to the 1,4-disubstituted piperazine on standing 6 to 8 days at room temperature (Eq 5) (*2798*).

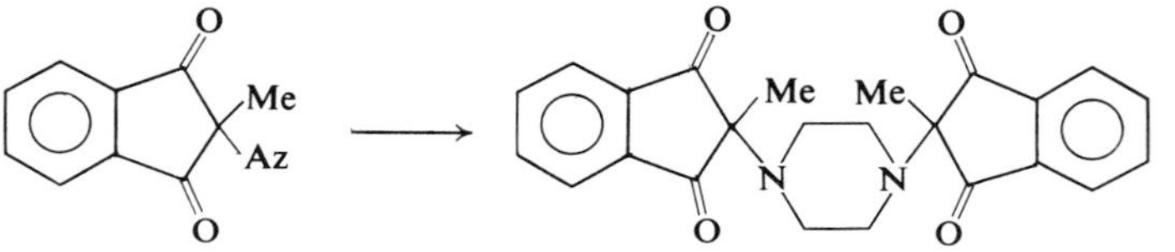

$$\text{(5)}$$

This change, and the analogous ones for other aziridinyl indandiones (*2518, 2551a*), may have been caused by HBr present as a trace impurity in the aziridine. The same mechanism for dimerization may apply to 1-(2,5-dichloro-3-thenyl)aziridine (*854*), and perhaps to that of 1-butylaziridine by 2,2,4,4-tetramethyl-1,3-cyclobutanedione (*4069*). 1-Phenethylaziridine is dimerized by heating with diethyl malonate (*3364*), and 1-butylaziridine with *p*-toluenesulfonic acid (*1607a*). 1-Benzylaziridine with this acid in alcohol behaves more spectacularly to yield a cyclic tetramer, a tetrazacyclododecane (*1607a*).

The pyrolysis of 1-(trialkylsilyl)aziridines at 250°–300°C to form 1,4-bis(trialkylsilyl)piperazines, or the same reaction at 200°C promoted by azobis(isobutyronitrile), apparently occurs by a different route (*2670*), as do the thermal and photochemical dimerizations of dimethyl 1-(*p*-methoxyphenyl)aziridine-2,3-dicarboxylate (**5**) and methyl 1-phenylaziridine-2-carboxylate, which have been attributed to C—C bond cleavage (*1795*).

5

Mixture of stereoisomers

Polymerization of Activated Aziridines

It has been known for some years that 1-acylated aziridines polymerize (to acyclic products, as is to be understood in following paragraphs also) very readily. The reaction is catalyzed not only by acids but by bases, and also often proceeds well when an acylated aziridine is merely heated. Notable examples are polymerization of 1-alkanoylaziridines (*70, 208, 3430*), aziridine-1-carboxylic esters and amides (*208, 354, 357, 1813, 2263, 3596*) and 1-arenesulfonylaziridines (*1854, 1934, 2334*), and MAPO (*3393*). It has been claimed, but not verified, that unbranched PEI of molecular weight up to 2000 can be obtained by hydrolyzing polymerized 1-benzenesulfonylaziridine with concentrated nitric acid at about 140°C (*3230*). 1-Perfluoroacylaziridines are polymerized by halide ions (*2886*). However, formation of 2-perfluoroalkyl-2-oxazolines is competitive with the polymerization. With iodide ion the oxazoline is the only product whereas fluoride or chloride ions gave only polymer. The claimed copolymerization of EI with ketene or diketene (*3435*) may well be merely the polymerization of 1-acylated EI. The effect of *C*-substituents on polymerizability is evident in terephthaloylbis(1-aziridines), of which the unsubstituted form with adipic acid yields a polymer of molecular weight about 3000, the 2-methyl derivative gives one of molecular weight about 1000, and the 2,2-dimethyl homolog undergoes only simple ring opening (*878*).

1-Thioacylaziridines, RC(S)Az, where R = Ar, ArO, ArS, or ArNH, undergo a unique 1,5-polymerization, more readily with basic catalysts, to yield polymers of form $(CH_2CH_2N{=}CR{-}S)_n$, with molecular weights in the thousands (*1927c*).

Activated aziridines can sometimes be dimerized to piperazines by treatment with nucleophiles, but for 1-acylaziridines the competitive rearrangement to substituted 2-oxazolines is overwhelming except with 1-aziridinecarboxanilide (**8**) (Eq 6).

A = MeSO$_2$ (**6**), ArSO$_2$ (**7**), PhNHCO (**8**), or Ar (**9**)
X = I or SCN

$$\text{(6)}$$

Yields for the reaction in acetone were nearly quantitative for **6** and **7**, and **8** gave no more than 22% of the piperazine; **9** in aqueous acetone produced the dimer in 37–67% yields (*1662*). Similar polymerization of 1,4-butanedisulfonylbis(1-aziridine), $AzSO_2(CH_2)_4SO_2Az$, was considered to give a polymer with piperazine rings in the chain (**10**), but the product was also crosslinked (*1124*).

$$\left[SO_2(CH_2)_4SO_2-N\bigcirc N \right]_n$$

10

An alternate route to poly(1-acylaziridines) is the acid-catalyzed polymerization of 2-alkyl- or 2-aryl-2-oxazolines (Eq 7) (*68, 289b, 662, 663a, 1039, 1365, 2020, 2667, 3184a, 3574*).

$$\underset{R}{\overset{\displaystyle N\!\!=\!\!\diagdown O}{\bigsqcup}} \xrightarrow{\text{acid or alkylating agent}} (CH_2CH_2N)_n \atop \underset{COR}{|} \qquad (7)$$

The structure of the products is well and independently authenticated, and the molecular weights are moderate, 3500–7000 (*3574*; cf. *67*). The reaction is initially first order in monomer (*3574*) and with mineral acid catalysts it is nonterminating, i.e., gives living polymers (*67*). While 1-acylaziridines are often readily rearranged to 2-oxazolines (see p. 282), their polymerization does not usually occur by way of such rearrangement.

CONSECUTIVE POLYMERIZATIONS AND COPOLYMERIZATIONS

Interesting possibilities for crosslinking are presented by monomers that contain both an aziridinyl group and an olefinic double bond. Since acid catalysts act much more readily on the aziridinyl group, and radicals almost solely on the double bond, polymerization may be effected by one route and crosslinking by the other. Difunctional monomers of this type are 1-allylaziridines (*919*), 2-(1-aziridinyl)ethyl methacrylate (*3739a*), 1-methacryloylaziridine (*703, 2305*), N-vinyl- and N-(2-propenyl)-1-aziridinecarboxamides (*559*), allyl 1-aziridinecarboxylate and the like (*2181*), 2-(1-aziridinecarboxamido)ethyl methacrylate ($CH_2\!=\!CMeCO_2CH_2CH_2NHCOAz$) and similar esters (*436*), N-vinyloxyalkyl-1-aziridinecarboxamides, vinyl 1-aziridinecarboxylate (*962*), and 1-(β-styrenesulfonyl)aziridine, $PhCH\!=\!CHSO_2Az$ (*1934*). An obvious possibility, mentioned in most of the references just cited, is vinylic copolymerization, as with styrene, methyl methacrylate, alkyl acrylates, and acrylonitrile; this yields polymers with reactive aziridinyl sites for binding them to other molecules. Reactivity ratios in vinyl copolymerization have been recorded as follows: $AzCONHCH\!=\!CH_2$ and styrene, $r_1 = 0.05 \pm 0.04$, $r_2 =$

14.5 ± 0.9; $AzCONHCH{=}CH_2$ and $CH_2{=}CMeCO_2Me$, $r_1 = 0.08 \pm 0.04$, $r_2 = 1.70 \pm 0.10$; $AzCONHCMe{=}CH_2$ and styrene, $r_1 = 0.01 \pm 0.03$, $r_2 = 15.7 \pm 0.08$ (*1924*). Heat or other radiation is reported to cause polymerization of $AzCH_2CHOHCH{=}CH_2$ through either the ring or the double bond (*2174a*).

Copolymerization of aziridines with other monomers has been reviewed (*2026*). Random copolymerization probably occurs for many mixtures of very similar aziridines, but this "ideal" behavior has been demonstrated for only one such pair, 1-(2-hydroxyethyl)aziridine and 1-(2-hydroxypropyl)aziridine (*884*). For these monomers the rate of copolymerization is essentially the sum of the rates of homopolymerization. The copolymerization of EI and 2-methylaziridine is known to give a copolymer and not a mixture of homo-polymers (*211*); and the same is evidently true of copolymerizations of (a) 1-substituted aziridines in which the substituent contains a masked (esterified) acid group with (b) a poly(1-aziridinyl) compound to serve as crosslinker. An example of this is the copolymerization of $AzCH_2CH_2P(O)(OEt)_2$ with $p\text{-}(AzCH_2CH_2)_2C_6H_4$. Such reactions, when followed by hydrolysis of the ester group, yield amphoteric ion-exchange resins (*1118, 1156, 1158, 2413, 2416*) (see p. 376). Copolymerizations of activated aziridines, such as $(2\text{-}MeAzCO_2CH_2)_2$ (*3383*) or $PhSO_2Az$ (*326*), with nonactivated (basic) ones probably produce complicated mixtures of copolymer structures by at least four different ring-opening reactions.

Alternating Copolymerization is known for aziridines, although it is prob-ably achieved by the mechanism usual in the radical-initiated process in only one case. Carbon monoxide and EI at above 500 atm, preferably 1500–2000 atm, and $100°\text{–}200°C$ in the presence of a metal carbonyl catalyst such as iron pentacarbonyl give rubbery copolymers containing very nearly two EI units to one CO unit (*1898*). This product probably has alternating $-CH_2CH_2NH-$ and $-CO-$ units in the main chain, since effecting the reaction in the presence of water gives β-alanine; alcohols, thiols, and some amines similarly yield derivatives of the β-amino acid (*1040*). Carbon monoxide and EI under irradiation with a ^{60}Co source, preferably at elevated temperatures, definitely produced poly-β-alanine, $(NHCH_2CH_2CO)_n$ (*2019*). Neither monomer homo-polymerized under these conditions. 2-Methylaziridine behaved like EI. When ethylene was added to a mixture of EI and carbon monoxide, irradiation or heating with α,α'-azobis(isobutyronitrile) led to an amorphous polymer con-taining $(NHCH_2CH_2CO)$, (CH_2CH_2CO), and $(NHCH_2CH_2CH_2CH_2CO)$ units; structure was determined by infrared analysis and identification of products of hydrolysis (*2021, 2023, 2024*). Increasing the concentration of ethylene in the monomer mixture increased the value of n in the

$$-NH(CH_2CH_2)_nCO-$$

units present, but a mixture of ethylene and EI did not copolymerize upon irradiation. The following mechanism is suggested (Eq 8) (*2024*):

Initiation

$$R\cdot + CH_2{=}CH_2 \longrightarrow RCH_2CH_2\cdot$$

$$RCH_2CH_2\cdot + CO \longrightarrow RCH_2CH_2CO\cdot$$

Propagation

$$RCH_2CH_2CO\cdot + AzH \longrightarrow RCH_2CH_2CONHCH_2CH_2\cdot$$

$$RCH_2CH_2CONHCH_2CH_2\cdot + CO \longrightarrow RCH_2CH_2CONHCH_2CH_2CO\cdot$$

$$RCH_2CH_2CONHCH_2CH_2\cdot +$$

$$CH_2{=}CH_2 \longrightarrow RCH_2CH_2CONHCH_2CH_2CH_2CH_2\cdot$$

$$RCH_2CH_2CONHCH_2CH_2\cdot + AzH \longrightarrow RCH_2CH_2CONHCH_2CH_2NHCH_2CH_2\cdot$$

$$(8)$$

In a more common pathway to alternating copolymers, an aziridine and the other monomer can form a 1:1 adduct, which then polymerizes. Copolymerization of 1-unsubstituted aziridines and olefin sulfides probably goes this way (*3061*). Cyclic anhydrides can combine with 1-alkylaziridines to form ring-opened dipolar intermediates such as **11**, which yield

$$(O_2CC_6H_4CONRCH_2CH_2)_n$$

readily (*841*);

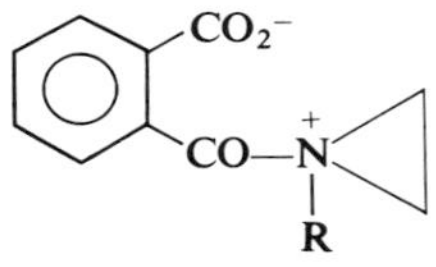

11

the related polymers from such anhydrides and activated aziridines (*1315*) are more highly crosslinked. The uncatalyzed copolymerization of aziridines and cyclic imides proceeds similarly to produce polyamides such as

$$(CH_2CH_2NHCOCH_2CH_2CO_2)_n,$$

from EI and succinimide; acid catalysts cause formation of materials richer in aziridine units (*1545, 2022, 3327, 3431*). Without catalyst, an excess of EI over succinimide at 50°–60°C gives a fusible branched-chain prepolymer that at 120°C is crosslinked to infusibility. $AzCOCH_2CH_2CONH_2$ does not produce a polymeric amide of the same kind, and neither does 3-(1-aziridinyl)-

succinimide. 1-Phenylaziridine and succinimide do not yield polymer at all, but simply the 2-anilinoethyl derivative of succinimide **12**.

12

An exotic polymer, $Az(AlH-NEt)_nAlHAz$, is formed from EI and $Et_3N \cdot AlH_3$, probably via $AzH \cdot AlH_3$ and $AzAlH_2$ (*1032*). A related one, $[(FCH_2CH_2NH)_2BF]_n$, is produced when BF_3 or $FCH_2CH_2NHBF_2$ reacts with excess EI (*3712*).

Not predominantly alternating in structure, but involving both monomer units in the chain, and probably formed via adducts, are the copolymers obtained from aziridines and aldehydes, especially formaldehyde, in inert diluents at low temperatures in the presence of anionic catalysts such as butyllithium (*2434a*). The composition in terms of monomer units may be varied over a wide range. The structure of copolymers of trioxane and 1-(hydrocarbonsulfonyl)aziridines formed with acid catalysts (*1127*) is unspecified, but paraformaldehyde and EI yield only modified PEI (*3626*).

A transition between alternating copolymers and PEI having *N*-pendant modifying groups is provided by aziridine–β-lactone systems. Mixtures (1:1) of EI and β-propiolactone with no catalyst, cationic catalyst, or anionic catalyst give copolymers having a 1:1 ratio of monomer units and some alternating structure, as shown by infrared spectra. The predominant pattern, however, is that of PEI with either $-CH_2CH_2CO_2H$ or $-COCH_2CH_2OH$ groups attached to the nitrogen atoms, depending on the polarity of the solvent used, and on the nature of the lactone (*1370, 2018*). Larger-ring lactones also yield copolymers with EI (*3433*). 1-Phenylaziridine and β-propiolactone without catalyst yield a true copolymer, rich in aziridine units ($r_1 = 7.5$, $r_2 = 0.15$, respectively) but containing lactone units in the main chain (*2025, 4088*).

The reaction of EI or other 1-unsubstituted aziridine with a cyclic alkylene carbonate has been supposed to proceed via an adduct, as shown in Eq 9, to a linear alternating copolymer (*979, 3434*) although such linearity has been found for copolymers of 1-phenylaziridine and carbon oxysulfide or carbon disulfide (*3272b*),

$$AzCO_2(CH_2CH_2OCH_2CH_2NHCO_2)_nCH_2CH_2OH \qquad (9)$$

but no evidence was given for the linear structure, and it appears at least equally likely that the product was PEI bearing $-CO_2CH_2CH_2OH$ groups on the nitrogen atoms. It is even less likely that polymers from EI and carbon disulfide have a linear chain with alternating monomer units (but cf. *3272b*).

The polymers formed from 1-unsubstituted aziridines and epoxides with boron trifluoride catalyst probably should not be called copolymers, since they are known to consist of chains of aziridine units with pendant 2-hydroxyalkyl groups on the nitrogen atoms (*2137, 2779, 2781, 2782, 2793*). Evidently these could be formed by either (a) adduction of the monomers and then polymerization, or (b) polymerization of the aziridine and then adduction. Studies (*2781, 2793*) addressed to this point have shown that path (b) is at least the predominant one. Activated aziridines also could not be copolymerized with epoxides, both acidic and basic catalysts yielding only homopolymers of the aziridines (*2793*). A number of patents claim the formation of cured polymers by the interaction of various basic aziridines and diepoxides (e.g., *3335, 3367, 3403*) but it is impossible to deduce the structure of the products from the evidence available. On the other hand, the uncatalyzed polymerization of 1-ethylaziridine and propylene sulfide gave a product containing predominantly sulfide units; in this competitive reaction, the sulfide was found to react 5.4 times as fast as the aziridine (*885*). Similarly 1-phenylaziridine and ethylene sulfide appeared to give only poly(ethylene sulfide) (*885*).

The copolymers of EI and dimethylketene (*1975*) or highly fluorinated olefins (*963*) may have been essentially PEI, PEI with pendant groups, or polymers having mixed units in the chain. However, the polymers made by treating mixtures of aziridines (such as EI) and unsaturated ethers with boron trifluoride etherate (*1439*) were probably mixtures of homopolymers.

Graft Copolymerization. The modification of PEI with monomers is discussed on p. 336; the graft copolymerization of aziridines is to be reviewed here. The polymer on which EI has been most often grafted is cellulose, to make ion-exchange materials; introduction of 2-aminoethyl groups, rather than PEI chains, is usually desired but is virtually impossible. The topic is treated on p. 224. A more complex polymer was made by combining 1-methacryloylaziridine with cellulose acetate, presumably to form 2-(methacrylamido)ethyl ethers of some hydroxyl groups, and graft polymerizing styrene to the cellulose chain by way of these ether groups (*1106*). Other modifications of carbohydrates with EI have been more concerned with the utility than the structure of the products: these were made from starch (*3163, 3840*), sorbitan (*321*), and plant gums (*2718*).

Some graft copolymerization of EI on poly(vinyl chloride), poly(vinyl alcohol), polyethylene, or polyacrylonitrile is effected by γ-ray irradiation, but since it is not inhibited by hydroquinone, the reaction must proceed ionically at reactive groups (such as OH) on the polymer generated by the radiation (*2639, 2640*). The product of modifying lignin with EI was very little characterized (*937*). On the other hand, the polymerization of EI by poly-(acrylic acid) or poly(methacrylic acid) (*1054*) quite evidently yields a graft copolymer with PEI side chains.

Copolymerization of diaziridinyl compounds with compounds containing two active hydrogen atoms deserves the name only to the extent that polyamides such as nylon 6-6 do.

$$n \; Az—Y—Az + n \; H—Y'—H \longrightarrow (Y—NHCH_2CH_2—Y'—CH_2CH_2NH)_n$$

Such polymers have been made with sufficient molecular weight to be film and fiber forming, but have apparently not been commercialized. Nevertheless they have been included as part of Table 5-IX, on p. 365.

MECHANISM OF POLYMERIZATION

Polymerization of *1-unsubstituted* aziridines may be treated as a special case of ring opening by amines (see p. 237). Initiation is effected by providing catalytic amounts of aziridinium ion and propagation by the ring-opening reaction (Eq 10).

$$AzH + H^+ \longrightarrow AzH_2^+ \qquad\qquad (10a)$$

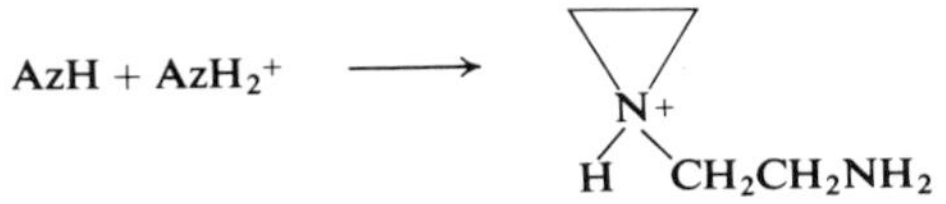

(10b)

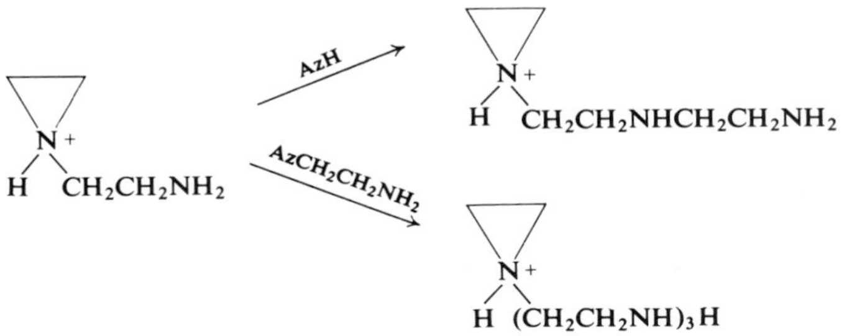

(10c)

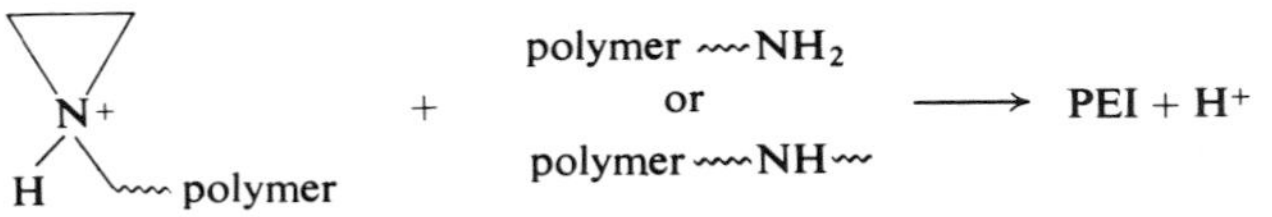

(10d)

The protons shown in Eq 10 are, of course, distributed among the several nitrogen atoms according to the respective base strengths of these nitrogen atoms, in a rapid equilibration. The concentration of the protonated aziridine species accordingly becomes lower and lower as polymerization proceeds to produce the more basic acyclic amino groups, and a marked decrease in rate is observed (*264, 1996, 1999, 2000*). In the early stages of polymerization the concentration of monomeric aziridine is relatively high and the propagation reaction occurring is primarily Eq 10b. However, as the concentration of dimer, 1-(2-aminoethyl)aziridine, increases, the formation of trimer and tetramer becomes important (Eq 10c). Subsequent reaction of these species (Eq 10d) yields polymer (*264, 265, 1996, 1997, 1999*). This path for polymerization was originally deduced from kinetic measurements and isolation or detection of the very low molecular weight oligomers (i.e., dimer, trimer, tetramer). More sophisticated gas–liquid chromatography techniques have recently been used to demonstrate the appearance and disappearance of the various oligomeric species (*963*). It is of interest here that in the polymerization of EI in methanol, the dimer was about 80% of the product and no product higher than tetramer was formed, up to about 50% conversion of EI. Continued reaction showed a decrease in dimer concentration. When all EI had been converted the product was shown to have a molecular weight of about 1000 (ebullioscopic). Continued reaction provided products of higher molecular weights (*963*).

Further basis for treating the polymerization as a ring-opening reaction by amines is provided by reports on polymerization of optically active 2-alkyl-aziridines into optically active polymers (*2576, 3471, 4194*). Ring opening thus occurs without affecting the optically active center, a result consistent with an S_N2 mechanism.

Ring-opening reactions subsequent to Eq 10c, leading to Eq 10d, provide a path for producing a highly branched polymer. As secondary amino groups are produced, they compete with the primary amino groups in attacking an aziridinium ring. Although the primary amino groups are inherently more reactive, the concentration of secondary amino groups is enough greater throughout the polymerization that a relatively large amount of reaction occurs at these groups.

All workers have not agreed on the degree of branching in PEI (*264, 265, 1996, 1999, 2128*). This is due in part to the difficulty in determination of the various types of amino nitrogen (tertiary, secondary, and primary) in the polymer (see p. 334). It has been reported that lower polymerization temperatures favor a lower degree of branching (*2128*). However, Van Slyke analysis for primary amino groups was used for determining the extent of branching and this method has been shown to be unsatisfactory when applied to PEI (*963*). A number of different preparations of PEI have been found to contain tertiary, secondary, and primary amino groups in a ratio of approximately 1:2:1 (*963, 2000*). Consistent with this result are the rate constants obtained for ring opening of the various aziridinium ions by various types of amino groups in a simulation (with the aid of a computer) of the polymerization kinetics for EI (*2000*). It has been reported (*4082*) but could not be verified (*963*) that in poly(2-methylaziridine) 95 % of the nitrogen atoms form secondary amino groups; if true this would mean that the polymer is substantially linear.

Branching may also result from ring opening of aziridinium ion by a tertiary aziridine nitrogen atom (Eq 11) (*265, 1996, 1999, 2000*).

$$AzCH_2CH_2NH_2 \;+\; \underset{\substack{\mid \\ H \quad CH_2CH_2NH_2}}{\overset{\bigvee}{N^+}} \quad \longrightarrow \quad \underset{\substack{\mid \\ H_2NCH_2CH_2 \;\; (CH_2CH_2NH)_2H}}{\overset{\bigvee}{N^+}} \qquad (11)$$

The relative importance of Eq 11 is difficult to assess. However, from the simulated kinetic data mentioned above, it was suggested that this reaction was more important in the initial stages of polymerization and reaction of secondary amino groups in the later stages (*2000*).

The nature of the termination reaction in polymerization of 1-unsubstituted aziridines has not been resolved. The rate becomes progressively lower as polymerization proceeds but, as already noted, this may be attributed to progressively lower concentrations of aziridinium ion resulting from competition of the acyclic amino groups with aziridine groups for the acid catalyst (*264, 1996, 1999*). Such might be called "kinetic termination" and would not represent chain termination.

There is no doubt, however, that chain termination occurs since limiting values of molecular weights are obtained (*963, 1999, 2128*). With anhydrous EI this number-average molecular weight (ebullioscopic) is about 3000 to 3500 (*963*). From polymerization of aqueous EI, higher-molecular-weight products are obtained (*963*).

To be consistent with the acceptable propagation reactions (Eq 10b, c, d), the termination mechanism would involve destruction of an aziridinium ring on a growing polymer chain by reaction with some nucleophile present in the medium. However, convincing arguments can be presented against termination by hydrolysis of the aziridinium ring and it has been shown that the molecular weight is not greatly influenced by the choice of mineral acid for catalyst (*1999*). This latter result shows that ring opening by the anion of the acid is of little importance since anions of different nucleophilicity were used (*963*). In nonaqueous solvents such termination by the anion is more reasonable, especially with strong nucleophiles (*264, 1999*).

An amine comparable in base strength to a vicinal polyamine (e.g., diethylenetriamine and triethylenetetramine) may be used in the polymerization of EI as a "chain stopper". The relationship of "one PEI chain for one amine molecule" (Eq 12) holds almost perfectly as long as the ratio of EI to amine does not predict a molecular weight greater than would be possible in the absence of the amine (963).

$$M_N = M_{Az} \text{ (moles of aziridine)/(moles of amine)} + M_{Am} \tag{12}$$

where M_N is number-average molecular weight of poly(aziridine); M_{Az}, the molecular weight of aziridine; and M_{Am}, the molecular weight of amine.

In view of the difficulties in assigning a termination reaction (termination in the polymerization of 1-alkylaziridines is also considered as pertinent; see p. 332) it does not seem unreasonable to suggest that formation of macrocyclic structures is the principal termination reaction (Eq 13)

$$\begin{array}{c} \text{[structure]} \\ \underset{H}{\overset{\displaystyle N^+}{\diagup\diagdown}} (CH_2CH_2NH)_x \end{array} \xrightarrow{-H^+} \left(\begin{array}{c} -CH_2CH_2N \diagup \\ (CH_2CH_2NH) \end{array} \right)_x \tag{13}$$

where x is sufficiently large to allow a back-side approach of a chain nitrogen atom to the aziridinium ring carbon atom.

The infrared absorption of commercial PEI indicated the presence of from 0.2 % to 5 % piperazine rings depending on the method of preparation (4177); but these are probably formed from ethylene dihalides used as initiators.

The mechanism for polymerization of *1-alkylaziridines* may be considered as analogous to that for 1-unsubstituted aziridines in that ring opening of aziridinium rings by an S_N2 reaction with amines (tertiary amine nitrogen atom of the 1-alkylaziridine) is involved. However, the polymerization does not occur by formation of oligomers and combination of the oligomers to form higher oligomers, etc., as it does with the 1-unsubstituted aziridines. Instead, the polymer molecule is built by reaction of monomer at the aziridinium ion end group of a polymer chain (Eq 14) (1999).

$$\underset{R}{\overset{\displaystyle N}{\diagup\diagdown}} \cdots \rightarrow \underset{R}{\overset{\displaystyle N^+}{\diagup\diagdown}} \text{polymer} \longrightarrow \underset{R}{\overset{\displaystyle N^+}{\diagup\diagdown}} CH_2CH_2NR\text{polymer} \tag{14}$$

Initiation may be effected with alkylating agents or with acids. However, the kinetic features of the polymerization are different for these two initiators. Each molecule of alkylating agent initiates a polymer chain that grows until the aziridinium ion end group is destroyed. With acids, a terminal secondary amino group is formed for each polymer chain initiated. Reaction of this group with an aziridinium ring end group regenerates the acid, which may initiate new polymer chains (Eq 15) (*1999*).

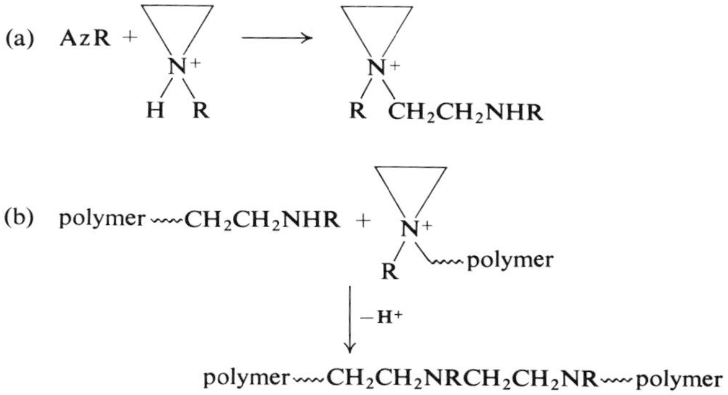
(a) AzR +
N+
H R
N+
R CH₂CH₂NHR
(b) polymer~~CH₂CH₂NHR +
N+
R ~~polymer
−H+
polymer~~CH₂CH₂NRCH₂CH₂NR~~polymer

(15)

In the alkylating-agent-catalyzed polymerization of 1-alkylaziridines, the reaction stops before all monomer is converted. From the relationship between conversion and initial catalyst concentration it was deduced that the polymerization could be represented as a second-order propagation and pseudo-first-order termination (*2000*). The kinetic expression derived was consistent with termination by ring opening of the aziridinium ring by a nitrogen atom in a polymer chain (Eq 16).

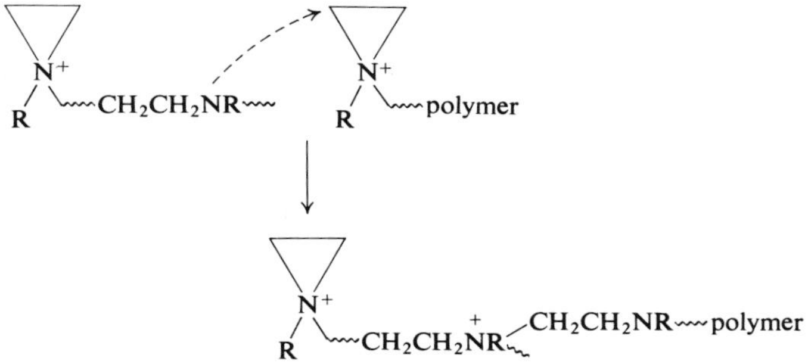
N+
R ~~CH₂CH₂NR~~
N+
R ~~polymer
N+
R ~~CH₂CH₂NR
CH₂CH₂NR~~polymer

(16)

In later work the presence of quaternary ammonium groups in poly(1-alkylaziridines) was established by NMR analysis. A proportionality between the concentration of such groups in the polymer and the initiator concentration was demonstrated. There was a 1:1 correspondence between the concentration of such groups and the concentration of secondary amine groups when the catalyst was a protonic acid (*963*).

Equation 16 represents a branching reaction. The degree of branching resulting from acid-catalyzed polymerization of aqueous 1-ethylaziridine was considerably less than that from similar polymerization of EI (*963*).

It is readily apparent that Eq 16 represents a "kinetic termination" but not a chain termination. In a study specifically directed towards identification of the chain-termination process, it was shown that the rate curves for disappearance of monomer were identical regardless of the mineral acid catalyst used in aqueous solution (HI, HBr, H_2SO_4, $HClO_4$) (963). Thus, ring opening of the aziridinium-ring end group by the anion from the acid is very improbable. Such ring opening has been indicated to occur with halide ions in nonpolar solvents, leading to piperazine rings (see p. 318).

Further, the number-average molecular weight for several such poly(1-alkylaziridines) (polymerization in aqueous solution with HI and $HClO_4$) was less than 2000. In such low-molecular-weight polymers, terminal piperazine rings would be easily observed by infrared analysis (minimum concentration of $C_4H_8N_2$ group would be 5% by weight) yet concentrations of such groups above the detectable limits (0.2% by weight in one case) could not be found (963). A sample of poly(1-ethylaziridine) of number-average molecular weight 1080 was shown to contain no hydroxyl groups (< 500 ppm), demonstrating the improbability of termination by aziridinium-ring hydrolysis (963). The infrared spectra of these polymers exhibited no extraneous absorptions readily attributable to end groups. As in the case of 1-unsubstituted aziridines, it seems most reasonable to attribute chain termination to formation of macrocyclic structures.

In the polymerization of 1-phenylaziridine with weak (such as acetic) or strong (such as trifluoroacetic) carboxylic acids, the rates of all steps of the process (initiation, propagation, and termination) increased with acid strength. Conversion and molecular weight of polymer increased with time when weak acids were used, but very rapidly approached limiting values with strong ones. The termination reaction was considered to be piperazine-ring formation (2018a).

Although very little data pertaining specifically to the mechanism for polymerization of *activated aziridines* has been reported, it is reasonable to assume operation of a process consistent with their other ring-opening reactions. Ring opening of activated aziridines by amides has been demonstrated (see p. 267). The reaction occurs in the absence of catalyst, and is faster in the presence of acid. Thus Eq 17 represents an acceptable propagation reaction.

$$\text{polymer}\!\sim\!\!\text{CH}_2\text{CH}_2\text{NHA} + \underset{\underset{A}{\overset{|}{N}}}{\triangledown} \longrightarrow \text{polymer}\!\sim\!(\text{CH}_2\text{CH}_2\text{NA})_2\text{H} \tag{17}$$

$$A = RCO, ROCO, RSO_2, R_2P(O), \text{etc.}$$

The susceptibility of these derivatives to attack by anionic reagents has also already been emphasized (see p. 206). This property provides a basis for an anionic polymerization mechanism (Eq 18) (*1999*) and indeed a number of base-catalyzed (or anion-catalyzed) polymerizations have been observed (*326, 2263, 2886*).

$$\text{polymer} \sim\!\sim\! CH_2CH_2\bar{N}A \xrightarrow{\quad\text{N}\quad} \text{polymer} \sim\!\sim\! CH_2CH_2NACH_2CH_2\bar{N}A$$

(18)

where A is the same as in Eq 17.

Polymers

PURIFICATION AND FRACTIONATION

Conventional methods for the purification of water-soluble polymers are applicable, e.g., electrodialysis to remove material of low molecular weight (*290, 2071, 3526*). Curtain electrophoresis, combining horizontal paper electrophoresis and descending paper chromatography, gave peculiar results; the fractionation achieved may have depended on the amount of chain branching rather than molecular weight (*2850*). Gel-permeation chromatography has also given separation of PEI fractions (*963*), and fractional precipitation has been successfully applied to PEI (*3510*) and to polymers of diethyl 1-aziridinyl-succinate and benzoylated PEI (*1789*).

Treatment of dilute aqueous PEI with enough sulfuric acid to protonate most of it causes the formation of a small water-rich and a large PEI-rich phase. Since the water-rich phase tends to contain the lower-molecular-weight material, some separation can be accomplished. This was verified by Sephadex gel filtration (*963*).

MOLECULAR WEIGHT

As for other polyelectrolytes, the determination of molecular weight of PEI presents difficulties, especially at the higher values. End-group analysis is useless because of the considerable amount of chain branching, although one chemical method—measurement of the amount of ethylene dibromide needed just to crosslink and insolubilize (gel) a sample—gave a reasonable value, $n = 35$ (*3230*). The colligative properties of PEI have been the basis of similar number-average molecular weights, 1160–3000 ($n = 27$–70) (*963, 2071, 2288, 3820*). Poly(D- or L-)-(2-methylaziridine) in benzene showed molecular weights (cryoscopic) of 2000–4000 (*2576*); a 1-ethylaziridine–epoxydodecane copolymer, a value of 788 (*2793*); and benzoylated PEI in chloroform, values up to $n = 74$ (*1789*).

Viscosity measurements are extremely useful for obtaining relative molecular weights of PEI samples, but their interpretation in terms of absolute molecular weight is somewhat hazardous because of the difficulty in establishing a reliable Staudinger constant K, especially for branched-chain polymers, and the necessity of suppressing ionization of the PEI or its salts by making the solution of high ionic strength. Nevertheless most values (viscosity-average) for the molecular weight have been so derived: $n = 57$ (*1996*), 40 (*3230*), 27–51 (*2071*), 100 (*1915, 3614*), and 1–770 (*923*). Similar values ranging from 17 to 93 were observed for fractions of benzoylated PEI in chloroform (*1789*).

A molecular weight of 30,000 ($n = 700$) attributed to PEI was obtained by light-scattering measurements (*1483*), and it is probable that the other high literature values not further identified have been so obtained: $n = 700$ (*2002*), 2100 (*2036*), or even beyond 2400 (*117, 4060*). Ultracentrifugation of a sample of commercial PEI yielded a similarly high value ($n = 790$) (*963*). Such high molecular weights are probably achieved by use of an ethylene dihalide or similar compound as a polymerization catalyst and crosslinker.

POLYETHYLENIMINE AS A BASE

Protonation of PEI has been studied by a number of workers independently, but with fairly concordant results. Isolation of the hydrochloride (*3044*) or the nitric and perchloric (*3043*) salts in nonaqueous solution was by conventional means, and the same procedure gave poly(1-methylaziridine) sulfate (*3044*). It was early noted (*2071*) that only part of the nitrogen atoms can be made positively charged. Titration curves (*290, 963, 2266, 2268, 3230, 3527*) show a rapid decrease of pH with volume of acid added, with no such inflection points as simple amines give. Added electrolyte, up to $2M$, raises the pH during titration and thus alters the shape of the curve, but does not make it any more amenable to interpretation by the Henderson-Hasselbalch equation for simple acids and bases nor by the Katchalsky or the Kotin-Nagasawa ones for polyelectrolytes. Changes in the titration curve are also produced by using different strong acids (*963, 3044*). Some authors (*290, 3044, 3230, 3527*) have sought to apply one or more of the equations mentioned to *portions* of the curve, but the validity of the results is doubtful. The fundamental difficulty, of course, is the interaction of near-neighbor amino groups, which is evidently much more complex than in polyacrylic acid, for example. Only about two-thirds of the nitrogen atoms of PEI are protonated at pH 4.4 (*3527*). The additional complication of chain branching, which means that primary, secondary, and tertiary nitrogen atoms are all present, makes it unlikely that the polybase properties of PEI can be interpreted as readily as those of polyvinylamine (*2049*).

It is noteworthy that potentiometric titration of solutions of PEI in acetic acid with strong acids (perchloric or *p*-toluenesulfonic) gives titration curves with inflection points suitable for determination of the equivalence point (*963*). However, equivalence points so obtained correspond to neutralization of only about 80 % of the nitrogen atoms. This same behavior is observed for poly(1-alkylaziridines), wherein different fractions of the total nitrogen present are protonated depending on the structure of the poly(1-alkylaziridine) (*963*). More significant is the fact that when PEI is acetylated with acetic anhydride in acetic acid and then titrated as above, the equivalence point obtained *does* correspond approximately to the total amount of nonacetylated tertiary amine nitrogen present in the acetylated PEI (*963*). If interaction of near-neighbor amino groups is responsible for the fractional neutralizations, this latter information suggests that branching sites (tertiary amine nitrogen atoms) are separated by at least one secondary amine group, as in **13**.

$$-NH-CH_2CH_2-N-CH_2CH_2-NH-CH_2CH_2-N-CH_2CH_2-NH-$$

$$
\begin{array}{ccc}
& CH_2 & \qquad CH_2 \\
& | & \qquad | \\
& CH_2 & \qquad CH_2 \\
& | & \qquad | \\
& NH & \qquad NH \\
& | & \qquad | \\
\end{array}
$$

13

A theoretical treatment of PEI as a polyelectrolyte (*3037*) is invalid because it neglects the extensive branching of the chain. The activity coefficient of chloride counterion in aqueous PEI hydrochloride solutions is raised by the presence of added salts, more so by 1:2 than by 1:1 electrolytes. This indicates that the charge distribution of an added small ion helps determine the distribution of counterions (*2267*). The mean activity coefficient of PEI hydrochloride is not equal to the activity coefficient of the chloride ion present; the same discrepancy exists for salts of polyanions, and is characteristic of polyelectrolytes (*1915*). The partial molal volumes of PEI and other polyelectrolytes have been measured by way of solution densities, and interpretations presented (*1915b*).

The titration behavior of PEI sufficiently crosslinked to constitute an anion-exchange resin of the weak-base type is very similar to that of PEI, except that even more of the nitrogen atoms in the resin cannot be protonated, even at pH 1–2 (*3231*). Other preparations and reactions of ion-exchange resins derived from PEI are discussed on p. 373.

The methylene protons in PEI show a reasonably sharp NMR singlet in aqueous salt solutions; they are probably in all all-*gauche* conformation. While extensive protonation tends to force successive nitrogen atoms to trans conformations, the counter ions of the salt solution impede this change and the spectrum is still complex in the presence of 100 % excess of acid (*2334a*).

In the presence of excess chloride or nitrate counter ions the variation of intrinsic viscosity with degree of protonation was small and about linear, but perchlorate ions produced a minimum in the curve, presumably because they stabilize intramolecular hydrogen bonds between protonated nitrogen atoms and unprotonated ones (*2334b*).

The formation of complexes by transition metal ions and PEI is easily demonstrated, and indeed solutions mixed in the ratio of one metal ion to four nitrogen atoms of PEI when evaporated yield glassy but nonhygroscopic solid complexes (*963, 3527*). Alteration of the acid–base titration curve of PEI by addition of metal ions—the Bjerrum method—permits the qualitative conclusion that stabilities of complexes are in the order

$$Cu(II) > Ni(II) > Zn(II) > Co(II) > Pb(II) > Mn(II) \quad (290).$$

The interpretation of either titrimetric or spectrophotometric results (the latter using the method of continuous variations) in terms of coordination number n of the metal ion and stability constant of the complex, however, is in an uncertain state. One investigator (*290*) has found n for copper (II) to be about 3, and the stability constant K_3 to be $10^{18.8}$, by both methods; another group (*3527*) reports n to approach 4 and K_4 to be $10^{16.6}$; a more recent report (*2849*) gives $n = 5$; and a fourth (*963*) did not find the Bjerrum method applicable at all. Results for Ni(II) were similar. Viscosity measurements indicate that in dilute solutions the metal ions crosslink extended chains (*3527*). In aqueous 1 M PEI that is 2 M in NaCl and 0.125–0.25 M in Zn(II) ions, NMR spectra show the methylene protons in Zn-coordinated PEI units to be different from those in unbound units. The coordination number of the zinc is four (*2334a*).

REPLACEMENTS OF HYDROGEN ATOMS IN PEI BY METHODS OTHER THAN CROSSLINKING

Methylation of PEI has been accomplished with dimethyl sulfate, but the product was used without characterization (*597*). Various alkylbenzylations produced a modified polymer in which about 50% of the nitrogen atoms were tertiary (*2562b*; cf. *1443a*).

Acylations are much more completely described. The earliest one (*3657*) broadly claimed products of modifying PEI with carboxylic acids, anhydrides, chlorides, or esters for a wide variety of uses. An acetyl derivative (*1128*) is soluble in water, and a benzoyl derivative (*1789, 1996*) in chloroform; sulfonyl (*2574*), thioacyl (*1927c*), phenylthiocarbamyl (*1927c*), and picryl (*1991*) derivatives have also been made.

While PEI catalyzes the hydrolysis of *p*-nitrophenyl acetate or laurate, such catalytic activity is improved by its modification with up to 20 mole % of lauroyl residues, as is the binding power for p-(phenylazo)-N,N-dimethylaniline. Polyethylenimine species so modified may be useful models of esterases (*2113a, 4094*). In a different catalytic process, PEI is more effective than simpler polyethylenepolyamines are in causing dedeuteration of isobutyraldehyde-2-*d*; the PEI reacts at the carbonyl group and then has other amino groups favorably situated to remove the deuteron (*1719a*). On the other hand, the EI–CuSO$_4$ complex does not have the same considerable ability to catalyze hydrolysis of diisopropyl fluorophosphate that the imidazole and ethylenediamine complexes do (*3722*). Polyethylenimine much increased the rate of an anion–anion reaction in aqueous solution (bromoacetate-thiosulfate), but did not affect those of cation–cation or anion–cation reactions. This primary salt effect was due to a lowering of the enthalpy and entropy of activation of the reaction (*1915a*).

The usual nitrosation procedures yield N-nitroso compounds (*1996*) but contrary to an earlier report (*1084*) these could not be reduced to poly(N-amino)-PEI (*1085*). Alkali and carbon disulfide converted PEI into a poly(dithiocarbamic acid) salt which could be alkylated and then used as a photosensitive material (*2756*). The polarization of the fluorescence of PEI having pendant 5-dimethylaminonaphthalene-1-sulfonyl groups indicated that such PEI exists as a rigid molecule that rotates as a unit (*3725*), but more recent work yielded relaxation times for this and the similar conjugate of PEI with fluorescein isocyanate that correspond better to a rotation of a segment of the PEI chain (about ten monomer units) in solution (*3510*).

Modification of PEI with 2-oxazolidinone and formaldehyde or with 3-hydroxymethyl-2-oxazolidinone yields about the same polymer as produced by polymerizing 3-(1-aziridinomethyl)-2-oxazolidinone: resins soluble in water but not in organic solvents, forming nonstoichiometric complexes with phenol or p-toluenesulfonic acid, presumably in part by hydrogen bonding (*4046, 4181*).

Like some other polymers, PEI treated with hydrogen peroxide and a titanous salt yields free radicals, studied by ESR (*1304a*).

Cationic Colloidal Behavior

The reactions of PEI as cationic colloidal substances are of importance in purification of water and waste water (p. 389). Colloidal acids, both inorganic (silica, alumina, clays) and organic (pectins, alginic acid, tannins, polyacrylic acid, polyacrolein–sulfurous acid adduct, etc.) are coagulated and precipitated by PEI (*168, 233, 886a, 887, 2070, 3179*); the progress of the reaction may be followed by measurement of turbidity (*374a, 963, 3528*), ζ potential or filtration time (*374a, 2036, 2255a*), or viscosity (*2324, 3800*). The flocculation of a silica sol (150 ppm) by PEI is believed due to charge neutralization (*963*).

Added aluminum ions (5–200 ppb) retard this flocculation, probably via aluminate ions, but calcium ions in turn partly offset the interference of the aluminum (963). The precipitation of some anionic colloids may be effected so as either to produce (2545) or avoid (3529) membranous gels. Fluorspar suspensions are not flocculated by PEI (4174). Poly(vinyl alcohol) and PEI or poly(2-methylaziridine) exhibit considerable evidence of interaction at low pH values (2324) but nearly ideal behavior in water otherwise (3800); poly-(ethylene oxide) and PEI also interact little (3800), but poly(N-vinylpyrroli-dinone) and especially carboxymethylcellulose show viscometric evidence of combining with PEI (963, 2869a), as does cellulose xanthate under favorable conditions (2869a). Starch xanthates are gelled by PEI (4117). As a protective colloid PEI is inferior to many others, but modifying it to make it amphoteric greatly increases its protective action on dispersions of gold (3530, 3531) or silver halide (2001). In the flocculation of a diluted polystyrene latex, adsorp-tion of PEI was very fast and the slow step was aggregation of primary particles (374a).

DEGRADATION

In some cases, notably those of poly(1-butylaziridine) and poly(1-phen-ethylaziridine), heat causes fairly smooth decomposition to piperazines (Eq 19) (265).

$$(NRCH_2CH_2)_n \longrightarrow \qquad\qquad (19)$$

The reaction is reminiscent of the breakdown of poly(ethylene oxide) to diox-ane, and that of poly(ethylene sulfide) to p-dithiane, both of which are pro-moted by either acids or nucleophiles. The same is true for polymers of aziridines (963). The decomposition of PEI itself without catalyst proved more difficult and less clean (265). Heated in air at 90°C, PEI disappeared completely into volatile products in 90 days (1033), evidently through autooxidation and probably some piperazine formation. Pyrolysis of PEI on a kaolin catalyst at 260°–450°C (3447) or in the presence of a hydrogen halide (2464) produces 1,4-diazabicyclo[2.2.2]octane (14) along with many other nitrogenous com-pounds.

14

Thermogravimetric analysis curves for PEI show rapid decomposition to begin in air at 250°C and in nitrogen at 300°C (*945, 4037*).

Pyrolysis of copolymers of 1-phenylaziridine and carbon oxysulfide or carbon disulfide predictably yields 3-phenyl-2-thiazolidinone or 3-phenyl-2-thiazolidine-2-thione, respectively (*3272b*).

The only other known degradation of polymers of aziridines is with an organoalkali compound, preferably butyllithium, to produce cleavage products with reactive end-groups useful in synthesis (*1700*). It must be supposed that this would apply best, or probably only, to the poly(1-hydrocarbyl)-aziridines.

OTHER REACTIONS

Since polymers of optically active aziridines retain the optical activity to a very high degree (*4194*), they have been examined as catalysts for asymmetric synthesis of benzaldehyde cyanohydrin, to serve as models of enzymes causing asymmetric synthesis. Optically active cyanohydrin was indeed produced, but whereas poly[(S)-2-isobutylaziridine] gave (−)-cyanohydrin (*3632*), the same polymer after crosslinking with 4-methyl-1,3-phenylene diisocyanate gave (+)-cyanohydrin. This is taken to indicate that conformation of the catalytic center is more important than configuration of the asymmetric carbon atom in determining the course of reaction (*3630*). Polymers of 1-alkyl-(S)-2-iso-butylaziridine have much less ability to cause stereospecific synthesis for the same reason (*3631*). The monomer (S)-2-isobutylaziridine, like some other optically active amines, catalyzes the asymmetric addition of 1-dodecanethiol to methyl methacrylate, and of 1,4-butanedithiol to ethylene dimethacrylate (*1905a*).

The modification of PEI and its homologs to yield ion-exchange resins, many of them amphoteric, is discussed elsewhere (p. 373). Not mentioned there is the crosslinking and gelling of PEI with the unusual reagent diphenyl hydrazodicarboxylate, $PhO_2CNHNHCO_2Ph$ (*3537a*).

A novel polymer is poly(1-aziridineacetic) acid, $[CH_2CH_2N(CH_2CO_2H)]_n$, made by polymerizing $AzCH_2CO_2Me$ and hydrolyzing the product (*168*). It is truly a synthetic ampholyte, of isoelectric point 2.7–2.9, with n about 40–130. However, "dealkylation" of polymers of $EtO_2CCH_2CHAzCO_2Et$ to PEI and fumaric acid is dominant over simple saponification in hot aqueous alkali, and is virtually complete in concentrated hydrochloric or hydrobromic acid (*1789*). Quaternizing poly(1-methylaziridine) with an acid such as bromo-acetic yields a polymeric betaine such as **15** (*2070*).

$$
\begin{array}{c}
Me \\
| + \\
(N\!-\!CH_2CH_2)_n \\
| \\
CH_2CO_2{}^-
\end{array}
$$

15

INDUSTRIAL APPLICATIONS OF AZIRIDINES

Commercial Development

Industrial production of EI and PEI began in Germany about 1938, when I.G. Farbenindustrie built and operated a plant in Ludwigshafen, using at first the 2-chloroethylamine route (*657, 1483*), with EI capacity of 120,000–140,000 lb/yr. During World War II production was at about this level; derivatives of EI so manufactured were used to waterproof textiles, improve coatings on plastic films, and give paper products wet strength.

After the war Badische Anilin- und Soda-Fabrik in Germany, and Chemirad Corporation in the United States (*111*), continued some production and distribution of EI and PEI, but the price remained relatively high ($2.50–$7/lb) and consumption correspondingly low. About 1960 Interchemical Corporation began advertising its ability to supply 2-methylaziridine and some derivatives. In 1963 The Dow Chemical Company announced its development of a new process for producing EI (*2760*), and later constructed a plant to produce 5–10 million lb/yr (*109*). The price of EI set by Dow decreased from $1.25/lb in 1963 to $0.85/lb in 1968. Union Carbide Corporation offered 1-(2-hydroxy-ethyl)aziridine for sale in 1964; and Dow, a series of derivatives and polymers from about that time on.

Usage of EI monomer in 1964 was estimated at over 1 million lb (*109*), but that of all alkylenimines, as monomers and polymers, was variously guessed as 1.5 million lb in 1963 (*110*) and 0.5 million lb in 1964 (*1483*). These numbers represent different opinions, not a decline in usage, and the consumption now is surely greater. The main derivatives accounting for this use are APO and the methyl homolog, apholate, TEM, and especially PEI.

Applications of Aziridines in Textile Chemistry

INTRODUCTION

The improvement of the properties of textiles by adding modifying substances to either yarns or woven goods is ancient. Such substances may alter the optical (dyeing, printing), mechanical (creaseproofing, shrinkproofing, water repellency, tensile strength improvement, stiffening), electrical (antistatic treatment), or chemical (flameproofing, rotproofing, mothproofing) characteristics of the product. The treatments ideally meet the following requirements:

1. They should produce the effect desired to maximum degree.
2. They should not adversely affect other properties of the material treated.
3. They should be easily applied at minimum cost.
4. They should resist destruction or removal by exposure to varying environments; that is, they should be fast to light, heat, air, laundering (including bleaches), perspiration, etc.

The principal utility of aziridines is to help meet the fourth requirement— permanency of the dye or finish. The latter may become associated with the fiber or textile by adhesion, formation in or transport into the fiber, or chemical combination with the fiber. Fastness usually increases in this order.

Adhesion in this case is mediated partly by adsorption; textile fibers, at least the cellulosic ones, tend to be negatively charged, so that cationic sites on dyes or polymers promote the desired fastness. More important, in dyeing of cellulose, is hydrogen bonding, but substantivity due to hydrogen bonding tends to yield poor wet-fastness because such bonds can be broken fairly readily in water. Formation of additives within fibers is illustrated in the use of vat and azoic dyes; transport into the fiber is illustrated by disperse dyes for cellulose acetate and by additives spun into the fiber. True chemical reaction with the textile fiber is very desirable but difficult to achieve on a practical basis. Reagents that esterify or etherify the hydroxyl groups of cellulose also hydrolyze readily, and sometimes polymerize. It is often a matter of doubt how much of a "fiber-reactive" agent really becomes covalently bound and how much is held by hydrogen bonding, etc.

Obviously the nature of the fiber is a major factor. The fastness of dyes and finishes on animal fibers, which have many reactive sites, tends to be much better than that on cotton. Viscose rayon and other synthetic fibers are still more difficult to modify permanently, with nonpolar polyolefin fibers such as polypropylene notoriously the worst.

Several brief reviews of the applications of aziridines and derivatives in textile chemistry have appeared (2382, 2845, 3643). These may be used along with general reference works in the field (1483, 2980, 3613, 4158).

REACTIVE DYES

Reactive dyes are those which react with the fiber to yield a covalent bond between the dye molecule and the fiber. The concept is a simple one, but it has been extensively developed only in the last 20 years, more in Europe than in the United States. Reviews are available (*4183, 649a*).

The aziridinyl group has naturally been among those introduced into dye molecules to cause reactivity toward functional groups in fibers, particularly the hydroxyl groups of cellulose (*303, 936, 2111, 3887*). Reactions of activated aziridines with such groups proceed rapidly and irreversibly; on the other hand, hydration and polymerization of the aziridine may compete successfully with the dye-binding alkylation of the fiber (*1979*), and the toxicity of the aziridines is a drawback. Probably for these reasons, reactive dyes containing the aziridinyl group (see Table 5-I) have not been commercialized.

Table 5-I

REACTIVE DYES CONTAINING THE AZIRIDINYL GROUP

Type of dye	Type of aziridinyl group	References
Azo	SO_2Az	*324, 1582, 1895, 4095*
Azo	SO_2(2-MeAz) or CO(2-MeAz)	*2892*
Phthalocyanine	SO_2Az	*695, 2378, 3441, 3706a*
Azo	Triazinyl-Az_2	*695, 2105, 2475, 2477*
Anthraquinone	Triazinyl-Az_2	*2475, 2477*
Anthraquinone	Az	*1912a, 3103*
Azo, etc.	NHCOAz	*3101*
Various	CH_2Az	*2970*
Azo	$COCH_2Az$	*693, 2891*
Azo	Various	*1911a*
Quinone vat	Various	*694*
Various	Az or NHCOAz	*700, 828*
Various	Various + urea	*3752*
Various	$SO_2CH_2CH_2NHQAz_n$[a]	*975*
Various	Various + a hydrazine	*696*
Various	Various with after-treatment for fastness	*697*

[a] Q = PO or PS, $n = 2$; or Q = CO, $n = 1$. This is as claimed; but chemically the structure $SO_2CH_2CH_2OCH_2CH_2NHQAz_n$ is more probable.

An alternative approach that avoids some of these problems is to use a functional group which can be changed under dyeing conditions into an aziridine or an aziridinium salt. This has been much more widely exploited. Usually the dye has low substantivity for cellulose (ability to be bound to the fiber) except in alkaline solutions. The usual groups employed to generate the aziridine function are $-SO_2NHCH_2CH_2X$ and $-CH_2NRCH_2CH_2X$, where X is either Cl or OSO_3H; the Levafix dyes (*2111*) are of this type. There is no doubt that the $-SO_2NHCH_2CH_2X$ in alkaline solution cyclizes to $-SO_2Az$; but the reaction of $-CH_2N(R)CH_2CH_2X$ with cellulose might be a direct second-order alkylation rather than go by way of first-order cyclization to **1**

$$-CH_2-\overset{\displaystyle \triangle}{\underset{\displaystyle R}{N^+}}$$

1

and ring opening by cellulosic hydroxyl. There is no experimental evidence on this. Because of both the difficulty of searching out all dyes that contain these "aziridinogen" functions and the considerable number of references to them, no literature is cited here.

TEXTILE DYEING AND PRINTING

The fastness of acidic dyes on cellulosic textiles is improved by concurrent application of a compound containing multiple aziridine rings, particularly APO and TEM (*175, 179, 220, 221, 383, 602, 3263, 3887*). The aziridine derivative may also be used in a post-dyeing step (*384, 1038, 2981*). Even reactive dyes are better bonded to cellulose by APO (*975, 2846, 3018*). Use of a curing agent such as zinc fluoroborate permits the fixation of a wider variety of dyes by APO (*3363*).

Among the first uses claimed for PEI was the "animalization" of cellulosic fibers—their modification to resemble wool and silk, at least in dyeability. Such improved dyeability and fastness of dyes applied along with PEI was claimed early (*1874*); it is advantageous to use a quaternized PEI (*402, 594, 597, 4054*), optionally along with a phenolic mordant (*1867*) or a urea–form-aldehyde resin (*402*). It is more usual to apply PEI after dyeing to obtain fastness (*169, 224, 599, 1115*); the polymer may be modified by condensation with urea or cyanic acid (*1210*), biguanide salts (*1890*), ethylenebis(dicyandi-amide) (*1891, 1897, 3502*), a hexitol and cupric ions (*1150*), or a chlorinated paraffin (*1191a*). Stripping of unbound PEI is done with boiling solutions of salts of strong acids (*598*).

Dyes themselves can be made to contain the $-CH_2CH_2NH-$ group derived from EI by ring opening. Besides the reactive dyes made by reaction of an aziridinyl-containing dye with hydrochloric acid,

$$\text{dye-Az} + \text{HCl} \rightarrow \text{dye-NHCH}_2\text{CH}_2\text{Cl}$$

phthalocyanine dyes containing the $SO_2NHCH_2CH_2NH_2$ group (*229*) and azo dyes containing the $SO_2NHCH_2CH_2SC(NR)(NR'R'')$ group (*1256*) or

$SO_2NHCH_2CH_2NR_2$ group (2476) have been claimed. Likewise PEI with a chlorotriazine azo dye (704) or 2,4-dinitrochlorobenzene (3360) yields modified dyes; the one from 2,4-dinitrochlorobenzene is fugitive but useful in

Table 5-II

USE OF AZIRIDINES IN TEXTILE PRINTING PASTES

Aziridinyl compound used	Polymer to be crosslinked	References
$(CONHCH_2CH_2Az)_2$	Acrylic polymer or copolymer	1227
–CH_2CH_2Az compound or	Acrylic polymer or copolymer	
$(CH_2)_n(SO_2Az)_2$	or casein, etc.[a]	773a
2,4,6-$(AzCH_2CH_2CO)_3$-H_6-s-		
triazine, TEM, etc.	Polyamine[a]	2112
p-$C_6H_4(COAz)_2$	Acidic alkyl resin	1244
$(CH_2)_6(NHCOAz)_2$	Acrylic polymer or copolymer[a]	201
TEM, APO, APS	Acrylic copolymer	1228, 1250
MAPO	Acrylic copolymer	647
TEM or APO	Acrylic copolymer or carboxy-methylcellulose	1222
$(CH_2)_n(SO_2Az)_2$	Acrylic polymer or copolymer	773, 773a
Compound containing 2 or more SO$_2$Az groups	Acrylic polymer or copolymer	1190
APS	—	1730
RNHPOAz$_2$, R$_2$NPOAz$_2$	Acrylic polymer or copolymer	1191
APS partly polymerized	Acrylic polymer or copolymer	1247
MAPO	Acrylic polymer or copolymer[b]	179, 420
APO	Acrylic or maleic copolymer[b]	7
RNHCONHPOAz$_2$	Acidic alkyd resin	3885a
AzCHOHCHOHAz types	—	3699
Polyaziridinyl compounds such as p-$C_6H_4(NHCOAz)_2$	—	1262
Polyaziridinyl compounds	Polymer containing R_4N^+ groups	207
Polyaziridinyl compounds	Acidic alkyd resin[a]	278, 1254, 1571
Polyaziridinyl compounds	Locust bean flour	1246
Polyaziridinyl compounds	Acrylic copolymer[a]	2084, 2463, 2665
An aziridinyl compound containing other reactive group	Acidic dyes	179
Aminoethylated polyvinyl alcohol, etc.	Vinyl-polymeric ester[a]	1146
PEI	A difunctional compound, e.g., an alkylene diisocyanate	2111a

[a] Product used as dispersion in water.
[b] Product used as dispersion in oil.

identifying textile fibers. Some claims for utility of aziridine derivatives for making dyes are vague (*1159, 1253, 2001, 3099*).

Textile printing with pigments, and more recently all-over coloration of textiles by the same means, requires a binder to cause adherence of the pigment to the fiber. The binder is dissolved or dispersed for application, and then cured, usually by baking. In one family of such binders, polymeric acids, especially polymers and copolymers of acrylic acids, are crosslinked with polyaziridinyl compounds; neutral resins may also be present. Thickening can be accomplished by emulsification of either an oil phase in water or a water phase in a nonaqueous one. Table 5-II treats the use of aziridines (or in one case, PEI) in pigment binding. Reactive dyes based on aziridine have also been claimed useful for textile printing (*1895, 2105*), but the only published commercial use of an aziridine derivative in textile printing has involved APO (*965*).

The wish to be able to dye mixed wool or rayon textiles evenly with minimum difficulty led to the idea of making the rayon as dye-reactive as the wool, i.e., of "animalizing" it. This can be done by modifying the fiber with additives before spinning or by treating the spun fiber; rayon so modified was formerly sold under the trade names Vistralan and Cupralan. While animalization has decreased in importance because of the development of new dyes and the difficulty in obtaining light-fastness in dyed animalized fibers, the subject is still of interest. It has been reviewed (*1307, 2979, 3787*). Aziridines have been extensively claimed for such pretreatment of cellulose and its derivatives, especially rayon; the literature is summarized in Table 5-III. An interesting

Table 5-III

PRETREATMENTS[a] FOR IMPROVING DYEABILITY OF CELLULOSE AND ITS DERIVATIVES

Form of cellulose treated	Aziridine or derivative used in treatment[b]	References
Cellulose and derivatives	AzH	*1110*
Cotton	$^+H_3NCH_2CH_2OSO_3^-$ + alkali	*1036, 1330, 1559, 2432*
Cotton	AzH + AcOH catalyst	*2580, 3191a*
Cotton and viscose rayon	AzH vapor	*971, 1293*
Viscose rayon, fresh	AzH	*2514*
Cellulose acetate	(Polyaziridinyl compound + NH₃ or amine)[b] spun in	*3147*
Cellulose esters	AzH	*1411, 3150*
Cellulose	AzCH₂CH₂CN	*2979*
Cotton	R₂NCH₂Az and homologs	*3354*
Cellulose	PEI (reported as polyvinylamine)	*2169*

Table 5-III—*continued*

Form of cellulose treated	Aziridine or derivative used in treatment[b]	References
Viscose rayon	PEI spun in or bath	1820, 1841, 1851, 3650
Cotton	Permethylated PEI	592, 1852
Viscose rayon	(Dye + PEI or protein or aminated polysaccharide) spun in	704
Cellulose	(PEI + C$_2$H$_2$ or AcCH=CH$_2$)	1877
Viscose rayon	(AzH or PEI or homologs + CS$_2$) spun in or bath	1070, 1828, 1870
Rayon contg. active H	A chloroalkylamine, then an aziridine	3149
Viscose rayon	(Aziridines + CS$_2$ + S) spun in or bath	1829
Viscose rayon	(Aziridines + CS$_2$ + alkali) spun in or bath	1830, 1869
Wood pulp	AzMe, then spun and cross-linked with epoxy resin	3599
Viscose rayon	(Aziridines + COS, CSCl$_2$, S$_2$Cl$_2$, or CH$_2$=CHNCS) spun in or bath	1831, 1843, 1844, 1872
Viscose rayon	(Aziridines or polymers + RNCO or RNCS) spun in or bath	1842, 1846, 3648
Cotton or viscose rayon	(Aziridines or polymers + ArNCO or ArNCS) spun in or bath	354, 1832
Viscose rayon	AzH, then PhNCO	1833
Viscose rayon	(AzH + PhOH + PhNCO)	1805
Cotton or viscose rayon	(Aziridines + CS$_2$ + ArNCO or ArNCS)	1075, 1868
Viscose rayon	(Aziridines + proteins + ArNCO or ArNCS) spun in	1073
Viscose rayon	(Aziridines or polymers + aldehydes or ketones)	3654
Viscose rayon	Various aziridine-based polymers, then aldehydes	1878, 1879
Viscose rayon	(Aziridines + phenols, etc. + RNCO or RNCS)	1849
Cellulose	(PEI or derivatives + ArNCO or ArNCS)	769
Viscose rayon	(H$_2$NCH$_2$CH$_2$)$_2$S (from AzH + H$_2$S) spun in	3544
Viscose rayon	(AzH + halogenated paraffin wax) spun in	3653
Viscose rayon	(Polyvinyl alcohol + H$_2$NCH$_2$CH$_2$Br)	1835
Viscose rayon	(Polyvinyl alcohol + AzH) spun in	1371
Viscose rayon	Starch aminated with AzH or otherwise, spun in	1372
Viscose rayon	(Aziridines + epoxides)	1837, 1840
Cotton	PEI + ethylene oxide + PhAc	1871
Viscose rayon	(Aziridines + polyepoxides)	1817
Viscose rayon	(PEI + aldehydes) spun in	2038

Table 5-III—*continued*

Form of cellulose treated	Aziridine or derivative used in treatment[b]	References
Cotton viscose rayon, or cellulose acetate	(PEI + tannins or other phenolic mordant) spun in	*1867*
Cellulose	$PhCHAz_2$ or $n\text{-}C_{17}H_{35}COAz$	*2381*
Viscose rayon	(Aziridines or polymers + RCO_2H or derivs.) spun in	*3653, 3657*
Cellulose	[Aziridines + $(CO_2R)_2$]	*197*
Cotton or viscose rayon	$(AzY)_nR$ [Y = CO, C(O)O, CH_2O or SO_2; $n = 1$ or 2]	*1814*
Cotton or viscose rayon	[$(AzY)_nR$ (Y = CO, C(O)O, CH_2O or SO_2; $n = 1$ or 2) + polymeric carboxylic acid]	*208*
Viscose rayon	Various aziridine-based polymers, then acid derivs.	*1812*
Cellulose	(Aziridines or polymers + $ROSO_3H$, $R = C_6$)	*1873, 3649*
Cotton	Adipoylbis-1-aziridines or TEM	*2381*
Cellulose	Polymers of $CH_2{=}CMeCOAz$	*703*
Cellulose	(Aziridines + ureas or thioureas)	*209*
Viscose rayon	$(CH_2)_6(NHCOAz)_2$	*3595*
Cellulose acetate	$(CH_2)_4(NHCOAz)_2$	*2034*
Viscose rayon	(PEI + acrylamide—Et acrylate copolymer) or (AzH + casein) spun in	*3594*
Cellulose	PEI + biguanides	*1892*
Viscose rayon	Sulfonylmono- or poly-1-aziridines such as $m\text{-}C_6H_4(SO_2Az)_2$	*326, 1854*
Viscose rayon	PEI + RNHCOAz or $Y(NHCOAz)_2$	*1879*
Cellulose	PEI + $ArSO_2Az$, or polymers of $p\text{-}H_2NC_6H_4SO_2Az$	*1806*
Cellulose	(AzH + a compound contg. a $=C=$ group) + vinyl monomer	*1809*
Cellulose	$R_2P(O)Az$ (R = Az, NH_2, NHR, NR_2, or OH)	*1732*
Viscose rayon	$RNHP(O)Az_2$	*1237*
Cellulose acetate	Aziridinyltriazines	*1731*
Cellulose acetate	(PEI + $CH_2{=}CHCN$) spun in	*416*
Various	APO	*183a*

[a] In the form of a bath except when otherwise specified.
[b] Parentheses indicate that the reagents they enclose are precombined.

suggestion chemically is to modify cellulose with 1-phenylaziridine and then couple diazonium salts with the reactive aromatic nuclei so attached (*2979*). Another is the application and curing of an aziridine in a pattern before dyeing, in order to produce printed color effects (*1807*).

Very similar work has been done with noncellulosic fibers. In particular the considerable literature on rendering polyolefin fibers dyeable (77) includes a number of references to aziridines, though it is uncertain whether any have had commercial use. Table 5-IV sets forth the processes described. The graft polymerization of EI on irradiated poly(vinyl chloride) fiber occurs not by radical ring opening but by reaction at acidic sites produced (2639).

Table 5-IV

PRETREATMENTS[a] FOR IMPROVING DYEABILITY OF NONCELLULOSIC FIBERS AND TEXTILES

Nature of fiber or textile	Aziridine or derivative used	References
Proteinaceous	AzH, 2-MeAzH, etc.	8, 3146
Poly(vinyl alcohol)	AzH, spun in	841
Polyacrylonitrile	AzH	1971
Olefin–acrylic copolymer	An aziridine, spun in or bath	158, 3588
Various	An aziridine, etc. + irradiation	2640
Poly(vinyl chloride)	Aq. $KBrO_3$–KBr–HCl, then AzH	1972
Polyolefins	Aq. $KBrO_3$–KBr–HCl, then AzH	1970
Polyolefin	Irradiation, then AcO_2H, then AzH, etc.	3600
Acrylonitrile–alkyl vinyl- phosphonate copolymers	$NCCH_2CH_2Az$, etc.	370
Wool	AzH + unsaturated esters	1471
—	$AzCH_2CHClCO_2R$	214
Polyolefin	Dibasic acid or anhydride spun in, then AzH, PEI, etc.	575, 579
Polyolefin	Polymeric acid spun in, then AzH or derivs.	3589
Polyolefin	Alkyl or aryl phosphate spun in, then AzH or derivs.	3583
Polyolefin	Sulfonation, then AzH	3586
Polyolefin	Haloaliphatic compound spun in, then + AzH, PEI, etc.	577
Polyolefin	Polyepichlorohydrin spun in, then + AzH, PEI, etc.	2288a
Polyolefin	MX_n or R_mMX_n (M = metal), then H_2O, then an aziridine	4191
Polyolefin	An alkylenebisamide spun in, then HX or I_2 or XCH_2CO_2H, then AzH, etc.	2086a
Polyolefin	$COCl_2$, then AzH	3036a
Polyolefin	Cyanuric chloride, then + amine such as AzH	2712
Polyolefin	Photochemical nitrosation, then + AzH, etc.	3587
Polyolefin	An aziridine–olefin copolymer spun in	3597
Polyolefin	n-$C_{18}H_{37}COAz$ spun in	3582
Poly(vinyl alcohol)	Aldehyde + AzH, etc.	1374, 2472
Polyester	AzR (R alkyl or aryl), then polymerize	1899

Table 5-IV—*continued*

Nature of fiber or textile	Aziridine or derivative used	References
Polyester, polyolefin polyamide	Aziridinyl compound, especially n-$C_{18}H_{37}NHCOAz$	1268
Poly(vinyl alcohol)	CH_2=$C(OMe)COAz$ polymers	2305
Various?	Aziridine–β-lactone copolymers	1370
Poly(vinyl alcohol)	Aziridines + (hydroxymethyl)urea spun in	3440
Poly(vinyl alcohol)	RNHCOAz or RNHCSAz	711, 2663, 2664
Poly(vinyl alcohol)	$(CH_2)_4(NHCOAz)_2$	2216
Wool	$(CH_2)_6(NHCOAz)_2$	2096
Proteinaceous	Az_2CO, APO	2142
Casein	AzH, then PhNCO	1833
Casein	RNHCOAz or $Y(NHCOAz)_2$	1875
Poly(vinyl alcohol)	APO	1733
Poly(vinyl alcohol)	APS spun in	1727
Polyacrylonitrile	RNHCOAz or RO_2CAz (R unsaturated), copolymerize and spin	2181
Polyolefin	Nitrogenous resin spun in, then + MAPO, etc.	417
Polyolefin	Sulfuric, sulfonic, or phosphoric acid, then RCOAz, APO, or PEI	1399
Polyamide or polyurethan	$Y(NHCOAz)_2$ or $(CONHCH_2CH_2Az)_2$ or $(CH_2)_n(SO_2Az)_2$	1804
Poly(vinyl alcohol)	Aziridinyltriazines	1731
Polyurethan	A tertiary amine containing also Az groups, etc.	1108
Polyolefin or polyacrylonitrile	Epichlorohydrin–amine adduct + another amine such as AzH	2605
Polyacrylonitrile	p-$(CH_2$=$CRCONH)C_6H_4SO_2Az$ (R = H or Me), copolymerize and spin	2659
Various	PEI, spun in	2595
Polyolefins	PEI or its derivatives spun in	45, 576, 577, 1294, 2596
Polyolefins	PEI + a dispersant spun in	2599
Poly(vinyl alcohol)	PEI, spun in	2380
Copolymer of vinyl alcohol with vinylpyridine	PEI, spun in	2207
Various	PEI (mixed with fiber monomer or polymer)	2592
Leather	Alkylated PEI	593
Polyolefin	Alkylbenzylated PEI spun in	2562b
Polyolefin	PEI or the like, optionally + metal salts	2601
Polyolefin	PEI or the like + Zn or Cd salts	2594
Polyolefin	PEI, etc., + o-hydroxynaphthoic acid	3634
Polyolefin	PEI or other N compound, then Cl_2 and a metal cyanamide	152a
Polyolefin	PEI, etc., + quaternized glycidylamine	149

Table 5-IV—*continued*

Nature of fiber or textile	Aziridine or derivative used	References
Polyolefin	PEI + epichlorohydrin spun in, then alkylation	2597
Polyolefin	PEI spun in, then + an acidic reagent	2562a
Various	Cyanoethylated PEI, spun in	416
Acrylonitrile copolymers	PEI, spun in	768
Polyamide or poly(vinyl chloride)	PEI + RNHCOAz or Y(NHCOAz)$_2$	1879
Polyamide	PEI + biguanides	1892
Various	PEI spun in, then diepoxides	45, 2600
Polypropylene	Sulfonation, then + PEI	2598
Polypropylene	Epoxy resin + HOCH$_2$CH$_2$NH$_2$ + PEI	2764
Poly(vinyl alcohol)	Aminated starch spun in	1373
Polyamide	Alkylating agent, then + PEI	439a
Poly(pivalolactone)	RAz or ArAz	992

^{a} In the form of a bath except when otherwise specified.

CREASE RESISTANCE AND FORM STABILITY

Crease-resisting finishes are used chiefly on cellulosic textiles, since other fibers either form stronger interfiber hydrogen bonds (protein fibers) or else are not hydrophilic and are not involved in the formation and breaking of hydrogen bonds that occurs in creasing. Regenerated cellulose requires more crease-resisting treatment than cotton.

Until recently the term crease resistance signified only the ability of a fiber or a textile to recover from bending or creasing when dry, but wet crease resistance is recognized as also very desirable, especially in wash-and-wear garments. The literature of the field is considerable (*2207a, 2443, 2488, 2724, 3333, 3581*). While aziridines have been studied repeatedly for imparting crease resistance, and even found superior in performance (*121, 925, 3334*), their cost and toxicity have apparently excluded them from commercial use (*2443, 2724*). Since the situation continues to change, application of aziridines to textiles for this purpose is reviewed here.

Ethylenimine itself produces no crease resistance (*1036*); a difunctional derivative is needed. Usually this is an activated aziridine: the only specifically claimed exceptions are for use of the EI–acrolein adduct (other aldehydes were no good) (*621, 3653*), 2-(1-aziridinyl)ethyl 2-methoxyethyl sulfone (*3381*), and 1,4-bis[3-(1-aziridinyl)propionyl]piperazine

$$[AzCH_2CH_2CON(CH_2CH_2)_2NCOCH_2CH_2Az]$$

and homologs (*1901*). *N*,*N'*-Alkylenebis(1-aziridinecarboxamides),

$$Y(NHCOAz)_2$$

were early claimed to have crease-resistant effects (*359, 1814*), and to anchor urea or melamine resins to the fiber for the purpose (*3302*). These have been shown to act by both polymerization and reaction with cellulose (*1994, 2032, 2033, 3562*). The similar alkylene bis(1-aziridinecarboxylates),

$$Y(O_2CAz)_2,$$

are also effective (*1814, 1931, 1994, 3520*), as are carbonylbis(1-aziridine), $COAz_2$ (*383, 622, 627, 1814, 2443, 3302, 3581*), polyaziridinyltriazine polymers (*3816, 3817*), SO_2Az_2 (*1814*), and other acylbis(1-aziridine) compounds, especially $(CH_2)_3(SO_2Az)_2$ (*1218*). Polyethylene containing pendant COAz, $AzCO_2$, or $P(O)Az_2$ groups serves the same purpose (*3384*), as also do vinyl copolymers of methacrylic acid (*991a*).

More attention has been given to APO than any other aziridine derivative for inducing crease resistance (*121, 4026*). It produces other valuable changes, particularly flame resistance, and is easy to apply (*969, 970, 2281, 2282, 2330, 2847*). Like other creaseproofing resins, it may be cured by γ-rays instead of heat (*1647, 1649*), is required in much larger amounts than can be accounted for by crosslinking (*2740*), may be made more effective if followed by application of an ethylene–propylene–acrylamide graft copolymer (*1249*), and causes little loss of tensile strength if yarn is mercerized slack and then stretched before treatment (*2641*). Reaction of APO with the glucose units of cellulose has been demonstrated (*3042*). Like most other nitrogenous finishes it causes yellowing when treated fabrics are bleached with chlorine bleaches and then scorched (*2280*). It may be used along with a saline swelling agent (such as lithium bromide) for cellulose (*756a, 1648, 2385*), with carboxymethylcellulose (*3013*), or with a chlorotriazine dye so as to give both color and wrinkle resistance (*2846*), or as an aftertreatment on textiles flameproofed with urea and diammonium hydrogen phosphate to yield crease resistance also (*3204*). The APO–thiourea and APO–urea copolymers followed by a methylolurea-type crosslinker produce particularly attractive results (*3566*).

Other aziridinylphosphorus compounds, some heterocyclic, are useful in producing wrinkle resistance: $Az_2P(O)NMeCH_2CH_2NMeP(O)Az_2$ (*628, 629*), $Az_2P(O)N(CH_2CH_2)_2NP(O)Az_2$ (*83*), $AzP(O)(OCH_2)_2C(CH_2O)_2P(O)Az$ (*2955*), $Y[P(O)(OR)Az]_2$ (Y = alkylene) (*1739*), $Q[P(O)Az_2]_n$ (*1902, 4175*), and especially the cyclic trimer $(PNAz_2)_3$ (*1724, 2847, 2957*).

Urea–formaldehyde (*3409*) and melamine–formaldehyde (*3410*) resins may be modified as anticrease agents by treatment with 2-aminoethyl hydrogen sulfate and alkali; this is nearly the same as modifying them with EI. The effect of formaldehyde itself as an anticrease agent is improved by mild pre-treatment of cotton with aziridinyl compounds, among others (*3480*).

Whereas cotton and rayon need crease resistance, wool is improved by shrinkproofing treatment. Crosslinking agents effect this change more or less well (*44, 936a, 4034*). While vinyl copolymers of $CH_2{=}CRCO_2YNHCOAz$ (R = H or Me, Y = alkylene) (*436*) and $CH_2{=}CHOYNHCOAz$ (*2520*) have been mentioned for the purpose, along with many other compounds, activated (*3382, 3384a*) and especially nonactivated polyfunctional aziridines (*2887, 3384, 3511–3513*) are better. Acylpoly-1-aziridines together with polyethylene–polyamines are also effective (*3514*), and the use of EI with a diisocyanate is recommended (*2177a*). Both crosslinking and polymerization are involved. Polyethylenimine alone (*2608*) or along with an epoxy resin (*244, 2819*) or other crosslinker (*1284a, 3780*) has some merit, preferably after a pretreatment of the wool with a little chlorine at pH 3–4 (*742, 1284b*).

The setting of creases in proteinaceous fabrics, or of waves in hair, usually depends on the breaking of disulfide bonds by mild reduction and reestablishing them in new orientation by mild oxidation. Thiol compounds have been much used as the reducing agents; and either 2-aminoethanethiol (producible from EI and H_2S) (see p. 230) or its *N*-acyl derivatives (*206, 222, 2202*) can serve the purpose.

The considerable sensitivity of either ordinary or prereduced wool to alkali is diminished by alkylation (evidently really crosslinking, since mono-functional reagents are ineffective) with such reagents as *N,N*-alkylenebis(1-aziridinecarboxamides) (*1214, 2096*). Concern has been expressed about the danger to workmen who might apply such potentially toxic agents, but it is noted that the finished textiles carry no such hazard (*44, 965*).

FLAMEPROOFING

The flameproofing of cellulosic textiles needs no defense of its utility. Tests for its effectiveness depend on both duration of flaming and duration of glow after ignition. Durable flameproofing finishes have been classified as pigment types, resin types, and cellulose-bonded types. The pigment types are difficult to make durable and are not of interest in this book. Aziridine derivatives hold the actual flameproofing agent in either physical or chemical union with the fabric. However, it is usually unknown how much they should be considered as merely physical adhesion promoters and how much as fiber-reactive binders, and no attempt will be made here so to classify them. Some of the many reviews on the subject are cited (*373, 868a, 976, 1345, 1352, 1353, 2844, 2920*).

Almost without exception the aziridine-based flameproofing finishes, like the majority of all such finishes, contain phosphorus compounds to make them effective. As Table 5-V shows, APO is by far the most common aziridine derivative used. Some commercial use has been made of the APO–tetrakis-(hydroxymethyl)phosphonium chloride finish, which is highly effective and durable (*131a, 529, 530, 966, 967*). Its action is mainly in the solid phase (*555*). The cured finish is nontoxic (*3808*).

Table 5-V

AZIRIDINES AND DERIVATIVES AS COMPONENTS OF FLAMEPROOFING FINISHES FOR
TEXTILES

Aziridine used (A)	Other flameproofing agent used (B)	References
AzH or PEI among other amines	$(HOCH_2)_4PCl$ or $(HOCH_2)_3PO^a$	*34, 3003, 3004, 3010, 3019*
$(AzCH_2)_2CHOH$	—	*2387*
APO	None (used on carboxymethylcellulose)	*3021*
APO	—	*969, 970, 2281, 2847, 2848, 4026*
APO among other monomers[b]	—	*1649*
Polyaziridinyl phosphorus oxides or sulfides	—	*625*
Polyaziridinyl phosphine oxide or sulfide polymers	—	*626*
APO or APS polymers with polyols	—	*623, 624*
APO or APS polymers with phenols	—	*36, 3014*
APO or APS polymers with carboxymethylcellulose	—	*3013*
APO or APS polymers with RCO_2H	—	*36, 3015*
APO or APS polymers with active H compounds	—	*36, 3016*
APO or APS polymers with amines or amides	—	*3011, 3012*
APO or APS	$(HOCH_2)_4PCl$ or $(HOCH_2)_3PO^a$	*35, 973, 974, 3006*
APO and $(HOCH_2)_3P$ + epi-chlorohydrin, then NH_3	—	*1240*
APO or APS	$(HOCH_2)_4PCl$ or $(HOCH_2)_3PO^a$	*120, 334, 530, 867, 868, 966–968, 1409, 2848, 3005, 3129*
APO or APS	$(HOCH_2)_4PCl$ or the like + urea	*2926a*

Table 5-V—*continued*

Aziridine used (A)	Other flameproofing agent used (B)	References
APO or the like	$(HOCH_2)_4PCl$ or the like + a S compound[a]	531
APO, APS, or the like	NH_4 borate + urea[a]	3020
APO or APS	$(NH_4)_2HPO_4$ + urea[c]	3204
APO or APS	$(NH_4)_2HPO_4$[c]	2554, 2555
APO	Resin from $NH_3 + (CH_2NH_2)_2 + P_2O_5$ or $POCl_3$[a]	3373
$MeNHP(O)Az_2$, $(MeNH)_2P(O)Az$, $MeNHP(O)(CH_2Cl)Az$	—	241a
APO or the like	Resin from $(PNCl_2)_n$ + MeOH + NH_3[a]	743
APO or APS or $Az_2P(O)CH=CH_2$	$ClCH_2P(O)(OH)_2$[c]	37, 3017
APO	Resin from $(CH_2NH_2)_2$ and a chlorinated polyphosphonate	3513a
$Az_2P(O)CH_2Cl$ or the like	—	231
APO	Thiourea[a]	958, 2282
APO	Sulfamides	2281a
APO	Guanidine phosphates[a]	659
APO	Poly(vinyl chloride), etc.[a]	1758
Polymers from APO + H_3PO_4	—	84
Polyaziridinylphosphine oxides or sulfides	$R_2NP(O)(NH_2)_2$, etc.[a]	1144
$[Az_2P(O)N(Me)CH_2]_2$	—	628, 629
$AzCH_2CH_2P(O)(OR)_2$	—	1119, 1157
$Y(OPOAz_2)_n$	—	1902
Aziridinyl derivs. of $(PNCl_2)_n$	—	1724, 2957
Metal complexes of poly-aziridinyl compounds	—	4026
PEI	NH_2SO_3H, etc.[d]	1498
PEI	Dipentaerythritol hexaortho-phosphate[d]	2388
PEI	Pentaerythritol tetraorthophosphate, etc.[d]	2389

[a] A and B precombined, applied, and cured.
[b] Cured with γ-rays or X-rays.
[c] B applied, then A and $Zn(BF_4)_2$, and cured.
[d] A applied first, then B, and cured.

WATER REPELLENCY

Water repellency is produced in textiles by hydrophobic coatings or impregnations. Since cellulosic textiles are highly hydroxylic and hydrophilic, the problem of reversing their properties and producing durable water-repellent finishes on cellulose is not simple. Here, as so often, an aziridine group can serve as a fiber-reactive portion of the water-repellent molecule, or PEI and its derivatives can serve as cationic adhesion promoters for the non-polar hydrophobe, probably in part by hydrogen bonding.

While the literature contains a number of recommendations for the use of aziridine derivatives in water-repellent finishes (*1037, 2587, 2881, 2920*) and some have appeared commercially, they do not rank as common ones. Now that EI is cheaper than formerly, the situation may change. Table 5-VI summarizes such use, classified by the hydrophobic agent or group.

Table 5-VI

AZIRIDINES AND DERIVATIVES AS COMPONENTS OF WATER-REPELLENT FINISHES FOR
TEXTILES

Aziridine used	References
Long-chain Alkyl Groups as Hydrophobic Agents; $R > C_8$, often C_{18}	
RNHCOAz[a]	*22, 115, 358, 422, 1053, 1197, 1198, 1235, 1239, 1259, 1887, 2708, 2713, 2753, 2765, 3235a, 3250a, 3292, 3521–3523, 3585, 4034*
RNHCSAz, etc.	*3652*
RO$_2$CAz	*1929, 3560*
RCOAz	*831, 833, 835, 1857*
2-(RNHCH$_2$CH$_2$CO)-4,6-(AzCH$_2$CH$_2$CO)$_2$-hexahydro-triazine	*834*
RAz and (CH$_2$)$_n$Az$_2$	*3512*
2,2-Dialkyl-AzH[b]	*1431*
PEI + RNCO	*1840*
PhCH$_2$Az + CS$_2$ + 1-C$_{10}$H$_7$NCO, then (RCO)$_2$O	*1812*
NH$_2$CH$_2$CH$_2$OSO$_3$H + ROSO$_3$Na + base	*184*
ArSO$_2$Az	*326*
Aziridines or polymers thereof + ROH, ROR, or RCO$_2$R[b]	*1822*
+ ArX or ArSO$_2$X[b]	*1823*
+ Aldehydes or ketones[b]	*3654*
+ RCO$_2$H, (RCO)$_2$O or RCO$_2$R[b]	*3657*
+ RCOCl[b]	*3655, 3657*
+ RCONH$_2$[b]	*2879*
+ Maleic anhydride + vinyl acetate copolymer[b]	*1877*
+ RCO$_2$H or haloparaffin wax[b]	*3653*
+ Epoxides	*1866, 1880*
+ Alkylureas or alkylthioureas[b]	*209*
DiAz-triazine or TEM + RNH$_2$ or R$_2$NH	*2179*
PEI along with paraffin wax	*3656*
PEI along with an insoluble soap	*1982*
Trimesoyltris(2-MeAz)	*3295*

Table 5-VI—*continued*

Aziridine used	References
Perfluoroalkyl Groups as Hydrophobic Agents	
$C_nF_{2n+1}COAz$ and $C_nF_{2n}(COAz)_2{}^c$	69, 2016, 2609, 2772a, 2885, 2885a, 2887, 4028
$C_nF_{2n+1}CONHCH_2COAz$ and $C_nF_{2n+1}NHCOAz$	2772a
$X(CF_2)_nCH_2NHCOAz$ (X = H or F, $n > 2$)	660a
$C_nF_{2n+1}SO_2NEtCH_2COAz$, etc.	24
$C_nF_{2n+1}CO_2H$ + APO or APS	736
$RP(O)Az_2$, R highly fluorinated	629a
A fluorocarbon deriv., preferably an acrylate, + AzH or $C_{17}H_{35}NHCOAz$, etc.	3212
PEI modified with $C_8F_{17}SO_2$ or $C_8F_{17}SO_2NEtCH_2CH_2$ groups	2574
A compound containing perfluoroalkyl groups ($\geq C_4$) + RCOAz (R > C_{10})	1051
A fluorocarbon deriv. + n-$C_{18}H_{37}Si(2\text{-MeAz})_3$	3213
Ethyl perfluorooctanoate + PEI	118, 4028
Other Groups as Hydrophobic Agents	
APS along with a silicone oil	3413
PEI or homolog + silicone oil	2549
Polyaziridinyl triazines and polymers	1223, 2381, 3819
Polyaziridinyl compound such as APO + a silicone oil or a fluorocarbon compound	729
APO + $(HOCH_2)_4PCl$ + a polymer or copolymer of $CH_2{=}CHCl$ + a polysiloxane + zirconium acetate latex^d	532

[a] The reagent may be used alone (*22, 115, 358, 422, 1197, 1259, 2709, 2753, 3493, 3521*) or along with a melamine resin (*1053, 2713, 2765*) or an acid curing agent (*3522, 3523*). Its aqueous dispersions are advantageously stabilized with alkali (*1198, 1235*). It is useful on polyester (*1239*) and polyvinyl (*1887*) fibers. It has had commercial use under the name "Perzistol VS" (*3302*: pp. 30, 868, 874, 901), "Primenit VS," and "Phobol PS," but it is better for reducing water absorption by hydrophilic fibers than for making them actually water-repellent.

[b] The patent claims for this use are vague.

[c] Particularly useful on wool.

[d] Confers also flame, rot, and weather resistance.

The perfluoroalkyl compounds in Table 5-VI also make fabrics oil-repellent; in fact, sometimes the oil repellency is much better than the water repellency (*2609, 4028*). Besides these, perfluoroalkyl phosphates used along with a cationic polymer such as PEI have been particularly recommended (*2386*). The long-chain alkyl compounds can usually function as softeners as well as water repellents, but that is discussed separately.

TEXTILE SOFTENING

Softening agents are frequently used as part of a textile finish applied primarily for some other purpose, to prevent loss of good hand or even to improve it. The majority of them have a cationic part of the molecule to promote attachment to the (negative) fiber, and a long alkyl chain (C_{12}–C_{18}) to give the softening effect. The treatment usually confers some water repellency also. Aziridines can function either as monomeric fiber-reactive components of molecules or as cationic polymers to hold the alkyl group to the fabric. Table 5-VII presents such uses of aziridines.

Table 5-VII

USE OF AZIRIDINES AND THEIR DERIVATIVES IN SOFTENING TEXTILES

Aziridine derivative used	References
RNHCOAz, R > C_{10}	358
RNHCOAz, R = C_{17} or C_{18}	225, 680, 2329
	2383, 3074, 3558
RO_2CAz, R = C_{18}	3298, 3560
RCOAz, R > C_7	680, 835, 1649, 1857
RO_2CCH_2Az, R = C_{14}	680
PEI or the like + $C_{17}H_{35}COX$	1840, 3655
PEI + ethylene oxide, then + BuO_2CCl	1880
Aziridines or polymers + RCO_2H or derivatives (vague)	3657
Aziridines or polymers + ROH or esters (vague)	1822
Aziridines or polymers + carbonyl compounds (vague)	831
AzH + $RCONH_2$	2879
$H_2NCH_2CH_2OSO_3H + ROSO_2Na + NaOH$	184
Aziridines + RNH_2 + AcOH, etc.	192
Aziridines + $RNHCONH_2$ or $RNHCSNH_2$	209
PEI and paraffin wax	3656
PEI and soaps	122
Polymer from RCOAz or RCO_2CH_2Az + high-molecular-weight RCO_2H	208

MISCELLANEOUS TEXTILE MODIFICATIONS

While cotton can be "aminized" with EI or 2-aminoethyl hydrogen sulfate, the product is of interest chiefly for its ion-exchange properties and will be discussed under that heading. Some such products when oxidized cautiously with aqueous chromic acid yield alkali-soluble cottons, of interest in making textiles of novelty weaves (3022).

The tensile strength of viscose rayon is increased by adding crosslinkers: PEI + RNHCOAz or $Y(NHCOAz)_2$ (1216), $NCCH_2CH_2Az$ (2710), $(CH_2)_6$-

(NHCOAz)$_2$ (*1865*, *3593*), TEM (*1865*), AzCONHC$_6$H$_3$MeNHCO$_2$CHMeCH$_2$-
O$_2$CNHC$_6$H$_3$MeNHCO$_2$(CHMeCH$_2$O)$_{34}$CONHC$_6$H$_3$MeNHCOAz   (*3592*)
(evidently made from polypropylene glycol, methyl-1,3-phenylene diisocyanate, and EI), or an aziridinyl-modified polyolefin (*3384*). An alternative once suggested is to spin the fibers into a bath more acid than usual,
which decomposes more xanthate groups, and then treat with EI (*1839*).
However, amination of cotton with 2-aminoethyl hydrogen sulfate and alkali
causes no increase in tensile strength, and even a small decrease (*1036*). Loss
of tear strength of natural or regenerated cellulose textiles on dyeing with
sulfur dyes is prevented by treatment with polyamines such as PEI (*596*).
Improved fibers are obtained from viscose solutions by adding a hydroxyethylated PEI to either the viscose or the acid coagulation bath (*235*).

   Similar crosslinking agents have been used on other fibers to improve
tensile strength and elasticity: (CH$_2$)$_2$(NHCOAz)$_2$ (*1984*), APO (*2771*), APS
(*1969*, *1984*), and TEM (*1969*) spun into cellulose acetate, and TEM (*2583*)
or (CH$_2$)$_6$(NHCOAz)$_2$ (*1160*, *1176*) used on polyurethan fibers, and various
other aziridinyl compounds (*1268*). Polyethylenimine may be spun into polypropylene which is then cold-drawn and shrunk to yield bulked yarn (*1294*),
or PEI may be mixed with urea and used with formaldehyde to finish leather
(*1195*). The stiffness of wool felts, as for hats, is improved by impregnating
with a polyaziridinyl compound such as APO, adding acid catalyst, and
curing (*1243*), but PEI applied to preoxidized moist wool fibers reduces felt-
ing tendency (*2716a*). Crimping of polyamide and polyester fibers is increased
by treatment with crosslinkers such as (CH$_2$)$_6$(NHCOAz)$_2$ (*236*).

   Aqueous slurries of alumina or silica used to impart antislip properties (to
minimize distortion and consequent fraying of textiles) to textile threads and
yarns are improved by addition of PEI, which stabilizes them (*864*, *893*;
cf. *889*) and enhances adhesion (*898a*; cf. *1840*); an aftertreatment with a
silicone then increases elasticity and softness (*898*). The alumina–silica treatment also helps soil resistance (*3717*).

   The accumulation of static charges on the surface of synthetic textiles is a
well-known nuisance which can be prevented by rendering the surface a better
conductor of electricity, usually by making it more hygroscopic. Polyethylenimines function well in this capacity, either alone (*276*, *1268*, *3326*, *3392*,
3421, *3795*), or modified by hydroxyalkylation (*1130*, *3417*, *3425*), introduction of CH$_2$CO$_2$H or CH$_2$SO$_3$H groups (*403*), treatment with a lauryl
alcohol–ethylene oxide–epichlorohydrin–NaOH reaction product (*660*), or
quaternized and used along with a surfactant (*217*). Copolymers of propiolactone and EI of low molecular weight are also considered useful (*1370*). The
relative triboelectric position of PEI—its tendency to gain a negative charge
from other polymer surfaces—puts it at the very top of the list (*3750*). In a
variant procedure, polyurethans made to have terminal NHCOAz groups are

cured on fabrics to give antistatic properties (*3811*). Still another antistatic finish contains an aminated polyethylene glycol as the agent and APO as the binder for it (*730*).

Finishes to increase resistance to soiling have been reviewed (*3717*); in general they are the same as those used to produce water repellency. Though conflicting to some extent, the evidence is that aziridines containing a hydrophobic part of the molecule are both effective and permanent (*390a, 3340, 3783*). When used along with colloidal alumina or silica for this purpose, the hydrophobic aziridine component improves softness also (*260*); but this application is limited to carpets, or at least to nonwash goods (*2326*). Ethyl perfluorooctanoate and EI used together on cotton gave a finish more subject to oily soiling than other hydrophobic finishes but also better in permitting removal of such soil and preventing its redeposition (*2609a*).

The use of substances known as optical bleaching agents or fluorescent brightening agents is relatively recent. The active compound is usually a stilbene or a heterocyclic analog of a stilbene; in any case the light absorber needs to be bound to the fabric. Ethylenimine has been proposed for use in making several fiber-reactive agents of this kind (*842, 2711, 2714–2716, 2447*).

It is of course desirable to reduce the susceptibility of textiles to degradation by physical or chemical attack. The stability of polypropylene fibers to heat and light is improved by modifying them with a phosphoric or phosphonic acid and then crosslinking with APO (*1398*); poly(vinyl chloride) is also stabilized by such crosslinkers (*2910*). Polyamide fibers are reportedly improved by heat-curing them with a diaziridinyl compound (*1818*), and discoloration and weakening of segmented elastomeric polyamide fibers by light and fumes is retarded by incorporation of titanium dioxide and a high-molecular-weight aliphatic amine that may be PEI (*142*). Microbiological degradation of cotton is inhibited by APO (*970, 3006, 4026, 4059*) and by a halophenol such as pentachlorophenol bound to the material with PEI (*2629*); polyaziridinyl–metal complexes have also been mentioned (*1397, 4026*). Aziridinyl compounds can either themselves mothproof wool or bond other mothproofers to it (*8, 1840, 2387, 3148*).

Use of Aziridine Derivatives in the Paper Industry

The main area of application of aziridine derivatives—chiefly PEI—in paper chemistry is as wet-end additives: substances mixed with the slurry of paper pulp, filler, etc., that is fed to the papermaking machine. Since this "furnish" is mostly water, the additives must be water-soluble or water-dispersible. Polyethylenimine has been used on a small scale for about 25 years as an additive (*2113, 3546*), chiefly to increase wet strength, although it also improves both drainage (rate of dewatering) of the paper stock on the machine wire and retention of fillers and fine paper fibers in the sheet. These will be discussed in turn. Both general and specific reviews are available (*590, 1483, 1536, 1956a, 2210, 2484, 2492, 2913a, 3120, 3366, 3706, 3794a, 4108*).

WET STRENGTH

Paper products that need to retain mechanical strength and shape during and after exposure to water—for example, paper towels, paper plates, and some cartons—require special treatment. This is not a matter of waterproofing, to prevent entry of water into the sheet, but of maintaining fiber–fiber bonds against being broken by water. Some resins used for the purpose, especially the formaldehyde–melamine and formaldehyde–urea types, function by polymerizing in and on the fibers so as to cement them together: drying and heating of the sheet is needed to cure the resin. There is evidence that such resins actually copolymerize with the cellulose to some extent (*291*).

Wilfinger (*1876, 3792*) first pointed out the value of PEI and its derivatives for improving both wet rub strength and wet burst strength, by application to either pulp or sheets. The usual application level is 1–1.5% of the pulp on a dry basis. Various initiators and special conditions have been claimed for making PEI of especial value as a wet strength resin (*650, 654, 706, 3580, 3807*).

Polyethylenimine attaches itself to pulp fibers, especially those containing hemicelluloses, more readily than the thermosetting resins, requiring only drying to develop wet strength in the paper (*1757, 3793, 3794*). It is more strongly cationic than the amide-based resins, and is adsorbed rapidly and surprisingly irreversibly on the pulp fibers (*3025, 3121, 3614*); the process may be followed by use of an electrical streaming current detector (*2067*). The claim that melamine–formaldehyde resins are more strongly *adsorbed* (*3682*) appears very doubtful. Again unlike resins that are not cationic, PEI is effective in alkaline solution, maximum uptake by pulp occurring at pH values 7–10 (*3121, 3793*). It is usual to find that PEI is deactivated as a wet-strength resin by papermakers' alum (aluminum sulfate), but improved PEI does not show this defect (*963, 4108*). In contrast to its action on paper sheet, which when treated has good wet strength, PEI produces little or no improvement in the wet or dry tensile strength of cotton or rayon yarns, which are comparatively very strong initially and moreover are too well purified to offer as many binding sites (*122*). For that matter, PEI somewhat decreases the dry strength of paper, either by reducing fiber flexibility and elasticity (*3121*) or by interfering with the fiber-to-fiber hydrogen bonding that occurs on drying.

Reworking of scrap high-wet-strength paper presents some difficulties, especially for that made with thermosetting resins and for PEI-treated paper after it has aged awhile (*2123*). A hypochlorite treatment may be useful (*1770*), but for fresh PEI-treated scrap, repulping in water acidified with hydrochloric acid or alum is effective (*3546*).

A disadvantage of all nitrogenous wet-strength resins is the tendency of the paper to lose brightness and gradually to yellow. This may be related to the yellowing of wash-and-wear cotton textiles made with such resins. It has also been attributed to the presence of soluble carbohydrates in the paper (*3025*). Quaternized PEI does not cause such yellowing but is only a retention aid, not a wet-strength agent (*3120*).

Various combinations involving PEI have been proposed as wet- and dry-strength resins: copolymers with 2-methylaziridine (*211*), urea–formaldehyde –PEI (*656*, *1981*), urea–formaldehyde–$H_3N^+CH_2CH_2OSO_3^-$–base (*3409*), urea–melamine–$H_3N^+CH_2CH_2OSO_3$ (*3410*), PEI made with polyacrylic acid (*1054*) or halohydrin (*650*) initiators, PEI salts with polymeric acids (*2379*), including partly hydrolyzed polyacrylamide (*1766*, *3035*, *3194*), PEI cross-linked with urea (*227*) or epichlorohydrin (*178*, *181*, *2379a*, *4114*), and urea–EI reaction products used along with a formaldehyde-based resin (*1261*). However, it has been shown that the increased PEI retention induced by addition of polymeric acids does not proportionately increase wet strength (*3121*). Increased crosslinking and increased strength can be achieved by the use of either a polysaccharide such as starch (*27*, *183*, *1316*), a water-soluble thermosetting aminoplast resin (*656*), *N,N'*-methylenebisacrylamide (*2340a*), or an organic polyisocyanate (*2777*), along with PEI. Polymers of aziridinyltriazines (*3819*) and 1-(2-hydroxyethyl)aziridines (*3628*) have been specified as additives, as have aminoethylated polymers made by treating starch (*1976a*), plant gums (especially guar) (*2718*), and polymeric carboxylic acids (*1287a*). Polymers of 2-methylaziridine are reported inactive in papermaking processes (*211*, *1483*).

Very strong paper, eminently suitable for making sandpaper, is made by saturating it with solutions of (a) a compound containing at least two acylated aziridine rings, such as APO, and (b) a compound having at least two active hydrogen atoms per molecule, especially a dithiol, and then heating to cause curing within the paper (*25*). It is also feasible to use APO or the like without added crosslinking agent (*2066*). Particularly hydrophilic paper products, such as towels, are producible by treating paper sheets with a polyhydroxylic colloidal material, e.g., poly(vinyl alcohol) or methylcellulose, and then PEI (*3693*).

RETENTION AID

The ability of water-soluble polymers to cause flocculation and deposition of paper fibers and fillers is well established (*1757*, *2431a*, *2887a*). While use of closed white-water systems on paper machines has reduced the problem of retention of fines, it still needs attention. Calcium carbonate pretreated with low-molecular-weight PEI is a convenient retention aid for calcium carbonate filler (*2256*). Polyethylenimine made with urea initiator (*3334a*), quaternized PEI (*653*), or PEI modified by crosslinking with epichlorohydrin (*196*) or polyvinyl alcohol and epichlorohydrin (*2256a*) or graft polymerizing it with acrylamide (*601*) is also recommended, but in any form its effectiveness decreases 70 seconds after addition to the pulp (*211*). Fine-fiber and filler retention, the latter at high levels, are improved by concurrent use of PEI or a like base and a polymeric acid such as polyacrylic acid or a plant gum (*132, 133, 3401*). Even when the total retention of filler is not increased, the filler is more effective in producing opacity when such a flocculant is used (*1957*). Dye and pigment retention is similarly enhanced with the product of condensing a polyalkylenepolyamine, such as PEI, with cyanamide, guanidine, or biguanide (*1721*). The performance of polyacrylic acids (*2677b*) and diethylamino ethers of starch (*1976, 1976a, 2677c*) as retention aids is improved by further aminating them with EI.

Coagulation of pulp fines also improves the drainage rate or freeness of the pulp; use of PEI (*211, 230, 1485, 3519a*) can raise machine capacity 10–15 %, by permitting faster operation and by reducing breakage (*2210, 3121*). The polymer made with an unsaturated acid or its derivative is especially claimed (*3328a*). Such use of PEI as a drainage aid (up to 0.5 % by weight) is permissible in paper for use in food packaging (*112*), and PEI is useful in making a cellulosic web for coating and use as a casing for meat products such as sausage (*901*).

SIZING

Internal sizing of paper to reduce water permeability and otherwise to improve its properties is effected with beater additives. The hydrophobic agents usually used adhere to the fiber better if a cationic polymer such as PEI or cationic starch is added also (*1980*). So used are long-chain acids or amines (*2262, 3034, 3840*), long-chain-alkyl chloroalkyl sulfones (*2591*), rosin soaps (*86, 2831, 2832*), organopolysiloxanes (*1163*), and latexes of thermoplastic resins (*2379, 2552, 3401, 3875, 3876*) and thermosetting resins (*3143*). Polyethylenimine partly acylated with C_{14}–C_{22} fatty acids can also serve (*3034*). The hydrophobic agent and the aziridine ring may be in the same molecule, as in N-octadecyl-1-aziridinecarboxamide, n-$C_{17}H_{35}$NHCOAz, used alone or along with starch (*1486*). An acidic polyester-activated aziridine dispersion as a beater additive makes paper both stronger and more transparent (*1a*). Polyethylenimine functions as a retention aid in oil-proofing paper with perfluorooctanoic acid (*2830*), polyfluoroalkyl phosphates (*2386*), or other perfluoroalkyl compounds (*2968*), rotproofing with a quaternary ammonium salt (*2833*), or flameproofing with inorganic anions, especially phosphate (*595*). Various aziridinylphosphorus compounds and their polymers have been suggested as flameproofers (*626, 958, 3011, 3014, 3015*). Stiffening of paper and especially paperboard can be effected with PEI lignosulfonate (*11*) or PEI and APO used together (*2778*). Paper made from acid- and oxidant-free pulp and containing PEI is coated or impregnated with metal-corrosion inhibitors to make a special wrapping paper (*3694*).

The *surface sizing* of paper has involved much less work with PEI, but two patents mention the polymer for use in such a process (*1282a, 1289*). Insulating paper is made by coating it with a solution of cellulose etherified with 1-(2-cyanoethyl)aziridine (*2206a*). A chloroform solution of terephthaloylbis-(1-aziridine), p-$C_6H_4(COAz)_2$, when used to impregnate paper and then cured with a polyester containing free acid groups, gives improved stability to the paper (*3294*). Similarly $C_{17}H_{35}NHCOAz$ and $(CH_2)_n(NHCOAz)_2$ are beneficial in the sizing of paper containing synthetic fibers by means of copolyamides (*2431*), and impregnating with APO and linoleic polymer acid, then curing, improves mechanical properties, especially water repellency (*4089*).

COATING

While good adhesion is one of the requirements in paper coating, PEI has not been directly incorporated in coating mixtures for this purpose; but it has been found to be a useful dispersant for clay in cationic latexes (*1673*). Cationic starch is valuable in paper coatings (*1533, 2678*) but apparently has been too expensive to find use; it is advantageously insolubilized before use by treatment with various agents, including PEI and poly(2-methylaziridine) (*2487*). Polyalkylenimines made by heating monomers with ureas or thioureas have been mentioned, too, for use in such coatings (*209*). The products made by modifying proteins, particularly casein, with EI or its 1-alkyl derivatives may be useful here (*71*).

Starch in which the granules have been insolubilized by heating with $C_{17}H_{35}NHCOAz$ has been suggested for use as a pigment in paper or leather (*210*). In a different application to pigments, phthalocyanines are stabilized in the preferred form by treatment with long-chain alkylureas, which may include n-$C_{17}H_{35}NHCOAz$ (*1019*). By various reactions aminoanthraquinone pigments themselves can be made to contain aziridinyl groups (*2891*).

Printing inks are obviously related to both textile printing pastes (see p. 345) and coatings (p. 381), but are mentioned here. Rapid-setting typographic inks can be produced by using a pigment binder consisting of an aziridine such as EI or APO and a polymeric acid such as rosin or modified rosin (*1911, 3070*). Writing inks may be made with PEI and an acid dye or a direct dye (*2798a*).

Use of Aziridines in Plastics

INTRODUCTION

For present purposes plastics are defined as solid organic polymers which are shaped into various useful forms. It is convenient to classify aziridines in plastics as (a) those that are used or proposed for use as major components and (b) those that function as additives and modifiers.

It may as well be admitted immediately that aziridines have been used as major components in very few plastics. Their ease of polymerization to solid products has led many applicants for composition-of-matter patents to allege that the polymers have general utility in the field, but most of these suggestions are vague, and unsupported by even laboratory experiments. A group of such broad claims was presented by early I. G. Farbenindustrie patents, and others have appeared since, as seen in Table 5-VIII. Somewhat more specific applications to forming films, fibers, and elastomers are proposed in the literature cited in Table 5-IX.

Table 5-VIII

USE OF AZIRIDINES AND THEIR DERIVATIVES AS MAJOR COMPONENTS IN GENERAL PLASTICS

Reagents used to form polymer	References
Aziridines + alkylxanthates	2395
EI + CS_2, S_2Cl_2, COS, or $CSCl_2$	1072
Aziridines + CS_2 + S	1829
Aziridines or their polymers + ArNCO or ArNCS	354, 1074, 1861
Aziridines or their polymers + polyphenols + ArNCO or ArNCS	1849
Aziridines + casein or like protein + ArNCO or ArNCS	1071
1-Glycidyl-2-alkylaziridines	3299
1-(2-Hydroxyalkyl)aziridine + a diglycidyl ether	3403
$Y(COAz)_2$ + polymeric higher polyenic fatty acids	1316
NH_2COAz or RNHCOAz types	357
RNHCOAz types	1858
$Y(NHCOAz)_2$ types (Y = nonaromatic)	355
RSO_2Az or $ArSO_2Az$ types	326
EI + cyclic anhydrides	3432
EI + cyclic imides	1545, 1687, 3327
1-Acryloylaziridines	2305
1-Acetoacetylaziridines	2001
1,1-Isophthaloylbisaziridines and 1,1,1-trimesoyltrisaziridines, homo- or copolymers	3295
RO_2CAz	2263
$Y(O_2CAz)_2$ + polyamines	3293
$Y(O_2CAz)_2$ homo- or copolymers	1693, 3296
$O[(CH_2)_nO_2CAz]_2$ and similar ones	3298

Table 5-VIII—*continued*

Reagents used to form polymer	References
A polyaziridinyl compound + a diphenol such as bisphenol A	*3405*
$(PNCl_2)_3$–AzH–polyfluoroalkanol reaction products	*2958*
1-Perfluoroacylaziridines	*24, 2886*
PEI + $ROCH_2NCO$ + minor reagents	*1124*
PEI + *m*-phenylenediamine + HCHO and/or CH_2Cl_2	*1534*

Several detailed studies of applications of aziridinyl compounds in plastics have discussed the use of adducts of EI with acrylonitrile (*3178*) or polyesters made from maleic acid (*1786*) as monomers for casting resins. These with acid or alkylating catalysts yield clear hard solids good for such specialty uses as embedding biological specimens, producing printers' type and engraving cuts, and filling teeth. The unusual tendency of polymerized aziridinyl compounds to adhere to solid surfaces makes it desirable to use special mold-release

Table 5-IX

USE OF AZIRIDINES AND THEIR DERIVATIVES AS MAJOR COMPONENTS IN FILM- AND
FIBER-FORMING POLYMERS AND ELASTOMERS

Reagents used to form polymer	References
Various aziridines alone or + epoxides, diamines or diacids (claims very doubtful)	*987*
$CH_2{=}CHCH_2Az$ polymers	*919*
RCHOHAz polymers	*3626*
$(CH_2)_3(NHCOAz)_2$ + a diamide	*1935*
$Y(NHCOAz)_2$ + a diamide	*1926, 1932, 1938, 1939*
RSO_2Az or $ArSO_2Az$	*2334*
$(CH_2)_4(SO_2Az)_2$ + a dithiol	*2661*
$RPO(O)Az_2$ or $ROP(S)Az_2$ + a diamine or a diacid	*1527*
$HS(CH_2)_nSH$ ($n = 2, 4, 5$ or 6) + AzH, then + chloride of diacid	*1932*
1-Hydrocarbylaziridine polymers + $X(CH_2)_nCO_2H$	*3174*
AzH + CO by use of $Fe(CO)_5$ and severe conditions	*1898*
$CH_2[NHCO-2-(1-R-Az)]_2$, optionally with polyamines or polyols	*151*
4-$OCNC_6H_4CH_2CH_2C_6H_4NHCOAz-4'$ polymers	*3477*
$RO[Si(OR)_2YCH(CH_2Az)O]_nH$ polymers and homologs thereof	*1590*
Aziridine–olefin sulfide copolymers	*3061*; cf. *1009a*
$Y(O_2CAz)_2$ + a dithiol	*1926, 1932*
$Y(NHCOAz)_2$ + a dithiol	*1939*
$AzH-C_2H_4$ copolymers used in mixture with butadiene–Me butadienecarboxylate copolymers	*158c*

agents—poly(vinyl alcohol) (*1226*) or silicones (*1232*)—for such castings. Other patents on this specific type of resins are cited in Table 5-X.

Table 5-X

ADDUCTS OF ETHYLENIMINE WITH DERIVATIVES OF UNSATURATED ACIDS OR WITH EPOXIDES AS MONOMERS FOR CASTING RESINS

Reagents used to form polymer	References
EI adduct with alkylene or arylene dicrotonates, optionally + acrylic acid	*1067, 1201, 1202, 1205, 3159*
EI adduct with polyester from a polyol + unsaturated dibasic acid such as maleic	*164, 1788, 2491*
$(AzCH_2CH_2CO_2)_nQ$ + epoxy resins	*3367*
$RO_2CCH_2CHAzCO_2R$ cured with $ArSO_2OMe$ (particularly for an outer layer in laminated contact lenses)	*1066*
$[SiR(CH_2CH_2Az)O]_n$ types containing 2 or more Az groups (particularly for dental fillings)	*1068*
$AzCH_2CH_2CN$, etc., cured with, e.g., Et_2SO_4 (while impregnated with graphite to make self-lubricating bearing)	*1055*
Various linear polymers with Az end groups, cured with $ArSO_2OR$ (particularly for dental impressions, etc.)	*1068, 1069*
$(p\text{-}AzCH_2CH_2CO_2CH_2CH_2OC_6H_4)_2CMe_2$ and similar esters (for dental use)	*1067*
EI adduct with N,N'-alkylene- or N,N'-arylenedimaleimides	*1545, 3327*

Degradation of poly(1-alkylaziridines), as of other like polymers, with organometallic reagents and subsequent hydrolysis yield fragments with reactive ends; these can be usefully repolymerized with difunctional reagents such as diisocyanates (*1700*).

MODIFIERS IN POLYMERIZATIONS AND PLASTICS

It is of interest, though mostly academic, that aziridines have been claimed as modifiers of vinyl polymerizations by each of the major mechanisms. The polymerization of ethylene by acid catalysts such as hydrogen fluoride is improved by an initiator such as EI (*389*); the carbanion-catalyzed polymerization of simple olefinic compounds can be similarly initiated (*390*); vinyl fluoride polymers and copolymers are producible by use of a coordination catalyst made from an alkylboron compound with a nitrogenous base which may be EI (*2593*); and radical-catalyzed vinyl polymerizations, as of acrylonitrile, are accelerated by PEI (*770*) and otherwise improved by use of organic hydroperoxide–aziridine reaction products, $ROOCH_2CH_2NH_2$ and the like, instead of the hydroperoxide as initiator (*1049*). Polymerization in water of a vinyl monomer in the presence of a bentonite (*946*) or silica gel (*948*) suspending agent is improved if a little PEI is also added.

The use of an aziridinyl derivative such as APO or APS to stop, not start, a vinyl polymerization catalyzed by a Ziegler-type catalyst prevents development of color in butadiene polymers (*1780*).

Among tertiary amines, 1-alkylaziridines were the most effective as catalysts for the reaction of polyols and polyisocyanates to give polyurethans (*480*, *481*); aziridines, not 1-substituted (*309*, *310*), or acylpolyaziridines such as APO (*312*) also improve the performance of the widely used catalyst triethylenediamine. Isocyanates alone are polymerized to the trimers, isocyanurates, by such mixed catalysts (*308*, *311*, *1129*, *3273*); but interestingly enough, phosphinous and phosphonous acid derivatives such as Az_2POAr and $AzP(OAr)_2$ are stabilizers for isocyanates (*1738*). Aziridines are among the cyclic amines usable along with acids in the controlled polymerization of formaldehyde (*3413a*). Aliphatic diisocyanates with 1-alkylaziridine catalysts also yield linear polymers (*1141*).

The use of aziridines and aziridine-generating reagents in producing accelerators for rubber vulcanization is old, and never achieved commercial status. Such use is reviewed in Table 5-XI merely to complete the record.

Table 5-XI

Use of Aziridines in Making Vulcanization Accelerators

Reagents	Product	References
An aziridine + CS_2	2-Mercaptothiazoline	3407
An aziridine + CS_2 + NaOH	$AzCS_2Na$ type[a]	2469, 3797
$AzCS_2Na^a$ + $(NH_4)_2S_2O_8$ or sulfur chlorides	$(AzCS)_2S_x$[a]	2469
An aziridine + NH_4SCN	Polymers	2468
An aziridine + Zn salt of 2-mercaptothiazoline	2-(2-Aminoethylthio)-thiazoline (?)	2004
An aziridine + $NH_2CS_2NH_4$	Polymers	2470
An aziridine + a thiuram disulfide	Polymers	1968

[a] These structures are certainly wrong; the products were most likely 2-mercaptothiazoline derivatives.

Fiber- and film-forming polymers containing chemically bound fluorescent moieties may be made with monomers containing aziridinyl (among many other) groups (*829*).

A wholly different modification—suppression of the tendency to accumulate a static charge—is produced in shock-resistant vinyl copolymers by milling-in a compound such as PEI (*3262*). Films sufficiently electrically conductive to be useful in circuitry are made from 7,7,8,8-tetracyanoquinodimethan, one of its salts, and quaternized PEI (*1447, 2358a*). Coating the grains of smokeless gunpowder with PEI of low molecular weight makes it free-flowing and static-free (*276*). These applications are obviously related to the uses of PEI on textiles discussed on p. 358. A silica filler aminated, as with EI or PEI, before use in rubber improves the resistance to aging (*2905a*). Complexes of dyestuffs and water-soluble polymers such as PEI are useful for coloring Portland cement (*3865b*).

CHAIN EXTENSION OF POLYMERS

The anionic polymerization of olefins can readily yield "living" polymers, with terminal organometallic linkages; these by any of the well-known reactions with carbon dioxide, ethylene oxide, and the like yield what are called terminally reactive (telechelic) polymers. End-to-end linking of these polymers by an appropriate difunctional compound then yields cured products, often elastomeric, of increased value structurally; the process is roughly comparable to vulcanization, but involves chain extension instead of crosslinking. If a trifunctional curing agent is used, both endlinking and crosslinking occur.

Preferred reagents for curing carboxyl-terminated telechelic diene polymers are APO and APS and their homologs, the products being useful in tire treads and molding resins (*19, 19a, 328, 2737, 3033, 3874*) and, with boron nitride, as caulking compositions (*2172a*). Also used are TEM or (PNAz$_2$)$_3$, optionally along with an organic peroxide (*1546, 2171*), or a more complex tris(1-aziridinyl) derivative (*1743*). The cure may be varied as desired by using a mixture of bis- and tris(1-aziridinyl) compounds, such as Az$_2$SO and APO (*2393*), or a mixture of monoacidic (semitelechelic) and diacidic polymers (*547, 1779, 3253, 3254*), the monoacid serving as a nonbleeding plasticizer. A butadiene–styrene copolymer compounded with dicumyl peroxide and MAPO was cured better than with either the peroxide or the aziridine alone (*2172*). In some cases an acidic carbon black is used to accelerate the curing (*1545a*), or (as for diene–vinylpyridine copolymers destined for rocket fuels) chloroacetic acid is blended in along with the MAPO (*367*). Both carboxyl-terminated telechelic polymers and butadiene–acrylic acid copolymers may be cured for rocket fuel use with APO and its relatives (*1784, 3393, 3729, 3846*), but the carboxylic derivative EtC(CH$_2$OCH$_2$CH$_2$COAz-2-Me)$_3$ is too reactive to be satisfactory. Concurrent use of a polyaziridinyl compound and an epoxy resin has been suggested (*148*) and also that of polyepoxide–2-methylaziridine adducts (*527*). Another rocket fuel containing ammonium perchlorate is cured with SO$_2$(CH$_2$CH$_2$Az)$_2$ (*682, 3385*), and one based on both ammonium nitrate and ammonium perchlorate as oxidizers is bonded with a carboxyl-terminated alkyd resin and a polyfunctional aziridine such as MAPO (*1475*). Ozonolysis of copolymers of isoolefins and conjugated diolefins and reduction or oxidation of the products yields polymers containing hydroxyl and/or carboxyl end-groups that can be cured to mastics with poly-(1-aziridinyl) compounds or other crosslinkers (*1079*).

As a variation, the telechelic polymer itself can be made to have terminal aziridinyl groups, and the molecules may then be linked by reaction with polyacids and anhydrides (*107, 177, 3811*) or with a catalyst such as methyl benzenesulfonate to yield elastomers (*1069*). Polymers containing alkali metal terminal atoms are treated with enough polyaziridinyl compound such as PhP(O)Az$_2$ that some aziridinyl function survives, as in

$$AzP(O)(Ph)NLiCH_2CH_2-\text{polymer chain}-CH_2CH_2NLiP(O)(Ph)Az,$$

and cautious hydrolysis yields the metal-free polymer (*1778*). If a trifunctional aziridinyl (or other) compound is used, not in excess, a branched-chain polymer is produced (*2876*).

$$\text{polymer chain}-Li + APO \rightarrow (\text{polymer chain}-CH_2CH_2NLi)_3PO$$

Polymers containing alkali metal atoms at both ends when combined with various reagents, including alkylenimines, yield telechelic polymers themselves of interest as monomers (*3873*).

The endlinking of carboxyl-terminated polymers other than those of hydrocarbons is of interest in producing coating materials rather than plastics, but is cited here (*2211, 3564, 3746*).

Chlorosulfonated polyethylene is advantageously crosslinked and cured by reaction of the SO$_2$Cl groups with acylpolyaziridines (*2692*); similar improvement of poly(vinyl chloride) or poly(vinylidene chloride) is effected with 2–6 % APO or a homolog (*651*), and of chlorinated polyethylene with MAPO (*2354b*). The endlinking or crosslinking of nonvinyl polymers can also be effected by the proper interaction of end groups and polyfunctional linking agent. Many of the products are elastomers. Reagents of this kind are reviewed in Table 5-XII, which also includes references on the curing of epoxy resins with aziridinyl compounds. A different kind of crosslinking and stabilization is effected by blending PEI, as a coordinating agent, into ethylene–methacrylic acid copolymers in which part of the acid groups are bound to transition metal ions (*992a*).

One known method for stabilizing halogen-containing polymers such as poly(vinyl chloride) is to add a reagent that absorbs liberated hydrogen halide by reacting with it. Aziridines certainly react readily enough, and have not been neglected in claims. Table 5-XIII records such reports, as well as those

Table 5-XII

Prepolymer type	Reactive group	Curing agent	References
Polyester	CO_2H ?	EI at 250°–320°C	2534
Polyester	CO_2H ?	$Y(NHCOAz)_2$	1016
Polyester	CO_2H	$(CH_2)_2(COAz)_2$	2990
Polyester	CO_2H	m-$C_6H_4(COAz)_2$, etc.	3295
Polyester	CO_2H	1,1-Isosebacoylbisaziridine, etc.	2569, 3743, 3744
Polyester	CO_2H	$(CH_2)_2(COAz)_2$ + an amide polymer	289
Polyester	CO_2H	1-Glycidylaziridines	3300
Polyester or polyacrylic	CO_2H	$Y(COAz)_2$	2
Polyester or polyacrylic	CO_2H	$Y(COAz)_2 + (PNAz_2)_3$ or the like	2838
Polyester or polyacrylic	CO_2H	$(CH_2)_n(O_2CAz)_2$	2, 2571
Polyester	CO_2H	$Q(O_2CAz)_n$	2573
Polyester	CO_2H	MAPO or MAPS	3713
Polyester	CO_2H	MAPO + $(2$-$MeAzCH_2CH_2)_2SO_2$	3439, 3714
Polyester	CO_2H	Polymer from a polyol + a diisocyanate + EI	1736, 1737
Polyester	CO_2H	$(PNAz_2)_n$, $n = 3$ or 4, + $Q(COAz)_n$	2568
Polyester	CO_2H	A polyaziridinyl compound[a]	3
Polyester	OH	Polyaziridinyltriazines	2180
Polyester	Active H	$Q(O_2C$-Y-$COAz)_n$	3537
Polyurethan	OH ?	AzH	1735
Polyurethan	OH	$Y(COAz)_2$	2751
Polyurethan	OH?	$Y(O_2CAz)_2$ or $Y(NHCOAz)_2$	1447a
Polyurethan	NCO	1-H-aziridines	3475a, 3811
Polyurethan	NCO	1-H-aziridines, then NH_3, etc.	1140
Polyurethan	OH ?	Alkyl 1-aziridinecarboxylate polymers	2263
Modified polyamide	$NHCH_2OH$, $NHCH_2OR$	Polyaziridinyl compound	829a, 2132a
Various	CO_2H	Polyaziridinyl compounds	1a
Various	CO_2H	Polyepoxide-aziridine adducts	526
Various	CO_2H	$Q[CO_2(CH_2)_mAz]_n$, $m = 1$–6, $n = 2$–4	960
Various	Active H	$2,4,6$-$(2$-$MeAz)_3$-s-triazine	836, 838
Epoxy	Epoxy	1-H-aziridine–RNH_2 or R_2NH reaction products	1255
Epoxy?	Epoxy	AzH	1718
Epoxy	Epoxy	$Y(COAz)_2$	1318
Epoxy	Epoxy	1-Allylaziridines	919
Epoxy	Epoxy	AzH adduct with, e.g., ethylene diacrylate	1258, 1907
Epoxy	Epoxy	$RN(POAz_2)_2$	963
Epoxy	Epoxy	$RR'NPOAz_2$ or $RR'NPSAz_2$ ($R = 2$-thiadiazolyl, $R' =$ alkyl or Ph)	82, 3187

Table 5-XII—*continued*

Prepolymer type	Reactive group	Curing agent	References
Epoxy	Epoxy	CH_2=$CHCH_2Az$ polymers	*919*
Epoxy	Epoxy	2-Aminoethyl methacrylates	*2501a*
Epoxy	Epoxy	An aziridinyl-*s*-triazine + dicyandiamide	*773b*
Epoxy	Epoxy	Poly(alkylenoxy)alkyl–O_2CAz–aliphatic polyamine adducts	*731a*
Silicone	CO_2H, OH, SH, or NH_2	$Q(COAz)_n$	*3742*
Highly fluorinated	OH or CO_2H	$Q(COAz)_n$, especially APO, APS, and $(CH_2)_n(O_2CAz)_2$	*3745*
Polyalkylene polysulfide	SH	$Q(COAz)_n$	*1314*
Epoxy	Epoxy	Compound containing an aziridine and a dihydropyran ring (among others)	*1753*
Epoxy	Epoxy	Polymer with NH_2 end groups, from a polysulfide polymer + an aziridine	*329*

[a] The mixture may be electrodeposited and then cured.

for stabilization of other polymers by aziridines and their derivatives; how much commercial use of this kind has been made is unknown.

A different sort of stabilization—the preservation of form by minimizing shrinkage during curing—is contributed by polyaziridinyltriazines in aminoplast resins (*3818*). Stabilization of diisocyanates before use in polyurethans can be effected by various 1-substituted aziridines (*2637a, 4077*) and aziridinyl derivatives of trivalent phosphorus (*1738*).

The ester-amides, $RCONR'CH_2CH_2O_2CR$, made by a ring-opening reaction of 1-R'-substituted aziridines with anhydrides of C_2–C_5 fatty acids (*3610*) and of dibasic acids in general (*219*), and that of phthalic anhydride in particular (*3609a*), are stated to be good plasticizers for poly(vinyl chloride) and cellulose acetate. 1-Oleoylaziridine has also been mentioned (*3274*). Related to this is the crosslinking in cellulose acetate films by $(CH_2)_4(COAz)_2$ and APS, which was most effective when the nitrogen content of the film was 0.8–2.0 % (*1985*). A claim that cotton cellulose can be made into a leatherlike material by impregnation and curing with 5 % EI (*3365*) appears questionable, but fibrous material *can* be so modified by such treatment with a film-forming vinyl polymer or copolymer and an acylbis(aziridine) such as $(CH_2)_6(COAz)_2$ or $MeC_6H_3(NHCOAz)_2$ as crosslinker (*200*). Paper containing PEI serves as a reinforcing base in which to produce a viscose-regenerated cellulose film, the strong sheets being used as casings for meat products such as sausage (*900*).

Crosslinking by EI or 2-methylaziridine of cellulose regenerated from viscose in a foamed state is a reasonable route to producing synthetic sponges (*2145*). When moist wood is impregnated with a solution of APO and the structure cured at 45°–150°C, it is resistant to warping and shrinkage, and to

Table 5-XIII

USE OF AZIRIDINES AND THEIR DERIVATIVES AS STABILIZERS FOR POLYMERS

Polymer stabilized	Stabilizer	References
Halogen-containing polymers	1-Acylaziridines	*2689*
Halogen-containing polymers	1-Acyl-2-methylaziridines	*1860*
Polymers and copolymers of $CH_2\!=\!CCl_2$	1-Acylaziridines	*205*
Halogen-containing polymers	1-Phosphorylaziridines such as APO	*1217, 2910*
Polymers and copolymers of $CH_2\!=\!CHCl$ and $CH_2\!=\!CCl_2$	APO and homologs or polymers	*651*
Halogen-containing polymers	MeCHOHCH$_2$Az or n-C$_{17}$H$_{35}$COAz	*2910, 2911*
Halogen-containing polymers	APS	*3697*
Unsaturated polyamide binders in printing inks	PEI (acetylated or not), etc.	*3140*
Polymers of cyclic acetals of polyols	Aziridines, etc.	*3533*
Polyformaldehyde	EI	*3698*
Polyformaldehyde	Aziridinyl compounds such as n-C$_{17}$H$_{35}$NHCOAz	*2039*
Formaldehyde–alkylene oxide copolymers	Nitrogenous compounds including n-C$_{17}$H$_{35}$NHCOAz or (CH$_2$)$_6$(COAz)$_2$	*1701*
Formaldehyde–alkylene oxide copolymers	An aziridinyl compound + a phenol or an arylamine	*1192*
Polyformaldehyde	Copolymerize with AzH or AzR	*1973*
Polyformaldehyde	Copolymerize with RSO$_2$Az or ArSO$_2$Az	*2123a*
Polyformaldehyde	EI + a dicarboxylic imide + dimethylformamide	*2580a*
Polyformaldehyde	Various aziridines	*486, 1974*
Polyurethans, especially fibers	Tertiary aliphatic amine containing an Az, etc., group	*1166*
Polyurethan films and fibers	Polyaziridinyl compounds	*1114*

decay and fire (*2065*). Untanned collagenic material is improved by treatment with a mono- or diaziridinyl compound having an acyl, carbalkoxy, carbamyl, alkane- or arenesulfonyl, or alkoxymethyl group in the 1-position (*199*). Ethylenimine has been tested along with other agents for stabilizing arterial grafts (*3871*) and minimizing their degeneration after transplant; but it caused calcification and undue rigidity (*1394*). Polyacrylamide with the appropriate degree of crosslinking, as with PEI, does not swell in petroleum but does so in water or brine and thus can block water intrusion in oil wells (*3772*). Other polymers with pendant amide groups are also crosslinked by PEI (*1237*).

Use of Aziridines in Ion-Exchange Media

Weakly basic ion-exchange resins invariably contain an abundance of amine nitrogen atoms, which supply the cationic sites at which exchange occurs. One of the classic ways to make such resins (*1675*) is to crosslink polyalkylenepolyamines sufficiently to give the necessary insolubility and structural strength, but not so much as to reduce penetrability and thus capacity for exchange. It was recognized early (*1534*) that PEI could thus be crosslinked with an aliphatic dihalide and/or formaldehyde; the structure could be made more rigid by including aniline or *m*-phenylenediamine.

For a resin made by crosslinking PEI with ethylene dibromide, the order of affinity for anions was acetate < chloride < nitrate < tosylate < 2-naphthalene-sulfonate < Orange II, the same as the order of decreasing swelling of the resin salts and approximately the order of increasing size of anions (*3231*). Epichlorohydrin has been repeatedly mentioned as crosslinker (*14, 172, 1122, 1532a, 3820a*); it gave better resins than dihalides, diepoxides, or diisocyanates (*3085*). Still another type of crosslinker contains two or more *N*-acyl or *N*-sulfonyl β-lactam groups (*4052*). If the resin is first gelled in an aqueous system containing emulsified liquids such as alkanes, drying produces a spongy resin of increased capacity (*1578*; cf. *3820a*). Resins crosslinked with epichloro-hydrin or formaldehyde may contain other components: vinylpyridines (*1184*), phenol (*421, 1189*), or *m*-phenylenediamine (*2945*). Crosslinking with poly-acrylic acid requires a higher temperature (*1008*). Homogeneous ion-exchange membranes for dialysis and electrodialysis have been made from PEI variously crosslinked (*1181, 1674, 2415, 2705, 2746, 3196, 3532, 3563*), sometimes in the presence of a support consisting of a textile fabric (*1178, 2706*) or paper (*1138*); but apparently these have been chiefly of laboratory interest. Resins contain-ing residues of chlorophyll (*497, 2274, 2275*) or hemin (*2274–2276*) derivatives have been made as enzyme models.

Only a few references deal with strong-base anion-exchange resins derived from the PEI structure. Quaternization of the weak-base type with methyl iodide converts only about half the nitrogen atoms (*3085*). A quaternary pyridinium salt, PEI, lignin, and epichlorohydrin together yield a mixed-base type (*2273*). Similarly, treating PEI with $PhOCH_2CH_2Cl$ and then with $PhOCH_2CH_2NMe_3Cl$ and acidic formaldehyde yields a resin in which some of the nitrogen atoms bear $CH_2CH_2OC_6H_4CH_2C_6H_4CH_2CH_2NMe_3Cl$

groups; such resins have reduced tendency to swell (*1134*). Another approach is to crosslink (as with epichlorohydrin) poly(1-alkylaziridines); the cross-linking quaternizes some of the nitrogen atoms (*1284*). These resins have improved stability to chemical degradation. The polymers of *N*-(2-chloro-ethyl)aziridine (*2562*) should have half the nitrogen atoms quaternized if all the chlorine atoms react.

The introduction of PEI chains into preformed polymers to obtain anion-exchange resins has not been overlooked. Chloromethylated crosslinked polystyrenes are swelled in an organic solvent and then aminated and cross-linked, as with PEI (*1188*). Alternatively the chloromethylated polymers are impregnated with excess EI in the cold and then heated to give resins with attached oligomeric EI units, of capacity up to 8 meq/gm of dry resin (*1186*). Lignin has also been modified with EI for the purpose (*937*), and polyvinyl alcohol) fabrics and films as well (*4081*). The polymer by far the most commonly aminated, however, is cellulose.

The reaction of cellulose and modified cellulose with aziridines and PEI has been of considerable interest in the textile and paper industries (see pp. 340–363). The simpler case is that of cellulose and PEI, since here the bonding can be only by adsorption; but this is strong and mostly irreversible when adequate surface is available for the heterogeneous reaction (*3121*). Sodium cellulose xanthate and PEI gave a resin which after extensive purification had a chloride ion exchange capacity of 4.2 meq/gm (versus a theoretical capacity of 9.3 meq/gm calculated from nitrogen content) (*3337*).

In the reaction of cellulose with EI or EI sources, there is great difficulty in establishing whether the nitrogen introduced is in the form of *O*-(2-amino-ethyl) groups (or oligomers thereof) or is PEI not washed out by whatever purification method was used. This is discussed on p. 224.

Table 5-XIV shows the results of various aminations of cellulose and its derivatives with EI or its precursors. High cost and low capacity have kept commercial interest in such ion-exchange materials small. Cellulose alkylated with diethylaminoethyl groups (DEAE-cellulose) is of similar nature and limitations. Of laboratory interest in paper electrophoresis is the use of PEI before staining; it is held by the paper and can serve as a reference substance for staining of proteins and lipoproteins (*3838*). Paper sheet or powder treated with PEI has anion-exchange properties and has had laboratory use for thin-layer or paper chromatographic separations (*2546, 2971, 2972, 3759*). A thin coating of PEI-treated cellulose on water-insoluble plastic sheets makes such sheets also useful in both paper and thin-layer chromatography (*2973*); such layers have been used in separation of nucleic acid bases, nucleosides, and nucleotides (*2828, 2944a*). Both the stability of the layers and the reproducibility of R_f values are excellent (*4142*). Columns of PEI-treated cellulose are especially good for the quantitative separation of nucleotides (*4024*).

Table 5-XIV

CELLULOSE-BASED ION-EXCHANGE MATERIALS MADE WITH AZIRIDINES AND
THEIR EQUIVALENTS

Cellulosic substrate	Aziridine or equivalent[a]	Ion-exchanging properties of product	References
Alkali cellulose	I	—	1618
Cellulose	II	—	1559, 2497, 2509
Cotton fabric	I, III	Dyeability	1036
Cotton fabric crosslinked as with $NH(CH_2CH_2OSO_3^-)_2$	I	Dyeability, etc.; mechanical properties improved	528
Cotton fabric	I, then II	Capacity 1.8 meq/mg	972, 1560, 3009
Na cellulose xanthate	I, II, III	Fibers crosslinked; dyeable (?)	2580
Cellulose fiber	I	Paper sheet used for separating complex anions	2063
Cellulose powder	I	Used for separating ovalbumin	3199
Cotton fiber	II	Dyeability	971
Cellulose acetate	IV	Dyeability	1411
Alkali cellulose or cellulose acetate	II, III, IV	None; no amination of cellulose	1309
Cellulose or (2-hydroxyethyl)-cellulose	II	Product containing adsorbed PEI only	2606, 2607
Paper	IV	3% N present; used for chromatographic separation of acids	2547
Alkali cellulose	I	Capacity 0.93 meq/gm	1959
Alkali cellulose	III	Very low N content and capacity	1959
Cellulose or poly(vinyl alcohol)	IV or homolog + acid or alkylating agent	Some capacity	1617
Cotton	IV + acetic acid	Moderate capacity	3191
Regenerated cellulose sponge	I	Some capacity	3355

[a] Aminoalkylating reagents are represented as follows: I, 2-aminoethyl hydrogen sulfate; II, EI vapor; III, 2-haloethylamine; IV, EI in solution.

Aziridines may serve not only to provide a basic chain upon which cross-linkers operate to give resins, but, when difunctional, as crosslinkers themselves. Only a few examples are available.

In the oldest one, PEI and lignin mixtures are crosslinked with bis(2-chloro-ethyl)methylamine, which reacts as the aziridinium ion (2273). The resins have only small capacity and swell badly, but they do have unusual ability to remove ligninsulfonic acids, as from sulfite liquor. Also described have been polyalkylenepolyamines crosslinked with bis- or tris(1-aziridinyl)triazines (*2355*), and resins formed by the interaction of a water-soluble ammonia–epichlorohydrin reaction product and PEI or preferably 1-alkylaziridine polymers to yield resins of high capacity and good mechanical properties (*1283*).

It is evident that resins containing a –N—C—C—N– grouping should chelate many metal ions. This has been of interest in salvaging, e.g., copper from very dilute aqueous wastes (*3231*), or in removing iron(III) from solutions of aluminum salts (*1185*). Chelation of metal ions, as by Co(II) and Co(III), also increases the basicity of the resins (*2717*). Resins have been made specifically for chelation by alkylating PEI with an unsaturated halide such as vinylbenzyl chloride or allyl chloride and then crosslinking by radical-induced vinyl polymerization (*3226*), or by using an EDTA–epoxy resin condensate to supply chelating sites and PEI to do the crosslinking (*3778*).

A kind of mixed-bed ion-exchange medium can be made from an anionic polymer such as sodium poly(styrenesulfonate) and a cationic one such as PEI, temporarily plasticized, to permit shaping it into, e.g., membranes, with soluble sodium or calcium salts that are then leached out (*2545*). However, a commoner approach to producing such media for deionizing water and aqueous solutions is to make each polymer molecule amphoteric. Acidic groups may be introduced into PEI before or after partial crosslinking and then the crosslinking finished. Acid groups have been supplied for the purpose by addition of acrylic acid (so as to yield $NHCH_2CH_2CO_2H$ groups) (*1187*) or a complex polyacid containing aldehyde groups (*3779*) or by metathesis with chloroacetic, chloromethylphosphonic, or *p*-bromobenzenearsonic acids (*1112*, *2412*, *3778a*), brominated EDTA or the like (*3778b*), or 4-chloropyridine-2,6-dicarboxylic acid (*380*). The product of the last reaction mentioned had a calcium ion capacity of 4.2 meq/gm and could separate calcium and strontium. Alternatively the copolymerization of compounds of type $(RO)_2P(O)CH_2CH_2Az$ and $C_6H_4(CH_2CH_2Az)_2$ (as crosslinker), with an alkyl sulfate catalyst, followed by saponification, gives amphoteric resins (*1156*, *2416*). As other sources of acid groups $AzCH_2CO_2Et$ (*1118*, *1158*), and $EtCHAzCO_2Me$ and $EtO_2CCH_2CHAzCO_2Et$ (*2413*) have been used, and TEM as crosslinker; the best resin was reported formed from the latter and $MeCHAzCO_2Et$ (*2413*). Cellulose may be treated with these aziridinyl esters and the product saponified with like results (*2414*). A chelating resin made from PEI, chloroacetic acid, and crosslinker was unequaled for the removal of trace impurities from lithium chloride brine (*439*).

Polyvinyl alcohol fibers or films are graft polymerized with acrylic acids and the copolymer treated with EI vapor to produce ion-exchange materials

(*2526b*); or the same supporting fibers are caused to react first with EI vapor and then with chloroacetic acid to form chelating structures (*1903a*).

Still another approach to producing an amphoteric ion-exchange resin is to insolubilize a water-soluble ionic polymer within a crosslinked polymer of opposite charge (*1631*). In such "snake-cage" composite resins, PEI "snake" may be formed within a "cage" of preformed sulfonated styrene–divinylbenzene copolymer (*1632, 3776a*) or sodium polyacrylate may be entrapped when a PEI–epichlorohydrin matrix is generated (*1633*).

There remains a small group of heterogeneous reports, not exactly on ion-exchange media but so closely related to the topics just discussed as to be appropriate for citation here. Filtration of used dry-cleaning solvents through the usual anionic filter (diatomaceous earth) is improved by coating the filter particles with a cationic polymer such as PEI (*1468a*); filter beds for water are similarly improved (*1546a*). Aqueous PEI (*1825, 3805*) and its carboxymethylated derivations (*1940*) have been claimed for stripping acid gases from mixtures, but these can hardly compete with 2-hydroxyethylamines; the same is true for extracting phenols from nonaqueous solution (*1710a*). Possibly the ability of PEI and homologous polymers to absorb acids is the reason for using it in tobacco smoke filters (*488, 1762*). Crosslinked, preferably with butadiene dioxide, it serves both as a good antiacid and a disintegrating agent in tablets containing aluminum hydroxide, with which it probably forms complexes (*26*). PEI orally administered can be used to lower blood cholesterol levels, presumably by preventing absorption of bile acids (*3821*), and an acetylated or otherwise acylated form can serve as a colloidal blood substitute (*1128*).

In the preparation of immunoadsorbents of high capacity, tris(2-methyl-1-aziridinyl)phosphine oxide (MAPO) was used to crosslink and insolubilize the protein component before coupling this with the antigens (*2763*).

Use of Aziridines and Their Derivatives in Adhesives

In this section only adhesion between preformed solids will be discussed. Adhesion of dyes to textiles is treated in the textile section, and adhesion of coatings in the section on coatings.

Adhesives have been classified as solvent-sensitive, pressure-sensitive, temperature-sensitive, and reaction-sensitive. Most of the applications of aziridines are in the latter class—thermosetting adhesives. Aziridinyl compounds and their polymers have unusual ability to promote adhesion; they are used either alone or as components of adhesive mixtures.

Table 5-XV presents the literature, nearly all patents, on the use of aziridines in adhesives in general. Almost no critical evaluations are possible, and most

Table 5-XV

USE OF AZIRIDINES IN GENERAL ADHESIVES

Adhesive composition (and adherends, if specified)	References
AzCH$_2$CH$_2$CN polymers (on nonporous surfaces)	3178
1-Glycidylaziridine polymers	3299
Aziridine–aldehyde copolymers	2434a
Y(NHCOCH$_2$CH$_2$Az)$_2$ polymers	151
AzH adducts with N,N'-alkylene- or N,N'-arylenedimaleimides	3327
AzH adducts with unsaturated alkyd resins, polymerized	1786, 1788
RCOAz polymers	67
CH$_2$=CMeCOAz polymers	703
Q(COAz)$_n$ polymers	3295, 3296
1-Alkylaziridine + phthalic anhydride	3609a
AzH + alkylene carbonate	979
1-Arylaziridine + RCO$_2$H, especially polyacrylic acid	208
Y(COAz)$_2$ + polyacylated polyamine + polyester containing CO$_2$H and OH groups	289
Q(O$_2$CAz)$_n$ polymers	3298
Q(O$_2$CAz)$_n$ + polymers containing CO$_2$H groups	2573
RNHCOAz or Q(NHCOAz)$_n$ polymers (on nonporous surfaces)	172, 1734, 1855
Polymers containing NHCOAz end groups + polyesters containing CO$_2$H groups	1737
Y(NHCOAz)$_2$, including 2,5-bis-AzCONHCH$_2$CH$_2$ derivatives of furan, tetrahydrofuran, and thiophene (on wood)	1927
APO or APS + phenols	3014
Polyaziridinyl compounds such as APO or Az$_2$SO + polymer containing CO$_2$H end groups	2393, 3033
(PNAz$_2$)$_3$ or (PNAz$_2$)$_4$ + polyols (in plywood)	2957
Epoxy resin cured with PEI	669
p-OCNC$_6$H$_4$CH$_2$CH$_2$C$_6$H$_4$NHCOAz-p polymers	3477
$^+$NH$_3$CH$_2$CH$_2$OSO$_3^-$ + OH$^-$ + urea + HCHO	3409
$^+$NH$_3$CH$_2$CH$_2$OSO$_3^-$ + OH$^-$ + melamine + HCHO	3410
Amine–HCHO resins (as from urea, melamine, casein, etc.) + TEM	3818
PEI + polyvinyl alcohol + other components (for heat-sealing of films)	3641a
PEI or like polymeric amine + insufficient crosslinker to cause gelling	1443
PEI and/or MeAz polymers used with a long-alkyl acrylate and/or alkyl propiolate (for gummed paper)	2589a

of the descriptions of use are very vague. Probably none has achieved commercial use unless in specialty items. It is evident that such adhesives are in general made not from PEI, but by polymerizing a 1-substituted aziridine, usually an activated one.

Pressure-sensitive adhesives, on the other hand, *are* producible from PEI, used along with poly(N-vinylpyrrolidone) (*186, 2896*), poly(vinyl alcohol)

(*2896*), or poly(vinyl alcohol) + a polybasic acid (*860*). However, PEI was considered inferior to some polyurethan, rubber latex, and polyacrylamide–glyoxal adhesives for surgical use (*755a, 1093*).

For laminating films and foils, PEI is recommended (see Table 5-XVI) and probably actually used. Other laminating adhesives based on aziridines usually contain an activated aziridine which is cured *in situ*.

Table 5-XVI

Use of Aziridinyl Compounds in Laminating Adhesives

Adherends	Adhesive	References
Glass plate + plastic sheet containing light-polarizing material	AzH–unsaturated ester adduct + Canada balsam + curing agent	*2015*
Glass + glass	AzH–unsaturated ester adduct + epoxy resin	*3367*
Glass + glass	Aziridinylorganosilicon compound–lactam copolymer	*2590*
Glass, ceramics, or metals	Poly(vinyl chloride) + alkylene dimethacrylate + APO, etc.	*1242*
Wood + wood, etc.	A polyaziridinyl compound + a polycarboxylic anhydride + water	*2967*
Wood	Polyacrylate latex containing $CO_2CH_2CHRNH_2$ groups	*999*
Paper	A polyaziridinyl compound such as APO + a Novolak resin	*3404*
Wood, paper, or cloth	TEM + alkyd resin containing OH groups	*2180*
Wood, cork, or paper	Epoxy resin + AzH + HCHO, etc.	*1052*
Glass + glass	Epoxy resin + APO	*3405*
Synthetic-fiber textiles + rubber	APO, TEM, etc.	*3122, 3123*
Paper + paper or foil	Vinyl acetate–acrylic acid copolymers + MAPO, etc.	*1600*
Glass + glass	$Q(O_2CAz)_n$ + polymeric acid	*2569*
Wood + thermoplastic resins	APO, etc. + acrylic copolymer containing CO_2H groups	*3555*
Glass cloth + glass cloth	$Q(COAz)_n$ or homolog + epoxy resin	*1318*
Glass cloth + glass cloth	PhOH–BzH resins + APO	*2897*
Glass cloth + glass cloth	Polysiloxane with active end groups + polyaziridinyl compound	*3742*
Glass cloth + glass cloth	Polysiloxane + PEI + other adhesive	*964*
Glass cloth + glass cloth	Polyaziridinyl compound + various other	*3383*
Glass cloth + glass cloth	Various polyaziridinyl compounds such as APO or $Y(COAz)_2$ + acid anhydride	*1315*
Glass cloth + glass cloth	Polymer of RO_2CAz	*2263*
Glass cloth + glass cloth or polyesters	Copolymer of activated and nonactivated aziridines	*4187*

Table 5-XVI—*continued*

Adherends	Adhesive	References
Paper + glass	HOCH$_2$CH$_2$Az polymer	3628
Polyolefin + other material	Ethylene–acrylic acid copolymer amino-ethylated with EI	4047
Paper + polyolefin film	PEI	16, 943, 1803, 2617, 2694
Paper + polyolefin film	Other adhesive containing a little PEI	951
Paper + polyolefin or poly(vinylidene chloride)	PEI	2012
Regenerated cellulose film + polyolefin	PEI	483, 2028, 2325
Regenerated cellulose film + poly(vinylidene chloride)	PEI	2248, 3323
Regenerated cellulose film + polyolefin	APS, TEM, etc.	3565a
Metal foil + polyolefin	PEI	955, 2249
Al foil or nylon + polypropylene	PEI + epoxy resin reaction product, then other adhesive	2602
Polyolefin + film of other polymer	PEI	942, 3069
Poly(vinyl chloride) film + (CF$_2$CClF)$_n$	PEI	1572a
Paper + paper	PEI + lignin	658
Polyimides + other polymers	PEI + R$_4$NCl + heat	2326a
Poly(vinyl fluoride) or wood + other surfaces	Polyacrylate latex containing CO$_2$CH$_2$CHRNH$_2$ groups	2498, 2499, 3266
Poly(vinyl fluoride) or a poly-imide + other surfaces	Polyacrylate latex containing CO$_2$CH$_2$CHRNH$_2$ groups + epoxy resin	990, 3669
Nylon or Dacron fabric + polyvinyl film	Dispersion containing poly(vinyl chloride), a plasticizer, and APO, APS, or the Me homologs	3515
Polypropylene film	PEI or 2-MeAzH polymer + other adhesive	3641
Polyester film	(CH$_2$)$_6$(NHCOAz)$_2$	20

Among the many special adhesives for joining rubber to tire cords, the aziridines have been mentioned mainly for use with polyester cords. Compounds containing two or more O$_2$CAz or NHCOAz groups are very suitable (*2982a, 2083, 3508, 3584, 3590, 3591, 3598, 3851a*) on polyalkylene terephthalates, as is a conventional vinylpyridine–butadiene copolymer latex mixed with a resorcinol–formaldehyde resin and doped with PEI (*1692, 2648*). Alternatively the polyester cord is pretreated with PEI and heated before further coating (*4061*). General utility in tire cord adhesives is claimed for APO and its homologs (*394*) and 1-allylaziridine polymers (*919*), and use specifically on rayon cords of $n\text{-}C_{18}H_{37}NHCOAz$ (47), and on polypivalolactone cords of mixtures containing PEI (3228b). A primary coat of epoxy resin, aziridinyl compound, and rubber latex may be used, then the conventional resorcinol–formalin–rubber latex mixture (475). Indeed $(CH_2)_6(NHCOAz)_2$ gave superior adhesion, but its toxicity was objectionable (1412).

With the increasing use of nonwoven fabrics in recent years, attention has been devoted to improving the binders by which the fibers are held together. For a mixed fabric containing viscose rayon, cotton, and poly(vinyl alcohol) fibers, a binder consisting of TEM, APO, or $(CH_2)_6(NHCOAz)_2$ is specified (1336). More generally, APO or APS or their homologs used along with a polymeric acid (591), 2-methylaziridine with a similar acid (2269a), EI with an acrylonitrile–butyl acrylate copolymer (2707), and compounds of type $(2\text{-MeAz})_3P{=}NSO_2Ar$ (3030) can serve to link the constituent fibers. Such use of an aziridine along with a vinyl polymer or copolymer improves wet strength (3206). In a related process, fiber flocks are bound to paper, leather, or cloth by use of an adhesive containing MAPO; the cured product is resistant to dry cleaning and washing (2423). Plastic foams may similarly be fixed to a surface by use of compounds containing NHCOAz groups (3534).

The use of aziridinyl compounds in adhesives for particulate material has been more limited, even in patent claims. When anhydrite $(CaSO_4)$ is mixed with water and allowed to set to constitute a floor, addition of PEI makes the floor more water-resistant, elastic, and shockproof (1973). A wood-particle board with magnesia-base binder is improved by inclusion of a little cationic electrolyte such as PEI (720). A sand–epoxy resin mixture for application to flooring was effectively cured with an amine–EI reaction product (1236a). Like the polyethylenepolyamines, PEI when variously modified by acylation or alkylation promotes good bonding between asphalt and rock aggregates used in road building (913, 1294a). Foundry molding compositions consisting of sand, clay, and water are treated with PEI or a homolog to serve as binder (3773). Finally, PEI is good for holding an antiblocking layer of finely divided silica on cellulosic filters (864), and acylated PEI similarly prevents blocking of cellulosic pressure-sensitive tapes (1687a, 3198).

Use of Aziridines and Their Derivatives in Coatings

The uses claimed for aziridines in finishing paints almost always involve them in the film-forming reaction, where they participate in curing, i.e., crosslinking, processes. The particular advantages most often cited are improved adhesion and solvent resistance. However, they have apparently never achieved commercial status as components of coatings, so that Table 5-XVII records possibilities rather than actualities.

Table 5-XVII

Use of Aziridines in Finishing Coatings

Aziridine used	Other components used	Special improvement claimed	References
EI or PEI	Copolymers of vinyl chloride	—	1570
EI	Various condensation polymers with NCO end groups	Flexibility	1736
EI, 2-MeAzH, etc.	Acrylate–methacrylate copolymers containing OH and CO_2H groups, thermosetting resin, etc.	Appearance	686
2-MeAzH	Epoxy resins	Flexibility, resistance	3335
2-MeAzH, etc.	Polyurethans with NCO end groups	—	3811
$PhCH_2CH_2Az$	Amine-cured epoxy resins	Water resistance on Al	2843
$HOCH_2CH_2Az$	Acrylic polymer latex, etc.	Adhesion, dispersion, nonyellowing	687
APO	Acrylic polymer, etc.	Appearance	3556
Glycidyl-Az and homologs	Polyacid or polyamine curing agents	—	2886
$CH_2[NHCO-2-(1-R–Az)]_2$	Optionally + polyamine or polyol	—	151
AzH–unsaturated ester adduct	Epoxy resins	Chemical resistance	1786, 3367
AzH–unsaturated ester adduct	Polymers or copolymers containing anhydride groups	—	2491
AzH–unsaturated bisamide adduct	—	—	3426
$CH_2{=}CMeCOAz$	Initiator of vinyl polymerization	—	2305
Acylbisaziridines	Polyurethans with OH end groups	—	2751
A bis(aziridinyl) compound such as $C_6H_4(CH_2CH_2Az)_2$	A diphenol + an epoxy resin	Chemical resistance, adhesion, flexibility	3406
$Y(COAz)_2$ (?)	Various	Heat and water resistance	1810
$Y(COAz)_2$	Vinyl polymers containing CO_2H groups	Flexibility	3746
$Y(COAz)_2$	Epoxy resins	—	1318
$Q(COAz)_n$	Various, CO_2H-containing	—	1a

TABLE 5-XVII—*continued*

Aziridine used	Other components used	Special improvement claimed	References
$Q(COAz)_n$	Polyalkylene polysulfides	—	*1314*
$m\text{-}C_6H_4(COAz)_2$, etc.	Polyesters with active end groups	—	*3295*
$Q(COAz)_n$	Polyesters with CO_2H end groups	Leather coating	*4*
$Y(COAz)_2$	Urea–melamine–HCHO prepolymers	—	*3296*
$Y(COAz)_2$	Polysiloxanes with active end groups	—	*3742*
$Y(COAz)_2$	Polyesters with CO_2H end groups	Flexibility	*2569, 3743, 3744*
$Y(O_2CAz)_2$	Polyamines	—	*3293*
$Q(O_2CAz)_n$	Polymers containing CO_2H groups	Adhesion	*2569, 2573*
$Q(O_2CAz)_n$, APO, etc.	Fluorinated polymers containing OH or CO_2H groups	Adhesion	*3745*
$Y(O_2CAz)_2$ or $Y(NHCOAz)_2$	Vinyl polymers containing OH groups	Electrical insulation	*1729*
RNHCOAz, etc.	Hydroxy acids	—	*1861*
$Y(NHCOAz)_2$	Acidic catalysts	—	*355*
RNHCOAz or $Y(NHCOAz)_2$	Methylcellulose or albumin	Leather coating	*2842*
RNHCOAz	Alkyd resins containing OH end groups	Water resistance	*1635*
RNHCOAz	Linseed oil, etc.	Adhesion to wet wood	*926*
Adducts of AzH with condensation polymers containing NCO end groups	Polyesters with active end groups	—	*1737*
Adducts of AzH with condensation polymers containing NCO end groups	Polyacids	—	*117*
RNHCOAz	—	Waterproofing masonry	*1257*
$RNHCO_2CH_2CH_2Az$	Styrene–maleic anhydride copolymers	—	*1592*
$RNHCONHCH_2CH_2Az$	Styrene–maleic anhydride copolymers	—	*1588*
$(Me_2N)_2P(O)NHCH_2CH_2Az$	Styrene–maleic anhydride copolymers	—	*4068*
Polyaziridinyltriazine + RNHCOAz or $Y(NHCOAz)_2$	—	—	*3817*

TABLE 5-XVII—*continued*

Aziridine used	Other components used	Special improvement claimed	References
Polyaziridinyltriazine	Polyols	—	3816
Polyaziridinyltriazine	Alkyd resins with OH end groups	Flexibility	2180
Polyaziridinyltriazine	Amines	—	2179
Polyaziridinyl phosphine oxides or sulfides	Phenols	—	3014
MAPO, MAPS, or TEM	Copolymers of unsaturated acids	Alkali resistance	3823
AzH + CS$_2$ or COS, S$_2$Cl$_2$, CSCl$_2$, or RNCS	—	—	1831
AzH + ArSO$_2$Az	Acid catalyst for copolymerization	—	326
RAz + phthalic anhydride	—	—	3609a
RAz + maleic anhydride	EI added at C=C double bonds	—	1590a
AzH + an unsaturated ether + BF$_3$	Used with a metallic drier	—	1439
AzH + polyolefin + unsaturated diester	—	—	1440
AzH or 2-MeAzH + acidic copolymer, as of CH$_2$=CMeCO$_2$H and its ester	(Used as latex)	Freeze–thaw resistance, etc.	686, 993, 999, 2498, 2499, 3696
AzH or 2-MeAzH + acidic copolymer	(Used as latex)	Metal enameling	995a, 2533a
AzH + acidic copolymer + NaHSO$_3$	(Used as latex)	No color development	3771
AzH + acidic aerated copolymer, as of CH$_2$=CMeCO$_2$H and its nitrile and esters	(Used as latex)	Metal coating	996
Copolymers of 2-(2-cyanoethylamino)ethyl acrylate or methacrylate (made from NCCH$_2$CH$_2$Az) and other acrylic esters	Those of latex lacquers	Adhesion	2502
AzH + ethylene–acrylic acid copolymer	Epoxides	—	4047
PEI	Ethylene oxide + a β-keto ester	—	1871
PEI	Vinyl chloride copolymers	—[a]	1354
PEI and polyhalophenols	Oil or latex paint	Antimicrobial	2629
PEI salt	Silica in aqueous dispersion	Cellophane coating	894
RCOAz polymers	Water-base paint	Thickener	67

[a] In corrosion-resistant paints, to improve elasticity, adhesion, and resistance to heat, acids, alkalies, and organic solvents, but the paints so modified have reduced pot life and poorer resistance to water and to yellowing.

By contrast, commercial application of aziridine derivatives, at least PEI, as priming coats to improve adhesion of finishing coatings dates back to World War II, when in Germany cellophane was made moisture-resistant by such a priming coat and then a barrier coating based on cellulose nitrate (*3302*). It is believed that some such uses of PEI are current, though not publicized. They are detailed in the patents summarized in Table 5-XVIII.

Table 5-XVIII

USE OF AZIRIDINES IN PRIMING COATINGS

Aziridine used	Substrate coated	Finishing coat	References
Y(NHCOAz)$_2$	Glass fibers	Poly(vinyl chloride)	*2882*
TEM	Cellophane	Various	*484*
TEM	Cellophane	Copolymers of CH$_2$=CHCl + CH$_2$=CCl$_2$ + maleic anhydride	*3565*
TEM	Fabric	Pressure-sensitive adhesive, as of rubber	*2277*
APO	Poly(ethylene terephthalate) film	Polyolefin	*1705*
PEI	Cellophane	Cellulose nitrate	*485, 2029, 3302*
PEI	Cellophane	Poly(vinyl chloride)	*612a, 2029*
PEI	Cellophane	Various	*1282, 2577a*
PEI	Cellophane	Vinylidene chloride copolymers	*482, 487, 2577a*
PEI	Cellophane	Polyethylene	*483*
PEI	Paper	Polyolefin	*1803*
PEI	Rayon fibers	Poly(vinyl chloride)	*745*
PEI	Rayon fibers	Various vinyl polymers	*2011*
PEI	Polyolefin film	Poly(vinylidene chloride)	*947*
PEI	Irradiated polyolefin film	Printing ink (printed designs)	*1508a*
PEI	Polyolefin film	Epoxy resin + vinyl polymer	*2603*
PEI	Oxidized polyolefin film	Cellulose nitrate or a polyamide	*1469*
PEI	Oxidized polyolefin film	Various	*3863*
PEI	Irradiated polyolefin film	(Meth)acrylic acid–(meth)-acrylic ester copolymer	*2584*
Polymerized APO	Cellophane	Various	*2257*
PEI + long-chain alkylating or acylating agent	Cellophane	Various	*3791*

Table 5-XVIII—*continued*

Aziridine used	Substrate coated	Finishing coat	References
PEI + long-chain alkylating or acylating agent	Glass	A Ti compound, to increase scratch resistance	886
PEI + a surfactant to prevent blocking	Various	Various	2037
PEI–aldehyde reaction product	Glass	Cellulose nitrate	1577
PEI–epoxy resin reaction product	Polyolefin	Vinyl copolymer	2604
PEI–RNCO reaction product	Fabric or film?	Pressure-sensitive adhesive	3197
PEI modified with urea and HCHO	Cellophane	Various	3829, 3830, 3832
PEI modified with urea and HCHO	Cellophane	For lithographic plates	3831
PEI salt with a polyacid	A water-resistant sheet	For lithographic plates	3750a
PEI and a gelatin solvent	A gelatin-coated plate	For lithography	1020c
PEI	Fibers	Binder to make non-woven fabrics	677a

Nearly all are concerned with PEI, and with coatings on plastic films to improve water resistance.

Aminopropylation of carboxyl groups in an acrylate–methacrylate–methacrylic acid copolymer with 2-methylaziridine makes it a much better dispersant for pigments, especially carbon black (*2889*).

Uses of Aziridines in Photography

The first application of aziridines to photographic technology to be mentioned might equally well have been noted in the section on coatings. In applying gelatin emulsions to a film base, TEM (*1366*) or PEI (*3078*) can be used as an anchor coat or priming coat.

Replacement of gelatin in silver halide emulsions by hydrophilic colloids such as PEI has been mainly of theoretical interest. PEI so used permits much less grain growth than poly[3-(1-aziridinyl)propionic acid] (*1087*). Polymers of 1-acetoacetylaziridine have been suggested as gelatin extenders (*2001*), and a more recent patent claims emulsions based on PEI and a gelling agent such as poly(vinyl alcohol) (*2567*). Addition of PEI to silver halide emulsions can so modify grain growth as to increase sensitivity (*1087*), but there are many other commoner ways to accomplish this. In particular, sensitization with gold and sulfur is enhanced by amines such as PEI (*1088, 2738*) or $AzCH_2CH_2CO_2Me$ (*1370*). Alternatively, in film that is already high-speed, fogging tendency is reduced by incorporation of polymers of TEM in the emulsion (*1368*). Compounds still containing an aziridine ring are also fog inhibitors (*1369*).

Lateral diffusion of dyes in the gelatin or other sensitized layer can be a problem in color photography. As in textile chemistry, the presence of an aziridine derivative minimizes such migration. Cited for such use have been PEI (*23, 995, 1913, 3081*) or products of its modification with diketene (*1995, 2001*) or urea (*3680*), as well as $COAz_2$, TEM, or APO (*383, 2143*). Combination of a dye component and an aziridinyl group to yield reactive dyes has been claimed (*1367, 2030*) as well as precombination of one of the color-forming compounds with PEI (*1863*).

Developer pastes can contain PEI as thickener and complexing agent, but many other amines can serve also (*1369a, 2259–2261*). In contact printing by diffusion of silver halide from a developed but not fixed emulsion to a print sheet, the number of copies obtainable is increased by having PEI in the print sheet to aid in the transfer (*1462, 3681*). Developer molecules themselves can be made less likely to undergo excess diffusion and cause fogging, by incorporating aziridinyl groups in them, as in 2,5-bis(1-aziridinyl)hydroquinone (*1913a, 1914*), or by attaching 3-(2,5-dihydroxyphenyl)propionyl groups to PEI to yield hydroquinone-type redox polymers (*3504, 3505*).

A well-known problem in the developing and fixing of photographic films, especially under tropical conditions where water temperatures are relatively high, is the mechanical weakness of the gelatin emulsion. Among the various hardeners used to overcome this difficulty [see a review (*3195*)], aziridines are often mentioned. Here compounds with intact but activated aziridine rings are usually used, to crosslink and cure the gelatin. Many such are claimed: $Cl(CH_2)_nNHCOAz$ (*546*), $HSCH_2CH_2Az$ (*1020a*), $ROCH_2NHCOAz$ (*1462a*), $RCONHCOAz$ (*702*), and $Y(NHCOAz)_2$ types (*3322*), $Q(CHRAz)_n$ (*1020b*), aliphatic compounds containing aziridinyl and other reactive functions (*1292*), $ArN=CAz_2$ (*1719*), TEM and similar triazines (*60, 1291, 3322, 3861*), APO and the like (*1291, 1461*), aziridinyl derivatives of $(PNCl_2)_3$ and $(PNCl_2)_4$ (*543*), $Y(SO_2Az)_2$ (*544*), $Q(N=PAz_3)_n$ (*4044*), and $PhSiAz_3$ (*1291*). Of ring-opened aziridine derivatives are mentioned $CO(NHCH_2CH_2Cl)_2$ (*545*), maleic acid–PEI condensation products (*1460*), PEI modified with pendant $COC_6H_4SO_3H$ groups (*1616*) or triazinol rings (*4136*), and a quaternized PEI bearing hydroxyalkyl and acid groups on nitrogen atoms (*2138a*).

Of interest in thermographic rather than photographic processes is that heat-sensitive copy sheets containing a noble metal soap and a reducing agent can be stabilized with activated aziridines, $Q(COAz)_n$ or $Q(O_2CAz)_n$ (*1519*).

Aziridine Derivatives as Surface-Active Agents

Without exception the claimed uses of aziridine derivatives as detergents, emulsifiers, and the like involve polymerized forms, wherein the polyamine chain serves as the hydrophilic part of the molecule. It is doubtful that poly-ethylenimines modified to contain a hydrophobic moiety have any advantage over the polyethylenepolyamines more frequently so modified, and that PEI derivatives have attained any commercial use as surfactants in this sense. This is not true for flocculation, which is discussed later in this section.

A group of patents, mostly old, claim modification of PEI with alkylating and/or acylating agents, including some long-chain ones (*209, 911, 1838, 1840, 1853, 2879, 3649, 3657*). Alternatively surface-active forms of PEI can be obtained by performing the polymerization in the presence of an alkylating agent (*1873*), a long-chain amine (*184, 1219*), or other active-hydrogen com-pound (*388, 3561*). Similar general claims for surface activity are made for the following products: EI–propylene oxide copolymers modified with hydro-phobic groups (*2779*); polymers of $Az(CH_2O)_nH$, when $n = 1$ or more (*3626*); aziridine–aldehyde copolymers (*2434a*); C-alkylpyrrolidines (from aziridines + higher olefins) converted to N-oxides (*1332*); and N-perfluoroacyl–PEI (*3519*). A germicidal detergent composition is formulated from a conventional surfactant, plain or modified PEI, and a heavy metal salt of 2-pyridinethiol 1-oxide (*2926b*), and a shampoo composition promoting wave set retention contains PEI with detergents (*2263a*).

The cationic nature of PEI derivatives gives them value in breaking emul-sions. Polyethylenimine slightly crosslinked with epichlorohydrin breaks oil-in-water emulsions (*1177*). Petroleum emulsions may also be destroyed with conventional breakers that have been made more cationic by treatment with EI (*870–877, 912*). Also of interest in petroleum production is the use of EI-based surfactants in water-flooding operations for secondary oil recovery (*917a, 2722*), in fluids for fracturing underground formations (*917a*), and in the prevention of scale formation or its removal from equipment by treatment with a modified but water-soluble form of PEI or poly(2-methylaziridine) (*917, 917a*). Modified forms of PEI of widely various types are claimed as foam suppressors (*915*), emulsifiers in drilling muds (*4040*), and as emulsion breakers and corrosion inhibitors (*916*).

Emulsification can also be promoted with cationic agents derived from PEI. Silica coated with PEI stabilizes oil-in-water dispersions (*949*) and aqueous suspensions of drugs (*1153*), and bituminous emulsions normally made with an anionic dispersant are improved with derivatives of PEI (*600, 913*). So also are washing and polishing compositions (*3700a*). Water-insoluble materials may be encapsulated in aqueous PEI by using a polymeric acid as coagulant (*2677a*).

Flocculation is a special manifestation of surface chemistry in which a dispersion of a solid in a liquid is destabilized and destroyed. The mechanisms are complex and still little understood, but when polymeric flocculants are used, both neutralization of ionic charge and mechanical entanglement of suspended particles are probably involved.

Charge neutralization was stressed in studies of the mutual precipitation of PEI and polymeric acids; pectins, agar, carrageenin, polyacrylic acid, and clay minerals were all thus flocculated (*887*). The process was suggested for clarification of fruit juices by precipitation of the pectins with PEI, with some concomitant removal of tannins (*233, 886*). Starch made cationic by amino-ethylation with EI has similar flocculating effect on organic polymeric acids and acidic minerals (*754, 2072*), as does aminoethylated guar gum (*2718*). This reaction is applied to the concentration of potash ores by flotation with polymeric acids, PEI being added to precipitate the latter (*3814a*). Floccula-tion of silica suspensions with PEI and/or aluminum perchlorate was measured by filtration time and correlated with ζ-potential; more flocculant was required to produce zero potential at pH 6.8 than at 5.0, and PEI was better than aluminum perchlorate or combinations of the two (*2036*). When proper precautions are taken, filtration time is a good measure of flocculation efficiency (*924*). However, PEI was less effective (in terms of concentration required) than several polyacrylamides or guar gum (*2035*). Patents claim the use of PEI or like cationic polymers to help remove alkali fluorosilicates from phosphate solutions (*1179*), suspended material from aqueous titanium sulfate (*2268a*) and sodium sulfoethylmethacrylate (*957*), and flue-dust ferric oxide from its suspensions (*3848*), and to improve the structure of soils (*2478, 2646*). The filterability of synthetic rubber latex coagulums, which may contain silica filler, can be similarly improved (*944, 2338, 3757*). An adduct of cellulose, propylene oxide, and an aziridine is claimed to be especially good for flocculations at high temperatures and pH about 7 (*1699*).

The principal application of PEI as a flocculant, however, is in the field of water purification and sewage disposal, where some commercial use is current. Both clarification of water and improvement of sewage sludge dewatering have been claimed. Any polymeric flocculant of this type, because of its cost, must be extremely effective in low concentration in order to compete with the alum or ferric salt conventionally used in coagulation processes. Polyethylenimine may be used alone (being made particularly for use as a flocculant) (*178, 952, 1009, 1304, 1413, 1414, 1485, 2924, 3757, 3807*) or along with a floc-weighting agent such as powdered iron ore (*378*), an anionic filter bed (*1547, 2649b*), or an anionic co-flocculant such as sodium poly(styrenesulfonate) (*944, 956, 2925*). The PEI may be chemically modified before use, as by quaternization (which makes it more chlorine-resistant (*841a, b, c*), grafting acrylamide units to the chain (*601*), or reaction with urea (*227*); EI–fluorinated olefin copolymers are similarly effective (*3545*). The addition of PEI or other cationic polyelectrolyte to the aeration tank in a laboratory model of the activated sludge process caused good flocculation of bacterial cells (*923a*) but, perhaps for this reason, retarded the digestion process (*3860, 4172*). The coagulum of paper fibers produced by treating waste water with polymers derived from *C*-alkylated aziridines and urea may be collected in a foam layer instead of a precipitate (*1267*).

It is presumably a surface effect that makes hydration of light soda ash easier in the presence of a little PEI (*3446*).

Aziridine Derivatives in Fuels

While the flame velocity (*1467a*) and ignitability (*562*) for EI burning in air are not exceptional, its ring-strain energy makes it an attractive component of high-energy fuels. These are commonly made up of one or more oxidizing and one or more oxidizable components. Liquid rocket fuels that undergo hypergolic (spontaneous) ignition can consist largely of EI, the oxidant being fuming nitric acid (*548, 2774*), or EI may be used simply as an additive to increase the specific impulse of the fuel (*2775, 2776*) or its sensitivity to ignition (*307*). 1-Aminoaziridine also has a high theoretical specific impulse (*1511, 1513, 1765*), as does the still more exotic 1,1′-biaziridine, Az–Az (*1510, 1512*). Ethylenimine can be used to form a complex with decaborane from mixtures of boranes (*2421*), but other amines are probably more suitable.

In the solid-fuel field, aziridine polymers may serve as the oxidizable component; salts of PEI with nitric and/or perchloric acid belong in this field (*3043*), as do the similar salts of poly{1-aminoaziridine) (*1712*), and mixtures of the polymer–decaborane complex with oxidants (*1711*). Solid fuels in which an aziridine acts as part of the binder are mentioned in the section on plastics (p. 368). A solid fuel from a diepoxide, triethylenetetramine, and *N,N′*-*m*-tolylenebis(1-aziridinecarboxamide), m-$C_6H_4(NHCOAz)_2$, can be formulated so as to leave most of the aziridine rings intact to contribute energy during the oxidation with nitric acid–dinitrogen tetroxide (lithergolic fuels for rockets) (*1063a*).

The only use of PEI in ordinary liquid fuels such as gasoline is as its salt with diesters of sulfo diacids, e.g., $HO_3SCH(CO_2R)CH_2CO_2R$; such a salt is effective, but not unique, in its ability to increase conductivity and thus reduce hazards from static electricity generated by pumping the fuel (*3674a, 3675*).

Polyethylenimine or a like polyamine modified with a long-chain alkyl-succinic anhydride is claimed to prevent carbon deposition in cracking of hydrocarbons (*2350*).

Use of Aziridine Derivatives in Lubricants

Of the thousands of additives that have been claimed to improve the properties of petroleum-based lubricating oils, only one small group contains the aziridine ring, and only a few are derivatives of PEI. Indeed, PEI, being highly polar, is not even soluble in such oils unless modified in some way with oleophilic groups.

Many additives, especially those designed to improve extreme-pressure service, contain halogen, sulfur, or phosphorus. The aziridines that have been claimed to increase load-bearing properties are 1,3-diaryl-2,2-dihaloaziridines (*3104*). An old patent (*327*) reports water-soluble products from EI and a thiol such as 1,6-hexanedithiol as anticorrosion and antisludging agents. Less specific, since other bases can serve instead of PEI, are claims for additives made by combining stilbene and phosphorus pentasulfide, then PEI (*189*), alkylhydroxyphenyl sulfides partly esterified with fatty acids and then neutralized with PEI (*204*), acids of phosphorus heated with excess 2-methylaziridine or 2-ethylaziridine (*9*), chlorinated polyisobutylene + PEI (*3228a*), and chlorinated polythio acids or esters modified with PEI (*212*). Antioxidants are formed by ring-opening addition of benzyl mercaptan to EI and condensation of the product with a phosphoric acid derivative, optionally with reductive debenzylation afterward (*819*).

Similar additives have been made from organic hydroxy acids and excess of a simple aziridine (*18*), fatty or naphthenic acids and PEI (*911*), an alkylsalicylic acid and PEI (*3676*), vinyl polymers containing carboxyl groups and a polymeric aziridine (*3048, 3677*), an epoxide, thiirane, or phenol ($\geq C_{10}$) and a polymeric aziridine (*3678*), an alkylphenol, formaldehyde, and PEI (*3691*) and condensation products of PEI and substituted succinic acids (*2350a*). Pour-point depressants are producible by making PEI with a long-chain alkyl end-group (*1750*) or modifying such a polymer with dibasic acids to form polyamides (*604a, 1752*), or by simply acylating PEI with, e.g., coconut oil fatty acids (*1751*).

Two other applications of aziridines in lubricants, while wholly different from those just discussed, will be mentioned. In sausage manufacturing, a cellulosic casing may be stuffed with meat and then the casing removed; but adhesion of sausage to the casing can cause difficulties. This can be prevented by coating the casing with a hydrophobic layer, as of *N*-octadecylethylenimine, the aziridine ring evidently serving to anchor the coating (*3760*). The lubrication of textile yarns to minimize damage by friction during weaving, known as warp sizing, is improved by the use of aminoethylated starch (from EI + starch) (2345, 2762).

Miscellaneous Minor Nonbiological Uses of Aziridines

Small amounts of PEI in baths used for the electrorefining of zinc or copper improve the density of the deposited metals, alone (2944) or along with amine oxides (3077). In metal pickling the same additive is an inhibitor yielding unusually smooth (180) and bright (3058a, 3141) surfaces. Deactivation of trace metal ions that catalyze the autooxidation of fats and oils, lubricants, rubber, gasoline, and other olefinic compounds can be accomplished with the product of condensing a salicylaldehyde with an aziridine having no 1-substituent (667), or with an aziridine–1,2-ethanedithiol reaction product (2489a). Related is the claimed use of Schiff bases from salicylaldehydes and $PhSCH_2CH_2NH_2$ (easily made from EI) as soil-bonding agents (2619) (see discussion of chelating ion-exchange resins on p. 376). Other EI-based chelating agents described are $S[CH_2CH_2N(CH_2CO_2H)_2]_2$ (3306), carboxymethylated reaction products of diethanolamine and EI (2177), poly(1-aziridinylacetic acid) [indirectly made (1532)], and poly[2-(1-aziridinyl)ethylphosphonic acid] (also made by polymerization of the ester, then hydrolysis) (1156). Polyethylenimine or carboxymethylated PEI, among other agents, can prevent exchange of sodium ions for calcium ions, with consequent swelling, in sausage casings made of calcium alginate (2341). Probably the corrosion-inhibiting effect of EI on steel (108, 240) is related to chelation. Polyethylenimine and a variety of alkylated and acylated forms of it have likewise been mentioned in patents as chelating agents (233, 911, 4106, 4188) and corrosion inhibitors for ferrous metals (914, 3805), and PEI mixed with hydroxylamine salts is good for cleaning metal chalcogenide deposits from metal surfaces (2630).

2-(3,5-Di-tert-butyl-4-hydroxybenzylamino)ethanethiol, made from the appropriate aziridine and hydrogen sulfide, and its derivatives are claimed as stabilizers of fuel against oxidation; presumably they function as both metal deactivators and conventional phenolic inhibitors (513).

Among the many claimed stabilizers for halogenated solvents are to be noted those containing various aziridines and derivatives, for 1,1,1-trichloroethane (379, 961, 1591, 2309, 2888), 1,2-dichloroethane (661), and tri- and tetrachloroethylenes (1584, 1591, 2309, 3332).

In a few cases aziridines provide useful synthetic pathways to nonnitrogenous compounds. The reduction of 1-acylaziridines with lithium aluminum hydride produces excellent yields of aldehydes corresponding to the acyl group (502–504, 509, 843, 2674, 3809, 3810, 3901). Spiro imidazolinium salts made from a spiro aziridine and a nitrile, when they contain a benzyl group on the onium nitrogen, have been suggested as benzylating agents for phenols (*2293*).

The reaction of lignin with EI yields a nitrogenous product of value as a fertilizer for plant growth (*940*); but this would be an expensive way to supply soil nitrogen. Similarly the regeneration or partial purification of spent caustic from hydrocarbon sweetening operations by treatment with an alkylenimine (*2481*) appears to be out of the question on a cost basis.

In the study of protein structure by hydrolytic degradation, EI is useful as a preliminary treatment to block mercapto groups (*574, 1548, 1753a, 2007, 2307, 2962, 3069, 3490a, 3633, 3787a, 4045, 4078, 4166*).

Both PEI and poly(2-methylaziridine), each of low molecular weight, have been found very efficient as liquid phases in gas–liquid chromatography for separating amines (*1539, 3300*).

BIOLOGICAL PROPERTIES AND USES OF AZIRIDINES

Introduction

Compounds containing the aziridine ring have profound effects on living cells, whereas the polymeric products, particularly PEI, produce no dramatic results. Although aziridines have some specific effects, they (and their usual precursors, the nitrogen mustards) usually cause much the same kind of changes as other powerful alkylating agents, such as esters of sulfuric and sulfonic acids, epoxides, and propiolactone. It is therefore usual to classify and discuss the aziridines as biological alkylating agents, which have been well reviewed (*43, 508, 744, 1641, 3068, 3776*). Because of the similarity in the effects of these substances to those of ionizing radiation, they have been called "radiomimetic" drugs. However, the term is then somewhat misapplied (*2346*); moreover it is fairly clear that the nonactivated aziridines, EI having been the chief one studied, are not typical biological alkylating agents in the same way that the activated ones (tepa, thiotepa, tretamine, etc.) are.

To quote from one of the reviews (*1641*) of this subject: "Information gathered during the Second World War on the chemistry, biochemistry, pharmacology, and pathology of the alkylating agents led to the proposal that some of them be used in the treatment of cancer. Their success as palliative therapeutic agents led, in turn, to more detailed studies. Investigations of the mutagenic action of alkylating agents apparently was the independent result of academic exploration of external factors that influence heredity. Study of the carcinogenic action of alkylating agents may have followed from theoretical considerations about the relationship between mutagenic and carcinogenic action. The compounds were at one time considered in the search for anti-fertility substances for man and are now being studied actively as chemo-sterilants for insects."

The question of mechanism of action has been of much interest: What do these alkylating agents alkylate to produce their effects? It is reasonably certain that nucleic acids, DNA and RNA, are sites of attack (e.g., *678, 936b, 2194, 2194a, 2278a, 2923a, 4212*), but enzymes, their cofactors, and other cellular components may be involved also; and alkylating agents do not all act alike. Frequently polyfunctional agents such as tepa or tretamine are found to have much greater effect than the same amount of the same function administered in monofunctional form. This suggests a crosslinking effect; but there are many exceptions. Thus knowledge of these processes remains grossly incomplete.

At the cellular level, three levels of effect may be distinguished (*3068*). In the mildest, cell division is delayed or prevented (cytostatic effect). Larger doses induce the formation of cells with altered genetic propeties (mutagenic effect), and still larger amounts cause death of the cell (cytotoxic effect). Unfortunately, these effects cannot be correlated well with many of the uses of aziridines to be discussed in this chapter; in particular it is not clear how far the antitumor properties of aziridines depend on cytostatic action rather than cytotoxic action.

Only a few examples of purely cytostatic action of aziridines have been clearly established; usually the influence cannot be limited to the stopping of cell division. Mitosis is inhibited by EI in *Escherichia coli* (*2347*) and phages of *E. coli* (*425*); by various 1-aziridinyl-substituted benzoquinones in *Neurospora crassa* (*2983*), *Microsporum canis* (*372*), wheat root (*749*), garlic root (*3617, 3621*), and chick fibroblast (*3028*) and tumor cell H. Ep. 2 (*4129*) tissue culture; by $CH_2{=}CHCHOHCH_2Az$ in *Neurospora* (*2982*), garlic (*905*), and fibroblast culture (*1346*); by $(AzCONH)_2(CH_2)_6$ and apholate in coccinellid insect larvae (*3289*); by tepa in wheat root (*749*) and onion and pea (*3617, 3618*); by AzAc in broad bean (*2743*); by thiotepa in cereal grains (*3268*); by tretamine in *E. coli* (*2050, 2347*), the yeast *Saccharomyces cerevisiae* (*2347*), several other yeasts (*2176*), wheat (*906*), white lupine (*764*), broad bean (*524, 2743*), sea urchin eggs (*763*), and rat intestine (*1347*); and by mitomycin C or porfiromycin in HeLa cells (*2390*), *S. cerevisiae* (*3799*), and garlic root (*3620*). *E. coli* phages are quite sensitive to some aziridines (*425*).

Mutagenic Effects of Aziridines

Of the many mutagenic chemicals, it has already been noted that the aziridines, which are very active, are considered to exert their effects by alkylating some part or parts of the nucleic acid structures involved in cell replication. They are among the so-called "radiomimetic" chemicals, but the spectrum of effects, such as the ratio of chromosome breaks to "gene" mutations, usually differs from that caused by high-energy radiation. General reviews of chemical mutagenesis are available (*159, 160, 2278, 2346, 2974, 2977, 3051, 3098*); one covers aziridines only (*286a*).

Table 6-I

AZIRIDINES INDUCING MUTATIONS IN MICROORGANISMS

Organism	Aziridine	Special effects	References
Coliphage T2	2,5-Az$_2$-3,6-(MeOCH$_2$CH$_2$O)$_2$-1,4-benzoquinone	—	869
Bacteriophage T4B	Tepa, metepa, apholate	—	977
Bacillus brevis GB	EI	Auxotrophic forms, etc.	2213a, 2354
B. megaterium	Tretamine	Phage formation, etc.	2363, 2719, 2720
B. megaterium	Az$_3$-1,4-benzoquinone, tretamine, mitomycin C	Lysinogenesis, etc.	2434
B. mesentericus	EI	—	2353a
Azotobacter suis	EI	—	2857a, 3046
Micrococcus lysodeiktikus	Various phosphorylated aziridines	Phage formation	3843
Streptococcus lactis	EI	Antagonism to *Bacterium dysenteriae*	3408
S. acetonicus	EI	Better yield of biacetyl	1538, 4065
Staphylococcus aureus	Thiotepa and other phosphorylated aziridines	Changes in nucleic acid synthesis	3844
Propionibacterium schermani	EI	Better yield of vitamin B$_{12}$	3707
Escherichia coli	Aziridinium form of N mustard	—	918
E. coli	Tepa, metepa, apholate	—	977
E. coli	2,5-Az$_2$-1,4-benzoquinone, tetramine	Morphology and streptomycin dependence	1940, 2485, 3374, 3453
E. coli	EI and eight of its derivatives	Streptomycin dependence	2857a, 3454
E. coli	Mitomycin C	Production of colicin	1886
E. coli	Mitomycin C	Phage formation, etc.	2785, 3869a
Pseudomonas pyocyanea	Tretamine	Phage formation	2363
Actinomyces (*Streptomyces*) sp.	EI	Better yield of antibiotics	50–54, 285, 286, 1014. 1478, 3054, 3055, 3055a, 3235, 3880, 4053, 4065, 4197
Streptomyces griseus	EI (most potent) and many derivatives	Leucine dependence	287
Neurospora crassa	EI, tretamine	—	2125; cf. 649

Table 6-I—*continued*

Organism	Aziridine	Special effects	References
N. crassa	EI, tepa, metepa, apholate	—	*2040, 3774*
Penicillium sp.	EI	Better yield of penicillins, etc.	*48, 49, 3053*
Aspergillus sp.	EI	Better yield of amylolytic enzymes or citric acid	*1446, 1522, 1535, 1900, 2166, 2166a*
Claviceps paspali	EI	Lysergic acid derivatives produced	*3102*
Schizosaccharomyces pombe	EI and many others	—	*1708, 4076*
Chlorella sp.	EI	Pigment formation	*91, 2079*
Paramecium aurelia	Aziridinium form of N mustard	—	*2918*
P. aurelia	Tretamine	—	*2086*
Trichothecium roseum	EI	Better yield of trichothecin	*2408*
Fusarium moniliforme	EI	Better yield of gibberellin	*1064*

Ethylenimine itself has been used much more than any of its derivatives as a mutagen. Indeed, it is one of the commonest reagents used by the geneticist to induce mutations. Some such work is of purely scientific interest; other studies have as a goal the development of improved organisms for human use.

Table 6-II

AZIRIDINES INDUCING MUTATIONS IN PLANTS

Plant	Aziridine	Results[a]	References
80 species, various	EI	A, D	*3892*
Pine	EI	A	*3849*
Barley	EI	A, B, D, F	*31, 103, 136, 137, 161a, 1029, 1030, 1031, 1059, 1558, 1638, 1696, 1709, 1710, 2130, 2357, 2375, 2575, 2679a, 3067, 3214, 3673, 3888, 4121, 4131, 4137, 4180*
Barley	Metepa	—	*3840a*
Barley	2-Et-2-PhAzH	A, B	*438*
Corn	EI	A, E	*396, 2375, 2376, 2376a*

Table 6–II—*continued*

Plant	Aziridine	Results[a]	References
Oats	EI	A	3730, 4201
Rice	EI	A, B	2053, 3845
Rye	EI	A	3888a
Rye	Thiotepa	C	3268
Wheat	EI	A, B, D, E	875, 1023, 1034, 1035, 1499, 1781, 2080, 2167, 2168, 2632, 3091a, 3221, 3249–3251, 3893–3897, 3899, 4119, 4121
Wheat	2,3,5-Az$_3$-1,4-benzo-quinone	A, F	751
Wheat	Thiotepa	C	2053
Wheat	2,5-Az$_2$-3,6-(PrO)$_2$-1,4-benzoquinone, tretamine, mitomycin C	F	750
Canary grass	EI	A, B	474
Onion	EI, 2-Az-4,6-(MeO)$_2$-s-triazine, tretamine	F	371
Flax	EI	—	3217
Paris and *Trillium* sp.	Thiotepa, mitomycin C	—	2479, 2480, 3491a
Arabidopsis thaliana (a crucifer)	EI	A, B	2505
Lentil	EI	—	3495
Chick-pea	EI	B	2375a
Pea	EI	A, B, D, E, F	32, 385–387, 1060, 1500, 3215, 3216, 3258, 3259, 3898, 4121
Pea	1-Az-piperidine, (AzCH$_2$)$_3$N	A, E	3898
Pea	EI and several derivatives	A, B, E	2136
Pea	Tepa	F, G	1500
Soy bean	EI	D	1059
Broad bean and other vetches	EI	A, B, D, G	263, 920, 1464, 2392, 2433a, 2969, 2969a, b, 3273a, 3870, 4041
Broad bean and other vetches	Tretamine	F	135, 1361, 2543, 2544, 2742, 2994, 4113
Broad bean and other vetches	Mitomycin C	F	2533
Cotton	EI	A, E	1881
Cucumber	EI	A	3551a
Jute	EI	A	437
Potato	EI	A, F	3494, 3496, 3497
Tomato	EI	A	291a, 1716, 2081

Table 6–II—*continued*

Plant	Aziridine	Results[a]	References
Tobacco	EI	A, B	*614, 3121a, 4160*
Tangiers pea	EI	F	*649b*
Lemon and orange	AzCH$_2$CH$_2$P(OEt)$_2$	A	*2068*
Chrysanthemum	EI	—	*456*
Lettuce	EI	A	*3551b*
Crepis capillaris	EI	A	*1004, 1005*
Hawks-beard	EI	F	*99, 3233a, 3252, 3257*
Wheat	Mitomycin C	F	*4029*
Love-in-a-mist and buckwheat	EI	A, C	*2894*

[a] *Results*—A = comparison with other mutagens made; B = chlorophyll mutations produced; C = effect decreased as ploidy increased; D = varietal differences in mutability observed; E = agronomic properties improved; F = effect on mitosis in roots studied; G = effect of mutagen blocked by thiols.

Table 6-III

Aziridines Inducing Mutations in Animals

Animal	Aziridine	References
Drosophila melanogaster	EI	*42, 582, 583, 2323a, 2399, 2880, 2975, 2976, 3747*
	2,5-Az$_2$-1,4-benzoquinone	*315, 1686, 1741, 2352, 2353, 3704*
	Tepa and relatives	*1290a, 1741, 2353*
	Tretamine	*1091, 1092, 1706, 1707, 3050, 3320*
	Mitomycin C	*2784*
A braconid wasp	Tepa	*2807*
Silkworm moth	EI	*2666*
Pleurodeles waltii eggs[a] (a salamander)	Tretamine	*3205*
Mouse	EI	*2409, 2710*
Mouse	Tepa, metepa, thiotepa	*1061a*
Mouse (bone marrow cells)[a]	Thiotepa	*141*
Mouse	Tretamine	*608, 610, 611, 858, 1061a*
Rat (bone marrow cells)[a]	Az$_2$P(O)N(CH$_2$CH$_2$)$_2$P(O)Az$_2$	*33*
Man (tissue culture cells)[a]	EI	*4021*
	Thiotepa	*1002, 1003, 1005a, 2808a*
	Mitomycin C	*2784*

[a] Genetic effect observed as chromosome breakage.

Microorganisms that give better yields of antibiotics and strains of crop plants having various advantages have been and are still thus sought. The applications of mutagens in plant breeding have been outlined (*1420*), and techniques for their use compared (*2840*).

Tables 6-I, 6-II, and 6-III present many references to the use of aziridines for inducing mutations. In Table 6-III, except as noted, the mutations were scored as sex-linked lethals or else as visible changes in the organism. The citation of the literature is very incomplete for work with *Drosophila*, since that is not considered applied genetics and in it the use of tretamine is quite common. Furthermore, the section on chemosterilization of insects (p. 407) should be compared, since that must often involve mutations to lethality. Whether EI is mutagenic in man is unknown (*78*).

Carcinogenic Effects of Aziridines

The tiny literature record on this subject has been reviewed (*3736, 3761*). Lung tumors have been induced in mice and rats by administration of tretamine (*3236, 3736*) and other aziridinyl compounds (*3237*), thymic tumors by 1-isopropyl-2-(2-naphthyl)aziridine (*1773*), leukemias by metepa (*1400*), various tumors in rats by tepa and apholate (*1573a*), and some sarcomas by use of EI (*909*), $(AzSO_2)_2(CH_2)_3$ (*3736*), and various simple 1-acylaziridines (*3735*), but there is no published evidence of tumor production in man by aziridines. Neither is there proof of connection between this limited carcinogenic action and the mutagenic activity of aziridines (*1641*).

Antimicrobial Effects

Ethylenimine and its simple homologs are too toxic for any use *in vivo* against protists (bacteria, amoebae, etc.), but have been repeatedly suggested for fumigative disinfection. The order of activity has been given as

$$AzCH_2CH_2NH_2 > EI > \text{ethylene oxide and ethylene sulfide}$$

(*2056, 2057, 2874*), and aziridines have been patented as germicides (*1463, 2495*); but they appear less practical as fumigants than ethylene oxide (*2874*), and dilution with carbon dioxide, while claimed (*1463*), is sure to destroy the active agent rapidly.

The claimed uses of aziridines of more complexity against protists are presented in Table 6-IV.

It is impossible to believe the old patented claim for varied uses of PEI as a disinfectant (*185*), but chlorophenols and EI give chlorophenyl 2-aminoethyl ethers good as germicides and fungicides (*404*). Similar claims are made

Table 6-IV

Use of Aziridines as Antiprotists[a]

Aziridinyl compound	Type of protist combated	References
Adducts of EI or 2-RAzH with bis(glycidyl ethers)	—	*941*
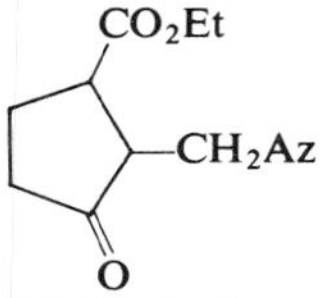 CO$_2$Et — CH$_2$Az (cyclopentanone structure)	Bacteria	*3416*
2,5-Az$_2$-hydroquinone	Amoebae, especially *Endamoeba histolytica*	*2453*
2,6-Az$_2$-*p*-benzoquinones and -hydroquinones	Amoebae	*1429*
2,5-(2-MeAz)$_2$-hydroquinone	Amoebae, bacteria	*2455*
2,6-Az$_2$- and (2-MeAz)$_2$-3,5-Z$_2$-*p*-benzoquinones (Z = Br, OEt, SEt)	Amoebae, bacteria	*2456*
2,6-Az$_2$-3,5-Z$_2$-hydroquinones (Z = halogen, OR, or SR)	Amoebae, bacteria	*705*
2,5-Az$_2$-3,6-(HO)$_2$-*p*-benzoquinone	Amoebae, bacteria	*2457*
2,5-Az$_2$-3,6-(RCONH)$_2$-*p*-benzoquinones	Amoebae, bacteria	*699, 708, 2454, 2458, 2459*
2,3,6-Az$_3$-*p*-benzoquinone and -hydroquinone	Amoebae, some bacteria	*879, 1429*
2,3,6-Az$_3$-5-RO-*p*-benzoquinones	Amoebae	*930*
2,5-Az$_2$-3,6-(RO)$_2$-*p*-benzoquinone	Anaerobic bacteria but few aerobic	*2173, 2174*
Various aziridinylbenzoquinones	Inactive against bacteria	*1640*
4-Az- and 4-(2-MeAz)-1,2-naphthoquinones	Amoebae	*3138*
MeO$_2$CCH$_2$CH$_2$COAz	Inactive against tuberculosis bacteria	*3201*
6-Az-demecolceine	Some activity against bacteria	*2513*
4,6-Az$_2$-2-(N$_2$CH)-*s*-triazine	Protozoa causing malaria	*1543*
Tretamine	*B. megaterium*[b]	*3154*
Tretamine	Protozoa causing malaria[c]	*74, 347, 1966, 3740*
Cl$_3$CSAz	*Staph. aureus, Salmonella typhosa*	*375*
Adducts of EI or 2-MeAzH with haloaryl isocyanates or isothiocyanates	Those causing blackhead in turkeys	*1295*
Adducts of AzCH$_2$CH$_2$CH$_2$OH and the like with ArNCS	Bacteria	*1589*
Cl$_3$C$_6$H$_2$OP(S)(OMe)Az	Bacteria	*3568*
Adducts of AzCO$_2$R and alcohols or acids	Bacteria	*1591, 1598*

Table 6-IV—*continued*

Aziridinyl compound	Type of protist combated	References
Haloaryl-OP(S)Az$_2$	Bacteria	*3569*
Thiotepa	Inactive against *Penicillium* spp.	*965*
Various	Inactive against *Agrobacterium* *tumefaciens*	*2420*

[a] The mitomycins are discussed separately.
[b] Nitriles have a protective effect against the drug.
[c] Drug reduced transmission of disease from chicks and by mosquitoes.

for "2-thiazolidinethione methiodide" (**1**), made from EI, carbon disulfide, and methyl iodide (*392*).

$$\text{HN}\diagdown\diagup\text{S} \quad \text{or} \quad \text{N}\diagdown\diagup\text{S}$$
$$\underset{\text{MeS}^+ \quad \text{I}^-}{} \qquad\qquad \underset{\text{Me}}{}$$

1

The products of ring opening of EI with hydrogen sulfide and thiols have been used in synthesis of compounds tested for inhibiting protist growth by antimetabolite activity, but these were not very effective (*275, 1480, 3181, 3203, 3786*).

A few acylated aziridines of type RNHP(O)Az$_2$ (*838, 2581*) and ROP(O)Az$_2$ (*837, 2582*) have antiviral properties, especially against encephalitis virus. Similar activity against some viruses is claimed for 1-(1-adamantyl)aziridine (*2835*). The effectiveness of TEM is increased by concurrent administration of a tetracycline antibiotic (*2869a*).

Among other inactivating agents, 1-acylaziridines, particularly 1-acetyl-aziridine, are effective in producing antigens from pathogenic bacteria and viruses (*499, 500, 1285, 1888, 1893, 2506, 3328*).

Fungicidal activity is described for Cl$_3$CSAz (*2459*), substituted 1-aziridine-carboxanilides and -thiocarboxanilides (*879*), haloalkyl-CR(OH)Az and –CR(OH)NH(CH$_2$)$_n$Az (*223*), Cl$_3$C$_6$H$_2$OP(S)(OMe)Az (*930*), haloaryl-OP(S)Az$_2$ (*2173*), *p*-ClC$_6$H$_4$CH$_2$SCOAz (*2732*), 2,6-(O$_2$N)$_2$-4-F$_3$CC$_6$H$_2$Az and homologs (*2203*), phenylhydrazine–EI reaction products (*1395*), and some steroidal aziridines (*4168, 4169*). However, some alkyl 3-(1-aziridinyl)-propionates were inactive (*3350*). The use of PEI along with a fungicidal ethylenebis(thiocarbamate) evidently helps in the application and adhesion of the active material on plants (*3049*).

The antibiotic and antitumor substances called mitomycins were discovered as products of growth of *Streptomyces caespitosus,* and mitomycin A (*1629*), mitomycin B (*1629*), and mitomycin C (*1507, 2104, 2221, 2224, 2230, 3727*) were obtained as pure compounds. Not long afterward porfiromycin was isolated from broth from cultures of *S. ardus* (*862, 1703, 3662*); and *S. griseovinaceus* (*2703*) and *S. verticillatus* (*411, 2284*) have been found also to produce these substances.

By a combination of chemical and physical methods, the mitomycins and porfiromycin were shown (*2530, 3378, 3635, 3672, 3716, 3726, 3748, 3749*) to be variant forms of the structure **2**,

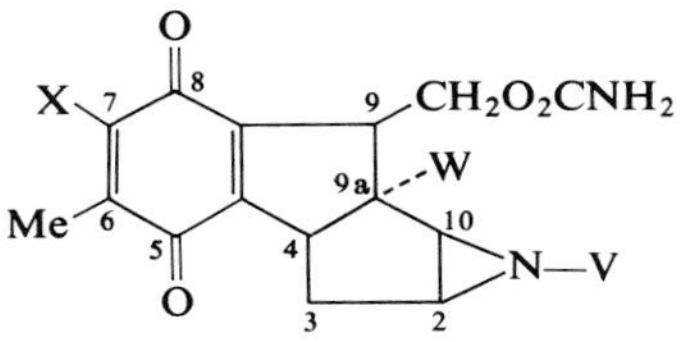

Mitosanes

2

called mitosanes for brevity. Assignment of the structures to the various mitomycins is shown in Table 6-V, to be read in conjunction with the general mitosane formula **2**.

Table 6-V

MITOSANES

	V	W	X
Mitomycin A	H	OMe	MeO
Mitomycin B	Me	OH	MeO
Mitomycin C	H	OMe	H_2N
Porfiromycin	Me	OMe	H_2N
N-Methylmitomycin A	Me	OMe	MeO

To be noted for present purposes is the hydrolytic behavior: in acid solution the aziridine ring is opened, whereas in alkaline solution replacement of X by OH takes place (*1415, 1416, 3173, 3664*). After such hydrolysis the hydroxyl group may be acylated (*2229*) or alkylated (*3173, 3665*) to produce new antibiotics. Similar solvolytic removal of the X group in mitomycin B yields the 7-amino (*2226*), 7-(substituted amino) (*2228, 4030*), or 7-(1-aziridinyl) (*2233, 4030*) analog, and mitomycin A produces similar derivatives (*2231, 2233, 4030*). Opening the aziridine ring in mitomycins with hydrogen fluoride (*2541*) or carboxylic anhydrides (*2219a*) also forms new bactericides.

Various alkylations and acylations of mitomycins A and C at the aziridine nitrogen atom are claimed for the same purpose (*2217, 2218, 2220, 2222, 2225, 2227, 2232, 2233, 2234, 2477a, 2530, 2540*). Still other variations are to cause reaction with thiols (*766*) or aldehydes (*765*), or hydrogenate and then oxidize with air, which introduces a double bond between carbons 9 and 9a with elimination of W (*766, 2219, 2829, 4143*), or to reduce with zinc and acetic anhydride in pyridine, which leads to structure **3** (*2223*).

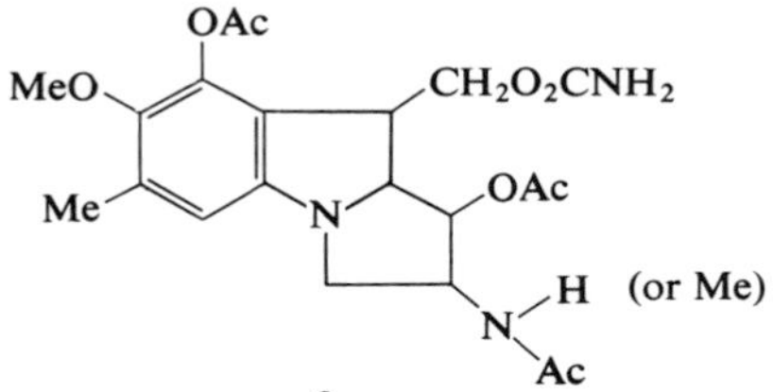

3

Mitomycin C and porfiromycin have some trypanocidal action *in vivo* (*1957a*).

In general all such modifications of the natural antibiotics are intended to improve their therapeutic value, by either increasing their bactericidal effects or decreasing their toxicities to the host. An approach in another direction, i.e., organic synthesis of simpler analogs, is represented by the preparation of many compounds of formula **4** (*63*; cf. *3026a*), including examples in which R^4 is Az or R^3 is CH_2O_2CAz.

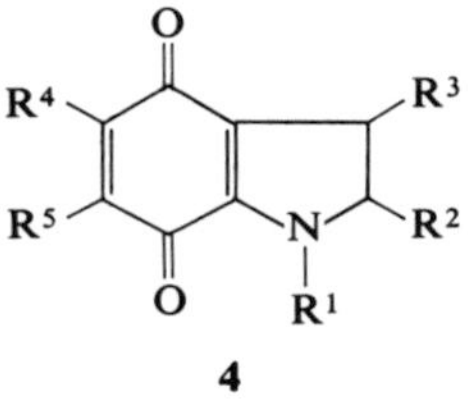

4

It is established that antibiotic activity in the mitomycins depends on the presence of the aziridine ring; the ring is apparently unmasked *in vivo* by reduction to a semiquinone stage (*2635, 3180*) and then may alkylate and crosslink DNA and inhibit its synthesis (*740, 2797*). Porfiromycin interferes with purine metabolism.

Of the thousands of chemically modified penicillins, only a very few have been made by the use of aziridines (*306, 1233, 2336, 2816*), and none of these are noteworthy. 1-Phenaceturoylaziridine-2-carboxylic acid, made as an analog of the penicillins, gives some of the color reactions but has only a little of the antibiotic activity of these drugs (*1684*).

The wide-spectrum antibiotic cycloserine, 4-amino-3-isoxazolidinone (**5**, R = H) (the natural one is the D form), is relatively simple in structure and may be prepared synthetically in a variety of ways. One of these involves aziridines as intermediates.

5

Methyl α-bromoacrylate (*1364*) or methyl 2,3-dibromopropionate (*2078, 3310*) may be treated with ammonia or an amine so as to produce an aziridine-2-carboxylic ester (see p. 34).

$$BrCH_2CHBrCO_2Me + RNH_2 \longrightarrow$$

This does not work for tritylamine, in which case the aziridine is made by *N*-tritylation and *O*-mesylation of serine methyl ester and subsequent ring closure with *N*-ethylpiperidine (*3311, 3315*).

$$HOCH_2CHNH_2CO_2Me \xrightarrow{Ph_3CCl,\ R_3N,\ MeSO_2Cl} MeSO_2OCH_2CH(NHCPh_3)CO_2Me$$

$$MeSO_2OCH_2CH(NHCPh_3)CO_2Me \xrightarrow{R_2NR'}$$

Treatment of the aziridinecarboxylic ester, N-substituted or not, with hydroxylamine yields the hydroxamic acid, which is then subjected to ring opening with hydrochloric acid (*1363, 1364, 2078, 3309, 3311, 3312, 3314*).

$$+ H_2NOH \longrightarrow$$

$$+ HCl \longrightarrow ClCH_2CH(NHR)CONHOH$$

When R is trityl, it is cleaved from the nitrogen atom in this step. Ring closure by base to the 3-isoxazolidinone derivative completes the synthesis (*3312, 3314*).

$$ClCH_2CH(NHR)CONHOH \xrightarrow{base} \mathbf{5}$$

Herbicidal and Insecticidal Effects

An old and very broad patent (*1864*) claims both aziridines and their polymers as general pesticides, but the polymers are definitely miscast as toxicants

Table 6-VI

USE OF AZIRIDINES AS PESTICIDES

Aziridine	Pest controlled	References
Polyhalophenol salts of aziridines	Weeds	*4099*
Polynitrophenol salts of aziridines	Weeds	*4100*
RNHCSAz (R = cyclooctyl)	Weeds	*223*
2-Cl$_3$C-4-Az-3,5,6-X$_3$-pyridine (at least 2 of the X = Cl)	Weeds, other pests	*2999*
3,4,5-Trichlorofuroyl-Az	Weeds, other pests	*2291*
CH$_2$=CHO(CH$_2$)$_n$CR$_2$NHCOAz (n = 1–7)	Insects	*2520*
RCOCH=CHAz and RCOCH$_2$CHAz$_2$	—	*216*
R$_2$NCHMeAz	Insects, rodents, nematodes	*2950*
RCOCH$_2$CH$_2$Az	—	*1080a*
RO$_2$CCH$_2$CH$_2$Az and homologs	Weeds, insects, nematodes	*1078*
(RO$_2$C)$_2$QCHR'Az	Weeds, insects, nematodes	*1076*
Haloalkyl-CR(OH)Az and -CR(OH)NH(CH$_2$)$_n$Az	Weeds, insects, nematodes	*1077*
(F$_3$C)$_2$C(OH)NHCH$_2$CH$_2$Az	—	*495a*
Tepa, thiotepa, ROPAz$_2$	Weeds	*2009*
Tepa	Grasses	*1754*
Tepa-Ph$_3$SnCl complex	Bacteria, weeds, mites, insects	*404a*
Thiotepa	Inactive against some common plants	*965*
AzP(O)–N(CH$_2$CH$_2$)$_2$N–P(O)Az$_2$ and homologs and analogs	Rodents	*83*
(RO)$_2$PAz and (RO)$_2$P(O)Az	Insects	*1523*
R$_2$P(S)Az	—	*1168*
(RO)$_2$P(S)SCHR'COAz	—	*3193*
Et(F)P(S)Az	Insects	*3164*
RO(RS)P(S)Az	Insects	*1120*
Halophenyl–OP(S)Az$_2$	Insects	*3569*
Halophenyl–OP(S)(OR)Az	Insects	*3568*
Adduct of ROPR'Az and an α-dicarbonyl compd. (R' = R or OR)	Insects	*377*
[(RO)$_2$P(O)]$_3$CSAz	Insects	*376*
Haloacyl-N=PAz$_3$	Weeds, insects	*515*
2-Pyrazinyl–OP(S)RR'	Insects	*2560, 2560a*
(R or R' or both = Az)		
3,6-Az$_2$-*s*-tetrazine	Weeds	*2359*

in themselves. They do have use in improving the persistence of copper ions intended to kill aquatic growths (*3517, 3518, 3545*) and the adherence of silica aerogel insecticides on animals (*890*). Ethylenimine itself has been studied as a fumigant against insects infesting stored products (*1611*), but many drawbacks are obvious.

Most aziridinyl-containing compounds claimed as pesticides contain also some other toxic function, so that it is difficult to tell which part of the molecule is effective. Table 6-VI presents a list of such compounds and references. Few if any of the claimed uses have become commercial.

A few compounds readily made by aziridine-ring opening remain to be noted. Ethylenimine with chlorophenols thus yields herbicidal 2-(aryloxy)-ethylamines (*404*), or with an *O,O*-dialkyl hydrogenphosphonothioate gives insecticidal $(RO)_2R(S)CH_2CH_2NH_2$ (*2213*). The reaction and products from alkyl 1-aziridinecarboxylates, $AzCO_2R$, and *O,O*-dialkyl dithiophosphates are similarly useful (*3369*). 2-(Benzylthio)ethylamine, from EI and α-toluene-thiol, with various phosphorus compounds yields pesticides (*819*). Alkyl 1-aziridinecarboxylates are ring-opened by carboxylic acids to alkyl carbamates, $R'CO_2CH_2CH_2NHCO_2R$, effective against the plum curculio (*2309*); ring opening with benzoyl chloride gives like products (*2308*). Carbon disulfide and EI readily yield thiazolidine-2-thione, which alone (*391*) or quaternized (*393*) is a defoliant and herbicide. Polymers of aziridinium tetraphenylborate have similar properties (*1058*). The product of reaction of EI and thiophenol, $PhSCH_2CH_2NH_2$, with substituted salicylaldehydes is converted into Schiff bases that are ascaricides, nematocides, and insecticides (*2619*). Substituted aziridines of the type $2,6-(O_2N)_2-4-F_3CC_6H_2Az$ can also be used to control nematodes and mites (*2203*).

Use of Aziridines as Sexual Chemosterilants

The reduction of insect population by production, in that population, of substantial numbers of sexually sterile individuals is still a relatively new technique of control compared to use of insecticides. The classic application of this has been the eradication of the screw-worm fly from the island of Curaçao and the southeastern United States by release of large numbers of irradiation-sterilized males. Such a method not only is superior on statistical grounds to the use of insecticides, but does not add any toxic substances to the environment. On the other hand, rearing and irradiating large numbers of insects is rarely practical, and substantial addition, even of sterilized individuals and on a temporary basis, to a pest population may be undesirable.

Chemosterilants have the same theoretical great mathematical advantage over insecticides, and if the other advantage, nonpollution of the environment, be sacrificed, the chemosterilants avoid the problem of rearing and sterilizing insects. They would simply be used instead of, or along with, insecticides.

Some requirements of a good chemosterilant are reasonably obvious. It should be effective at very low dosage, and preferably inactive on nonpest organisms; and its effects should be permanent. However, it should not decrease either the life span or the mating aggressiveness of the insect, and the ratio of lethal dose to sterilizing dose should be high. The compound should, of course, not be expensive.

The development and evaluation of chemosterilants is currently of great interest in applied entomology, and has been reviewed repeatedly in some detail (*154, 428, 431, 432, 569, 1953, 2116, 2238, 2327, 3290, 3291, 4104*). The present account is therefore largely devoted to a synopsis and tabulation of the work reported with aziridines.

Table 6-VII

AZIRIDINES ACTIVE AS INSECT CHEMOSTERILANTS

Insect species and mode of application[a]	References
Tepa	
Japanese beetle, T	*2250a*
Boll weevil, O	*4093*
Mosquitoes, T	*2496, 3756, 3837*
Eye gnat, O	*2644*
Olive fly, O	*2770*
Mexican fruit fly, OT	*633, 3219, 3837*
Housefly, OT	*343, 1380, 1503, 1505, 1506, 2243,*
	2515, 3086, 3087, 3837, 4017
Screw-worm fly, OT	*1505*
Stable fly, T	*1614*
The fly *Ophyra aenescens*, O	*3088*
Metepa	
Various insects	*3837*
Locust borer	*3825*
Mosquito, T	*2496*
Eye gnat, O	*2644*
Olive fly, O	*2770*
Housefly, O	*1503, 1505, 2237, 2978, 3837, 4017*
Screw-worm fly, OT	*618, 1505*
Blow fly, O	*2978*
Stable fly, T	*618, 1614*
Thiotepa	
Boll weevil, O	*4093*
Armyworm, O	*631*
Housefly, etc., O	*630, 2244, 3837, 3865c*
Screw-worm fly	*810*

Table 6-VII—*continued*

Insect species and mode of application[a]	References
$ArP(O)(2\text{-}MeAz)_2$	
Housefly, O	433, 818, 1380, 2237, 2242, 2884, 3837
$F_2P(O)Az$	
Housefly, O	2922
$ROP(O)Az_2$	
Housefly, O	433, 2242
$(RO)_2P(O)Az$, $(RO)_2P(S)Az$	
Boll weevil, O	4093
Housefly, O	433, 1380, 2959, 2960, 2978
$ROP(S)Az_2$, $RSP(S)Az_2$	
Various insects, OT	59a, 820, 1380, 1506, 4002
$(EtO)_2P(S)OCH_2CH_2Az$	
Housefly, O	1380
$RR'P(Y)Az$, wherein $R' = R$, RO, or Az	
Various insects	3368
$RNHP(O)Az_2$	
Housefly, O	433, 1380, 1506, 2242
$R_2NP(O)Az_2$, $R_2NP(S)Az_2$[b]	
Boll weevil, O	4093
Housefly, O	433, 629, 1380, 2243, 2244, 3865c
$RO_2CNHP(O)Az_2$	
Boll weevil, O	4093
Housefly, screw-worm fly, O	813, 1506, 2304
$RNHCONHP(O)Az_2$	
Boll weevil, O	4093
Housefly, screw-worm fly, O	2956, 2961, 2978, 4033
Apholate	
Green peach aphid, OT	1613
Cabbage maggot, O	3444
Onion maggot, O	2351
Silkworm moth, O	1722
Boll weevil[c]	2959
Black vine weevil, OT?	778
Honeybee, O	1989
Mexican bean beetle, O	588
Mosquitoes, T	1354a, 2496, 2644, 3756
Eye gnat, O	4167
Pomace fly, O	571, 4203
Housefly, OT	1503, 1505, 1609, 2243, 2515, 2978, 3039, 3086
Fruit fly, O	1691
Face fly, OT	1580, 1581
Stable fly, T	1614

Table 6-VII—*continued*

Insect species and mode of application[a]	References
Apholate Analogs	
Boll weevil, O	4093
Housefly, screw-worm fly, OT	604, 1505, 1506, 1380, 2242, 2789, 2790, 3039
Az_2SO, Az_2SO_2, Az_2S_2, and Homologs	
Various insects, O	427, 1380, 2821, 3835, 3836
Various $RCOAz$ and $Y(COAz)_2$	
Various insects, OT	1380, 1505, 2821, 3834
Various $RNHCOAz$ and $Y(NHCOAz)_2$	
Boll weevil, O	4093
Housefly, screw-worm fly, OT	254, 430, 816, 1380, 1434, 1505, 1506, 2978, 3040, 3082, 3283
Various $RN{=}CAz_2$ and $Y(N{=}CAz_2)_2$	
Various insects	2788
$MeSO_2Az$, Cl_3CSAz	
Housefly, O	2821
Az_2-pyrimidines	
Boll weevil	4093
Tretamine	
Boll weevil, O	4093
Housefly, O	810, 2242, 2244, 2884
Screw-worm fly, T[d]	1380, 2242
Various 2,5-Az_2-1,4-benzoquinones and Hydroquinones	
Boll weevil, O	4093
Housefly, O	1380, 2242
Various R_2NCOCH_2Az, $RNHCOCH_2Az$, and $Y(NHCOCH_2Az)_2$	
Boll weevil, O	4093
Housefly, O	1380, 2821, 3276, 3278, 3280
$Y(O_2CCH_2Az)_2$[e]	
Housefly, O	2242, 3279
Mitomycin C[e]	
Boll weevil, O	4093
Housefly, O	2805
Porfiromycin	
Housefly, O	1380, 2129
Mexican fruit fly, housefly, screw-worm fly, O	2743a, 3666a

[a] T = topical application (dipping, spotting, spraying, or exposure to residues); O = oral administration.

[b] Including aphamide.

[c] Males only.

[d] Activity increased by extraoptimal temperatures.

[e] Very little activity.

Table 6-VIII

COMPARISONS OF SELECTED AZIRIDINES AS INSECT CHEMOSTERILANTS

Insect species and mode of application[a]	Results Safety margin[b]	Vigor of males	References
Tepa			
German cockroach, O	Good	—	537
Pea aphid, O	Fair	—	366
Citrus red mite, T	Poor	Good	783
Fall armyworm, O	—	Good	3855
Corn earworm, armyworm, granulate cutworm, O	Good	—	3856
Carpenterworm, T	Fair	Good	3330
Cabbage looper, OT	Fair	Poor	1688, 1689, 1774, 1775
Gypsy moth, T	Good	Good	737, 738
Codling moth, T	—	Fair	1634; cf. 2618
Egyptian cotton leafworm, OT	Good	—	3577
Tobacco budworm, T	—	—	1303a
Red bollworm	—	Good	570
European corn borer, OT	Fair	Poor	4070
Boll weevil, OI	Poor[c]	—	1650
Plum curculio, T	Poor	—	3041
Banded cucumber beetle, OT	Poor[c]	—	782
Cereal leaf beetle	Poor	Good	1089
Japanese beetle, T	Fair	—	2250
Mosquitoes, O[d]T	Varies[e,f]	Varies[e]	847, 849, 850, 1022, 2106a, 2634, 3155, 3755, 4066
Tsetse fly, TI	Poor	Good	846
Mediterranean fruit fly	Good?[g]	—	2769
Various fruit flies, OT	Good	—	2061
Housefly, OTI	Good[g]	Good	634, 635, 637, 741, 1502, 2106a, 2645, 2821, 3155
Face fly, OT	Good	—	1581
Little housefly, OT	Poor	Good	859
Stable fly, OT	—	Poor	1615
Screw-worm fly, OT	Fair?	—	811
Metepa			
German cockroach, O	Poor	—	537
Pea aphid, O	Poor	—	366
Tobacco budworm, T	—	—	1303a
Bollworm, O	—	Poor	3341
Pink bollworm, T	Good	Good	2791
Cabbage looper, OT	—	Poor	1688, 1775

Table 6-VIII—*continued*

Insect species and mode of application[a]	Results		References
	Safety margin[b]	Vigor of males	
Metepa			
Gypsy moth	Poor	—	*737*
Azuki bean weevil, T	Good	—	*427, 2652, 3239*
Egyptian cotton leafworm, OT	Good	—	*3577*
Banded cucumber beetle, OT	Poor?	—	*782*
Japanese beetle, T	Fair	—	*2250*
Mosquitoes, O[d]T	Varies[e,h,i]	Varies[e]	*848, 1022, 2042, 2106a, 2634, 4066*
Tsetse fly, T	Poor	—	*616*
Mediterranean fruit fly	Poor?[g]	—	*2769*
Various fruit flies, OT	Good	—	*2061*
Housefly, OTI	Poor	Good	*634, 848, 1502, 2645, 2821*
Thiotepa			
German cockroach, O	Poor	—	*537*
Various moths	Good	Good	*533*
Mosquitoes, T	Good[g]	Good	*348, 3100, 3777*
Housefly, O	Good[f]	—	*632, 2805, 2821*
Little housefly, OT	Poor	Good	*859*
Pomace fly, OT	Good	Good	*2082*
Screw-worm fly, OT	Good	Poor	*809, 811, 814*
$RNHP(O)Az_2$, $Me_2NP(O)Az_2$, $(Me_2N)_2P(O)Az$			
Tobacco budworm, T	—	—	*1303a*
Housefly, O	Variable	Good	*637, 1643*a
Screw-worm fly, OT	Good[f]	Poor	*815*
$R_2NP(O)Az$, $ArNHCONHP(O)Az_2$, $(CH_2)_4(NHCOAz)_2$			
Screw-worm fly	Good	Good	*817*
Aphamide			
German cockroach, O	Poor	—	*537*
Citrus red mite, T	Poor	Good	*783*
Plum curculio, T	Poor	—	*1644*
Mosquitoes, T	Poor?	—	*3755*
Apholate			
German cockroach, O	Poor	—	*537*
Pea aphid, O	Good	—	*366*
Citrus red mite, T	Poor	Good	*783*
Spider mites, OT	Good?	Poor	*3292*
Tobacco budworm, T	—	—	*1303a*
Bollworm	—	Poor	*3341*
Fall armyworm, O	—	Good	*3855*
Cabbage looper, OT	Fair	Poor	*1688, 1775*
Gypsy moth	Poor?	—	*737*
Azuki bean weevil, T	—	Good	*2652–2654*

Table 6-VIII—*continued*

Insect species and mode of application[a]	Results		References
	Safety margin[b]	Vigor of males	
Apholate			
Boll weevil, OT	Poor[c]	Poor	*1472, 1643, 1652, 2328*
Mexican bean beetle, OT	Poor	—	*1690, 4204*
Various moths	Good	Good	*533*
Plum curculio, T	Poor	—	*2250, 3041*
Japanese beetle, T	Fair	—	*2250, 3041*
Mosquitoes, OT[c]	Varies[i,j]	Varies[e]	*847, 850, 854a, 1022, 1645, 2042, 2106a, 2483, 2634, 2644, 3754, 3755, 4066*
Tsetse fly, T	Poor	—	*616*
Mediterranean fruit fly	—	Good	*2768*
Various fruit flies, OT	Good	—	*2061*
Sheep blowfly, OT	Fair	Good	*4211*
Green sheep blowfly, OT	—	Good	*2557*
Housefly, OTI[b]	Fair[f,h]	Good	*634, 741, 1502, 1608, 2106a, 2240, 2461, 2465, 2805, 2851*
Face fly, OT	Good	—	*1581*
Stable fly, OT	—	Poor	*1615*
Screw-worm fly, OT	Fair	—	*617*
2,5-Az$_2$-3,6-(MeOCH$_2$CH$_2$O)$_2$-1,4-benzoquinone			
Stable fly, OT	—	Poor	*1615*
Screw-worm fly, OT	Good	—	*811*
Tretamine			
Tobacco budworm, T	—	—	*1303a*
Various moths	Good	Good	*533*
Various fruit flies, OT	Good	—	*2061*
Housefly, O	Fair?	—	*2099*
Screw-worm fly, OT	Good	Poor	*809, 811, 814*

[a] O = oral administration; T = topical (dipping, spotting, spraying, or exposure to residues); I = injection.

[b] Ratio of lethal or life-shortening dose to effective dose.

[c] Duration of sterility poor.

[d] Includes feeding on mice treated with chemosterilant.

[e] Varies with species.

[f] Permanent sterility.

[g] Duration of sterility fair.

[h] Resistance to the chemosterilant allegedly can be developed but this later was not observed (*2613*).

[i] Susceptibility to a virus infection and ability to transmit the disease increased.

[j] Resistance developed but did not extend markedly to tepa and metepa (*4144*).

The numerous screening tests that have been carried out are summarized in Table 6-VII and more intensive tests of promising ones, especially tepa and apholate, in Table 6-VIII. In general, alkyl groups on the carbon atoms of the aziridine ring reduce chemosterilant activity. With rare exceptions, adult insects are more susceptible than those in earlier stages of the life cycle (*4032*), males are more susceptible to chemosterilants than females, and administration by feeding is more effective than by contact. For houseflies at least, repellency of chemosterilants in baits can be overcome (*1381*). Use of apholate as a systemic chemosterilant for protection of cattle against warble flies is impractical because of its toxicity to the host (*2076*).

Only a few field tests have been reported. Apholate-sterilized male boll weevils were required in overwhelming numbers to achieve control, partly because they did not compete effectively in mating (*857, 4036*). Most of the crop from an isolated mango grove was protected from the Mexican fruit fly by release of tepa-sterilized males (*3220*), and populations of fruit flies (*Drosophila melanogaster*) were greatly reduced in tomato field plots by release of apholate-sterilized adults (*4122*) or use of baited jars containing apholate (*4123*). Cornmeal baits containing tepa (*2241, 3087*), metepa (*2239, 2516*), or apholate (*1504, 2516*) reduced housefly populations in 4–5 weeks, but the decrease was only temporary, partly because of reinfestation from outside the experimental area. Similarly, when applied to desert potholes, apholate caused only temporary control of a species of mosquito, presumably because the treatment did not reach all overlapping generations (*2311*).

A few papers report studies of the mode of action of aziridine derivatives as chemosterilants. While the presence of two or more aziridinyl groups per molecule of chemosterilant is not essential for activity, it is apparently advantageous (*812, 4017*); this suggests a crosslinking action. Tepa (*636, 1651*), metepa (*619, 2893*), and thiotepa (*4141*) are degraded rapidly (half-life 2–5 hours) in houseflies and other animals. Relatively large doses produce degeneration of reproductive organs (*314, 571, 1650, 2610–2612, 2644, 2963, 3305*); dominant lethal mutations are induced by smaller amounts (*2100, 2246, 2247, 4105*). It is both supposed (*2085, 2806, 4126*) and questioned (*1642*) that aziridines act by interfering with synthesis and metabolism of nucleic acids.

There is one record (*1281*) of considerable reduction in reproductive capacity of saprophytic nematodes exposed to tretamine or 2,5-bis(1-aziridinyl)-3,6-(2-methoxyethoxy)benzoquinone, and a similar study of the effect of thiotepa on a tapeworm (*Hymenolepis diminuta*) parasitic on the confused flour beetle (*2535*).

Studies of chemosterilization of vertebrates have been aimed at producing a better understanding of reproductive processes, and perhaps ultimately birth control, rather than pest eradication. No serious consideration of aziridines for limiting human fertility is possible at present because of their toxicity. Their action as antifertility agents in higher animals, as well as that of other alkylating agents, has been reviewed repeatedly (*1641, 1943, 1944, 1946, 1952, 1986*), and is also summarized in Table 6-IX.

Table 6-IX

AZIRIDINES AS CHEMOSTERILANTS OF VERTEBRATES

Aziridine	Animal	Effect	References
EI	Rat	Reduced fertility	*3864b*
2-Az-1,4-benzoquinone	Rat	Atrophy of testes	*1456*
Tepa	Rat	Temporary sterility	*1945, 1950*
Tepa	Male rabbit	Sterility	*1062*
Thiotepa	Male rat	Temporary sterility	*1945, 1950*
Thiotepa	Rat and dog	Atrophy of testes	*1573*
Metepa	Male rat	Sterility	*1400, 1401*
Metepa	Male rat	Degradation of metepa	*2893*
$[Az_2P(O)]_2O$	Male rodent	Temporary sterility	*1948*
$(AzSO_2)_2(CH_2)_3$, Az_2SO, $AzCO_2Et$, $AzCONH_2$	Male rat	Temporary sterility	*1945, 1950*
$AzCONHMe$, $AzCONMe_2$	Male rat	Prolonged sterility	*1944*
Apholate	Chicken	Sterility	*1704, 1704a*
$(AzCH_2CONH)_2$-$(CH_2)_8$, apholate	Japanese quail	Reduced fertility	*3229a*
$1,4-(AzCH_2CONH)_2$-cyclohexane	Japanese quail	Reduced fertility	*3276, 3229a*
Various $(AzCH_2CONH)_2Y$	Male mouse	Sterility	*3275*
Tretamine	Starling	Atrophy of gonads	*858*
Tretamine	Redwinged blackbird	Atrophy of testes	*3674*
Tretamine	Male mouse	Temporary sterility	*607, 609, 858, 1948, 3232*
Tretamine	Female mouse	Sterility	*606*
Tretamine	Mouse	Atrophy of testes	*2628*
Tretamine	Male rat	Sterility	*400, 776, 1944, 1948, 1951, 3372*
Tretamine	Male rabbit	Sterility	*1311, 1943, 2833a*
Mitomycin C	Rat and dog	Atrophy of testes	*1573*

Toxicology of Aziridines

Obviously the toxic properties of aziridines are desirable when they are used as pesticides, and undesirable when in their drug use or by accidental exposure they adversely affect human subjects. Indeed their toxicity to humans has restricted their use as chemical intermediates, as drugs, and as poisons for unwanted plant and animals. Their sexual chemosterilant properties have already been discussed.

A general review of the toxicology of alkylating agents to vertebrates is given by Hayes (*1641*); as may be expected, the symptoms and systemic effects are often similar to those produced by high-energy radiation. The cytotoxic effects are most marked in fast-growing tissues: bone marrow, the lymphatic system, the intestinal mucosa, the gonads, embryos, and tumors. These effects predictably lead to severe anemia, vomiting and other gastrointestinal disturbances, and sterility. Ethylenimine (*752*) and tretamine (*746*) have caused retinal damage and blindness in test animals. There is also a delayed lethal effect, apparently not traceable directly to the tissue derangements mentioned.

The high toxicity to test animals of EI (*1391, 2362*), 2-methylaziridine (*1388*), and what was probably camphenimine (*1006*) was among the properties first reported for these compounds. A marked effect of EI on test animals is kidney necrosis, which is not characteristic of the alkylating agents, but which has been noted repeatedly (*2164, 2306, 2755*) and even recommended as a means of studying renal pathology (*2411*). In one experiment in which its effect on the kidney was unexpectedly low, it was administered as the "acetate" (*3455*); the material injected may have been partially hydrated and detoxified by the acid. Massive doses cause rapid death of rats by respiratory arrest, but sublethal amounts produce a severe diuretic effect (*1477*). This is not caused by thiotepa, but is induced to varying degrees by other acylated aziridines; a series of papers reports studies of the mechanism of such diuresis (*752, 775, 1482, 1947, 1949, 1962, 1963*).

When sublethal doses of ^{14}C-labeled EI were administered intraperitoneally to rats, about half the ^{14}C appeared in the urine (though mostly not as EI), a little was expired as CO_2 and perhaps EI, and the rest was widely distributed in body tissues (*4208*).

A very different locus, the hypothalamus, is damaged by the diquaternary aziridinium ion **6**, formed by spontaneous cyclization of 1,1′-bis(2-chloroethyl)-4,4-bipiperidine; the substance has a specific obesifying effect in mice (*2923, 3079*; cf. *2919*).

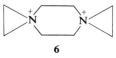

6

Two human fatalities have been reported as a result of poisoning by EI (*3524*), and the symptoms caused by exposure have been described repeatedly. The vapor, after a few hours delay, causes inflammation of the respiratory tract and eyes, nausea and vomiting, and albuminuria (*852, 2312b, 2563, 3758*).

Symptoms may persist for weeks or months after severe exposure. The most detailed accounts of such poisoning also describe treatment, which is essentially symptomatic (*3524, 3758*). Ethylenimine in liquid form can be absorbed through the skin and is a severe vesicant, but skin contact with the vapor is less dangerous (*1996, 2563, 3524, 3758*). The compound was at one time considered for use as a chemical warfare agent (*1991*) and studies of its penetration of gas mask canisters were made (*2289*). Some aziridines may also act as allergens and sensitize the exposed person to further contact (*2820*), although APO and APS were not found extremely allergenic to persons working with them (*965*), and EI itself has not sensitized industrial workers exposed to it (*963, 3524*).

While the Threshold Limit Values tolerable for repeated exposure without injury, based on single exposure of animals, were fixed for several years at 5 ppm in air (10 mg/m³) for EI and 25 ppm for 2-methylaziridine (*79*), they have recently been lowered to 0.5 ppm and 2 ppm, respectively (*78*), as a result of reevaluation of the data from of the animal tests in 1948.

To make a comparison with other toxic chemicals: the acute lethality, by inhalation, of EI to rats or dogs and cats is somewhat less than that of hydrogen cyanide, hydrogen sulfide, diisopropyl fluorophosphate, methyl isocyanate, phosgene, acrolein, arsine, cyanogen chloride, ketene, and chloropicrin. Such toxicity of EI is about the same as that of chlorine, nickel carbonyl, methyl silicate, 2-chloroethanol, dimethyl sulfate, diborane, and acrylonitrile (*10*).

Most studies of toxicity of other aziridines have been carried out in connection with the use of nitrogen mustards and 1-substituted aziridines in tumor chemotherapy. The nitrogen mustards come into consideration because of the tendency of those having the nitrogen unsubstituted with strongly electron-withdrawing groups to cyclize to the aziridinium ion form (see p. 2).

$$>N-CH_2CH_2Cl \underset{+Cl^-}{\overset{-Cl^-}{\rightleftharpoons}}$$

Indeed it appears that much of the toxicity of the nitrogen mustards is due to such aziridinium ions (*123, 490, 1090, 1355, 1490, 1492, 2870*), and maintenance of low pH of stored solutions of bis(2-chloroethyl)methylamine is recommended to minimize the isomerization (*345a*). However, it is impractical here to review all the toxicity data on nitrogen mustards, and only those compounds will be considered which were clearly used in the aziridinium form.

Table 6-X presents the accumulated quantitative data on toxicity of aziridines to animals. The LD₅₀ values, the dose at which half the animals may be

Table 6-X

TOXICITY OF AZIRIDINES

Aziridine	Test animal	Doses given	Method of dosage[a]	Total test period (days)	LD_{50} (μmole/kg)	References
EI	Mouse	—	A	10	$(3.9)^b$	3264
		—	A	—	$(0.40–0.46)^c$	3865
EI	Rat	1	B	14	350	3318
		—	A	14	—	585, 586
		—	A	—	$(1.9)^i$	963
		1	D	28	88	1962
EI	Guinea pig	—	A	14	—	585
		1	B	14	≈ 350	585
		—	C	14	330	585
EI	Rabbit	1	B	—	330	963
		1	C	—	330	963
2-MeAzH	Rat	1	B	14	330	3318
		—	A	14	—^{d}	586, 3317
2-MeAzH	Guinea pig	—	C	14	750	3317
AzCH$_2$CH$_2$OH	Rat	1	B	14	850	3316
AzCH$_2$CH$_2$OH	Rabbit	—	C	14	290	3316
HOCH$_2$CH$_2$AzMe$^+$ Cl$^-$	Mouse	1	D	—	30–50	123, 1492
HOCH$_2$CH$_2$AzMe$^+$ Cl$^-$	Rabbit	1	D	—	20–40	123
HOCH$_2$CH$_2$AzEt$^+$ Cl$^-$	Mouse	1	D	—	30–50	123, 1355
HOCH$_2$CH$_2$AzEt$^+$ Cl$^-$	Rabbit	1	D	—	30–40	123
HOCH$_2$CH$_2$Az(CH$_2$CH$_2$Cl)$^+$ Cl$^-$	Mouse	1	D	—	8	1490
(HOCH$_2$CH$_2$)$_2$Az$^+$ Cl$^-$	Mouse	1	D	—	30	1490
ClCH$_2$CH$_2$AzMe$^+$ Cl$^-$	Mouse	1	D	—	9–15	123
ClCH$_2$CH$_2$AzEt$^+$ Cl$^-$	Mouse	1	D	—	11	123
ClCH$_2$CH$_2$AzEt$^+$ Cl$^-$	Rat	1	D	—	≈ 3	123
ClCH$_2$CH$_2$AzEt$^+$ Cl$^-$	Rabbit	1	D	—	≈ 17	123
AzCH$_2$CHOHCH=CH$_2$	Rat	5	D	21	90–240	3158
1,4-(AzCH$_2$CONH)$_2$-cyclohexane	Mouse	1	B	—	250	3276
(AzCH$_2$CONH)$_2$(CH$_2$)$_8$	Mouse	1	B	—	345	3276
2,5-Az$_2$-pBQ^e	Mouse	1	B	14	105	989
2,5-Az$_2$-pBQ^e	Rat	1	B	14	800	989
	Rat	1	D	—	9.8	989
2-Az-5-MeO-pBQ^e	Rat	1	B	14	2000	989
	Rat	1	D	14	31	989
2,5-Az$_2$-3,6-(MeO)$_2$-pBQ^e	Mouse	1	B	14	220	989

Table 6-X—*continued*

Aziridine	Test animal	Doses given	Method of dosage[a]	Total test period (days)	LD_{50} (μmole/kg)	References
2,5-Az$_2$-3,6-(EtO)$_2$-pBQ^e	Mouse	1	B	14	300	*989*
2,5-Az$_2$-3,6-(PrO)$_2$-pBQ^e	Mouse	1	B	14	300	*989*
	Mouse	1	D	14	10	*989*
2,5-Az$_2$-3,6-(MeOCH$_2$CH$_2$O)$_2$-pBQ^e	Mouse	1	B	14	150	*989*
	Mouse	1	D	14	45	*989*
	Mouse	5	D	21	9.3–24	*3158*
2,5-Az$_2$-3,6-(MeOCH$_2$CH$_2$O)$_2$-pBQ^e	Rat	1	D	14	8	*3158*
	Rat	5	D	21	2.5–3.6	*3158*
2,5-Az$_2$-3,6-(morpholino)$_2$-pBQ^e	Rat	1	B	14	35	*989*
	Rat	1	D	14	9	*3158*
2,5-Az$_2$-3,6-(AcNH)$_2$-pBQ^e	Rat	6	D	—	4.4	*1406*
2,5-Az$_2$-3,6-(EtCONH)$_2$-pBQ^e	Mouse	5	D	21	9	*3158*
2,5-Az$_2$-3,6-(EtCONH)$_2$-pBQ^e	Rat	5	D	21	2.1–2.3	*3158*
2,5-Az$_2$-3,6-(EtO$_2$CNH)$_2$-pBQ^e	Rat	1	B	14	18	*989*
	Rat	1	D	14	9	*3158*
Az$_3$-pBQ^e	Mouse	1	B	14	40	*989*
	Mouse	1	D	14	3	*3158*
	Mouse	5	D	21	0.8–0.9	*3158*
Az$_3$-pBQ^e	Rat	1	B	14	10–40	*989*
	Rat	1	D	14	1–2	*3158*
	Rat	5	D	21	0.30–0.37	*3158*
Az$_3$-pBQ^e	Dog, cat	1	B	14	10	*989*
Az$_4$-pBQ^e	Mouse	5	D	21	7	*3158*
Az$_4$-pBQ^e	Rat	1	B	14	7	*989*
	Rat	1	D	14	0.3	*3158*
2,5-Az$_2$-1,4-C$_6$H$_2$(OH)$_2$	Rat	1	B	—	650	*989*
2-Az-5,6,7,8-H$_4$-1,4-NQ^f	Mouse	1	B	14	4200	*989*
2-Az-5,6,7,8-H$_4$-1,4-NQ^f	Rat	1	B	14	1800	*989*
	Rat	1	D	14	60	*3158*
2-Az-3-Cl-5,6,7,8-H$_4$-1,4-NQ^f	Rat	1	B	14	12000	*989*
	Rat	1	D	14	240	*989*
4-Az-1,2-NQ^f	Mouse	1	B	14	1100	*989*
4-Az-1,2-NQ^f	Rat	1	D	14	170	*989*
Az$_2$CO	Rat	5	D	21	56–74	*3158*
p-(AzCO)$_2$C$_6$H$_4$	Mouse	5	D	21	110	*3158*
p-(AzCO)$_2$C$_6$H$_4$	Rat	5	D	21	60–120	*3158*
AzCO$_2$Me	Rat	1	D	28	85	*1962*
AzCO$_2$Et	Rat	1	D	28	85	*1962*
AzCO$_2$Pr	Rat	1	D	28	140	*1962*
AzCO$_2$-iso-Pr	Rat	1	D	28	140	*1962*
AzCO$_2$Bu	Rat	1	D	28	105	*1962*
m-AzCO$_2$C$_6$H$_4$-iso-Pr	House-fly	1	C	—	>2400	*1090*

Table 6-X —*continued*

Aziridine	Test animal	Doses given	Method of dosage[a]	Total test period (days)	LD$_{50}$ (μmole/kg)	References
(AzCONH)$_2$(CH$_2$)$_6$	Mouse	1	D	—	22	2872
		5	D	—	9	2872
(AzCONH)$_2$(CH$_2$)$_6$	Rat	1	D	—	6	2872
		5	D	—	2	2872
(AzCH$_2$CONH)$_2$(CH$_2$)$_8$	Mouse	1	B	5	3400	3229a
		1	D	5	280	3229a
(AzCH$_2$CONH)$_2$-1,4-c-C$_6$H$_{10}$	Mouse	1	B	5	250	3229a
(*trans*)		1	D	5	160	3229a
m-(AzCONH)$_2$C$_6$H$_4$	Mouse	1	D	—	86	2872
		5	D	—	26	2872
m-(AzCONH)$_2$C$_6$H$_4$	Rat	1	D	—	44	2872
		5	D	—	14	2872
AzCMe=NNHC$_6$H$_4$NO$_2$-p	Mouse	?	D?	—	1700	2349a
Tretamine	Mouse	1	B	—	70	2872
		5	B	21	43	3158
		1	D	—	14	2872
		5	D	—	5	2872
		5	D	21	4.6–5.7	3158
		1?	D	30	0.36/mouse	153
Tretamine	Rat	1	B	—	60	2872
		5	B	21	54–140	3158
		1	D	—	5	2872
		5	D	—	2	2872
		6	D	—	3.7	1406
		5	D	21	1.3–2.6	3158
		1?	D	—	5.5	989
2,6-Az$_2$-4-NH$_2$-s-triazine	Mouse	1	D	—	10	2872
		5	D	—	4	2872
2,6-Az$_2$-4-NH$_2$-s-triazine	Rat	1	D	—	4	2872
		5	D	—	2	2872
In the following, R = 4,6-Az$_2$-2-s-triazinyl						
N-Formyl-O-R-L-tyrosine	Mouse	?	D?	—	210	3210
	Rat	?	D?	—	200	3210
N-Acetyl-O-R-L-tyrosine	Mouse	?	D?	—	150	3210
Me ester	Rat	?	D?	—	50	3210
N-Acetyl-N-R-DL-	Mouse	?	D?	—	110	3210
phenylalanine Me ester	Rat	?	D?	—	50	3210
Et R-acetamidomalonate	Mouse	?	D?	—	200	3210
	Rat	?	D?	—	50	3210
2-Az-4,5-Cl$_2$-pyrimidine	Rat	5	D	21	$\approx$30	3158
2,4-Az$_2$-6-Me-5-NO$_2$-pyrimidine	Rat	5	D	21	10	3158

Table 6-X—*continued*

Aziridine	Test animal	Doses given	Method of dosage[a]	Total test period (days)	LD_{50} (μmole/kg)	References
Mitomycin C	Mouse	1	D	—	15–27	3727
		1	D	—	25	2873
		5	D	—	7	2873
		5	D	—	2.4	4176
		5	D	21	1.5–2.2	3158
Mitomycin C	Rat	1	D	—	7.5	2873
		6	D	—	3.3	1406
		5	D	—	1.4	3089
		5	D	—	3	2873
		5	D	21	1.4–1.7	3158
Mitomycin C	Cat	1	D	—	6	2873
Mitomycin C	Dog	1	D	—	$\approx$3	2873
		5	D	—	$\approx$0.36	2873
Porfiromycin	Mouse	5	D	—	13	4176
Methylmitomycin A	Mouse	—	—	—	14	4102
Various mitomycin derivatives	Mouse	1?	D?	—	Various	2580b
Tepa	Mouse	1	B	—	270	3450a
		1	D	—	190	3450a
		5	D	21	80	3158
Tepa	Rat	1	B	22	210	1401
		1	B	—	170[g]	2184
		1	C	22	500	1401
		1	D	—	50	3450a
		5	D	21	12.6–23	3158
Metepa	Rat	1	B	22	630–1000	1401
		1	C	22	850	1401
$(2,2\text{-Me}_2\text{Az})_3\text{PO}$	Mouse	1	B	—	677	4130
		1	D	—	230–400	4130
$\text{Az}_2\text{P(O)NHMe}$	Mouse	1	B	—	11[g]	670
$\text{Az}_2\text{P(O)NHEt}$	Mouse	1	B	—	23[g]	670
$\text{Az}_2\text{P(O)NHPr}$	Mouse	1	B	—	13[g]	670
$\text{Az}_2\text{P(O)NEt}_2$	Mouse	—	B	—	370	3450a
		—	D	—	220	3450a
$\text{Az}_2\text{P(O)NEt}_2$	Rat	—	B	—	390	3450a
		—	D	—	75	3450a
$\text{Az}_2\text{P(O)NEt}_2$	Dog	—	D	—	20	3450a
$\text{Az}_2\text{P(O)NHBu}$	Rat	5	D	21	17	3158
$(2\text{-Et-1-Az})_2\text{P(O)NHBu}$	Rat	5	D	21	190–250	3158
$\text{Az}_2\text{P(O)NBu}_2$	Mouse	5	D	21	95	3158
$\text{Az}_2\text{P(O)NBu}_2$	Rat	5	D	21	45–57	3158
$\text{Az}_2\text{P(O)N(CH}_2\text{CH}_2\text{Cl})_2$	Mouse	1	D	—	70	679
$\text{Az}_2\text{P(O)N(CH}_2\text{CH}_2\text{Cl})_2$	Rat	1	B	—	86[g]	2184
		5	D?	17	7	679

Table 6-X—*continued*

Aziridine	Test animal	Doses given	Method of dosage[a]	Total test period (days)	LD_{50} (μmole/kg)	References
$Az_2P(O)NHCH_2CH_2CO_2Et$	Rat	1	B	—	210[g]	2184
$Az_2P(O)NHCHMeCO_2Et$	Rat	1	B	—	300[g]	2184
$Az_2P(O)NHCHBuCO_2Et$	Rat	1	B	—	760[g]	2184
$Az_2P(O)NHCH$-$(CH_2CH_2CH_2SMe)CO_2Et$	Rat	1	B	—	170[g]	2184
$Az_2P(O)NHCHPhCH_2CO_2Et$	Rat	1	B	—	360[g]	2184
$Az_2P(O)NHPh$	Rat	1	B	—	230[g]	2184
$Az_2P(O)N(Ph)CH_2CH{=}CH_2$	Mouse	—	D	—	75	1455
$1\text{-}[Az_2P(O)]\text{-}2,5\text{-}Me_2\text{-}$ pyrrolidine	Rat	5	D	21	31	3158
$1\text{-}[(2\text{-}Me\text{-}1\text{-}Az)_2P(O)]\text{-}2,5\text{-}Me_2\text{-}$ pyrrolidine	Rat	5	D	21	36	3158
$1\text{-}[Az_2P(O)]\text{-}H_6\text{-}azepine$	Mouse	—	D	—	160	1496
$1\text{-}[Az_2P(O)]\text{-}H_6\text{-}azepine$	Dog	—	D	—	24	1496
$4\text{-}[Az_2P(O)]\text{-}morpholine$	Rat	6	D	—	160	1406
$2\text{-}[Az_2P(O)NEt]\text{-}thiazole$	Rat	5	D	21	57–71	3158
$2\text{-}[Az_2P(O)NH]\text{-}pyrimidine$	Mouse	—	B?	—	600[g]	672
$2\text{-}[Az_2P(O)NH]\text{-}4\text{-}R\text{-}6\text{-}R'\text{-}$ pyrimidine						
R = H, R' = H	Rat	1	B	—	560[g]	2184
R = H, R' = Cl	Rat	1	B	—	1200[g]	2184
R = H, R' = Me	Rat	1	B	—	210[g]	2184
R = H, R' = OMe	Rat	1	B	—	170[g]	2184
R = H, R' = NMe_2	Rat	1	B	—	7.5[g]	2184
R = H, R' = $NMeCH_2Ph$	Rat	1	B	—	290[g]	2184
R = Cl, R' = Me	Rat	1	B	—	1300[g]	2184
$2\text{-}[Az_2P(O)NEt]\text{-}thiadiazole$	Rat	—	B	—	21	3285a
$Az_2P(O)\text{-}N(CH_2CH_2)_2N\text{-}R$						
R = CO_2Me	Rat	1	B	—	180[g]	2184
R = $CONEt_2$	Rat	1	B	—	760[g]	2184
R = $P(O)(NMe_2)_2$	Rat	1	B	—	290[g]	2184
R = $P(O)Az_2$	Mouse	—	B	—	26	2268b
R = $P(O)Az_2$	Mouse	—	D?	—	110[g]	672
R = $P(O)Az_2$	Rat	—	B	—	23	2268b
R = $P(O)Az_2$	Mouse, rat	—	D	—	360–430[g]	2903
$Az_2P(O)N{=}C(OEt)Me$	Mouse	1	D	—	50[g]	670
$Az_2P(O)NHCO_2Me$	Mouse	1	D	—	32	267
$Az_2P(O)NHCO_2Et$	Mouse	1	D	—	30	267
$Az_2P(O)NHCO_2CH_2Ph$	Mouse	1	D	—	28	267
$Az_2P(O)NHBz$	Mouse	—	D	—	150	2268b
$Az_2P(O)NHBz$	Rat	—	D	—	210	2268b
$Az_2P(O)NHBz$	Rabbit	—	B	—	63	2268b
$Az_2P(O)NHCOC_6H_4F\text{-}p$	Mouse	—	D	—	80–90	2268b
$Az_2P(O)NHCOC_6H_4F\text{-}p$	Rat	—	D	—	80–90	2268b
		—	B	—	270	2268b

Table 6-X *—continued*

Aziridine	Test animal	Doses given	Method of dosage[a]	Total test period (days)	LD_{50} (μmole/kg)	References
$Az_2P(O)NHCONHPh$	Mouse	—	B	—	310	*1455a*
		—	D	—	110	*1455a;* *cf. 883*
$Az_2P(O)NHCONHPh$	Rat	—	B	—	114	*1455a*
		—	D	—	75	*1455a*
$Az_2P(O)NHCONHC_6H_4Cl$-o	Mouse	—	—	—	175[g]	*883*
$Az_2P(O)NHCONH$-1-$C_{10}H_7$	Mouse	1	D?	—	300	*2204*
$Az_2P(O)NHCONH$-1-$C_{10}H_7$	Rat	1	D?	—	250	*2204*
$(2,2$-$Me_2Az)_2P(O)NHCO_2Et$	Mouse	1	D	—	2200	*4023*
$Az_2P(O)N{=}CAzPh$	Mouse	—	—	—	130[g]	*883*
$Az_2P(O)N{=}CAzC_6H_4Cl$-p	Mouse	—	—	—	96[g]	*883*
$Az_2P(O)N{=}CAzC_6H_4Br$-p	Mouse	—	—	—	73[g]	*883*
$Az_2P(O)OMe$	Mouse	1	D	15	150–300	*615*
		1	D		63[g]	*670*
$Az_2P(O)OEt$	Mouse	1	D	15	34–70	*615*
		1	D		3[g]	*670*
$Az_2P(O)OEt$	Rat	1	B	—	34[g]	*2184*
$(2,2$-$Me_2Az)_2P(O)OEt$	Mouse	1	D	—	730	*4023*
$Az_2P(O)OPr$	Mouse	1	D		21[g]	*670*
$Az_2P(O)OBu$	Mouse	1	D		23[g]	*670*
$Az_2P(O)O$-n-C_6H_{13}	Mouse	5	D	21	130	*3158*
$Az_2P(O)O$-n-C_6H_{13}	Rat	5	D	21	43–94	*3158*
$Az_2P(O)Ph$	Rat	1	B	—	1700[g]	*2184*
$Az_2P(O)(OC_6H_4NO_2$-$p)$	Rat	1	B	—	22[g]	*2184*
p-$C_6H_4[OP(O)Az_2]_2$	Mouse	1	B	—	150	*3410a*
$Az_2P(O)Me$	Mouse	1	D	15	340	*615*
		1	B	—	30[g]	*670*
$Az_2P(O)Et$	Mouse	1	B	—	29[g]	*670*
$Az_2P(O)Pr$	Mouse	1	B	—	26[g]	*670*
$Az_2P(O)Bu$	Mouse	1	B	—	56[g]	*670*
$Az_2P(O)CH{=}CH_2$	Mouse	1	B	—	25[g]	*670*
$[Az_2P(O)CH_2]_2$	Mouse	1	B	—	18[d]	*670*
$Az_2P(O)CH_2CH_2P(O)(OEt)_2$	Mouse	1	B	—	53[g]	*670*
$Az_2P(O)CH_2CH_2P(O)(OBu)_2$	Mouse	1	B	—	47[g]	*670*
$AzP(O)(NHPr)_2$	Mouse	1	B	—	270[g]	*670*
$Az_2P(O)NHCONHPh$	Mouse	—	—	—	84[g]	*883*
$Az_2P(O)NHCONHC_6H_4Cl$-p	Mouse	—	—	—	175[g]	*883*
$AzP(O)(OMe)_2$	Mouse	1	D	15	1300–2000	*615*
$AzP(O)(OEt)_2$	Mouse	1	D	15	550	*615*
Thiotepa	Mouse	5	D	21	32–57	*3158*
Thiotepa	Rat	—	B	—	210[g]	*2184*
		—	D	—	55	*989*
		1	D	—	44	*3377*
		1	D	30	46–50	*419*
		6	D	—	25	*1406*
		5	D	21	15–22	*3158*

Table 6–X—Continued

Aziridine	Test animal	Doses given	Method of dosage[a]	Total test period (days)	LD$_{50}$ (μmole/kg)	References
Thiotepa	Rabbit	1	D	—	39	2532
1-Az$_2$P(S)-pyrrolidine	Rat	5	D	21	25–29	3158
1-(2-MeAz)$_2$P(S)-pyrrolidine	Rat	5	D	21	170–200	3158
4-Az$_2$P(S)-morpholine	Mouse	5	D	21	120–140	3158
4-Az$_2$P(S)-morpholine	Rat	5	D	21	31–52	3158
Az$_2$P(S)-N(CH$_2$CH$_2$)$_2$N-CONEt$_2$	Rat	1	B	—	660	2184
Az$_2$P(S)–N(CH$_2$CH$_2$)$_2$N–P(O)-(NMe$_2$)$_2$	Rat	1	B	—	680	2184
Az$_2$P(S)OBu	Rat	5	D	21	29–50	3158
(2-MeAz)$_2$P(S)OBu	Rat	5	D	21	78–95	3158
Az$_2$P(S)CH$_2$CH$_2$P(O)(OEt)$_2$	Mouse	1	B	—	19[g]	670
Az$_2$P(S)CH$_2$CH$_2$P(O)(OBu)$_2$	Mouse	1	B	—	124[g]	670
AzP(S)(Me)F	Rat	—	B	—	360	3164
AzP(S)(Et)F	Rat	—	B	—	330	3164
Apholate[h]	Chicken	1	B	—	64	3233
Apholate	Japanese quail	1	B	—	46–53	3233
Apholate	Rat	—	D?	—	52–57	1405
		1	B	22	250–290	1401
		1	C	22	≈ 1000–2000	1401
Apholate	Rabbit	—	D?	—	8–9	1405
Apholate	Mouse	1	B	—	280–490	3039
P$_3$N$_3$Az$_5$Cl	Mouse	1	B	—	180	3039
P$_3$N$_3$Az$_5$OMe	Mouse	1	B	—	330	3039
P$_3$N$_3$Az$_5$NMe$_2$	Mouse	1	B	—	330	3039
P$_3$N$_3$Az$_4$(OMe)$_2$(2,2-)	Mouse	1	B	—	770	3039
P$_3$N$_3$Az$_4$(NMe$_2$)$_2$(2,4-)	Mouse	1	B	—	260	3039
P$_3$N$_3$Az$_2$(NMe$_2$)$_4$(2,2,4,4-)	Mouse	1	B	—	1460	3039
Az$_3$P=NBz	Mouse	—	—	—	130[g]	883
Az$_3$P=NCOC$_6$H$_4$Cl-o	Mouse	—	—	—	84[g]	883
Az$_3$P=NCOC$_6$H$_4$Cl-p	Mouse	—	—	—	58[g]	883
Az$_3$P=NCOC$_6$H$_4$NO$_2$-m	Mouse	—	—	—	410[g]	883
Az$_3$P=NCOC$_6$H$_4$NO$_2$-p	Mouse	—	—	—	62[g]	883
Az$_3$P=NCOC$_6$H$_4$Br-p	Mouse	—	—	—	65[g]	883
Az$_3$P=NSO$_2$Ph	Mouse	—	—	—	210[g]	883

[a] A = inhalation; B = ingestion; C = absorption through skin; D = injection.
[b] Lethal concentration for 50%, 10 minutes exposure, in mg/l of air.
[c] Lethal concentration for 50%, 2 hours exposure, in mg/l of air.
[d] About 15% as toxic as EI.
[e] pBQ = p-benzoquinone.
[f] NQ = naphthoquinone.
[g] LD$_{100}$; LD$_{50}$ perhaps about 80% of this.
[h] Toxicity for striped killifish, grass shrimp, and mud snails has been reported (1041).
[i] Lethal concentration for 50%, 1 hour exposure, in mg/l of air.

expected to die, are expressed in μmole/kg of body weight (rather than the more usual mg/kg) to allow for differences in molecular weight (*3158*). Since toxicity is due to the aziridine ring, it might have been more informative to express toxicity as (number of aziridine rings per molecule) $\times$ μmole/kg of body weight; but this has not been done. A related compilation including information on toxicity of some aziridinyl phosphorus compounds is to be noted (*3567*), but toxicological data from two articles available only as abstracts (*670, 2702*) are not in Table 6-X. A few other records of animal poisoning by aziridines may be noted (*2871, 3857, 3858*), but the teratogenic effect of these drugs is noted here only by way of a review (*728a*). Polyethylenimine has extremely low toxicity in comparison to aziridines (*1483, 3120*), and in fact it is claimed for internal use as a drug (*3821*) and as an additive for animal feeds (*2589*). Its use in cellophane for food wrappings has been authorized in the United States (*113*).

Administration of bone marrow (*76, 2335*), thiosulfate ions (*414, 2279*), other substances containing mercapto groups (*76, 153, 748, 2279*), or antihistamines (*3045*) sometimes protects animals from toxicity of alkylating agents, including aziridines; but it is probable that the antitumor effect of the drugs is also cut by such antidotes. The function, and indeed the stability, of traces of substituted aziridines in animal feeds (*2589, 3478*) is not yet clear.

The toxicity (LD_{50}) of PEI has been reported (*238*) as follows: mouse, oral, about 2.8 gm/kg; rat, oral, about 3 gm/kg; guinea pigs, oral, 1.6 gm/kg killed 6 out of 10; mouse, subcutaneous, about 230 mg/kg; mouse, intraperitoneal, about 40 mg/kg; mouse, intravenous, 5 mg/kg killed 6 out of 20; rat, intraperitoneal, about 70 mg/kg; cats, intravenous, 10 mg/kg killed.

Uses of Aziridines as Anticancer Drugs

This aspect of the biological effects of aziridines has had much more study, and motivated more publications, than any other by far. Indeed, the literature on it is so voluminous that it cannot be reviewed in the detailed manner used in the rest of this book. The present chapter will (a) give some general background, (b) tabulate aziridines that have been screened as antitumor agents, and (c) discuss briefly the possible mode of action of these drugs. Articles reporting tests of known compounds on various tumors, those on clinical comparisons of drugs, and the many on effects of aziridines on physiological processes are mostly passed over, in order to keep the chapter within reasonable bounds.

As has already been noted, the aziridines are classified among biological alkylating agents, and have often been presumed to function as such in combating tumor growth. The possibility of using them so was recognized as the result of research on nitrogen mustard chemical warfare agents in World War

II. This showed that such agents owe at least part of their cytotoxic effects to the aziridinium ions formed by spontaneous cyclization (*1473*), and it is common practice to review nitrogen mustards and aziridines together. A number of general digests of their chemotherapeutic uses are available (*138, 338, 509, 561, 1050, 3450, 3879*), as well as more specific ones on aziridinyl quinones (*1423, 2853, 2855*), tretamine (*2044, 3056*), thiotepa (*114, 3492, 3882*), and aziridinylphosphorus compounds (*673*). A list of 648 aziridines screened for antitumor activity or at least made for screening was published in 1963 (*1497*).

The aziridines that have had most clinical use are tretamine [approved for human use (*114*)], thiotepa, tetramin (AzCH$_2$CHOHCH=CH$_2$), tepa, and perhaps trenimon, 2,5-Az$_2$-3,6-(MeOCH$_2$CH$_2$O)$_2$-*p*-benzoquinone. Like other alkylating agents, they have greatest effectiveness, i.e., palliative value, on leukemias and other lymphomas, such as Hodgkin's disease, and are of little value against solid tumors. The great defect of all such drugs is their poor chemotherapeutic index; they do not kill malignant tissue much better than they do normal tissue. In spite of the enormous variety tested, the various alkylating agents do not differ very much in their effectiveness. These matters are discussed at length in the reviews cited. A recent suggestion is the use of DNA pretreated with a difunctional reagent such as tretamine (*2649*); another employs injected bacteria (*Clostridium* sp.) along with tumor inhibitors such as aziridinyl compounds in therapy (*2528*).

Table 6-XI presents a list of compounds that have been tested against cancer or prepared for such testing. This list is supplementary to the long one in Cancer Chemotherapy Reports (*1497*), and to be used in conjunction with it. Compounds in the published list for which journal references were cited are

Table 6-XI

AZIRIDINES TESTED AGAINST CANCER OR MADE FOR SUCH TESTING

Compound	CCR[a] No.	References
Aziridines 1-Substituted with Aliphatic Group		
AzCH$_2$OH	—	*1717*
AzCHOHMe	—	*1717*
AzCHOHCH=CH$_2$	—	*173, 182*
AzCHOHCMe=CH$_2$	—	*182*
AzCHOHPr	—	*1717*
AzCHOH-iso-Pr	—	*1717*
AzCH$_2$CHOHCH=CH$_2$	22	*182, 3700*
AzCH$_2$CHOHEt	24	*3023*
AzCHMeCHMeOH	25	*3023*

Table 6-XI—*continued*

Compound	CCR[a] No.	References
Aziridines 1-Substituted with Aliphatic Group		
DL-[2-(CH$_2$=)Az]CH$_2$CHOHCH=CH$_2$ and	27	448
DL-[2-(CH$_2$=)Az]CH(CH$_2$OH)CH=CH$_2$		
AzCH$_2$CMe(OH)C≡CH	29	241
AzCH$_2$CHOHCH=CHMe	—	2930
AzCH$_2$CHOHCMe=CH$_2$	—	2930
(2-MeAz)CH$_2$CHOHCH=CH$_2$	—	3700
(2-MeAz)CH$_2$CHOHCH=CH$_2$ + (2-MeAz)CH(CH$_2$OH)CH=CH$_2$	33	447
(2-MeAz)CH$_2$CMe(OH)C≡CH	36	241
(2-MeAz)CH$_2$CMe(OH)CH=CH$_2$	37	3700
(2,2-Me$_2$Az)CH$_2$CHOHCH=CH$_2$ +		
(2,2-Me$_2$Az)CH(CH$_2$OH)CH=CH$_2$	38	447
1-Az-cyclohexanol	—	1717
AzCH$_2$CH(OEt)CH=CH$_2$	—	3359
AzCHOH-n-C$_6$H$_{13}$	—	1717
2-Az-1-(HC≡C)-cyclohexanol	—	241
2-Az-1-(H$_2$C=CH)-cyclohexanol	—	3700
(2-BuAz)CH$_2$CHOHCH=CH$_2$	—	182
AzCHPhCH$_2$CHO	—	1717
2-(2-MeAz)-1-(HC≡C)-cyclohexanol	—	241
2-(2-MeAz)-1-(H$_2$C=CH)-cyclohexanol	—	3700
[2,2-(CH$_2$)$_5$Az]CH$_2$CHOHC≡CH	—	241
[2,2-(CH$_2$)$_5$Az]CH$_2$CHOHCH=CH$_2$	—	182, 3700
2-Az-5-(CH$_2$=CMe)-2-Me- + 2-Az-4-(CH$_2$=CMe)-1-Me-cyclohexanol	—	188
AzCHPhCH$_2$CHOHAz	—	1717
AzCH$_2$CH$_2$OAc	47	3625
AzCH$_2$CH$_2$O$_2$CEt	48	3625
DL-AzCH$_2$CH(OAc)CH=CH$_2$ + DL-AzCH(CH$_2$OAc)CH=CH$_2$	51	2529
AzCH$_2$CH(OAc)CH=CH$_2$	—	3359
AzCH$_2$CH$_2$O$_2$C-iso-Pr	—	3625
AzCH$_2$CHOHCH$_2$OCH$_2$CH=CH$_2$	—	198
AzCH(2-furyl)CH$_2$CHO	—	1717
AzCH(CH$_2$OCPr)CH=CH$_2$	—	3358
AzCH$_2$CH(O$_2$CPr)CH=CH$_2$	—	3359
(2-MeAz)CH$_2$CHOHCH$_2$OCHMeCH=CH$_2$	—	198
AzCH(2-furyl)CHOHAz	—	1717
AzCH(CH$_2$O$_2$C-n-C$_5$H$_{11}$)CH=CH$_2$	—	3358
AzCH$_2$CH(O$_2$C-n-C$_5$H$_{11}$)CH=CH$_2$	—	218, 3359, 3686
AzCH(CH$_2$O$_2$CCH=CHPh)CH=CH$_2$	—	3358
AzCH$_2$CH(O$_2$CCH=CHPh)CH=CH$_2$	—	3359
AzCH$_2$CH(O$_2$CC$_{15}$H$_{31}$)CH=CH$_2$	—	174, 218, 3359, 3686
AzCH$_2$CHOHCH$_2$SCH$_2$CH=CH$_2$	—	198
AzCH(CH$_2$OCO$_2$Et)CH=CH$_2$	—	3358

Table 6-XI—continued

Compound	CCR[a] No.	References
2-MeAzCH$_2$CH(CH=CH$_2$)SCH$_2$CHMeNH$_2$	—	195
Az$_2$CH$_2$	58	3625
AzCH$_2$CH$_2$N=CHPh	—	1717
AzCH$_2$CH$_2$N=CH-2-furyl	—	1717
AzCH$_2$CHOHCH$_2$NMeCH$_2$CH=CH$_2$	—	198
AzCH$_2$CHOHCH$_2$NPrCH$_2$CH=CH$_2$	—	198
AzCH$_2$CH(O$_2$CNHEt)CH=CH$_2$	—	3359
AzCHOHCH$_2$CH$_2$CHOHAz	71	3625
AzCH$_2$CHOHCH$_2$CH$_2$CH=CHCHOHCH$_2$Az	—	182
AzCH$_2$CH(O$_2$CNHBu)CH=CH$_2$	—	3359
AzCH$_2$CH(O$_2$CNEt$_2$)CH=CH$_2$	—	3359
AzCH(CH$_2$O$_2$CNHPh)CH=CH$_2$	—	3358
AzCH$_2$CH(O$_2$CNHPh)CH=CH$_2$	—	3359
AzCH$_2$CH(O$_2$CNPh$_2$)CH=CH$_2$	—	3359
[AzCH$_2$CH(CH=CH$_2$)O]$_2$CO	—	3359
6-Az-6-deoxy-1,2-O-isopropylidene-D-glucofuranose	—	3686
1,6-Az$_2$-1,6-dideoxy-D-mannitol	—	676
[AzCH$_2$CH(CH=CH$_2$)O$_2$CCH$_2$CH$_2$]$_2$	—	3359
2-AzCH$_2$-benzimidazole	79	3282
2-AzCH$_2$CH$_2$NH-quinoline	—	2921
3,5-(AzCH$_2$)$_2$-2,6-Me$_2$-pyridine	—	2550
3-AzCH$_2$CH$_2$NH-6-Cl-pyridazine	—	2731; cf. 2206, 3424
4-AzCH$_2$CH$_2$NH-3,6-Cl$_2$-pyridazine	—	3414
4-AzCH$_2$CH$_2$NH-3,6-Br-pyridazine	—	3414

Aziridines 1-Substituted with Aralkyl or Aromatic Group

Compound	CCR[a] No.	References
1-(2-MeAz)-2-indanol	—	3096
4-Az-1,2-C$_{10}$H$_5$(OH)$_2$	—	1162,1169, 1421, 1428
4-(2-MeAz)-1,2-C$_{10}$H$_5$(OH)$_2$	—	1421
3-Az-2-Cl-1,4-C$_{10}$H$_4$(OH)$_2$	—	2452
2,5-(2-MeAz)$_2$-1,4-C$_6$H$_2$(OH)$_2$	106	2455
2,6-Az$_2$-3,5-Br$_2$-1,4-C$_6$(OH)$_2$	—	2450, 2452
2,5-Az$_2$-3,6-Cl$_2$-1,4-C$_6$(OH)$_2$	—	2452
2,6-Az$_2$-3,5-(EtO)$_2$-1,4-C$_6$(OH)$_2$	129	1131, 2450
2,5-Az$_2$-3,6-(EtO)$_2$-1,4-C$_6$(OH)$_2$	130	705, 2452
2,5-Az$_2$-3,6-(PrO)$_2$-1,4-C$_6$(OH)$_2$	—	2452
2,5-Az$_2$-3,6-(BuO)$_2$-1,4-C$_6$(OH)$_2$	—	1131
2,5-Az$_2$-3,6-(MeS)$_2$-1,4-C$_6$(OH)$_2$	—	705
2,6-Az$_2$-3,5-(EtS)$_2$-1,4-C$_6$(OH)$_2$	—	2450, 2452
2,5-Az$_2$-3,6-(EtS)$_2$-1,4-C$_6$(OH)$_2$	—	705, 2452
2,5-Az$_2$-3,6-(MeOCH$_2$CH$_2$O)$_2$-1,4-C$_6$(OH)$_2$	—	2452

Table 6-XI—*continued*

Compound	CCR[a] No.	References
(1-Aziridinyl) Quinones		
(*p*BQ = *p*-benzoquinone; NQ = naphthoquinone)		
2-Az-5,6-Me₂-*p*BQ	—	1131, 1421
2-Az-1,4-NQ	116	1117
2-Az-5,6,7,8-H₄-1,4-NQ	—	1421, 1427
2-Az-3-Me-1,4-NQ	—	1117
4-(2-MeAz)-1,2-NQ	—	1421, 1428
4-(2,2-Me₂Az)-1,2-NQ	—	1421, 1428
4-Az-3-Cl-1,2-NQ	—	1162, 1421, 3138
2-Az-3-Cl-1,4-NQ	121	1117, 1154
4-(2-MeAz)-3-Cl-1,2-NQ	—	1162, 1421, 3138
4-(2,2-Me₂Az)-3-Cl-1,2-NQ	122	1162, 1421, 3138
4-Az-3-MeO-1,2-NQ	—	1162, 1421
2-Az-3-MeO-1,4-NQ	124	1111, 1421
2-Az-3-EtO-1,4-NQ	—	1131
2-Az-3-PhO-1,4-NQ	—	1131, 1151, 1421
2-Az-3-(*p*-MeC₆H₄O)-1,4-NQ	—	1151, 1421
2-Az-3-MeS-1,4-NQ	—	1111, 1131
2-Az-3-EtS-1,4-NQ	—	1131
2-Az-3-PhS-1,4-NQ	—	3124
2-Az-3-(*p*-MeC₆H₄S)-1,4-NQ	—	3124
2-Az-3-PhCH₂S-1,4-NQ	—	1131
2-Az-3-(*p*-ClC₆H₄S)-1,4-NQ	—	3124
2-Az-3-(Ac₂CH)-1,4-NQ	—	1170
2-Az-3-(HOCH₂CH₂S)-1,4-NQ	—	1421
2-Az-3-(HOCH₂CH₂CH₂S)-1,4-NQ	—	1421
2,5-(2-MeAz)₂-*p*BQ	—	1117, 1151
2,3-Az₂-1,4-NQ	—	1171
2,5-Az₂-3-Cl-*p*BQ	—	1117, 1154
2,6-Az₂-3,5-Br₂-*p*BQ	—	2450
2,5-Az₂-3,6-Br₂-*p*BQ	—	1117, 1154
2,6-(2-MeAz)₂-3,5-Br₂-*p*BQ	—	2450
2,5-Az₂-3,6-Cl₂-*p*BQ	127	1117, 1151
2,5-(2-MeAz)₂-3,6-Cl₂-*p*BQ	—	1117
2-Az-3-AcNH-1,4-NQ	—	1133, 1421
2-Az-3-AcNMe-1,4-NQ	—	1133, 1421
2-Az-3-AcNEt-1,4-NQ	—	1133, 1421
2,5-Az₂-3,6-(HO)₂-*p*BQ	—	1050
2,6-(2-MeAz)₂-3,5-(MeO)₂-*p*BQ	—	2450
2,5-Az₂-3,6-(MeO)₂-*p*BQ	—	1111
2,5-Az₂-3,6-(PrO)₂-*p*BQ	131	1131

Table 6-XI—*continued*

Compound	CCR[a] No.	References
(1-Aziridinyl) Quinones		
(pBQ = p-benzoquinone; NQ = naphthoquinone)		
2,5-(2-MeAz)$_2$-3,6-(EtO)$_2$-pBQ	—	*1131*
2,5-Az$_2$-3,6-(PhO)$_2$-pBQ	—	*1151, 1421*
2,5-Az$_2$-3,6-(MeS)$_2$-pBQ	—	*1131*
2,5-Az$_2$-3,6-(EtS)$_2$-pBQ	—	*1131*
2,5-(2-MeAz)$_2$-3,6-(EtS)$_2$-pBQ	—	*1131*
2,5-Az$_2$-3,6-(PhS)$_2$-pBQ	—	*1131, 1421*
2,5-Az$_2$-3,6-(PhCH$_2$S)$_2$-pBQ	—	*1131*
2-Az-3-MeSO$_2$NMe-1,4-NQ	—	*1165, 1421*
2-Az-3-MeSO$_2$NCH$_2$CH=CH$_2$-1,4-NQ	—	*1165*
2,5-Az$_2$-3,6-(MeOCH$_2$CH$_2$O)$_2$-pBQ	134	*1131, 1421*
2,5-Az$_2$-3,6-(EtOCH$_2$CH$_2$O)$_2$-pBQ	—	*1131*
2,5-Az$_2$-3,6-(MeSCH$_2$CH$_2$O)$_2$-pBQ	—	*1421*
2,5-Az$_2$-3,6-(MeOCH$_2$CH$_2$S)$_2$-pBQ	—	*1421*
2,5-Az$_2$-3,6-(EtSCH$_2$CH$_2$O)$_2$-pBQ	—	*1421*
2,5-Az$_2$-3,6-(morpholino-Y)$_2$	—	*1396*
Y = –CH$_2$CH$_2$O–, –CH$_2$CH$_2$CH$_2$O–, –CMe$_2$O–		
2,5-Az$_2$-3,6-(HOCH$_2$CH$_2$CH$_2$S)$_2$-pBQ	—	*1421*
2,5-Az$_2$-3,6-(p-MeOC$_6$H$_4$S)$_2$-pBQ	—	*1131, 1421*
(3-Az-1,4-NQ-2-SCH$_2$)$_2$	—	*1131*
4-Az-1,2-NQ-phenazine with (CH$_2$NH$_2$)$_2$	—	*1421*
4-Az-1,2-NQ-phenazine with o-C$_6$H$_4$(NH$_2$)$_2$	—	*1421*
4-Az-3-Cl-1,2-NQ-phenazine with o-C$_6$H$_4$(NH$_2$)$_2$	—	*1421*
4-Az-1,2-NQ-phenazine with 3-Me-1,2-C$_6$H$_3$(NH$_2$)$_2$	—	*1421*
2,3,6-Az$_3$-pBQ	135	*1429*
6,7-Az$_2$-quinoline-5,8-dione	—	*1171*
Az$_4$-pBQ	137	*1756*
2,5-Az$_2$-3,6-dipiperidino-pBQ	—	*1173*
2,5-Az$_2$-3,6-(AcNH)$_2$-pBQ	138	*1133, 1421*
		2450, 2454
2,5-(2-MeAz)$_2$-3,6-(AcNH)$_2$-pBQ	139	*2450, 2454*
2,5-Az$_2$-3,6-(EtCONH)$_2$-pBQ	140	*2450, 2454*
2,5-(2-MeAz)$_2$-3,6-(EtCONH)$_2$-pBQ	141	*2450, 2454*
2,5-Az$_2$-3,6-dimorpholino-pBQ	—	*1173*
2,5-Az$_2$-3,6-(PrCONH)$_2$-pBQ	142	*2450, 2454*
2,5-Az$_2$-3,6-(Me$_2$NCH$_2$CH$_2$O)$_2$-pBQ	—	*1131*
2,5-Az$_2$-3,6-(c-C$_6$H$_{11}$CONH)$_2$-pBQ	143	*2458*
2,5-Az$_2$-3,6-(n-C$_6$H$_{13}$CONH)$_2$-pBQ	—	*699*
2,5-Az$_2$-3,6-(n-C$_{15}$H$_{31}$CONH)$_2$-pBQ	—	*699*
2,5-Az$_2$-3,6-(Et$_2$NCH$_2$CH$_2$S)$_2$-pBQ	—	*1131*
2,5-Az$_2$-3,6-(IMeEt$_2$NCH$_2$CH$_2$S)$_2$-pBQ	—	*1421*
2,5-Az$_2$-3,6-(H$_2$NCH$_2$CONH)$_2$-pBQ	—	*2402*
2,5-Az-3,6-(AzCH$_2$CONH)$_2$-pBQ	—	*2402*
2,5-Cl$_2$-3,6-(AzCH$_2$CONH)$_2$-pBQ	—	*2402*

Table 6-XI—*continued*

	Compound		CCR[a] No.	Refer- ences

Aziridines 1-Substituted with Heterocyclic Group

Compound	CCR[a] No.	References
4-Az-coumarin	—	*1437*
4-Az-7-MeO-coumarin	—	*1437*
4-Az-7,8-(MeO)$_2$-coumarin	—	*1437*
3-Az-6-Br-pyridazine	—	*3424*
3-Az-6-MeSO$_2$-pyridazine	—	*2731*
1-(ClCH$_2$CH$_2$)-1-(4-pyrimidinyl)aziridinium picrate	—	*3190*
6-Az-3-Cl-pyridazine	—	*3424*
3-(or 6-)Az-6-(or 3-)Cl-4-Me-pyridazine	—	*3418*
3-(or 6-)Az-6-(or 3-)Cl-4-MeO-pyridazine	—	*3418*

Pyrimidines
(substituents as shown)

2-	4-	5-	6-	CCR[a] No.	References
Az	H	H	H	147	*81*
MeS	Az	CH$_2$OH	H	159	*2139*
MeS	Az	H	CO$_2$Me	162	*2139*
MeS	Az	CO$_2$Et	H	163	*2139*
Cl	Az	H	CO$_2$Me	166	*2139*
MeS	Az	Br	H	167	*2139*
MeS	Az	Br	Me	168	*2139*
MeS	Az	Br	Cl	169	*2139*
p-ClC$_6$H$_4$CH$_2$S	Az	Br	H	170	*2139*
p-ClC$_6$H$_4$CH$_2$S	Az	Br	Me	171	*2139*
2,4-Cl$_2$C$_6$H$_3$CH$_2$S	Az	Br	H	172	*2139*
MeS	Az	H	Cl	173	*2139*
MeS	Az	Ph	Cl	174	*2139*
Cl	Az	H	H	—	*81*
Cl	Az	Br	Me	178	*1042*
Cl	Az	Me	H	179	*2139*
MeS	2-MeAz	H	Cl	181	*2139*
Az	NHC$_6$H$_4$F-p	NO$_2$	Me	—	*1042*
Cl	Az	Cl	Me	—	*1042*
Az	Az	H	H	—	*81*
Az	Az	H	Me	—	*2550*
Az	Az	NO$_2$	Me	191	*1042*
H	Az	H	SO$_2$Me	—	*2731*

Table 6-XI—*continued*

Compound	CCR[a] No.	References
2-Az-4,6-(Me$_2$N)$_2$-s-triazine	209	*3126*
2-(Az$_2$C=N)-4,6-Cl$_2$-triazine	—	*3091*
2-(Az$_2$C=N)-4-Az-6-Cl-triazine	—	*3091*
2-R-4,6-Az$_2$-s-triazines,		
R = H	210	*3126*
4-MeOC$_6$H$_4$CH$_2$O	—	*2208*
4-EtOC$_6$H$_4$CH$_2$O	—	*2208*
4-O$_2$NC$_6$H$_4$CH$_2$O	—	*2208*
3,4-(MeO)$_2$C$_6$H$_3$CH$_2$O	—	*2208*
3,4-(HCO$_2$)$_2$C$_6$H$_3$CH$_2$O	—	*2208*
3-O$_2$N-4-MeOC$_6$H$_3$CH$_2$O	—	*2208*
p-MeO$_2$CCH(NHCHO)CH$_2$C$_6$H$_4$O	—	*336*
p-MeO$_2$CCH(NHAc)CH$_2$C$_6$H$_4$O	—	*336*
ClCH$_2$CH$_2$NH	227	*3126*
Et$_2$N	228	*3126*
Az$_2$C=N	—	*3091*
(Et$_2$N)$_2$C=N	—	*3091*
Piperidino	—	*3442*
Morpholino	—	*3442*
4-Me-piperidino	—	*3442*
p-AcC$_6$H$_4$NH	—	*1297*
p-EtCOC$_6$H$_4$NH	—	*1297*
EtO$_2$CCH$_2$NH	230	*3442*
MeO$_2$CCHMeNH	231	*3442*
EtO$_2$CCHMeNH	233	*3442*
Me$_2$CHCH(CO$_2$Et)NH	—	*3442*
PhCH$_2$O$_2$CCHMeNH	—	*3442*
EtO$_2$CCHMeNPh	—	*3442*
EtO$_2$CCH$_2$CH(CO$_2$Et)NH	235	*3442*
EtO$_2$CCH$_2$CH$_2$CH(CO$_2$Et)NH	236	*3442*
p-MeO$_2$CCH(NHAc)CH$_2$C$_6$H$_4$NH	—	*336*
(EtO$_2$C)$_2$C(NHAc)	—	*336*
N$_2$CH	—	*1683*
1,4-(4,6-Az$_2$-2-triazinyl)$_2$-piperazine	—	*3442*
2-Az-3-Cl-quinoxaline	258	*3690*
2-Az-3-Cl-6-O$_2$N-quinoxaline	—	*3419*
4-Az-7-Cl-quinoline	—	*2837*
6-Az-9-(tetrahydropyran-2-yl)-9H-purine	270	*3557*
6-Az-2-Cl-7-Me-purine	—	*3667*
9-Az-6-Cl-2-MeO-acridine	—	*2837*

1-Aziridinylalkanoic Derivatives

Compound	CCR No.	References
AzCH$_2$CH$_2$CO$_2$Me	—	*3625*
AzCH$_2$CH$_2$CO$_2$CH=CH$_2$	285	*3625*

Table **6-XI**—*continued*

Compound	CCR[a] No.	References
1-Aziridinylalkanoic Derivatives		
AzCH$_2$CH$_2$CO$_2$CH$_2$CH=CH$_2$	287	*3625*
(AzCH$_2$CH$_2$CO$_2$CH$_2$)$_2$	—	*3625*
2-AzCH$_2$-3-oxocyclopentane-1-CO$_2$Et	—	*3416*
AzCH$_2$CH$_2$CON(CH$_2$CH=CH$_2$)$_2$		*2560b*
1,4-(AzCH$_2$CH$_2$CO)$_2$-piperazine	—	*1901*
1,4-[(2-MeAz)CH$_2$CH$_2$CO]$_2$-piperazine	—	*1901*
1,4-[(2,2-Me$_2$Az)CH$_2$CH$_2$CO]$_2$-piperazine	—	*1901*
1-Aziridinecarboxylic Esters		
AzCO$_2$CH$_2$CH=CH$_2$	312	*3625*
(AzCO$_2$CH$_2$)$_2$CMe$_2$	317	*3625*
(*p*-AzCO$_2$C$_6$H$_4$)$_2$CMe$_2$	318	*3625*
(AzCO$_2$CH$_2$)$_2$	319	*3625*
(AzCO$_2$CH$_2$CH$_2$)$_2$O	321	*3625*
Steroid Derivatives		
16-Az-3β-HO-5-pregnen-20-one	—	*3161, 3321* *4017*
16-Az-3β-HO-5-pregnen-20-one acetate	—	*3161*
16-Az-4-pregnen-3,20-dione	—	*3161, 3321* *4017*
16-AzCH$_2$-5β-HO-5-androsten-17-one	—	*3161, 4019*
16-AzCH$_2$-5β-HO-5-androsten-17-one acetate	—	*3161, 4019*
16-AzCH$_2$-4-androstene-3,17-dione	—	*3161*
16-Az-3-MeO-1,3,5(10)-estratrien-17-one	—	*4019*
Sugar Derivatives		
Glucosyl-NHCOAz	—	*933*
Tetraacetylglucosyl-NHCOAz	—	*933*
1-Aziridinecarbothionamides, AzCSNHR		
(AzCSNH)$_2$(CH$_2$)$_2$	—	*1116*
(AzCSNH)$_2$(CH$_2$)$_4$	—	*1116*
[(2-MeAz)CSNHCH$_2$]$_2$	—	*1116*
[(2,2-Me$_2$Az)CSNHCH$_2$]$_2$	—	*1116*
(AzCSNH)$_2$(CH$_2$)$_6$	367	*1116*
p-(AzCSNH)$_2$C$_6$H$_4$	368	*1116*
p-(AzCSNHCH$_2$)$_2$C$_6$H$_4$	—	*1116*

Table 6-XI—*continued*

Compound	CCR[a] No.	References
1-Aziridinecarbothionamides, AzCSNHR		
(3-AzCSNH-4-MeOC$_6$H$_3$)$_2$CH$_2$	—	1116
1,3,5-(AzCSNH)$_3$-2-MeC$_6$H$_2$	—	1116
4-(AzCSNH)-2-MeC$_6$H$_3$NHCOAz	—	1116
Glucosyl-NHCSAz	—	933
Tetraacetylglucosyl-NHCSAz	—	933
Other Urea and Thiourea Derivatives		
(BP = biphenyl)		
4,4'-(AzCONH)$_2$-3,3'-Me$_2$-BP	—	1147
4,4'-(AzCONH)$_2$-3,3'-Cl$_2$-BP	—	1147
4,4'-(AzCONH)$_2$-3,3'-(MeO)$_2$-BP	—	1147
4,4'-(AzCONH)$_2$-2,2'-(MeO)$_2$-BP	—	1147
4,4'-(AzCONH)$_2$-3,3'-(EtO)$_2$-BP	—	1147
4,4'-(AzCONH)$_2$-3,3'-(PhO)$_2$-BP	—	1147
4,4'-(AzCONH$_2$-2,2',6,6'-(MeO)$_4$-BP	—	1147
4,4'-(AzCONH)$_2$-2-O$_2$N-BP	—	1147
AzCONHP(O)Cl$_2$	—	605
AzCONHP(O)(NHPh)$_2$	—	605
(AzCONH)$_3$PO	—	605
Other 1-Acylaziridines		
(CH$_2$)$_2$(COAz)$_2$	—	106a
Various 3-oxocyclopentanecarbonyl-Az	—	4048
2-Furoyl-Az	—	1717
(5-Br-2-furoyl)-Az	—	1717
(5-O$_2$N-2-furoyl)-Az	—	1717
m-(ClCH$_2$CH$_2$)$_2$NC$_6$H$_4$COAz	—	3701
p-(ClCH$_2$CH$_2$)$_2$NC$_6$H$_4$COAz	—	3503
p-(ClCH$_2$CH$_2$)$_2$NC$_6$H$_4$(CH$_2$)$_n$COAz (*n* = 0 to 3)	—	878
Quinoxaline-1,4-dioxide-2-COAz	—	3036
CH$_2$(COAz)$_2$	—	424
(CH$_2$)$_3$(COAz)$_2$	410	3625
AzCMe=NNHC$_6$H$_4$NO$_2$-*p*	—	2349a
Az$_2$SO	435	1961
2-(2,5-Dioxo-4-imidazolidinyl)ethanesulfonyl-Az	—	2342
Compounds Having Aziridinyl N Linked to P		
(BuS)$_2$PAz	—	3110
Ethylene 1-Az-phosphonite	—	1530

Table 6-XI—*continued*

Compound	CCR[a] No.	References
Compounds Having Aziridinyl N Linked to P		
Propylene 1-Az-phosphonite	—	1530
1,2-Me$_2$-ethylene 1-Az-phosphonite	—	1530
Trimethylene 1-Az-phosphonite	—	1530
1-Me-trimethylene 1-Az-phosphonite	—	1530
Me$_2$P(S)Az	—	1168
Et$_2$P(S)Az	—	1168
PhP(O)(OEt)Az	—	1136
MeP(O)(NHCH$_2$CH=CH$_2$)Az	—	671
(EtO)$_2$P(O)Az	—	1136
(EtS)$_2$P(O)Az	—	3110
(BuO)$_2$P(O)Az	—	1136
O,O-1-Me-trimethylene 1-Az-phosphonothioate	—	1530
o-Phenylene 1-Az-phosphonate	—	3107
(PhO)$_2$P(O)N=CPhAz	—	2190
1-Az-(3-HO-1,1-Me$_2$-2-butenyl)phosphinothioic acid, intramol. *O*-ester	—	3168
(ClCH$_2$CH$_2$)$_2$NP(O)(NH$_2$)Az	—	1348
(ClCH$_2$CH$_2$)$_2$NP(O)(NH-cyclohexyl)Az	—	1348
(CH$_2$=CHCH$_2$NH)$_2$P(O)Az	—	671
(ClCH$_2$CH$_2$)$_2$NP(O)(OH)Az, salt with cyclohexylamine	—	1348
(ClCH$_2$CH$_2$)$_2$NP(O)(OCH$_2$Ph)Az	—	1348
(ClCH$_2$CH$_2$)$_2$NP(O)(NR$_2$)Az, various values of R	—	2041
PhP(O)(NEt$_2$)Az	—	1136
(ClCH$_2$CH$_2$)$_2$NP(O)(OCH$_2$CH$_2$Cl)Az	—	1348
(ClCH$_2$CH$_2$)$_2$NP(O)(OPh)Az	—	1348
(Et$_2$N)$_2$P(O)Az	—	1136
PhNEtP(O)(NHPh)Az	—	1136
(Piperidino)$_2$P(O)Az	—	1136
(Morpholino)(piperidino)P(O)Az	—	1136
(Morpholino)$_2$P(O)Az	—	1136
(H$_6$-Azepin-1-yl)$_2$P(O)Az	451	3624
(2-Methyl-3-thiazolidinyl)-P(O)Az$_2$	—	1906
Et$_2$NP(O)(OEt)Az	—	1136
PhP(S)(OEt)Az	—	1136
(MeO)$_2$P(S)Az	454	517
(EtO)$_2$P(S)Az	455	1136
O,O-Ethylene 1-Az-phosphonothioate	—	1530, 3110
O,O-1-Me-trimethylene 1-Az-phosphonothioate	—	1530
MeP(S)(NHCH$_2$CH=CH$_2$)Az	—	671
PhP(S)(NEt$_2$)Az	—	1136
(Me$_2$N)$_2$P(S)Az	—	1136
(CH$_2$=CHCH$_2$NH)$_2$P(S)Az	—	671
H$_6$-Azepin-1-yl-P(S)(Cl)Az	457	3624
(H$_6$-Azepin-1-yl)$_2$P(S)Az	458	3624

Table 6-XI—*continued*

Compound	CCR[a] No.	References
Compounds Having Aziridinyl N Linked to P		
5-[$Az_2P(O)CH_2$]-4-Me-uracil	—	337
$EtOP(O)(2,2-Me_2Az)_2$	—	4023
$PhP(S)Az_2$	477	517
$2-C_{10}H_7OP(O)Az_2$	506	3113
$2-C_{10}H_7OP(S)Az_2$	507	3113
$4-H_2N-2-MeS-5$-pyrimidinylmethyl-$OP(O)Az_2$	—	1726
$EtOP(S)Az_2$	513	517, 1206
$EtOP(S)(2-MeAz)_2$	514	1421
$ClCH_2CH_2OP(S)Az_2$	515	517
$PrOP(S)Az_2$	516	517
$PrOP(S)(2-MeAz)_2$	517	517
$BuOP(S)Az_2$	518	517
iso-$BuOP(S)Az_2$	—	1206
$n-C_5H_{11}OP(S)Az_2$	—	1206
$Me_2CHCH_2CH_2OP(S)Az_2$	520	517
$c-C_6H_{11}-OP(S)Az_2$	—	1206
$n-C_{17}H_{35}CO_2CH_2CH_2OP(O)Az_2$	—	292
$n-C_{17}H_{35}CO_2CH_2CH(O_2CC_{17}H_{35}-n)-CH_2OP(O)Az_2$	—	292
$n-C_{10}H_{21}OP(S)Az_2$	524	517
$PhOP(S)Az_2$	525	517, 1206
$PhOP(S)(2-MeAz)_2$	526	517
$p-ClC_6H_4OP(S)Az_2$	527	517
$p-MeC_6H_4OP(S)Az_2$	528	517
$p-MeOC_6H_4OP(S)Az_2$	529	517
$4-Cl-3-MeC_6H_4O-P(S)Az_2$	530	517
$EtOP(S)(2,2-Me_2Az)_2$	531	517
$PrOP(S)(2,2-Me_2Az)_2$	532	517
$PhOP(S)(2,2-Me_2Az)_2$	533	517
$MeNHP(O)Az_2$	—	1212
$MeCH{=}CHCH_2NHP(O)Az_2$	536	1224
$BuNHP(O)Az_2$	537	1212
$c-C_6H_{11}NHP(O)Az_2$	—	1350, 3900
$Me(CH_2)_6NHP(O)Az_2$	—	933
$C_8H_{17}NHP(O)Az_2$	—	1212
Pinocamphyl-$NHP(O)Az_2$	—	2908a
$Me(CH_2)_{11}NHP(O)Az_2$	—	933
$p-PhCH_2O_2CCH_2C_6H_4NHP(O)Az_2$	—	3900
$MeO_2CCHMeNHP(O)Az_2$	—	669a
$HOCH_2CH_2CH_2NHP(O)Az_2$	—	1350
$p-FC_6H_4NHP(O)Az_2$	—	2930
$MeONHP(O)Az_2$	—	605
$p-F_3CC_6H_4NHP(O)Az_2$	—	2930
$p-EtO_2CCH_2C_6H_4NHP(O)Az_2$	—	2120

Table 6-XI—*continued*

Compound	CCR[a] No.	References
Compounds Having Aziridinyl N Linked to P		
p-EtO$_2$OCH$_2$C$_6$H$_4$NHP(S)Az$_2$	—	2120
p-EtO$_2$CCH(NHAc)C$_6$H$_4$NHP(O)Az$_2$	—	2120
p-EtO$_2$CCH(CH$_2$Ph)NHCOC$_6$H$_4$NHP(O)Az$_2$	—	2120
p-EtO$_2$CCH(iso-Pr)NHCOCH(NHAc)C$_6$H$_4$NHP(O)Az$_2$	—	2120
p-MeO$_2$CCH$_2$CH$_2$CH$_2$C$_6$H$_4$NHP(O)Az$_2$	—	3900
m-HO$_2$CCH(NH$_2$)CH$_2$C$_6$H$_4$NHP(O)Az$_2$	—	2444
p-HO$_2$CCH(NH$_2$)CH$_2$C$_6$H$_4$NHP(O)Az$_2$	—	2444
p-EtO$_2$CCH(iso-Bu)NHCOCH$_2$C$_6$H$_4$NHP(O)Az$_2$	—	3900
p-EtO$_2$CCH(CH$_2$Ph)NHCOCH$_2$C$_6$H$_4$NHP(O)Az$_2$	—	3900
p-EtO$_2$CCH(CH$_2$Ph)NHCOCH$_2$CH$_2$CH$_2$C$_6$H$_4$NHP(O)Az$_2$	—	3900
o-FC$_6$H$_4$CONHP(O)Az$_2$	—	2930
m-FC$_6$H$_4$CONHP(O)Az$_2$	—	2930
p-FC$_6$H$_4$CONHP(O)Az$_2$	565	2930
p-F$_3$CC$_6$H$_4$CONHP(O)Az$_2$	—	2930
EtO$_2$CNHP(O)(2-MeAz)$_2$	—	270
EtO$_2$CNHP(O)(2-EtAz)$_2$	—	270
EtO$_2$CNHP(O)(2,3-Me$_2$Az)$_2$	—	270
EtO$_2$CNHP(O)(2,2,3-Me$_3$Az)$_2$	—	270
c-C$_6$H$_{11}$O$_2$CNHP(O)Az$_2$	—	271
Various 4-substituted-2-[Az$_2$P(O)NH]-pyrimidines	—	671
2-[(2-MeAz)$_2$P(O)NH]-pyrimidine	—	4133
3-[Az$_2$P(O)NH]-pyridazine	—	3420
3-[Az$_2$P(O)NMe]-pyridazine	—	3420
3-[Az$_2$P(O)NH]-6-Cl-pyridazine	—	3420
3-[Az$_2$P(O)NMe]-6-Cl-pyridazine	—	3420
5-Glucosyl-O$_2$CNHP(O)Az$_2$	—	271
5-Uracil-O$_2$CNHP(O)Az$_2$	—	271
Et$_2$NCONHP(O)Az$_2$	—	271
RNHCONHP(O)Az$_2$		
R = CH$_2$=CHCH$_2$	—	1193
Bu	—	1193
iso-Bu	—	1193
Ph	—	1193
c-C$_6$H$_{11}$	—	1193, 2189
o-ClC$_6$H$_4$	—	2189
p-ClC$_6$H$_4$	—	1193, 2189
p-BrC$_6$H$_4$	—	2189
PhCH$_2$	—	1193
o-MeC$_6$H$_4$	—	2189
p-MeC$_6$H$_4$	—	271, 1193, 2189
4-Me-c-C$_6$H$_{10}$	—	1193
2-Cl-4-MeC$_6$H$_3$	—	1193

Table 6-XI—*continued*

Compound	CCR[a] No.	References
Compounds Having Aziridinyl N Linked to P		
RNHCONHP(O)Az$_2$		
R = PhCH$_2$CH$_2$	—	1193
PhCH=CHCH$_2$	—	1193
o-MeOC$_6$H$_4$	—	2189
p-MeOC$_6$H$_4$	—	1193
p-MeO-c-C$_6$H$_{10}$	—	1193
1-C$_{10}$H$_7$	—	2189
2-C$_{10}$H$_7$	—	2189
EtO$_2$CCHMe	—	2189
iso-BuNHCONHP(O)(2-MeAz)$_2$	—	1193
iso-BuNHCONHP(O)(2,2-Me$_2$Az)$_2$	—	1193
PhNHCONHP(O)(2-MeAz)$_2$	—	1193
p-ClC$_6$H$_4$NHCONHP(O)(2-MeAz)$_2$	—	1193
(c-C$_6$H$_{11}$)$_2$NCONHP(O)Az$_2$	—	271
(ClCH$_2$CH$_2$)$_2$NP(O)Az$_2$	573	1348
CH$_2$=CHCH$_2$NHP(O)Az$_2$	—	1224
CH$_2$=CHCH$_2$NEtP(O)Az$_2$	574	1224
(CH$_2$=CHCH$_2$)$_2$NP(O)Az$_2$	575	1224
iso-Bu$_2$NP(O)Az$_2$	577	2810a
(n-C$_8$H$_{17}$)$_2$NP(O)Az$_2$	—	2810a
[c-C$_6$H$_{11}$N(CH$_2$CH=CH$_2$)]P(O)Az$_2$	580	1224
[p-ClC$_6$H$_4$N(CH$_2$CH=CH$_2$)]P(O)Az$_2$	—	1224
[PhCH$_2$N(CH$_2$CH=CH$_2$)]P(O)Az$_2$	581	1224
[p-MeC$_6$H$_4$N(CH$_2$CH=CH$_2$)]P(O)Az$_2$	—	1224
[PhCH=CHN(CH$_2$CH=CH$_2$)]P(O)Az$_2$	582	1224
CH$_2$=CHCH$_2$NPhP(O)Az$_2$	584	1224
3-[Az$_2$P(Y)NH(CH$_2$)$_n$]-indoles	—	2613a
(Y = O or S)		
2-[Az$_2$P(O)NH]-5-Me-1,3,4-thiadiazole	—	3427, 3428
2-[Az$_2$P(O)NEt]-1,3,4-thiadiazole	585	3186, 3420
2-[Az$_2$P(O)NH]-5-Et-1,3,4-thiadiazole	—	3427, 3428
2-[Az$_2$P(O)NEt]-5-Me-1,3,4-thiadiazole	—	3420
2-[Az$_2$P(O)NEt]-5-Cl-1,3,4-thiadiazole	—	3420
2-[Az$_2$P(O)NEt]-5-Br-1,3,4-thiadiazole	—	3420
2-[Az$_2$P(O)NH]-5-Pr-1,3,4-thiadiazole	—	3427, 3428
2-[Az$_2$P(O)NPh]-1,3,4-thiadiazole	—	84, 87, 3420
2-[Az$_2$P(O)NH]-5-Ph-1,3,4-thiadiazole	—	3427, 3428
AzCAr=NP(O)Az$_2$, Ar = Ph, p-ClC$_6$H$_4$, or p-BrC$_6$H$_4$	—	2190
Y[CAz=NP(O)Az$_2$]$_2$, Y = m-C$_6$H$_4$ or p-C$_6$H$_4$	—	2940
CH$_2$=CHCH$_2$NHP(S)Az$_2$	586	1224
HOCH$_2$CH$_2$CH$_2$NHP(S)Az$_2$	587	1350
MeOCH$_2$CH$_2$CH$_2$NHP(S)Az$_2$	—	1350
c-C$_6$H$_{11}$NHP(S)Az$_2$	588	1350, 3900
(CH$_2$=CHCH$_2$)$_2$NP(S)Az$_2$	592	1224

Table 6-XI—*continued*

Compound	CCR[a] No.	References
Compounds Having Aziridinyl N Linked to P		
$MeO_2CNHP(S)Az_2$	—	*269, 271*
$EtO_2CNHP(S)Az_2$	—	*271*
$PhCH_2OCNHP(S)Az_2$	—	*271*
$p\text{-}[Az_2P(S)NH]C_6H_4CH_2CHNH_2CO_2H$	—	*2444*
$3\text{-}[Az_2P(S)NH]\text{-pyridazine}$	—	*3420*
$3\text{-}[Az_2P(S)NMe]\text{-pyridazine}$	—	*3420*
$3\text{-}[Az_2P(S)NH]\text{-6-Cl-pyridazine}$	—	*3420*
$3[Az_2P(S)NMe]\text{-6-Cl-pyridazine}$	—	*3420*
$H_6\text{-Azepin-1-yl-}P(S)Az_2$	607	*3624*
$1\text{-}[Az_2P(S)]\text{-4-Me-piperazine}$	—	*1161*
$H_6\text{-Azepin-1-yl-}P(O)Az_2$	620	*3624*
$p\text{-}C_6H_4[OP(O)Az_2]_2$	621	*3468*
$CH{=}CHCH_2N[P(O)Az_2]_2$	—	*3188*
$BuN[P(O)Az_2]_2$	—	*3188*
$c\text{-}C_6H_{11}N[P(O)Az_2]_2$	—	*3188*
$PhCH_2N[P(O)Az_2]_2$	—	*3188*
$ArCON{=}PAz_3$		
Ar = Ph, $o\text{-}ClC_6H_4$, $p\text{-}ClC_6H_4$, $o\text{-}BrC_6H_4$, $p\text{-}BrC_6H_4$, $m\text{-}O_2NC_6H_4$, and $p\text{-}O_2NC_6H_4$	—	*2190*
$ArSO_2N{=}PAz_3$		
Ar = Ph	636	*2190, 3112, 3468*
$p\text{-}ClC_6H_4$	637	*2190, 3112, 3468*
$p\text{-}MeC_6H_4$	638	*2190, 3112*
$p\text{-}MeOC_6H_4$	—	*2190, 3468*
$p\text{-}MeOC_6H_4$	639	*2190, 3112, 3468*
$p\text{-}O_2NC_6H_4$	—	*2190*
$p\text{-}Az_3P{=}NC_6H_4$	—	*3114*
$Y(N{=}PAz_3)_2$		
$Y = m\text{-}C_6H_4(CO)_2$, $p\text{-}C_6H_4(CO)_2$, $m\text{-}C_6H_4(SO_2)_2$, $\text{-}SO_2\text{-}$	—	*2940*
$Y = p\text{-}C_6H_4(SO_2)_2$	—	*2940, 3468*
$p\text{-}AzSO_2C_6H_4N{=}PAz_3$	—	*3468*
Phosphorylated Steroids		
$Cholesterol\text{-}OP(O)Az_2$	—	*2858*
$Estrone\text{-}OP(O)Az_2$	—	*2858*
$Diethylstilbestrol\text{-}[OP(O)Az_2]_2$	—	*2858*
$Testosterone\text{-}OP(O)Az_2$	—	*2858*
$Estradiol\text{-}[OP(O)Az_2]_2$	—	*2858*
$Cholesterol\text{-}OP(S)Az_2$	—	*2858*
$Estrone\text{-}OP(S)Az_2$	—	*2858*

Table 6-XI—*continued*

Compound	CCR[a] No.	References

Mitomycin Derivatives

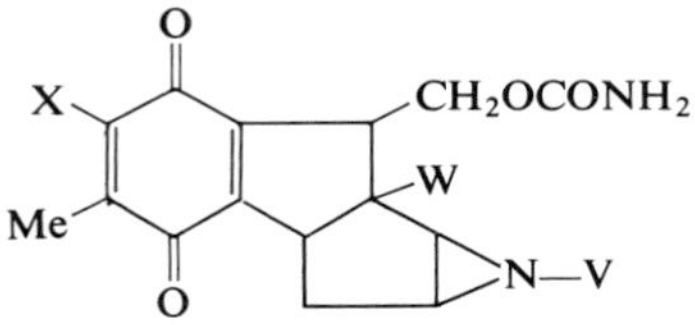

V =	W =	X =	References
H	OMe	OH	2229
COCH$_2$Cl	OMe	NH$_2$	2227
Bz	OMe	NH$_2$	2227
SO$_2$Me	OMe	NH$_2$	2227
SO$_2$C$_6$H$_4$Me-*p*	OMe	NH$_2$	2227
Ac	OMe	OAc	2229
Bz	OMe	OBz	2229
Me	OH	NH$_2$	2226
CO$_2$Et	OMe	NH$_2$	2227
Maleoyl	OMe	NH$_2$	2227
Phthaloyl	OMe	NH$_2$	2227
Phthaloylglutamyl	OMe	NH$_2$	2227

not now included, but those for which only accession numbers were cited *are* listed again. The earliest record of screening for each compound has been sought.

The mechanism by which aziridines exert their antitumor activity remains to be discussed, but cannot be expounded with any confidence. As has already been noted, most opinion has associated the cytostatic and cytotoxic effects of such drugs with their alkylating ability (*3068*). A recent study, however, has indicated that antitumor activities of tretamine, tepa, and Az$_2$P(O)NHCO$_2$Et parallel their rates of hydrolysis rather than the rates at which they alkylate 4-(*p*-nitrobenzyl)pyridine (*266*). Since the rate of hydrolysis of aziridinyl quinones rises exponentially with decreasing pH, and decreased pH is characteristic of tumor cells, it has been suggested that hydrogen peroxide formed by intracellular redox reactions of quinones is the real cytostatic agent (*331, 1759*); but this idea can scarcely explain the activity of nonquinonoid antitumor drugs. Efforts have been made, without notable success, to correlate such activity with magnetic susceptibility and electron delocalization (*2486,*

2946) and with partition coefficients between benzene and aqueous phosphate buffer solutions (*3331*).

Antitumor activity has been claimed for polymers produced by treating 1-(1-aziridinyl)-3-buten-2-one with copper, nickel, cobalt, or iron salts (*127*); but toxicity also increased. The metal–nitrogen bond may be responsible. The antitumor activity of iododeoxyuridine or 5-iododeoxycytidine was increased by prior complexing with PEI (*3833*); this must be related to the observation that PEI is preferentially adsorbed by tumor cells and greatly reduced the growth of mouse ascites tumors (*75*). Polymers from 1-(2-hydroxy-3-butenyl)-aziridines had antitumor action only if they retained some aziridinyl groups (*988a*).

Aziridines as Adrenomotor Antagonists

2-Haloalkylamines of the type $RR'NCH_2CH_2X$ wherein at least one of the R groups is benzyl or substituted benzyl have been known for about 20 years to possess a remarkable ability to prevent the usual effects of administration of adrenaline or stimulation of adrenergic nerves in the animal body. The antagonism to adrenaline is often complete and long-lasting. This aspect of pharmacology has been competently reviewed (*316, 319, 1516, 2696, 3611*), and the convincing evidence that these drugs are active only as they cyclize to aziridinium ions has been cited in Chapter 1 (p. 4). They have had considerable use in physiological research and a little in human therapy, e.g., for treatment of hypertension and of some vascular disorders. Such medical applications are discussed by Graham (*1516*). The inhibition of erythrocyte acetylcholinesterase by 1,1-dimethyl-2-phenylaziridinium ion is specific and irreversible (*320, 2942a*). A similar long-lasting and specific blocking action on acetylcholine receptors is shown by the aziridinium ion from

$$Ph_2C(OH)CO_2CH_2CH_2NMeCH_2CH_2Cl \ (\textit{1470}).$$

Aziridines as Sources of Antiradiation Agents

A research program notable in recent years has been the development of chemicals which will counteract the dire effects of ionizing radiations on living things, particularly the higher animals. These agents are preferably effective after exposure, but ones that confer protection by administration before exposure are also of interest. On the whole the most potent protective agents discovered have been 2-aminoethanethiol, $H_2NCH_2CH_2SH$, and its derivatives; the field has been reviewed (*259, 2522, 3218*). It is mentioned now because one of the best routes for synthesis of these substances is the opening of the aziridine ring with thiols (see p. 230). It is inappropriate here to discuss the still poorly understood mechanism by which these compounds exert their effect, or to give references to the extensive testing of 2-aminoethanethiol and salts of S-(2-aminoethyl)isothiourea, $H_2NCH_2CH_2SC(=NH)NH_2$. Aziridines have been used to produce both N-substituted (458, 690, 1277, 1488, 1495, 1755, 3090, 4020) and S-substituted 2-aminoethanethiols (494, 1277, 1312, 1755, 2425, 2883, 3182, 3622, 4001) for trial, but the program is obviously in the experimental stage. Of interest here is the observation that compounds containing mercapto groups reduced the chemosterilant effect of apholate on the housefly (1286a).

Use of Aziridines in Synthesis of Other Drugs

The reactions involved here are more systematically discussed in Chapter 3, and the pharmaceutical applications, being mostly in the form of patent claims, are not well known if indeed they have been verified clinically. What is presented is necessarily a relatively uncritical synopsis of the literature.

SEDATIVES AND TRANQUILIZERS

Various 2-aminobenzophenones react with aziridines to yield benzodiazepines (7) for this use (1743, 1745, 1747, 3000, 3001, 3090)

7

and a different route to diazepines involves an aziridine intermediate (1360, 1744). Other ring expansions and openings yielding sedatives and hypnotics start with aziridines (885a, 1481, 2286, 3241, 3242, 3248). Some aziridines themselves, in spite of their potential toxicity, are claimed to have tranquilizing and antidepressive effects (1767, 3243, 3245, 3248, 4085); the arylmercapto amines from arenethiols and aziridines are also effective (692, 701).

Some aziridines, especially 1-phenethyl- and 1-isopropyl-2-phenylaziridine, have been shown to have high activity as monoamine oxidase inhibitors (3248a).

MISCELLANEOUS DRUGS OF SPECIFIED ACTIVITY

Substituted guanidines, either made by aziridine ring opening (*3324*) or still containing such a ring (*2812*), help counteract hypertension. More detailed claims for use against disorders of lipid metabolism are made for "cytidine-5'-diphosphate ethanolamine," made by the esterification of cytidine-5'-diphosphate with EI (*3475*). Probably of physiological rather than therapeutic interest is the prolonged drop in blood pressure caused by acetylated forms of 2-aminoethanethiol (*2201*). Ring openings of EI with *N*-(*m*-chlorophenyl)-*N*-phenylcarbamoyl chloride (*824*) or of an 2-alkoxy-2-(*p*-methoxyphenyl)-3,3-dimethylaziridine with water and acid (*1919*) constitute one step in the synthesis of appetite inhibitors (anorectic agents), and thiols and aziridines similarly can lead ultimately to heterocyclic local anesthetics (*2767*) or anthelmintics (*1407, 1899a, 4080*). Camphidine (*3486*) or 4-(*p*-chlorophenyl)-perhydroazepine (*3488*) and EI with an acid catalyst, then by reaction with an *S*-alkylisothiourea, yield *N*-(2-guanidinoethyl) derivatives for treating muscular disorders. Among other polymeric amines, PEI orally administered is useful to combat hyperacidity (*26, 26a*) and to bind bile acids in the intestinal tract and thus lower blood cholesterol levels and relieve pruritis due to biliary stasis (*3821*). A few compounds containing the aziridine ring are claimed: 1-[β-(5-nitro-2-furyl)acryloyl]aziridine for combating trematode parasites (*666*), and steroidal aziridines as hormonal regulators (*440, 985, 2531*).

DRUGS OF UNSPECIFIED ACTIVITY

Vague claims for pharmacological value have been made for the products of aminoethylating theophylline and other xanthines (*145, 147*), cyclic imides (*143, 144*), and flavanoid glucosides (*2236*) with EI. Several patents include the aziridinyl group among other secondary amino groups in compounds broadly claimed as drugs (*1767a, 2814, 2815, 2816a, 2817, 2817a, 3538a, 3660, 3663, 3666, 3668*), but it is probable that the pyrrolidino or the piperidino group is a better choice.

ANALYTICAL METHODS FOR AZIRIDINES AND DERIVATIVES

Chemical Methods

Procedures for the detection and determination of EI and other compounds containing the aziridine ring mostly depend on the unusual features of that ring, particularly its cleavability. There is no such unique character associated with PEI, and it is not easily distinguished from similar polyalkylenepoly-amines. The field has been reviewed only incompletely (*1444, 1967, 2320, 3619*).

PRECIPITATION

Precipitation of EI from aqueous solution with bulky anions such as BiI_4^- and HgI_4^{2-} [as the Cu(II) complex] is known (*1444*; cf. *3851*), and indeed $NaBPh_4$ has even been suggested for the gravimetric determination of EI as $AzH_2^+BPh_4^-$ (*1967*). However, none of these methods is specific or well enough worked out to be of interest.

TITRATION

Titrimetric methods for determining aziridines, like those for oxiranes, usually involve opening the ring with an excess of a nucleophilic anion. While many of the procedures may be applied equally well to both activated aziridines and basic aziridines, the differences in the nature of the ring-opening reactions should be recognized; see appropriate sections of Chapter 3. For example, basic aziridines must be treated with a large excess of acid to convert them completely to aziridinium ions, which then undergo ring opening by the nucleophile. Unless this is done, unprotonated aziridine molecules may react as nucleophiles toward protonated ones, and such reaction (polymerization) consumes none of the added nucleophile and no acid; but such consumption is the basis of the method. In contrast, while the activated aziridine is much less basic, the tendency for the unprotonated aziridine to act as a nucleophile is negligible, and consequently little more than the stoichiometric amount of acid is necessary. In another difference, a protonated activated aziridine reacts with the added nucleophile virtually instantaneously, whereas the protonated basic aziridine reacts more slowly, enough so as to require increased time or temperature or both.

Failure of the several methods based on ring opening is due in most cases to competitive ring opening by water or other nucleophile that does not consume acid.

The aziridine **1** may represent either a basic aziridine converted to aziridinium ion or a transitory protonated activated aziridine. Obviously the ratio of rate constants, k_1/k_2, should be as high as possible; this is achieved by the choice of an anion, B^-, of high nucleophilicity. The overall rate for the first reaction relative to the second may also be increased by using as large an excess of B^- as is feasible. In applying the various methods to specific analytical problems, consideration should always be given to the possible presence of other nucleophilic materials. For certain aziridines, such as MAPO, still other competitive side reactions may exist.

It is possible to titrate EI and the simple basic aziridines with acid in cold aqueous or nonaqueous solution, but the method is useful only in the absence of amines or other basic materials having K_b values close to those of the aziridines (*1967, 2071, 2767a, 2916, 3230*).

The oldest procedure based on ring opening prescribes heating the sample with excess standard hydrobromic acid (or standard hydrochloric acid and sodium bromide), and back-titrating the excess acid.

$$AzH_2^+ + Br^- \rightarrow BrCH_2CH_2NH_2$$

Since details of the method are somewhat inaccessible (*395, 1967*), it is summarized here. It applies only to EI and its water-soluble nonactivated derivatives.

A sample containing up to 40 meq of aziridine rings is titrated to a methyl orange end point with 1.00N HCl and then treated with 50.0 ml of 1.00N HCl and 20 ml of saturated aqueous sodium bromide solution. The mixture is boiled for 15 minutes, cooled, and back-titrated to the methyl orange end point with 1.00N NaOH.

A similar method that is applicable to water-insoluble aziridines employs standard pyridine hydrochloride in pyridine as the acid source, and thymolphthalein–phenolphthalein as the indicator (*964, 1583*). In this case pyridine is the nucleophile causing the ring opening. The method is generally applicable to activated aziridines.

Although it has been successfully applied to some basic aziridines, it should be noted that the aziridine is not converted to the aziridinium ion completely; some of the free base form is present. Thus a ring-opening reaction between basic aziridine and aziridinium ion which does not consume acid is possible.

Also suitable for certain water-insoluble aziridines such as APO is treatment of a sample in an inert solvent (acetone, chloroform, benzene, or chlorobenzene) with excess tetraethylammonium bromide or, preferably, iodide, and direct titration with standard perchloric acid in glacial acetic acid or dioxane, with crystal violet as indicator (*1977*).

The highly nucleophilic thiosulfate ion has been extensively used in determining aziridines. It was first employed in analysis for the aziridinium ions arising by spontaneous cyclization of 2-chloroethylamines (nitrogen mustards). Thiosulfate was added to a bicarbonate-buffered solution and the excess was titrated iodimetrically (*1492*). The procedure has been used by many investigators (p. 5). Buffering the sample to a pH of about 4 during the reaction with thiosulfate is desirable to minimize further cyclization (*728, 3270*). However, unless the reaction with thiosulfate is fast relative to reaction with water —and sometimes it is not (*280, 1620, 2109, 3269*)—hydrolysis will destroy some aziridinium ion. Thus some complex aziridinium picrylsulfonates of high purity showed only 93–96% of the theoretical thiosulfate consumption (*65*). When the reaction with thiosulfate is slow, the results may be a measure of not only the aziridinium ion but also the open-chain form, by an S_N2 reaction of the latter (*2109*).

A Bunte anion

As a variation, either the excess thiosulfate or the Bunte anion may be determined polarographically (*2343, 2426, 2427, 3869*).

For aziridines themselves, the thiosulfate method is reasonably general for water-soluble samples. Again iodimetric determination of the excess has been used (*964*). A faster route is to add excess thiosulfate, titrate rapidly to pH 4 (methyl orange or pH meter) with standard acid, let stand a half hour, and titrate to pH 10.2 (phenolphthalein or meter) with standard base (*62, 2321, 2964, 3080, 3839*). The acid protonates the ring to form the aziridinium ion, which reacts rapidly. The procedure gives good results (>99%) for both EI and some activated forms (tretamine, APO, thiotepa, etc.) but not for 1-arenesulfonylaziridines nor $(2,2\text{-Me}_2\text{Az})_3\text{PO}$. Later workers reported results less good: 51–53% assay on $(2,2\text{-Me}_2\text{Az})_2\text{P(O)NHCO}_2\text{Et}$ (*270*), 92–96% assay on pure APO, and 96% on pure TEM, but 100% on apholate (*343a*). For 2-methylaziridine, titration to a phenol red end point is recommended; potentiometric titration to pH 5.7 gives results that are low by 1% to 3% (*4082*).

A very rapid and reproducible procedure, of interest because it is suitable for methanol-soluble samples, uses excess potassium thiocyanate in methanol, standard *p*-toluenesulfonic acid, and potassium hydroxide as the titrant (*3153, 4155*).

$$\text{Az}^+\text{RH} + \text{SCN}^- \rightarrow \text{RNHCH}_2\text{CH}_2\text{SCN}$$

The method gave somewhat less than theoretical results on hindered activated aziridines, but only a few such compounds were tested.

COLORIMETRY

A qualitative and quantitative but nonspecific method of analysis for EI depends on color formation with *sym*-trinitrobenzene (*1967*). Both basic and activated aziridines may be detected by reaction with thiourea, rearrangement of the $\text{H}_2\text{N}\text{—C—C—SC(NH)NH}_2$ to $\text{HS—C—C—NHC(NH)NH}_2$ with alkali, and formation of a purple color (due to the mercapto group) with nitroprusside (*3460*).

Alkylating agents of many kinds react with γ-(4-nitrobenzyl)pyridine to yield a blue dye which is distinctive and stable enough to constitute the basis of both detection and determination of such agents. The reaction was first used quantitatively to determine the sulfur mustard $\text{S(CH}_2\text{CH}_2\text{Cl})_2$, and was applied to aziridines by Epstein, Rosenthal, and Ess (*1061*). The alkylation of the pyridine is effected by heating with the aziridine at a pH of 4.0–4.4 and the color is developed by adding potassium carbonate or other base. Absorption at 540–600 mμ, properly corrected, is a measure of alkylating agent; since the maximum varies with structure of the aziridine and composition of the medium, the method should be validated by use of a known sample. The procedure has been used repeatedly for detecting (1349) and determining (161, 1351, 1442, 2107, 2397, 2618, 2854, 2988, 3347, 3485) nitrogen mustards. Both aziridines and nitrogen mustards react with the pyridine reagent in an S_N2 reaction, for which good rate constants can be obtained (266). The process may be considered as a measure of the aziridinium form and not the 2-chloroethyl form of the mustards. Most papers recommend only minor variations from the original procedure, but in the presence of biological fluids, an extraction of the dye into a nonaqueous layer for measurement is advantageous (3485, 3619).

A modified procedure for determining EI itself permits raising the temperature to decrease the time required. One ml of sample is mixed with 1 ml of 2-butoxyethanol containing 0.1 gm of γ-(4-nitrobenzyl)pyridine. The solution is heated for 5 minutes at about 185°C, cooled in an ice bath, and treated with 1 ml of 2-butoxyethanol saturated with cesium carbonate. The absorption is read at 562 mμ (963).

The method is also useful for APO, tretamine, and aziridinylbenzoquinones (343, 2738a, 2987, 3619), but the alkylation with some complex aziridinium ions (65) and with $Az_2P(O)NHCO_2Et$ and its homologs (268) is so slow that the procedure appears unsuitable for determining such compounds.

A more rapid method for determining traces of EI itself employs the Folin reagent for amino acids, 1,2-naphthoquinone-4-sulfonic acid; but the method is inapplicable to 1-substituted aziridines, and there is danger of interference by other nontertiary amines, though not ammonia (2270, 3059). The procedure requires only reaction for a few minutes at a pH of about 10, extraction of the dye with chloroform, and reading absorbance at 420 mμ. It has been recommended for monitoring plant and laboratory atmospheres for EI vapor, and is sensitive down to 1 ppm (779, 1961). Reading the absorbance at 255 mμ extends the sensitivity to 0.2 ppm (554). However, gas chromatography may well be more convenient (963).

Analytical differentiation between aziridines and many nitrogen mustards of the type $RN(CH_2CH_2Cl)_2$ can be effected with 8-quinolinol, which gives a color reaction only with the latter (3602). Similarly p-phenylphenol reacts primarily with bis(2-chloroethyl)ethylamine rather than the aziridinium form, to yield a colored compound measurable by spectrofluorimetry (2523). However, a similar procedure (extraction with benzene or chloroform–methanol, heating with 2-naphthol and acid, extraction of the dye, and reading the fluorescence at 355 mμ induced by activation at 290 mμ) works well for traces of tepa and thiotepa (2524, 2525).

Of the several methods that have been mentioned (*664, 665, 2904, 2913*) for the detection of PEI in paper, the ones based on enhanced dyeability with eosin and especially on nitrosation appear best. The paper is subjected to preliminary reduction with sodium hydrosulfite to eliminate interferences, then treated with nitrous acid, washed clean, and tested for nitroso groups with diphenylamine (blue color produced). Traces of PEI can be determined in water by adding the naphthoquinone reagent previously referred to, a little trisodium phosphate buffer, and some aqueous sodium bisulfite, and reading absorbance at 425 mμ (*963*). The copper(II) chelate of PEI is also suitable for the spectrophotometric determination (by absorbance at 635 mμ) of either the polymer (*2849*) or of copper (*2849, 3883*). As an alternative, both copper sulfate and eosin are added and the color due to the PEI–Cu(II)–eosin complex read (*554*).

POLAROGRAPHY

The concentration of aziridinyl rings in solutions of some nitrogen mustards (*2427, 3869*), aziridinylbenzoquinones (*106, 293, 330, 331, 3718, 3719, 4004, 4011, 4012*), and aziridinyl derivatives of mannitol (*1960*) has been determined polarographically, but this specialized electroanalytical method has not been used routinely.

Physical Methods

The abundance of physical analytical methods and instruments for their application needs no emphasis. Those cited here are only those in which a measurement was clearly applied to the detection or the determination of an aziridine or its polymer. Obviously others could be so used.

CHROMATOGRAPHY

Paper chromatography has been tested for the identification of EI (*1300, 2556*), 1-(2-hydroxyethyl)aziridine (*1300*), tepa (*2525*), and thiotepa (*2525, 2577*). Thin-layer chromatography on alumina is usable for tepa (*343a, 4017*), tretamine (*343a, 2577*), and a considerable series of 1-aziridinecarboxamides (*1301*), and column chromatography on silica gel–sodium sulfate to concentrate tepa from complex mixtures and permit its colorimetric determination (*739, 771*). The original articles should be consulted for the solvent systems used and the R_f values observed, which are too numerous to tabulate here. Ligand-exchange liquid chromatography has been investigated for separating aziridines in mixtures (*4202*). In hydrogenolytic gas chromatography EI yielded ethane (*343*).

Gas–liquid partition chromatography has been used in analysis for EI (964, 1488a, 2781); since access to details of the methods may be difficult, they are given here. A general-purpose column for use is an 8-ft by 0.25-inch stainless steel tube packed with 30% Dow Polyglycol E6000 on 30–70 mesh Celite and equipped with a thermal conductivity detector. Column temperature is kept at 90°–110°C and helium pressure at 10 lb/sq. inch. A similar column for 2-methylaziridine analysis contained Carbowax 20M on Chromosorb W and was used at 115°–120°C (4082). Another partitioning liquid useful for the separation of EI is Oronite's Dispersant NI-W. A 6-ft by $\frac{3}{16}$-inch fluorocarbon column packed with 30% Dispersant NI-W on Chromosorb W, 80–100 mesh, is operated at 100°C and an argon gas pressure of 30 lb/sq. inch with a hydrogen flame ionization detector for the determination of EI in the presence of water (964).

Separation of EI can also be effected on a 10-ft by 0.25-inch aluminum column containing 30% Triton X-100 on Applied Science Laboratories' Gas Chrom P, 100–200 mesh. The column is operated isothermally at 45° to 100°C, depending on the application, and is used with a thermal conductivity detector or, if water is present, a hydrogen flame ionization detector. The flow rate of helium carrier gas through the column and the thermal conductivity detector is 40% on a Brooks Rotameter 1A-15-1 tube (stainless steel ball). The rate is about 20 ml/minute with the hydrogen flame ionization detector. This column is also effective for analysis for 1-(2-aminoethyl)aziridine (963). Columns with Apiezon L on Celite 545 have also been used (98a).

Trace quantities of EI in air, water, or other substances can be detected by using the previously described Triton X-100 column and a hydrogen flame ionization detector or a 16-ft by 0.25-inch Micro-Tek aluminum column with 15 weight % Tergitol 35 on Chromosorb W, 60–80 mesh, which has been treated with 2% potassium hydroxide solution. The column is operated at 130°C with helium carrier gas at 40 lb/sq. inch at the head of the column. The lower limit of detection will depend upon the stability of the flame unit used. Two to 5 ppm can easily be detected with a stable instrument (807a, 963).

Several columns, each in conjunction with a hydrogen flame ionization detector, have been used for determination of trace quantities of impurities in EI. A 10-ft by $\frac{3}{16}$-inch aluminum column packed with 10% UCON 50HB2000 and 10% glycerol on Chromosorb W, 80–100 mesh, is operated at 80°C (partitioning liquid loss is excessive at temperatures higher than 90°C) with a helium carrier gas flow rate of 20 ml/minute. An 8-ft by $\frac{3}{16}$-inch aluminum column packed with 7.5% di(2-ethylhexyl) sebacate and 22.5% diglycerol on Chromosorb W is used at 80°C and helium gas flow at 50% on a Brooks Rotameter 1A-15-1 tube (Pyrex ball). The advantage of these columns is that the EI is held up, allowing trace impurities, which would normally be hidden in the EI tail, to emerge before the EI. The range of detection of impurities depends on the sensitivity to the particular impurity. Impurities have been detected in the 0.1 ppm range. To obtain maximum sensitivity, the flow rates of hydrogen and air to the flame ionization detector are adjusted for each application (*964*). Similar columns with polyethylene glycol 4000 on Chromosorb P or W used at 85°–100°C detected 0.001 % 2-aminoethanol or 0.005 % water in EI (*3501a*).

Gas–liquid partition chromatography has been used also to determine a substituted 1,2-divinylaziridine (*3389*) (silicone oil on firebrick) and traces of aziridinyl chemosterilants (*457, 771*), to separate *cis*- and *trans*- 1,2,3-trialkylaziridines (*3679*) (didecyl phthalate, Silicone 550, or Amine 220 on Chromosorb W-HMDS), and to study stabilities, retention times, and structures of 1-aziridinecarboxamides (*3885*) (QF-1 fluorosilicone and methyl chlorophenyl silicone), and to determine 1-benzoyl-2-ethylaziridine in the presence of its rearrangement products (oxazolines) (ethylene glycol succinate or diethylene glycol succinate on Diatoport-S) (*4154*). Again the number of variables involved is so considerable that retention times are not worth restating here.

Owing to the strong tendency of PEI to be adsorbed on paper, it does not migrate in paper chromatography, at least under the conditions tested (*1417*); but it has been fractionated as the acetate by combined paper chromatography and paper electrophoresis (*2850*). The oligomers of EI are distinguishable by paper chromatography with 1-butanol–acetic acid–water–pyridine (9:2:4:6) as solvent and ninhydrin as color former (*265, 2641*).

SPECTROMETRY

An extensive comparison of infrared spectra of 1-substituted aziridines (*3349*) contains many suggestions for determining the concentration of such compounds in mixtures. An absorption band at 1230 cm^{-1} was used to follow disappearance of 2-ethyl-2-phenylaziridine by hydration (*1026*). Infrared spectroscopy has been employed to detect the reaction products of APO with the cellulose of cotton textiles, but the method is not very sensitive (*2490, 2554, 3612*). Better results were obtained by examining the products of hydrolysis of textiles so treated (*2553*). 2,5-Dipropoxy-3,6-(1-aziridinyl)-1,4-benzoquinone has been determined on the basis of its ultraviolet absorption maximum (in cyclohexane) at 340 mμ (*3839*).

NMR spectrometry has been more useful for structure proof than for measurement of concentration of aziridines. Ethylenimine and tepa have been so determined (*343a*), and aziridines and aziridinium ions formed from nitrogen mustards (*2310, 2865, 3347*), as well as some isomeric aziridines (*2165*), including the *cis–trans* forms of substituted aziridines and derived quaternary salts (*445, 446, 451, 454, 1467b, 1625*). The water content of MAPO is determinable by either NMR or infrared techniques (*4190*). A discussion of the analysis of PEI by infrared absorption is available (*945*).

OTHER METHODS

Analysis of systems consisting essentially of EI, its polymers, and water has been effected by viscometry and refractometry (*1996*) and by dilatometry (*2641*).

ANALYSIS OF ETHYLENIMINE

Nearly pure EI (>95 %) may be analyzed (*963*) for total impurities by determination of the melting point from a time–temperature curve and application of the equation

$$\text{Mole } \% \text{ purity} = 100 - 1.98 \, (73.97 - \text{m.p. in } {}^{\circ}\text{C})$$

The procedure is essentially that of ASTM D1015 (*90*). Water in EI is conveniently measured by gas–liquid partition chromatography on a column of 30 % Triton X-100 on Gas Chrom P at 75°C, the column being preconditioned by water injection (*963*).

8

HANDLING AND STORAGE OF AZIRIDINES

Toxicity

PRECAUTIONS

The principal difficulty in the handling of aziridines, and particularly EI itself, arises from the high toxicity of these compounds. Furthermore the toxic effects are often manifest only after some delay. The toxicology is discussed in Chapter 6; precautions and first aid measures are added here. Medical attention should be obtained in case of *any* known or suspected exposure.

Ethylenimine and 2-methylaziridine present the greatest danger because their vapor pressures are ordinarily high enough to generate an inhalation hazard. Because of the ammonialike odor of EI vapor, most persons find the breathing of high concentrations to be objectionable or even intolerable. However, the detection of odor should not be relied on to prevent over-exposure; repeated exposures to the vapors at concentrations low enough not to cause discomfort can still have serious consequences. The odor threshold for EI is reported as 2 ppm (*1269*). A threshold limit value of 0.5 ppm in air for continuous exposure has been set (*78*).

Liquid EI and the 2-methyl homolog rapidly cause severe burns of the skin and of the eye, and have acute oral toxicity.

In laboratory operations where minimum exposures are likely, persons handling EI or 2-methylaziridine should wear chemical workers' goggles and rubber gloves, and should use a laboratory hood (*964, 4082*). Where there is danger of more extensive exposure, as in industrial use, full protective clothing (suitable respiratory equipment, slicker suit, boots, and rubber gloves) should be worn, and a safety shower should be readily accessible. Details on such protective clothing have been published (*964*). For low concentrations of vapor, a full-face gas mask with a fresh ammonia (silica gel) canister or a breathing apparatus with air supply should be used; for longer exposures to moderate or high concentrations, only a breathing apparatus with air supply is recommended.

Spilled EI should be flushed away with plenty of water, and persons not equipped with protective clothing and special breathing apparatus excluded from the area until the danger is past.

FIRST-AID MEASURES

Skin Contact. Upon any suspected contact immediately flush the skin with large amounts of water while removing contaminated clothing, including shoes. Wash the affected area with soap and plenty of water. Get medical attention promptly. Destroy contaminated shoes and wash contaminated clothing before reuse. During and after removal, contaminated clothing must be handled with great care to prevent skin contact. Skin contact with EI may not produce evidence of burns for several hours and the resulting burns will be severe and require long periods of time to heal. Erythema usually develops within a few hours followed by vesiculation and progression into full-thickness skin burns. Immediate and prolonged decontamination (at least 30 minutes) with copious amounts of water will considerably lessen the severity of skin burns.

Eye Contact. Wash the eyes immediately with plenty of flowing water for at least 30 minutes and obtain medical attention promptly.

Swallowing. If conscious, patient should drink large amounts of milk or water immediately. Call a physician immediately.

Vapor Inhalation. Remove to fresh air any person who shows ANY SIGNS of illness that may be due to an exposure of EI. Call a physician immediately. The victim should be kept warm and quiet until the physician arrives. If breathing stops, start artificial respiration.

Other Hazards

Both EI and 2-methylaziridine are highly flammable; the flash point of EI is $-11.1°C$ (12°F), about like that of benzene. Both the U.S. Coast Guard (*1269*) and the U.S. Interstate Commerce Commission (*1270*) classify these as inflammable liquids, and prescribe conditions for their shipment.

The polymerization of undiluted EI or 2-methylaziridine by traces of acids or other catalysts (*365, 1999, 2018*) is likely to be explosively violent. Care must be taken to avoid such combination.

Hazards of Derivatives

Derivatives of EI should be considered toxic in rough proportion to the fraction of the molecule that is aziridine ring, although as this becomes smaller the volatility decreases and thus also the danger from inhaling the vapors. The tendency to explosive polymerization by acids also persists (e.g., *2686*). Special and understandable instability is reported for 1-chloroaziridine, which has exploded after storage (*116, 1509*), and 1,1'-biaziridine, Az–Az, which is dangerous when heated in air (*1510*).

By way of contrast, it may be worth repeating here that polymers of EI (*1483, 3120*), and those of APO on and with textiles (*44, 965, 3808*), present no unusual toxicity.

Materials of Construction

Glass, 304 and 316 stainless steel, and mild steel are satisfactory materials in which to store and process EI and its aqueous solutions. Most copper alloys are unsuitable because EI dissolves the copper to form complexes. Silver solder must not be used in fabricating equipment for the purpose because EI converts it into an unknown but explosive substance (*964*).

Most types of rubber are badly swelled by EI, as are plastics in general, but ethylene–propylene synthetic rubber may be satisfactory for gaskets. Teflon and Garlock 900 gaskets are suitable.

Table 8-I shows the effect of EI on various materials, and Table 8-II that of aqueous EI (except as noted).

Aqueous PEI may be stored or shipped in glass, 5052 aluminum, or steel coated with, e.g., Heresite, polyethylene, Unichrome B-124, or Amercoat 75. Mild steel and especially galvanized steel are corroded and are unsuitable container materials (*963*).

Stability and Stabilization

In general, aziridines are stable when well purified and can be kept at room temperature for extended periods if acid impurities are excluded or prevented from forming. It is standard practice to store EI itself over solid sodium hydroxide, which dissolves only in traces but reacts with any atmospheric carbon dioxide that may have gained entrance and thus prevents polymerization. Alkalies and surfactants are also claimed to stabilize aqueous dispersions of 1-aziridinecarboxamides to be used for textile treating (*658a, 1198, 1235*). The half-life of EI as a 20% aqueous solution has been measured under

Table 8-I

RATES OF CORROSION IN ETHYLENIMINE[a,b]

Material	Corrosion (mils/year)	Material	Corrosion (inches/year)
Ferrous Metals and Alloys		*Nonmetals*	
Armco Ingot Iron		Amerplate 95 Y elastomer	—[f]
(0.0057% C)	0.023	Ethylene–propylene	
Cast iron (2.8% C)	0.37[c]	elastomer 404	< 0.001
Cupronickel 30%	0.000	Haveg 41 resin	4.3535[d,e]
Drum Steel 17E (0.03%)	0.018	Haveg 43 resin	2.3993
Duraloy HCA	0.0000	Haveg 60 resin	0.416
Fire Box Steel A212B		Heresite M-66 resin	0.0585[e]
(0.19% C)	0.022	Johns-Manville 61 asbestos	< 0.001
Mild steel (0.047% C)	0.026	Johns-Manville 91 asbestos	< 0.001
Stainless Steel type 304	0.031	Karbate AB graphite	0.00227
Stainless Steel type 316	0.16	Neoprene 333 elastomer	—[g]
		Nitrile compound 464	—[g]
Nonferrous Metals and Alloys		Nordel 1704-C rubber	0.00629
Admiralty brass, inhibited	2.89[d]	Parker "O"-ring	
Aluminum alloy No.		terpolymer	< 0.003
6061-TG	0.3	Phenolic resin TK-2	—[d]
Brass	0.127[d]	Polyethylene	—[i]
Bronze	2.36[d,e]	Ethylene–ethyl acrylate	
Copper	1.77[d,e]	copolymer (90:10)	—[i]
Monel	0.5	SBR 660-4 rubber	—[g]
Nickel	0.16	Teflon	—[i]
Lead, tin	Very small (5000)	Viton A elastomer	—[d,g]

[a] Total immersion, static system, 48 hours at 54.5°C; procedure from J. H. Perry, "Chemical Engineers' Handbook," 4th ed., p. 23–67. McGraw-Hill, New York, 1963.
[b] Dow Chemical Co. data (964).
[c] Gained weight.
[d] Colored EI.
[e] Polymerized EI.
[f] Disintegrated.
[g] Swelled greatly.
[h] At 30°C.
[i] Swelled somewhat.

a variety of conditions; the results are reproduced in Table 8-III (964). Dilute aqueous solutions of thiotepa were stable for months at temperatures below 20°C, but deteriorated rapidly at higher ones, especially in the presence of oxygen, carbon dioxide, or light (2316). Water-insoluble aziridinylbenzoquinones can be dissolved in ethylene glycol and the solution diluted with water for drug use (*1458*); nonionic surfactants have also been tested for dispersing these agents (*1457*). Both simple alcohols (*832*), urethan (*2759*), and poly-ethylene glycols (*2659, 2759*), are alleged to stabilize various aziridinyl drugs

Table 8-II

RATES OF CORROSION IN AQUEOUS ETHYLENIMINE[a,b]

Material	Corrosion (mils/year)
Admiralty, inhibited	37.6
Stainless steel	0.1
Mild steel	1.06
Monel	0.22

[a] Total immersion, static system, 48 hours in 40% EI–60% water at 80°C; procedure as cited in Table I.
[b] Dow Chemical Co. data (*964*).

Table 8-III

STABILITY OF ETHYLENIMINE[a,b]

Solvent	Temp. (°C)	Half-life (hours)
Water[c]	5	232
Water[c]	25	104
Water[c]	50	38
Water[c]	100	0.7
5% aq. NaOH	25	394
1% aq. NaOH	100	14.9
5% aq. NaOH	100	103
10% aq. NaOH	100	99.7
1% aq. NEt$_3$	100	2.3
5% aq. NEt$_3$	100	14.0
10% aq. NEt$_3$	100	17.1
1% aq. (CH$_2$NH$_2$)$_2$	30	394
1% aq. (CH$_2$NH$_2$)$_2$	50	34.3
None[d]	54	9000

[a] 20 wt % solution used except as specified.
[b] Dow Chemical Co. data (*964*).
[c] Distilled water of pH 7.
[d] In sealed metal container with flake NaOH.

in aqueous solution. APO in *nonaqueous* solution is said to keep better in the presence of organic peroxides or dehydrating agents (*1236*).

A very different stabilization of simple aziridines is accomplished by converting them to their sulfate salts, which can be preserved surprisingly well (*2093*).

Industrial Handling

A brochure on EI (*964*) provides detailed information on suitable tanks, pumps, valves, and gauges, and procedures for unloading large shipping containers.

REFERENCES

References have been arranged alphabetically in a main series and a supplementary list. In the main series, some numbers have been skipped because of elimination of duplicate references.

1. E. Abderhalden and M. Paquin, *Ber.* **53**, 1125 (1920).
1a.J. F. Abere (to Minnesota Mining and Manufacturing Co.), U.S. 3,267,054 (1966); Brit. 1,014,302 (1965).
2. J. F. Abere and R. D. Lowrey (to Minnesota Mining and Manufacturing Co.), U.S. 3,147,161 (1964).
3. J. F. Abere (to Minnesota Mining and Manufacturing Co.), U.S. 3,268,433 (1966).
4. J. F. Abere (to Minnesota Mining and Manufacturing Co.), U.S. 3,316,202 (1967).
5. R. J. Abraham and W. A. Thomas, *Chem. Commun.* p. 413 (1965).
6. R. A. Abramovitch and B. A. Davis, *Chem. Rev.* **64**, 149 (1964).
7. J. R. Abrams (to Interchemical Corp.), U.S. 3,138,567 (1964).
8. Aceta G. m. b. H., Fr. 794,750 (1936); *C. A.* **30**, 5334; Neth. 46,320 (1939).
9. C. E. Adams and B. H. Shoemaker [to Standard Oil Co. (Indiana)], U.S. 2,372,244 (1945).
10. E. M. Adams, *Houston Conf., Comm. Hazardous Mater., 1966.* National Research Council—National Academy of Science—National Academy of Engineering, 1967.
11. J. W. Adams (to American Can Co.), U.S. 3,180,787 (1965).
12. R. Adams and T. L. Cairns, *J. Am. Chem. Soc.* **61**, 2464 (1939).
13. R. Adams and V. V. Jones, *J. Am. Chem. Soc.* **71**, 3826 (1949).
14. E. M. Adaskin, N. L. Luk'yanova, and S. L. Gutina, *Gidrolizn. i Lesokhim. Prom.* **11** (8), 15 (1958); via *C. A.* **53**, 7462.
15. B. Adcock and A. Lawson, *J. Chem. Soc.* p. 474 (1965).
16. Adcote Chemicals, Inc., Belg. 646,783 (1964); *C. A.* **63**, 8605; Neth. appl. 6,402,461 (1965).
17. W. E. Adelmann, *Dissertation Abstr.* **19**, 1190 (1958).
18. D. E. Adelson, G. L. Perry, and G. G. Pritzker (to Shell Development Co.), U.S. 2,628,941 (1953).
19. A. Adicoff and A. A. Yukelson, *J. Appl. Polymer Sci.* **10**, 159 (1966).
19a.A. Adicoff and A. A. Yukelson, *J. Appl. Polymer Sci.* **12**, 1959 (1968).
20. Aeisawa Seisakusho Co. Ltd., Japan. 19,960 ('67).
22. T. Agawa, T. Minami, and S. Komori, *Technol. Rept. Osaka Univ.* **16**, 725 (1966); via *C.A.* **67**, 33769.
23. Agfa A.-G., Ger. 928,268 (1955); *C. A.* **52**, 10780.
24. A. H. Ahlbrecht and T. S. Reid (to Minnesota Mining and Manufacturing Co.), U.S. 3,198,754 (1965).
25. A. H. Ahlbrecht (to Minnesota Mining and Manufacturing Co.), U.S. 3,240,579 (1966); Brit. 985,213 (1965).

26. C. Ainsworth *et al.* (to Eli Lilly and Co.), U.S. 3,224,940 (1965).
26a. C. Ainsworth and R. R. Pfeiffer (to Eli Lilly and Co.), U.S. 3,332,841 (1967).
27. T. Aitken, W. V. Cross, and F. W. Webking (to Nalco Chemical Co.), U.S. 3,264,174 (1966).
28. S. Akerfeldt, *Acta Chem. Scand.* **17**, 329 (1963).
29. S. Akerfeldt and L. Fagerlind, *J. Med. Chem.* **10**, 115 (1966).
30. S. Akerfeldt and M. Hellstrom, *Acta Chem. Scand.* **20**, 1418 (1966).
31. A. I. Akhund-Zade, *Izv. Akad. Nauk Azerb. SSR, Ser. Biol. Nauk* p. 40 (1966); via *C.A.* **67**, 61399.
32. A. I. Akhund-Zade and V. V. Khvostova, *Genetika* No. 6, 47 (1966); via *C.A.* **65**, 9310.
33. A. P. Akif'ev, *Vliyanie Ioniz. Izluch. Nasledstvennost, Akad. Nauk SSSR* p. 157 (1966); via *C.A.* **67**, 10242.
34. Albright and Wilson Ltd., Brit. 764,313 (1956); Fr. 1,116,796 (1956); Ger. 1,045,097 (1958).
35. Albright and Wilson Ltd., Brit. 837,709 (1960).
36. Albright and Wilson Ltd., Brit. 837,710 (1960); Austrian 227,471 (1960); Can. 654,627 (1962).
37. Albright and Wilson Ltd., Brit. 901,463 (1962).
38. K. Alder and G. Stein with W. Friedrichsen, *Ann. Chem.* **501**, 1 (1933); K. Alder and G. Stein, *ibid.* **504**, 216 (1933); **515**, 185 (1935); K. Alder and R. Ruehmann, *ibid.* **566**, 1 (1950).
39. K. Alder *et al.*, *Chem. Ber.* **87**, 1752 (1954).
40. V. T. Aleksanyan *et al.*, *Dokl. Akad. Nauk SSSR* **171**, 95 (1966); *Dokl. Chem. (English Transl.)* **169-171**, 1027 (1966).
41. B. H. Alexander *et al.*, *J. Chem. Eng. Data* **7**, 263 (1962).
42. M. L. Alexander and E. Glanges, *Proc. Natl. Acad. Sci. U.S.* **53**, 282 (1965).
43. P. Alexander and J. T. Lett, *Biochem. Pharmacol.* **4**, 34 (1960).
44. P. Alexander, *Melliand Textilber.* **35**, 3 (1954); via *C.A.* **48**, 6131.
45. L. Alexandru *et al.*, *Faserforsch. Textiltech.* **16**, 433 (1965); via *C.A.* **64**, 11360.
46. J. Algar, A. Hickey, and P. G. Sherry, *Proc. Roy. Irish Acad.* **B49**, 109 (1943).
47. Algemene Kunstseide Unie N. V., Neth. appl. 6,609,491 (1967); via *C. A.* **67**, 12380.
47a. Y. Ali *et al.*, *Carbohydrate Res.* **7**, 255 (1968).
48. S. I. Alikhanyan *et al.*, *Antibiotiki* **2**, 33 (1957); via *C.A.* **51**, 16674.
49. S. I. Alikhanyan and L. N. Borisova, *Izv. Akad. Nauk SSSR, Ser. Biol.* No. 2, 74 (1956); via *C. A.* **50**, 9506.
50. S. I. Alikhanyan and N. I. Zhdanova, *Dokl. Akad. Nauk SSSR* **133**, 454 (1960); via *C. A.* **55**, 3715.
51. S. I. Alikhanyan, S. Yu. Gol'dat, and A. F. Tetevyatnik, *Dokl. Akad. Nauk SSSR* **115**, 1015 (1957); *via C. A.* **52**, 3913.
52. S. I. Alikhanyan, E. S. Morozova, and S. I. Veselova, *Antibiotiki* **6**, 1055 (1961); via *C. A.* **56**, 14716.
53. S. I. Alikhanyan and N. B. Romanova, *Antibiotiki* **10**, 1113 (1965); via *C. A.* **64**, 10123.
54. S. I. Alikhanyan and V. G. Zhdanov, *Dokl. Akad. Nauk SSSR* **125**, 1353 (1959); via *C. A.* **53**, 18164.
55. P. I. Alimov and L. A. Antokhina, *Izv. Akad. Nauk SSSR, Ser. Khim.* p. 1316 (1964); *Bull. Acad. Sci. USSR, Div. Chem. Sci. (English Transl.)* p. 1220 (1964).
56. P. I. Alimov and L. N. Nevkova, *Izv. Akad. Nauk SSSR, Ser. Khim.* p. 1298 (1965); *Bull Acad. Sci. USSR, Div. Chem. Sci. (English Transl.)* p. 1271 (1965).

57. All-Union Scientific-Research Chemical-Pharmaceutical Institute, U.S.S.R. 158,278 (1963), via *C. A.* **60**, 9293.
58. All-Union Scientific-Research Chemical-Pharmaceutical Institute, U.S.S.R. 168,294 (1965); via *C. A.* **63**, 5608.
59. All-Union Scientific-Research Institute of Chemical Reagents and Pure Chemical Substances, U.S.S.R. 178,378 (1966); via *C. A.* **64**, 19570.
60. C. F. H. Allen and D. M. Burness (to Eastman Kodak Co.), U.S. 2,983,611 (1961).
61. C. F. H. Allen, F. W. Spangler, and E. R. Webster, *Org. Syn.* Coll. Vol. **4**, 433 (1963).
62. E. Allen and W. Seaman, *Anal. Chem.* **27**, 540 (1955).
63. G. R. Allen, Jr. and J. F. Poletto (to American Cyanamid Co.), U.S. 3,265,698 (1966); Belg. 653,057 (1965).
64. J. F. Allen and N. B. Chapman, *J. Chem. Soc.* p. 1076 (1961).
65. J. F. Allen and N. B. Chapman, *J. Chem. Soc.* p. 1482 (1960).
67. Allied Chemical Corp., Belg. 666,828 (1965); via *C. A.* **65**, 10689; Fr. 1,450,751 (1966); Neth. appl. 6,509,052 (1966); T. G. Bassiri, A. Leory, and M. Litt, *J. Polymer Sci.* **B5**, 871 (1967).
68. Allied Chemical Corp., Neth. appl. 6,610,443 (1967); via *C. A.* **67**, 33166.
69. Allied Chemical Corp., Belg. 654,666 (1965); Neth. appl. 6,412,323 (1965); Fr. 1,412,237 (1965); Brit. 1,015,630 (1966); Indian 96,113 (1966).
70. Allied Chemical Corp., Japan. 2912 ('67).
71. Allied Colloids (Manufacturing) Co. Ltd. and R. Gill, Brit. 678,103 (1952).
72. N. L. Allinger and V. Zalkow, *J. Org. Chem.* **25**, 701 (1960).
73. G. H. Alt and W. S. Knowles, *J. Org. Chem.* **25**, 2047 (1960).
74. R. M. Altman, *Am. J. Hyg.* **77**, 221 (1963).
75. E. J. Ambrose, D. M. Easty, and P. C. T. Jones, *Brit. J. Cancer* **12**, 439 (1958).
76. J. L. Ambrus *et al.*, *Proc. Intern. Symp. Bone Marrow Therapy Chem. Protect. Irradiated Primates, Rijswijk, Neth., 1962* p. 339. Radiobiol. Inst., The Hague, Neth., via *C. A.* **59**, 2082.
77. American Association of Textile Chemists and Colorists, *Am. Dyestuff Reptr.* **54**, 107 (1965).
78. American Conference of Governmental Industrial Hygienists, pamphlet, quoted in full in *J. Chem. Educ.* **44**, A45 (1967); *ibid.*, "Documentation of Threshold Limit Values," Rev. ed., p. 84, 1966.
79. American Conference of Governmental Industrial Hygienists, *J. Occupational Med.* **5**, 491 (1963); *Arch. Environ. Health* **7**, 592 (1963); **9**, 545 (1964).
80. American Cyanamid Co., Can. 491,492 (1953).
81. American Cyanamid Co., Can. 517,305 (1955).
83. American Cyanamid Co., Ger. 1,014,543 (1957); *C. A.* **54**, 18564.
84. American Cyanamid Co., Fr. 1,520,998 (1968).
86. American Cyanamid Co., Neth. appl. 6,505,960 (1965); Belg. 651,846 (1965); Fr. 1,434,578 (1966); Brit. 1,108,035 (1968).
87. American Cyanamid Co., Ger. 1,227,466 (1966); via *C.A.* **66**, 28777.
89. American Cyanamid Co., South Africa 65/6108.
90. American Society for Testing Materials, *Am. Soc. Testing Mater., ASTM Std.* **18**, 145 (1966).
91. I. D. Amikeeva, V. A. Shevchenko, and E. N. Vaulina, *Tr. Mosk. Obshch. Ispyt. Prir., Otd. Biol.* **22**, 149 (1966); via *Bibliog. Agr.* **31**, 48313.
92. A. G. Anastassiou, *J. Org. Chem.* **31**, 1131 (1966).
93. A. G. Anastassiou, H. E. Simmons, and F. D. Marsh, *J. Am. Chem. Soc.* **87**, 2296 (1965).

94. A. G. Anastassiou, *J. Am. Chem. Soc.* **88**, 2322 (1966).
95. A. G. Anastassiou and H. E. Simmons, *J. Am. Chem. Soc.* **89**, 3177 (1967).
96. A. G. Anastassiou, *J. Am. Chem. Soc.* **87**, 5512 (1965).
97. A. G. Anastassiou and R. P. Cellura, *Chem. Commun.* p. 762 (1967).
98. J. R. Anderson and N. J. Clark, *J. Catalysis* **5**, 250 (1966).
98a. A. Andersons and M. V. Shimanskaya, *Piperazin, Akad. Nauk Latv. SSSR, Inst. Org. Sin.* p. 131 (1965); via *C. A.* **66**, 61625.
99. V. S. Andreev, B. N. Sidorov, and N. N. Solokov, *Genetika* No. 6, 28 (1966); via *C. A.* **65**, 9354.
100. K. A. Andrianov, V. I. Sidorov, and L. M. Khananashvili, *Zh. Obshch. Khim.* **36**, 168 (1966); *J. Gen. Chem. USSR (English Transl.)* **36**, 178 (1966).
101. K. A. Andrianov, V. I. Sidorov, and L. M. Khananashvili, *Dokl. Akad. Nauk SSSR* **158**, 868 (1964); *Proc. Acad. Sci. USSR, Chem. Sect. (English Transl.)* **158**, 987 (1964).
102. V. I. Andrianov *et al.*, *Zh. Strukt. Khim.* **8**, 100 (1967); *J. Struct. Chem. (English Transl.)* **8**, 82 (1967).
103. A. F. Androshchuk, *Ukr. Botan. Zh.* **23**, 28 (1966); via *Bibliog. Agr.* **31**, 55901.
104. F. A. L. Anet and J. M. Osyany, *J. Am. Chem. Soc.* **89**, 352 (1967).
105. F. A. L. Anet, R. D. Trepka, and D. J. Cram, *J. Am. Chem. Soc.* **89**, 357 (1967).
106. A. Anhalt and H. Berg, *J. Electroanal. Chem.* **4**, 218 (1962).
106a. V. N. Anisimov, *Vop. Onkol.* **13** (2), 91 (1967); via *C. A.* **66**, 114477.
107. Anonymous, *Chem. Process.* **28**, 65 (1965).
108. Anonymous, *Chem. Week* **90** (19), 82 (1962).
109. Anonymous, *Chem. Week* **96** (6), 58 (1965).
110. Anonymous, *Chem. Week* **92** (26), 23 (1963).
111. Anonymous, *Chem. Eng. News* **36** (42), 25 (1958); *Chem. Week* **91** (26), 13 (1962).
112. Anonymous, *Federal Register* **28**, 348 (1963).
113. Anonymous, *Federal Register* **27**, 11640 (1962); **31**, 13793 (1966).
114. Anonymous, *Federal Register* **30**, 6497 (1965).
115. Anonymous, "Developments in the Wear Resistance of Textiles and Related Papers Published in Germany during World War II," *Publication Board Rept. (U.S.)* PB 99,296 (1939-1947); *Bibliog. Tech. Rept. (U.S.)* **13**, 91.
116. Anonymous, *Chem. Eng. News* **42** (8), 41 (1964).
117. Anonymous, *Chem. Eng.* **70** (15), 96 (1963).
118. Anonymous, *Chem. Eng. News* **46** (6), 51 (1968).
119. Anonymous, *Chem. Eng.* **72** (22), 243 (1965).
120. Anonymous, *Chem. Eng. News* **41** (7), 49 (1963).
121. Anonymous, *Chem. Week* **93** (12), 99 (1963).
122. Anorgana G.m.b.H., *Publication Board Rept. (U.S.)* PB 70,345, Frames 18620–24a (1937-1941); via *Bibliog. Sci. Ind. Rept. (U.S.)* **6**, 674.
123. W. P. Anslow *et al.*, *J. Pharmacol. Exptl. Therap.* **91**, 224 (1947).
124. V. K. Antonov and A. Ya. Berlin, *Zh. Obshch. Khim.* **30**, 151 (1960); *J. Gen. Chem. USSR (English Transl.)* **30**, 161 (1960).
125. V. K. Antonov, *Zh. Obshch. Khim.* **29**, 1132 (1959); *J. Gen. Chem. USSR (English Transl.)* **29**, 1102 (1959).
126. V. K. Antonov and A. Y. Berlin, *Zh. Obshch. Khim.* **29**, 4003 (1959); *J. Gen. Chem. USSR (English Transl.)* **29**, 3962 (1959).
127. A. V. Arbatskii *et al.*, *Khim.-Farm. Zh.* **1**, 34 (1967); via *C. A.* **67**, 62693.
128. S. Archer *et al.*, *J. Am. Chem. Soc.* **83**, 2386 (1961).
129. A. Arens and G. Vanags, *Dokl. Akad. Nauk SSSR* **129**, 98 (1959); via *C. A.* **54**, 7671.

130. A. Arens, V. Mikstais, and G. Vanags, *Latvijas PSR Zinatnu Akad. Vestis, Kim. Ser.* p. 371 (1963); via *C.A.* **60**, 1661.
131. A. Arens, V. Mikstais, and G. Vanags, *Dokl. Akad. Nauk SSSR* **145**, 1279 (1962); *Proc. Acad. Sci. USSR, Chem. Sect.* (*English Transl.*) **145–147**, 743 (1962).
131a. Arkansas State Board of Health, *Textile Ind.* **132** (4), 159 (1968).
132. H. F. Arledter (to Hurlbut Paper Co.), U.S. 2,943,013 (1960).
133. H. F. Arledter (to The Mead Corporation), U.S. 3,184,373 (1965).
134. Armour and Co., Brit. 877,671 (1961).
135. T. J. Arnason and R. Wakonig, *Can. J. Genet. Cytol.* **1**, 16 (1959); R. Wakonig and T. J. Arnason, *Proc. 10th Intern. Congr. Genet., Montreal, 1958* Vol. 2, p. 305. Univ. of Toronto Press, Toronto, 1959.
136. T. J. Arnason *et al.*, *Can. J. Genet. Cytol.* **4**, 172 (1962).
137. T. J. Arnason, L. M. El-Sadek, and J. L. Minocha, *Can. J. Genet. Cytol.* **8**, 746 (1966).
138. H. Arnold, *Strahlentherapie* **119**, 147 (1962).
139. H. Arnold, *Fortschr. Chem. Forsch.* **7**, 196 (1966).
140. H. Arnold and H. Bekel, *Arzneimittel-Forsch.* **14**, 750 (1964); via *C. A.* **62**, 428.
141. M. A. Arsen'eva and A. V. Golovkina, *Vliyanie Ioniz. Izluch. Nasledstvennost, Akad. Nauk SSSR* p. 122 (1966); via *C. A.* **67**, 8466.
142. H. C. Arvidson and N. Blake (to du Pont de Nemours and Co.), U.S. 2,999,839 (1961); Fr. 1,225,758 (1960); Brit. 881,635 (1961); Ger. 1,126,603 (1962).
143. Arzneimittelfabrik Krewel-Leuffen G. m. b. H., Ger. 1,169,453 (1964); *C. A.* **61**, 4385.
144. Arzneimittelfabrik Krewel-Leuffen G. m. b. H., Ger. 1,173,101 (1964); *C. A.* **61**, 12012.
145. Arzneimittelfabrik Krewel-Leuffen G. m. b. H., Ger. 1,122,534 (1962); *C. A.* **56**, 14306.
147. Arzneimittelfabrik Krewel-Leuffen G. m. b. H., Ger. 1,141,288 (1962); *C. A.* **58**, 10213.
148. Asahi Chemical Industry Co., Ltd., Japan. 1438 ('66).
149. Asahi Chemical Industry Co., Ltd., Neth. appl. 6,415,122 (1965).
150. Asahi Chemical Industry Co., Ltd., Japan. 9,152 ('65); via *C. A.* **63**, 4305.
151. Asahi Chemical Industry Co., Ltd., Japan. 15,838 ('65); via *C. A.* **63**, 18385.
152. Asahi Chemical Industry Co., Ltd., Japan. 18,337 ('66); via *C. A.* **66**, 37756.
152a. Asahi Chemical Industry Co., Ltd., Japan. 5555 ('68).
153. M. Asano *et al.*, *Arch. Pathol.* **75**, 250 (1963).
154. K. R. S. Ascher, *World Rev. Pest Control* **3**, 7 (1964).
154a. F. Asinger, H. Berding, and H. Offermans, *Monatsh. Chem.* **99**, 2084 (1968).
155. F. Asinger, F. J. Schmitz, and B. Reichel, *Ann. Chem.* **652**, 50 (1962).
155a. F. Asinger *et al.*, *Monatsh. Chem.* **99**, 2090 (1968).
156. F. Asinger, H. Diem, and W. Schaefer, *Monatsh. Chem.* **95**, 1335 (1964).
157. Asta-Werke Chemische Fabrik A.-G., Ger. 1,046,621 (1958); Brit. 822,775 (1959); Neth. 94,346 (1960); Can. 629,657 (1961).
158. Y. Atarashi (to Toyo Rayon Co.), U.S. 3,205,156 (1965).
158a. R. S. Atkinson, *Chem. Commun.* p. 676 (1968).
158b. R. S. Atkinson and C. W. Rees, *Chem. Commun.* p. 631 (1968).
158c. S. M. Atlas, Fr. 1,493,045 (1967); via *POST-P* **3**, 2388.
159. C. Auerbach, *Ann. N.Y. Acad. Sci.* **68**, 731 (1958).
160. C. Auerbach, *Science* **158**, 1141 (1967).
161. R. K. Ausman *et al.*, *J. Am. Med. Assoc.* **178**, 735 (1961).
161a. V. A. Avetisov and S. A. Valeva, *Genetika* **4** (5), 31 (1968); via *C. A.* **69**, 49647.

161b. M. G. Avetyan and S. G. Matsoyan, U.S.S.R. 201,414 (1967); via *C. A.* **69**, 27231.

162. W. I. Awad, S. M. A. R. Omran, and F. Nagieb, *Tetrahedron* **19**, 1591 (1963).

163. W. I. Awad *et al.*, *J. Chem. Soc.* p. 2040 (1965).

164. E. A. Babenkova and G. A. Shtraikhman, *Zh. Prikl. Khim.* **40**, 1783 (1967); *J. Appl. Chem. USSR (English Transl.)* **40**, 1715 (1967).

164a. E. S. Babichev and V. A. Shokol, *Ukr. Khim. Zh.* **22**, 215 (1956); via *C. A.* **51**, 423.

164b. F. L. Bach and E. Cohen, *Chem. Commun.* p. 415 (1968).

165. H. J. Backer, *Rec. Trav. Chim.* **69**, 1223 (1950).

166. J. Baddiley and E. M. Thain, *J. Chem. Soc.* p. 800 (1952).

167. R. C. Badger, Jr., *Dissertation Abstr.* **26**, 1342 (1965).

168. Badische Anilin- und Soda-Fabrik, A.-G., Ger. 806,992 (1951); via *C. A.* **45**, 9230.

169. Badische Anilin- und Soda-Fabrik, A.-G., Fr. 1,498,727 (1967).

170. Badische Anilin- und Soda-Fabrik, A.-G., Ger. 1,073,498 (1960); *C. A.* **55**, 17650.

171. Badische Anilin- und Soda-Fabrik, A.-G., Ger. 935,545 (1955); *C. A.* **52**, 20195.

172. Badische Anilin- und Soda-Fabrik, A.-G., Ger. Appl. B6595 (1941); via R. Wegler, *in* "Methoden der organischen Chemie" (Houben-Weyl) 4th ed. (E. Mueller, ed.), Vol. 14, Part 2, p. 575. Thieme, Stuttgart, 1963.

173. Badische Anilin- und Soda-Fabrik, A.-G., Swiss 339,929 (1959); via *Chem. Zentr.* p. 9652 (1960).

175. Badische Anilin- und Soda-Fabrik, A.-G., Belg. 613,442 (1962), via *C. A.* **58**, 622; Swiss 377,312 (1964).

176. Badische Anilin- und Soda-Fabrik, A.-G., Belg. 649,882 (1964); Neth. appl. 6,407,592 (1965); Fr. 1,400,134 (1965); via *C. A.* **63**, 580.

177. Badische Anilin- und Soda-Fabrik, A.-G., Belg. 650,991 (1965); via *C. A.* **64**, 11422.

178. Badische Anilin- und Soda-Fabrik, A.-G., Belg. 649,883 (1964); Fr. 1,400,223 (1966); Neth. 6,407,587 (1966); Brit. 1,065,114 (1967).

179. Badische Anilin- und Soda-Fabrik, A.-G., Belg. 631,294 (1963); Brit. 987,373 (1965); Ger. 1,239,265 (1967).

180. Badische Anilin- und Soda-Fabrik, A.-G., Belg. 680,930 (1966); Neth. appl. 6,606,627 (1966); via *C. A.* **66**, 118190.

181. Badische Anilin- und Soda-Fabrik, A.-G., Belg. 686,361 (1967).

182. Badische Anilin- und Soda-Fabrik, A.-G., Fr. 1,126,399 (1956); Swiss 339,928 (1957); Ger. 1,004,614 (1957); Brit. 783,728 (1957).

183. Badische Anilin- und Soda-Fabrik, A.-G., Brit. 1,110,004 (1968).

183a. Badische Anilin- und Soda-Fabrik, A.-G., Ger. 1,268,582 (1968).

184. Badische Anilin- und Soda-Fabrik, A.-G., Ger. 801,745 (1951); *C. A.* **45**, 3608.

185. Badische Anilin- und Soda-Fabrik, A.-G., Ger. 802,346 (1951); *C. A.* **45**, 5372.

186. Badische Anilin- und Soda-Fabrik, A.-G., Ger. 1,009,807 (1957); Fr. 1,193,628 (1959); Brit. 811,135 (1959).

187. Badische Anilin- und Soda-Fabrik, A.-G., Brit. 821,192 (1959); Fr. 1,215,544 (1960).

188. Badische Anilin- und Soda-Fabrik, A.-G., Ger. 1,054,998 (1959); Brit. 839,305 (1960).

189. Badische Anilin- und Soda-Fabrik, A.-G., Ger. 843,852 (1952); *C. A.* **49**, 4984.

190. Badische Anilin- und Soda-Fabrik, A.-G., Ger. 845,802 (1952); *C. A.* **48**, 7053.

191. Badische Anilin- und Soda-Fabrik, A.-G., Ger. 851,196 (1952); *C. A.* **52**, 10200.

192. Badische Anilin- und Soda-Fabrik, A.-G., Ger. 857,495 (1952); *C. A.* **52**, 10188.

193. Badische Anilin- und Soda-Fabrik, A.-G., Ger. 858,700 (1952); *C. A.* **52**, 5456.

194. Badische Anilin- und Soda-Fabrik, A.-G., Brit. 832,002 (1959).

195. Badische Anilin- und Soda-Fabrik, A.-G., Ger. 1,029,000 (1958); Fr. 1,253,212 (1957); Brit. 823,482 (1959).

196. Badische Anilin- und Soda-Fabrik, A.-G., Neth. appl. 6,612,293 (1967); via *C. A.* **67**, 65085.
197. Badische Anilin- und Soda-Fabrik, A.-G., Ger. 858,846 (1952); *C. A.* **52**, 10200.
198. Badische Anilin- und Soda-Fabrik, A.-G., Belg. 566,909 (1958); Austrian 202,992 (1959); Swiss 342,228 and 342,229 (1959); Ger. 1,115,256 (1961); Brit. 860,285 (1961).
199. Badische Anilin- und Soda-Fabrik, A.-G., Ger. 863,982 (1953); *Chem. Zentr.* p. 8764 (1953).
200. Badische Anilin- und Soda-Fabrik, A.-G., Ger. 864,856 (1953); *Chem. Zentr.* p. 7451 (1953).
201. Badische Anilin- und Soda-Fabrik, A.-G., Ger. 867,085 (1953); *Chem. Zentr.* p. 9029 (1953).
202. Badische Anilin- und Soda-Fabrik, A.-G., Ger. 871,149 (1953); *Chem. Zentr.* p. 8718 (1953).
203. Badische Anilin- und Soda-Fabrik, A.-G., Ger. 872,269 (1954); via *Chem. Zentr.* p. 7418 (1953).
204. Badische Anilin- und Soda-Fabrik, A.-G., Ger. 874,912 (1953); *C. A.* **52**, 11405.
205. Badische Anilin- und Soda-Fabrik, A.-G., Ger. 879,312 (1953); *C. A.* **52**, 9662.
206. Badische Anilin- und Soda-Fabrik, A.-G., Ger. 892,888 (1953); *C. A.* **52**, 12336; Swiss 304,712 (1955).
207. Badische Anilin- und Soda-Fabrik, A.-G., Ger. 895,744 (1953); *C. A.* **52**, 13284.
208. Badische Anilin- und Soda-Fabrik, A.-G., Ger. 900,137 (1953); *C. A.* **52**, 15136.
209. Badische Anilin- und Soda-Fabrik, A.-G., Ger. 907,698 (1954); I. G. Farben-industrie A.-G., Belg. 450,588 (1944); via *C. A.* **41**, 7818.
210. Badische Anilin- und Soda-Fabrik, A.-G., Ger. 909,569 (1954); *C. A.* **52**, 8597.
211. Badische Anilin- und Soda-Fabrik, A.-G., Fr. 1,443,777 (1966); via *C. A.* **66**, 56919.
212. Badische Anilin- und Soda-Fabrik, A.-G., Ger. 1,002,329 (1957); *C. A.* **53**, 22893.
213. Badische Anilin- und Soda-Fabrik, A.-G., Ger. 1,040,037 (1958); *C. A.* **55**, 6496.
214. Badische Anilin- und Soda-Fabrik, A.-G., Belg. 706,149 (1968); Neth. appl. 6,714,989 (1968).
215. Badische Anilin- und Soda-Fabrik, A.-G., Ger. 1,111,186 (1961); *C. A.* **56**, 7221.
216. Badische Anilin- und Soda-Fabrik, A.-G., Ger. 1,111,637 (1961); *C. A.* **56**, 7279.
217. Badische Anilin- und Soda-Fabrik, A.-G., Ger. 1,123,282 (1962); *C. A.* **57**, 4904; Fr. 1,302,794 (1962).
218. Badische Anilin- und Soda-Fabrik, A.-G., Ger. 1,124,040 (1962); *C. A.* **57**, 4634.
219. Badische Anilin- und Soda-Fabrik, A.-G., Fr. 1,129,932 (1957); *Chem. Zentr.* p. 14465 (1958).
220. Badische Anilin- und Soda-Fabrik, A.-G., Belg. 631,190 (1963); Brit. 965,392 (1964); Ger. 1,186,026 (1965).
221. Badische Anilin- und Soda-Fabrik, A.-G., Fr. 1,315,333 (1963); Belg. 631,585 (1963); Ger. 1,159,899 (1963); Austrian 233,509 (1964); Brit. 970,923 (1964) and 982,270 (1965).
222. Badische Anilin- und Soda-Fabrik, A.-G., Ger. 893,795 (1953); Brit. 718,063 (1954).
223. Badische Anilin- und Soda-Fabrik, A.-G., Brit. 847,573 (1960).
224. Badische Anilin- und Soda-Fabrik, A.-G., Ger. 1,135,859 (1962); *C. A.* **57**, 16921; Belg. 616,731 (1962).
225. Badische Anilin- und Soda-Fabrik, A.-G., Ger. 1,142,831 (1963); *C. A.* **58**, 8088.
226. Badische Anilin- und Soda-Fabrik, A.-G., Belg. 706,150 (1968); Neth. appl. 6,715,049 (1968).

227. Badische Anilin- und Soda-Fabrik, A.-G., Belg. 622,590 (1963); Ger. 1,169,131 (1964); *C. A.* **59**, 8940.
228. Badische Anilin- und Soda-Fabrik, A.-G., Brit. 784,058 (1960).
229. Badische Anilin- und Soda-Fabrik, A.-G., Ger. 1,198,471 (1965); *C. A.* **63**, 18316.
230. Badische Anilin- und Soda-Fabrik, A.-G., Ger. 1,225,862 (1966); *C. A.* **66**, 20153; Fr. 1,445,142 (1966).
231. Badische Anilin- und Soda-Fabrik, A.-G., Ger. 1,234,671 (1967); *C. A.* **67**, 12485.
233. Badische Anilin- und Soda-Fabrik, A.-G., Fr. 1,425,700 (1966); via *C. A.* **65**, 20251.
234. Badische Anilin- und Soda-Fabrik, A.-G., Fr. 1,442,792 (1966).
235. Badische Anilin- und Soda-Fabrik, A.-G., Fr. 1,455,536 (1966); Neth. appl. 6,515,064 (1966); via *C. A.* **65**, 13861.
236. Badische Anilin- und Soda-Fabrik, A.-G., Neth. appl. 6,607,766 (1966); via *C. A.* **67**, 22848.
238. Badische Anilin- und Soda-Fabrik, A.-G., results released through Chemirad Corporation, 1961.
239. Badische Anilin- und Soda-Fabrik, A.-G., Fr. 1,451,146 (1966).
240. Badische Anilin- und Soda-Fabrik, A.-G., Fr. 1,479,183 (1967); via *C. A.* **67**, 109734.
241. Badische Anilin- und Soda-Fabrik, A.-G., Ger. 1,031,307 (1958); Brit. 823,002 (1959).
242. Badische Anilin- und Soda-Fabrik, A.-G., Belg. 704,847 (1968).
243. E. Baer and J. Maurukas, *J. Biol. Chem.* **212**, 39 (1955).
244. M. Bahr, *Z. Ges. Textil.-Ind.* **66**, 519 (1964); via *Chem. Zentr.* No. 3, abstr. 2851 (1966).
244a. E. Baier and H. Luebbers (to Farbwerke Hoechst), U.S. 3,364,240 (1968).
245. A. S. Bailey, J. J. Merer, and J. E. White, *Chem. Commun.* p. 4 (1965); A. S. Bailey and J. J. Wedgwood, *J. Chem. Soc., C, Org.* p. 682 (1968).
246. B. R. Baker and T. Neilson, *J. Org. Chem.* **29**, 1047 (1964).
247. B. R. Baker and T. Neilson, *J. Org. Chem.* **29**, 1051 (1964).
248. B. R. Baker and T. Neilson, *J. Org. Chem.* **29**, 1057 (1964).
249. B. R. Baker and T. Neilson, *J. Org. Chem.* **29**, 1063 (1964).
250. B. R. Baker and T. L. Hullar, *J. Org. Chem.* **30**, 4038 (1965).
251. B. R. Baker and T. L. Hullar, *J. Org. Chem.* **30**, 4045 (1965).
252. B. R. Baker and T. L. Hullar, *J. Org. Chem.* **30**, 4049 (1965).
253. B. R. Baker and T. L. Hullar, *J. Org. Chem.* **30**, 4053 (1965).
254. D. R. Baker, M. E. Brokke, and D. J. Broadbent (to Stauffer Chemical Co.), U.S 3,250,674 (1966).
255. G. A. Balaev, V. M. Al'bitskaya, and A. A. Petrov, *Zh. Obshch. Khim.* **31**, 1861 (1961); *J. Gen. Chem. USSR (English Transl.)* **31**, 1741 (1961).
256. A. A. Balandin *et al.*, *Dokl. Akad. Nauk SSSR* **165**, 99 (1965); *Proc. Acad. Sci. USSR, Chem. Sect. (English Transl.)* **163–165**, 1057 (1965).
257. J. E. Baldwin and R. A. Smith, *J. Org. Chem.* **32**, 3511 (1967).
257a. J. E. Baldwin *et al.*, *J. Am. Chem. Soc.* **90**, 5325 (1968).
258. E. T. Baliga, A. K. Tantamaa, and E. Whalley, *J. Phys. Chem.* **69**, 1751 (1965).
259. V. S. Balubukha, ed., "Chemical Protection of the Body Against Ionizing Radiation." Macmillan, New York, 1964.
260. W. Bandel, *Melliand Textilber.* **38**, 648 (1957).
261. W. B. Bang, *Dissertation Abstr.* **24**, 3552 (1964).
262. R. E. Banks and G. J. Moore, *J. Chem. Soc., C, Org.* p. 2304 (1966).
262a. R. C. Bansal, E. J. Eisenbraun, and P. W. Flanigan, *J. Am. Chem. Soc.* **88**, 1837 (1966).
263. A. Baranauskaite and V. Rancelis, *Lietuvos TSR Aukstuju Molyklu Mokslo Darbai: Biol.* **6**, 11 (1966); via *C. A.* **66**, 104197.

264. W. G. Barb, *J. Chem. Soc.* p. 2564 (1955).
265. W. G. Barb, *J. Chem. Soc.* p. 2577 (1955).
266. T. J. Bardos *et al.*, *J. Med. Chem.* **8**, 167 (1965).
267. T. J. Bardos *et al.*, *Nature* **183**, 399 (1959).
268. T. J. Bardos, Z. F. Chmielewicz, and C. K. Navada, *J. Pharm. Sci.* **54**, 399 (1965).
269. T. J. Bardos, R. D. Dillard, and Z. B. Papanastassiou, *Chem. & Ind.* (*London*) p. 1464 (1963).
270. T. J. Bardos *et al.*, *J. Pharm. Sci.* **54**, 187 (1965).
271. T. J. Bardos and Z. B. Papanastassiou (to Armour Pharmaceutical Co.), U.S. 3,201,313 (1965).
272. T. J. Bardos, C. Szantay, and C. K. Navada, *J. Am. Chem. Soc.* **87**, 5796 (1965).
273. A. D. Barford and A. C. Richardson, *Carbohydrate Res.* **4**, 408 (1967).
275. J. W. Barnett, *J. Chem. Soc.* p. 5 (1944).
276. C. J. Barr (to Olin Mathieson Chemical Corp.), U.S. 2,960,393 (1962); Ger. 1,122,422 (1962).
277. O. O. Bartan, O. V. Krylov, and E. A. Fokina, *Kinetika Kataliz* **7**, 280 (1966); *Kinetics and Catalysis* (*English Transl.*) **7**, 260 (1966).
278. H. Bartl *et al.* (to Farbwerke Hoechst), U.S. 2,961,349 (1960); Indian 61,493 (1958); Fr. addn. 72,212 (1960); Ger. 1,104,927 (1961).
279. P. D. Bartlett, S. D. Ross, and C. G. Swain, *J. Am. Chem. Soc.* **69**, 2971 (1947).
280. P. D. Bartlett, S. D. Ross, and C. G. Swain, *J. Am. Chem. Soc.* **71**, 1415 (1949).
281. P. D. Bartlett *et al.*, *J. Am. Chem. Soc.* **69**, 2977 (1947).
282. D. H. R. Barton, *S. African Ind. Chemist* **15** (12), 229 (1961); via *C. A.* **58**, 8001.
283. D. H. R. Barton and L. R. Morgan, Jr., *J. Chem. Soc.* p. 622 (1962).
284. O. O. Bartan and O. V. Krylov, *Izv. Akad. Nauk SSSR, Ser. Khim.* p. 2053 (1965); *Bull. Acad. Sci. USSR, Div. Chem. Sci.* (*English Transl.*) p. 2019 (1965).
285. Yu. E. Bartoshevich, L. M. Filippova, and R. G. Kostyanovskii, *Genetika* No. 4, 147 (1966); via *C. A.* **65**, 5693.
286. Yu. E. Bartoshevich, *Dokl. Akad. Nauk SSSR* **162**, 193 (1965); via *C. A.* **63**, 4708.
286a. Yu. E. Bartoshevich, *Supermutageny, Akad. Nauk SSSR, Inst. Khim. Fiz.* p. 211 (1966); via *C. A.* **67**, 40067.
287. Yu. E. Bartoshevich and R. G. Kostyanovskii, *Antibiotiki* **10**, 1069 (1965); via *C. A.* **64**, 20257; Yu. E. Bartoshevich, *Tr. Mosk. Obshchest. Ispyt. Prir. Otd. Biol.* **22**, 124 (1966); via *C. A.* **68**, 102802.
288. A. K. Barua *et al.*, *Abstr. Papers, 147th Am. Chem. Soc. Meeting, Philadelphia, 1964* p. M-27.
289. M. I. Bassin (to Minnesota Mining and Manufacturing Co.), U.S. 3,157,607 (1964).
289a. T. G. Bassiri, A. Levy, and M. Litt (to Allied Chemical Corp.), U.S. 3,293,245 (1966).
289b. T. G. Bassiri. A. Levy, and M. Litt, *Polymer Letters* **5**, 871 (1967); *J. Polymer Sci. Part A-1* **6**, 1883 (1968).
290. R. Bastian, *Dissertation Abstr.* **16**, 30 (1966).
291. N. A. Bates, *Tappi* **49**, 184 (1966).
291a. G. G. Batikyan and V. S. Pogosyan, *Biol. Zh. Arm.* **20** (5), 3 (1967); via *C. A.* **67**, 89931.
292. S. G. Batrakov *et al.*, *Zh. Obshch. Khim.* **37**, 426 (1967); *J. Gen. Chem. USSR* (*English Transl.*) **37**, 398 (1967).
293. E. Bauer and H. Berg, *Chem. Zvesti* **18**, 454 (1964); via *C. A.* **61**, 11375.
294. H. E. Baumgarten and J. M. Petersen, *J. Am. Chem. Soc.* **82**, 459 (1960).
295. H. E. Baumgarten, J. M. Petersen, and D. C. Wolf, *J. Org. Chem.* **28**, 2369 (1963).
296. H. E. Baumgarten *et al.*, *J. Am. Chem. Soc.* **85**, 3303 (1963).
297. H. E. Baumgarten *et al.*, *J. Org. Chem.* **31**, 3708 (1966).

298. H. E. Baumgarten, R. L. Zey, and H. Knolls, *J. Am. Chem. Soc.* **83**, 4469 (1961).

299. H. E. Baumgarten and F. A. Bower, *J. Am. Chem. Soc.* **76**, 4561 (1954).

300. H. E. Baumgarten, *J. Am. Chem. Soc.* **84**, 4975 (1962).

302. J. N. Baxter and J. Cymerman-Craig, *J. Chem. Soc.* p. 1940 (1953).

303. O. Bayer, *Angew. Chem.* **73**, 125 and 343 (1961).

304. P. I. Bebesel and C. N. Turcanu, *Studii Cercetari Chim.* **14**, 861 (1966); via *C. A.* **67**, 64125.

305. A. L. J. Beckwith and J. W. Redmond, *Australian J. Chem.* **17**, 1859 (1966); *Chem. Commun.* p. 165 (1967).

306. Beecham Research Laboratories, Ltd., Brit. 891,777 (1962).

307. R. L. Beegle, R. C. Brown, and C. M. James (to Aerojet-General Corp.), U.S. 3,132,060 (1964); S. Afr. 62/1828; Belg. 627,768 (1963); Ger. 1,167,238 (1964); Brit. 999,066 (1965).

308. B. D. Beitchman, *Ind. Eng. Chem., Prod. Res. Develop.* **5**, 35 (1966).

309. B. D. Beitchman, *Rubber Age* (*N. Y.*) **98** (2), 65 (1966).

310. B. D. Beitchman (to Air Products and Chemicals, Inc.), U.S. 3,146,219 (1964); Japan. 118 ('66).

311. B. D. Beitchman (to Air Products and Chemicals, Inc.), U.S. 3,154,522 (1964).

312. B. D. Beitchman and J. H. Krause (to Air Products and Chemicals, Inc.), U.S. 3,179,628 (1965).

312a. M. A. Belaventsev *et al.*, U.S.S.R. 213,826 (1968); via *C. A.* **69**, 35423.

313. J. S. Belew, C. E. Grabiel, and L. B. Clapp, *J. Am. Chem. Soc.* **77**, 1110 (1955).

315. H. J. Belitz, *Z. Vererbungslehre* **90**, 223 (1959).

316. B. Belleau, *Proc. 1st Intern. Pharmacol. Meeting, Stockholm, 1961* Vol. 7, p. 75. Macmillan, New York, 1963.

317. B. Belleau, *J. Med. Pharm. Chem.* **1**, 327 (1959).

318. B. Belleau, *J. Med. Pharm. Chem.* **1**, 343 (1959).

319. B. Belleau, *Can. J. Biochem. Physiol.* **36**, 731 (1958).

320. B. Belleau and H. Tani, *Mol. Pharmacol.* **2**, 411 (1966).

320a. J A. Benckiser G. m. b. H. Chemische Fabrik, Brit. 858,453 (1961); Ger. 1,082,266 (1960).

320b. J. A. Benckiser G. m. b. H. Chemische Fabrik, Brit. 865,848 (1961).

321. G. Bencze, E. Olasz, and J. Pogany, Hung. 147,657 (1960); via *C. A.* **58**, 12661.

321a. H. S. Bender, F. C. Loew, and P. Resnick (to Interchemical Corp.), U.S. 3,390,167 (1968).

322. G. Benoit and A. Funke, *Bull. Soc. Chim. France* p. 946 (1955).

323. J. L. Benoit-Guyot, A. Boucherie, and G. Carraz, *Bull. Soc. Chim. France* p. 1660 (1965).

324. J. Benz, L. Schneider, and H. Siegrist (to Sandoz Ltd.), U.S. 3,035,043 (1962); Fr. 1,217,337 (1960); Brit. 910,024 (1962); Swiss 387,194 and 392,889 (1965); Ger. 1,208,022 (1965).

325. G. J. Berchet (to du Pont de Nemours and Co.), U.S. 2,212,146 (1940); Brit. 543,998 (1942).

326. G. J. Berchet (to du Pont de Nemours and Co.), U.S. 2,269,997 (1942).

327. G. J. Berchet (to du Pont de Nemours and Co.), U.S. 2,304,623 (1942).

328. M. B. Berenbaum (to Thiokol Chemical Corp.), U.S. 3,235,589 (1966); Brit. 957,652 (1964).

328a. M. B. Berenbaum and L. Citarel (to Thiokol Chemical Corp.), U.S. 3,382,237 (1968).

328b. M. B. Berenbaum and L. Citarel (to Thiokol Chemical Corp.), U.S. 3,388,140 (1968).

329. M. B. Berenbaum (to Thiokol Chemical Corp.), U.S. 3,322,851 (1967); Fr. 1,455,156 (1966); Brit. 1,102,535 and 1,102,536 (1968).

330. H. Berg, *Chem. Zvesti* **16**, 342 (1962); via *C. A.* **58**, 11301.

331. H. Berg and G. Horn, *Naturwissenschaften* **50**, 356 (1963).

333. E. D. Bergmann and A. Kaluszyner, *Rec. Trav. Chim.* **78**, 289 (1956).

334. J. B. Berkowitz-Mattuck and T. Noguchi, *J. Appl. Polymer Sci.* **7**, 709 (1963).

336. A. Ya. Berlin and V. K. Antonov, *Zh. Obshch. Khim.* **30**, 282 (1960); *J. Gen. Chem. USSR* (*English Transl.*) **30**, 302 (1960).

337. A. Ya. Berlin and M. N. Vasil'eva, *Zh. Obshch. Khim.* **28**, 1063 (1958); *J. Gen. Chem. USSR* (*English Transl.*) **28**, 1033 (1958).

338. A. Ya. Berlin and L. S. Yaguzhinskii, *Usp. Khim.* **34**, 1293 (1965); *Russ. Chem. Rev.* (*English Transl.*) **34**, 537 (1965).

339. A. Ya. Berlin and A. N. Makarova, *Zh. Obshch. Khim.* **30**, 1380 (1960); *J. Gen. Chem. USSR* (*English Transl.*) **30**, 1411 (1960).

340. A. Ya. Berlin and A. N. Makarova, *Zh. Obshch. Khim.* **30**, 1582 (1960); *J. Gen. Chem. USSR* (*English Transl.*) **30**, 1587 (1960).

341. K. D. Berlin and L. A. Wilson, *Chem. Commun.* p. 280 (1965).

342. W. G. Berly *et al.*, *Biochem. J.* **58**, 660 (1954).

343. M. Beroza, *Anal. Chem.* **34**, 1801 (1962).

343a. M. Beroza and A. B. Borkovec, *J. Med. Chem.* **7**, 44 (1964).

344. R. S. Berry, D. Cornell, and W. Lwowski, *J. Am. Chem. Soc.* **85**, 1199 (1963).

345. E. Bertanalffy, Chemisch-pharmazeutische Fabrik, Austrian 167,872 (1951); via *C. A.* **46**, 6797.

345a. E. Bertele *et al.*, *Angew. Chem.* **76**, 393 (1964); *Angew. Chem. Intern. Ed. Engl.* **3**, 490 (1964).

346. A. Bertho, T. Curtius, and F. Schmidt, *Ber.* **60**, 1717 (1927); A. Bertho, *J. Prakt. Chem.* [2] **120**, 89 (1928).

347. D. S. Bertram, S. C. Srivastava, and A. S. Msangi, *J. Trop. Med. Hyg.* **67**, 51 (1964).

348. D. S. Bertram, *Trans. Roy. Soc. Trop. Med. Hyg.* **57**, 322 (1963).

350. H. Bestian, *Ann. Chem.* **566**, 210 (1950).

351. H. Bestian, *in* "Methoden der organischen Chemie" (Houben-Weyl) 4th ed. (E. Mueller, ed.), Vol. 11, Part 2, pp. 223ff. Thieme, Stuttgart, 1958.

353. H. Bestian, *Angew. Chem.* **62**, 451 (1950).

354. H. Bestian, J. Nuesslein, and J. Monheim (to General Aniline and Film Corp.), U.S. 2,317,965 (1943); I. G. Farbenindustrie A.-G., Ital. 363,580 (1938); Brit. 501,595 (1939); Ger. 689,151 and 700,072 (1940); Neth. 49,475 (1940); Fr. 840,709 and 840,773 (1939); Belg. 429,142 (1939).

355. H. Bestian (to General Aniline and Film Corp.), U.S. 2,265,416 (1941); I. G. Farbenindustrie A.-G., Belg. 445,976 (1942); Ger. 907,699 (1954).

356. H. Bestian (to Farbwerke Hoechst), U.S. 2,302,288 (1942); Ger. 863,343 (1945).

357. H. Bestian (to General Aniline and Film Corp.), U.S. 2,312,863 (1943).

358. H. Bestian and G. von Finck (to I. G. Farbenindustrie), U.S. 2,314,968 (1943); Fr. 865,869 (1940); Ger. 731,667 (1943); Neth. 55,567 (1943).

359. H. Bestian and M. O. Schuermann (vested in the Alien Property Custodian), U.S. 2,327,760 (1943).

360. H. Bestian (vested in the Alien Property Custodian), U.S. 2,339,046 (1944).

361. H. Bestian (to Farbwerke Hoechst), U.S. 2,596,200 (1952); Swiss 275,434 (1951), 278,839, 278,840 and 278,841 (1952); Ger. 836,353 (1952); Austrian 172,328 (1952); Swed. 134,449 (1952); Brit. 693,611 (1953).

362. H. Bestian (to Farbwerke Hoechst), U.S. 2,626,931 (1953); Ger. 888,170 (1948).

363. H. Bestian, *Publication Board Report* (*U.S.*) PB 76,498 (1939); *Bib. Sci. Ind. Rept.* (*U.S.*) **7**, 576.
364. H. Bestian (to General Aniline and Film Corp.), U.S. 2,288,178 (1942); Swiss 222,445 and 222,446 (1942).
365. H. Bestian, *in* "Methoden der organischen Chemie" (Houben-Weyl) 4th ed. (E. Mueller, ed.), Vol. 11, Part 2, p. 227. Thieme, Stuttgart, 1958.
366. O. P. Bhalla and A. G. Robinson, *J. Econ. Entomol.* **59**, 378 (1966).
367. C. C. Bice (to Phillips Petroleum Co.), U.S. 3,154,527 (1964); 3,239,469 (1966).
368. J. H. Biel *et al.*, *J. Am. Chem. Soc.* **77**, 2250 (1955).
369. J. H. Biel, W. K. Hoya, and H. A. Leiser, *J. Am. Chem. Soc.* **81**, 2527 (1959).
370. G. Bier, A. G. M. Gumboldt, and W. von Happe (to Farbwerke Hoechst), U.S. 3,036,052 (1962); Ger. 1,105,175 (1961).
371. J. J. Biesele *et al.*, *Nature* **166**, 1112 (1950); *Exptl. Cell Res.* Suppl. II, p. 279 (1952).
372. P. Biggio, P. Pinette, and G. L. Gessa, *Boll. Soc. Ital. Biol. Sper.* **43**, 288 (1967); via *C. A.* **67**, 97978.
373. X. Bilger and G. Mangeney, *Teintex* **29**, 837 (1964); *Melliand Textilber.* **46**, 294 (1965); *C. A.* **63**, 722.
374. T. Bing, *K'un Ch'ung Hsueh Pao* (*Acta Entomol. Sinica*) **14**, 250 (1965); via *Rev. Appl. Entomol.* **54B**, 38.
374a. F. B. Birkner and J. J. Morgan, *J. Amer. Water Works Assoc.* **60**, 175 (1968).
375. G. H. Birum (to Monsanto Chemical Co.), U.S. 2,809,912 (1957).
376. G. H. Birum (to Monsanto Chemical Co.), U.S. 2,813,819 (1957).
377. G. H. Birum and J. L. Dever (to Monsanto Chemical Co.), U.S. 2,961,455 (1960); Brit. 925,991 (1963); Ger. 1,211,204 (1966).
378. D. S. Blaisdell and R. E. B. Klaas, U.S. 3,142,638 (1964).
379. M. J. Blankenship (to The Dow Chemical Co.), U.S. 3,328,474 (1967); Belg. 662,519 (1965).
380. E. Blasius and B. Brozio, *J. Chromatog.* **18**, 572 (1965).
381. A. H. Blatt, *J. Am. Chem. Soc.* **61**, 349 (1939).
382. H. M. Blatter (to Ciba Corp.), U.S. 3,165,529 (1965).
383. V. A. Blinov, *Tekstil'n. Prom.* **21** (7), 74 (1961); via *C. A.* **56**, 4990.
384. V. A. Blinov and O. M. Cherntsov, U.S.S.R. 132,188 (1960); via *C. A.* **55**, 5974.
385. S. Blixt, L. Ehrenberg, and O. Gelin, *Agr. Hort. Genet.* **18**, 109 (1960); via *Hort. Abstr.* **30**, 5461.
386. S. Blixt, *Agr. Hort. Genet.* **22**, 171 (1964); via *Nucl. Sci. Abstr.* **19**, 7043.
387. S. Blixt, L. Ehrenberg, and O. Gelin, *Agr. Hort. Genet.* **21**, 178 (1963); via *Nucl. Sci. Abstr.* **19**, 35962; *ibid.* **24**, 111 (1966); via *C. A.* **69**, 84181.
388. H. S. Bloch and D. R. Strehlau (to Universal Oil Products Co.), U.S. 2,839,568 (1958).
389. H. S. Bloch (to Universal Oil Products Co.), U.S. 3,017,400 (1962).
390. H. S. Bloch (to Universal Oil Products Co.), U.S. 3,113,165 (1963).
390a. W. Bloechl, Brit. 1,122,404 (1968).
391. H. Bluestone (to Diamond Alkali Co.), U.S. 2,860,962 (1958).
392. H. Bluestone (to Diamond Alkali Co.), U.S. 2,953,573 (1960).
393. H. Bluestone (to Diamond Alkali Co.), U.S. 3,020,143 (1962).
394. M. Blumberg (to Interchemical Corp.), U.S. 3,156,606 (1964).
395. K. Blumrich, *Publication Board Report* (*U.S.*) PB 70,066, Frames 5686-6 and 5928-9 (1943); *Bib. Sci. Ind. Rept.* (*U.S.*) **6**, 669.
396. O. V. Blyandur and V. N. Lysikov, *Tr. Mosk. Obshchest. Ispyt. Prir.* **23**, 116 (1967); via *C. A.* 67, 71213.
397. H. Bock and H. T. Dieck, *Chem. Ber.* **99**, 213 (1966).

398. H. Bock and W. Wiegraebe, *Chem. Ber.* **99**, 1068 (1966).
400. M. Bock and H. Jackson, *Brit. J. Pharmacol.* **12**, 1 (1957).
401. M. Bockmuehl and G. Ehrhart, *Ann. Chem.* **561**, 52 (1949).
402. K. Boeckmann and C. Taube (to Farbenfabriken Bayer), U.S. 3,141,728 (1964); Ger. 1,124,467 (1962).
403. Boehme Fettchemie G. m. b. H., Ger. 1,113,676 (1959); *C. A.* **56**, 4998.
404. C. H. Boehringer Sohn, Ger. 1,020,031 (1957); *C. A.* **54**, 2258.
404a. C. H. Boehringer Sohn, Neth. appl. 6,612,312 (1967); via *C. A.* **67**, 73687.
405. W. R. Boell, W. Pretzer, and E. Vogel, *Tetrahedron Letters* p. 3613 (1965).
406. M. Boese, *Ber.* **53B**, 2000 (1920).
407. M. T. Bogert and E. J. Mills, Jr. (to E. R. Squibb and Sons), U.S. 2,358,786 (1944).
408. Yu. I. Bogodist, *Ukr. Khim. Zh.* **33**, 87 (1967); via *C. A.* **66**, 94989.
409. Yu. I. Bogodist and L. D. Protsenko, *Ukr. Khim. Zh.* **32**, 1094 (1966); via *C. A.* **66**, 94988.
410. Yu. I. Bogodist, *Ukr. Khim. Zh.* **32**, 1091 (1966); via *C. A.* **66**, 37870.
411. N. Bohonos *et al.* (to American Cyanamid Co.), U.S. 3,219,530 (1965).
412. P. Boldt and F. Vardakis, *Angew. Chem.* **77**, 1137 (1965); *Angew. Chem. Intern. Ed. Engl.* **4**, 1078 (1965).
413. B. G. Boldyrev and V. T. Kolesnikov, *Zh. Obshch. Khim.* **36**, 634 (1966); *J. Gen. Chem. USSR (English Transl.)* **36**, 649 (1966).
414. G. Bonadonna and D. A. Karnovsky. *Clin. Pharmacol. Therap.* **6**, 50 (1965).
415. W. A. Bonner and F. D. Mango, *J. Org. Chem.* **29**, 29 (1964).
416. A. Bonvicini and C. Caldo (to "Montecatini" Societa . . .), U.S. 3,037,835 (1962); Austrian 219,184 (1959); Fr. 1,228,704 (1960).
417. A. Bonvicini and E. Ildos (to "Montecatini" Societa . . .), U.S. 3,321,267 (1967); Fr. 1,357,989 (1964); Ger. 1,224,263 (1966).
418. S. Bookman, *Ber.* **28**, 3111 (1895).
419. I. U. Boone, B. S. Rogers, and D. L. Williams, *Toxicol. Appl. Pharmacol.* **4**, 344 (1962).
420. A. Booth, R. A. Pizzarello, and J. E. De Graff (to Interchemical Corp.), U.S. 3,093,602 (1963); Fr. 1,232,024 (1960); Brit. 877,865 (1961); Can. 680,189 (1964).
421. C. Boresch, W. Hagge, and M. Quaedvlieg (to Farbenfabriken Bayer), U.S. 2,859,186 (1958); Fr. 1,124,355 (1956).
422. H. C. Borghetty, *Rayon Syn. Textiles* **30** (11), 79 (1949); **31** (1), 85, (2), 81, (3), 85, and (4), 81 (1950); *C. A.* **46**, 9315.
424. L. B. Borisov *et al.*, *Byul. Eksperim. Biol. i Med.* **55** (6), 76 (1963); via *Federation Proc.* **23**, T925; L. B. Dashkevich and V. G. Beilin, *Zh. Obshch. Khim.* **32**, 2423 (1962); *J. Gen. Chem. USSR (English Transl.)* **32**, 2391 (1962).
425. L. B. Borisov, G. S. Yakovleva, and S. V. Livshina, *Byul. Eksperim. Biol. i Med.* **60** (12), 90 (1965); via *C. A.* **64**, 13240.
426. A. B. Bořkovec and C. W. Woods, *Advan. Chem. Ser.* **41**, 47 (1963).
427. A. B. Bořkovec, S. Nagasawa, and H. Shinohara, *J. Econ. Entomol.* **61**, 695 (1968).
428. A. B. Bořkovec, *Residue Rev.* **6**, 87 (1964).
430. A. B. Bořkovec and C. W. Woods, *J. Med. Chem.* **8**, 545 (1965).
431. A. B. Bořkovec, *Science* **137**, 1034 (1962).
432. A. B. Bořkovec, *Advan. Pest Control Res.* **7**, 1 (1966).
433. A. B. Bořkovec, C. W. Woods, and R. T. Brown, *J. Med. Chem.* **9**, 522 (1966); cf. C. W. Woods and A. B. Bořkovec, *Abstr. Papers, 150th Am. Chem. Soc. Meeting, Atlantic City, 1965*, p. A-21.
434. N. Bortnick *et al.*, *J. Am. Chem. Soc.* **78**, 4358 (1956).
435. N. M. Bortnick *et al.*, *J. Am. Chem. Soc.* **78**, 4039 (1956).

436. N. M. Bortnick (to Rohm and Haas Co.), U.S. 2,686,772 (1954).

437. S. Bose and A. De, *Trans. Bose Res. Inst. (Calcutta)* **27**, 13 (1964); via *C. A.* **65**, 14119.

438. S. Bose, *Experientia* **21**, 506 (1965).

439. J. Bosholm, *J. Chromatog.* **21**, 286 (1966).

439a. H. H. Bosshard and A. Eschenmoser (to Ciba Ltd.), U.S. 3,340,210 (1967).

440. G. A. Boswell, Jr. and R. M. Scribner (to du Pont de Nemours and Co.), U.S. 3,201,426 (1965).

440a. K. Bott, *Angew. Chem.* **79**, 943 (1967); *Angew. Chem. Intern. Ed. Engl.* **6**, 946 (1967).

441. A. T. Bottini and R. E. Olsen, *Org. Syn.* **44**, 53 (1964).

442. A. T. Bottini, V. Dev, and M. Stewart, *J. Org. Chem.* **28**, 156 (1963).

443. A. T. Bottini and R. L. Van Etten, *J. Org. Chem.* **30**, 2994 (1965).

444. A. T. Bottini and R. E. Olsen, *J. Am. Chem. Soc.* **84**, 195 (1962).

445. A. T. Bottini and R. L. Van Etten, *J. Org. Chem.* **30**, 575 (1965).

446. A. T. Bottini, R. L. Van Etten, and A. J. Davidson, *J. Am. Chem. Soc.* **87**, 755 (1965).

447. A. T. Bottini and V. Dev, *J. Med. Pharm. Chem.* **5**, 925 (1962).

448. A. T. Bottini and V. Dev, *J. Org. Chem.* **27**, 968 (1962).

449. A. T. Bottini and J. D. Roberts, *J. Am. Chem. Soc.* **79**, 1462 (1957).

450. A. T. Bottini, B. J. King, and R. E. Olsen, *J. Org. Chem.* **28**, 3241 (1963).

451. A. T. Bottini, B. F. Dowden, and L. Sousa, *J. Am. Chem. Soc.* **87**, 3249 (1965).

452. A. T. Bottini, B. F. Dowden, and R. L. Van Etten, *J. Am. Chem. Soc.* **87**, 3251 (1965).

452a. A. T. Bottini and J. J. Dolhun, *J. Org. Chem.* **33**, 3904 (1968).

453. A. T. Bottini and J. D. Roberts, *J. Am. Chem. Soc.* **80**, 5203 (1958).

454. A. T. Bottini and J. D. Roberts, *J. Am. Chem. Soc.* **78**, 5126 (1956).

455. M. M. Boudakian and E. R. Shipkowski (to Olin Mathieson Chemical Corp.), Can. 776,686 (1968).

456. H. J. M. Bowen, *Use Induced Mutat. Plant Breed., Rept. FAO-IAEA Tech. Meet., Rome, 1964* p. 695. Pergamon Press, Oxford, 1965; via *Bibliog. Agr.* **31**, 48323.

457. M. C. Bowman and M. Beroza, *J. Assoc. Offic. Agr. Chemists* **49**, 1046 (1966).

457a. D. W. Boykin, Jr., A. B. Turner, and R. E. Lutz, *Tetrahedron Letters* p. 817 (1967).

458. F. Bracco, Ger. 1,062,705 (1959); *C. A.* **55**, 22241.

459. N. O. Brace, *J. Org. Chem.* **26**, 4005 (1961).

460. N. O. Brace and W. B. McCormack, *J. Org. Chem.* **26**, 5091 (1961).

460a. E. G. Brain, F. P. Doyle, and M. D. Mehta, *J. Chem. Soc.* p. 633 (1961).

461. J. v. Braun, *Ber.* **70**, 979 (1937).

462. J. v. Braun, K. Heider, and E. Mueller, *Ber.* **50**, 1637 (1917); **51**, 273 (1918).

463. J. v. Braun and W. Pinkernelle, *Ber.* **70**, 1230 (1937).

464. G. I. Braz and Y. I. Vorob'eva, U.S.S.R. 60,202 (1941), via *Chem. Zentr.* Part II, 2851 (1942).

465. G. I. Braz, V. K. Antonov, and K. N. Kurdyumova, *Tr. Inst. Eksperim. i Klin. Onkol., Akad. Med. Nauk SSSR* **2**, 124 (1960); via *C. A.* **59**, 11491.

466. G. I. Braz and V. A. Skorodumov, *C. R. Acad. Sci. URSS* **55**, 315 (1947); via *C. A.* **41**, 6527.

467. G. I. Braz and V. A. Skorodumov, *Dokl. Akad. Nauk SSSR* **59**, 489 (1948); via *C. A.* **42**, 6747.

468. G. I. Braz, *Dokl. Akad. Nauk SSSR* **87**, 589 (1952); via *C. A.* **48**, 113.

469. G. I. Braz, *Dokl. Akad. Nauk SSSR* **87**, 747 (1952); via *C. A.* **48**, 569.

470. G. I. Braz, *Zh. Obshch. Khim.* **25**, 763 (1955); *J. Gen. Chem. USSR (English Transl.)* **25**, 731 (1955).

471. G. I. Braz and V. A. Skorodumov, *Zh. Obshch. Khim.* **26**, 770 (1956); *J. Gen. Chem. USSR (English Transl.)* **26**, 881 (1956).

472. G. I. Braz, *Zh. Obshch. Khim.* **25**, 1413 (1955); *J. Gen. Chem. USSR (English Transl.)* **25**, 1359 (1955).

473. G. I. Braz, V. K. Antonov, and K. N. Kurdyumova, *Zh. Obshch. Khim.* **28**, 2972 (1958); *J. Gen. Chem. USSR (English Transl.)* **28**, 3001 (1958).

474. D. E. Bremer-Reinders, *Proc. 11th Intern. Congr. Genet., The Hague, 1963* Vol. 1, p. 216. Pergamon Press, Oxford, 1965; via *Plant Breed. Abstr.* **34**, 1484.

475. Bridgestone Tire Company, Japan. 9004 ('67); via *C. A.* **67**, 91508.

477. R. K. Brinton and D. H. Volman, *J. Chem. Phys.* **20**, 25 (1952).

478. R. K. Brinton, *Can. J. Chem.* **38**, 1339 (1960).

479. R. K. Brinton, *J. Phys. Chem.* **68**, 2652 (1964).

480. J. W. Britain and P. G. Gemeinhardt, *J. Appl. Polymer Sci.* **4**, 207 (1960).

481. J. W. Britain (to Mobay Chemical Co.), U.S. 3,054,757 (1962); Can. 680,302 (1964).

482. British Cellophane Ltd., Brit. 766,827 (1957).

483. British Cellophane Ltd., Brit. 786,764 (1957).

484. British Cellophane Ltd., Brit. 810,007 (1959).

485. British Cellophane Ltd., Brit. 813,863 (1959).

486. British Industrial Plastics Ltd., Belg. 668,467 (1966); Neth. appl. 6,510,737 (1966); Fr. 1,446,560 (1966); Brit. 1,041,523 (1966).

487. British Sidac Ltd. and A. Copple, Brit. 812,130 (1959).

448. British-American Tobacco Co., Belg. 652,215 (1964); Fr. 1,402,649 (1965); Neth. appl. 6,409,658 (1965); via *C. A.* **64**, 12959.

489. F. H. Brock, *Abstr. Papers, 145th Am. Chem. Soc. Meeting, New York, 1963* p. T-46.

490. N. Brock and H. J. Hohorst, *Arzneimittel-Forsch.* **11**, 164 (1961).

491. W. R. Brode and M. W. Hill, *J. Am. Chem. Soc.* **69**, 724 (1947).

492. S. J. Brois, *J. Org. Chem.* **27**, 3532 (1962).

493. S. J. Brois and G. P. Beardsley, *Tetrahedron Letters* p. 5113 (1966).

494. S. J. Brois, *Publication Board Rept. (U.S.)* PB 135,447; via *C. A.* **54**, 12090.

495. S. J. Brois, *Abstr. Papers, 153rd Am. Chem. Soc. Meeting, Miami Beach, 1967* abstr. O-73.

495a. S. J. Brois (to Esso Research and Development Co.), U.S. 3,401,164 (1968).

495b. S. J. Brois, *Tetrahedron Letters* p. 5997 (1968).

496. R. E. Brooks *et al., Tetrahedron* **22**, 1279 (1966).

497. W. Broser and W. Lautsch, *Naturwissenschaften* **38**, 209 (1951).

498. D. M. Brown and G. O. Osborne, *J. Chem. Soc.* p. 2590 (1957).

499. F. Brown, B. Cartwright, and D. L. Stewart, *J. Gen. Microbiol.* **31**, 179 (1963).

500. F. Brown *et al., J. Hyg.* **61**, 337 (1963).

502. H. C. Brown and A. Tsukamoto, *J. Am. Chem. Soc.* **83**, 2016 (1961).

503. H. C. Brown and A. Tsukamoto, *J. Am. Chem. Soc.* **86**, 1089 (1964).

504. H. C. Brown and A. Tsukamoto, *J. Am. Chem. Soc.* **83**, 4549 (1961).

505. H. C. Brown and M. Gerstein, *J. Am. Chem. Soc.* **72**, 2926 (1950).

506. I. Brown and O. E. Edwards, *Can. J. Chem.* **43**, 1264 (1965).

507. S. C. Brown, *Nucleonics* **4** (5), 139 (1949).

508. S. S. Brown, *Advan. Pharmacol.* **2**, 243 (1963).

509. W. A. Brown and F. D. Mango, *J. Org. Chem.* **29**, 29 (1964).

510. K. Brueckner *et al., Chem. Ber.* **94**, 2897 (1961).

510a. T. C. Bruice *et al., J. Am. Chem. Soc.* **89**, 2106 (1967).

511. Y. A. Bruk and F. Y. Rachinskii, *Zh. Obshch. Khim.* **34**, 2983 (1964); *J. Gen. Chem. USSR (English Transl.)* **34**, 3018 (1964).

512. Y. A. Bruk and F. Y. Rachinskii, *Biol. Aktivn. Soedin., Akad. Nauk SSSR* p. 183 (1965); via *C. A.* **64**, 6539.

513. Y. A. Bruk, *et al.*, USSR 194,834 (1967); via *C. A.* **69**, 10243.

515. H. F. Brust (to The Dow Chemical Co.), U.S. 3,071,574 (1963).
516. B. Buchner, G. G. Kertesz, and A. F. Jackson, *J. Org. Chem.* **27**, 1051 (1962).
518. R. E. Buckles and G. V. Mock, *J. Am. Chem. Soc.* **70**, 1275 (1948).
519. R. E. Buckles and W. J. Probst, *J. Org. Chem.* **22**, 1728 (1957).
520. D. Buckley and H. B. Henbest, *J. Chem. Soc.* p. 1888 (1956).
521. R. Bucourt and M. Vignau, *Bull. Soc. Chim. France* p. 1190 (1961).
522. R. Bucourt, J. Valls, and R. Joly (to Laboratories Français de Chimiotherapie), U.S. 2,920,080 (1960); Fr. 1,195,252 (1959).
524. M. Buiatti and V. N. Ronchi, *Caryologia* **16**, 397 (1963).
524a. N. A. Buina, I. A. Nuretdinov, and N. P. Grechkin, *Izv. Akad. Nauk SSSR, Ser. Khim.* p. 217 (1967); *Bull. Acad. Sci. USSR, Div. Chem. Sci. (English Transl.)* p. 216 (1967).
525. G. J. Buist and H. J. Lucas, *J. Am. Chem. Soc.* **79**, 6157 (1957).
526 G. F. Bulbenko, R. H. Gobran, and E. A. Blommers (to Thiokol Chemical Corp.), U.S. 3,405,121 (1968).
527. G. F. Bulbenko, R. H. Gobran, and E. A. Blommers (to Thiokol Chemical Corp.), U.S. 3,329,674 (1967).
528. A. L. Bullock and J. D. Guthrie (to U.S. Department of Agriculture), U.S. 2,971,815 (1961).
529. J. B. Bullock and C. M. Welch, *Textile Res. J.* **36**, 441 (1966).
530. J. B. Bullock, C. M. Welch, and J. D. Guthrie, *Textile Res. J.* **34**, 691 (1964).
531. J. B. Bullock and C. M. Welch (to U.S. Department of Agriculture), U.S. 3,278,497 (1966).
532. J. B. Bullock and C. M. Welch (to U.S. Department of Agriculture), U.S. 3,318,659 (1967).
533. M. A. Bulyginskaya, *Entomol. Obozrenie* **44**, 738 (1965); via *C. A.* **64**, 16555.
534. C. L. Bumgardner, K. S. McCallum, and J. P. Freeman, *J. Am. Chem. Soc.* **83**, 4417 (1961).
535. C. L. Bumgardner, K. J. Martin, and J. P. Freeman, *J. Am. Chem. Soc.* **85**, 97 (1963).
536. J. F. Bunnett, *J. Am. Chem. Soc.* **83**, 4968 (1961).
537. G. S. Burden and B. J. Smittle, *Florida Entomologist* **46**, 229 (1963).
540. A. B. Burg and C. E. Good, *J. Inorg. & Nucl. Chem.* **2**, 237 (1956).
541. S. I. Burmistrov *et al.*, *Ukr. Khim. Zh.* **30**, 934 (1964); via *C. A.* **62**, 2747.
542. S. I. Burmistrov and V. I. Markov, U.S.S.R. 159,848 (1964); via *C. A.* **60**, 12018.
542a. S. I. Burmistrov *et al.*, U.S.S.R. 209,453 (1968); via *C. A.* **69**, 35916.
543. D. M. Burness and M. D. Sterman (to Eastman Kodak), U.S. 3,271,175 (1966); Belg. 656,174 (1964); Ger. 1,229,386 (1966).
544. D. M. Burness (to Eastman Kodak Co.), U.S. 2,964,404 (1960).
545. D. M. Burness (to Eastman Kodak Co.), U.S. 3,106,468 (1963).
546. D. M. Burness (to Eastman Kodak Co.), U.S. 3,338,715 (1967).
547. C. H. Burnside (to North American Aviation, Inc.), U.S. 3,305,523 (1967).
548. J. M. Burton (to Phillips Petroleum Co.), U.S. 2,769,304 (1956).
549. D. H. Buss, L. D. Hall, and L. Hough, *J. Chem. Soc.* p. 1616 (1965).
550. D. H. Buss, L. Hough, and A. C. Richardson, *J. Chem. Soc.* p. 2736 (1965).
551. D. H. Buss, L. Hough, and A. C. Richardson, *J. Chem. Soc.* p. 5295 (1963).
552. R. Buyle, *Chem. & Ind. (London)* p. 195 (1966).
553. A. M. Buzueva, *Khim. Geterotsikl. Soedin., Akad. Nauk Latv. SSR* p. 157 (1968); via *Chem. Zentr.* No. 60, abstr. 654 (1968).
554. M. S. Bykhovskaya and R. V. Makedonskaya, *Zh. Anal. Khim.* **22**, 621 (1967); *J. Anal. Chem. USSR (English Transl.)* **22**, 537 (1967).
555. G. A. Byrne, D. Gardiner, and F. H. Holmes, *J. Appl. Chem. (London)* **16**, 81 (1966).

556. V. F. Bystrov and V. P. Lezina, *Opt. i Spektroskopiya* **16**, 790 (1964), *Opt. Spectry.* (*USSR*) (*English Transl.*) **16**, 430 (1964).

557. V. F. Bystrov *et al.*, *Opt. i Spektroskopiya* **19**, 217 (1965); *Opt. Spectry.* (*USSR*) (*English Transl.*) **19**, 122 (1965).

558. V. F. Bystrov, O. A. Yuzhakova, and R. G. Kostyanovskii, *Dokl. Akad. Nauk SSSR* **147**, 843 (1962); *Proc. Acad. Sci. USSR, Chem. Sect.* (*English Transl.*) **145–147**, 1049 (1962).

558a. G. A. Cabat, *Dissertation Abstr.* **B28**, 4926 (1968).

559. J. I. G. Cadogan and L. C. Thomas, *J. Chem. Soc.* p. 2248 (1960).

560. T. L. Cairns, *J. Am. Chem. Soc.* **63**, 871 (1941).

561. P. Calabresi and A. D. Welch, *Ann. Rev. Med.* **13**, 147 (1962).

562. H. F. Calcote *et al.*, *Ind. Eng. Chem.* **44**, 2656 (1952).

563. D. W. Cameron and R. G. F. Giles, *Chem. Commun.* p. 573 (1965); *J. Chem. Soc., C, Org.* p. 1461 (1968).

564. B. K. Campbell and K. N. Campbell, *J. Org. Chem.* **9**, 178 (1944).

565. K. N. Campbell, A. H. Sommers, and B. K. Campbell, *Org. Syn.* Coll. Vol. **3**, 148 (1955).

566. K. N. Campbell *et al.*, *J. Org. Chem.* **8**, 103 (1943).

567. K. N. Campbell, A. H. Sommers, and B. K. Campbell, *J. Am. Chem. Soc.* **68**, 140 (1946).

568. K. N. Campbell *et al.*, *J. Org. Chem.* **9**, 184 (1944).

569. D. G. Campion, *Pest Artic. News Sum.* **11**, 467 (1965).

570. D. G. Campion, *Nature* **214**, 1031 (1967).

571. G. T. Cantwell and H. J. Henneberry, *J. Insect Pathol.* **5**, 251 (1963).

572. R. V. Capeller *et al.*, *Helv. Chim. Acta* **40**, 1652 (1957).

573. B. Capon, *Quart. Rev.* (*London*) **18**, 62 and 72 (1964).

574. G. L. Capp, D. A. Rigas, and R. T. Jones, *Science* **157**, 65 (1967).

575. V. Cappuccio and U. Riboni (to "Montecatini" Societa . . .), U.S. 3,112,159 (1963); Hung. 149,405 (1961); Brit. 893,605 (1962).

576. V. Cappuccio, F. Vacanti, and P. Maltese (to "Montecatini" Societa . . .), U.S. 3,107,228 (1963); V. Cappuccio, P. Maltese, and F. Vacanti (to "Montecatini" Societa . . .), U.S. 3,312,755 (1967); Fr. 1,190,703 (1959); Austrian 210,055 (1960); Brit. 873,830 (1961).

577. V. Cappuccio and U. Riboni (to "Montecatini" Societa . . .), U.S. 3,126,246 (1964); S. Afr. 60/187; Austral. 249,479 (1960); Indian 70,343 (1961); Fr. 1,245,274 (1961); Austrian 215,604 (1961); Brit. 884,665 (1961); Neth. 101,434 (1962); Can. 669,779 (1963); Ger. 1,223,493 (1966).

579. V. Cappuccio and U. Riboni (to Montecatini Edison S. p. A.), U.S. 3,320,226, (1967).

582. G. Cardinali and G. Morpurgo, *Ric. Sci.* **25**, 55 (1955); via *C. A.* **52**, 15756.

583. G. Cardinali, *Nature* **173**, 825 (1954).

584. G. Caronna and S. Palazzo, *Gazz. Chim. Ital.* **82**, 292 (1952).

585. C. P. Carpenter, H. F. Smyth, Jr., and C. B. Shaffer, *J. Ind. Hyg. Toxicol.* **30**, 2 (1948).

586. C. P. Carpenter, H. F. Smyth, Jr., and U. C. Pozzani, *J. Ind. Hyg. Toxicol.* **31**, 343 (1949).

587. W. Carpenter, A. Haymaker, and D. W. Moore, *J. Org. Chem.* **31**, 789 (1966).

588. J. L. Carrillo, A. Ortega, and J. Rodriguez, *Agr. Tec. Mex.* **2**, 168 (1963).

589. H. E. Carter, *Org. Reactions* **3**, 198 (1946).

590. J. P. Casey, "Pulp and Paper: Chemistry and Chemical Technology," 2nd ed., Vol. II: "Papermaking,". Wiley (Interscience), New York, 1960.

591. N. S. Cassel (to Interchemical Corp.), U.S. 2,949,386 (1960).

592. Cassella Farbwerke Mainkur, A.-G., Ger. 822,241 (1951); *C. A.* **48**, 4227.
593. Cassella Farbwerke Mainkur, A.-G., Ger. 832,438 (1952); *Chem. Zentr.* p. 5011 (1952).
594. Cassella Farbwerke Mainkur, A.-G., Ger. 831,540 (1952); *C. A.* **49**, 5853.
595. Cassella Farbwerke Mainkur, A.-G., Ger. 863,450 (1953); *C. A.* **52**, 15069.
596. Cassella Farbwerke Mainkur, A.-G., Ger. 871,592 (1953); *C. A.* **52**, 15083.
597. Cassella Farbwerke Mainkur, A.-G., Swiss 297,371 (1954); Ger. 958,379 (1957); *C. A.* **53**, 6639.
598. Cassella Farbwerke Mainkur, A.-G., Ger. 1,014,961 (1957); *C. A.* **54**, 16856.
599. Cassella Farbwerke Mainkur, A.-G., Ger. 1,140,172 (1962); *C. A.* **59**, 7705.
600. Cassella Farbwerke Mainkur, A.-G., Ger. 1,163,726 (1964); Fr. 1,345,630 (1964); *C. A.* **60**, 15669.
601. Cassella Farbwerke Mainkur, A.-G., Ger. 1,182,433 (1964); Fr. 1,363,033 (1964); Brit. 987,329 (1965).
602. Cassella Farbwerke Mainkur A.-G., Brit. 1,034,606 (1966).
603. N. C. Castellucci *et al.*, *Chem. Commun.* p. 473 (1967).
604. R. E. Castle and S. S. Ristich, *J. Agr. Food Chem.* **14**, 301 (1966).
604a. Castrol Ltd., Neth. appl. 6,709,004 (1968); Belg. 700,617 (1967).
605. L. A. Cates, *J. Med. Chem.* **10**, 924 (1967).
606. B. M. Cattanach, *Intern. J. Radiation Biol.* **1**, 288 (1959).
607. B. M. Cattanach, *Effects Ionizing Radiation Reprod. System, Proc. Intern. Symp., Colo. State Univ., 1962* p. 415. Pergamon Press, Oxford, 1964.
608. B. M. Cattanach, *Z. Vererbungslehre* **90**, 1 (1959).
609. B. M. Cattanach and R. G. Edwards, *Proc. Roy. Soc. Edinburgh* **B67**, Part 1, 54 (1957–1958).
610. B. M. Cattanach, *Z. Vererbungslehre* **92**, 165 (1961).
611. B. M. Cattanach, *Mutation Res.* **3**, 346 (1966).
612. G. Cavallini and F. Ravenna, *Farmaco (Pavia), Ed. Sci.* **12**, 151 (1957); via *C. A.* **51**, 11245.
612a. Cellophane Investments Co. Ltd., Brit. 1,082,984 (1967).
613. P. R. Certain, V. S. Watts, and J. H. Goldstein, *Theoret. Chim. Acta* **2**, 324 (1964).
614. T. Cervigni and G. T. Scarascia, *Comit. Nazl. Energia Nucl.* **CNEN-118**, 343 (1961); via *C. A.* **57**, 4991.
615. P. Chabrier *et al.*, *Compt. Rend. Soc. Biol.* **158**, 2057 (1964).
616. P. R. Chadwick, *Nature* **204**, 299 (1964).
616a. J. C. Chalchat, F. Theron, and R. Vessiere, *Compt. Rend.* **C267**, 426 (1968).
617. W. F. Chamberlain, *J. Econ. Entomol.* **55**, 240 (1962).
618. W. F. Chamberlain and C. C. Barrett, *J. Econ. Entomol.* **57**, 267 (1964).
619. W. F. Chamberlain and E. W. Hamilton, *J. Econ. Entomol.* **57**, 800 (1964).
620. S. C. Chan and F. Leh, *Australian J. Chem.* **19**, 2271 (1966).
620a. L. M. Chance, D. G. Daigle, and G. L. Drake, Jr., *J. Chem. Eng. Data* **13**, 442 (1968).
621. L. H. Chance, R. M. Perkins, and W. A. Reeves, *Textile Res. J.* **30**, 305 (1960).
622. L. H. Chance, R. M. Perkins, and W. A. Reeves, *Textile Res. J.* **30**, 918 (1960).
623. L. H. Chance, G. L. Drake, Jr., and W. A. Reeves (to U.S. Department of Agriculture), U.S. 2,870,042 (1959).
624. L. H. Chance, G. L. Drake, Jr., and W. A. Reeves (to U.S. Department of Agriculture), U.S. 2,886,538 (1959).
625. L. H. Chance, G. L. Drake, Jr., and W. A. Reeves (to U.S. Department of Agriculture), U.S. 2,891,877 (1959).
626. L. H. Chance, G. L. Drake, Jr., and W. A. Reeves (to U.S. Department of Agriculture), U.S. 2,901,444 (1959).

627. L. H. Chance and W. A. Reeves (to U.S. Department of Agriculture), U.S. 3,038,776 (1962).

628. L. H. Chance (to U.S. Department of the Navy), U.S. 3,146,228 (1964).

629. L. H. Chance (to U.S. Department of Agriculture), U.S. 3,205,034 (1965).

629a L. H. Chance and J. P. Moreau, *Abstr. Papers, 156th Am. Chem. Soc. Meeting, Atlantic City, 1968* abstr. CELL-14.

630. J. T.-P. Chang, C.-P. Tsao, and Y.-C. Chiang, *K'un Ch'ung Hsueh Pao* **12**, 394 (1963); via *C. A.* **60**, 3314.

631. J. T.-P. Chang and Y.-C. Chiang, *K'un Ch'ung Hsueh Pao* **12**, 538 (1963); via *C. A.* **60**, 12431.

632. J. T.-P. Chang and Y.-C. Chiang, *K'un Ch'ung Hsueh Pao* **13**, 679 (1964); via *C. A.* **62**, 11089; cf. T.-P. Ts'ao and J. T.-P. Chang, *K'un Ch'ung Hsueh Pao* **15**, 13 (1966); via *C. A.* **65**, 9656.

633. S. C. Chang and A. B. Bořkovec, *J. Econ. Entomol.* **59**, 102 (1966).

634. S. C. Chang and A. B. Bořkovec, *J. Econ. Entomol.* **57**, 488 (1964).

635. S. C. Chang, *J. Econ. Entomol.* **58**, 669 (1965).

636. S. C. Chang, A. B. Bořkovec, and C. W. Woods, *J. Econ. Entomol.* **59**, 937 (1966).

637. S. C. Chang and A. B. Bořkovec, *J. Econ. Entomol.* **59**, 1359 (1966).

638. S. C. Chang and A. B. Bořkovec, *Abstr. Papers, 150th Am. Chem. Soc. Meeting, Atlantic City, 1965* p. A-26.

640. N. B. Chapman, K. Clarke, and R. D. Strickland, *Proc. Roy. Soc.* **B163**, 116 (1965).

641. N. B. Chapman *et al.*, *Chem. & Ind.* (*London*) p. 805 (1952).

642. N. B. Chapman and A. J. Tompsett, *J. Chem. Soc.* p. 1291 (1961).

643. N. B. Chapman and D. J. Triggle, *J. Chem. Soc.* p. 1385 (1963).

644. N. B. Chapman and J. W. James, *J. Chem. Soc.* p. 2103 (1954).

645. N. B. Chapman and D. J. Triggle, *J. Chem. Soc.* p. 4835 (1963).

646. P. Charpentier, *Compt. Rend.* **225**, 306 (1947).

647. V. L. Chase and E. Messmer (to Interchemical Corp.), U.S. 3,223,669 (1965); Fr. 1,376,041 (1964); Japan. 9156 ('66); Brit. 1,035,445 (1966).

648. F. D. Chattaway and G. D. Parkes, *J. Chem. Soc.* p. 1307 (1925).

649. K. L. Chaudhuri, *Sci. Culture* (*Calcutta*) **32**, 419 (1966).

649a. M. A. Chekalin, *Zh. Vseso. Khim. Obshchestva im. D. I. Mendeleeva* **11**, 43 (1966); *Mendeleev Chem. J.* (*English Transl.*) **11**, 40 (1966).

649b. N. M. Chekalin, *Tsitol. Genet., Akad. Nauk Ukr. SSR* **2** (2), 138 (1968); via *C. A.* **69**, 16874.

650. Chemirad Corp., Brit. 1,020,811 (1966).

651. Chemirad Corp., Brit. 1,057,175 (1967).

653. Chemirad Corp., Brit. 996,388 (1965); Ger. 1,208,170 (1965).

654. Chemirad Corp., Brit. 1,008,464 (1965).

656. Chemirad Corp., Fr. 1,449,286 (1966); Brit. 1,125,792 (1968).

657. Chemirad Corp., "*Ethylene Imine*" (an undated booklet).

658. Chemirad Corp., Brit. 1,069,223 (1967).

658a. Chemische Fabrik Pfersee, Belg. 571,306 (1962); via *Chem. Zentr.* No. 7-8, abstr. 3026 (1965).

659. Chemische Fabrik Pfersee, Neth. appl. 6,602,865 (1966); via *C. A.* **66**, 29995.

659a. Chemische Fabrik Pfersee, Ger. 1,272,298 (1968).

660. Chemische Fabrik Stockhausen et Cie, Belg. 630,432 (1963); *C. A.* **60**, 13386; Ger. 1,217,330 (1966).

661. Chemische Werke Huels A.-G., Ger. 1,144,702 (1963); *C. A.* **59**, 6420.

662. Chemische Werke Huels A.-G., Fr. 1,427,414 (1966); via *C. A.* **65**, 8917.

663. Chemische Werke Huels A.-G., Fr. 1,513,142 (1968).

663a. Chemische Werke Huels A.-G., Ger. 1,263,300 (1968); *C. A.* **68**, 96350.
664. M. Chêne and O. Martin-Borret, *Assoc. Tech. Ind. Papetiére, Bull.* No. 5, p. 218 (1957); *C. A.* **52**, 12398.
665. M. Chêne, *Papeterie* **86**, 1155 (1964); via *C. A.* **62**, 1839.
666. H.-Y. Cheng *et al.*, *Yao Hsueh Hsueh Pao* **10**, 407 (1963); via *C. A.* **59**, 13982.
667. J. A. Chenicek (to Universal Oil Products Co.), U.S. 2,530,650 (1950).
668. E. Cherbuliez, S. Colak-Antic, and J. Rabinowitz, *Arch. Sci. (Geneva)* **18**, 282 (1965); via *C. A.* **64**, 1913.
669. I. Z. Chernin and I. A. Goroshkova, *Klei i Tekhinol. Skleivaniya, Sb. Statei* p. 145 (1960); via *C. A.* **56**, 10393.
669a. V. A. Chernov and V. B. Lytkina, *Vopr. Onkol.* **5**, 552 (1959); via Cheymol *et al.* (673).
670. V. A. Chernov, S. M. Volodarskaya, and A. I. Gavrilova, *Farmakol. i Toksikol.* **28**, 70 (1965); *C. A.* **62**, 15243.
671. V. A. Chernov and S. M. Volodarskaya, *Vopr. Onkol.* **9** (7), 5 (1963); via *C. A.* **60**, 1021.
671a. V. A. Chernov and B. T. Garibdzhanyan, *Farmakol. i Toksikol.* **28**, 340 (1965); via *C. A.* **63**, 12143.
672. V. A. Chernov, A. A. Grushina, and L. G. Lytkina, *Farmakol. i Toksikol.* **26**, 102 (1963); via *C. A.* **59**, 5665.
673. J. Cheymol *et al.*, *Biol. Med. (Paris)* **56**, 519 (1967).
675. R. F. Childs and A. W. Johnson, *Chem. Commun.* p. 95 (1965).
676. Chinoin Gyógyszer és Vergyészeti Termékek Gyára R.T., Austrian 243,806 (1965); via *C. A.* **64**, 6739.
677. Chinoin Gyógyszer és Vergyészeti Termékek Gyára R.T., Belg. 613,335 (1962); *C. A.* **58**, 2502.
677a. D. S. Chisholm (to The Dow Chemical Co.), U.S. 3,301,932 (1967).
677b. R. A. Chittenden and L. C. Thomas, *Spectrochim. Acta* **22**, 1449 (1967).
678. Z. F. Chmielewicz *et al.*, *Abstr. Papers, 147th Am. Chem. Soc. Meeting, Philadelphia, 1964* p. M-27; *Cancer Res.* **A27**, 1248 (1967).
679. C.-H. Chou, H.-C. Liang, and P. Hsu, *Yao Hsueh Hsueh Pao* **11**, 617 (1964); via *C. A.* **62**, 979.
680. H. Chou and W.-L. Yang, *Fang Chih Chi Shu* No. 2, 37 (1964); via *C. A.* **62**, 13309.
681. H. Chou, *Hua Hsueh Tung Pao* No. 3, 33 (1964); via *C. A.* **61**, 5589.
682. R. C. Christena and E. Broderick (to Thiokol Chemical Corp.), U.S. 3,235,544 (1966); Brit. 1,003,385 (1965); Japan. 28,565 ('65).
682a. R. C. Christena and E. Broderick (to Thiokol Chemical Corp.), U.S. 3,244,697 (1967).
683. H. N. Christensen, *J. Biol. Chem.* **135**, 399 (1940).
684. J. E. Christensen and L. Goodman, *J. Org. Chem.* **28**, 847 (1963).
685. J. E. Christensen and L. Goodman, *J. Am. Chem. Soc.* **82**, 4738 (1960).
686. R. M. Christenson, S. Porter, Jr., and A. Halcoussis (to Pittsburgh Plate Glass Co.), U.S. 3,290,416 and 3,290,417 (1966); Brit. 1,109,643 (1968); Neth. appl. 6,607,546 (1966).
687. R. M. Christenson, S. Porter, Jr., and A. Halcoussis (to Pittsburgh Plate Glass Co.), U.S. 3,325,443 (1967).
688. Christiaens Soc., Neth. appl. 6,508,663 (1966); Belg. 666,353 (1966); Fr. M4686 (1966); via *C. A.* **64**, 15904.
689. A. Chrzaszezewska and W. Dawid, *Lodz. Towarz. Nauk.: Wydzial III, Acta Chim.* **11**, 127 (1966); via *C. A.* **66**, 104544.
690. S.-H. Chu and H. G. Mautner, *J. Org. Chem.* **26**, 4498 (1961).

691. Ciba A.-G., Fr. 1,336,403 (1963); *C. A.* **60**, 2917.
692. Ciba Ltd., Neth. appl. 6,707,726 (1968); Belg. 699,290 (1967).
693. Ciba Ltd., Swiss 369,839 (1963); *C. A.* **60**, 5669.
694. Ciba Ltd., Fr. 1,205,384 (1960); Belg. 609,295 (1962); Brit. 923,090 (1963).
695. Ciba Ltd., Swiss 366,607 (1963); *C. A.* **60**, 3141.
696. Ciba Ltd., Belg. 622,423 (1963); Swiss 386,385 (1965); Brit. 982,913 (1965); Ger. 1,212,487 (1966).
697. Ciba Ltd., Brit. 877,948 (1961); Ger. 1,143,784 (1963).
698. Ciba Ltd., Brit. 884,258 (1961).
699. Ciba Ltd., Austrian 217,452 (1961); Fr. M197 (1961); Indian 67,819 (1961); Ger. 1,125,431 (1962); Fr. 1,292,946 (1962); Brit. 889,514 (1962); Swiss 377,823 (1964).
700. Ciba Ltd., Brit. 920,801 (1963).
701. Ciba Ltd., Belg. 699,422 (1967).
702. Ciba Ltd., Neth. appl. 6,707,198 (1968).
702a. Ciba Ltd., Belg. 709,377 (1968).
703. Ciba Ltd., Ger. 1,066,745 (1959); *C. A.* **55**, 19334.
704. Ciba Ltd., Belg. 609,054 (1962); Brit. 1,009,911 (1965).
705. Ciba Ltd., Austrian 193,859 (1957); Ger. 1,058,514 (1959); Swiss 334,841 and 334,842 (1959); Brit. 825,760 (1959).
706. Ciba Soc. Anonymous, Fr. 1,506,467 (1967).
708. Ciba Soc. Anonymous, Fr. 1,163,465 (1958); *Chem. Zentr.* 17306 (1959).
710. E. Cioranescu *et al.*, *Acad. Rep. Populare Romine, Studii Cercetari Chim.* **10**, 81 (1962); via *C. A.* **58**, 6741.
711. City of Nagoya, Japan. 8895 ('55); via *C. A.* **52**, 4200.
712. L. B. Clapp, *J. Am. Chem. Soc.* **70**, 184 (1948).
713. L. B. Clapp and J. W. Watjen, *J. Am. Chem. Soc.* **75**, 1490 (1953).
714. L. B. Clapp, *J. Am. Chem. Soc.* **73**, 2584 (1951).
715. L. B. Clapp *et al.*, *J. Am. Chem. Soc.* **77**, 5116 (1955).
716. D. T. Clark, *Theoret. Chim. Acta* **10**, 111 (1968).
717. R. A. Clark, *Dissertation Abstr.* **B27**, 1082 (1966).
718. R. D. Clark, *Dissertation Abstr.* **26**, 3035 (1965).
719. R. D. Clark and G. K. Helmkamp, *J. Org. Chem.* **29**, 1316 (1964).
720. J. A. Clarke (to The Dow Chemical Co.), U.S. 3,317,442 (1967).
721. C. S. Cleaver and C. G. Crespan, *J. Am. Chem. Soc.* **87**, 3716 (1965).
722. C. S. Cleaver (to du Pont de Nemours), U.S. 3,255,157 (1966).
722a. J. Cleophax, S. D. Gero, and R. D. Guthrie, *Tetrahedron Letters* p. 567 (1967).
722b. J. Cleophax, S. D. Gero, and J. Hildesheim, *Chem. Commun.* p. 95 (1968).
723. R. O. Clinton *et al.*, *J. Am. Chem. Soc.* **70**, 950 (1948).
724. G. L. Closs and S. J. Brois, *J. Am. Chem. Soc.* **82**, 6068 (1960).
724a. G. L. Closs and W. A. Boell, *J. Am. Chem. Soc.* **85**, 3904 (1963).
725. J. E. Cobb (to The Dow Chemical Co.), U.S. 3,179,655 (1965); Belg. 625,995 (1962); Fr. 1,341,871 (1963); Japan. 11,381 ('64); Brit. 973,956 (1964); Ital. 680,058 (1965); Can. 740,905 (1966); Ger. 1,262,278 (1968).
726. B. Cohen, E. R. Van Artsdalen, and J. Harris, *J. Am. Chem. Soc.* **70**, 281 (1948).
727. B. Cohen, E. R. Van Artsdalen, and J. Harris, *J. Am. Chem. Soc.* **74**, 1875 (1952).
728. B. Cohen, E. R. Van Artsdalen, and J. Harris, *J. Am. Chem. Soc.* **74**, 1878 (1952).
728a. R. L. Cohen, *Advan. Pharmacol.* **4**, 263 (1966).
729. S. Cohen (to Millmaster Onyx Corp.), U.S. 3,242,117 (1966).
730. S. Cohen (to Millmaster Onyx Corp.), U. S. 3,258,358 (1966).

730a. W. P. Coker, P. M. Phillips, and G. R. Miller (to The Dow Chemical Co.), U. S. 3,338,885 (1967); Belg. 662,519 (1965); Fr. 1,455,085 (1966); Ital. 754,891 (1967); Brit. 1,075,585 (1967).

731. W. P. Coker (to The Dow Chemical Co.), U.S. 3,326,895 (1967); Neth. appl. 6,600,635 (1966); Belg. 676,417 (1966); Fr. 1,468,054 (1966); Ital. 758,397 (1967); Can. 751,455 (1967); Brit. 1,080,900 (1967); Japan 8271 ('68).

731a. W. P. Coker and R. E. Lane, Jr. (to The Dow Chemical Co.), U.S. 3,359,303 (1967).

732. G. H. Coleman and G. P. Waugh, *Proc. Iowa Acad. Sci.* **40**, 115 (1933).

733. G. H. Coleman and C. S. Nicholopoulos, *Proc. Iowa Acad. Sci.* **49**, 286 (1942).

734. G. H. Coleman and J. E. Callen, *J. Am. Chem. Soc.* **68**, 2006 (1946).

735. G. H. Coleman, *J. Am. Chem. Soc.* **50**, 2739 (1928).

736. Colgate-Palmolive Co., Fr. 1,399,085 (1965); Brit. 1,065,033 (1967).

737. C. W. Collier and J. E. Downey, *J. Econ. Entomol.* **58**, 649 (1965).

738. C. W. Collier and J. E. Downey, *J. Econ. Entomol.* **60**, 265 (1967).

739. C. W. Collier and R. Tardif, *J. Econ. Entomol.* **60**, 28 (1967).

740. J. F. Collins, *Brit. Med. Bull.* **21**, 223 (1965).

741. I. Combiescu, M. Duport, and A. Enescu, *Arch. Roumaines Pathol. Exptl. Microbiol.* **26**, 205 (1967); via *C. A.* **67**, 81445.

742. Commonwealth Scientific and Industrial Research Organization, Neth. appl. 6,409,279 (1965); *C. A.* **63**, 13484; Belg. 651,439 (1965); *C. A.* **64**, 8385; Fr. 1,411,809 (1965).

743. Compagnie française des matières colorantes, Belg. 628,277 (1963); Fr. 1,322,330 (1963); Brit. 1,032,275 (1966).

744. "Comparative Clinical and Biological Effects of Alkylating Agents," *Ann. N.Y. Acad. Sci.* **68**, 657 (1958).

745. Comptoir des textiles artificiels, Viscose Française and Givet-Izieux, Fr. 1,106,707 (1955); *C. A.* **53**, 10792.

746. J. W. Conklin, A. C. Upton, and K. W. Christenberry, *Cancer Res.* **25**, 20 (1965).

747. T. A. Connors *et al.*, *Chem. & Ind.* (*London*) p. 1017 (1962).

748. T. A. Connors and L. A. Elson, *Biochem. Pharmacol.* **11**, 1221 (1962).

749. D. G. Constantinescu *et al.*, *Compt. Rend.* **253**, 1061 (1961).

750. D. G. Constantinescu *et al.*, *Compt. Rend.* **255**, 1357 (1962).

751. D. G. Constantinescu *et al.*, *Compt. Rend.* **256**, 3878 (1963); *Pharmazie* **18**, 699 (1963).

751a. A. J. Costanza and G. E. Meyer (to Goodyear Tire and Rubber Co.), U.S. 3,388,107 (1968).

752. B. S. V. Constatt *et al.*, *Verhandl. Deut. Ges. Pathol.* **50**, 429 (1966); via *C. A.* **66**, 93546.

753. A. G. Cook and E. K. Fields, *J. Org. Chem.* **27**, 3686 (1962).

754. S. R. B. Cooke, N. F. Schulz, and E. W. Lindroos, *Mining Eng.* **4**, 697 (1952).

755. R. C. Cookson *et al.*, *J. Chem. Soc.*, C, *Org.* p. 928 (1967).

755a. C. W. Cooper and R. D. Falb, *Ann. N.Y. Acad. Sci.* **146**, 214 (1968).

756. W. Cooper and R. K. Smith, *Makromol. Chem.* **40**, 148 (1960).

756a. A. S. Cooper, Jr. *et al.* (to U.S. Department of Agriculture), U.S. 3,285,690 (1966).

757. A. C. Cope *et al.*, *J. Am. Chem. Soc.* **71**, 554 (1949).

758. A. C. Cope *et al.*, *J. Am. Chem. Soc.* **73**, 1199 (1951).

759. E. J. Corey *et al.*, *J. Am. Chem. Soc.* **89**, 2797 (1967).

760. E. J. Corey and M. Chaykovsky, *J. Am. Chem. Soc.* **84**, 3782 (1962); **87**, 1353 (1965).

761. D. W. Cornell, R. S. Berry, and W. Lwowski, *J. Am. Chem. Soc.* **88**, 544 (1966).

762. D. W. Cornell, R. S. Berry, and W. Lwowski, *J. Am. Chem. Soc.* **87**, 3626 (1965).

763. I. Cornman and M. Evans, *Biol. Bull.* **103**, 44 (1952).
764. C. Corradi, E. Grossi, and V. Guzzon, *Atti Soc. Lombarda Sci. Med. Biol.* **13**, 58 (1958); via *C. A.* **52**, 17418.
765. D. B. Cosulich, J. B. Patrick, and R. P. Williams (to American Cyanamid Co.), U.S. 3,214,439 (1965).
766. D. B. Cosulich, J. B. Patrick, and R. P. Williams (to American Cyanamid Co.), U.S. 3,214,440 (1965).
767. R. J. Cotter and R. F. Beach, *J. Org. Chem.* **29**, 751 (1964).
768. Courtaulds Ltd., Brit. 796,294 (1958).
769. Courtaulds Ltd., E. E. Tallis, and W. J. C. Field, Brit. 536,686 (1941).
770. Courtaulds Ltd., Brit. 830,011 (1960).
771. H. C. Cox, J. R. Young, and M. C. Bowmann, *J. Econ. Entomol.* **60**, 1111 (1967).
772. J. D. Cox, *Tetrahedron* **19**, 1175 (1963).
773. K. Craemer and F. Hoelscher (to Badische Anilin- und Soda-Fabrik, A.-G.), U.S. 2,719,831 (1955); Brit. 701,139 (1953); Ger. 908,009 (1954).
773a. K. Craemer and F. Hoelscher (to Badische Anilin- und Soda-Fabrik, A.-G.), U.S. 2,813,083 (1957); Ger. 918,922 (1954); Brit. 709,954 (1954).
773b. D. E. Cragar and D. O. Bowen (to The Dow Chemical Co.), U.S. 3,366,601 (1968).
774. A. W. Craig and H. Jackson, *Brit. J. Pharmacol.* **10**, 321 (1955).
775. A. W. Craig, H. Jackson, and R. M. V. James, *Brit. J. Pharmacol.* **21**, 590 (1963).
776. A. W. Craig, B. W. Fox, and H. Jackson, *Nature* **181**, 353 (1958); H. Jackson, A. W. Craig, and B. W. Fox, *Acta Unio Intern. Contra Cancrum* **16**, 673 (1960); via *C. A.* **54**, 23049.
777. D. J. Cram and M. J. Hatch, *J. Am. Chem. Soc.* **75**, 33 (1953).
778. W. T. Cram, *J. Econ. Entomol.* **60**, 885 (1967).
779. T. R. Crampton, *Analyst* **90**, 107 (1965).
782. C. S. Creighton, E. R. Cuthbert, Jr., and W. J. Reid, Jr., *J. Econ. Entomol.* **59**, 163 (1966).
783. A. W. Cressmann, *J. Econ. Entomol.* **56**, 111 (1963).
784. N. H. Cromwell, *Record Chem. Progr.* (*Kresge-Hooker Sci. Lib.*) **19**, 215 (1958).
785. N. H. Cromwell, *J. Am. Chem. Soc.* **69**, 258 (1947).
786. N. H. Cromwell and D. J. Cram, *J. Am. Chem. Soc.* **65**, 301 (1943).
787. N. H. Cromwell and I. H. Witt, *J. Am. Chem. Soc.* **65**, 308 (1943).
788. N. H. Cromwell, R. D. Babson, and C. E. Harris, *J. Am. Chem. Soc.* **65**, 312 (1943).
789. N. H. Cromwell and R. S. Johnson, *J. Am. Chem. Soc.* **65**, 316 (1943).
790. N. H. Cromwell and M. A. Graff, *J. Org. Chem.* **17**, 414 (1952).
791. N. H. Cromwell, *Trans. N.Y. Acad. Sci.* **68**, 721 (1957).
792. N. H. Cromwell and H. Hoeksema, *J. Am. Chem. Soc.* **71**, 708 (1949).
793. N. H. Cromwell and R. A. Wankel, *J. Am. Chem. Soc.* **71**, 711 (1949).
795. N. H. Cromwell et al., *J. Am. Chem. Soc.* **79**, 922 (1957).
796. N. H. Cromwell et al., *J. Am. Chem. Soc.* **73**, 1044 (1951).
797. N. H. Cromwell and M. C. McMaster, *J. Org. Chem.* **32**, 2145 (1967).
798. N. H. Cromwell and J. A. Caughlan, *J. Am. Chem. Soc.* **67**, 2235 (1945).
799. N. H. Cromwell et al., *J. Am. Chem. Soc.* **73**, 2803 (1951).
800. N. H. Cromwell and G. D. Mercer, *J. Am. Chem. Soc.* **79**, 3815 (1957).
801. N. H. Cromwell and G. D. Mercer, *J. Am. Chem. Soc.* **79**, 3819 (1957).
802. N. H. Cromwell, R. E. Bamburg, and J. L. Adelfang, *J. Am. Chem. Soc.* **82**, 4241 (1960).
803. N. H. Cromwell, *J. Am. Chem. Soc.* **81**, 4702 (1959).
804. N. H. Cromwell et al., *J. Am. Chem. Soc.* **75**, 5384 (1953).
805. N. H. Cromwell and R. P. Cahoy, *J. Am. Chem. Soc.* **80**, 5524 (1958).

806. N. H. Cromwell and R. J. Mohrbacher, *J. Am. Chem. Soc.* **75**, 6252 (1953).
807. N. H. Cromwell and H. Hoeksema, *J. Am. Chem. Soc.* **71**, 716 (1949).
807a. F. R. Cropper and S. Kaminsky, *Anal. Chem.* **35**, 735 (1963).
808. M. Crowther and W. R. Nummy (to Arnold Hoffman and Co., Inc.), U.S. 2,806,839 (1957).
809. M. M. Crystal, *Exptl. Parasitol.* **15**, 249 (1964).
810. M. M. Crystal and L. E. LaChance, *Biol. Bull.* **125**, 270 (1963).
811. M. M. Crystal, *J. Econ. Entomol.* **56**, 468 (1963).
812. M. M. Crystal, *J. Econ. Entomol.* **59**, 577 (1966).
813. M. M. Crystal, *J. Econ. Entomol.* **59**, 580 (1966).
814. M. M. Crystal, *J. Econ. Entomol.* **58**, 678 (1965).
815. M. M. Crystal, *J. Econ. Entomol.* **57**, 726 (1964).
816. M. M. Crystal, *J. Econ. Entomol.* **60**, 1005 (1967).
817. M. M. Crystal, *J. Med. Entomol.* **2**, 317 (1965).
818. M. M. Crystal, *J. Econ. Entomol.* **60**, 880 (1967).
818a. B. M. Culbertson and S. Dietz, *Can. J. Chem.* **46**, 3399 (1968).
819. G. G. Curtis and B. Buchner (to Continental Oil Co.), U.S. 3,286,002 (1966).
819a. G. G. Curtis and B. Buchner (to Continental Oil Co.), U.S. 3,337,656 (1967).
820. G. G. Curtis, E. Buchner, and B. Buchner (to The American Agricultural Chemical Co.), U.S. 3,207,661 (1965).
821. T. Curtius and W. Doerr, *J. Prakt. Chem.* (2) **125**, 425 (1930).
822. T. Curtius and A. Bertho, *Ber.* **59**, 565 (1926).
823. T. Curtius and F. Schmidt, *Ber.* **55**, 1571 (1922).
824. J. W. Cusic and H. S. Lowrie (to G. D. Searle and Co.), U.S. 3,140,286 (1964).
825. J. Cymerman-Craig, *et al.*, *Australian J. Chem.* **9**, 89 (1956).
826. S. Daehne, J. Ranft, and H. Paul, *Tetrahedron Letters* p. 3355 (1964).
827. S. Daehne, H. Paul, and D. Leupold, *Z. Naturforsch.* **20b**, 76 (1965); *C. A.* **63**, 159.
828. Dainicheseika Color and Chemicals Manufacturing Co. Ltd., Belg. 637,190 (1964); Neth. 300,513 (1965); Brit. 1,065,961 (1967).
829. Dainichiseika Color and Chemicals Manufacturing Co., Ltd., Neth. appl. 6,516,714 (1966); via *C. A.* **66**, 66228.
829a. Dai-Nippon Ink and Chemicals, Inc., Japan. 10,635 ('68).
830. Dai-Nippon Ink and Chemicals, Inc., Japan. 3034 ('64); via *C. A.* **61**, 10658.
831. Dai-Nippon Ink and Chemicals, Inc., Japan. 15,598 ('67).
832. Dai-Nippon Ink and Chemicals, Inc., Japan. 7778 ('64); via *C. A.* **61**, 11860; Fr. M5393 (1967).
833. Dai-Nippon Ink and Chemicals, Inc., Japan. 23,633 ('63); vi *C. A.* **60**, 2796.
834. Dai-Nippon Ink and Chemicals, Inc., Japan. 5892 ('63); via *C. A.* **59**, 12974.
835. Dai-Nippon Ink and Chemicals, Inc., Japan. 7725 ('64).
836. Dai-Nippon Ink and Chemicals, Inc. Japan. 22,044 ('67).
837. Dai-Nippon Pharmaceutical Co., Ltd., Japan. 10,466 ('59); via *C. A.* **54**, 18547.
838. Dai-Nippon Pharmaceutical Co., Ltd., Japan. 10,467 ('59); via *C. A.* **54**, 18548.
839. Dai-Nippon Printing Ink Mfg. Co., Ltd., Japan. 11,621 ('66).
840. F. S. Dainton and K. J. Ivin, *Quart. Rev.* **12**, 61 (1958).
841. Daiwa Spinning Co., Japan. 10,369 ('57); via *C. A.* **52**, 21144.
841a. M. T. Dajani (to Nalco Chemical Co.), U.S. 3,409,547 (1968).
841b. M. T. Dajani, J. D. Ingraham, and W. F. Lorene (to Nalco Chemical Co.), U.S. 3,408,292 (1968).
841c. M. T. Dajani and T. G. Cocks (to Nalco Chemical Co.), U.S. 3,408,293 (1968).
842. G. F. D'Alelio (to Dal Mon Research Co.), U.S. 3,327,018 (1967).
843. F. Dallacker, K. Ulrichs, and M. Lipp, *Ann. Chem.* **667**, 50 (1966).

844. F. Dallacker, *Ann. Chem.* **665**, 78 (1963).
845. F. D'Amato *et al.*, *Energia Nucl. Agr.* p. 279 (1963); via *Nucl. Sci. Abstr.* **17**, 38689.
846. D. A. Dame and H. R. Ford, *Bull. Entomol. Res.* **56**, 649 (1966).
847. D. A. Dame, D. B. Woodward, and H. R. Ford, *Mosquito News* **24**, 1 (1964).
848. D. A. Dame and C. H. Schmidt, *J. Econ. Entomol.* **57**, 77 (1964).
849. D. A. Dame and C. H. Schmidt, *J. Econ. Entomol.* **57**, 669 (1964).
850. D. A. Dame and H. R. Ford, *Nature* **201**, 733 (1964).
851. D. Danchev, D. Dalev, and L. Velichkov, *Farmatsiya (Sofia)* **15** (4), 202 (1965); via *C. A.* **64**, 3447.
852. J. P. Danehy and D. J. Pflaum, *Ind. Eng. Chem.* **30**, 778 (1938).
852a. F. A. Daniher, M. T. Melchior, and P. E. Butler, *Chem. Commun.* p. 931 (1968).
853. A. Darapsky and H. Spannagel, *J. Prakt. Chem.* [2] **92**, 272 (1915).
854. C. M. Darling, *Dissertation Abstr.* **27B**, 3875 (1967).
854a. M. Das, *Bull. World Health Org.* **36**, 949 (1967).
855. L. B. Dashkevich and V. G. Beilin, *Zh. Obshch. Khim.* **32**, 2423 (1962); *J. Gen. Chem. USSR (English Transl.)* **32**, 2391 (1962).
856. L. B. Dashkevich and V. G. Beilin, U.S.S.R. 176,285 (1965); via *C. A.* **64**, 12643.
857. T. B. Davich *et al.*, *J. Econ. Entomol.* **58**, 127 (1965).
858. D. E. Davis, *Anat. Record* **142**, 353 (1962).
859. H. G. Davis and G. W. Eddy, *J. Econ. Entomol.* **59**, 993 (1966).
860. J. J. Davis and J. Sirota (to National Starch Co.), U.S. 3,249,572 (1966); Neth. appl. 6,414,632 (1965); Belg. 657,093 (1965); Fr. 1,427,829 (1966); Brit. 1,087,554 (1967).
861. S. J. Davis and C. S. Rondestvedt, Jr., *Chem. & Ind. (London)* p. 845 (1956).
861a. A. R. Day and A. D. Lourie, U.S. 3,388,128 (1968).
862. C. De Boer *et al.*, *Antimicrobial Agents Ann.* 17 (1961).
863. O. de Booseré, *Bull. Soc. Chim. Belges* **32**, 26 (1923).
864. E. Debus (to Deutsche Gold- und Silber-Scheideanstalt), U.S. 3,379,546 (1968); Belg. 655,148 (1965); Neth appl. 6,412,000 (1965); Fr. 1,410,531 (1965); Ger. 1,189,949 (1965); Brit. 1,019,129 (1966).
867. K. M. Decossas, *Textile Ind.* **125** (4), 135 (1961).
868. K. M. Decossas, H. L. E. Vix, and E. L. Patton, *Am. Dyestuff Reptr.* **51**, P318 (1962).
868a. K. M. Decossas *et al.*, *Textile Ind.* **130** (7), 128 (1966).
869. L. Degen, *Pathol. Microbiol.* **26**, 237 (1963).
870. M. De Groote and K.-T. Shen (to Petrolite Corp.), U.S. 2,792,353 and 2,792,354 (1957); 2,828,283 and 2,839,489 (1958).
871. M. D. De Groote and O. H. Pettingill (to Petrolite Corp.), U.S. 2,839,471 (1958).
872. M. De Groote and K.-T. Shen (to Petrolite Corp.), U.S. 2,828,277, 2,854,431–2,854,433, 2,864,793, and 2,864,796–2,867,798 (1958).
873. M. De Groote and K.-T. Shen (to Petrolite Corp.), U.S. 2,854,427, 2,854,429, 2,864,787, 2,864,792, 2,864,800–2,864,801, and 2,864,806 (1958).
874. M. De Groote and J. P. Cherry (to Petrolite Corp.), U.S. 3,066,159 (1962).
875. M. De Groote (to Petrolite Corp.), U.S. 2,792,366 and 2,792,379 (1957); 2,819,224, 2,819,226, 2,828,283, and 2,828,825 (1958).
876. M. De Groote and O. H. Pettingill (to Petrolite Corp.), U.S. 3,121,749 and 3,121,750 (1964).
877. M. De Groote and K.-T. Shen (to Petrolite Corp.), U.S. 3,186,951 (1965).
877a. J. Degutis and D. Sukeliene, *Zh. Vseso. Khim. Obshchestva im. D. I. Mendeleeva* **6**, 583 (1961); via *C. A.* **56**, 5908.
878. G. J. Del Franco *et al.*, *J. Polymer Sci.* **B5**, 487 (1967).
878a. I. E. Den Besten and C. R. Wenger, *J. Am. Chem. Soc.* **87**, 5500 (1965).
879. H. D. Deppe and L. Lutzmann, *Arch. Hyg. Bakteriol.* **148**, 108 (1964); *C. A.* **61**, 2211.

880. G. I. Derkach and L. I. Samarai, *Zh. Obshch. Khim.* **33**, 1587 (1963); *J. Gen. Chem. USSR (English Transl.)* **33**, 1549 (1963).

881. G. I. Derkach, *Zh. Obshch. Khim.* **32**, 2992 (1962); *J. Gen. Chem. USSR (English Transl.)* **32**, 2942 (1962).

883. G. I. Derkach and I. M. Loseva, *Fiziol. Aktiv. Veshchestva, Akad. Nauk Ukr. SSR* . . . p. 57 (1966); via *C. A.* **67**, 98715.

884. O. C. Dermer and W. A. Ames, *J. Polymer Sci.* **A2**, 4151 (1964).

885. O. C. Dermer, WADC Tech. Rept. 55–447 (1956) (PB 121,796); *U.S. Govt. Research Rept.* **27**, 169 (1957).

885a. G. de Stevens, W. Knoll, and H. M. Blatter (to Ciba Corp.), U.S. 3,151,116 (1964).

885b. G. de Stevens and M. Sklar, *J. Org. Chem.* **28**, 3210 (1963).

886. R. H. Dettre and J. A. Nelson (to du Pont de Nemours and Co.), U.S. 3,161,536 (1964).

886a. H. Deuel, J. Solms, and A. Denzler, *Mitt. Gebiete Lebensm. Hyg.* **45**, 73 (1954).

887. H. Deuel, J. Solms, and A. Denzler, *Helv. Chim. Acta* **36**, 1671 (1953).

888. A. S. Deutsch and P. E. Fanta, *J. Org. Chem.* **21**, 892 (1956).

889. Deutsche Gold- und Silber-Scheideanstalt A.-G., Belg. 700,114 (1967).

890. Deutsche Gold- und Silber-Scheideanstalt A.-G., Belg. 674,442 (1966).

891. Deutsche Gold- und Silber-Scheideanstalt A.-G., Ger. 889,444 (1953); *Chem. Zentr.* p. 4949 (1957).

893. Deutsche Gold- und Silber-Scheideanstalt A.-G., Neth. appl. 6,512,426 (1966); via *C. A.* **66**, 57426.

894. Deutsche Gold- und Silber-Scheideanstalt A.-G., Neth. appl. 6,512,217 (1966); Belg. 670,122 (1966); via *C. A.* **65**, 9178.

895. C. S. Dewey and R. A. Bafford, *J. Org. Chem.* **30**, 491 (1965).

896. C. S. Dewey and R. A. Bafford, *J. Org. Chem.* **30**, 495 (1965).

897. C. S. Dewey and R. A. Bafford, *J. Org. Chem.* **32**, 3100 (1967).

898. De Wit's Textiel Nijverheid N. V., Ger. 1,119,815 (1961); *C. A.* **56**, 14502.

898a. De Wit's Textiel Nijverheid N.V., Ger. 1,081,410 (1960); *C. A.* **55**, 13868.

899. M. Dexter (to J. R. Geigy A.-G.), U.S. 3,150,160 (1964); Ger. 1,155,122 (1963); Brit. 945,015 (1964).

900. C. H. Dexter and Sons Inc., Fr. 1,475,129 (1967); via *C. A.* **67**, 74671.

901. Dexter Corp., Brit. 1,091,105 (1967).

902. J. A. Deyrup and R. B. Greenwald, *Tetrahedron Letters* p. 321 (1965).

903. J. A. Deyrup and R. B. Greenwald, *J. Am. Chem. Soc.* **87**, 4538 (1965).

903a. J. A. Deyrup and C. L. Moyer, *Abstr. Papers 156th Am. Chem. Soc. Meeting, Atlantic City, 1968* abstr. ORGN-2.

904. J. A. Deyrup and R. B. Greenwald, *Tetrahedron Letters* p. 5091 (1966).

904a. J. A. Deyrup and S. C. Clough, *J. Am. Chem. Soc.* **90**, 3592 (1968).

905. G. Deysson and R. Truhaut, *Compt. Rend. Soc. Biol.* **153**, 281 (1959).

906. G. Deysson and R. Truhaut, *Compt. Rend. Soc. Biol.* **150**, 1171 (1956).

906a. C. R. Dick (to The Dow Chemical Co.), U.S. 3,359,270 (1967).

907. C. R. Dick, *J. Org. Chem.* **32**, 72 (1967).

908. C. R. Dick (to The Dow Chemical Co.), U.S. 3,373,162 (1968).

909. F. Dickens and J. Cooke, *Brit. J. Cancer* **19**, 404 (1965).

910. F. H. Dickey, W. Fickett, and H. J. Lucas, *J. Am. Chem. Soc.* **74**, 944 (1952).

911. W. J. Dickson and F. W. Jenkins (to Petrolite Corp.), U.S. 3,301,783 (1967).

912. W. J. Dickson (to Petrolite Corp.), U.S. 2,792,370–2,792,373 (1957).

913. W. J. Dickson and F. W. Jenkins (to Petrolite Corp.), U.S. 3,259,513 (1965).

914. W. J. Dickson and F. W. Jenkins (to Petrolite Corp.), U.S. 3,262,791 (1966).

915. W. J. Dickson and F. W. Jenkins (to Petrolite Corp.), U.S. 3,313,736 (1967).

916. W. J. Dickson and F. W. Jenkins (to Petrolite Corp.), U.S. 3,344,083 (1967).
917. W. J. Dickson and F. W. Jenkins (to Petrolite Corp.), U.S. 3,251,778 (1966).
917a. W. J. Dickson and F. W. Jenkins (to Petrolite Corp.), U.S. 3,347,789 (1967).
918. N. V. Di Modrone and M. Simonetta, *Gazz. Chim. Ital.* **79**, 822 (1949).
919. H. J. Dishburger (to The Dow Chemical Co.), U.S. 3,231,563 (1966); Fr. 1,449,447 (1966); Belg. 621,233 (1966); Brit. 1,111,827 (1968).
920. V. Ya. Dishler *et al.*, *Vliyanie Ioniz. Izluch. Nasledstvennost, Akad. Nauk SSSR* p. 277 (1966); via *C. A.* **67**, 8479.
921. J. S. Dix (to Phillips Petroleum Co.), U.S. 3,205,224 (1965).
922. J. S. Dix and C. R. Bresson, *J. Org. Chem.* **32**, 282 (1967).
923. J. K. Dixon *et al.*, *J. Colloid Interface Sci.* **23**, 465 (1967).
923a. J. K. Dixon and M. W. Zielyk, *Abstr. Papers, 156th Am. Chem. Soc. Meeting, Atlantic City, 1968* abstr. COLL-42.
924. J. K. Dixon, V. K. La Mer, and H. B. Linford, *J. Water Pollution Control Federation* **39**, 647 (1967).
924a. B. A. Dmitriev, N. E. Bairimova, and N. K. Kochetkov, *Izv. Akad. Nauk SSSR, Ser. Khim.* p. 2691 (1967); via *C. A.* **69**, 27687.
925. W. Doecke, *Deut. Textiltech.* **10**, 354 (1960); *C. A.* **54**, 25849.
926. R. H. Dogget and A. R. Johnson (to A. D. Little, Inc.), U.S. 2,886,455 (1959).
926a. L. J. Dolby and H. Biere, *J. Am. Chem. Soc.* **90**, 2699 (1968).
927. J. E. Dolfini, *J. Org. Chem.* **30**, 1298 (1965).
928. J. E. Dolfini and D. M. Dolfini, *Tetrahedron Letters* p. 2053 (1965).
929. J. E. Dolfini and J. D. Simpson, *J. Am. Chem. Soc.* **87**, 4381 (1965).
930. G. Domagk and W. Gauss (to Farbenfabriken Bayer), U.S. 3,025,289 (1962); Ger. 1,079,052 (1960); Brit. 850,508 (1960).
931. A. S. R. Donald and R. E. Marks, *Chem. & Ind.* (*London*) p. 1340 (1965).
932. P. F. Donovan, W. R. Smith, and D. A. Conley, *J. Org. Chem.* **32**, 2036 (1967).
933. H. Dorn, *Monatsber. Deut. Akad. Wiss. Berlin* **3**, 683 (1961); via *C. A.* **58**, 5666; H. Dorn and M. Schuett, *Z. Chem.* **7**, 182 (1967).
934. A. Dornow and W. Schacht, *Chem. Ber.* **82**, 464 (1949).
935. A. Dornow and E. Schleese, *Chem. Ber.* **91**, 1830 (1958).
936. B. C. M. Dorset, *Textile Mfr.* **91**, 418 (1965).
936a. B. C. M. Dorset, *Textile Mfr.* **94**, 24 (1968).
936b. J. Doskočil, *Coll. Czech. Chem. Commun.* **30**, 2434 (1965).
937. J. B. Doughty, *Forest Prod. J.* **13**, 413 (1963).
938. J. B. Doughty, C. L. Lazzell, and A. R. Collett, *J. Am. Chem. Soc.* **72**, 2866 (1950).
939. J. B. Doughty (to West Virginia Pulp and Paper Co.), U.S. 2,842,534 (1958).
941. The Dow Chemical Co., Fr. 1,448,507 (1966); Belg. 670,264 (1966); Neth. appl. 6,512,597 (1966); via *C. A.* **65**, 10566; Japan. 4347 ('68).
942. The Dow Chemical Co., Austral. appl. 58,927 (1960).
943. The Dow Chemical Co., Belg. 604,838 (1961); Brit. 919,065 (1963); Fr. 1,348,013 (1964) in part.
944. The Dow Chemical Co., Belg. 622,154 (1963); Brit. 1,254,592 (1967).
945. The Dow Chemical Co., "Polyethylenimine" brochure (1968).
946. The Dow Chemical Co., Brit. 802,061 (1958).
947. The Dow Chemical Co., Brit. 910,875 (1962).
948. The Dow Chemical Co., Brit. 952,351 (1964); Ger. 1,211,017 (1966).
949. The Dow Chemical Co., Brit. 952,352 (1964).
951. The Dow Chemical Co., Belg. 627,193 (1963); Fr. 1,348,013 (1964) in part; Brit. 986,317 (1965); Ital. 681,347 (1965); Can. 716,137 (1965).
952. The Dow Chemical Co., Ger. 1,114,151 (1961); *C. A.* **56**, 8524.

955. The Dow Chemical Co., Austral. appl. 58,928 (1960).
956. The Dow Chemical Co., Belg. 612,513 (1962); Brit. 963,157 and 967,607 (1964).
957. The Dow Chemical Co., Neth. appl. 6,602,767 (1966); via *C. A.* **66**, 55955.
958. The Dow Chemical Co., Neth. appl. 6,508,322 (1965); Belg. 666,043 (1965); Fr. 1,449,744 (1966); Japan. 22,439 ('67).
959. The Dow Chemical Co., Neth. appl. 6,711,729 (1968); Belg. 703,093 (1968).
960. The Dow Chemical Co., Belg. 702,436 (1968).
961. The Dow Chemical Co., Brit. 1,075,585 (1967).
962. The Dow Chemical Co., Fr. 1,478,633 (1967); via *C. A.* **67**, 108564; Neth. appl. 6,602,828 (1967); Japan. 4347 ('68); Brit. 1,116,005 (1968).
963. The Dow Chemical Co., unpublished work.
964. The Dow Chemical Co., "Ethylenimine" brochure (1965).
964a. Dowsmith, Inc., Fr. 1,490,767 (1967); via *POST-P* **3**, 1401.
965. G. L. Drake, Jr., B. M. Kopacz, and F. S. Perkerson, *U.S. Dept. Agr.*, *ARS* **ARS 72-14** (1958).
966. G. L. Drake, Jr., *Quart. Nat. Fire Protect. Assoc.* **57**, 83 (1963–1964).
967. G. L. Drake, Jr., J. V. Beninate, and J. D. Guthrie, *Am. Dyestuff Reptr.* **50**, P129 (1961).
968. G. L. Drake, Jr., E. K. Leonard, and W. A. Reeves, *Textile Ind.* **130** (12), 145, 147, and 192 (1966).
969. G. L. Drake, Jr. and J. D. Guthrie, *Textile Res. J.* **29**, 155 (1959).
970. G. L. Drake, Jr. *et al.*, *Am. Dyestuff Reptr.* **51**, P272 (1962).
971. G. L. Drake, Jr., W. A. Reeves, and J. D. Guthrie, *Textile Res. J.* **23**, 639 (1953).
972. G. L. Drake, Jr. and J. D. Guthrie (to U.S. Department of Agriculture), U.S. 2,751,278 (1956).
973. G. L. Drake, Jr., W. A. Reeves, and L. H. Chance (to U.S. Department of Agriculture), U.S. 2,886,539 (1959).
974. G. L. Drake, Jr., W. A. Reeves, and L. H. Chance (to U.S. Department of Agriculture), U.S. 2,911,325 (1959).
975. G. L. Drake, Jr., R. M. Perkins, and W. A. Reeves (to U.S. Department of Agriculture), U.S. 3,197,269 (1965).
976. G. L. Drake, Jr., *Am. Dyestuff Reptr.* **56**, P560 (1967).
977. J. W. Drake, *Nature* **197**, 1028 (1963).
978. F. Drawert and K. H. Reuther, *Chem. Ber.* **93**, 3066 (1960).
979. E. K. Drechsel (to American Cyanamid Co.), U.S. 2,824,857 (1958); Can. 611,257 (1960).
979a. G. Drefahl, K. Ponsold, and D. Eichhorn, *Chem. Ber.* **101**, 1633 (1968).
980. G. Drefahl, K. Ponsold, and B. Schoenecker, *Chem. Ber.* **97**, 2014 (1964).
981. G. Drefahl and M. Huebner, *J. Prakt. Chem.* [4] **23**, 149 (1964).
981a. P. Drefahl and K. Drefahl, *J. Prakt. Chem.* [4] **38**, 168 (1968).
982. G. Drefahl, K. Ponsold, and B. Schoenecker, *Chem. Ber.* **98**, 186 (1965).
983. G. Drefahl, K. Ponsold, and B. Schoenecker, *Z. Chem.* **5**, 268 (1965); via *C. A.* **63**, 11649.
984. G. Drefahl and K. Ponsold, *Chem. Ber.* **93**, 519 (1960).
985. G. Drefahl, K. Ponsold, and B. Schoenecker, Ger. (East) 33,855 (1964); via *C. A.* **63**, 11674.
986. U. Drehmann and K. Wiesener, *J. Prakt. Chem.* [4] **7**, 304 (1959).
987. C. Dreyfus, Fr. 957,308 (1950); *Chem. Zentr.* Part I, 1234 (1951).
988. H. Dreyfus, Brit. 485,768 (1938); *C. A.* **32**, 8158.
988a. L. M. Dronova *et al.*, *Izv. Akad. Nauk SSSR, Ser. Biol.* **31**, 896 (1966); via *C. A.* **66**, 17847.

989. H. Druckrey *et al.*, *Arzneimittel-Forsch.* **6**, 539 (1956).
990. E. I. du Pont de Nemours and Co., Belg. 692,284 (1967); Neth. appl. 6,700,228 (1967).
991. E. I. du Pont de Nemours and Co., S. Afr. 64/3485; Belg. 646,581 (1964); *C. A.* **63**, 14727; Neth. appl. 6,403,294 (1965); *C. A.* **63**, 9838.
991a. E. I. du Pont de Nemours and Co., Fr. 1,500,695 (1967); via *C. A.* **69**, 60017.
992. E. I. du Pont de Nemours and Co., Brit. 1,100,580 (1968); via *POST-P* **3**, 1490.
992a. E. I. du Pont de Nemours and Co., Brit. 1,125,549 (1968).
993. E. I. du Pont de Nemours and Co., Belg. 672,290 (1966); Neth. appl. 6,514,668 (1966); Fr. 1,463,985 (1967); Ger. 1,097,069 (1967); Brit. 1,097,169 (1967).
994. E. I. du Pont de Nemours and Co., Neth. 292,605 (1965); via *C. A.* **64**, 4970.
995. E. I. du Pont de Nemours and Co., Fr. 1,422,674 (1965); via *C. A.* **66**, 33528.
995a. E. I. du Pont de Nemours and Co., Fr. 1,494,692 (1967); via *POST-P* **3**, 3317.
996. E. I. du Pont de Nemours and Co., Belg. 672,961 (1966); via *C. A.* **66**, 77067.
997. E. I. du Pont de Nemours and Co., Ger. 1,181,182 (1964); Brit. 990,005 (1965); *C. A.* **62**, 9010.
998. E. I. du Pont de Nemours and Co., Fr. 1,383,044 (1964); Japan. 28,570 ('65); Ger. 1,243,685 (1967).
999. E. I. du Pont de Nemours and Co., Neth. appl. 6,401,270 (1964); Belg. 643,538 (1964); Fr. 1,386,655 (1965); Brit. 1,088,109 (1967).
999a. R. G. Dubenko and E. F. Gorbenko, *Zh. Org. Khim.* **4**, 634 (1968); via *C. A.* **69**, 2620.
1000. R. G. Dubenko and P. S. Pelkis, *Zh. Obshch. Khim.* **34**, 679 (1964); *J. Gen. Chem. USSR (English Transl.)* **34**, 682 (1964).
1001. R. G. Dubenko and P. S. Pelkis, *Zh. Obshch. Khim.* **34**, 3481 (1964); *J. Gen. Chem. USSR (English Transl.)* **34**, 3524 (1964).
1002. N. P. Dubinin, E. P. Vaulin, and E. G. Saprykina, *Vliyanie Ioniz. Izluch. Nasledstvennost, Akad. Nauk SSSR* p. 46 (1966); via *C. A.* **67**, 10065.
1003. N. P. Dubinin and E. G. Saprykina, *Dokl. Akad. Nauk SSSR* **158**, 956 (1964); via *C. A.* **62**, 2121.
1004. L. G. Dubinina and N. P. Dubinin, *Dokl. Akad. Nauk SSSR* **175**, 213 (1967); via *C. A.* **67**, 97765; *Genetika* **4** (2), 5 (1968); via *C. A.* **68**, 12253.
1005. N. P. Dubinin and R. G. Dubinina, *Magy. Tud. Akad. Biol. Tud. Oszt. Kozlem.* **10**, 165 (1967); via *C. A.* **69**, 95325.
1005a. N. P. Dubinin, Yu. A. Mitrovanov, and E. S. Manuilova, *Izv. Akad. Nauk SSSR, Ser. Biol.* p. 477 (1967); via *C. A.* **67**, 80830.
1006. P. Duden and A. E. Macintyre, *Ber.* **33**, 481 (1900).
1007. P. Duden and A. E. Macintyre, *Ann. Chem.* **313**, 59 (1900).
1008. J. R. Dudley (to American Cyanamid Co.), U.S. 2,582,194 (1952).
1009. I. R. Dunlap, Austral. 216,301 (1956).
1009a. Dunlop Co. Ltd., Fr. 1,479,869 (1967); via *C. A.* **67**, 109179.
1010. G. E. Dunn, R. H. Meen, and G. F. Wright, *J. Am. Chem. Soc.* **74**, 1344 (1952).
1011. R. G. Dunning (to Chemirad Corp.), U.S. 3,326,897 (1967); Brit. 962,866 (1964).
1012. W. Duntze *et al.*, *Z. Krebsforsch.* **64**, 503 (1962); via *C. A.* **59**, 13944.
1013. G. J. Durant, J. H. Turnbull, and W. Wilson, *Chem. & Ind.* (*London*) p. 157 (1958).
1014. N. D. Duseeva, *Antibiotiki* **9**, 408 (1964); via *Biol. Abstr.* **46**, 66755.
1015. D. Dvornik and G. Schilling, *J. Med. Chem.* **8**, 466 (1965).
1016. Dynamit A.-G., Ger. 934,502 (1944); *Chem. Zentr.* p. 5703 (1956).
1017. B. G. Dzantiev and A. V. Shishkov, *Chem. Effects Nucl. Transformations* . . . **1**, 209 (1965); via *C. A.* **63**, 10946.
1018. J. E. Earley *et al.*, *J. Am. Chem. Soc.* **80**, 3458 (1958).
1019. J. W. Eastes and T. F. Cooke (to American Cyanamid Co.), U.S. 2,699,443 (1955).

1020. Eastman Kodak Co., Belg. 705,512 (1968).
1020a. Eastman Kodak Co., Fr. 1,504,888 (1967).
1020b. Eastman Kodak Co., Fr. 1,506,894 (1967).
1021. G. G. Ecke and W. E. Zitelli, *J. Org. Chem.* **31**, 2006 (1966).
1022. G. W. Eddy, A. R. Roth, and L. R. Abrahamsen, *Mosquito News* **25**, 169 (1965).
1023. L. H. Edwards and N. D. Williams, *Crop Sci.* **6**, 271 (1966).
1024. O. E. Edwards, *Chem. Can.* **13**, 40 (1961).
1025. S. Eguchi and Y. Ishii, *Bull. Chem. Soc. Japan* **36**, 1434 (1963).
1026. S. Eguchi, Y. Iwata, and Y. Ishii, *Nippon Kagaku Zasshi* **85**, 707 (1964); via *C. A.* **62**, 12996.
1027. Egyesült Gyógyszerés Tápszergyár, Brit. 923,052 (1963); Ger. 1,129,148 (1962).
1029. L. Ehrenberg, U. Lundqvist, and G. Stroem, *Hereditas* **44**, 330 (1958).
1030. L. Ehrenberg, A. Gustafsson, and U. Lundqvist, *Hereditas* **47**, 243 (1961).
1031. L. Ehrenberg, A. Gustafsson, and U. Lundquist, *Hereditas* **45**, 351 (1959).
1032. R. Ehrlich *et al.*, *Inorg. Chem.* **3**, 628 (1964).
1033. W. Eichelberger, *Kunststoffe-Plastics* **7**(5), 148 (1960); *C. A.* **54**, 23413.
1034. N. S. Eiges, *Radiobiologiya* **4**, 170 (1964); via *C. A.* **61**, 15013.
1035. N. S. Eiges and S. A. Valeva, *Radiobiologiya* **1**, 304 (1961); via *Plant Breed. Abstr.* **32**, 3101.
1036. U. Einsele, *Melliand Textilber.* **45**, 641 (1964); *C. A.* **61**, 5839.
1037. U. Einsele, *Melliand Textilber.* **41**, 721 (1960); *C. A.* **54**, 18967.
1038. J. Eisele *et al.* (to Badische Anilin- und Soda-Fabrik), U.S. 2,813,773 (1957); Ger. 925,042 (1955).
1039. A. A. Eisenbraun (to Allied Chemical Corp.), U.S. 3,312,714 (1967).
1040. J. L. Eisenmann (to Ionics, Inc.), U.S. 3,321,514 (1967); Brit. 1,034,298 (1966).
1041. R. Eisler, *Progressive Fish Culturist* **28**, 154 (1966).
1042. R. C. Elderfield and R. Nandan, *J. Org. Chem.* **25**, 1583 (1960).
1043. R. C. Elderfield and H. A. Hageman, *J. Org. Chem.* **14**, 605 (1949).
1044. R. C. Elderfield and R. S. McElhinney, *J. Org. Chem.* **26**, 1917 (1961).
1045. L. Eldjarn, K. F. Nakken, and A. Pihl, *Acta Chem. Scand.* **11**, 1085 (1957).
1047. J. A. Elvidge, *Ann. Rept. Progr. Chem.* (*Chem. Soc. London*) **45**, 216 (1948).
1048. H. Emde, *Helv. Chim. Acta* **12**, 399 (1929).
1049. W. S. Emerson and B. S. Wildi (to Monsanto Chemical Co.), U.S. 2,703,816 (1955).
1050. P. Emmelot, *Mol. Pharmacol.* **2**, 53 (1964).
1051. H. Enders *et al.* (to Chemische Fabrik Pfersee), U.S. 3,232,790 (1966).
1052. H. Enders *et al.* (to Chemische Fabrik Pfersee,) U.S. 3,326,894 (1967).
1053. H. Enders, H. Deiner, and E. W. Kurz (to Chemische Fabrik Pfersee), U.S. 3,148,164 (1964).
1054. D. J. Endsley and B. W. Wilson (to The Dow Chemical Co.), U.S. 3,280,218 (1966).
1055. W. Engelmann and W. Graupner, Ger. (East) 10,562 (1955); via *C. A.* **52**, 17576.
1056. E. L. Englehardt *et al.*, *Abstr. Papers, 12th Intern. Congr. Pure Appl. Chem., New York, 1951*, p. 341.
1057. M. A. Englin *et al.*, *Zh. Obshch. Khim.* **30**, 2371 (1960); *J. Gen. Chem. USSR* (*English Transl.*) **30**, 2353 (1960).
1058. W. D. English (to U.S. Borax and Chemical Corp.), U.S. 3,024,230 (1962).
1059. V. B. Enken, *Izv. Sibirsk. Otd. Akad. Nauk SSSR, Ser. Biol.-Med. Nauk* No. 12, 52 (1963); via *Plant Breed. Abstr.* **34**, 5316.
1060. V. B. Enken and K. K. Sidorova, *Vliyanie Ioniz. Izluch. Nasledstvennost, Akad. Nauk SSSR* p. 287 (1966); via *C. A.* **67**, 8480.
1061. J. Epstein, R. W. Rosenthal, and R. J. Ess, *Anal. Chem.* **27**, 1435 (1955).
1061a. S. S. Epstein and H. Shafner, *Nature* **219**, 385 (1968).

1062. H. Eriksson, *Arkiv Zool.* [2] **16**, 543 (1965).
1063. M. Erlenbach and A. Sieglitz (to Farbwerke Hoechst), U.S. 2,654,737 (1953); Ger. 830,048 (1952); Brit. 692,368 (1953); Swiss 296,339 (1954).
1063a. R. Erlmeier and G. Spengler, *Brennstoff-Chem.* **49**, 136 (1968).
1064. L. I. Erokhina and E. V. Solokova, *Genetika* No. 1, 109 (1966); via *Nucl. Sci. Abstr.* **20**, 32991.
1065. A. Eschenmoser *et al.*, *Angew. Chem.* **76**, 393 (1964); *Angew. Chem. Intern. Ed. Engl.* **3**, 490 (1964).
1066. ESPE Fabrik Pharmazeutischer Praeparate G.m.b.H., Belg. 616,333 (1962); *C. A.* **60**, 10888.
1067. ESPE Fabrik Pharmazeutischer Praeparate G.m.b.H., Brit. 1,054,635 (1967).
1068. ESPE Fabrik Pharmazeutischer Praeparate G.m.b.H., Ger. 1,166,471 (1964); *C. A.* **60**, 16073.
1069. ESPE Fabrik Pharmazeutischer Praeparate G.m.b.H., Fr. 1,423,660 (1966); Brit. 1,044,753 (1966).
1070. P. Esselmann, K. Koesslinger, and J. Duesing (to I. G. Farbenindustrie), U.S. 2,261,240 (1941); Neth. 49,734 (1940); Ger. 714,790 (1941).
1071. P. Esselmann and J. Duesing (to W. H. Duisberg), U.S. 2,220,441 (1940); Ger. 672,855 (1939) and 702,855 (1941).
1072. P. Esselmann, K. Koesslinger, and J. Duesing (to I. G. Farbenindustrie), U.S. 2,208,095 (1940).
1073. P. Esselmann and J. Duesing (to W. H. Duisberg), U.S. 2,232,318 (1941); I. G. Farbenindustrie A.-G., Fr. 840,773 (1937); Brit. 501,653 (1939); Ger. 672,855 (1939) and 702,855 (1941); Ital. 366,639 (1938).
1074. P. Esselmann and J. Duesing (to W. H. Duisberg), U.S. 2,257,162 (1941).
1075. P. Esselmann and J. Duesing (to W. H. Duisberg), U.S. 2,257,163 (1941); Brit. 518,369 (1940); Ger. 737,667 (1943); Neth. 51,825 (1942); I. G. Farbenindustrie A.-G., Ital. 374,783 (1939); Brit. 518,369 (1940).
1076. Esso Research and Engineering Co., Neth. appl. 6,618,440 (1967).
1077. Esso Research and Engineering Co., Neth. appl. 6,700,050 (1967); Fr. 1,506,174 (1967); *C. A.* **70**, 3824.
1078. Esso Research and Engineering Co., Neth. appl. 6,700,051 (1967).
1079. Esso Research and Engineering Co., Neth. appl. 6,509,365 (1966); Belg. 667,543 (1965); Fr. 1,455,231 (1966); Brit. 1,096,598 (1967).
1080. Esso Research and Engineering Co., Fr. 1,514,219 (1968).
1080a. Esso Research and Engineering Co., Fr. 1,507,033 (1968).
1081. M. G. Ettlinger and F. Kennedy, *Chem. & Ind.* (*London*), p. 166 (1956).
1082. H. Euler, *Arkiv Kemi, Mineral. Geol.* **1**, 67 (1903); *Ann. Chem.* **330**, 280 (1904).
1083. G. E. Evans and T. Hoffman, *Proc. Iowa Acad. Sci.* **57**, 235 (1950).
1084. R. F. Evans, *Chem. & Ind.* (*London*) p. 915 (1958).
1085. R. F. Evans and J. I. Jones, *J. Chem. Soc.* p. 3523 (1963).
1087. F. Evva, *Z. Wiss. Phot. Photophysik Photochem.* **52**, 1 (1957); via *C. A.* **51**, 16158.
1088. F. Evva, *Z. Wiss. Phot., Photophysik Photochem.* **52**, 136 (1958); via *C. A.* **52**, 18038.
1089. M. I. Ezuch and R. A. Hoopingarner, *J. Econ. Entomol.* **60**, 907 (1967).
1090. M. A. H. Fahmy *et al.*, *J. Agr. Food Chem.* **14**, 79 (1966).
1091. O. G. Fahmy and M. J. Fahmy, *J. Genet.* **54**, 146 (1956).
1092. O. G. Fahmy and M. J. Fahmy, *J. Genet.* **53**, 563 (1955).
1093. R. D. Falb, R. I. Leininger, and C. W. Cooper, *Abstr. Papers, 148th Am. Chem. Soc. Meet., Chicago, 1964* p. T-14.
1094. P. Fanta, *Chem. Heterocyclic Compds.* **19**, Part 1, 524 (1964).
1095. P. E. Fanta and E. N. Walsh, *J. Org. Chem.* **31**, 59 (1966).

1096. P. E. Fanta and A. S. Deutsch, *J. Org. Chem.* **23**, 72 (1958).
1097. P. E. Fanta and M. K. Kathan, *J. Heterocyclic Chem.* **1**, 293 (1964).
1098. P. E. Fanta, *J. Chem. Soc.* p. 1441 (1957).
1099. P. E. Fanta *et al.*, *J. Org. Chem.* **31**, 3113 (1966).
1100. P. E. Fanta and E. N. Walsh, *J. Org. Chem.* **30**, 3574 (1965).
1101. P. E. Fanta *et al.*, *J. Org. Chem.* **28**, 413 (1963).
1102. P. E. Fanta, R. Golden, and H. J. Hsu, *J. Chem. Eng. Data* **9**, 246 (1964).
1103. P. E. Fanta, U.S. 2,766,232 (1956).
1104. R. E. Fanta, R. J. Smat, and J. R. Krikau, *J. Heterocyclic Chem.* **5**, 419 (1968).
1105. P. E. Fanta and E. N. Walsh, *J. Chem. Eng. Data* **11**, 115 (1966).
1106. G. Faraone *et al.*, *J. Appl. Polymer Sci.* **5**, 16 (1961).
1108. Farbenfabriken Bayer A.-G., Belg. 655,445 (1965); Fr. 1,416,009 (1965); Ger. 1,204,406 (1965); Brit. 1,057,428 (1967).
1109. Farbenfabriken Bayer A.-G., Austrian 196,389 (1956); Ger. 1,047,203 (1958); via *C. A.* **55**, 4530.
1110. Farbenfabriken vorm. Friedr. Bayer and Co., Ger. 363,192 (1922); *Chem. Zentr.* Part II, 276 (1923); Ger 368,413 (1923); *Chem. Zentr.* Part II, 755 (1923).
1111. Farbenfabriken Bayer A.-G., Ger. 955,597 (1957); *C. A.* **53**, 16071.
1112. Farbenfabriken Bayer A.-G., Ger. 1,168,078 (1964); Brit. 976,568 (1964).
1113. Farbenfabriken Bayer A.-G., Belg. 617,873 (1962); *C. A.* **59**, 636.
1114. Farbenfabriken Bayer A.-G., Ger. 1,267,782 (1968); via *POST-P* **3**, 1781.
1115. Farbenfabriken Bayer A.-G., Brit. 736,914 (1955); Ger. 928,713 (1955).
1116. Farbenfabriken Bayer A.-G., Fr. 1,093,362 (1955); Austrian 184,918 (1956); Brit. 753,247 (1956); Ger. 970,463 (1958).
1117. Farbenfabriken Bayer A.-G., Fr. 1,118,425 (1956); Brit. 762,723 (1956); Ger. 967,344 (1957).
1118. Farbenfabriken Bayer A.-G., Ger. 1,160,183 (1963); Fr. 1,278,553 (1962) in part; Brit. 976,570 (1964); *Chem. Zentr.* No. 42, abstr. 2583 (1964).
1119. Farbenfabriken Bayer A.-G., Ger. 1,175,242 (1964); *C. A.* **61**, 13346.
1120. Farbenfabriken Bayer A.-G., Ger. 1,177,161 (1964); *C. A.* **61**, 14640.
1122. Farbenfabriken Bayer A.-G., Belg. 650,632 (1965), via *C. A.* **63**, 4459; Neth. appl. 6,407,663 (1965).
1124. Farbenfabriken Bayer A.-G., Neth. appl. 6,601,400 (1966), via *C. A.* **66**, 19202; Fr. 1,466,892 (1967).
1125. Farbenfabriken Bayer A.-G., Fr. 1,182,074 (1957); Ger 1,126,396 (1962); Neth. 107,964 (1964); *C. A.* **57**, 9664.
1126. Farbenfabriken Bayer A.-G., Ger. 1,131,694 (1962); *C. A.* **57**, 13609.
1127. Farbenfabriken Bayer A.-G., Japan. 8708 ('67).
1128. Farbenfabriken Bayer A.-G., Ger. 1,020,789 (1957); *C. A.* **54**, 11393.
1129. Farbenfabriken Bayer A.-G., Belg. 647,984 (1964); Neth. appl. 6,405,473 (1964); Brit. 1,001,746 (1965); Ger. 1,203,792 (1965); Fr. 1,401,513 (1963).
1130. Farbenfabriken Bayer A.-G., Brit. 765,658 (1957); Fr. addn. 67,639 (1958); Swiss 332,057 (1958).
1131. Farbenfabriken Bayer A.-G., Brit. 793,796 (1958); Ger. 943,166 (1956).
1132. Farbenfabriken Bayer A.-G., Brit. 793,860 (1958).
1133. Farbenfabriken Bayer A.-G., Brit. 796,218 (1958); Ger. 1,010,968 (1957).
1134. Farbenfabriken Bayer A.-G., Brit. 799,620 (1958); Ger. 1,031,964.
1135. Farbenfabriken Bayer A.-G., Brit. 805,518 (1958); Austrian 198,254 (1958); Fr. addn. 81,102 (1963).
1136. Farbenfabriken Bayer A.-G., Ger. 963,876 (1957); Brit. 808,638 (1959).
1137. Farbenfabriken Bayer A.-G., Brit. 818,517 (1959); Ger. 1,044,816 (1958).

1138. Farbenfabriken Bayer A.-G., Ger. 1,020,600 (1958); Brit. 824,191 (1959).
1139. Farbenfabriken Bayer A.-G., Ger. 1,068,006 (1959); Brit. 837,159 (1960).
1140. Farbenfabriken Bayer A.-G., Fr. 1,508,209 (1968).
1141. Farbenfabriken Bayer A.-G., Ger. 1,272,540 (1968); *C. A.* **69**, 52640.
1142. Farbenfabriken Bayer A.-G., Ger. 865,596 (1953); *C. A.* **52**, 17287.
1143. Farbenfabriken Bayer A.-G., Brit. 866,434 (1961).
1144. Farbenfabriken Bayer A.-G., Fr. 1,197,507 (1959); Can. 620,703 (1961); Brit. 892,131 (1962).
1145. Farbenfabriken Bayer A.-G., Ger. 900,814 (1954); *C. A.* **49**, 3241.
1146. Farbenfabriken Bayer A.-G., Ger. 908,133 (1954); *C. A.* **52**, 10600.
1147. Farbenfabriken Bayer A.-G., Ger. 911,016 (1954); *C. A.* **52**, 11937.
1148. Farbenfabriken Bayer A.-G., Ger. 939,151 (1956); *C. A.* **53**, 8096.
1149. Farbenfabriken Bayer A.-G., Ger. 948,330 (1956); Can. 613,181 (1961); *C. A.* **53**, 6267.
1150. Farbenfabriken Bayer A.-G., Ger. 953,519 (1956); *C. A.* **53**, 1760.
1151. Farbenfabriken Bayer A.-G., Ger. 963,153 (1957); *C. A.* **53**, 13173.
1153. Farbenfabriken Bayer A.-G., Ger. 956,099 (1957); *C. A.* **53**, 6547.
1154. Farbenfabriken Bayer A.-G., Ger. 967,793 (1957); *C. A.* **53**, 13173.
1155. Farbenfabriken Bayer A.-G., Ger. 967,794 (1957); *C. A.* **53**, 13174.
1156. Farbenfabriken Bayer A.-G., Brit. 976,566 (1964); Ger. 1,191,966 (1965).
1157. Farbenfabriken Bayer A.-G., Ger. 1,153,022 (1963); Brit. 976,569 (1964).
1158. Farbenfabriken Bayer A.-G., Brit. 976,570 (1964).
1159. Farbenfabriken Bayer A.-G., Brit. 978,089 (1964); Fr. 1,363,063 (1964).
1160. Farbenfabriken Bayer A.-G., Belg. 629,235 (1963); Fr. 1,353,195 (1964); Brit. 978,673 (1964).
1161. Farbenfabriken Bayer A.-G., Ger. 1,020,631 (1957); *C. A.* **54**, 5713.
1162. Farbenfabriken Bayer A.-G., Ger. 1,032,254 (1958); *C. A.* **55**, 11435.
1164. Farbenfabriken Bayer A.-G., Fr. 1,411,819 (1965); Belg. 651,846 (1965); Brit. 1,035,876 (1966).
1165. Farbenfabriken Bayer A.-G., Ger. 1,047,203 (1958); *C. A.* **55**, 4530.
1166. Farbenfabriken Bayer A.-G., Brit. 1,057,428 (1967); Neth. 6,412,962 (1965); Belg. 655,445 (1965); Fr. 1,416,009 (1965); Ger. 1,204,406 (1965).
1167. Farbenfabriken Bayer A.-G., Ger. 1,064,520 (1959); *C. A.* **55**, 21144.
1168. Farbenfabriken Bayer A.-G., Fr. 1,174,704 (1959); Ger. 1,087,130 (1960); *C. A.* **55**, 15846.
1169. Farbenfabriken Bayer A.-G., Ger. 1,087,131 (1960); Neth. 108,671 (1964); Swiss 389,616 (1965); *C. A.* **55**, 16508.
1170. Farbenfabriken Bayer A.-G., Ger. 1,087,607 (1960); *C. A.* **55**, 17650.
1171. Farbenfabriken Bayer A.-G., Ger. 1,098,762 (1960); Brit. 864,747 (1961); Swiss 390,920 (1965); Fr. 1,444,655 (1966).
1172. Farbenfabriken Bayer A.-G., Ger. 1,108,233 (1961); Brit. 890,554 (1962); Swiss 388,336 (1965).
1173. Farbenfabriken Bayer A.-G., Ger. 1,108,693 (1961); *C. A.* **56**, 10101.
1174. Farbenfabriken Bayer A.-G., Ger. 1,145,633 (1963); *C. A.* **59**, 11664.
1175. Farbenfabriken Bayer A.-G., Ger. 1,224,265 (1966); *C. A.* **66**, 11799.
1176. Farbenfabriken Bayer A.-G., Belg. 636,976 (1963); Ger. 1,157,386 (1963); *C. A.* **60**, 5721; Fr. 1,373,230 (1964); Neth 297,478 (1965).
1177. VEB Farbenfabrik Wolfen, Ger. (East) 13,244 (1957); *C. A.* **53**, 6592.
1178. VEB Farbenfabrik Wolfen, Ger. (East) 17,670 (1959); *C. A.* **54**, 25389.
1179. VEB Farbenfabrik Wolfen, Ger. (East) 20,722 (1961); via *Chem. Zentr.* p. 13314 (1961).

1180. VEB Farbenfabrik Wolfen, Fr. 1,244,000 (1961); Ger. 1,234,221 (1967); via *C. A.* **67**, 82083.
1181. VEB Farbenfabrik Wolfen, Ger. (East) 24,444 (1962); via *C. A.* **59**, 10311.
1182. VEB Farbenfabrik Wolfen, Brit. 897,746 (1962).
1184. VEB Farbenfabrik Wolfen, Ger. (East) 14,221 (1957); via *C. A.* **53**, 8480; Ger. 1,056,371 (1959); via *C. A.* **55**, 5809.
1185. VEB Farbenfabrik Wolfen, Ger. 1,093,784 (1960); *C. A.* **55**, 17954.
1186. VEB Farbenfabrik Wolfen, Ger. 1,144,007 (1963); Brit. 942,422 (1963); Fr. 1,312,060 (1962).
1187. VEB Farbenfabrik Wolfen, Ger. (East) 12,316 (1956); via *C. A.* **53**, 3544; Ger. 1,056,825 (1959); Brit. 837,599 (1960).
1188. VEB Farbenfabriken Wolfen, Belg. 666,668 (1965); Fr. 1,428,239 (1966); Brit. 1,058,625 (1967).
1189. VEB Farbenfabrik Wolfen, Ger. (East) 33,164 (1964); *C. A.* **63**, 5851.
1190. Farbwerke Hoechst A.-G., Ger. 913,165 (1954); *Chem. Zentr.* p. 6140 (1955).
1191. Farbwerke Hoechst A.-G., Ger. 1,041,466 (1958); Brit. 868,935 (1961).
1191a. Farbwerke Hoechst A.-G., Ger. 1,062,667 (1959); Brit. 864,034 (1961).
1192. Farbwerke Hoechst A.-G., Japan. 7708 ('67).
1193. Farbwerke Hoechst A.-G., Belg. 610,695 (1962); via. *C. A.* **58**, 505.
1195. Farbwerke Hoechst A.-G., Belg. 686,996 (1967).
1197. Farbwerke Hoechst A.-G., Brit. 795,380 (1958).
1198. Farbwerke Hoechst A.-G., Ger. 964,316 (1957); Brit. 799,045 (1958).
1199. Farbwerke Hoechst A.-G., Ger. 832,152 (1948); *Chem. Zentr.* p. 1353 (1954).
1200. Farbwerke Hoechst A.-G. Ger. 834,990 (1952); *C. A.* **51**, 14819.
1201. Farbwerke Hoechst A.-G., Ger. 838,449 (1952); *Chem. Zentr.* p. 6954 (1952).
1202. Farbwerke Hoechst A.-G., Ger. 839,861 (1952); *Chem. Zentr.* p. 6773 (1952).
1203. Farbwerke Hoechst A.-G., Ger. 849,407 (1952); *C. A.* **52**, 11945.
1204. Farbwerke Hoechst A.-G., Ger. 850,613 (1952); *C. A.* **52**, 14695.
1205. Farbwerke Hoechst A.-G., Ger. 851,852 (1952); *Chem. Zentr.* p. 7350 (1953).
1206. Farbwerke Hoechst A.-G., Fr. 1,177,837 (1959); Ger. 1,048,583 (1959); Brit. 854,443 (1960); Neth. 96,688 (1961); Can. 610,010 (1960); Swiss 353,365 (1960).
1207. Farbwerke Hoechst A.-G., Ger. 854,651 (1952); *C. A.* **52**, 10200.
1208. Farbwerke Hoechst A.-G., Ger. 858,847 (1952); *C. A.* **52**, 12922.
1209. Farbwerke Hoechst A.-G., Ger. 859,025 (1952); *Chem. Zentr.* p. 4780 (1953).
1210. Farbwerke Hoechst A.-G., Fr. 1,185,865 (1959); Austrian 209,305 (1960); Brit. 862,710 (1961).
1211. Farbwerke Hoechst A.-G., Ger. 863,055 (1953); *Chem. Zentr.* p. 4950 (1953).
1212. Farbwerke Hoechst A.-G., Fr. 1,175,550 (1959); Brit. 864,021 (1961).
1213. Farbwerke Hoechst A.-G., Ger. 864,867 (1953); Neth. 57,084 (1946); via *Chem. Zentr.* p. 3663 (1953).
1214. Farbwerke Hoechst A.-G., Ger. 868,285 (1953); *Chem. Zentr.* p. 6596 (1953); Ger. 872,037 (1953); *Chem. Zentr.* p. 82 (1953).
1215. Farbwerke Hoechst A.-G. Ger. 870,855 (1953); Swiss 220,745 (1942).
1216. Farbwerke Hoechst A.-G., Ger. 873,082 (1953); *Chem. Zentr.* p. 455 (1954).
1217. Farbwerke Hoechst A.-G., Ger. 879,314 (1953); *C. A.* **52**, 9655.
1218. Farbwerke Hoechst A.-G., Ger. 880,740 (1953); *Chem. Zentr.* p. 685 (1954).
1219. Farbwerke Hoechst A.-G., Ger. 881,659 (1953); *C. A.* **52**, 11892.
1220. Farbwerke Hoechst A.-G., Ger. 888,853 (1953); *C. A.* **52**, 12894.
1221. Farbwerke Hoechst A.-G., Ger. 889,748 (1953); *C. A.* **52**, 10595.
1222. Farbwerke Hoechst A.-G., Ger. 896,790 (1953); *Chem. Zentr.* p. 2919 (1954).
1223. Farbwerke Hoechst A.-G., Brit. 905,647 (1963).

1224. Farbwerke Hoechst A.-G., Belg. 575,311 (1959); Fr. 1,227,284 (1960); Ger. 1,083,267 (1960); Brit. 906,428 (1962); Swiss 377,358 (1964).
1226. Farbwerke Hoechst A.-G., Ger. 910,726 (1954); *C. A.* **52**, 10647.
1227. Farbwerke Hoechst A.-G., Ger. 912,451 (1954); *Chem. Zentr.* p. 928 (1955).
1228. Farbwerke Hoechst A.-G., Ger. 914,123 (1954); *C. A.* **52**, 17741.
1230. Farbwerke Hoechst A.-G., Ger. 915,743 (1954); *C. A.* **52**, 11471.
1231. Farbwerke Hoechst A.-G., Brit. 916,368 (1963).
1232. Farbwerke Hoechst A.-G., Ger. 927,831 (1955); *C. A.* **52**, 1680.
1233. Farbwerke Hoechst A.-G., Ger. 932,066 (1965); *C. A.* **52**, 18469.
1235. Farbwerke Hoechst A.-G., Ger. 946,132 (1956); *C. A.* **52**, 16754.
1236. Farbwerke Hoechst A.-G., Ger. 953,078 (1956); *C. A.* **53**, 5285.
1236a. Farbwerke Hoechst A.-G., Ger. 1,218,718 (1966); *C. A.* **66**, 76541.
1237. Farbwerke Hoechst A.-G., Ger. 1,000,007 (1957); *C. A.* **54**, 6150.
1238. Farbwerke Hoechst A.-G., Ger. 1,010,063 (1957); *C. A.* **54**, 2177.
1239. Farbwerke Hoechst A.-G., Ger. 1,012,586 (1957); *C. A.* **54**, 1890.
1240. Farbwerke Hoechst A.-G., Belg. 701,987 (1968); Neth. appl. 6,710,389 (1968).
1242. Farbwerke Hoechst A.-G., Belg. 648,685 (1964); Fr. 1,396,952 (1965); Brit. 1,024,492 (1966).
1243. Farbwerke Hoechst A.-G., Ger. 1,023,446 (1958); *C. A.* **54**, 14716.
1244. Farbwerke Hoechst A.-G., Fr. 1,352,660 (1964); Ger. 1,209,097 (1966); Brit. 1,028,614 (1966).
1245. Farbwerke Hoechst A. G., Ger. 1,243,687 (1967); *C. A.* **67**, 90650.
1246. Farbwerke Hoechst A.-G., Ger. 1,044,028 (1958); *C. A.* **54**, 23353; Indian 60,743 (1958).
1247. Farbwerke Hoechst A.-G., Ger. 1,044,761 (1958); *C. A.* **54**, 23350.
1248. Farbwerke Hoechst A.-G., Ger. 1,044,827 (1958); *C. A.* **55**, 1442.
1249. Farbwerke Hoechst A.-G., Neth. appl. 6,400,799 (1964); Belg. 643,310 (1964); Fr. 1,389,063 (1965); Brit. 1,059,543 (1967).
1250. Farbwerke Hoechst A.-G., Ger. 1,060,350 (1959); *C. A.* **55**, 8878.
1252. Farbwerke Hoechst A.-G., Ger. 1,077,217 (1960); *C. A.* **55**, 15509.
1253. Farbwerke Hoechst A.-G., Ger. 1,137,744 (1962); Brit. 916,368 (1963); Fr. 1,341,454 (1963).
1254. Farbwerke Hoechst A.-G., Fr. 1,132,865 (1957); Austrian 191,839 (1957); Indian 60,228 (1958); *Chem. Zentr.* p. 13638 (1958).
1255. Farbwerke Hoechst A.-G., Ger. 1,139,268 (1962); Fr. 1,293,793 (1962); Austrian 229,587 (1963); Brit. 983,238 (1965).
1256. Farbwerke Hoechst A.-G., Ger. 1,172,660 (1964); Fr. 1,370,441 (1964); Brit. 1,064,141 (1967).
1257. Farbwerke Hoechst A.-G., Belg. 654,202 (1964); Neth. appl. 6,411,771 (1965)· via *C. A.* **63**, 17674; Fr. 1,410,796 (1965); Ger. 1,194,754 (1965).
1258. Farbwerke Hoechst A.-G., Fr. 1,331,186 (1962).
1259. Farbwerke Hoechst A.-G., Fr. 1,383,422 (1964); *C. A.* **62**, 9023; Belg. 644,251 (1964).
1261. Farbwerke Hoechst A.-G., Neth. appl. 6,410,003 (1965); Belg. 652,509 (1965).
1262. Farbwerke Hoechst A.-G., Ger. 907,409 (1954); *Chem. Zentr.* p. 8450 (1954).
1263. Farbwerke Hoechst A.-G., Ger. 914,325 (1949); *C. A.* **52**, 11471.
1264. Farbwerke Hoechst A.-G., Ger. 888,170 (1948); *Chem. Zentr.* p. 4500 (1957).
1266. Farbwerke Hoechst, Ger. 870,557 (1953); *Chem. Zentr.* p. 7982 (1954).
1267. Farbwerke Hoechst A.-G., Belg. 661,140 (1965); via *C. A.* **65**, 1953; Fr. 1,431,240 (1966).
1268. Farbwerke Hoechst A.-G., Ger. 1,248,858 (1967); Brit. 1,095,116 (1967).

1269. Code of Federal Regulations, Title 46, "Shipping," Parts 146 and 149, p. 31 and p. 232. Coast Guard, 1967; U.S. Coast Guard Manual CG 388, "Chemical Data Guide for Bulk Shipment by Water," p. 65. Coast Guard, 1966.

1270. Code of Federal Regulations, Title 49, "Transportation", Parts 71 and 90, p. 16 and p. 117. Interstate Commerce Commission, 1967.

1271. L. R. Fedor *et al.*, *J. Am. Chem. Soc.* **88**, 108 (1966).

1272. L. A. Fedotova and M. G. Voronkov, *Khim. Geterotsikl. Soedin., Akad. Nauk Latv. SSSR* p. 846 (1965); *Chem. Heterocyclic Compounds (English Transl.)* **1**, 573 (1965).

1272a.L. A. Fedotova and M. G. Voronkov, *Khim. Geterotsikl. Soedin., Akad. Nauk Latv. SSSR* p. 603 (1967).

1273. L. A. Fedotova and D. O. Rinkis, U.S.S.R. 179,310 (1966); via *C. A.* **65**, 2222.

1273a. L. A. Fedotova, M. G. Voronkov, and D. Rinkis, U.S.S.R. 194,811 (1967); via *C. A.* **69**, 35917.

1274. F. Feher and B. Degen, *Angew. Chem.* **79**, 690 (1967); *Angew. Chem. Intern. Ed. Engl.* **6**, 703 (1967).

1275. P. W. Feit and O. T. Nielsen, *J. Med. Chem.* **10**, 697 (1967).

1276. P. W. Feit, *Acta Chem. Scand.* **16**, 522 (1962).

1277. E. Felder, F. Bonati, and S. Bianchi, *Experientia* **15**, 32 (1959).

1279. I. Kh. Fel'dman and V. N. Mikhailova, *Zh. Obshch. Khim.* **33**, 38 (1963); *J. Gen. Chem. USSR (English Transl.)* **33**, 33 (1963).

1280. I. Kh. Fel'dman and L. F. Mikheeva, *Zh. Obshch. Khim.* **33**, 2116 (1963); *J. Gen. Chem. USSR (English Transl.)* **33**, 2061 (1963).

1281. J. Feldmesser, M. Beroza, and R. V. Rebois, *J. Parasitol.* **48**, No. 2, Sect. 2, 44 (1962).

1282. "Feldmuehle" Papier- und Zellstoffwerke, A.-G., Ger. 752,810 (1953); *Chem. Zentr.* p. 4978 (1954).

1282a."Feldmuehle" Papier- und Zellstoffwerke, A.-G., Fr. 1,306,296 (1963); *Chem. Zentr.* No. 22, abstr. 3024 (1965).

1283. C. A. Feldt and G. T. Kekish (to Nalco Chemical Co.), U.S. 3,092,617 (1963).

1284. C. A. Feldt and G. T. Kekish (to Nalco Chemical Co.), U.S. 3,234,150 (1966).

1284a.H. D. Feldtman, J. R. McPhee, and W. V. Morgan, *Textile Mfr.* **93**, 122 (1967).

1284b.H. D. Feldtman and J. R. McPhee, *Textile Res. J.* **36**, 935 (1966).

1284c.D. Felix *et al.*, *Helv. Chim. Acta* **51**, 1461 (1968).

1285. O. N. Fellowes, *J. Immunol.* **95**, 1100 (1965); **99**, 508 (1967).

1286. F. C. Ferguson, W. C. Wescoe, and P. Theodore, *J. Pharmacol. Exptl. Therap.* **100**, 100 (1950).

1286a.F. R. Ferrer, D. S. Grosch, and F. E. Guthrie, *J. Econ. Entomol.* **61**, 719 (1968).

1287. A. Ferretti and G. Tesi, *Tetrahedron Letters* p. 2975 (1964).

1287a.J. Fertig, E. D. Mazzarella, and M. Skoultchi (to National Starch and Chemical Corp.), U.S. 3,372,149 (1968); Fr. 1,468,789 (1967); Brit. 1,101,758 (1968).

1287b.G. F. Field, W. J. Zally, and L. H. Sternbach, *Tetrahedron Letters* p. 2609 (1966).

1288. E. K. Fields and J. M. Sandri, *Chem. & Ind. (London)* p. 1216 (1959).

1289. H. Fikentscher *et al.* (to Badische Anilin- und Soda-Fabrik), U.S. 3,174,874 (1965); Belg. 610,467 (1960); Ger. 1,108,436 (1961); Brit. 897,804 (1962).

1290. A. Filbey and L. R. Buzbee (to Ethyl Corp.), U.S. 2,893,871 (1959); Brit. 772,988 (1957); Can. 611,998 (1961).

1290a.L. M. Filippova, O. A. Pan'shin, and R. G. Kostyanovskii, *Genetika* No. 8, 134 (1967); via *C. A.* **68**, 93905.

1291. VEB Filmfabrik Agfa Wolfen, Ger. 1,081,169 (1960); *C. A.* **55**, 17323.

1292. VEB Filmfabrik Agfa Wolfen, Ger. 1,109,875 (1961); *C. A.* **56**, 1094.

1293. H. Fink and R. Stahn (to I. G. Farbenindustrie), U.S. 2,097,120 (1937); Fr. 793,179 (1936); Brit. 460,590 (1937); Neth. 41,802 (1937); Ger. 662,335 (1938).

1294. A. Fior and E. Del Mauro (to "Montecatini" Societa ...), U.S. 3,137,989 (1964); Brit. 904,417 (1962); S. Afr. 60/611; Austral. appl. 57,461 (1960); Fr. addn. 77,174 (1962).

1294a. Firma Wm. Hilgers, Fr. 1,478,039 (1967); via C. A. **67**, 118931.

1295. B. C. Fischback and G. H. Harris (to The Dow Chemical Co.), U.S. 2,775,587 (1956); Brit. 790,982 (1958); Can. 568,769 (1959).

1296. F. Fischer and E. Hoffmann, J. Prakt. Chem. [4] **14**, 119 (1961).

1297. F. Fischer and H. J. Siemann, Z. Chem. **5**, 155 (1965).

1298. F. Fischer and H. Roensch, Z. Chem. **3**, 265 (1963).

1299. F. Fischer and H. Roensch, Chem. Ber. **94**, 901 (1961).

1300. L. Fishbein and M. A. Cavanaugh, J. Chromatog. **20**, 283 (1965).

1301. L. Fishbein, J. Chromatog. **26**, 522 (1967).

1302. D. Fleš and A. Markovac-Prpić, Arhiv Kem. **27**, 211 (1955); via C. A. **50**, 11951.

1303. D. Fleš and A. Markovac-Prpić, Arhiv Kem. **26**, 239 (1954); via C. A. **50**, 928.

1303a. H. M. Flint et al., J. Econ. Entomol. **61**, 939 (1968).

1304. H. G. Flock (to Calgon Corp.), U.S. 3,288,640 (1966); Can. 771,612 (1967).

1304a. R. E. Florin, F. Sicilio, and L. A. Wall, J. Res. Natl. Bur. Stand. **A72**, 49 (1968).

1305. T. A. Foglia and D. Swern, J. Org. Chem. **32**, 75 (1967).

1306. E. P. Fokin, S. A. Russkikh, and V. V. Russkikh, Izv. Sibirsk. Otd. Akad. Nauk SSSR, Ser. Khim. Nauk No. 3, 121 (1965); via C. A. **64**, 17516.

1306a. P. J. Foley and R. S. Neale, J. Chem. Eng. Data **13**, 593 (1968).

1306b. K. H. Ford and M. M. Joullié, J. Heterocyclic Chem. **3**, 529 (1966).

1307. D. Fornelli, Am. Dyestuff Reptr. **37**, 853 and 882 (1948).

1308. E. R. A. Forshaw (to Shell Oil Co.), U.S. 3,153,079 (1964); Fr. 1,306,628 (1963); Brit. 938,053 (1963).

1309. P. Fournier, Ann. Chim. (Paris) [12] **7**, 75, especially p. 97 et seq. (1952).

1310. F. W. Fowler, A. Hassner, and L. A. Levy, J. Am. Chem. Soc. **89**, 2077 (1967).

1311. B. W. Fox et al., J. Reprod. Fertility **5**, 13 (1963).

1312. W. O. Foye, R. N. Dewall, and J. Mickles, J. Pharm. Sci. **51**, 168 (1962).

1313. S. Fraenkel and M. Cornelius, Ber. **51**, 1660 (1918).

1314. P. Fram (to Minnesota Mining and Manufacturing Co.), U.S. 3,119,782 (1964).

1315. P. Fram (to Minnesota Mining and Manufacturing Co.), U.S. 3,225,013 (1965).

1316. P. Fram and G. H. Smith (to Minnesota Mining and Manufacturing Co.), U.S. 3,318,930 (1967).

1318. P. Fram and R. R. Charbonneau (to Minnesota Mining and Manufacturing Co.), U.S. 3,079,367 (1963).

1319. L. Francesconi and G. Sanna, Gazz. Chim. Ital. **45**, part I, 35 (1915).

1320. L. Francesconi and N. Granata, Gazz. Chim. Ital. **45**, part I, 167 (1915).

1321. B. V. Franko and C. D. Lunsford, J. Med. Pharm. Chem. **2**, 523 (1960).

1322. J. E. Franz and C. Osuch, Tetrahedron Letters p. 837 (1963).

1323. J. E. Franz, J. Org. Chem. **31**, 2847 (1966).

1324. J. E. Franz, C. Osuch, and M. W. Dietrich, J. Org. Chem. **29**, 2922 (1964).

1325. J. E. Franz and C. Osuch (to Monsanto Co.), U.S. 3,284,444 (1966).

1326. V. Franzen and H. E. Driesen, Tetrahedron Letters p. 661 (1962); Chem. Ber. **96**, 1881 (1963).

1327. M. E. Freed and A. R. Day, J. Org. Chem. **25**, 2108 (1960).

1328. L. D. Freedman and G. O. Doak, J. Am. Chem. Soc. **77**, 6635 (1955).

1329. J. P. Freeman and W. H. Graham, J. Am. Chem. Soc. **89**, 1761 (1967).

1330. E. Freiser, Z. Ges. Textil-Ind. **60**, 977 (1958); C. A. **53**, 8636.

1332. M. I. Fremery (to Shell Oil Co.), U.S. 3,228,957 (1966); Belg. 657,090 (1965); Neth. appl. 6,414,636 (1965); Fr. 1,439,024 (1966); Brit. 1,025,440 (1966); Japan. 17,981 ('66); Angew. Chem. **78**, 1024 (1966); Angew. Chem. Intern. Ed. Engl. **5**, 975 (1966).

1333. M. I. Fremery (to Shell Oil Co.), U.S. 3,259,632 (1966).
1334. M. I. Fremery (to Shell Oil Co.), U.S. 3,277,114 (1966).
1336. Carl Freudenberg K.-G., Ger. 1,128,832 (1962); Brit. 935,770 (1963).
1338. H. Freundlich and H. Kroepelin, *Z. Physik. Chem.* **122**, 39 (1926).
1339. H. Freundlich and W. Neumann, *Z. Physik. Chem.* **87**, 69 (1914).
1340. H. Freundlich and G. Salomon, *Helv. Chim. Acta* **17**, 88 (1934).
1341. H. Freundlich and G. Salomon, *Z. Physik. Chem.* **A166**, 161 (1933).
1342. H. Freundlich and G. Salomon, *Z. Physik. Chem.* **A166**, 179 (1933).
1343. H. Freundlich and F. Juliusburger, *Z. Physik. Chem.* **A146**, 321 (1930).
1344. H. Freundlich and G. Salomon, *Ber.* **66B**, 355 (1933).
1345. J. G. Frick, Jr. *et al.*, *Publication Board Rept.* (*U.S.*), PB 151,550; *C. A.* **54**, 11491.
1346. L. Friederici, *Aertzl. Forsch.* **10**, 527 (1956).
1347. N. B. Friedman *et al.*, *Cancer Res.* **15**, 479 (1955).
1348. O. M. Friedman *et al.*, *J. Med. Chem.* **6**, 50 (1963).
1349. O. M. Friedman, K. Pollak, and E. Khedouri, *J. Med. Chem.* **6**, 462 (1963).
1350. O. M. Friedman *et al.*, *J. Med. Chem.* **6**, 449 (1963).
1351. O. M. Friedman and E. Boger, *Anal. Chem.* **33**, 906 (1961).
1352. E. P. Frieser, *Spinner Weber & Textilveredl.* **79**, 1140 and 1144 (1961); *C. A.* **57**, 1114.
1353. I. E. Frieser, *Melliand Textilber.* **39**, 795 (1958); *C. A.* **52**, 19148.
1354. H. Frischmann, *F.A.T.I.P.E.C.* **7**, 94 (1964); via *C. A.* **61**, 12149.
1354a.G. Frizzi and T. Maxia, *Atti Assoc. Genet. Ital.* **11**, 249 (1966); via *C. A.* **67**, 18920.
1355. J. S. Fruton and M. Bergmann, *J. Org. Chem.* **11**, 543 (1946).
1356. J. S. Fruton, W. H. Stein, and M. Bergmann, *J. Org. Chem.* **11**, 559 (1946).
1357. J. S. Fruton *et al.*, *J. Org. Chem.* **11**, 571 (1946).
1358. J. S. Fruton, *in* "Heterocyclic Compounds" (R. C. Elderfield, ed.), Vol. I, Chapter 2. Wiley, New York, 1950.
1359. E. M. Fry, *J. Org. Chem.* **30**, 2058 (1965).
1360. R. I. Fryer and L. H. Sternbach (to Hoffmann-La Roche), U.S. 3,261,867 (1966); Fr. 1,375,300 (1964); Neth. 298,186 (1964); Belg. 637,329 (1964); Brit. 982,909 (1965).
1361. V. Fucik, A. Michaelis, and R. Rieger, *Biochem. Biophys. Res. Commun.* **13**, 366 (1963).
1362. J. J. Fuerholzer, *Dissertation Abstr.* **26**, 3629 (1966).
1363. A. Fuerst and E. Kyburz (to Hoffmann-La Roche), U.S. 3,021,335 (1962); Brit. 856,393 (1960); Swiss 373,384 and 376,921 (1964).
1364. A. Fuerst, E. Kyburz, and S. Majnoni (to Hoffmann-La Roche), U.S. 3,072,636 (1963); Brit. 847,205 (1960); Austrian 207,373 and 228,384 (1960); Indian 65,575 (1960); Fr. 1,215,684 (1960); Ger. 1,126,879 (1962); Swiss 362,078 (1962); Can. 669,707 (1963).
1365. R. Fuhrmann, E. C. Lazar, and J. F. Van Pepper (to Allied Chemical Corp.), U.S. 3,373,194 (1968); Neth. appl. 6,610,443 (1967); Fr. 1,487,711 (1967).
1366. Fuji Photo Film Co., Ltd., Japan. 5793 ('63); via *C. A.* **59**, 14177.
1367. Fuji Photo Film Co., Ltd., Belg. 656,456 (1965); Japan. 8550 ('66); via *C. A.* **65**, 5573.
1368. Fuji Photo Film Co., Ltd., Belg. 675,007 (1966); Japan. 4134 ('68).
1369. Fuji Photo Film Co., Ltd., Brit. 1,064,805 (1967); Belg. 662,747 (1965); Fr. 1,436,221 (1966).
1369a.Fuji Photo Film Co., Ltd., Neth. appl. 6,717,016 (1968).
1370. K. Fukui *et al.* (to Sumitomo Chemical Co.), U.S. 3,375,231 (1968); Japan. 20,524 ('64); Brit. 1,020,617 (1966); Ger. 1,221,448 (1966).
1371. O. Fukushima and H. Kurashige (to Kurashiki Rayon Co.), U.S. 3,066,107 (1962); Japan. 22,906 and 22,907 ('61); Can. 697,001 (1964).
1372. O. Fukushima (to Kurashiki Rayon Co.), U.S. 3,066,032 (1962).

1373. O. Fukushima and K. Matsubayashi (to Kurashiki Rayon Co. and Air Reduction Co.), U.S. 3,067,152 (1962).
1374. O. Fukushima and H. Kurashige (to Air Reduction Co. and Kurashiki Rayon Co.), U.S. 3,142,532 (1964).
1375. T. R. Fukuto and E. M. Stafford, *J. Am. Chem. Soc.* **79**, 6083 (1957).
1375a. E. Funakubo *et al.*, *Chem. Ber.* **96**, 2035 (1963).
1376. A. Funke and G. Benoit, *Bull. Soc. Chim. France* p. 1021 (1953).
1377. K. Furukawa, S. Yamanaka, and R. Oda, *J. Chem. Soc. Japan., Ind. Chem. Sect.* **54**, 664 (1951); via *C. A.* **48**, 2648.
1378. K. Furukawa, S. Yamanaka, and R. Oda, *J. Chem. Soc. Japan, Ind. Chem. Sect.* **54**, 666 (1951), via *C. A.* **48**, 2648.
1379. R. C. Fuson and C. L. Zirkle, *J. Am. Chem. Soc.* **70**, 2760 (1948).
1380. R. L. Fye, H. K. Gouck, and G. C. LaBrecque, *J. Econ. Entomol.* **58**, 446 (1965); R. L. Fye, G. C. LaBrecque, and H. K. Gouck, *ibid.* **59**, 485 (1966); R. L. Fye, *ibid.* **60**, 605 (1967).
1381. R. L. Fye and G. C. LaBrecque, *J. Econ. Entomol.* **60**, 1284 (1967).
1382. N. W. Gabel, *J. Org. Chem.* **29**, 3129 (1964).
1383. S. Gabriel and H. Ohle, *Ber.* **50**, 804 (1917).
1384. S. Gabriel and H. Ohle, *Ber.* **50**, 815 (1917).
1385. S. Gabriel, *Ber.* **21**, 1049 (1888).
1386. S. Gabriel, *Ber.* **22**, 1139 (1889).
1387. S. Gabriel and J. Colman, *Ber.* **47**, 1866 (1914).
1388. S. Gabriel and C. F. von Hirsch, *Ber.* **29**, 2747 (1896).
1389. S. Gabriel and R. Stelzner, *Ber.* **29**, 2381 (1896).
1390. S. Gabriel and G. Eschenbach, *Ber.* **30**, 2494 (1897).
1391. S. Gabriel, *Ber.* **21**, 2664 (1888).
1392. S. Gabriel and R. Stelzner, *Ber.* **28**, 2929 (1895).
1393. H. C. Gabsch, *Naturwissenschaften* **49**, 106 (1962).
1394. G. G. Gade *et al.*, *Surgery* **39**, 515 (1956).
1395. V. R. Gaertner (to Monsanto Chemical Co.), U.S. 2,965,536 (1960).
1395a. V. R. Gaertner, *Tetrahedron Letters* p. 5919 (1968).
1396. I. Gagauzov and D. Dalev, *Farmatsiya* (*Sofia*) **17**, 7 (1967); via *C. A.* **67**, 53844.
1397. Gagliardi Research Corporation, *Chem. Week* **102** (5), 25 (1968).
1398. D. D. Gagliardi, *Am. Dyestuff Reptr.* **54**, P472 (1965).
1399. D. D. Gagliardi, U.S. 3,314,743 (1967).
1400. T. B. Gaines and R. D. Kimbrough, *Bull. World Health Organ.* **34**, 317 (1966).
1401. T. B. Gaines and R. D. Kimbrough, *Bull. World Health Organ.* **31**, 737 (1964).
1402. E. Gallegos and R. W. Kiser, *J. Phys. Chem.* **65**, 1177 (1961).
1403. V. S. Gandhi and E. Schwenk, *J. Indian Chem. Soc.* **39**, 306 (1962).
1404. C. R. Ganellin, D. R. Hollyman, and H. F. Ridley, *J. Chem. Soc., C, Org.* p. 2220 (1967).
1405. K. P. Ganina, *Uch. Zap., Kievsk. Nauchn.-Issled. Rentgeno-Radiol. i Onkol. Inst.* **7**, 177 (1961); via *C. A.* **60**, 8505.
1406. S. Garattini and V. Palma, *Cancer Chemotherapy Rept.* **13**, 9 (1961).
1407. M. Garber and B. Miller (to American Cyanamid), U.S. 3,297,708 (1967); S. Afr. 65/6109 (1966); Belg. 674,078 (1966); Fr. 1,481,053 (1967); Neth. appl. 6,515,470 (1967).
1408. J. Gardent, *Compt. Rend.* **243**, 63 (1956).
1409. H. K. Gardner, G. L. Drake, Jr., and N. B. Knoepfler, *Hospitals* **37** (16), 123 (1963); via *Rev. Text. Progr.* **15**, 408.
1410. T. S. Gardner, *J. Polymer Sci.* **1**, 289 (1946).

1411. T. S. Gardner (to Eastman Kodak Co.), U.S. 2,518,676 (1950).
1412. N. L. Garetovskaya and N. V. Beljaeva, *Kauchuk i Rezina* **25**, 29 (1966); via *C. A.* **65**, 17173.
1413. D. C. Garms and F. E. Norton (to The Dow Chemical Co.), U.S. 3,210,308 (1965); Brit. 1,003,356 (1965); Fr. 1,383,770 (1965); Neth. 295,004 (1965); Belg. 657,545 (1965); Can. 761,538 (1967); Ital. 699,290 (1965).
1414. D. C. Garms (to The Dow Chemical Co.), U.S. 3,275,588 (1966); Belg. 639,551 (1964); Neth. 300,100 (1965); Ger. 1,216,542 (1966); Brit. 1,002,703 (1965).
1415. E. R. Garrett, *J. Med. Chem.* **6**, 488 (1963).
1416. E. R. Garrett and W. Schroeder, *J. Pharm. Sci.* **53**, 917 (1964).
1417. J. Gasparic *et al.*, *Collection Czech. Chem. Comm.* **26**, 2950 (1961).
1418. E. W. Gassenmeier and C. Schuster (to Badische Anilin- und Soda-Fabrik), U.S. 2,694,704 (1954); Ger. 879,695 (1953); Brit. 712,720 (1954); Fr. 1,055,622 (1954).
1419. P. G. Gassman and A. Fentiman, *J. Org. Chem.* **32**, 2388 (1967).
1420. H. Gaul, *Radiation Botany* **4**, 155 (1964).
1421. W. Gauss and S. Petersen, *Angew. Chem.* **69**, 252 (1957).
1422. W. Gauss, M. Pestemer, and S. Peterson, *Helv. Chim. Acta* **39**, 330 (1956).
1423. W. Gauss and S. Petersen, *Med. Chem., Abhandl. Med.-Chem. Forschungsstaetten Farbwerke Hoechst A.-G.* **7**, 649 (1963).
1424. W. Gauss and S. Petersen, *Angew. Chem.* **70**, 703 (1958).
1425. W. Gauss, *Chem. Ber.* **91**, 2216 (1958).
1426. W. Gauss, P. Moser, and G. Schwartzenbach, *Helv. Chim. Acta* **35**, 2359 (1952).
1427. W. Gauss, S. Petersen, and G. Domagk (to Schenley Industries), U.S. 2,868,782 (1959); Can. 611,837 (1961); Austrian 198,254 (1957); Fr. addn. 81,102/1,118,425 (1963); Ger. 1,024,083 (1958); Brit. 805,518 (1958).
1428. W. Gauss and S. Petersen (to Farbenfabriken Bayer), U.S. 2,964,522 (1960); Austrian 197,367 (1957); Brit. 806,079 (1958); Ger. 1,021,849 (1958).
1429. W. Gauss and G. Domagk (to Schenley Industries), U.S. 2,976,279 (1961); Can. 582,610 (1959); Ger. 1,044,816 (1958); Brit. 818,517 (1959).
1430. G. Gavlin and K. Hattori (to The Richardson Co.), U.S. 3,052,669 (1962).
1431. G. Gavlin and K. Hattori (to The Richardson Co.), U.S. 3,100,789 (1963).
1432. G. Gavlin and K. Hattori (to The Richardson Co.), U.S. 3,169,143 (1965).
1433. C. S. Gebelein, G. Swift, and D. Swern, *J. Org. Chem.* **32**, 3314 (1967).
1434. Q. A. Geering, P. J. Brooker, and J. H. Parsons, *J. Econ. Entomol.* **58**, 574 (1965).
1435. J. R. Geigy A.-G., Swiss 270,826 (1951); *C. A.* **46**, 2574.
1436. J. R. Geigy A.-G., Swiss 274,692 (1951); *C. A.* **46**, 4573.
1437. J. R. Geigy A.-G., Swiss 387,045 (1965); *C. A.* **63**, 8322.
1438. G. Geiseler and W. Koenig, *Z. Physik. Chem. (Leipzig)* **227**, 81 (1964).
1439. E. M. Geiser (to Universal Oil Products Co.), U.S. 2,998,415 (1961).
1440. E. M. Geiser (to Universal Oil Products Co.), U.S. 3,068,209 (1962).
1441. T. A. Geissman and A. Armen, *J. Am. Chem. Soc.* **77**, 1623 (1955).
1442. T. A. Geissman, H. Hochman, and R. T. Fukuto, *J. Am. Chem. Soc.* **74**, 3313 (1952).
1443. Gelatin and Glue Research Assn., Belg. 653,465 (1965); Fr. 1,422,903 (1966); Brit. 1,101,291 (1968).
1444. P. A. Gembitskii, N. M. Loim, and D. S. Zhuk, *Usp. Khim.* **35**, 229 (1966); *Russ. Chem. Rev. (English Transl.)* **35**, 105 (1966).
1445. P. A. Gembitskii, D. S. Zhuk, and V. A. Kargin, "Khimiya Etilenimina." Nauka Moscow, 1966.
1446. S. B. Gendina, *Tr., Vses. Nauchn.-Issled. Inst. Fermentnoi i Spirt. Prom.* **16**, 58 (1965); via *C. A.* **65**, 1084.

1447. General Electric Co., Neth. appl. 6,510,986 (1966); via *C. A.* **65**, 7382; Fr. 1,456,735 (1966); Brit. 1,117,481 (1968).
1447a. General Tire and Rubber Co., Fr. 1,486,844 (1967); via *POST-P* **3**, 1201.
1448. W. J. Gensler and B. A. Brooks, *J. Org. Chem.* **31**, 568 (1966).
1449. W. J. Gensler, *J. Am. Chem. Soc.* **70**, 1843 (1948).
1450. W. J. Gensler, *J. Am. Chem. Soc.* **69**, 1966 (1947).
1451. W. J. Gensler and W. R. Koehler, *J. Org. Chem.* **27**, 2754 (1962).
1452. W. J. Gensler and J. C. Rockett, *J. Am. Chem. Soc.* **77**, 3262 (1955).
1453. W. J. Gensler, B. A. Brooks, and W. R. Koehler, *J. Org. Chem.* **30**, 4365 (1965).
1454. W. J. Gensler and J. C. Rockett, *J. Am. Chem. Soc.* **74**, 4451 (1952).
1455. D. Gericke, *Intern. Symp. Chemotherapy: 2nd, Naples, 1961* Vol. 3, p. 94. Karger, Basel, 1963; via Cheymol *et al.* (673).
1455a. D. Gericke, *Neoplasma* **11**, 329 (1964); via Cheymol *et al.* (673).
1456. N. Gerlich, *Naturwissenschaften* **46**, 148 (1959).
1457. N. Gerlich, *Naturwissenschaften* **44**, 282 (1957).
1458. N. Gerlich, *Naturwissenschaften* **43**, 396 (1956).
1459. J. A. Gervasi, M. Brown, and L. A. Bigelow, *J. Am. Chem. Soc.* **78**, 1679 (1956).
1460. Gevaert Photo Producten N. V., Ger. 1,069,867 (1959); Brit. 860,631 (1961).
1461. Gevaert Photo Producten N. V., Belg. 575,440 (1959); Brit. 918,950 (1963).
1462. Gevaert Photo Producten N. V., Ger. 1,118,007 (1961); Brit. 950,960 and 961,177 (1964).
1462a. Gevaert-Agfa N. V., Neth. appl. 6,608,174 (1966); Belg. 682,427 (1966); Fr. 1,483,147 (1967); via *C. A.* **67**, 27583.
1463. R. Gewalt and E. Stein, Ger. 1,058,221 (1959); Belg. 556,423 (1960); *Chem. Zentr.* p. 14796 (1960).
1464. M. V. Ghatnekar, *Caryologia* **17**, 219 (1964).
1465. R. Ghirardelli and H. J. Lucas, *J. Am. Chem. Soc.* **77**, 106 (1955).
1466. R. Ghirardelli and H. J. Lucas, *J. Am. Chem. Soc.* **79**, 734 (1957).
1467. C. F. Gibbs, L. Hough, and A. C. Richardson, *Carbohydrate Res.* **1**, 290 (1965).
1467a. G. J. Gibbs and H. F. Calcote, *J. Chem. Eng. Data* **4**, 226 (1959).
1467b. B. Giese and R. Huisgen, *Tetrahedron Letters* p. 1889 (1967).
1468. C. Giessner-Prettre, *Ann. Phys. (Paris)* [13] **9**, 557 (1964).
1468a. H. S. Gilbert (to The Dow Chemical Co.), U.S. 3,368,678 (1968).
1469. S. G. Gilbert and J. T. Mergy (to Milprint, Inc.), U.S. 3,111,418 (1963).
1470. E. W. Gill and H. P. Rang, *Mol. Pharmacol* **2**, 284 (1966).
1471. R. Gill (to Allied Colloids), U.S. 2,677,681 (1954); Brit. 760,311 (1956).
1472. F. R. Gilliland, Jr. and T. B. Davich, *J. Econ. Entomol.* **59**, 1209 (1966); **61**, 852 (1968).
1473. A. Gilman and F. S. Philips, *Science* **103**, 409 (1946).
1474. H. Gilman *et al.*, *J. Am. Chem. Soc.* **67**, 2106 (1945).
1475. J. N. Godfrey (to Atlantic Research Corp.), U.S. 3,203,842 (1965).
1476. A. Goeksel, *Rev. Fac. Sci. Univ. Istanbul* **21C**, 72 (1956); *C. A.* **51**, 4978.
1477. V. Goerisch and W. Grund, *Arch. Exptl. Pathol. Pharmacol.* **236**, 207 (1959).
1478. S. Yu. Gol'dat, *Genetika* No. 1, 106 (1965); via *C. A.* **64**, 2459; S. Yu. Gol'dat, R. V. Sokolova, and L. P. Kadakova, *Antibiotiki* **9**, 211 (1964); via *Chem. Zentr.* No. 37, abstr. 1330 (1965).
1479. A. A. Goldberg, *J. Chem. Soc.* p. 826 (1945).
1480. A. A. Goldberg and W. Kelly, *J. Chem. Soc.* p. 1919 (1948).
1481. M. W. Goldberg and H. H. Lehr (to Hoffmann-La Roche), U.S. 2,755,278 (1956).
1482. E. L. Goldblatt *et al.*, *Proc. Soc. Exptl. Biol. Med.* **123**, 845 (1966).
1483. A. Goldstein, *in* "Encyclopedia of Polymer Science and Technology" (N. G. Gaylord and N. M. Bikales, eds.), Vol. 1, p. 734. Wiley (Interscience), New York, 1964.

1484. A. Goldstein and F. A. Nowak, Jr. (to Chemirad Corp.), U.S. 3,194,826 (1965); Fr. 1,350,893 (1964).
1485. A. Goldstein and J. W. Brook (to Chemirad Corp.), U.S. 3,294,723 (1966).
1486. A. Goldstein and J. W. Brook (to Chemirad Corp.), U.S. 3,310,460 (1967).
1488. M. H. Gollis, R. J. Wineman, and J. C. James (to Monsanto Research Corp.), U.S. 3,312,732 (1967).
1488a. R. V. Golovnya, G. A. Mironov, and I. L. Zhuravleva, *Zh. Anal. Khim.* **22**, 797 (1967); *J. Anal. Chem. USSR (English Transl.)* **22**, 676 (1967).
1489. C. Golumbic and M. Bergmann, *J. Org. Chem.* **11**, 536 (1946).
1490. C. Golumbic, M. A. Stahmann, and M. Bergmann, *J. Org. Chem.* **11**, 550 (1946).
1491. C. Golumbic, J. S. Fruton, and M. Bergmann, *J. Org. Chem.* **11**, 581 (1946).
1492. C. Golumbic, J. S. Fruton, and M. Bergmann, *J. Org. Chem.* **11**, 518 (1946).
1493. R. Gompper and W. Toepfli, *Chem. Ber.* **95**, 2861 (1962).
1494. R. Gompper and W. Haegele, *Angew. Chem.* **74**, 753 (1962); *Angew. Chem. Intern. Ed. Engl.* **1**, 553 (1962).
1494a. W. D. Good *et al.*, *Proc. JANAF Thermochem. Working Group Symp., Douglas Advan. Res. Lab., Huntington Beach, Calif., 1968.* Chem. Propulsion Inform. Agency (to be published).
1495. L. Goodman, J. E. Christensen, and S. L. Holton, *Armed Services Technical Information Agency (U.S.) Document* AD 434,058 (1964).
1496. L. Goodman *et al.*, *Proc. Am. Assoc. Cancer Res.* **3**, 233 (1961).
1497. T. H. Goodridge, W. T. Huntress, and R. P. Bratzell, *Cancer Chemotherapy Rept.* **26**, 341 (1963).
1498. W. E. Gordon (to du Pont de Nemours and Co.), U.S. 2,286,726 (1942).
1499. V. E. Gorin, *Izv. Sibirsk. Otd. Akad. Nauk SSSR, Ser. Biol.-Med. Nauk* No. 3, 117 (1964); via *C. A.* **63**, 2097.
1500. S. A. Gostimskii and V. V. Khvostova, *Dokl. Akad. Nauk SSSR* **162**, 197 (1965); via *C. A.* **63**, 4670.
1501. H. Goto, *J. Fac. Textile Sci. Technol., Shinshu Univ.* **8**, 19 (1962); via *C. A.* **61**, 3050.
1502. H. K. Gouck and G. C. LaBrecque, *U.S. Dept. Agr., ARS* **ARS 33-87** (1963).
1503. H. K. Gouck, *J. Econ. Entomol.* **57**, 239 (1964).
1504. H. K. Gouck, D. W. Meifert, and J. B. Gahan, *J. Econ. Entomol.* **56**, 445 (1963).
1505. H. K. Gouck *et al.*, *J. Econ. Entomol.* **56**, 506 (1963).
1506. H. K. Gouck and G. C. LaBrecque, *J. Econ. Entomol.* **57**, 663 (1964).
1507. A. Gourevitch, B. Chertow, and J. Sein (to Bristol-Myers Co.), U.S. 3,042,582 (1962); Brit. 871,481 (1961); Ger. 1,217,548 (1966).
1507a. L. P. Gozman, *Zh. Obshch. Khim.* **37**, 2732 (1967); via *C. A.* **69**, 66826.
1508. W. R. Grace and Co., Fr. 1,327,460 (1963); *C. A.* **59**, 12844.
1508a. W. R. Grace and Co., Belg. 652,377 (1965); *C. A.* **64**, 12919.
1509. A. F. Graefe, *Chem. Eng. News* **36** (43), 52 (1958).
1510. A. F. Graefe and R. E. Meyer, *J. Am. Chem. Soc.* **80**, 3939 (1958).
1511. A. F. Graefe (to Aerojet-General Corp.), U.S. 2,944,051 (1960).
1512. A. F. Graefe and R. E. Meyer (to Aerojet-General Corp.), U.S. 3,070,596 (1962).
1513. A. F. Graefe (to Aerojet-General Corp.), U.S. 3,173,910 (1965).
1514. J. D. P. Graham, *J. Physiol. (London)* **135**, 62P (1957).
1515. J. D. P. Graham and M. A. Karrar, *J. Med. Chem.* **6**, 103 (1963).
1516. J. D. P. Graham, *Progr. Med. Chem.* **2**, 132 (1962).
1517. J. D. P. Graham, *Brit. J. Pharmacol.* **12**, 489 (1957).
1518. J. D. P. Graham, *J. Med. Pharm. Chem.* **2**, 499 (1960).
1518a. V. A. Grakauskas, A. J. Tomasewski, and J. P. Horwitz, *J. Am. Chem. Soc.* **80**, 3155 (1958).

1519. E. A. Grant, Jr. (to Minnesota Mining and Manufacturing Co.), U.S. 3,028,254 (1962); Fr. 1,269,464 (1961); Ger. 1,145,644 (1963); Brit. 967,440 (1964).

1520. P. Gray and A. Jones, *Trans. Faraday Soc.* **61**, 2161 (1965).

1521. P. Gray and A. Jones, *Can. J. Chem.* **43**, 3485 (1965).

1522. R. N. Grebeshova and S. G. Tul'kes, *Tr. Mosk. Obshch. Ispyt. Prir., Otd. Biol.* **22**, 243 (1966); via *Bibliog. Agr.* **31**, 48364.

1523. N. P. Grechkin, *Khim. Primen. Fosfororgan. Soedin., Akad. Nauk SSSR, Tr. 1-oi Konf.*, p. 243 (1955); via *C. A.* **52**, 241.

1524. N. P. Grechkin and I. A. Nuretdinov, *Izv. Akad. Nauk SSSR, Otd. Khim. Nauk* p. 295 (1962); *Bull. Acad. Sci. USSR, Div. Chem. Sci.* (*English Transl.*) p. 272 (1962).

1524a. N. P. Grechkin, R. R. Shagidullin, and L. N. Grishina, *Izv. Akad. Nauk SSSR, Ser. Khim.* p. 854 (1968); via *C. A.* **69**, 86264.

1525. N. P. Grechkin and I. A. Nuretdinov, *Izv. Akad. Nauk SSSR, Otd. Khim. Nauk* p. 302 (1963); *Bull. Acad. Sci. USSR, Div. Chem. Sci.* (*English Transl.*) p. 275 (1963).

1526. N. P. Grechkin, *Izv. Akad. Nauk SSSR, Otd. Khim. Nauk* p. 538 (1956); via *C. A.* **51**, 1933.

1527. N. P. Grechkin, *Dokl. Akad. Nauk SSSR* **133**, 592 (1960); *C. A.* **54**, 24480.

1528. N. P. Grechkin, *Izv. Akad. Nauk SSSR, Otd. Khim. Nauk* p. 1053 (1957). *Bull. Acad. Sci. USSR, Div. Chem. Sci.* (*English Transl.*) p. 1084 (1957).

1529. N. P. Grechkin and I. A. Nuretdinov, *Izv. Akad. Nauk SSSR, Ser. Khim.* p. 1105 (1965); *Bull. Acad. Sci. USSR, Div. Chem. Sci.* (*English Transl.*) p. 1072 (1965).

1530. N. P. Grechkin and L. N. Grishina, *Dokl. Akad. Nauk SSSR* **146**, 1333 (1962); via *Proc. Acad. Sci. USSR, Chem. Sect.* (*English Transl.*) **145-147**, 922 (1962).

1531. N. P. Grechkin and L. N. Grishina, *Izv. Akad. Nauk. SSSR, Ser. Khim.* p. 1502 (1965); *Bull. Acad. Sci. USSR, Div. Chem. Sci.* (*English Transl.*) p. 1472 (1965).

1531a. J. L. Greene, Jr., A. M. Williams, and J. A. Montgomery, *J. Med. Chem.* **7**, 20 (1964).

1532. H. P. Gregor, D. H. Gold, and G. K. Hoeschele, *J. Am. Chem. Soc.* **77**, 4743 (1955).

1532a. H. P. Gregor, I. F. Miller, and O. W. Weber, *National Aeronautics and Space Administration* (*U.S.*) *Accession No.* N66-33449, Rept. No. NASA-CR-65450; via *C. A.* **66**, 119156.

1533. D. S. Greif, *Tappi* **43**, 254 (1960).

1534. R. Griessbach, E. Meier, and H. Wassenegger (to I. G. Farbenindustrie A.-G.), U.S. 2,223,930 (1940); Fr. 830,227 (1938); Brit. 489,173 (1938); Farbenfabrik Bayer A.-G., Ger. 974,941 (1961).

1535. Iv. Grigorov *et al., Izv. Mikrobiol. Inst., Bulgar. Akad. Nauk* **19**, 115 (1967); via *C. A.* **68**, 112486.

1536. E. P. Grimshaw, *Plastics Inst.* (*London*), *Trans.* **20** (42), 9 (1952).

1537. E. I. Grinblat and I. Y. Postovskii, *Dokl. Akad. Nauk SSSR* **133**, 847 (1960); via *C. A.* **54**, 24756.

1538. A. G. Grinevich, *Uzbeksk. Biol. Zh.* **10**, 16 (1966); via *C. A.* **64**, 17997.

1539. K. Grob, *J. Gas Chromatog.* **2**, 80 (1964).

1540. A. Gruen and R. Limpaecher, *Ber.* **60**, 151 (1927).

1541. C. J. Grundmann, H. Schroeder, and R. F. W. Raetz, *J. Org. Chem.* **23**, 1522 (1958).

1542. C. J. Grundmann and E. Kober, *J. Am. Chem. Soc.* **79**, 944 (1957).

1543. C. J. Grundmann and E. Kober (to Olin Mathieson Chemical Corp.), U.S. 2,867,621 (1959); Brit. 769,722 (1957).

1544. C. J. Grundmann and E. Kober (to Olin Mathieson Chemical Corp.), U.S. 3,022,303 (1962).

1545. F. Grundschober and J. Sambeth, *J. Polymer Sci.* **C16**, 2087 (1967).

1545a. J. T. Gruver (to Phillips Petroleum Co.), U.S. 3,264,251 (1966); S. Afr. 62/2305; Brit. 944,267 (1963); Fr. 1,333,247 (1963); Japan. 27,622 ('64).

1546. J. T. Gruver (to Phillips Petroleum Co.), U.S. 3,097,193 (1963).
1546a. K. W. Guebert and I. C. Jones, Jr. (to The Dow Chemical Co.), U.S. 3,352,424 (1967); Can. 747,727 (1966).
1547. K. W. Guebert and J. D. Laman (to The Dow Chemical Co.), U.S. 3,242,073 (1966); Can. 730,505 (1966); Ital. 716,981 (1966); Brit. 1,043,616 (1966); Fr. 1,390,538 (1965); Ger. 1,227,426 (1966); Belg. 644,772 (1964).
1548. J. R. Guest and C. Yanovsky, *J. Biol. Chem.* **241**, 1 (1966).
1549. E. Gulbins, R. Morlock, and K. Hamann, *Ann. Chem.* **698**, 180 (1966).
1550. W. S. Gump and E. J. Nikawitz, *J. Am. Chem. Soc.* **72**, 1309 (1950).
1551. K.-D. Gundermann and G. Holtmann, *Chem. Ber.* **91**, 160 (1958).
1552. K.-D. Gundermann and H.-J. Rose, *Chem. Ber.* **92**, 1081 (1959).
1553. K.-D. Gundermann *et al.*, *Chem. Ber.* **93**, 1632 (1960).
1554. W. F. Gunn, Jr. and M. M. Joullié, *J. Org. Chem.* **32**, 53 (1967).
1555. W. H. H. Gunther and H. G. Mautner, *J. Am. Chem. Soc.* **82**, 2762 (1962).
1556. S. Gurin, A. M. Delluva, and D. I. Crandall, *J. Org. Chem.* **12**, 606 (1947).
1557. S. Gurin, A. M. Delluva, and D. I. Crandall, *J. Org. Chem.* **12**, 612 (1947).
1558. A. Gustafsson, *Hereditas* **50**, 211 (1963).
1559. J. D. Guthrie, *Textile Res. J.* **17**, 625 (1947).
1560. J. D. Guthrie, *Ind. Eng. Chem.* **44**, 2187 (1952).
1561. R. D. Guthrie and D. Murphy, *J. Chem. Soc.* p. 5288 (1963).
1562. R. D. Guthrie *et al.*, *Proc. Chem. Soc.* p. 84 (1963).
1563. R. D. Guthrie and D. Murphy, *J. Chem. Soc.* p. 3828 (1965).
1564. R. D. Guthrie and D. King, *Carbohydrate Res.* **3**, 128 (1966–1967).
1565. E. Gutierrez Rios, A. Rodriguez, and A. Santos, *Anales Real Soc. Españ. Fis. Quím. (Madrid)* **B63**, 297 (1967); via *C. A.* **67**, 15237.
1566. V. Gutmann, P. Heilmayer and K. Utvary, *Monatsh. Chem.* **92**, 322 (1961).
1567. H. S. Gutowsky, *Ann. N. Y. Acad. Sci.* **70**, 786 (1958).
1568. H. S. Gutowsky, M. Karplus, and D. M. Grant, *J. Chem. Phys.* **31**, 1278 (1959).
1569. H. S. Gutowsky *et al.*, *J. Am. Chem. Soc.* **76**, 4242 (1954).
1569a. Gyógyszeripari Kutato Intezet, Hung. 150,476 (1963); via *C. A.* **60**, 4242.
1570. W. Gysin (to Badische Anilin- und Soda-Fabrik), U.S. 2,823,191 (1958); Ger. 952,201 (1956); Fr. 1,114,150 (1956).
1571. H. Haakh and A. Rueckert (to Farbwerke Hoechst), U.S. 2,933,416 (1960); Ger. 971,871 (1959); Brit. 810,548 (1959).
1572. R. Haberl, *Monatsh. Chem.* **89**, 814 (1958).
1572a. K. R. Habermann (to Allied Chemical Corp.), U.S. 3,355,347 (1967); Belg. 670,586 (1965); Neth. appl. 6,512,928 (1966).
1573. Y. Hada, *Osaka Shiritsu Daigaku Igaku Zasshi* **9**, 4177 (1960); via *C. A.* **55**, 10718.
1573a. Z. Hadidian *et al.*, *J. Nat. Cancer Inst.* **41**, 985 (1968).
1573b. K. Hafner and K. Goliasch, *Chem. Ber.* **94**, 2909 (1961).
1574. K. Hafner and C. Koenig, *Angew. Chem.* **75**, 89 (1963); *Angew. Chem. Intern. Ed. Engl.* **2**, 96 (1963).
1575. K. Hafner, D. Zinser, and K. L. Moritz, *Tetrahedron Letters* p. 1733 (1964).
1576. K. Hafner, W. Kaiser, and R. Puttner, *Tetrahedron Letters* p. 3953 (1964).
1577. L. Hagan and V. D. Celentano (to Olin Mathieson Chemical Corp.), U.S. 3,011,910 (1961); Brit. 917,050 (1963).
1578. W. Hagge, G. Naumann, and O. Schneider (to Farbenfabriken Bayer), U.S. 3,210,299 (1965); Belg. 622,716 (1963); Brit. 967,772 (1964); Ger. 1,174,983 (1964).
1579. C. S. Hahn, *Daehan Hwahak Hwoejee* **7**, 230 (1963); via *C. A.* **61**, 13298.
1580. J. A. Hair and E. C. Turner, Jr., *J. Econ. Entomol.* **59**, 452 (1966).
1581. J. A. Hair and T. R. Adkins, Jr., *J. Econ. Entomol.* **57**, 586 (1964).

1582. A. J. Hall, *Textile World* **111**, 80 (1961).
1582a. R. H. Hall and G. F. Wright, *J. Am. Chem. Soc.* **73**, 2208 (1951).
1583. G. E. Ham, *J. Org. Chem.* **29**, 3052 (1964).
1584. G. E. Ham (to The Dow Chemical Co.), U.S. 3,198,806 (1965).
1585. G. E. Ham and P. M. Phillips (to The Dow Chemical Co.), U.S. 3,242,165 (1966).
1586. G. E. Ham (to The Dow Chemical Co.), U.S. 3,243,429 (1966).
1587. G. E. Ham (to The Dow Chemical Co.), U.S. 3,247,220 (1966).
1588. G. E. Ham (to The Dow Chemical Co.), U.S. 3,280,106 (1966).
1589. G. E. Ham (to The Dow Chemical Co.), U.S. 3,312,687 (1967).
1590. G. E. Ham (to The Dow Chemical Co.), U.S. 3,322,694 (1967).
1590a. G. E. Ham and J. E. Stevens (to The Dow Chemical Co.), U.S. 3,354,126 (1967).
1591. G. E. Ham and L. Levine (to The Dow Chemical Co.), U.S. 3,326,962 (1967).
1592. G. E. Ham (to The Dow Chemical Co.), U.S. 3,337,533 (1967).
1593. G. E. Ham, *Abstr. Papers, 147th Am. Chem. Soc. Meeting, Philadelphia, 1964* p. N-16.
1594. G. E. Ham and P. M. Phillips (to The Dow Chemical Co.), U.S. 3,324,120 (1967).
1595. G. E. Ham and L. Levine (to The Dow Chemical Co.), U.S. 3,320,302 (1967).
1595a. G. E. Ham, H. L. Hairston, and D. A. Tomalia (to The Dow Chemical Co.), U.S. 3,409,618 (1968).
1596. G. E. Ham and P. M. Phillips (to The Dow Chemical Co.), U.S. 3,280,110 (1966).
1596a. G. E. Ham and P. M. Phillips (to The Dow Chemical Co.), U.S. 3,324,130 (1968).
1597. G. E. Ham and C. H. Klentsch (to The Dow Chemical Co.), U.S. 3,280,109 (1966).
1598. G. E. Ham (to The Dow Chemical Co.), U.S. 3,382,270 (1968).
1599. K. Hamann, *Angew. Chem.* **63**, 231 (1951).
1600. C. L. Hamermesh *et al.* (to Interchemical Corp.), U.S. 3,077,427 (1963).
1601. C. F. Hammer and S. R. Heller, *Chem. Commun.* p. 919 (1966).
1602. W. E. Hanby *et al.*, *J. Chem. Soc.* p. 519 (1947).
1603. G. R. Handrick *et al.*, *J. Med. Chem.* **8**, 762 (1965).
1605. B. Hansen, *Acta Chem. Scand.* **17**, 1483 (1963).
1606. B. Hansen, *Acta Chem. Scand.* **16**, 1927 (1962).
1607. B. Hansen, *Acta Chem. Scand.* **16**, 1945 (1962).
1607a. G. R. Hansen and T. E. Burg, *J. Heterocyclic Chem.* **5**, 305 (1968).
1608. E. J. Hansens and P. Granett, *J. Econ. Entomol.* **58**, 157 (1965).
1609. E. J. Hansens, *J. Econ. Entomol.* **58**, 944 (1965).
1610. U. Harder, E. Pfeil, and K. F. Zenner, *Chem. Ber.* **97**, 510 (1964).
1611. P. K. Harein and R. S. Soles, *J. Econ. Entomol.* **57**, 369 (1964).
1612. M. D. Harmony and M. Sancho, *J. Chem. Phys.* **47**, 1911 (1967).
1613. F. H. Harries and W. G. Wiles, *J. Econ. Entomol.* **59**, 694 (1966).
1614. R. L. Harris, *J. Econ. Entomol.* **55**, 882 (1962).
1615. R. L. Harris and E. D. Frazar, *J. Econ. Entomol.* **59**, 1171 (1966).
1616. R. M. Hart and A. H. De Cat (to Gevaert Photo-Producten), U.S. 3,230,201 (1966); Ger. 1,136,110 (1962); Belg. 604,417 (1961); Brit. 932,620 and 939,250 (1963).
1617. R. J. Hartman and E. J. Fujiwara, U.S. 2,972,606 (1961).
1618. M. Hartman (to Soc. pour l'ind. chim. à Bâle), U.S. 1,777,970 (1930).
1619. G. R. Harvey and K. W. Ratts, *J. Org. Chem.* **31**, 3907 (1966).
1620. S. C. Harvey and M. Nickerson, *J. Pharmacol. Exptl. Therap.* **109**, 328 (1953).
1621. A. Hassner and C. Heathcock, *J. Org. Chem.* **30**, 1748 (1965).
1622. A. Hassner and C. Heathcock, *Tetrahedron Letters* p. 393 (1963).
1623. A. Hassner, M. E. Lorber, and C. Heathcock, *J. Org. Chem.* **32**, 540 (1967).
1624. A. Hassner and C. Heathcock, *Tetrahedron* **20**, 1037 (1964).
1625. A. Hassner and C. Heathcock, *Tetrahedron Letters* p. 1125 (1964).
1626. A. Hassner and F. W. Fowler, *Tetrahedron Letters* p. 1545 (1967).

1627. A. Hassner and C. Heathcock, *J. Org. Chem.* **29**, 3640 (1964).
1628. A. Hassner and L. A. Levy, *J. Am. Chem. Soc.* **87**, 4203 (1965).
1629. T. Hata *et al.*, *J. Antibiotics (Tokyo)* **A9**, 141 (1956); *C. A.* **53**, 20248.
1630. M. J. Hatch and D. J. Cram, *J. Am. Chem. Soc.* **75**, 38 (1953).
1631. M. J. Hatch, J. A. Dillon, and H. B. Smith, *Ind. Eng. Chem.* **49**, 1812 (1957).
1632. M. J. Hatch (to The Dow Chemical Co.), U.S. 3,041,292 (1962); Brit. 795,624 (1958); Fr. 1,140,490 (1957); Can. 589,371 (1959); Ger. 1,156,236 (1963).
1633. M. J. Hatch (to The Dow Chemical Co.), U.S. 3,205,184 (1965).
1634. D. O. Hathaway, L. V. Lydin, and B. A. Butt, *J. Econ. Entomol.* **59**, 851 (1966).
1635. K. H. Hauck and F. Hecker-Over, Ger. 1,045,652 (1958); *C. A.* **55**, 2138.
1637. M. Hauptschein and M. Braid (to Pennsalt Chemical Corp.), U.S. 3,248,419 (1966).
1639. A. W. Hay, A. L. Thompson, and C. A. Winkler, *Can. J. Res.* **26B**, 175 (1948).
1640. S. Hayashi *et al.*, *Chem. & Pharm. Bull. (Tokyo)* **11**, 948 (1963); via *C. A.* **59**, 10656.
1641. W. J. Hayes, Jr., *Bull. World Health Organ.* **31**, 721 (1964).
1642. W. J. Hayes, Jr., *Abstr. Papers, 150th Am. Chem. Soc. Meeting, Atlantic City, 1965* p. A-29.
1643. J. W. Haynes, P. A. Hedin, and T. B. Davich, *J. Econ. Entomol.* **59**, 1014 (1966).
1643a. S. B. Hays, *J. Econ. Entomol.* **61**, 800 (1968).
1644. S. B. Hays and J. H. Cochran, *J. Econ. Entomol.* **57**, 217 (1964).
1645. E. I. Hazard *et al.*, *Science* **145**, 500 (1964).
1646. R. Hazard *et al.*, *Therapie* **20**, 173 (1965); via *C. A.* **62**, 14663.
1647. G. Heberlein, F. Muenzel, and W. Kung (to Heberlein and Co.), U.S. 3,140,197 (1964); Ger. 1,113,677 (1961); Brit. 906,324 (1962); Swiss 368,465 (1963) and 383,326 (1964).
1648. Heberlein and Co. A.-G., Swiss 388,246 (1965); *C. A.* **63**, 11771.
1649. Heberlein and Co. A.-G., Brit. 930,427 (1963); Swiss 395,014 (1965).
1649a. G. Hecht and C. Gloxhuber, *Med. Chem.* **7**, 666 (1963); via *Chem. Zentr.* No. 19, abstr. 1093 (1965).
1650. P. A. Hedin *et al.*, *J. Econ. Entomol.* **60**, 209 (1967).
1651. P. A. Hedin, G. Wiygul, and N. Mitlin, *J. Econ. Entomol.* **60**, 215 (1967).
1652. P. A. Hedin, C. P. Cody, and A. C. Thompson, Jr., *J. Econ. Entomol.* **57**, 270 (1964).
1653. J. P. Heeschen, *Dissertation Abstr.* **20**, 3090 (1960).
1654. H. W. Heine and H. S. Bender, *J. Org. Chem.* **25**, 461 (1960).
1655. H. W. Heine and A. B. Smith, *Angew. Chem.* **75**, 669 (1963); *Angew. Chem. Intern. Ed. Engl.* **2**, 400 (1963).
1656. H. W. Heine, *Angew. Chem.* **74**, 772 (1962); *Angew. Chem. Intern. Ed. Engl.* **1**, 528 (1962).
1657. H. W. Heine and D. L. Tomalia, *J. Am. Chem. Soc.* **84**, 993 (1962).
1658. H. W. Heine, B. L. Kapur, and C. S. Mitch, *J. Am. Chem. Soc.* **76**, 1173 (1954).
1659. H. W. Heine and Z. Proctor, *J. Org. Chem.* **23**, 1554 (1958).
1660. H. W. Heine, M. E. Fetter, and E. M. Nicholson, *J. Am. Chem. Soc.* **81**, 2202 (1959).
1661. H. W. Heine *et al.*, *J. Am. Chem. Soc.* **76**, 2503 (1954).
1662. H. W. Heine, W. G. Kenyon, and E. M. Johnson, *J. Am. Chem. Soc.* **83**, 2570 (1961).
1663. H. W. Heine, *J. Am. Chem. Soc.* **85**, 2743 (1963).
1664. H. W. Heine and A. C. Brooker, *J. Org. Chem.* **27**, 2943 (1962).
1665. H. W. Heine and R. Peavy, *Tetrahedron Letters* p. 3123 (1965).
1666. H. W. Heine and F. Scholer, *Tetrahedron Letters* p. 3667 (1964).
1667. H. W. Heine, *J. Am. Chem. Soc.* **78**, 3708 (1956).
1668. H. W. Heine and B. L. Kapur, *J. Am. Chem. Soc.* **77**, 4892 (1955).
1669. H. W. Heine and M. S. Kaplan, *J. Org. Chem.* **32**, 3069 (1967).
1670. H. W. Heine, D. C. King, and L. A. Portland, *J. Org. Chem.* **31**, 2662 (1966).

1671. H. W. Heine and T. Newton, *Tetrahedron Letters* p. 1859 (1967).
1672. H. W. Heine, R. Peavy, and A. J. Durbetaki, *J. Org. Chem.* **31**, 3924 (1966).
1672a. H. W. Heine, G. J. Blosick, and G. B. Lowrie, *Tetrahedron Letters* p. 4801 (1968).
1673. E. J. Heiser, R. W. Morgan, and A. S. Reder, *Tappi* **45**, 588 (1962).
1674. F. Helfferich, *Z. Elektrochem.* **56**, 947 (1952).
1675. F. Helfferich, "Ion Exchange." McGraw-Hill, New York, 1962.
1676. C. Hell and O. v. Guenthert, *J. Prakt. Chem.* [2] **52**, 193 (1895).
1677. C. Hell and R. Poliakoff, *Ber.* **25**, 640 (1892).
1678. G. Heller and H. Lauth, *Ber.* **52**, 2295 (1919).
1679. Hellerman, *in* "Heterocyclic Compounds" (R. C. Elderfield, ed.), Vol. 1, p. 74. Wiley, New York, 1950; personal communication to J. S. Fruton.
1680. G. K. Helmkamp, R. D. Clark, and J. R. Koskinen, *J. Org. Chem.* **30**, 666 (1965).
1682. J. A. Hendry and R. F. Homer, *J. Chem. Soc.* p. 328 (1952).
1683. J. A. Hendry, F. L. Rose and A. L. Walpole, *J. Chem. Soc.* p. 1134 (1958).
1684. K. R. Henery-Logan and A. M. Limburg, *Tetrahedron Letters* p. 4615 (1966).
1685. K. R. Henery-Logan and R. A. Clark, *Abstr. Papers, 150th Am. Chem. Soc. Meeting, Atlantic City, 1966* p. S–72; *Tetrahedron Letters* p. 801 (1968).
1686. H. Henke, G. Hoehne, and H. A. Kuenkel, *Z. Krebsforsch.* **62**, 347 (1958).
1687. Henkel et Cie G.m.b.H., Ger. 724,037 (1942); *C. A.* **37**, 5520.
1687a. Henkel et Cie G.m.b.H., Fr. 1,503,104 (1967); via *C. A.* **69**, 78551.
1688. T. J. Henneberry and A. N. Kishaba, *J. Econ. Entomol.* **59**, 156 (1966).
1689. T. J. Henneberry, H. H. Shorey, and A. N. Kishaba, *J. Econ. Entomol.* **59**, 573 (1966).
1690. T. J. Henneberry, F. F. Smith, and W. L. McGovern, *J. Econ. Entomol.* **57**, 813 (1964).
1691. T. J. Henneberry, H. C. Mason, and W. L. McGovern, *J. Econ. Entomol.* **60**, 853 (1967).
1692. G. Hennemann (to American Enka Corp.), U.S. 3,156,606 (1964) and 3,305,430 (1967).
1693. J. H. Hennes (to The Dow Chemical Co.), U.S. 3,169,122 (1965).
1694. G. F. Hennion and P. E. Butler, *J. Org. Chem.* **27**, 2088 (1962).
1695. G. F. Hennion and A. C. Hazy, *J. Org. Chem.* **30**, 2650 (1965).
1696. W. Hentrich, *Z. Pflanzenzuecht.* **56**, 132 (1966).
1697. H. R. Henze and W. D. Compton, *J. Org. Chem.* **22**, 1036 (1957).
1699. Hercules Inc., Neth. appl. 6,701,828 (1967).
1700. Hercules Inc., Brit. 1,078,751 (1967).
1701. H. D. Hermann and E. Fischer (to Farbwerke Hoechst), U.S. 3,316,207 (1967); Belg. 626,284 (1962); Fr. 1,356,557 (1964); Brit. 994,205 (1965).
1702. P. Hermann, K. Stalla, and M. Zaoral, *Acta Chem. Acad. Sci. Hung.* **44**, 219 (1965).
1703. R. R. Herr *et al.*, *Antimicrobial Agents Ann.* p. 23 (1961).
1704. R. B. Herrick and M. Sherman, *Toxicol. Appl. Pharmacol.* **9**, 293 (1966).
1704a. R. B. Herrick, M. Sherman, and T. R. Batra, *Poultry Sci.* **46**, 1045 (1967).
1705. O. Herrmann and H. Mueller (to Kalle and Co.), U.S. 2,911,321 (1959).
1706. I. H. Herskowitz, *Genetics* **40**, 574 (1955).
1707. I. H. Herskowitz, *Genetics* **41**, 605 (1956).
1708. H. Heslot, *Abhandl. Deut. Akad. Wiss. Berlin, Kl. Med.* p. 98 (1960).
1709. H. Heslot *et al.*, *Effects Ionizing Radiations Seeds, Proc. Symp., Karlsruhe, 1960* p.243. I.A.E.A., Vienna, 1961; via *C. A.* **56**, 13269; *Oleagineux* **17**, 537 (1962).
1710. H. Heslot and R. Ferrary, *Ann. Inst. Natl. Rech. Agron.* **44**, 133 (1958); via *Plant Breed. Abstr.* **29**, 3850.
1710a. H. V. Hess and G. B. Arnold (to Texas Co.), U.S. 2,618,666 (1952).
1711. H. P. Heubusch (to Bell Aerospace Corp.), U.S. 3,099,629 (1963).
1712. H. P. Heubusch (to Bell Aerospace Corp.), U.S. 3,211,720 (1965).

1713. B. L. Hicks, T. E. Turner, and W. W. Widule, *J. Chem. Phys.* **21**, 564 (1953).
1714. Z. A. Hicks and G. H. Coleman, *Proc. Iowa Acad. Sci.* **53**, 207 (1946).
1715. W. Hieber and R. Wiesboeck, *Chem. Ber.* **91**, 1146 (1958).
1716. G. J. Hildering, *Euphytica* **12**, 113 (1963).
1717. S. Hillers and M. Lidaks, *Puti Sinteza i Izyskaniya Protivoopukholevykh Preparatov* . . . p. 193 (1962); via *C. A.* **58**, 4531.
1718. S. Hillers and Ya. A. Kastron, U.S.S.R. 167,922 (1964); via *C. A.* **62**, 16464.
1719. W. Himmelmann *et al.* (to Agfa), U.S. 3,220,848 (1965); Ger. 1,165,405 (1964).
1719a. J. Hine, F. E. Rogers, and R. E. Notari, *J. Am. Chem. Soc.* **90**, 3279 (1968).
1720. J. Hine, "Physical Organic Chemistry," 2d ed., p. 146. McGraw-Hill, New York, 1962.
1721. A. J. Hinton and V. G. Morgan (to Imperial Chemical Industries), U.S. 3,049,468 (1962); Brit. 851,546 (1960); Can. 688,161 (1964).
1722. C. Hirano, *Botyu-Kagaku* **30**, 109 (1965); via *C. A.* **64**, 18079.
1723. P. v. Hirsch, *Ber.* **23**, 964 (1890).
1723a. G. H. Hitchings (to The Wellcome Foundation), Can. 514,927 (1955).
1724. S. R. Hobart, G. L. Drake, Jr., and J. D. Guthrie, *Am. Dyestuff Reptr.* **51**, 657 (1962).
1725. J. Hoch, *Compt. Rend.* **198**, 1865 (1934).
1726. J. J. Hodan and H. Tieckelmann, *J. Org. Chem.* **26**, 4429 (1961).
1727. Hodogaya Chemical Co., Ltd., Japan. 211 ('58); via *C. A.* **52**, 21143.
1728. Hodogaya Chemical Co., Ltd., Japan. 3579 ('61); via *C. A.* **58**, 10172.
1729. Hodogaya Chemical Co., Ltd., Japan. 4442 ('59); via *C. A.* **54**, 13687.
1730. Hodogaya Chemical Co., Ltd., Japan. 7637 ('57); via *C. A.* **52**, 21138.
1731. Hodogaya Chemical Co., Ltd., Japan. 7684 ('56); via *C. A.* **52**, 16754.
1732. Hodogaya Chemical Co., Ltd., Japan. 7685 ('56); via *C.A.* **52**, 16754.
1733. Hodogaya Chemical Co., Ltd., Japan. 8492 ('57); via *C. A.* **53**, 734.
1734. Hodogaya Chemical Co., Ltd., Japan. 10,319 ('60); via *C. A.* **55**, 8947.
1735. Hodogaya Chemical Co., Ltd., Japan. 10,320 ('60); via *C. A.* **55**, 8948.
1736. Hodogaya Chemical Co., Ltd., Japan. 16,850 ('62); via *C. A.* **59**, 8895.
1737. Hodogaya Chemical Co., Ltd., Japan. 17,392 ('62); via *C. A.* **59**, 8895.
1738. Hodogaya Chemical Co., Ltd., Japan. 17,970 ('66).
1739. Hodogaya Chemical Co., Ltd., Brit. 984,278 (1965); Ger. 1,263,291 (1968).
1741. G. Hoehne, C. Bertram, and G. Schubert, *Acta Unio Intern. Contra Cancrum* **16**, 658 (1960).
1742. H. T. Hoffman, Jr., G. E. Evans, and G. Glockler, *J. Am. Chem. Soc.* **73**, 3028 (1951).
1743. J. A. Hoffman and J. C. Oppelt (to American Cyanamid Co.), U.S. 3,378,535 (1968).
1744. F. Hoffmann-La Roche and Co., A.-G., Neth appl. 6,515,759 (1966); Belg. 673,109; S. Afr. 65/6298; Brit. 1,124,245 and 1,124,246 (1968).
1745. F. Hoffmann-La Roche and Co., A.-G., Belg. 646,617 (1964); S. Afr. 62/3136; Brit. 1,012,260 (1965).
1746. F. Hoffmann-La Roche and Co., A.-G., Brit. 1,124,247 (1968).
1746a. F. Hoffmann-La Roche and Co., A.-G., Brit. 1,124,248 (1968).
1747. F. Hoffmann-La Roche and Co., A.-G., Brit. 1,017,276 (1966).
1747a. J. A. Hoffman (to American Cyanamid Co.), U.S. 3,393,184 (1968).
1748. A. W. von Hofmann, *Ber.* **23**, 3297 (1890).
1749. A. W. von Hofmann, *Ber.* **23**, 3723 (1890).
1750. W. C. Hollyday, Jr. (to Esso Research and Development Co.), U.S. 2,744,071 (1956); Fr. 1,069,428 (1954).
1751. W. C. Hollyday, Jr. (to Esso Research and Development Co.), U.S. 2,852,467 (1958); Ger. 962,367 (1957).
1752. W. C. Hollyday, Jr. (to Esso Research and Development Co.), U.S. 2,859,208 (1958).

1753. R. T. Holm and P. H. Williams (to Shell Oil Co.), U.S. 3,232,901 (1966).
1753a. A. Holmgren, R. N. Perham, and A. Baldesten, *Eur. Polymer J.* **5**, 352 (1968).
1754. T. W. Holmsen and J. K. Leasure, *Science* **153**, 1659 (1966); cf. W. Klassen and T. H. Chang, *ibid.* **154**, 920 (1966).
1755. S. L. Holton *et al.*, *Can. J. Chem.* **42**, 2147 (1964).
1756. H. Holzer *et al.*, *Angew. Chem.* **70**, 439 (1958).
1757. J. Homolova, *Papir Celulosa* **22** (7), 181 (1967); via *C. A.* **67**, 109818.
1757a. B. R. Honovski, *J. Am. Chem. Soc.* **36**, 1028 (1914).
1758. Hooker Chemical Co., Neth. appl. 6,410,278 (1965); Fr. 1,410,476 (1965); Belg. 669,025 (1966); *C. A.* **63**, 13482.
1759. G. Horn, *Chem. Zvesti* **18**, 363 (1964); via *C. A.* **61**, 15947.
1760. I. Horner and H. Lang, *Chem. Ber.* **89**, 2768 (1956).
1761. L. Horner and A. Christmann, *Angew. Chem.* **75**, 707 (1963); *Angew. Chem. Intern. Ed. Engl.* **2**, 599 (1963).
1762. H. G. Horsewell and G. H. Rayner (to Brown and Williamson Tobacco Co.), U.S. 3,340,879 (1967).
1763. A. G. Hortmann and D. A. Robertson, *J. Am. Chem. Soc.* **89**, 5974 (1967).
1764. T. Horvath and L. Vargha, *Acta Unio Intern. Contra Cancrum* **20**, 71 (1964); via *C. A.* **61**, 9916.
1765. D. Horvitz (to FMC Corporation), U.S. 3,210,396 (1965).
1766. Hoshihikari Chemical Industry Co., Japan. 18,401 ('66).
1767. W. J. Houlihan (to Sandoz Inc.), U.S. 3,318,952 (1967).
1767a. W. J. Houlihan (to Sandoz Inc.), U.S. 3,351,584 (1967).
1768. H. O. House and W. F. Berkowitz, *J. Org. Chem.* **28**, 307 (1963).
1769. H. O. House and W. F. Berkowitz, *J. Org. Chem.* **28**, 2271 (1963).
1770. R. R. House and Y. Jen (to American Cyanamid Co.), U.S. 2,872,313 (1959).
1771. C. C. Howard and W. Marckwald, *Ber.* **32**, 2036 (1899).
1772. J. C. Howard and G. Klein, *J. Org. Chem.* **27**, 3701 (1962).
1773. R. Howe, *Nature* **207**, 594 (1965).
1774. A. F. Howland, P. Vail, and T. J. Henneberry, *J. Econ. Entomol.* **59**, 194 (1966).
1775. A. F. Howland, P. Vail, and T. J. Henneberry, *J. Econ. Entomol.* **58**, 635 (1965).
1777. E. Hoyer, *Z. Anorg. Allgem. Chem.* **312**, 282 (1961).
1778. H. L. Hsieh (to Phillips Petroleum Co.), U.S. 3,251,812 (1966); Brit. 944,538 (1963); Fr. 1,326,703 (1963); Ger. 1,170,645 (1964).
1779. H. L. Hsieh (to Phillips Petroleum Co.), U.S. 3,177,190 (1965).
1780. H. L. Hsieh (to Phillips Petroleum Co.), U.S. 3,213,074 (1965).
1781. C.-M. Hsu, *Radiobiologiya* **4**, 444 (1964); via *C. A.* **62**, 10790.
1782. G. Huber, O. Schier, and J. Druey, *Helv. Chim. Acta* **43**, 1787 (1960).
1784. P. S. Hudson and C. C. Bice (to Phillips Petroleum Co.), U.S. 3,087,844 (1963).
1786. R. Huettel, W. Schoenthaler, and R. Mueller, *Farbe Lack* **67**, 71 (1961); *C. A.* **55**, 15954.
1787. R. Huettel, *Fette, Seifen, Anstrichmittel* **64**, 107 (1962).
1788. R. Huettel, Ger. 1,020,790 (1957); *C. A.* **54**, 10393.
1789. R. Huettel and K. G. Loesch, *Fette, Seifen, Anstrichmittel* **66**, 803 (1964).
1790. R. Huettel *et al.*, *Fette, Seifen, Anstrichmittel* **68**, 453 (1966).
1792. J. W. Huffman and T. Kamiya, *Tetrahedron Letters* p. 1857 (1966); J. W. Huffman, T. Kamiya, and C. B. S. Rao, *J. Org. Chem.* **32**, 700 (1967).
1793. R. Huisgen, D. Vossius, and M. Appl, *Chem. Ber.* **91**, 12 (1958).
1794. R. Huisgen, *Angew. Chem.* **72**, 359 (1960).
1795. R. Huisgen *et al.*, *Tetrahedron Letters* p. 397 (1966).
1796. R. Huisgen, G. Szeimies, and L. Moebius, *Chem. Ber.* **99**, 475 (1966).

1797. R. Huisgen *et al.*, *Tetrahedron* **21**, 3311 (1966).
1798. R. Huisgen *et al.*, *Chem. Ber.* **98**, 3992 (1965).
1799. R. Huisgen, W. Scheer, and H. Huber, *J. Am. Chem. Soc.* **89**, 1753 (1967).
1800. R. Huisgen, R. Sustmann, and K. Bunge, *Tetrahedron Letters* p. 3603 (1966).
1801. C. P. Humrichouse, *Dissertation Abstr.* **B27**, 1416 (1966).
1802. C. C. Hunt and F. S. Philips, *J. Pharmacol. Exptl. Therap.* **95**, 131 (1949).
1803. A. R. Hurst (to Morton International), U.S. 3,230,135 (1966).
1804. I. G. Farbenindustrie A.-G., Neth. appl. 108,822 (1940); via Wigman (3787).
1805. I. G. Farbenindustrie A.-G., Ital. 381,029 (1940); via *Chem. Zentr.* Part I, 2953 (1942); Neth. 52,193 (1942).
1806. I. G. Farbenindustrie A.-G., Neth. 52,945 (1942).
1807. I. G. Farbenindustrie A.-G., Neth. 56,842 (1944).
1808. I. G. Farbenindustrie A.-G., Neth. 63,864 (1949).
1809. I. G. Farbenindustrie A.-G., Neth. 53,494 (1942).
1810. I. G. Farbenindustrie A.-G., Belg. 450,975 (1943); *C. A.* **41**, 7816.
1811. I. G. Farbenindustrie A.-G., Ital. 381,164 (1940); via *Chem. Zentr.* Part I, 2732 (1942).
1812. I. G. Farbenindustrie A.-G., Ital. 384,352 (1940); via *Chem. Zentr.* Part I, 3275 (1942).
1813. I. G. Farbenindustrie A.-G., Belg. 445,688 (1942); *C. A.* **39**, 648.
1814. I. G. Farbenindustrie A.-G., Belg. 445,753 (1942); via *C. A.* **39**, 627.
1816. I. G. Farbenindustrie A.-G., Belg. 445,945 (1942); *C. A.* **39**, 840; Ger. 753,128 (1952).
1817. I. G. Farbenindustrie A.-G., Belg. 447,230 (1942); via *C. A.* **39**, 1086.
1818. I. G. Farbenindustrie A.-G., Belg. 448,291 (1943); *C. A.* **41**, 6411.
1819. I. G. Farbenindustrie A.-G., Swiss 213,247 (1941) and 222,442 (1942); Fr. 857,722 (1940); via *Chem. Zentr.* Part I, 3148 (1941).
1820. I. G. Farbenindustrie A.-G., Brit. 461,666 (1937).
1821. I. G. Farbenindustrie A.-G., Swiss 222,443 and 222,444 (1942); via *Chem. Zentr.* Part I, 1517 (1943).
1822. I. G. Farbenindustrie A.-G., Fr. 810,395 (1937) in part; Brit. 466,344 (1937).
1823. I. G. Farbenindustrie A.-G., Fr. 810,395 (1937); Ger. 662,451 (1938); Brit. 466,345 (1937).
1825. I. G. Farbenindustrie A.-G., Brit. 470,440 (1937).
1827. I. G. Farbenindustrie A.-G., Brit. 488,581 (1937); Ger. 648,000 (1937).
1828. I. G. Farbenindustrie A.-G., Brit. 491,565 (1938); Fr. 831,554 (1938); Ger. 676,197 (1939); Belg. 425,553 (1938); Neth. 48,242 (1940).
1829. I. G. Farbenindustrie A.-G., Brit. 495,964 (1938); Belg. 427,083 (1938); Fr. addn. 49,309 (1939); Ger. 678,907 (1939); Neth. 49,609 (1940) and 51,328 (1941).
1830. I. G. Farbenindustrie A.-G., Brit. 495,965 (1938); Belg. 427,084 (1938); Ger. 678,908 (1939); Fr. addn. 49,310 (1939); Neth. 49,778 (1941).
1831. I. G. Farbenindustrie A.-G., Brit. 496,052 (1938); Neth. 49,731 (1941).
1832. I. G. Farbenindustrie A.-G., Ital. 363,577 (1938); Brit. 501,804 (1939); Fr. 841,158 (1939); Neth. 52,168 (1942).
1833. I. G. Farbenindustrie A.-G., Fr. 847,694 (1939); Brit. 509,852 (1939).
1835. I. G. Farbenindustrie A.-G., Fr. 792,453 (1935); Ger. 625,446 (1936); via *Chem. Zentr.* Part I, 4992 (1936).
1836. I. G. Farbenindustrie A.-G., Ger. 648,761 (1937); *C. A.* **31**, 8547.
1837. I. G. Farbenindustrie A.-G., Ger. 651,797 (1937); *C. A.* **32**, 686; Fr. 810,395 (1937).
1838. I. G. Farbenindustrie A.-G., Ger. 655,742 and 655,743 (1938); *C. A.* **32**, 3865.
1839. I. G. Farbenindustrie A.-G., Ger. 657,742 (1938); Neth. 44,824 (1939).
1840. I. G. Farbenindustrie A.-G., Fr. 810,395 (1937), in part; via *C. A.* **32**, 686; Ger. 666,646 (1938) and 715,155 (1941).
1841. I. G. Farbenindustrie A.-G., Ger. 676,117 (1939); *Chem. Zentr.* Part I, 807 (1940).

1842. I. G. Farbenindustrie A.-G., Ger. 681,520 (1939); via *C. A.* **36**, 2086; included in Belg. 429,331 (1939).
1843. I. G. Farbenindustrie A.-G., Ger. 688,379 (1940); Neth. 48,276 (1940).
1844. I. G. Farbenindustrie A.-G., Ger. 688,380 (1940); Neth. 48,329 (1940).
1845. I. G. Farbenindustrie A.-G., Swiss 220,925 (1942); via *Chem. Zentr.* Part I, 1107 (1943).
1846. I. G. Farbenindustrie A.-G., Ger. 692,695 (1940); Neth. 48,338 (1940).
1847. I. G. Farbenindustrie A.-G., Ger. 695,331 (1940); *C. A.* **35**, 5128; Fr. 853,460 (1940).
1848. I. G. Farbenindustrie A.-G., Ger. 698,597 (1940); *C. A.* **35**, 6602.
1849. I. G. Farbenindustrie A.-G., Ital. 384,352 (1940); *Chem. Zentr.* Part I, 3276 (1942); Ger. 701,003 (1941); Neth. 51,867 (1942); *Chem. Zentr.* Part I, 2717 (1942).
1850. I. G. Farbenindustrie A.-G., Ger. 707,757 (1940); *C. A.* **36**, 2565; Fr. 853,460 (1940).
1851. I. G. Farbenindustrie A.-G., Ger. 709,721 (1941), via *C. A.* **37**, 3620; Swiss 193,353 (1938).
1851a. I. G. Farbenindustrie A.-G., Ger. 710,276 (1941); *C. A.* **37**, 3768.
1851b. I. G. Farbenindustrie A.-G., Ger. 711,408 (1941); *C. A.* **37**, 4077.
1852. I. G. Farbenindustrie A.-G., Ger. 714,585 and 715,605 (1941).
1853. I. G. Farbenindustrie A.-G., Ger. 717,155 (1942); *C. A.* **38**, 2345.
1854. I. G. Farbenindustrie A.-G., Ger. 729,208 (1942); *C. A.* **38**, 376.
1855. I. G. Farbenindustrie A.-G., Belg. 440,651 (1941); Ger. 729,248 (1942); *C. A.* **38**, 3055; Neth. 54,146 (1943).
1856. I. G. Farbenindustrie A.-G., Ger. 735,008 (1943); *C. A.* **38**, 12514; Fr. 871,242 (1942).
1857. I. G. Farbenindustrie A.-G., Ger. 736,194 (1943); *C. A.* **38**, 1251.
1858. I. G. Farbenindustrie A.-G., Fr. 870,187 (1941); Ger. 737,199 (1943); *C. A.* **38**, 3757; Neth. 58,960 (1947).
1859. I. G. Farbenindustrie A.-G., Ger. 740,723 (1943); *C. A.* **40**, 1170
1860. I. G. Farbenindustrie A.-G., Ger. 742,427 (1943); *C. A.* **38**, 549.
1861. I. G. Farbenindustrie A.-G., Ital. 384,351 (1940); Ger. 745,472 (1943); *C. A.* **40**, 2035.
1862. I. G. Farbenindustrie A.-G., Ger. 747,733 (1944).
1863. I. G. Farbenindustrie A.-G., Ger. 756,711 (1953); *Chem. Zentr.* p. 11349 (1954).
1864. I. G. Farbenindustrie A.-G., Fr. 809,414 (1937); via *Chem. Zentr.* Part II, 2060 (1937).
1865. I. G. Farbenindustrie A.-G., Fr. 874,039 (1942); via *Chem. Zentr.* Part I, 352 (1943); cf. L. H. Smith, *Publication Board Rept.* (*U.S.*) PB 7416, p. 873 (1946). ,
1866. I. G. Farbenindustrie A.-G., Fr. 884,271 (1943); via A. M. Paquin, "Epoxydverbindungen und Epoxyharze," p. 469. Springer, Berlin, 1958.
1867. I. G. Farbenindustrie A.-G., Brit. 496,944 (1938); Fr. 838,151 (1939); Ger. 714,789 (1941); Neth. 50,009 (1941).
1868. I. G. Farbenindustrie A.-G., Neth. 50,107 (1941).
1869. I. G. Farbenindustrie A.-G., Neth. 51,329 (1941); via *Chem. Zentr.* Part I, 954 (1942).
1870. I. G. Farbenindustrie A.-G., Fr. 831,574 (1938); Brit. 493,509 (1938); Ger. 693,662 (1940); Neth. 49,731 (1940).
1871. I. G. Farbenindustrie A.-G., Ger. 656,934 (1938); *C. A.* **32**, 4356.
1872. I. G. Farbenindustrie A.-G., Ger. 688,337 (1940); Neth. 48,330 (1940).
1873. I. G. Farbenindustrie A.-G., Ger. 711,671 (1941); *C. A.* **37**, 4077.
1874. I. G. Farbenindustrie A.-G., Fr. 779,583 (1935); via *C. A.* **29**, 5673; Ger. 727,917 (1942).
1875. I. G. Farbenindustrie A.-G., Ger. 738,000 (1943); Neth. 54,564 (1943).
1876. I. G. Farbenindustrie A.-G., Ger. 758,570 (1953); *Chem. Zentr.* p. 6170 (1953); Belg. 446,575 (1942); Fr. 884,560 (1943); Norweg. 68,131 (1947).

1877. I. G. Farbenindustrie A.-G., Fr. 839,537 (1939); *C. A.* **33**, 7930.
1878. I. G. Farbenindustrie A.-G., Ital. 382,444 (1940); *Chem. Zentr.* Part I, 3275 (1942); Neth. 54,903 (1943).
1879. I. G. Farbenindustrie A.-G., Neth. appl. 106,583 (1940); via Wigman (3787).
1880. I. G. Farbenindustrie A.-G., Fr. 810,395 (1937) in part; via *C. A.* **32**, 696; Ger. 654,840 (1937); via *C. A.* **32**, 3521.
1881. S. I. Ibragimov and R. I. Koval'chuk, *Tr. Mosk. Obshch. Ispyt. Prir.* **23**, 179 (1966); via *C. A.* **67**, 72670.
1882. K. Ichimura and M. Ohta, *Tetrahedron Letters* p. 807 (1966).
1883. K. Ichimura and M. Ohta, *Bull. Chem. Soc. Japan* **40**, 432 (1967).
1884. M. Igarashi, *Bull. Chem. Soc. Japan* **34**, 369 (1961).
1885. R. W. Ihndris, *Cancer Chemotherapy Rept.* **15**, 67 (1961).
1886. T. Iijima, *Biken's J.* **5**, 1 (1962); via *C. A.* **57**, 14274.
1887. T. Imai, *Nagoyashi Kogyo Kenkyusho Kenkyu Hokoku* **18**, 42 (1958); via *C. A.* **52**, 13273.
1888. Imperial Chemical Industries, Can. 600,700 (1960).
1889. Imperial Chemical Industries, Ltd., Brit. 680,652 (1952).
1890. Imperial Chemical Industries, Ltd., A. Lowe, J. A. Moyse, and A. M. Wooler, Brit. 755,478 (1956).
1891. Imperial Chemical Industries, Ltd., A. Lowe, J. A. Moyse, and A. M. Wooler, Brit. 755,519 (1956); Ger. 1,082,050 (1960).
1892. Imperial Chemical Industries, Ltd., Brit. 798,061 (1958).
1893. Imperial Chemical Industries, Can. 600,699 (1960); Ger. 1,041,648 (1948); Brit. 806,949 and 806,950 (1959).
1894. Imperial Chemical Industries, Ltd., Brit. 810,568 (1959).
1895. Imperial Chemical Industries, Ltd., Fr. 1,206,008 (1960); Brit. 830,246 (1960); Ger. 1,138,736 (1962).
1896. Imperial Chemical Industries, Ltd., Brit. 823,709 (1959).
1897. Imperial Chemical Industries, Ltd., Brit. 890,518 (1962).
1898. Imperial Chemical Industries, Ltd., Brit. 911,486 (1962).
1899. Imperial Chemical Industries, Ltd., Brit. 1,040,730 (1966).
1899a. Imperial Chemical Industries Ltd., Brit. 1,109,148 (1968).
1900. A. A. Imshenitskii and L. A. Kuzyurina, *Mikrobiologiya* **35**, 812 (1966); via *C. A.* **67**, 71341f.
1901. S. Inaba, A. Misaki, and C. Saito (to Sumitomo Chemical Co.), U.S. 3,196,156 (1965); Belg. 646,325 (1964); Japan. 23,022 ('65); Ger. 1,216,313 (1966); Brit. 1,021,946 (1966).
1902. A. P. Ingram (to The Dow Chemical Co.), U.S. 3,270,005 (1966); Belg. 662,571 (1965); Fr. 1,440,090 (1966); Can. 774,132 (1967); Brit. 1,101,688 (1968); Ital. 754,940 (1967).
1903. S. A. Inkina *et al.*, U.S.S.R. 190,521 (1966); via *C. A.* **68**, 79530.
1904. H. Inokawa, *Bull. Chem. Soc. Japan* **37**, 568 (1964).
1905. H. Inokawa, *Nippon Kagaku Zasshi* **84**, 932 (1963); via *C. A.* **61**, 13225; *Bull. Chem. Soc. Japan* **37**, 568 (1964).
1905a. S. Inoue *et al.*, *Makromol. Chem.* **112**, 66 (1968).
1906. Institut Organicheskogo Sinteza, Brit. 1,052,711 (1966); Japan. 2102 ('68).
1907. Institute of High Molecular Compounds, U.S.S.R. 172,488 (1965); *C. A.* **63**, 18402.
1908. Institute of Organic Chemistry, Siberian Dept., Academy of Sciences, U.S.S.R. 170,935 (1965); via *C. A.* **63**, 13180.
1909. Institute of Organic Chemistry, Siberian Dept., Academy of Sciences, U.S.S.R. 172,837 (1966); via *C. A.* **64**, 671.

1910. Interchemical Corp., Fr. 1,358,669 (1964); Belg. 630,415 (1963); *C. A.* **61**, 4312.
1911. Interchemical Corp., Belg. 650,775 (1964); Neth. appl. 6,407,981 (1965); *C. A.* **63**, 13580.
1911a. Interchemical Corp., Brit. 1,123,404 (1968).
1912. Interchemical Corp., "MAPO", Bull. CD-107 (1960).
1912a. Interchemical Corp., Brit. 1,108,635 (1968).
1913. International Polaroid Corp., Ger. 1,140,079 (1962); *Chem. Zentr.* p. 21784 (1963).
1913a. International Polaroid Corp., Ger. 1,122,835 (1962); *C. A.* **57**, 327.
1914. International Polaroid Corp., Ger. 1,149,249 (1963); Belg. 621,626 (1963); Brit. 960,782 (1964); Fr. 1,338,941 (1964).
1915. N. Ise and T. Okubo, *J. Phys. Chem.* **70**, 2400 (1966).
1915a. N. Ise and F. Matsui, *J. Am. Chem. Soc.* **90**, 4242 (1968).
1915b. N. Ise and T. Okubo, *J. Am. Chem. Soc.* **90**, 4527 (1968).
1916. M. Ishidate, Y. Sakurai, and S. Owari, *Pharm. Bull.* (*Tokyo*) **5**, 203 (1957); via *C. A.* **52**, 6242.
1917. Y. Ishii, S. Eguchi, and T. Hironaka, *Kogyo Kagaku Zasshi* **68**, 293 (1965); via *C. A.* **62**, 16168.
1917a. K. Isomura, S. Kobayashi, and H. Taniguchi, *Tetrahedron Letters* p. 3499 (1968).
1918. K. Issleib and D. Haferburg, *Z. Naturforsch.* **20b**, 916 (1965).
1919. Y. J. L'Italien (to Parke, Davis and Co.), U.S. 3,278,600 (1966).
1920. S. Z. Ivin *et al.*, *Zh. Obshch. Khim.* **35**, 1218 (1965); *J. Gen. Chem. USSR* (*English Transl.*) **35**, 1221 (1965).
1921. Y. Iwakura, A. Nabeya, and T. Nishiguchi, *J. Org. Chem.* **32**, 2362 (1967).
1922. Y. Iwakura, *Chem. High Polymers* (*Tokyo*) **3**, 121 (1946); via *C. A.* **44**, 1106.
1923. Y. Iwakura *et al.*, *J. Chem. Soc. Japan, Ind. Chem. Sect.* **58**, 123 (1955); via *C. A.* **50**, 4008.
1924. Y. Iwakura, N. Nakabayashi, and H. Suzuki, *Makromol. Chem.* **78**, 168 (1964).
1925. Y. Iwakura and A. Nabeya, *Bull. Tokyo Inst. Technol.* **42**, 69 (1961); via Y. Iwakura *et al.*, *J. Org. Chem.* **30**, 3410 (1965).
1926. Y. Iwakura and M. Sakamoto, *J. Polymer Sci.* **47**, 277 (1960).
1927. Y. Iwakura *et al.*, *Kobunshi Kagaku* **15**, 298 (1958); via *C. A.* **54**, 10988.
1927a. Y. Iwakura *et al.*, *J. Polymer Sci. Part A-1* **5**, 3193 (1967).
1927b. Y. Iwakura, A. Nabeya, and T. Nishiguchi, *Yuki Gosei Kagaku Kyokai Shi* **26**, 101 (1968).
1927c. Y. Iwakura, A. Nabeya, and T. Nishiguchi, *J. Polymer Sci. Part A-1* **6**, 2591 (1968).
1928. Y. Iwakura, M. Sakamoto, and H. Yasuda, *Nippon Kagaku Zasshi* **82**, 606 (1961); via *C. A.* **56**, 8534.
1929. Y. Iwakura and Y. Tezuka, *Seni-i Gakkaishi* **17**, 681, 687, and 693 (1961); via *C. A.* **55**, 21603.
1930. Y. Iwakura and A. Nabeya, *Nippon Kagaku Zasshi* **77**, 773 (1956); via *C. A.* **52**, 9028.
1931. Y. Iwakura and Y. Tezuka, *Seni-i Gakkaishi* **17**, 794 (1961); via *C. A.* **55**, 24710.
1932. Y. Iwakura, M. Sakamoto, and Y. Awata, *J. Polymer Sci.* **A2**, 881 (1964).
1933. Y. Iwakura and A. Nabeya, *J. Org. Chem.* **25**, 1118 (1960).
1934. Y. Iwakura *et al.*, *Kogyo Kagaku Zasshi* **68**, 1222 (1965); via *C. A.* **63**, 9852.
1935. Y. Iwakura, Japan. 1689 ('53); via *C. A.* **48**, 4255.
1936. Y. Iwakura and A. Nabeya, *J. Org. Chem.* **26**, 4384 (1961).
1937. Y. Iwakura, Japan. 2975 ('53); via *C. A.* **49**, 4014.
1938. Y. Iwakura, Japan. 3294 ('57); via *C. A.* **52**, 5881.
1939. Y. Iwakura, M. Sakamato, and M. Yoneyama, *J. Polymer Sci., Part A-1* **4**, 159 (1966).
1940. V. N. Iyer and W. Szybalski, *Appl. Microbiol.* **6**, 23 (1958); *Proc. Natl. Acad. Sci. U.S.* **44**, 446 (1958).

1941. M. Izumi, *Pharm. Bull.* (*Tokyo*) **3**, 88 (1955); via *C. A.* **50**, 7724.
1942. E. L. Jackson, *J. Org. Chem.* **16**, 1899 (1951).
1943. H. Jackson, *Pharmacol. Rev.* **11**, 135 (1959).
1944. H. Jackson, *Fortschr. Arzneimittelforsch.* **7**, 146 (1964).
1945. H. Jackson, A. W. Craig, and B. W. Fox, *Brit. J. Pharmacol.* **14**, 149 (1959).
1946. H. Jackson, *Pharm. J.* [4] **184**, 151 (1960).
1947. H. Jackson and R. M. V. James, *Brit. J. Pharmacol.* **25**, 223 (1965).
1948. H. Jackson, B. W. Fox, and A. W. Craig, *J. Reprod. Fertility* **2**, 447 (1961).
1949. H. Jackson and R. M. V. James, *Brit. J. Pharmacol.* **21**, 581 (1963).
1950. H. Jackson, *Chem. & Ind.* (*London*) p. 949 (1957).
1951. H. Jackson and M. Bock, *Nature* **175**, 1037 (1955).
1952. H. Jackson, *J. Fac. Radiologists* **9**, 217 (1958).
1953. H. Jackson, "Antifertility Compounds in the Male and Female," p. 85. Thomas, Springfield, Illinois, 1966.
1954. T. B. Jackson and J. O. Edwards, *J. Am. Chem. Soc.* **83**, 355 (1961).
1955. T. B. Jackson and J. O. Edwards, *Inorg. Chem.* **1**, 398 (1962).
1955a.T. B. Jackson et al., *Inorg. Chem.* **5**, 2046 (1966).
1956. M. E. Jacox and D. E. Milligan, *J. Am. Chem. Soc.* **85**, 278 (1963).
1956a.G. Jacquelin, *ATIP* **22**, 129 (1968); via *C. A.* **69**, 97807.
1957. G. Jacqueline and H. Bourglas, *Tech. Rech. Papetiéres* **4**, 42 (1964); via *C. A.* **62**, 9347.
1957a.J. J. Jaffe, *Nature* **213**, 704 (1967).
1958. F. Jakob and P. Schlack, *Chem. Ber.* **96**, 88 (1963).
1959. A. O. Jakubovic and B. N. Brook, *Polymer* **2**, 18 (1961).
1960. B. Jámbor, I. P. Horváth, and L. Institoris, *Acta Chem. Acad. Sci. Hung.* **39**, 411 (1963); **53**, 85 (1967); *Magy. Kem. Folyoirat* **73**, 332 (1967); via *C. A.* **67**, 102840.
1961. R. M. V. James, *Nature* **209**, 518 (1966).
1962. R. M. V. James, *Biochem. Pharmacol.* **14**, 915 (1965).
1963. R. M. V. James and H. Jackson, *Biochem. Pharmacol.* **14**, 1847 (1965).
1964. J. W. S. Jamieson and C. A. Winkler, *J. Phys. Chem.* **60**, 1542 (1956).
1965. J. W. S. Jamieson, G. R. Brown, and W. K. Hancock, *Can. J. Chem.* **43**, 1973 (1965).
1966. H. Jamnback, *J. Econ. Entomol.* **60**, 390 (1967).
1967. J. Janecke and W. Bathe, *in* "Methoden der organischen Chemie" (Houben-Weyl), 4th ed. (E. Mueller, ed.), Vol. 11, Part 2, p. 262. Thieme, Stuttgart, 1958.
1968. J. E. Jansen (to B. F. Goodrich Co.), U.S. 2,460,581 (1949).
1969. Japan, Bureau of Industrial Technics, Japan. 8114 ('60); via *C. A.* **57**, 6163.
1970. Japan, Bureau of Industrial Technics, Japan. 188 ('62); via *C. A.* **59**, 10292.
1971. Japan, Bureau of Industrial Technics, Japan. 5295 ('62); via *C. A.* **59**, 11720.
1972. Japan, Bureau of Industrial Technics, Japan. 5843 ('62); via *C. A.* **59**, 11719.
1972a.Japan, Bureau of Industrial Technics, Japan. 5292 ('62); via *C. A.* **59**, 11720.
1973. Japan Catalytic Chemical Industry Co., Ltd., Japan. 1950 ('65).
1974. Japan Catalytic Chemical Industry Co., Ltd., Japan. 8788 ('66).
1975. Japanese Association for Research on Polymers, Japan. 22,076 ('65); via *C. A.* **64**, 3716.
1976. W. Jarowenko (to National Starch and Chemical Corp.), U.S. 3,331,833 (1967).
1976a.W. Jarowenko (to National Starch and Chemical Corp.), U.S. 3,354,034 (1967).
1976b. M. Jautelat and J. D. Roberts, *J. Am. Chem. Soc.* **91**, 642 (1969).
1977. R. R. Jay, *Anal. Chem.* **36**, 667 (1964).
1978. J. Jaz, E. D. de Hault, and R. Navette, *Tetrahedron Letters* p. 2751 (1965).
1979. K.-T. Jen and L. S. Efros, *Zh. Obshch. Khim.* **33**, 966 (1963); *J. Gen. Chem. USSR* (*English Transl.*) **33**, 954 (1963).

1980. Y. Jen and C. H. Clinton, *Pulp Paper Mfr.* **28** (2), 50 (1965).
1981. Y. Jen, S. T. Moore, and T. J. Suen (to American Cyanamid Co.), U.S. 2,885,318 (1959).
1982. Y. Jen (to American Cyanamid Co.), U.S. 2,977,245 (1961).
1983. J. Jentzsch and R. Mayer, Ger. (East) 51,641 (1966); *C. A.* **66**, 95031.
1984. Y. Jo and R. Murase, *Sen-i Kogyo Shikensho Iho* **45**, 87 (1958); via *C. A.* **55**, 4968.
1985. Y. Jo and M. Kamiya, *Sen-i Kogyo Shikensho Iho* **45**, 99 (1958); via *C. A.* **55**, 4968.
1986. W. Joechle, *Angew. Chem.* **74**, 667 (1962); *Angew. Chem. Intern. Ed. Engl.* **1**, 537 (1962).
1989. C. A. Johansen and R. D. Redmond, *J. Apicult. Res.* **4**, 55 (1965).
1989a. C. K. Johnson, *J. Org. Chem.* **32**, 1508 (1967).
1990. D. E. Johnson, R. S. Bruenner, and A. J. Di Milo, *Ind. Eng. Chem., Prod. Res. Develop.* **5**, 53 (1966).
1991. J. R. Johnson, *Publication Board Rept.* (*U.S.*) PB 31,093 (1941); via *Bibliog. Sci. Ind. Rept.* **2**, 785 (1946).
1992. R. D. Johnson, R. J. Myers, and W. D. Gwinn, *J. Chem. Phys.* **21**, 1425 (1953).
1993. R. L. Johnson, C. W. Rees, and C. E. Smithen, *Proc. Chem. Soc.* p. 217 (1964).
1994. F. B. Jones et al., *Textile Res. J.* **31**, 57 (1961).
1995. G. D. Jones, *J. Appl. Polymer Sci.* **6**, 15 (1962).
1996. G. D. Jones et al., *J. Org. Chem.* **9**, 125 (1944).
1997. G. D. Jones, *J. Org. Chem.* **9**, 484 (1944).
1998. G. D. Jones, J. Zomlefer, and K. Hawkins, *J. Org. Chem.* **9**, 500 (1944).
1999. G. D. Jones, in "The Chemistry of Cationic Polymerization" (P. H. Plesch, ed.), p. 513. Macmillan, New York, 1963.
2000. G. D. Jones, D. C. MacWilliams, and N. A. Braxtor, *J. Org. Chem.* **30**, 1994 (1965).
2001. G. D. Jones (to General Aniline and Film Corp.), U.S. 2,587,329 (1952); Brit. 671,917 (1947); Can. 581,017 (1959).
2002. J. I. Jones, *Chem. & Ind.* (*London*) p. 1454 (1956).
2003. P. C. Jones (to B. F. Goodrich Co.), U.S. 2,264,759 (1941).
2004. P. C. Jones and R. A. Mathes (to B. F. Goodrich Co.), U.S. 2,409,685 (1946).
2005. R. G. Jones et al., *J. Am. Chem. Soc.* **78**, 6027 (1956).
2007. R. T. Jones, *Cold Spring Harbor Symp. Quant. Biol.* **29**, 297 (1964).
2008. P. K. Joseph and M. M. Joullié, *J. Med. Chem.* **7**, 801 (1964).
2009. M. J. Josephs (to The Dow Chemical Co.), U.S. 3,156,552 (1964); Brit. 1,060,439 (1967).
2011. J. L. Justice (to American Viscose Corp.), U.S. 2,940,889 (1960).
2012. J. L. Justice and C. M. Rosser (to American Viscose Corp.), U.S. 2,999,782 (1961).
2013. P. K. Kadaba and J. O. Edwards, *J. Org. Chem.* **25**, 1431 (1960).
2014. P. K. Kadaba and J. O. Edwards, *J. Org. Chem.* **26**, 2331 (1961).
2015. E. Kaesemann and K. Kaesemann, Fr. 1,056,742 (1954); Ger. 947,570 (1957); *C. A.* **52**, 19239.
2016. I. Kageyama et al., *Kogyo Kagaku Zasshi* **65**, 1207 (1962); via *C. A.* **58**, 1576.
2017. T. Kagiya et al., *J. Polymer Sci.* **B4**, 257 (1966).
2018. T. Kagiya et al., *Kogyo Kagaku Zasshi* **68**, 1741 (1965); *J. Polymer Sci.* **B3**, 617 (1965).
2018a. T. Kagiya, T. Kondo, and K. Fukui, *Bull. Chem. Soc. Japan* **41**, 2473 (1968).
2019. T. Kagiya et al., *J. Polymer Sci. Part A-1* **4**, 293 (1966).
2020. T. Kagiya et al., *J. Polymer Sci.* **B4**, 441 (1966).
2021. T. Kagiya et al., *J. Polymer Sci., Part A-1* **4**, 2171 (1966).
2022. T. Kagiya et al., *J. Polymer Sci., Part A-1* **4**, 2081 (1966).
2023. T. Kagiya et al., *J. Polymer Sci., Part A-1* **5**, 1645 (1967).

2024. T. Kagiya *et al.*, *J. Polymer Sci.*, *Part A-1* **5**, 2031 (1967).

2025. T. Kagiya, T. Kondo, and K. Fukui, *Bull. Chem. Soc. Japan* **41**, 1682 (1968).

2026. T. Kagiya and T. Ichida, *Kagaku To Kogyo* (*Tokyo*) **18**, 25 (1967); via *C. A.* **67**, 32936.

2027. D. W. Kaiser and F. E. Schaefer (to American Cyanamid Co.), U.S. 2,653,934 (1953).

2028. Kalle and Co., A.-G., Belg. 615,578 (1962); *C. A.* **58**, 10406.

2029. Kalle and Co., A.-G., Ger. 753,191 (1953); *Chem. Zentr.* p. 204 (1954).

2030. Kalle and Co., A.-G., Ger. 1,062,247 (1959); *C. A.* **55**, 15447.

2031. G. Kamai and Z. L. Khisamova, *Dokl. Akad. Nauk SSSR* **156**, 365 (1964); *Proc. Acad. Sci. USSR, Chem. Sect.* (*English Transl.*) **154-156**, 485 (1964).

2032. M. Kamiya and Y. Shiro, *Bull. Textile Res. Inst.* **29**, 39 (1954); via *J. Polymer Sci.* **27**, 255.

2033. M. Kamiya and Y. Jo, *Sen-i Kogyo Shikensho Iho* **34**, 45 (1955); via *C. A.* **55**, 4968.

2034. K. Kanamaru and S. Ota, *Kogyo Kagaku Zasshi* **60**, 452 (1957); *C. A.* **53**, 6621.

2035. J. C. Kane, V. K. La Mer, and H. B. Linford, *J. Phys. Chem.* **68**, 2273 (1964).

2036. J. C. Kane, V. K. La Mer, and H. B. Linford, *J. Am. Chem. Soc.* **86**, 3450 (1964).

2037. W. P. Kane (to du Pont de Nemours and Co.), U.S. 3,297,476 (1967).

2038. Kanegafuchi Spinning Co., Ltd., Japan. 9677 ('60); via *C. A.* **55**, 7859.

2039. Kanegafuchi Spinning Co., Ltd., Japan. 1947 ('65).

2040. A. R. Kaney and K. C. Atwood, *Nature* **201**, 1006 (1964).

2040a. S. Kano and T. Nishide, Japan 26,772 ('67); via *C. A.* **69**, 51588.

2041. W.-I. Kao *et al.*, *Yao Hsueh Hsueh Pao* **12**, 672 (1965); via *C. A.* **64**, 8017.

2042. K. D. Kappus and E. C. Corristan, *Am. J. Trop. Med. Hyg.* **16**, 539 (1967).

2043. J. V. Karabinos and K. T. Serijan, *J. Am. Chem. Soc.* **67**, 1856 (1945).

2044. D. A. Karnovsky, *Proc. 2nd Natl. Cancer Conf.* p. 594 (1954).

2045. D. V. Kashelikar and P. E. Fanta, *J. Org. Chem.* **26**, 1841 (1961).

2046. D. V. Kashelikar and P. E. Fanta, *J. Am. Chem. Soc.* **82**, 4930 (1960).

2047. D. V. Kashelikar and P. E. Fanta, *J. Am. Chem. Soc.* **82**, 4927 (1960).

2049. A. Katchalsky, J. Mazur, and P. Spilnik, *J. Polymer Sci.* **23**, 513 (1957).

2050. B. J. Katchman, E. Spoerl, and H. E. Smith, *Science* **121**, 97 (1955).

2051. K. Kato, *Nippon Kagaku Zasshi* **83**, 1276 (1962); via *C. A.* **59**, 11325.

2052. J. J. Kaufman, *J. Am. Chem. Soc.* **84**, 4393 (1962).

2053. T. Kawai and H. Sato, *Bull. Natl. Inst. Agr. Sci., Tokyo* **D13**, 133 (1965); via *Bibliog. Agr.* **30**, 43319; H. Sato and T. Kawai, *Jap. J. Breed.* **15** (3), 67 (1965); via *Bibliog. Agr.* **30**, 16956.

2054. R. L. Kay, *U.S. At. Energy Comm.* **NYO-10695** (1963); via *Nucl. Sci. Abstr.* **18**, 206 (1964); *C. A.* **61**, 11387.

2055. R. L. Kay, G. A. Vidulich, and J. Berberian, *J. Chem. Phys.* **47**, 866 (1967).

2056. S. Kaye, *Am. J. Hyg.* **50**, 289 (1949).

2057. S. Kaye, *Am. J. Hyg.* **50**, 296 (1949).

2058. L. G. Kazankina and S. I. Burmistrov, *Ukr. Khim. Zh.* **30**, 1198 (1964); via *C. A.* **62**, 9085.

2059. L. G. Kazankina and S. I. Burmistrov, *Ukr. Khim. Zh.* **33**, 303 (1967); via *C. A.* **67**, 43515.

2060. J. F. W. Keana, S. B. Keana, and D. Beetham, *J. Org. Chem.* **32**, 3057 (1967).

2061. I. Keiser, L. F. Steiner, and H. Kamasaki, *J. Econ. Entomol.* **58**, 682 (1965).

2062. P. C. Kelley, *Dissertation Abstr.* **26**, 7038 (1965).

2063. N. F. Kember and R. A. Wells, *Nature* **175**, 512 (1955).

2064. M. K. Kemp and W. H. Flygare, *J. Am. Chem. Soc.* **90**, 6267 (1968).

2065. D. L. Kenaga (to The Dow Chemical Co.), U.S. 3,242,004 (1966); *Forest Prod. J.* **16**, 21 (1966).

2066. D. L. Kenaga (to The Dow Chemical Co.), U.S. 3,312,520 (1967); Can. 775,071 (1968); Fr. 1,518,994 (1968).

2067. D. L. Kenaga, W. A. Kindler, and F. J. Meyer, *Tappi* **50**, 381 (1967).

2068. I. G. Kerkadze, *Genetika* No. 12, 52 (1966); via *C. A.* **66**, 73345.

2070. W. Kern and I. Loeflund (to Deutsche Gold- und Silber . . .), U.S. 3,127,374 (1964); Ger. 1,063,806 (1959); Neth. 108,917 (1964).

2071. W. Kern and E. Brenneisen, *J. Prakt. Chem.* [2] **159**, 193 and 219 (1941).

2072. R. W. Kerr and H. Neukom, *Staerke* **4**, 255 (1952).

2073. J. F. Kerwin *et al.*, *Science* **113**, 315 (1951).

2074. J. F. Kerwin *et al.*, *J. Am. Chem. Soc.* **69**, 2961 (1947).

2075. J. F. Kerwin *et al.*, *J. Am. Chem. Soc.* **73**, 5681 (1951).

2076. M. A. Khan, *Can. J. Comp. Med. Vet. Sci.* **27**, 233 (1963).

2077. M. S. Kharasch and H. M. Priestley, *J. Am. Chem. Soc.* **61**, 3425 (1939).

2078. R. M. Khomutov *et al.*, *Zh. Obshch. Khim.* **29**, 642 (1959); *J. Gen. Chem. USSR* **29**, 636 (1959).

2079. V. I. Khropova, K. V. Kvitko, and I. A. Zakharov, *Issled. Genet.* No. 2, p. 69 (1964); via *Nucl. Sci. Abstr.* **20**, 3716.

2080. V. V. Khvostova *et al.*, *Mutation Res.* **2**, 339 (1965).

2081. V. V. Khvostova *et al.*, *Radiobiologiya* **2**, 790 (1962); via *C. A.* **59**, 1971.

2082. H. Kido and E. M. Stafford, *J. Econ. Entomol.* **59**, 1064 (1966).

2082a. K. Kigane, H. Togawa, and S. Yamada (to Teikoku Rayon Co.), U.S. 3,179,547 (1965); Fr. 1,310,104 (1962).

2083. K. Kigane, S. Yamada, and Y. Isozaki (to Teijin Co.), U.S. 3,272,676 (1966); Japan. 20,956 and 20,957 ('63); Brit. 983,818 (1965).

2084. Y. Kikuchi and S. Katagiri, Japan. 587 ('65).

2085. W. W. Kilgore and R. R. Painter, *Biochem. J.* **92**, 353 (1964).

2086. R. F. Kimball, *Science* **154**, 422 (1966).

2086a. H. Kimura *et al.* (to Nippon Rayon Co., Ltd.), U.S. 3,383,161 (1968).

2087. S. Kimura, *Nippon Kagaku Zasshi* **82**, 78 (1961); via *C. A.* **56**, 10069.

2088. S. Kimura and Y. Yudawa, *Nippon Kagaku Zasshi* **82**, 225 (1961); via *C. A.* **56**, 10069.

2089. J. F. Kincaid and F. C. Henriques, Jr., *J. Am. Chem. Soc.* **62**, 1474 (1940).

2090. H. Kindler *et al.*, *Chem.-Ing.-Tech.* **37**, 400 (1965).

2090a. H. Kindler, U. Soenksen, and A. Wittwer (to Badische Anilin- und Soda-Fabrik), U.S. 3,398,183 (1968); Neth. appl. 6,511,306 (1966); Belg. 669,164 (1966); Fr. 1,446,186 (1966); Brit. 1,111,854 (1968).

2091. F. E. King and R. Robinson, *J. Chem. Soc.* p. 270 (1933).

2092. F. E. King, *J. Chem. Soc.* p. 1318 (1949).

2093. D. N. Kinsey, F. R. Jensen, and J. H. Hennes (to The Dow Chemical Co.), U.S. 3,248,385 (1966); Can. 759,461 (1967).

2094. A. I. Kiprianov and G. G. Dyadyuska, *Zh. Obshch. Khim.* **29**, 1708 (1959); *J. Gen. Chem. USSR (English Transl.)* **29**, 1685 (1959).

2095. A. V. Kirsanov *et al.*, U.S.S.R. 148,059 (1962); via *C. A.* **58**, 9142.

2096. W. Kirst, *Melliand Textilber.* **29**, 236 (1948); *C. A.* **44**, 9677.

2097. R. W. Kiser and T. W. Lapp, *Inorg. Chem.* **1**, 401 (1962).

2098. R. W. Kiser and E. J. Gallegos, *J. Phys. Chem.* **66**, 947 (1962).

2099. J. B. Kissam and S. B. Hays, *J. Econ. Entomol.* **59**, 748 (1966).

2100. J. B. Kissam, J. A. Wilson, and S. B. Hays, *J. Econ. Entomol.* **60**, 1130 (1967).

2101. H. M. Kissman, D. S. Tarbell, and J. Williams, *J. Am. Chem. Soc.* **75**, 2959 (1953).

2102. H. M. Kissman and D. S. Tarbell, *J. Am. Chem. Soc.* **74**, 4317 (1952).

2103. K. Kitahonoki *et al.*, *Tetrahedron Letters* p. 1059 (1965); K. Kotera *et al.*, *Tetrahedron* **24**, 6177 (1968).

2103a. K. Kitahonoki, Y. Takano, and H. Takahashi, *Tetrahedron* **24**, 4605 (1968).

2104. Kitasato Research Foundation, Japan. 7597 ('59); via *C. A.* **54**, 3869.

2105. Kiwa Chemical Industry Co., Japan. 5834 ('61); via *C. A.* **56**, 1563.

2106. D. Klamann *et al.*, *Chem. Ber.* **100**, 1870 (1967).

2106a. W. Klassen and F. Matsumura, *Nature* **209**, 1155 (1966).

2107. O. Klatt, A. C. Griffin, and J. S. Stehlin, Jr., *Proc. Soc. Exptl. Biol. Med.* **104**, 629 (1960).

2108. D. L. Klayman, W. F. Gilmore, and T. R. Sweeney, *Chem. & Ind. (London)* p. 1632 (1965).

2109. D. L. Klayman, J. W. Lown, and T. R. Sweeney, *J. Org. Chem.* **30**, 2275 (1965).

2110. D. L. Klayman, *J. Org. Chem.* **30**, 2454 (1965).

2111. K. G. Kleb, E. Siegel, and K. Sasse, *Angew. Chem.* **76**, 423 (1964); *Angew. Chem. Intern. Ed. Engl.* **3**, 408 (1964).

2111a. H. Kleiner, O. Bayer, and B. Becht (to Farbenfabriken Bayer), U.S. 2,643,958 (1953); Brit. 723,767 (1955).

2112. H. Kleiner, O. Bayer, and B. Becht (to Farbenfabriken Bayer), U.S. 2,762,718 and 2,762,719 (1956); Ger. 913,164 (1954).

2112a. R. F. Klemm, *Can. J. Chem.* **43**, 2633 (1965).

2113. G. M. Kline, *Mod. Plastics* **23** (2), 152A, specifically 152L (1945).

2113a. I. M. Klotz and A. R. Sloniewsky, *Biochem. Biophys. Res. Commun.* **31**, 426 (1968).

2114. G. W. Klumpp *et al.*, *Ann. Chem.* **706**, 47 (1967).

2115. C. A. Knight, Jr., J. G. Pucknat, and P. Resnick, *Abstr. Papers, 145th Am. Chem. Soc. Meeting, New York, 1963* p. Q-77.

2116. E. F. Knipling, *J. Econ. Entomol.* **53**, 415 (1960); *Sci. Am.* **203** (4), 54 (1960); *J. Econ. Entomol.* **55**, 782 (1962).

2117. L. Knorr and G. Meyer, *Ber.* **38**, 3129 (1905).

2118. L. Knorr, H. Hoerlein, and P. Roth, *Ber.* **38**, 3136 (1905).

2119. L. Knorr, *Ber.* **37**, 3507 (1904).

2120. I. L. Knunyants *et al.*, *Dokl. Akad. Nauk SSSR* **142**, 370 (1962); *Proc. Acad. Sci. USSR, Chem. Sect. (English Transl.)* **142-144**, 49 (1962).

2121. I. L. Knunyants and Yu. V. Zeifman, *Izv. Akad. Nauk SSSR, Ser. Khim.* p. 711 (1967); *Bull. Acad. Sci. USSR, Div. Chem. Sci. (English Transl.)* p. 695 (1967).

2122. Y. Kobayashi, L. A. Chasin, and L. B. Clapp, *Inorg. Chem.* **2**, 212 (1963).

2123. L. Kobor, *Papiripar Magy. Graf.* **6**, 145 (1962); via *C. A.* **58**, 2564.

2123a. E.-U. Kocher *et al.* (to Farbenfabriken Bayer), U.S. 3,390,130 (1968); Belg. 666,013 (1965); Neth. appl. 6,507,417 (1966); Ger. 1,231,009 (1966); Brit. 1,113,274 (1968); Fr. 1,533,189 (1968).

2124. W. R. Koehler, *Dissertation Abstr.* **21**, 760 (1960).

2125. G. K. Koelmark and M. Westergaard, *Hereditas* **39**, 209 (1953).

2126. H. Koenig, H. Metzger, and K. Seelert, *Chem. Ber.* **98**, 3724 (1965).

2127. K. H. Koenig and G. Letsch, *Chem. Ber.* **92**, 1789 (1959).

2127a. N. H. Koenig (to U.S. Department of Agriculture), U.S. 3,388,964 (1968).

2128. H.-G. Koennecke and M. Heise, *J. Prakt. Chem.* [4] **9**, 232 (1959).

2128a. K. W. F. Kohlrausch and A. W. Reitz, *Z. Phys. Chem.* **B45**, 249 (1939).

2129. R. E. Kohls, A. J. Lemin, and P. W. O'Connell, *J. Econ. Entomol.* **59**, 745 (1966).

2130. M. Kojima, *Yakugaku Zasshi* **79**, 1 (1956); via *C. A.* **53**, 10185.

2131. M. Kojima, *Yakugaku Zasshi* **79**, 20 (1959); via *C. A.* **53**, 10186.

2132. Kokoku Chemical Industry Co., Japan. 8619 ('68); via *C. A.* **69**, 52740.

2133. I. Yu. Kokoreva *et al.*, *Dokl. Akad. Nauk SSSR* **166**, 155 (1966); via *C. A.* **64**, 12523.

2134. M. B. Kolesova and Kh. L. Muravich-Aleksandr, *Zh. Obshch. Khim.* **34**, 3515 (1964); *J. Gen. Chem. USSR (English Transl.)* **34**, 3561 (1964).

2135. I. I. Kolodkina *et al.*, *Zh. Org. Khim.* **2**, 66 (1966); via *C. A.* **64**, 14087.

2136. P. V. Kolotenkov, N. N. Zoz, and S. I. Makarova, *Supermutageny, Akad. Nauk SSSR, Inst. Khim. Fiz.* p. 135 (1966); via *C. A.* **67**, 41105.

2137. S. Komori and Y. Oshiro, *Japan.* 16,077 ('66); via *C. A.* **66**, 19069.

2137a. S. Komori and Y. Oshiro, *Japan* 20,043 ('67); via *C. A.* **69**, 19002; S. Komori *et al.*, *Kogyo Kagaku Zasshi* **71**, 1091 (1968).

2138. Konishiroku Photographic Industry Co. Ltd., Japan 4131 ('68).

2139. H. C. Koppel, R. H. Springer, and C. C. Cheng, *J. Org. Chem.* **26**, 1884 (1961).

2139a. H. C. Koppel *et al.*, *J. Org. Chem.* **27**, 3614 (1962).

2140. K. A. Kornev and V. A. Vonsyatskii, *Ukr. Khim. Zh.* **24**, 226 (1958); via *C. A.* **52**, 18279.

2141. K. A. Kornev and L. D. Protsenko, *Ukr. Khim. Zh.* **22**, 782 (1956); via *C. A.* **51**, 8675.

2142. A. I. Korolev *et al.*, U.S.S.R. 115,470 (1958); via *C. A.* **53**, 12694.

2143. A. I. Korolev *et al.*, U.S.S.R. 118,702 (1959); via *C. A.* **53**, 21311.

2145. E. L. Kosak and E. J. Quinn (to General Mills, Inc.), U.S. 3,186,858 (1965).

2146. R. G. Kostyanovskii and V. F. Bystrov, *Dokl. Akad. Nauk SSSR* **148**, 839 (1963); *Proc. Acad. Sci. USSR, Chem. Sect. (English Transl.)* **148-150**, 97 (1963).

2147. R. G. Kostyanovskii and V. F. Bystrov, *Izv. Akad. Nauk SSSR, Otd. Khim. Nauk* p. 171 (1963); *Bull. Acad. Sci. USSR, Div. Chem. Sci. (English Transl.)* p. 151 (1963).

2148. R. G. Kostyanovskii and A. K. Prokof'ev, *Izv. Akad. Nauk SSSR, Ser. Khim.* p. 175 (1965); *Bull. Acad. Sci. USSR, Div. Chem. Sci. (English Transl.)* p. 159 (1965).

2149. R. G. Kostyanovskii and O. A. Pan'shin, *Izv. Akad. Nauk SSSR, Otd. Khim. Nauk* p. 182 (1963); *Bull. Acad. Sci. USSR, Div. Chem. Sci. (English Transl.)* p. 164 (1963).

2150. R. G. Kostyanovskii, *Zh. Vses. Khim. Obshchestva im. D. I. Mendeleeva* **10**, 231 (1965); via *C. A.* **63**, 1759.

2151. R. G. Kostyanovskii and O. A. Pan'shin, *Izv. Akad. Nauk SSSR, Ser. Khim.* p. 564 (1965); *Bull. Acad. Sci. USSR, Div. Chem. Sci. (English Transl.)* p. 549 (1965).

2152. R. G. Kostyanovskii and O. A. Pan'shin, *Izv. Akad. Nauk SSSR, Ser. Khim.* p. 567 (1965); *Bull. Acad. Sci. USSR, Div. Chem. Sci. (English Transl.)*, p. 553 (1965).

2152a. R. G. Kostyanovskii, O. A. Pan'shin, and V. F. Bystrov, *Izv. Akad. Nauk SSSR, Otd. Khim. Nauk* p. 931 (1962); *Bull. Acad. Sci. USSR, Div. Chem. Sci. (English Transl.)* p. 869 (1962).

2152b. R. G. Kostyanovskii, O. A. Pan'shin, and T. Z. Papoyan, *Dokl. Akad. Nauk SSSR* **177**, 1099 (1967); *Dokl. Chem. (English Transl.)* **177**, 1160 (1967).

2152c. R. G. Kostyanovskii, Z. E. Samoilova, and I. I. Chervin, *Tetrahedron Letters* p. 3025 (1968).

2152d. R. G. Kostyanovskii, I. I. Chervin, and O. A. Pan'shin, *Izv. Akad. Nauk SSR, Ser. Khim.* p. 1423 (1968).

2153. R. G. Kostyanovskii and O. A. Pan'shin, *Izv. Akad. Nauk SSSR, Ser. Khim.* p. 740, 1965; *Bull. Acad. Sci. USSR, Div. Chem. Sci. (English Transl.)* p. 721 (1965).

2154. R. G. Kostyanovskii, *Dokl. Akad. Nauk SSSR* **135**, 853 (1960); via *C. A.* **55**, 12380.

2155. R. G. Kostyanovskii, *Dokl. Akad. Nauk SSSR* **139**, 877 (1961); via *C. A.* **56**, 1440.

2156. R. G. Kostyanovskii and O. A. Yuzhakova, *Dokl. Akad. Nauk SSSR* **159**, 142 (1964); *Proc. Acad. Sci. USSR, Chem. Sect. (English Transl.)*, **157-159**, 1152 (1964).

2157. R. G. Kostyanovskii, O. A. Yuzhakova, and V. F. Bystrov, *Zh. Vses. Khim. Obshchestva im. D. I. Mendeleeva* **10**, 229 (1965); via *C. A.* **63**, 1684.

2158. R. G. Kostyanovskii and O. A. Pan'shin, *Izv. Akad. Nauk SSSR, Ser. Khim.* p. 1554 (1964); *Bull. Acad. Sci. USSR, Div. Chem. Sci. (English Transl.)* p. 1469 (1964).

2159. R. G. Kostyanovskii and V. F. Bystrov, *Izv. Akad. Nauk SSSR, Otd. Khim. Nauk* p. 1488 (1962); *Bull. Acad. Sci. USSR, Div. Chem. Sci. (English Transl.)* p. 1404 (1962).

2160. R. G. Kostyanovskii, O. A. Yuzhakova, and V. F. Bystrov, *Izv. Akad. Nauk SSSR, Otd. Khim. Nauk* p. 1666 (1962); *Bull. Acad. Sci. USSR, Div. Chem. Sci. (English Transl.)* p. 1576 (1962).

2161. R. G. Kostyanovskii and A. K. Prokof'ev, *Dokl. Akad. Nauk SSSR* **164**, 1054 (1965); *Proc. Acad. Sci. USSR, Chem. Sect. (English Transl.)* **163-165**, 969 (1965).

2162. R. G. Kostyanovskii and O. A. Yuzhakova, *Zh. Obshch. Khim.* **32**, 2743 (1962); *J. Gen. Chem. USSR (English Transl.)* **32**, 2700 (1962).

2163. R. G. Kostyanovskii and A. K. Prokof'ev, *Izv. Akad. Nauk SSSR, Ser. Khim.* p. 473 (1967); *Bull. Acad. Sci. USSR, Div. Chem. Sci. (English Transl.)* p. 469 (1967).

2164. T. Kosugi, *Beitr. Pathol. Anat. Allgem. Pathol.* **77**, 1 (1927).

2165. K. Kotera, T. Okada, and S. Miyazaki, *Tetrahedron Letters* p. 841 (1967); *Tetrahedron* **24**, 5677 (1968).

2165a. K. Kotera *et al.*, *Tetrahedron* **24**, 3681 (1968).

2165b. K. Kotera *et al.*, *Tetrahedron Letters* p. 5759 (1968).

2166. S. P. Kovalenko, *Dokl. Akad. Nauk SSSR* **158**, 960 (1964); via *C. A.* **62**, 2003.

2166a. S. P. Kovalenko, *Tr. Mosk. Obshch. Ispyt. Prir., Otd. Biol.* **22**, 170 (1966); via *C. A.* **68**, 112488.

2167. N. N. Kozhanova and N. N. Zoz, *Agrokhimiya* No. 11, 123 (1966); via *C. A.* **66**, 8872.

2168. N. N. Kozhanova, N. V. Grigorova, and N. N. Zoz, *Supermutageny, Akad. Nauk SSSR, Inst. Khim. Fiz.* p. 140 (1966); via *C. A.* **67**, 41106.

2169. I. Krabbe (née Zeitler) *et al.*, Ger. 865,901 (1953); *Chem. Zentr.* p. 936 (1955).

2170. W. Krabbe and K. H. Schmidt, *Ber.* **72**, 381 (1939); W. Krabbe, A. Seher, and E. Polzin, *ibid.* **74**, 1892 (1941).

2171. G. Kraus and G. A. Moczvgemba, *J. Polymer Sci.* **A2**, 277 (1964).

2172. G. Kraus and J. T. Gruver (to Phillips Petroleum Co.), U.S. 3,153,639 (1964)

2172a. G. Kraus and J. T. Gruver (to Phillips Petroleum Co.), U.S. 3,362,931 (1968).

2173. D. Krebs, *Arzneimittel-Forsch.* **12**, 588 (1962).

2174. D. Krebs and H. Blass, *Zentr. Bakteriol. Parasitenk., Abt. I. Orig.* **200**, 468 (1966); via *C. A.* **65**, 19029.

2174a. B. A. Krentsel, Yu. V. Korshak, and E. P. Tyurina, *Puti Sinteza Izyskaniya Protivopukholevykh Prep.* No. 2, 113 (1967); via *C. A.* **69**, 61521.

2175. H. Krieger, *Suomen Kemistilehti* **B36**, 68 (1963); via *C. A.* **59**, 7453.

2176. H. Kroeger, *Arzneimittel-Forsch.* **7**, 147 (1957).

2177. H. Kroll and M. Knell (to Geigy Chemical Corp.), U.S. 2,831,885 (1958).

2179. E. L. Kropa and H. P. Wohnsiedler (to American Cyanamid Co.), U.S. 2,582,594 (1952); Can. 534,950 (1956).

2180. E. L. Kropa and H. P. Wohnsiedler (to American Cyanamid Co.), U.S. 2,582,704 (1952); Can. 530,725 (1956).

2181. E. L. Kropa and E. W. Malmberg (to American Cyanamid Co.), U.S. 2,655,494 (1953).

2182. A. A. Kropacheva and N. M. Kashnikova, *Zh. Obshch. Khim.* **35**, 2229 (1965); *J. Gen. Chem. USSR (English Transl.)* **35**, 2219 (1965).

2183. A. A. Kropacheva, N. M. Kashnikova, and V. A. Parshina, *Zh. Obshch. Khim.* **34**, 530 (1964); *J. Gen. Chem. USSR (English Transl.)* **34**, 532 (1964).

2184. A. A. Kropacheva, N. V. Sazonov, and A. V. Parshina, *Khim. i Primenenie Fosfororgan. Soedin. Akad. Nauk SSSR, Kazansk. Filial, Trudy 2-oi Konf.* p. 366 (1962); via Tolkmith (3567).

2185. A. A. Kropacheva and N. M. Kashnikova, *Zh. Obshch. Khim.* **38**, 136 (1968); *J. Gen. Chem. USSR (English Transl.)* **38**, 135 (1968).

2186. A. A. Kropacheva, L. E. Mukhina, and N. M. Kashnikova, *Puti Sinteza i Izyskaniya Protivoopukholevykh Preparatov* . . . p. 174 (1962); via *C. A.* **58**, 5664.

2187. A. A. Kropacheva and V. A. Parshina, *Zh. Obshch. Khim.* **29**, 556 (1959); *J. Gen. Chem. USSR (English Transl.)* **29**, 553 (1959).

2188. A. A. Kropacheva and N. M. Kashnikova, *Puti Sinteza Izyskaniya Protivoopukholevykh Prep., Tr. 2-oi Simp., Moscow 1967*, 90; via *C. A.* **70**, 11427.

2189. A. A. Kropacheva *et al., Zh. Obshch. Khim.* **32**, 1540 (1962); *J. Gen. Chem. USSR (English Transl.)* **32**, 1526 (1962).

2190. A. A. Kropacheva, G. I. Derkach, and A. V. Kirsanov, *Zh. Obshch. Khim.* **31**, 1601 (1961); *J. Gen. Chem. USSR (English Transl.)* **31**, 1489 (1961).

2191. A. A. Kropacheva and L. E. Mukhina, *Zh. Obshch. Khim.* **31**, 2437 (1961); *J. Gen. Chem. USSR (English Transl.)* **31**, 2274 (1961).

2192. A. A. Kropacheva and N. V. Sazonov, *Zh. Obshch. Khim.* **31**, 3601 (1961); *J. Gen. Chem. USSR (English Transl.)* **31**, 3357 (1961).

2193. A. A. Kropacheva, N. V. Sazonov, and S. I. Sergievskaya, *Zh. Obshch. Khim.* **32**, 3796 (1962); *J. Gen. Chem. USSR (English Transl.)* **32**, 3723 (1962).

2194. K. E. Kruglyakova *et al., Dokl. Akad. Nauk SSSR* **161**, 718 (1965); via *C. A.* **63**, 2032.

2194a. K. E. Kruglyakova *et al., Biofizika* **12**, 330 (1967); via *C. A.* **67**, 8009.

2195. P. J. Krusic, *Dissertation Abstr.* **B27**, 3890 (1967).

2196. O. V. Krylov and O. L. Bartan, U.S.S.R. 172,726 (1965); via *C. A.* **63**, 18296.

2197. E. Kuh and D. R. Seeger (to American Cyanamid Co.), U.S. 2,670,347 (1954); Brit. 729,586 (1955); Can. 491,654 (1953); Fr. 1,072,482 (1954).

2198. E. Kuh and R. L. Shepherd (to American Cyanamid Co.), U.S. 2,672,459 (1954); Can. 491,655 (1953).

2199. R. Kuhn and F. Drawert, *Ann. Chem.* **590**, 55 (1954).

2200. R. Kuhn, G. Quadbeck, and E. Roehm, *Chem. Ber.* **86**, 468 (1953).

2201. R. Kuhn and G. Quadbeck, *Chem. Ber.* **84**, 844 (1951).

2202. R. Kuhn and G. Quadbeck (to Badische Anilin- und Soda-Fabrik), U.S. 2,751,409 (1956); Ger. 932,374 (1955).

2203. S. J. Kuhn (to The Dow Chemical Co.), U.S. 3,297,682 (1967).

2204. G. I. Kulik and I. M. Loseva, *Farmakol. i Toksikol. Sb.* p. 109 (1964); via *C. A.* **64**, 13256.

2205. M. Kulka, *Can. J. Chem.* **37**, 325 (1959).

2206. M. Kumagai, *Nippon Kagaku Zasshi* **82**, 227 (1961); via *C. A.* **56**, 10139.

2207. Kurashiki Rayon Co., Japan. 1664 ('58); via *C. A.* **52**, 21144.

2207a. Kurashiki Rayon Co., Japan. 26,143 ('67).

2208. K. N. Kurdymova and A. Ya. Berlin, *Zh. Obshch. Khim.* **33**, 129 (1963); *J. Gen. Chem. USSR (English Transl.)* **33**, 121 (1963).

2208a. N. Kuroki, *Seni-i Gakkaishi* **23**, 309 (1967); vai *POST-J* **3**, 554 (1968). via *C. A.* **66**, 113230.

2209. P. Kurtz, H. Gold, and H. Disselnkoetter, *Ann. Chem.* **624**, 1 (1959).

2210. M. Kusak and M. Weinfurt, *Papir Celulosa* **19** (5), 129 (1964); via *C. A.* **61**, 9670.

2211. L. Kutik (to Interchemical Corp.), U.S. 3,017,293 (1961).

2212. I. I. Kuz'menko and L. B. Rapp, *Prob. Organ. Sinteza, Akad. Nauk SSSR, Otd. Obshch. i Tekhn. Khim.* p. 316 (1965); via *C. A.* **64**, 6597.

2213. E. V. Kuznetsov, S. G. Tsarev, and L. I. Sitnikova, U.S.S.R. 179,528 (1966); via *C. A.* **65**, 2126.

2213a. E. I. Kvarnikov and V. I. Sudenko, *Tsitol. Genet., Akad. Nauk Ukr.* **1**, 61 (1967); via *C. A.* **66**, 113230.

2214. H. Kwart and A. A. Khan, *J. Am. Chem. Soc.* **89**, 1951 (1967).

2215. E. Kyburz *et al.*, *Helv. Chim. Acta* **49**, 359 (1966).

2216. Kyoji Oshima, Japan. 63 ('57); via *C. A.* **52**, 15920.

2217. Kyowa Fermentation Industry Co., Ltd., Japan. 6358 ('67); via *C. A.* **67**, 21901.

2218. Kyowa Fermentation Industry Co., Ltd., Japan. 22,379 ('67); Fr. 1,478,345 and M4923 (1967).

2219. Kyowa Fermentation Industry Co., Ltd., Fr. M5329 (1967).

2220. Kyowa Fermentation Industry Co., Ltd., Japan. 22,378 ('67).

2221. Kyowa Fermentation Industry Co., Ltd., Japan. 5400 ('62); via *C. A.* **59**, 6955.

2222. Kyowa Fermentation Industry Co., Ltd., Belg. 668,788 (1965); Fr. 1,449,946 (1966); Neth. appl. 6,510,520 (1966); Japan. 9354 ('67); Brit. 1,110,035 (1968).

2223. Kyowa Fermentation Industry Co., Ltd., Belg. 671,904 (1966); via *C. A.* **65**, 13663; Neth. appl. 6,514,382 (1966).

2224. Kyowa Fermentation Industry Co., Ltd., Japan. 9,094 ('61); via *C. A.* **56**, 2518.

2225. Kyowa Fermentation Industry Co., Ltd., Japan. 13,760 ('65); Brit. 1,102,259 (1968).

2226. Kyowa Fermentation Industry Co., Ltd., Japan. 18,116 ('65); via *C. A.* **64**, 5098.

2227. Kyowa Fermentation Industry Co., Ltd., Japan. 18,117 and 18,118 ('65); via *C. A.* **64**, 8139; Belg. 655,399 (1965); Fr. 1,437,402 (1966); via *C. A.* **65**, 20128; Neth. appl. 6,412,941 (1966); via *C. A.* **65**, 13712.

2228. Kyowa Fermentation Industry Co., Ltd., Brit. 1,099,814 (1968).

2229. Kyowa Fermentation Industry Co., Ltd., Belg. 666,697 (1965); Neth. appl. 6,508,896 (1966); Japan. 22,380 ('67); via *C. A.* **65**, 8916.

2230. Kyowa Fermentation Industry Co., Ltd. and K. Kenkyusho, Brit. 830,874 (1960); Ger. 1,059,623 (1959).

2231. Kyowa Fermentation Industry Co. Ltd., Fr. 1,449,947 (1966); Brit. 1,110,036 (1968).

2232. Kyowa Fermentation Industry Co., Ltd., Brit. 1.099,648 (1968).

2233. Kyowa Fermentation Industry Co., Ltd., Belg. 648,956 (1964); via *C. A.* **63**, 18034; Neth. appl. 6,406,466 (1965); Fr. 1,421,318 (1965).

2234. Kyowa Fermentation Industry Co., Ltd., Brit. 1,101,500 (1968).

2235. Y. J. L'Italien (to Parke, Davis and Co.), U.S. 3,278,600 (1966).

2236. Laboratories Coupin, Fr. 1,221,869 (1960); via *C. A.* **56**, 10047.

2237. G. C. LaBrecque, D. W. Meifert, and H. K. Gouck, *Florida Entomologist* **46**, 7 (1963).

2238. G. C. LaBrecque, *Advan. Chem. Ser.* **41**, 42 (1963).

2239. G. C. LaBrecque, D. W. Meifert, and R. L. Fye, *J. Econ. Entomol.* **56**, 150 (1963).

2240. G. C. LaBrecque, D. W. Meifert, and C. N. Smith, *Science* **136**, 388 (1962).

2240a. G. C. LaBrecque and C. N. Smith, eds., " Principles of Insect Chemosterilization." Appleton-Century-Crofts, New York, 1968.

2241. G. C. LaBrecque, C. N. Smith, and D. W. Meifert, *J. Econ. Entomol.* **55**, 449 (1962).

2242. G. C. LaBrecque and H. K. Gouck, *J. Econ. Entomol.* **56**, 476 (1963).

2243. G. C. LaBrecque, *J. Econ. Entomol.* **54**, 684 (1961).

2244. G. C. LaBrecque, P. H. Adcock, and C. N. Smith, *J. Econ. Entomol.* **53**, 802 (1960).

2245. G. Labruto and L. Irrera, *Gazz. Chim. Ital.* **64**, 136 (1934).

2246. L. E. La Chance and M. M. Crystal, *Biol. Bull.* **125**, 280 (1963).

2247. L. E. La Chance and M. M. Crystal, *Genetics* **51**, 699 (1965).

2248. G. H. Lacy and R. R. Chervenak (to The Dow Chemical Co.), U.S. 3,033,707 (1962); Belg. 589,932 (1960); Fr. 1,262,069 (1961); Ital. 629,181 (1961); Austral. 244,571 (1963); Brit. 913,289 (1963); Can. 708,138 (1965); Swiss 392,065 (1965); Swed. 225,192 (1968).

2249. G. H. Lacy and R. R. Chervenak (to The Dow Chemical Co.), U.S. 3,140,196 (1964); Belg. 589,928 (1960); Fr. 1,263,329 (1961); Ital. 631,189 (1961); Brit. 899,829 (1962); Austral. 245,963 (1964); Swiss 392,875 (1965); Swed. 225,193 (1968).

2250. T. L. Ladd, Jr., *J. Econ. Entomol.* **59**, 422 (1966).

2250a. T. L. Ladd, Jr., C. W. Collier, and E. L. Plasket, *J. Econ. Entomol.* **61**, 942 (1968).

2251. A. Ladenburg and J. Abel, *Ber.* **21**, 758 and 2706 (1888).

2252. A. Ladenburg, *Ber.* **19**, 780 (1886); **20**, 442 (1887).

2253. A. Ladenburg, *Ber.* **16**, 1149 (1883).

2254. G. J. Laemmle, Jr. (to Jefferson Chemical Co.), U.S. 2,776,972 (1957).

2255. G. J. Laemmle, Jr. (to Jefferson Chemical Co.), U.S. 3,037,042 (1962).

2255a. J. F. Lafaye and G. Jacquelin, *Paperi Puu* **50** (4a), 155 (1968); via *C. A.* **68**, 106198.

2256. P. Lagally (to Chemirad Corporation), U.S. 3,252,852 (1966); Brit. 996,389 (1965).

2256a. P. Lagally and J. W. Brook (to Chemirad Corp.), U.S. 3,348,997 (1967).

2257. E. Lakatos *et al.* (to Kalle and Co.), U.S. 2,784,116 (1957); Fr. 1,121,423 (1956).

2258. R. F. Lambert, G. Thompson, and C. E. Kristofferson, *J. Org. Chem.* **29**, 3116 (1964).

2259. E. H. Land *et al.* (to Polaroid Corp.), U.S. 2,857,274 (1958); Ger. 1,012,176 (1957).

2260. E. H. Land *et al.* (to Polaroid Corp.), U.S. 2,857,275 (1958).

2261. E. H. Land *et al.* (to Polaroid Corp.), U.S. 2,857,276 (1958); Ger. 1,068,118 (1959).

2262. C. G. Landes and W. F. Reynolds, Jr. (to American Cyanamid Co.), U.S. 2,698,793 (1955).

2263. R. E. Lane, Jr. and G. E. Ham (to The Dow Chemical Co.), U.S. 3,264,368 (1966); Brit. 1,114,125 (1968); Fr. 1,456,667 (1966); Belg. 668,007 (1966); Can. 745,236 (1966); Ital. 745,669 (1967).

2263a. E. W. Lang (to The Procter and Gamble Co.), U.S. 3,400,198 (1968).

2264. F. Langer, E. Zbinal, and R. Wessely, *Monatsh. Chem.* **90**, 623 (1959).

2265. I. Langman, A. E. McKay, and G. F. Wright, *J. Org. Chem.* **14**, 550 (1949).

2266. S. Lapanje *et al.*, *J. Am. Chem. Soc.* **83**, 1590 (1961).

2267. S. Lapanje, P. F. Jones, and S. A. Rice, *J. Am. Chem. Soc.* **85**, 883 (1963).

2268. S. Lapanje, *Vestn. Sloven. Kem. Drustva* **9**, 5 (1962); via *C. A.* **60**, 2362.

2268a. Laporte Titanium Ltd., Belg. 696,455 (1968).

2268b. L. F. Larionov, "Khimioterapia Zlokachestvenych Opukholej." Gosud. Izdat. Med. Literat., Moskva, 1962; via Cheymol *et al.* (673).

2269. R. A. Lasselle and S. A. Sundet, *J. Am. Chem. Soc.* **63**, 2374 (1941).

2269a. C. J. Lattarulo and J. J. R. Luzzi (to Interchemical Corp.), U.S. 3,113,038 (1963).

2270. J. J. Latterell and H. F. Walton, *Anal. Chim. Acta* **32**, 101 (1965).

2271. A. Lattes, A. de Savignac, and J. Carles, *Compt. Rend.* **253**, 2714 (1961); A. de Savignac, A. Lattes, and J. Carles, *J. Chromatog.* **7**, 261 (1962).

2272. A. Lattes, R. Martino, and R. Mathis-Noel, *Compt. Rend.* **C263**, 49 (1966).

2273. W. Lautsch, *Die Chemie* **57**, 149 (1944); via *C. A.* **40**, 5915.

2274. W. Lautsch *et al.*, *Naturwissenschaften* **38**, 210 (1951).

2275. W. Lautsch *et al.*, *Kolloid-Z.* 12572 (1952).

2276. W. Lautsch, W. Biedermann, and W. Broser, *Naturwissenschaften* **38**, 260 (1954).

2277. P. B. Lavanchy (to Johnson and Johnson), U.S. 2,922,723 (1960).

2278. P. D. Lawley, *Progr. Nucleic Acid Res. Mol. Biol.* **5**, 89 (1966).

2278a. P. D. Lawley and P. D. Brookes, *J. Mol. Biol.* **25**, 143 and **29**, 537 (1967).

2279. W. Lawrence, Jr. *et al.*, *J. Surg. Res.* **4**, 483 (1964).

2280. R. B. LeBlanc and A. P. Ingram, Jr., *Textile Res. J.* **32**, 284 (1962).

2281. R. B. LeBlanc, *Am. Dyestuff Reptr.* **53**, P291 (1964).

2281a. R. B. LeBlanc and R. H. Symm (to The Dow Chemical Co.), US 3,409,463 (1968).

2282. R. B. LeBlanc, *Textile Res. J.* **35**, 341 (1965).

2282a. H. Z. Lecher and E. Kuh (to American Cyanamid Co.), U.S. 2,654,738 (1953); Can. 491,651 (1953).

2283. J. A. Leermakers, *J. Am. Chem. Soc.* **55**, 2719 (1933).

2284. D. V. Lefemine *et al.*, *J. Am. Chem. Soc.* **84**, 3184 (1962).

2285. R. Lehmann and E. Grivsky, *Bull. Soc. Chim. Belges* **55**, 52 (1946).

2286. H. Lehr, S. Karlan, and M. W. Goldberg, *J. Med. Chem.* **6**, 136 (1963).

2287. T. Lehrfeld, *Ber.* **14**, 1816 (1881).

2288. E. Leibnitz, H.-G. Koennecke, and G. Gawalek, *J. Prakt. Chem.* [4] **6**, 289 (1958).

2288a. G. Leicht (to "Montecatini" Societa...), U.S. 3,288,897 (1966); Fr. 1,357,296 (1964).

2289. P. A. Leighton, *Publication Board Rept. (U.S.)* PB A 50,817; via *Bibliog. Sci. Ind. Rept.* **5**, 474.

2290. P. A. Leighton, W. A. Perkins, and M. L. Renquist, *J. Am. Chem. Soc.* **69**, 1540 (1947).

2291. E. Leon, E. D. Weil, and J. Linder (to Hooker Chemical Corp.), U.S. 3,158,624 (1964).

2292. N. J. Leonard, *Record Chem. Progr. (Kresge-Hooker Sci. Lib.)* **26**, 211 (1965).

2293. N. J. Leonard and L. E. Brady, *J. Org. Chem.* **30**, 817 (1965).

2294. N. J. Leonard and J. V. Paukstelis, *J. Org. Chem.* **30**, 821 (1965).

2295. N. J. Leonard *et al.*, *J. Org. Chem.* **28**, 1499 (1963).

2296. N. J. Leonard and G. L. Shoemaker, *J. Am. Chem. Soc.* **71**, 1762 (1949).

2297. N. J. Leonard, E. F. Kiefer, and L. E. Brady, *J. Org. Chem.* **28**, 2850 (1963).

2298. N. J. Leonard *et al.*, *J. Org. Chem.* **29**, 3383 (1964).

2299. N. J. Leonard, R. Y. Ning, and R. L. Booth, *J. Org. Chem.* **30**, 4357 (1965).

2300. N. J. Leonard and K. Jann, *J. Am. Chem. Soc.* **84**, 4806 (1962).

2301. N. J. Leonard and K. Jann, *J. Am. Chem. Soc.* **82**, 6418 (1960).

2302. N. J. Leonard and B. Zwanenburg, *J. Am. Chem. Soc.* **89**, 4456 (1967).

2303. S. Le Reste and L. Sparfel, *Compt. Rend.* **C263**, 442 (1966).

2304. J. B. Lesh and C. W. Damaskees (to Armour Pharmaceutical Co.), U.S. 3,264,178 (1966); Fr. 1,397,493 (1965); Brit. 1,042,903 (1966).

2305. E. Leumann *et al.* (to Ciba), U.S. 2,830,045 (1958); Brit. 799,657 (1958); Ger. 1,088,056 (1960).

2306. C. Levaditi, *Arch. Intern. Pharmacodyn.* **8**, 45 (1901).

2307. E. D. Levin and V. M. Stepanov, *Khim. Prirodn. Soedin., Akad. Nauk Uz. SSR* **2**, 444 (1966); via *C. A.* **67**, 64679.

2308. L. Levine (to The Dow Chemical Co.), U.S. 3,356,710 (1967).

2309. L. Levine and G. E. Ham (to The Dow Chemical Co.), U.S. 3,326,968 (1967).

2310. P. L. Levins and Z. B. Papanastassiou, *J. Am. Chem. Soc.* **87**, 826 (1965).

2311. L. L. Lewallen, H. C. Chapman, and W. H. Wilder, *Mosquito News* **25**, 16 (1965).

2312. Y. S. Li and M. D. Harmony, *Abstr. Papers, 153rd Am. Chem. Soc. Meeting, Miami Beach, 1967* abstr. R-40.

2312a. M. Yu. Lidak *et al.*, U.S.S.R. 199,893 (1968).

2312b. M. I. Lidak *et al.*, *Klin. Med.* (Moscow) **46**, 142 (1968); via *Cumulated Index Medicus.*

2313. M. Lidaks, S. Hillers, and A. Medne, *TioTEFA, Akad. Nauk Latv. SSR., Inst. Organ. Sinteza* p. 5 (1961); via *C. A.* **58**, 3375.

2314. M. Lidaks and S. Hillers, *Puti Sinteza i Izyskaniya Protivoopukholevykh Preparatov ...* p. 150 (1962); via *C. A.* **58**, 4491.

2315. M. Lidaks and S. Hillers, *Latvijas PSR Zinatnu Akad. Vestis* No. 7, p. 49 (1961); via *C. A.* **57**, 12404.

2316. M. Lidaks, Z. Lein, and M. V. Shimanskaya, *Latvijas PSR Zinatnu Akad. Vestis* No. 11, p. 87 (1959); via *C. A.* **54**, 23193.

2317. M. Lidaks and S. Hillers, *Latvijas PSR Zinatnu Akad. Vestis, Kim. Ser.* No. 1, p. 81 (1961); via *C. A.* **58**, 4567.

2318. M. Lidaks, S. Hillers, and A. Medne, *Latvijas PSR Zinatnu Akad. Vestis* No. 1, p. 87 (1959); via *C. A.* **53**, 17992.

2318a. M. Lidaks and S. Hillers, *Latvijas PSR Zinatnu Akad. Vestis* No. 5, p. 99 (1961); via *C. A.* **56**, 4706.

2319. M. Lidaks and S. Hillers, *Latvijas PSR Zinatnu Akad. Vestis, Kim. Ser.* No. 2, p. 211 (1961); via *C. A.* **58**, 4530.

2320. M. Lidaks, Z. Lejins, and M. V. Shimanskaya, *TioTEFA, Akad. Nauk Latv. SSR, Inst. Organ. Sinteza* p. 9 (1961); via *C. A.* **58**, 1304.

2321. M. Lidaks, J. Lisis, and A. Veiss, *Latvijas PSR Zinatnu Akad. Vestis* No. 2, p. 101 (1960); via *C. A.* **55**, 25602.

2322. M. V. Likhosherstov and R. A. Arkhangel'skaya, *Zh. Obshch. Khim.* **7**, 1914 (1937); via *C. A.* **32**, 519.

2323. M. V. Likhosherstov, R. A. Arkhangel'skaya, and T. V. Shalaeva, *Zh. Obshch. Khim.* **9**, 2085 (1939); via *C. A.* **34**, 3674.

2323a. J. K. Lim and L. A. Snyder, *Mutation Res.* **6**, 129 (1968).

2324. M. K. Lindemann and F. R. Eirich, *Abst. Papers, 142nd Am. Chem. Soc. Meeting, Atlantic City, 1962* p. I-2.

2325. Lindgens and Sohne, Belg. 614,293 (1962); Fr. 1,316,133 (1963); via *Chem. Zentr.* No. 23, abstr. 2840 (1965).

2326. K. Lindner, *Fette, Seifen, Anstrichmittel* **65**, 96 (1963).

2326a. W. B. Lindsey (to du Pont de Nemours and Co.), U.S. 3,361,586 (1968); Neth. appl. 6,512,677 (1966).

2327. A. W. Lindquist, *J. Wash. Acad. Sci.* **51**, 109 (1961).

2328. D. A. Lindquist *et al.*, *J. Econ. Entomol.* **57**, 745 (1964).

2329. F. Linke, M. Seidel, and W. Linke, *SVF Fachorgan Textilveredlung* **19**, 630 (1964); via *J. Soc. Dyers Colourists* **81**, 69.

2330. Liparo S. A., Brit. 950,073 (1964).

2331. E. Lippert and H. Prigge, *Ann. Chem.* **659**, 81 (1962).

2332. E. Lippert and H. Prigge, *Ber. Bunsenges. Physik. Chem.* **67**, 554 (1963).

2333. E. Lippert and H. Prigge, *Ber. Bunsenges. Physik. Chem.* **67**, 415 (1963).

2333a. E. R. Lippincott, G. Nagarajan, and J. M. Stutman, *J. Phys. Chem.* **70**, 78 (1966); cf. G. Nagarajan, *Z. Naturforsch.* **21a**, 238 (1966).

2334. M. H. Litt and T. G. Bassiri (to Allied Chemical Corp.), U.S. 3,314,924 (1967); Belg. 654,601 (1965); Neth. appl. 6,412,214 (1965); Indian 96,113 (1966); Brit. 1,063,345 and 1,063,346 (1967); Japan. 2834 ('67); Ger. 1,237,781 (1967).

2334a. K.-J. Liu, *Preprints Sci. Papers, Intern. Symp. Macromol. Chem., Tokyo-Kyoto, 1966* **7**, 50.

2334b. K.-J. Liu, *Macromolecules* **1**, 390 (1968).

2335. H. L. Lochte, Jr. *et al.*, *Blood* **21**, 424 (1963).

2336. Loevens Kemiske Fabrik ved A. Kongsted, Brit. 891,174 (1962).

2337. A. Loewenstein, J. F. Neumer, and J. D. Roberts, *J. Am. Chem. Soc.* **82**, 3599 (1960).

2337a. P. Loewrigkeit *et al.*, *J. Org. Chem.* **33**, 3344 (1968).

2338. H. Logemann and W. Lehmann (to Farbenfabriken Bayer), U.S. 3,122,518 (1964); Ger. 1,147,031 (1963).

2339. A. L. Logothetis, *J. Org. Chem.* **29**, 3049 (1964).

2340. A. L. Logothetis, *J. Am. Chem. Soc.* **87**, 749 (1965).

2340a. H. Lomas (to Ontario Research Foundation), U.S. 3,386,880 (1968).

2341. L. Longmaack (to Wolff and Co.), U.S. 2,973,274 (1961); Ger. 1,020,225 (1957); Brit. 862,671 (1961).
2342. M. Lora-Tamayo *et al.*, *Anales Real Soc. Españ. Fis. Quim.* (*Madrid*) **B62**, 173 (1966); via *C. A.* **65**, 13685.
2343. N. G. Lordi and J. E. Christian, *J. Am. Pharm. Assoc.* **45**, 530 (1956).
2344. J. R. Lotz, B. P. Block, and W. C. Fernelius, *J. Phys. Chem.* **63**, 541 (1959).
2345. J. B. Lovelace and W. E. Patterson (to Pittsburgh Plate Glass Co.), U.S. 3,167,468 (1965); Fr. 1,325,980 (1962); Brit. 997,051 (1965).
2346. A. Loveless, "Genetic and Allied Effects of Alkylating Agents." Penn. State Univ. Press, University Park, Pennsylvania, 1966.
2347. L. E. Loveless, E. Spoerl, and T. H. Weisman, *J. Bacteriol.* **68**, 637 (1954).
2348. J. V. Lowe, Jr., T. A. Oda, and R. Evans, *J. Org. Chem.* **28**, 1496 (1963).
2349. J. R. Lowell, Jr. and G. K. Helmkamp, *J. Am. Chem. Soc.* **88**, 768 (1966).
2349a. M. O. Lozinskii *et al.*, *Fiziol. Aktiv. Veshchestva, Akad. Nauk Ukr. SSR . . .*, p. 50 (1966); via *C. A.* **67**, 53846.
2350. Lubrizol Corp., Fr. 1,360,302 (1964); via *C. A.* **62**, 3865.
2350a. Lubrizol Corp., Fr. 1,457,520 (1966); via *C. A.* **67**, 4685.
2351. W. H. Luckmann, G. Gangrade, and D. B. Broersma, *J. Econ. Entomol.* **60**, 737 (1967).
2352. H. Lueers, *Naturwissenschaften* **43**, 206 (1956).
2353. H. Lueers and G. Roehrborn, *Mutation Res.* **2**, 29 (1965).
2353a. T. M. Luginina, *Mikrobiol. Zh., Akad. Nauk Ukr. RSR* **29**, 507 (1967); via *C. A.* **68**, 93745.
2354. A. A. Lukin and I. N. Polyakova, *Antibiotiki* **12**, 658 (1967); via *C. A.* **67**, 106186.
2354a. F. L. Luknitskii and B. A. Vovsi, *Zh. Org. Khim.* **3**, 794 (1967); via *C. A.* **67**, 43395.
2354b. R. B. Lund *et al.* (to Allied Chemical Corp.), U.S. 3,379,707 (1968).
2355. L. A. Lundberg (to American Cyanamid Co.), U.S. 2,620,315 (1952).
2356. R. T. Lundquist and A. Ruby, *Appl. Spectry.* **20**, 258 (1966).
2357. U. Lundqvist and D. von Wettstein, *Hereditas* **48**, 342 (1962).
2358. C. Luner and H. Gesser, *J. Phys. Chem.* **62**, 1148 (1958).
2358a. J. H. Lupinski, K. D. Koppel, and J. J. Hertz, *J. Polymer Sci.* **C16**, 1561 (1967).
2359. A. W. Lutz and B. L. Walworth (to American Cyanamid Co.), U.S. 3,166,399 (1965); Fr. 1,384,159 (1965).
2360. R. E. Lutz *et al.*, *J. Org. Chem.* **15**, 181 (1950).
2361. R. E. Lutz and A. B. Turner, *J. Org. Chem.* **33**, 516 (1968).
2362. R. Luzzatto, *Arch. Farmacol. Sper.* **17**, 455 (1914); via *C. A.* **9**, 335.
2363. A. Lwoff *et al.*, *Compt. Rend.* **234**, 2308 (1952).
2364. W. Lwowski, *Angew. Chem.* **70**, 483 (1958).
2365. W. Lwowski, T. J. Maricich, and T. W. Mattingly, Jr., *J. Am. Chem. Soc.* **85**, 1200 (1963).
2366. W. Lwowski and T. W. Mattingly, Jr., *J. Am. Chem. Soc.* **87**, 1947 (1965).
2367. W. Lwowski and T. J. Maricich, *J. Am. Chem. Soc.* **87**, 3630 (1965).
2368. W. Lwowski and G. T. Tisue, *J. Am. Chem. Soc.* **87**, 4022 (1965).
2369. W. Lwowski and J. S. McConaghy, Jr., *J. Am. Chem. Soc.* **87**, 5490 (1965).
2370. W. Lwowski and F. P. Woerner, *J. Am. Chem. Soc.* **87**, 5491 (1965).
2371. W. Lwowski and T. W. Mattingly, Jr., *Tetrahedron Letters* p. 277 (1962).
2372. W. Lwowski and R. L. Johnson, *Tetrahedron Letters* p. 891 (1967).
2373. W. Lwowski, *Angew. Chem.* **79**, 922 (1967); *Angew. Chem. Intern. Ed. Engl.* **6**, 897 (1967).
2374. R. E. Lyle and W. E. Krueger, *J. Org. Chem.* **32**, 3613 (1967).
2375. V. N. Lysikov and O. V. Blyandur, *Supermutageny, Akad. Nauk SSSR, Inst. Khim. Fiz.* p. 159 (1966); via *C. A.* **67**, 41108.

2375a. V. N. Lysikov *et al.*, *Tr. Kishinev. Sel'skokhoz. Inst.* **46**, 83 (1967); via *C. A.* **69**, 74552.

2376. V. N. Lysikov and O. V. Blyandur, *Tr. Kishinev. Sel'skokhoz. Inst.* **37**, 84 (1964); via *C. A.* **63**, 13955.

2376a. V. N. Lysikov and Z. A. Orinshtein, *Tr. Kishinev. Sel'skokhoz. Inst.* **46**, 154 (1967); via *C. A.* **69**, 74553.

2377. D. A. Lyttle and H. G. Petering (to Upjohn Co.), U.S. 2,957,875 (1960).

2378. S. Machida, J. Machida, and H. Tanaka, *Yuki Gosei Kagaku Kyokai Shi* **20**, 70 (1962); via *C. A.* **56**, 13049.

2379. S. Machida, T. Yoshii, and H. Yamada, *Kami-pa Gikyoshi* **19**, 389 (1965); via *C. A.* **63**, 18451.

2379a. S. Machida *et al.*, *Kami-pa Gikyoshi* **21**, 432 (1967); via *C. A.* **67**, 118303.

2380. S. Machida, *Seni-i Gakkaishi* **14**, 892 (1958); via *C. A.* **53**, 4746.

2381. S. Machida *et al.*, *Yuki Gosei Kagaku Kyokai Shi* **19**, 913 (1961); via *C. A.* **56**, 6204.

2382. S. Machida, *Kagaku No Ryoiki* **16**, 865 (1962); via *C. A.* **59**, 1560.

2383. Z. Machnowska, *Prace Inst. Wlokiennicktwa* **12**, 333 (1962); via *C. A.* **60**, 5693.

2384. G. E. Maciel and G. B. Savitsky, *J. Phys. Chem.* **69**, 3925 (1965).

2385. C. H. Mack and C. P. Wade (to U.S. Department of Agriculture), U.S. 3,268,291 (1966).

2386. A. K. Mackenzie (to du Pont de Nemours and Co.), U.S. 3,112,241 (1963).

2387. H. W. Mackinney (to Chemirad Corp.), U.S. 3,165,509 (1965).

2388. A. MacLean and S. F. Marrian (to Imperial Chemical Industries, Ltd.), U.S. 2,470,042 (1949).

2389. A. MacLean and S. F. Marrian (to Imperial Chemical Industries, Ltd.), U.S. 2,472,335 (1949); Fr. 966,611 (1950).

2390. W. E. Magee and O. V. Miller, *Biochim. Biophys. Acta* **55**, 818 (1962).

2391. D. D. Magnelli *et al.*, *Inorg. Chem.* **5**, 457 (1966).

2392. G. Magri-Allegra and L. Zannone, *Atti Assoc. Genet. Ital.* **8**, 334 (1963); via *Plant Breed. Abstr.* **32**, 1271; *Use Induced Mutations Plant Breed. Rept. FAO-IAEA Tech. Meeting, Rome, 1964* p. 215. Pergamon Press, Oxford, 1965; via *C. A.* **66**, 44311.

2392a. Magyar Állam, Hung. 144,772 (1959); via *Chem. Zentr.* p. 4816 (1963).

2393. J. E. Mahan (to Phillips Petroleum Co.), U.S. 3,214,421 (1965).

2394. G. Maier, *Angew. Chem.* **79**, 446 (1967); *Angew. Chem. Intern. Ed. Engl.* **6**, 402 (1967).

2395. W. Maier (to I. G. Farbenindustrie), U.S. 2,148,909 (1939); Fr. 808,307 (1937); Ger. 644,575, 648,000, and 648,761 (1937); Brit. 476,570 (1937) and 488,581 (1938).

2396. P. Maitland, *Ann. Rept. Progr. Chem.* (*Chem. Soc. London*) **36**, 243 (1939).

2397. J. C. Maitlen and L. M. McDonough, *J. Econ. Entomol.* **60**, 1391 (1967).

2398. W. Majert and A. Schmidt, *Ber.* **23**, 3718 (1890).

2399. Y. Makao, *Idengaku Zasshi* **40**, Suppl. 107 (1965); via *C. A.* **65**, 10931.

2399a. S. P. Makarov, I. V. Ermakova, and V. A. Shpanskii, *Zh. Obshch. Khim.* **36**, 1419 (1966); *J. Gen. Chem. USSR* (*English Transl.*), **36**, 1426 (1966).

2400. A. N. Makarova and I. G. Spasskaya, *Tr. Inst. Onkol., Akad. Med. Nauk SSSR* **2**, 132 (1962); via *C. A.* **59**, 13907.

2400a. A. N. Makarova *et al.*, *Puti Sinteza i Izyskaniya Protivoopukholevykh Preparatov* . . . p. 165 (1962); via *C. A.* **58**, 5629.

2401. A. N. Makarova and A. Ya. Berlin, *Zh. Obshch. Khim.* **29**, 666 (1959); *J. Gen. Chem. USSR* (*English Transl.*) **29**, 659 (1959).

2402. A. N. Makarova, Z. M. Egorova, and A. Ya. Berlin, *Zh. Obshch. Khim.* **32**, 1285 (1962); *J. Gen. Chem. USSR* (*English Transl.*) **32**, 1259 (1962).

2403. A. N. Makarova, M. P. Gribkova, and A. Ya. Berlin, *Zh. Obshch. Khim.* **30**, 1577 (1960); *J. Gen. Chem. USSR (English Transl.)* **30**, 1583 (1960).

2404. A. N. Makarova, V. S. Martynov, and A. Ya. Berlin, *Zh. Obshch. Khim.* **33**, 1643 (1963); *J. Gen. Chem. USSR (English Transl.)* **33**, 1601 (1963).

2405. A. N. Makarova and A. Ya. Berlin, *Zh. Obshch. Khim.* **31**, 2353 (1961); *J. Gen. Chem. USSR (English Transl.)* **31**, 2193 (1961).

2406. A. N. Makarova and A. Ya. Berlin, *Zh. Obshch. Khim.* **34**, 3037 (1964); *J. Gen. Chem. USSR (English Transl.)* **34**, 3073.

2406a. A. N. Makarova and A. Ya. Berlin, *Zh. Obshch. Khim.* **37**, 637 (1967); via *C. A.* **67**, 43530.

2407. A. N. Makarova and A. Ya. Berlin, *Zh. Obshch. Khim.* **29**, 3959 (1959); *J. Gen. Chem. USSR (English Transl.)* **29**, 3919 (1959).

2408. R. A. Maksimova, *Sel'skokhoz. Biol.* **1**, 280 (1966); via *C. A.* **65**, 17657.

2409. A. M. Malashenko and I. K. Egorov, *Genetika* No. 3, 59 (1967); via *C. A.* **67**, 19460.

2410. A. M. Malashenko and I. K. Egorov, *Genetika* **4**, 21 (1968); via *C. A.* **68**. 94304.

2410a. I. E. Mamaeva, N. V. Sazonov, and A. A. Kropacheva, *Khim.-Farm. Zh.* **2**, 31 (1968); via *C. A.* **69**, 77204.

2411. E. E. Mandel and H. Popper, *A. M. A. Arch. Pathol.* **52**, 1 (1951).

2412. G. Manecke and H. Heller, *Makromol. Chem.* **59**, 106 (1963).

2413. G. Manecke and A. Grohmann, *Makromol. Chem.* **82**, 146 (1965).

2414. G. Manecke and P. Gergs, *Naturwissenschaften* **50**, 322 (1963).

2415. G. Manecke and K. F. Bonhoeffer, *Z. Elektrochem.* **55**, 475 (1951).

2416. G. Manecke and H. Heller, *Angew. Chem.* **72**, 523 (1960).

2417. G. Manecke and H. Heller, *Chem. Ber.* **95**, 2700 (1962).

2418. G. Manecke, H. P. Aurich, and P. Gergs, *Chem. Ber.* **99**, 2444 (1966).

2419. D. Mangrana, Span. 233,559 (1957); *C. A.* **52**, 3860.

2420. P. Manil and J. Fourneau, *Ann. Inst. Pasteur* **90**, 381 (1956).

2421. D. J. Mann and H. C. Kaufman (to Thiokol Chemical Corp.), U.S. 3,037,846 (1962).

2422. S. L. Mannatt, D. D. Elleman, and S. J. Brois, *J. Am. Chem. Soc.* **87**, 2220 (1965).

2423. J. F. Manning and D. J. McKendry (to Interchemical Corp.), U.S. 3,130,065 (1964).

2425. E. D. Manolov, *Farmatsiya (Sofia)* **14** (1), 11 (1964); via *C. A.* **61**, 11982.

2426. R. Mantsavinos and J. E. Christian, *J. Am. Pharm. Assoc.* **47**, 570 (1958).

2427. R. Mantsavinos and J. E. Christian, *Anal. Chem.* **30**, 1071 (1958).

2428. W. Marckwald and O. Frobenius, *Ber.* **34**, 3544 (1901).

2429. W. Marckwald, *Ber.* **33**, 764 (1900).

2430. W. Marconi *et al.*, *Gazz. Chim. Ital.* **92**, 1062 (1962); via *C. A.* **58**, 12507.

2431. B. S. V. Marek and J. Gneisz (to Société de la Viscose Suisse), U. S. 3,141,813 (1964); Ger. 1,226,409 (1966).

2431a. F. Marek, J. Bicanova, and F. Mikula, *Papir Celulosa* **22** (7), 183 (1967); via *C. A.* **67**, 109808.

2432. M. F. Margavio and J. D. Guthrie, *Am. Dyestuff Reptr.* **54**, P788 (1965).

2433. G. Mariani and L. Zannone, *Energia Nucl. Agri.* p. 353 (1963); via *Nucl. Sci. Abstr.* **17**, 38692.

2433a. D. Marinkovic and D. Kanazir, *Bull. Boris Kidrich Inst. Nucl. Sci.* 17 (2), 137 (1966); via *C. A.* **66**, 16550.

2434. E. Marjai and G. Ivanovics, *Acta Microbiol. Acad. Sci. Hung.* **11**, 193 (1964).

2434a. H. F. Mark (to Chemirad Corp.), U.S. 3,296,209 (1967); Brit. 1,014,152 (1965).

2435. R. Markiw and J. S. Roth, *Abstr. Papers, 152nd Am. Chem. Soc. Meeting, New York, 1966* abstr. C-61.

2436. V. I. Markov and S. I. Burmistrov, *Zh. Obshch. Khim.* **35**, 153 (1965); *J. Gen. Chem. USSR (English Transl.)* **35**, 153 (1965).

2437. V. I. Markov and S. I. Burmistrov, *Zh. Obshch. Khim.* **35**, 158 (1965); *J. Gen. Chem. USSR (English Transl.)* **35**, 158 (1965).
2438. V. I. Markov, S. I. Burmistrov, and O. N. Dolgopolov, *Zh. Obshch. Khim.* **35**, 162 (1965); *J. Gen. Chem. USSR (English Transl.)* **35**, 162 (1965).
2439. V. I. Markov and S. I. Burmistrov, U.S.S.R. 176,306 (1965); via *C. A.* **64**, 11175.
2439a. V. I. Markov, U.S.S.R. 209,454 (1968); via *C. A.* **69**, 35918 (but the abstract there should read CH_2N_2 instead of C_2H_2).
2440. Y. V. Markova, K. K. Kuzmina, and M. N. Shchukina, *Zh. Obshch. Khim.* **30**, 1039 (1960); *J. Gen. Chem. USSR (English Transl.)* **30**, 1054 (1960).
2441. F. D. Marsh and H. E. Simmons, *J. Am. Chem. Soc.* **87**, 3529 (1965).
2442. F. D. Marsh and M. E. Hermes, *J. Am. Chem. Soc.* **86**, 4506 (1964).
2443. J. T. Marsh, "Crease Resisting Fabrics." Reinhold, New York, 1962.
2443a. D. Martin and A. Weiss, *Chem. Ber.* **99**, 3367 (1966).
2443b. M. M. Martin and R. A. Koster, *J. Org. Chem.* **33**, 3428 (1968).
2444. A. P. Martinez, W. W. Lee, and L. Goodman, *J. Med. Chem.* **7**, 224 (1964).
2445. V. S. Martynov, A. N. Makarova, and A. Y. Berlin, *Biol. Aktivn. Soedin., Akad. Nauk SSSR* p. 129 (1965); via *C. A.* **63**, 18252.
2446. V. S. Martynov, A. N. Makarova, and A. Y. Berlin, *Zh. Obshch. Khim.* **34**, 2807 (1964); *J. Gen. Chem. USSR (English Transl.)* **34**, 2833 (1964).
2446a. V. S. Martynov, A. N. Makarova, and A. Y. Berlin, *Zh. Obshch. Khim.* **37**, 70 (1967); *J. Gen. Chem. USSR (English Transl.)* **37**, 62 (1967).
2447. T. Maruyama, N. Kuroki, and K. Konishi, *Bull. Univ. Osaka Prefect.* **A13**, 135 (1964); via *C. A.* **63**, 1913.
2448. A. Marxer, *Experientia* **11**, 184 (1955); *Helv. Chim. Acta* **39**, 335 (1956).
2450. A. Marxer, *Helv. Chim. Acta* **40**, 502 (1957); cf. *Chimia* **10**, 260 (1956).
2451. A. Marxer, *Helv. Chim. Acta* **38**, 1473 (1955).
2453. A. Marxer (to Ciba Corp.), U.S. 2,770,617 (1956); Brit. 809,535 (1959); Ger. 1,088,495 (1960); Swiss 340,231 (1959).
2454. A. Marxer (to Ciba, Ltd.), U.S. 2,802,001 (1957); Brit. 838,993 (1960); Ger. 1,117,585 (1961).
2455. A. Marxer (to Ciba Corp.), U.S. 2,833,760 (1958); Austrian 193,364 (1957); Brit. 821,924 (1959); Ger. 1,088,496 (1960) and 1,135,910 (1962).
2456. A. Marxer (to Ciba, Ltd.), U.S. 2,841,581 (1958); Brit. 825,557 and 825,558 (1959); Ger. 1,052,404 (1959).
2457. A. Marxer (to Ciba, Ltd.), U.S. 2,893,991 (1959); Ger. 1,067,818 (1959).
2458. A. Marxer (to Ciba, Ltd.), U.S. 3,040,030 (1962); Ger. 1,125,432 (1962); Brit. 888,303 (1962); Swiss 378,326 (1964); Indian 68,597 (1961).
2459. A. Marxer (to Ciba, Ltd.), U.S. 3,211,721 (1965); Austrian 214,839 (1958); Austral. 53,861 (1959); Brit. 884,258 (1961); Fr. 1,272,930 (1961); Ger. 1,129,955 (1962); Swiss 372,672 (1963).
2460. S. Masamune and N. T. Castellucci, *Angew. Chem.* **76**, 569 (1964); *Angew. Chem. Intern. Ed. Engl.* **3**, 582 (1964).
2461. H. C. Mason and F. F. Smith, *J. Econ. Entomol.* **60**, 1127 (1967).
2462. E. J. Masters and M. T. Bogert, *J. Am. Chem. Soc.* **64**, 2709 (1942).
2463. T. Masumoto and S. Yamazaki, Japan. 586 ('65).
2464. P. M. T. Matell, J. T. Tornquist, and O. R. Steijner, U.S. 3,242,183 (1966).
2468. R. A. Mathes (to B. F. Goodrich Co.), U.S. 2,376,796 (1945).
2469. R. A. Mathes and P. C. Jones (to B. F. Goodrich Co.), U.S. 2,407,566 (1946).
2470. R. A. Mathes (to B. F. Goodrich Co.), U.S. 2,422,578 (1947).
2471. L. Mathus, *Bull. Soc. Chim. Belges* **34**, 285 (1925).

2472. K. Matsubayashi and O. Fukushima (to Kurashiki Rayon Co.), U.S. 3,137,675 (1964); Belg. 665,403 (1965); Fr. 1,450,593 (1966); Brit. 1,104,632 and 1,104,633 (1968).
2473. K. Matsui and Y. Soeda, *Yuki Gosei Kagaku Kyokai Shi* **20**, 354 (1962); via *C. A.* **57**, 991.
2474. K. Matsui *et al.*, *Yuki Gosei Kagaku Kyokai Shi* **20**, 363 (1962); via *C. A.* **57**, 991.
2475. K. Matsui and Y. Soeda, *Yuki Gosei Kagaku Kyokai Shi* **20**, 371 (1962); via *C. A.* **57**, 990.
2476. K. Matsui, E. Kobayashi, and K. Suzuki, *Yuki Gosei Kagaku Kyokai Shi* **20**, 445 (1962); via *C. A.* **57**, 4793.
2477. K. Matsui and M. Soeda, Japan. 11,442 ('63); via *C. A.* **60**, 13354.
2477a. M. Matsui *et al.* (to Kyowa Fermentation Industry Co.), U.S. 3,410,867 (1968); Japan. 21,853 ('65); Brit. 1,090,707 (1967).
2478. S. Matsuo and H. Konishi (to Daiichi Kogyo Seiyaku Co., Ltd.), U.S. 3,312,070 (1967).
2479. H. Matsuura, S. Tanifuji and M. Iwafuchi, *J. Fac. Sci., Hokkaido Univ., Ser.* V **8**, 57 (1962); via *C. A.* **60**, 14814.
2480. H. Matsuura *et al.*, *J. Fac. Sci., Hokkaido Univ., Ser.* V **8**, 75 (1962); via *C. A.* **60**, 14814.
2481. W. J. Mattox (to Esso Research and Engineering Co.), U.S. 3,291,566 (1966).
2483. T. Maxia, *Rend. Seminario Fac. Sci. Univ. Cagliari* **36**, 51 (1966); via *C. A.* **66**, 45762.
2484. C. S. Maxwell, *Ind. Eng. Chem.* **55** (5), 31 (1963).
2485. R. E. Maxwell and V. S. Nickel, *Science* **120**, 270 (1954).
2486. G. Mayr and G. C. Rabotti, *Experientia* **13**, 252 (1957).
2487. E. D. Mazzarella and E. Dalton (to National Starch and Chemical Corp.), U.S. 3,320,080 (1967); Neth. appl. 6,507,161 (1965).
2488. L. W. Mazzeno, Jr., R. M. Reinhardt, and W. A. Reeves, *Am. Dyestuff Reptr.* **52**, P909 (1963).
2489. E. T. McBee, Office of Ordnance Research Rept. No. 1395:5 (AD 254,983); via *U.S. Govt. Res. Rept.* **36**, 14.
2489a. L. J. McCabe (to Mobil Oil Corp.), U.S. 3,399,041 (1968).
2490. E. R. McCall, *Appl. Spectry.* **18**, 81 (1965).
2491. J. C. McClendon and C. R. Dick (to The Dow Chemical Co.), U.S. 3,262,991 (1966).
2492. H. H. McClure, *Can. Pulp Paper Ind.* **17** (6), 48 (1964).
2493. J. S. McConaghy, Jr. and W. Lwowski, *J. Am. Chem. Soc.* **89**, 2357 (1967).
2494. J. S. McConaghy, Jr. and W. Lwowski, *J. Am. Chem. Soc.* **89**, 4450 (1967).
2495. J. E. W. McConnell and C. P. Collier, U.S. 3,042,533 (1962).
2496. E. M. McCray, Jr. and H. F. Schoof, *J. Econ. Entomol.* **60**, 60 (1967).
2496a. R. S. McDaniel and A. C. Oehlschlager, *Can. J. Chem.* **46**, 2316 (1968).
2497. A. W. McDonald, G. C. Humphreys, and J. N. Grant, *Textile Res. J.* **30**, 312 (1960).
2498. M. J. McDowell and E. R. Werner, Jr. (to du Pont de Nemours and Co.), U.S. 3,261,797 (1966); Belg. 671,509 (1966).
2499. M. J. McDowell and T. B. Hill (to du Pont de Nemours and Co.), U.S. 3,309,331 (1967).
2500. S. M. McElvain and T. A. Lies, *J. Am. Chem. Soc.* **82**, 164 (1960).
2501. S. M. McElvain and E. H. Pryde, *J. Am. Chem. Soc.* **71**, 326 (1949).
2501a. R. T. McFadden (to The Dow Chemical Co.), U.S. 3,336,358 (1967); Belg. 667,260 (1966); Fr. 1,441,131 (1966); Ital. 719,679 (1966); Can. 771,701 (1967); Brit. 1,090,228 (1968).
2502. R. T. McFadden and C. R. Dick (to The Dow Chemical Co.), U.S. 3,338,954 (1967); Belg. 701,074 (1968).

2503. G. H. McIntyre, Jr., B. P. Block, and W. C. Fernelius, *J. Am. Chem. Soc.* **81**, 529 (1959).

2504. A. F. McKay, D. L. Garmaise, and A. Halasz, *Can. J. Chem.* **34**, 1567 (1956).

2505. A. D. McKelvie, *Nature* **195**, 409 (1962); *Radiation Botany* **3**, 105 (1963).

2506. P. D. McKercher and A. R. Giordasso, *Arch. Ges. Virusforsch.* **20**, 34 and 54 (1957).

2507. D. E. McLaughlin *et al.*, *J. Inorg. & Nucl. Chem.* **18**, 118 (1961).

2509. O. J. McMillan, Jr. *et al.*, *Am. Dyestuff Reptr.* **48** (17), 37 (1959).

2510. C. H. McMullen and C. J. Stirling, *J. Chem. Soc., B, Phys. Org.* p. 1217 (1966).

2510a. J. S. Meek and J. S. Fowler, *J. Org. Chem.* **33**, 3418 (1968).

2511. G. Meguerian and L. B. Clapp, *J. Am. Chem. Soc.* **73**, 486 (1951).

2512. G. Meguerian and L. B. Clapp, *J. Am. Chem. Soc.* **73**, 2121 (1951).

2513. R. Meier, B. Schaer, and L. Neipp, *Experientia* **10**, 74 (1954).

2514. W. Meier (to I. G. Farbenindustrie), U.S. 2,122,801 (1938); Fr. 808,310 (1937); Brit. 476,431 (1937); Ger. 644,925 (1937); Neth. 44,824 (1939).

2515. D. W. Meifert, R. L. Fye, and G. C. LaBrecque, *Florida Entomologist* **46**, 161 (1963).

2516. D. W. Meifert *et al.*, *J. Econ. Entomol.* **60**, 480 (1967).

2517. J. Meinwald, Y. C. Meinwald, and T. N. Baker, III, *J. Am. Chem. Soc.* **86**, 4074 (1964).

2518. T. Meirovics and G. Vanags, *Latvijas PSR Zinatnu Akad. Vestis, Khim. Ser.* p. 102 (1966); via *C. A.* **65**, 13626.

2519. J. Meisenheimer and L.-H. Chou, *Ann. Chem.* **539**, 70 (1939).

2520. S. Melamed (to Rohm and Haas Co.), U.S. 2,694,693 (1954); Brit. 763,634 and 763,635 (1956); Ger. 1,025,878 (1958).

2521. S. Melamed and W. H. Watanabe (to Rohm and Haas Co.), U.S. 2,816,094 (1957).

2522. H. J. Melching and C. Straffer, *Progr. Drug Res.* **9**, 11 (1966).

2523. L. B. Mellett and L. A. Woods, *Cancer Res.* **20**, 518 (1960).

2524. L. B. Mellett, P. E. Hodgson, and L. A. Woods, *J. Lab. Clin. Med.* **60**, 818 (1962).

2525. L. B. Mellett and L. A. Woods, *Cancer Res.* **20**, 524 (1960).

2526. G. A. Melson and R. G. Wilkins, *J. Chem. Soc.* p. 4208 (1962).

2526a. P. G. Mente, H. W. Heine, and G. R. Scharoubim, *J. Org. Chem.* **33**, 4547 (1968).

2526b. A. I. Meos *et al.*, U.S.S.R. 192,404 (1967); via *C. A.* **68**, 79073.

2527. E. Merck A.-G., Ger. 1,054,088 (1959); *C. A.* **55**, 8439.

2528. Merck and Co., Inc., Belg. 650,279 (1965); via *C. A.* **64**, 7976.

2529. Merck and Co., Inc., Brit. 963,627 (1964); Japan. 5934 ('64); Fr. 1,519,483 (1968).

2530. Merck and Co., Inc., Ger. 1,184,348 (1964); *C. A.* **62**, 11646.

2531. E. Merck A.-G., Ger. 1,147,577 (1963); via *Chem. Ber.* **98**, 186.

2532. G. Mergina, *Latvijas PSR Zinatnu Akad. Vestis* No. 6, p. 97 (1962); via *C. A.* **57**, 17330.

2533. T. Mertz, *Science* **133**, 329 (1961).

2533a. K. J. Mesec (to du Pont de Nemours and Co.), U.S. 3,386,939 (1968).

2534. Metallgesellschaft A.-G., Neth. appl. 6,517,136 (1966); via *C. A.* **66**, 29546.

2535. D. F. Mettrick and J. R. Parnell, *Exptl. Parasitol.* **20**, 17 (1967).

2536. H. Metzger and K. Seelert, *Z. Naturforsch.* **18b**, 335 (1963).

2537. J. Metzger and J.-L. Larice, *Bull. Soc. Chim. France* p. 575 (1965).

2538. W. Meyer zu Reckendorf, *Chem. Ber.* **97**, 325 (1964).

2539. W. Meyer zu Reckendorf, *Chem. Ber.* **98**, 93 (1965).

2540. W. E. Meyer, J. B. Patrick, and J. H. Mowat (to American Cyanamid Co.), U.S. 3,226,393 (1965).

2541. W. E. Meyer and J. H. Mowat (to American Cyanamid Co.), U.S. 3,230,233 (1966).

2542. J. V. Michael and W. A. Noyes, Jr., *J. Am. Chem. Soc.* **85**, 1228 (1963).

2543. A. Michaelis, H. Nicoloff, and R. Rieger, *Biochem. Biophys. Res. Commun.* **9**, 280 (1962).
2544. A. Michaelis and R. Rieger, *Nature* **199**, 1014 (1963).
2545. A. S. Michaels (to Amicon Corp.), U.S. 3,271,496 (1966).
2546. F. Micheel and W. Leifels, *Mikrochim. Acta* p. 467 (1961).
2547. F. Micheel and W. Schminke, *Chem. Ber.* **91**, 984 (1958).
2548. J. G. Michels and G. Gever, *J. Am. Chem. Soc.* **78**, 5349 (1956).
2549. Midland Silicones Ltd., Brit. 802,540 (1958).
2550. B. M. Mikhailov and T. K. Kozminskaya, *Zh. Obshch. Khim.* **26**, 2042 (1956); *J. Gen. Chem. USSR (English Transl.)* **26**, 2275 (1956); L. F. Larionov, *Acta Unio Intern. Contra Cancrum* **13**, 393 (1957); via *C. A.* **52**, 4853.
2551. V. A. Mikhalev, M. I. Dorokhova, and N. E. Smolina, *Zh. Obshch. Khim.* **30**, 3714 (1960); *J. Gen. Chem. USSR (English Transl.)* **30**, 3679 (1960).
2551a. U. Mikstais, I. Lavrinovics, and A. Arens Rizh, *Zh. Org. Khim.* **4**, 313 (1968); *J. Org. Chem. USSR (English Transl.)* 4, 304 (1968).
2552. Miles Laboratories Inc., Belg. 612,789 (1962); Brit. 998,521 (1965).
2553. S. H. Miles, *Am. Dyestuff Reptr.* **53**, P440 (1965).
2554. T. D. Miles, F. A. Hoffman, and A. Merola, *Am. Dyestuff Reptr.* **49**, P596 (1960).
2555. T. D. Miles, F. A. Hoffman, and A. Merola (to U.S. Secretary of the Army), U.S. 3,085,029 (1963).
2556. T. D. Miles and A. C. Delasanta, *Anal. Chem.* **31**, 2051 (1959).
2557. E. S. Millar, *New Zealand J. Agr. Res.* **8**, 295 (1965).
2558. D. J. Millen and J. Zabicky, *Nature* **196**, 889 (1962).
2559. D. J. Millen and J. Zabicky, *J. Chem. Soc.* p. 3080 (1965).
2560. B. Miller and D. W. Long (to American Cyanamid Co.), U.S. 3,172,888 (1965); Fr. 1,282,807 (1962); Brit. 948,522 (1964).
2560a. B. Miller and D. W. Long (to American Cyanamid Co.), U.S. 3,395,224 (1968).
2560b. E. E. Miller and K. C. Tsou, *Cancer Res.* **27**, 1496 (1967).
2561. G. R. Miller *et al.* (to The Dow Chemical Co.), U.S. 3,336,294 (1967); Belg. 594,895 (1961); Brit. 933,528 (1965); Can. 649,353 (1962) reissued as 662,407 (1963); Fr. 1,266,865 (1961); Japan. 2481 ('64).
2562. G. R. Miller (to The Dow Chemical Co.), U.S. 3,240,776 (1966); Neth. appl. 6,516,581 (1966); Belg. 767,079 (1966); Ital. 735,576 (1966); Fr. 1,460,279 (1967); Brit. 1,075,524 (1967); Can. 761,453 (1967).
2562a. R. Miller, F. C. Loveless, and M. Farber (to Uniroyal Inc.), U.S. 3,361,843 (1968); United States Rubber Co., Neth. appl. 6,507,660 (1965).
2562b. R. Miller, M. Farber, and F. C. Loveless (to Uniroyal, Inc.), U.S. 3,399,251 (1968); Fr. addn. 91,789 (1968); Brit. 1,118,685 (1968).
2563. E. J. Mills and M. T. Bogert, *J. Am. Chem. Soc.* **62**, 1173 (1940).
2563a. N. Milstein, *J. Chem. Eng. Data* **13**, 275 (1968).
2563b. N. Milstein, *J. Heterocyclic Chem.* **5**, 339 (1968).
2564. F. Minisci, R. Galli, and M. Cecere, *Chim. Ind. (Milan)* **48**, 132 (1966); via *C. A.* **64**, 12514.
2565. F. Minisci and R. Galli, *Tetrahedron Letters* p. 167 (1964).
2566. F. Minisci, R. Galli, and M. Cecere, *Chim. Ind. (Milan)* **48**, 347 (1966); via *C. A.* **65**, 2140.
2567. Minnesota Mining and Manufacturing Co., Belg. 673,549 (1966); Fr. 1,473,350 (1967); via *C. A.* **67**, 86474.
2568. Minnesota Mining and Manufacturing Co., Neth. appl. 6,602,416 (1967).
2569. Minnesota Mining and Manufacturing Co., Brit. 954,195 (1964); Can. 680,335 (1964).
2570. Minnesota Mining and Manufacturing Co., Brit. 956,006 (1964).

2571. Minnesota Mining and Manufacturing Co., Brit. 956,008 (1964).

2573. Minnesota Mining and Manufacturing Co., Fr. 1,284,105 (1962); Japan. 13,347 ('66); Can. 680,335 (1964); via *Chem. Zentr.* No. 10, abstr. 29 (1966).

2574. Minnesota Mining and Manufacturing Co., Fr. 1,437,500 (1966); Brit. 1,106,642, 1,106,643, and 1,107,260 (1968); Ger. 1,259,333 (1968).

2575. J. L. Minocha and T. J. Arnason, *Can. J. Genet. Cytol.* **5**, 105 (1963).

2576. Y. Minoura, M. Takebayashi, and C. C. Price, *J. Am. Chem. Soc.* **81**, 4689 (1959).

2577. H. N. Mirkina and V. T. Kharlamov, *Metody Analiza Radioaktivn. Preparatov, Sb. Statei* p. 155 (1965); via *C. A.* **63**, 9744.

2577a. R. L. Mitchell, C. F. Murphy, and D. Allen (to Rayonier Inc.), U.S. 3,364,061 (1968); Belg. 659,913 (1965); Neth. appl. 6,501,570 (1966).

2578. R. W. Mitchell, J. C. Burr, Jr., and J. A. Merritt, *Spectrochim. Acta* **23A**, 195 (1967).

2579. R. A. Mitsch, E. W. Neuvar, and P. H. Ogden, *J. Heterocyclic Chem.* **4**, 389 (1967).

2580. Mitsubishi Rayon Co., Ltd., Japan. 10,497 ('65).

2580a. Mitsubishi Rayon Co., Ltd., Japan. 26,868 ('67); via *POST-P* **3**, 87.

2580b. S. Miyamura *et al.*, *J. Antibiotics* (*Tokyo*) **A20** (2), 72 (1967); *C. A.* **67**, 61785.

2581. T. Mizuma, Y. Minaki, and S. Toyoshima, *Yakugaku Zasshi* **81**, 48 (1961); via *C. A.* **55**, 13403.

2582. T. Mizuma, Y. Minaki, and S. Toyoshima, *Yakugaku Zasshi* **81**, 51 (1961); via *C. A.* **55**, 12379.

2583. K. Mizutani, E. Shiraki, and S. Suzuki, *Kogyo Kagaku Zasshi* **63**, 1514 (1960); via *C. A.* **56**, 13113.

2584. Mobil Oil Co., Belg. 696,807 (1967).

2585. J. G. Moffatt and H. G. Khorana, *J. Am. Chem. Soc.* **83**, 663 (1961).

2586. M. Mokotoff, *J. Org. Chem.* **33**, 2556 (1968).

2587. J. L. Moilliet, ed., "Waterproofing and Water-Repellency." American Elsevier Publishing Co., New York, 1963.

2588. J. D. C. Mole and E. E. Turner, *Chem. & Ind.* (*London*) p. 582 (1939).

2589. Monsanto Co., S. Afr. 67/0210; Neth. appl. 6,614,764 (1967); Fr. 1,502,976 (1967).

2589a. Monsanto Co., Fr. 1,517,784 (1968).

2590. Monsanto Co., Brit. 1,069,087 and 1,069,752 (1967); Belg. 648,691 (1964); Fr. 1,401,564 (1965).

2591. Monsanto Co., Brit. 1,113,039 (1968).

2592. "Montecatini" Societa . . ., Japan. 2469 ('66).

2593. "Montecatini" Societa . . ., Belg. 635,081 (1963); Brit. 1,029,635 (1966); Fr. 1,367,086 (1964); Ital. 678,674 (1964); Neth. 295,229 (1965).

2594. "Montecatini" Societa . . ., Fr. 1,446,285 (1966); via *C. A.* **66**, 56535.

2595. "Montecatini" Societa . . ., Austral. appl. 50,219 (1959).

2596. "Montecatini" Societa . . ., Ital. 587,008 (1959), via *C. A.* **55**, 10910; Austral. appl. 57,463 (1960); Ger. 1,251,903 (1967).

2597. "Montecatini" Societa . . ., Hung. 149,766 (1962); Can. 687,254 (1964); via *Chem. Zentr.* p. 18682 (1963).

2598. "Montecatini" Societa . . ., Ital. 584,249 (1958); via *C. A.* **53**, 22973.

2599. "Montecatini" Societa . . ., Ital. 608,856 (1960); Fr. 1,248,765 (1961); Indian 70,732 (1961); Brit. 893,604 (1962).

2600. "Montecatini" Societa . . ., Austral. appl. 59,572 (1960); Austrian 219,001 (1962); Brit. 942,131 (1963); Ger. 1,170,363 (1964).

2601. "Montecatini" Societa . . ., Belg. 627,902 (1963); Brit. 960,798 (1964) and 992,012 (1965).

2602. "Montecatini" Societa . . ., Neth. appl. 6,605,286 (1966); via *C. A.* **66**, 66286; Fr. 1,477,211 (1967); via *C. A.* **67**, 82771.

2603. "Montecatini" Societa . . ., Neth. appl. 6,502,828 (1965); Belg. 661,113 (1965); Brit. 1,092,786 (1967).

2604. "Montecatini" Societa . . ., Belg. 680,114 (1966); Neth. appl. 6,605,287 (1966).

2605. "Montecatini" Societa . . ., Ger. 1,238,214 (1967); via *C. A.* **67**, 64895.

2606. G. Montegudet, *Peintures, Pigments, Vernis* **34**, 204, 271, and 311 (1958).

2607. G. Montegudet, *Compt. Rend.* **242**, 1998 (1956).

2608. J. E. Moore and C. E. Pardo, Jr. (to U.S. Department of Agriculture), U.S. 2,925,317. (1960).

2608a. J. Moravec and J. Smrt, *Coll. Czech. Chem. Commun,* **33**, 1768 (1968).

2609. J. P. Moreau, S. E. Elizey, Jr., and G. L. Drake, Jr., *Am. Dyestuff Reptr.* **56**, 117 (1967).

2609a. J. P. Moreau and G. L. Drake, Jr., *Am. Dyestuff Reptr.* **57**, 683 (1968).

2610. P. B. Morgan and G. C. LaBrecque, *J. Econ. Entomol.* **55**, 626 (1962).

2611. P. B. Morgan and G. C. LaBrecque, *J. Econ. Entomol.* **57**, 896 (1964).

2612. P. B. Morgan, *Abstr. Papers, 150th Am. Chem. Soc. Meeting, Atlantic City, 1965* p. A-27.

2613. P. B. Morgan *et al., J. Econ. Entomol.* **60**, 1064 (1967).

2613a. L. M. Morozovskaya *et al., Khim. Org. Soedin. Fosfora* ..., p. 223 (1967); ⸢via *C. A.* **69**, 77047.

2614. H. G. Morren, Brit. 750,363 (1956).

2614a. E. R. Morris and J. C. J. Thynne, *Trans. Faraday Soc.* **64**, 3021 (1968).

2615. D. C. Morrison (to Fundamental Research Co.), U.S. 3,294,838 (1966).

2616. D. F. Morrow and M. E. Butler, *J. Heterocyclic Chem.* **1**, 53 (1964).

2616a. F. S. Mortimer, *J. Mol. Spectry.* **5**, 199 (1960).

2617. Morton Salt Co., Fr. 1,399,731 (1965); Brit. 1,046,295 (1966).

2618. V. S. Mosienko, V. F. Novikova, and N. D. Dumbadze, *Lab. Delo* p. 430 (1967); via *C. A.* **67**, 72143.

2619. R. D. Moss and P. M. Hamilton (to The Dow Chemical Co.), U.S. 3,147,307 (1964).

2620. H. Moureu *et al., Bull. Soc. Chim. France* p. 296 (1952).

2621. H. Moureu and P. Chovin, with M. Ducros, *Bull. Soc. Chim. France* p. 586 (1953).

2622. H. Moureu and C. Dufraisse, *Bull. Soc. Chim. France* **41**, 850 (1927).

2623. H. Moureau, P. Chovin, and L. Petit, *Compt. Rend.* **243**, 910 (1956); *Bull. Soc. Chim. France* p. 1785 (1956).

2624. H. Moureau, P. Chovin, and L. Petit, *Bull. Soc. Chim. France* p. 1573 (1955).

2626. M. Mousseron, F. Winternitz, and R. Dennilauler, *Compt. Rend.* **239**, 278 (1954).

2627. M. Mousseron, F. Winternitz, and R. Dennilauler, *Compt. Rend.* **241**, 805 (1955).

2628. J. Moutschen, *Genetics* **46**, 291 (1961).

2629. C. L. Moyle and R. L. Johnson (to The Dow Chemical Co.), U.S. 3,033,746 (1962); Belg. 615,597 (1962); Fr. 1,318,112 (1963); Ital. 684,950 (1962); Ger. 1,160,140 (1964); Can. 678,149 (1964); Brit. 964,186 (1964).

2630. D. E. Muehlberg and F. N. Teumac (to The Dow Chemical Co.), U.S. 3,282,851 (1966).

2631. E. Mueller and E. W. Schmidt, *Chem. Ber.* **97**, 2614 (1964).

2632. G. T. S. Mugnozza and L. M. Monti, *Mutation Res.* **3**, 298 (1966).

2633. L. E. Mukhina and A. A. Kropacheva, *Zh. Obshch. Khim.* **38**, 313 (1968); via *C. A.* **69**, 59168.

2634. M. S. Mulla, *Mosquito News* **24**, 212 (1964).

2634a. L. L. Miller and J. Hamer, "1,2-Cycloaddition Reactions. The Formation of Three- and Four-Membered Heterocycles," p. 5. Wiley (Interscience), New York, 1967.

2635. H. Murakami, *J. Theoret. Biol.* **10**, 236 (1966).
2636. M. Murakami and T. Fukumoto, *Mem. Inst. Sci. Ind. Res., Osaka Univ.* **12**, 169 (1955); via *C. A.* **50**, 16700.
2637. M. Murakami and T. Fukumoto, *Nippon Kagaku Zasshi* **76**, 270 (1955); via *C. A.* **51**, 17805.
2637a. T. Murakami, S. Morisaki, and K. Hiiro (to Hodogaya Chemical Co.), U.S. 3,260,702 (1966); Brit. 1,030,394 (1966).
2638. Kh. L. Muravich-Aleksandr, A. V. El'tsov, and M. B. Kolesova, *Sintez Prirodn. Soedin.* . . . p. 251 (1965); via *C. A.* **65**, 3875.
2639. T. Muroi *et al.*, *Seni-i Gakkaishi* **15**, 833 (1959); via *C. A.* **54**, 1918.
2640. T. Muroi (to Japan, Bureau of Industrial Technics), U.S. 3,154,479 (1964); Fr. 1,229,071 (1960); Ger. 1,129,925 (1962); Brit. 923,851 (1963).
2641. A. L. Murphy, M. F. Margavio, and C. M. Welch, *Am. Dyestuff Reptr.* **53**, P42 (1964).
2644. W. S. Murray and W. E. Bickley, *Univ. Maryland, Agr. Expt. Sta., Bull.* **A-134** (1964).
2645. C. M. Murvosh, G. C. LaBrecque, and C. N. Smith, *J. Econ. Entomol.* **57**, 89 (1964).
2646. D. R. Mussell, U.S. 2,745,815 (1956); Ger. 1,031,324 (1958).
2647. A. Mustafa, S. M. A. D. Sayed, and S. Khattab, *J. Am. Chem. Soc.* **78**, 145 (1956).
2648. N. V. Onderzoekings Instituut Research, Belg. 612,198 (1962); Neth. 103,985 (1963); Brit. 962,174 (1964).
2649. H. M. Nachf, Fr. M3014 (1965); Brit. 1,049,424 (1966); Ger. 1,240,868 (1967).
2649a. M. V. Nadkarni, E. I. Goldenthal, and P. K. Smith, *Cancer Res.* **14**, 559 (1954).
2649b. L. E. Nagan (to Nalco Chemical Co.), U.S. 3,131,144 (1964).
2650. K. Nagarajan and C. L. Kulkarni, *Tetrahedron Letters* p. 2717 (1968).
2650a. H. T. Nagasawa and H. R. Gutmann, *J. Org. Chem.* **23**, 487 (1958).
2651. H. T. Nagasawa and J. A. Elberling, *Tetrahedron Letters* p. 5393 (1966).
2652. S. Nagasawa and H. Shinohara, *Entomol. Exptl. Appl.* **6**, 263 (1963).
2653. S. Nagasawa and H. Shinohara, *Japan. J. Appl. Entomol. Zool.* **9**, 271 (1965); via *Rev. Appl. Entomol.* **A53**, 488.
2654. S. Nagasawa and H. Shinohara, *Japan. J. Appl. Entomol. Zool.* **8**, 272 (1964); via *Rev. Appl. Entomol.* **A54**, 151.
2655. W. Nagata *et al.*, *J. Am. Chem. Soc.* **89**, 5045 (1967).
2655a. W. Nagata *et al.*, *J. Am. Chem. Soc.* **89**, 5046 (1967); **90**, 1650 (1968).
2656. K. G. Naik, R. K. Trivedi, and S. M. Mehta, *J. Indian Chem. Soc.* **20**, 369 (1943).
2657. H. Najer *et al.*, *Bull. Soc. Chim. France* p. 323 (1963).
2658. H. Najer *et al.*, *Compt. Rend.* **253**, 2369 (1961).
2659. K. Nakabayashi (to Sumitomo Chemical Co.), U.S. 3,014,902 (1962); Japan. 13,943 ('60) and 10,349 ('61); Can. 599,191 (1960); Brit. 845,823 (1960); Fr. 1,294,104 (1962); Ger. 1,227,613 (1966).
2660. N. Nakabayashi and Y. Iwakura, *Makromol. Chem.* **81**, 180 (1965).
2661. N. Nakabayashi, E. Masuhara, and Y. Iwakura, *Makromol. Chem.* **107**, 94 (1967).
2662. K. Nakajima, *Nippon Kagaku Zasshi* **82**, 737 (1961); via *C. A.* **59**, 617.
2663. M. Nakajima and R. Oshima, Japan. 2110 ('54); via *C. A.* **49**, 2088.
2664. M. Nakajima and R. Oshima, Japan. 2518 ('57); via *C. A.* **52**, 4997.
2665. M. Nakamura and M. Takashima, Japan. 588 ('65).
2666. Y. Nakao, *Japan. J. Genet.* **40**, Suppl., 107 (1965); via *C. A.* **65**, 10931.
2667. N. S. Nametkin, I. A. Grushevenko, and V. N. Perchenko, *Dokl. Akad. Nauk SSSR* **162**, 347 (1965); *Proc. Acad. Aci. USSR, Chem. Sect.* (*English Transl.*) **160–162**, 468 (1965).

2668. N. S. Nametkin, V. N. Perchenko, and I. A. Grushevenko, *Dokl. Akad. Nauk SSSR* **158**, 404 (1964); *Proc. Acad. Sci. USSR, Chem. Sect.* (*English Transl.*) **157–159**, 898 (1964).

2669. N. S. Nametkin, V. N. Perchenko, and L. G. Batalova, *Dokl. Akad. Nauk SSSR* **158**, 660 (1964); *Proc. Acad. Sci. USSR, Chem. Sect.* (*English Transl.*) **157–159**, 953 (1964).

2670. N. S. Nametkin, V. N. Perchenko, and L. G. Batalova, *Dokl. Akad. Nauk SSSR* **160**, 1087 (1965); *Proc. Acad. Sci. USSR, Chem. Sect.* (*English Transl.*) **160–162**, 167 (1965).

2671. N. S. Nametkin, I. A. Grushevenko, and V. N. Perchenko, *Izv. Akad. Nauk SSSR, Ser. Khim.* p. 737 (1966); *Bull. Acad. Sci. USSR, Div. Chem. Sci.* (*English Transl.*) p. 699 (1966).

2672. N. S. Nametkin *et al.*, *Intern. Symp. Organosilicon Chem., Sci. Commun., Prague, 1965* p. 323. Prague, 1965; via *C. A.* **65**, 8948.

2673. N. S. Nametkin *et al.*, *Khim. Geterotsikl. Soedin., Akad. Nauk Latv. SSR* p. 106 (1967); via *C. A.* **67**, 21960.

2673a. N. S. Nametkin, V. S. Perchenko, and E. S. Vasil'eva, *Izv. Akad. Nauk SSSR, Ser. Khim.* p. 213 (1968); via *C. A.* **69**, 86712.

2674. V. L. Narayanan (to E. R. Squibb and Co., Inc.), U.S. 3,300,480 (1966); Neth. appl. 6,613,252 (1967).

2675. C. P. Nash and G. E. Maciel, *J. Phys. Chem.* **68**, 832 (1964).

2676. A. H. Nathan and M. T. Bogert, *J. Am. Chem. Soc.* **63**, 2361 (1941).

2677. U. S. National Bureau of Standards, *Natl. Bur. Std.* (*U.S.*), *Monograph* **34**, Vol. 2, Sect. 432.475 (1964).

2677a. National Cash Register Co., Ger. 1,265,130 (1968); *C. A.* **68**, 106154.

2677b. National Starch and Chemical Corp., Brit. 1,101,758 (1968).

2677c. National Starch and Chemical Co., Fr. 1,499,781 (1967); via *C. A.* **69**, 60169.

2678. Nationale Zetmeelindustrie N. V., Brit. 944,804 (1963).

2679. V. A. Naumov, *Dokl. Akad. Nauk SSSR* **169**, 839 (1966); via *C. A.* **65**, 17819.

2679a. M. M. Nawar, *Dissertation Abstr.* **B27**, 44 (1966).

2680. R. S. Neale, *Tetrahedron Letters* p. 483 (1966).

2681. R. S. Neale and R. L. Hinman, *J. Am. Chem. Soc.* **85**, 2666 (1963).

2682. R. S. Neale, *J. Am. Chem. Soc.* **86**, 5340 (1964).

2683. R. S. Neale, *J. Org. Chem.* **32**, 3263 (1967).

2684. R. S. Neale and N. L. Marcus, *J. Org. Chem.* **32**, 3273 (1967).

2685. P. W. Neber and A. Friedolsheim, *Ann. Chem.* **449**, 109 (1926).

2686. R. Neidlein and W. Haussmann, *Angew. Chem.* **77**, 506 (1965); *Angew. Chem. Intern. Ed. Engl.* **4**, 521 (1965); *Arch. Pharm.* **300**, 609 (1967).

2687. J. Nelles, *Publication Board Rept.* (*U.S.*) PB 76479 (1939).

2688. J. Nelles, E. Tietz, and O. Bayer (to General Aniline and Film Corp.), U.S. 2,233,296 (1941); I. G. Farbenindustrie A.-G., Belg. 449,535 (1943).

2689. J. Nelles and O. Bayer (to I. G. Farbenindustrie A.-G.), U.S. 2,302,362 (1942); Ger. 732,087 (1943).

2690. R. A. Nelson and R. S. Jessup, *J. Res. Natl. Bur. Std.* **48**, 206 (1952).

2691. V. G. Nemets and G. G. Tsybaeva, *Tr. Leningr. Tekhnol. Inst. im. Lensoveta* **60**, 49 (1960); via *C. A.* **55**, 20943.

2692. A. Nersasian, K. F. King, and I. R. Johnson, *J. Appl. Polymer Sci.* **8**, 337 (1964).

2693. R. G. Neville and G. Gorin, *J. Am. Chem. Soc.* **78**, 4893 (1956).

2694. F. C. Newmaker, Jr. (to The Dow Chemical Co.), U.S. 3,096,602 (1963); Belg. 630,735 (1963).

2695. M. Nickerson and W. S. Gump, *J. Pharmacol. Exptl. Therap.* **97**, 25 (1949).

2696. M. Nickerson, *Pharmacol. Rev.* **1**, 27 (1949).
2698. M. Nickerson, L. S. Goodman, and G. Nomaguchi, *J. Pharmacol.* **89**, 167 (1947).
2699. R. Nicoletti and M. L. Forcellese, *Tetrahedron Letters* p. 153 (1965); *Gazz. Chim. Ital.* **97**, 148 (1967); *C. A.* **67**, 32540.
2700. R. Nicoletti, M. L. Forcellese, and C. Germani, *Gazz. Chim. Ital.* **97**, 685 (1967); *C. A.* **67**, 64153.
2701. E. E. Nifant'ev, A. I. Gavrilova, and N. K. Bliznyuk, *Zh. Obshch. Khim.* **36**, 363 (1966); *J. Gen. Chem. USSR (English Transl.)* **36**, 377 (1966).
2701a. E. E. Nifant'ev, A. I. Zavalishina, and I. V. Komlev, *Zh. Obshch. Khim.* **37**, 2497 (1967); via *C. A.* **68**, 87347.
2702. S. V. Nikol'aeva, L. D. Protsenko, and K. A. Kornev, *Farmakol. i Toksikol. Sb.* No. 1, 103 (1964); via *C. A.* **64**, 14890.
2703. Nippon Antibiotic Substances Science Assoc., Japan. 2898 ('56); via *C. A.* **51**, 9100.
2705. A. Nishihara, Y. Mineki, and M. Sekino, *Rept. Res. Lab., Asahi Glass Co., Ltd.* **6**, 20 (1956); via *C. A.* **50**, 12351.
2706. A. Nishihara (to Asahi Glass Co.), U.S. 3,152,061 (1964).
2707. H. Nishimoto, *Nippon Gomu Kyokaishi* **36**, 1020 (1963); via *C. A.* **61**, 3263.
2708. H. Nishimura and H. Takamatsu, *Yakugaku Zasshi* **84**, 817 (1964); via *C. A.* **62**, 1588.
2709. Nisshin Fibers Co., Japan. 3999 ('55); via *C. A.* **51**, 13414.
2710. Nisshin Spinning Co., Ltd., Japan. 16,462 ('62); via *C. A.* **59**, 10285.
2711. Nisshin Spinning Co., Ltd., Japan. 29,011 ('65); via *C. A.* **64**, 11356.
2712. Nisshin Spinning Co., Ltd., Japan. 6235 ('66); via *C. A.* **65**, 7356.
2713. Nisshin Textiles Co., Japan. 3499 ('52); via *C. A.* **47**, 8386.
2714. Nisso Chemical Industries, Ltd., Japan. 13,490 ('64); via *C. A.* **62**, 2860.
2715. Nisso Chemical Industries, Ltd., Japan. 18,179 ('64).
2716. Nisso Chemical Industries, Ltd., Japan. 8137 ('67); via *C. A.* **67**, 74483.
2716a. I. W. S. Nominee Co. Ltd., Neth. appl. 6,613,490 (1967); via *C. A.* **68**, 40963.
2717. S. Nonogaki, S. Makishima, and Y. Yoneda, *J. Phys. Chem.* **62**, 601 (1958); *Kogyo Kagaku Zasshi* **61**, 457 and 459 (1958).
2718. R. Nordgren (to General Mills, Inc.), U.S. 3,303,184 (1967).
2719. J. H. Northrop, *Biochem. Z.* **338**, 230 (1963).
2720. J. H. Northrop, *J. Gen. Physiol.* **46**, 971 (1963).
2721. K. Y. Novitskii, L. V. Brattava, and Y. K. Yur'ev, *Zh. Organ. Khim.* **1**, 1097 (1965); *J. Org. Chem. USSR (English Transl.)* **1**, 1107 (1965); U.S.S.R. 164,300 (1964); via *C. A.* **62**, 569.
2722. T. J. Nowak and H. F. Keller, Jr. (to Union Oil Co.), U.S. 2,802,784 (1957).
2722a. H. Nozaki, Y. Okuyama, and S. Fujita, *Can. J. Chem.* **46**, 3333 (1968).
2723. T. Nozoe, K. Takase, and M. Tada, *Bull. Chem. Soc. Japan* **38**, 247 (1965).
2724. A. C. Nuessle, *Textile Ind.* **123** (10), 116 (1959).
2724a. M. Numata and H. Hagiwara, *Chem. Pharm. Bull. (Tokyo)* **16**, 311 (1968).
2725. I. A. Nuretdinov and N. P. Grechkin, *Izv. Akad. Nauk SSSR, Ser. Khim.* p. 1883 (1964); *Bull. Acad. Sci. USSR, Div. Chem. Sci. (English Transl.)* p. 1784 (1964).
2726. I. A. Nuretdinov and N. P. Grechkin, *Izv. Akad. Nauk SSSR, Ser. Khim.* p. 1466 (1966); *Bull. Acad. Sci. USSR, Div. Chem. Sci. (English Transl.)* p. 1408 (1966).
2727. I. A. Nuretdinov *et al.*, *Izv. Akad. Nauk SSSR, Ser. Khim.* (*English Transl.*) p. 839 (1966); *Bull. Acad. Sci. USSR, Div. Chem. Sci. (English Transl.)* p. 803 (1966).
2728. I. A. Nuretdinov and N. P. Grechkin, *Izv. Akad. Nauk SSSR, Ser. Khim.* p. 439 (1967); *Bull. Acad. Sci. USSR, Div. Chem. Sci. (English Transl.)* p. 424 (1967).
2728a. I. A. Nuretdinov and N. P. Grechkin, *Izv. Akad. Nauk SSSR, Ser. Khim.* p. 1143 (1968); via *C. A.* **69**, 106349.

2729. I. A. Nuretdinov and N. P. Grechkin, *Izv. Akad. Nauk SSSR, Ser. Khim.* p. 436 (1967); *Bull. Acad. Sci. USSR, Div. Chem. Sci.* (*English Transl.*) p. 421 (1967).
2729a. I. A. Nuretdinov, N. A. Buina, and N. P. Grechkin, *Zh. Obshch. Khim.* **37**, 959 (1967) via *C. A.* **68**, 105307n.
2729b. I. A. Nuretdinov and N. P. Grechkin, *Izv. Akad. Nauk SSSR, Ser. Khim.* p. 1363 (1968); via *C. A.* **69**, 77359.
2730. N. I. Nuzhdin and N. S. Samokhvalova, *Dokl. Akad. Nauk SSSR* **166**, 1217 (1966); *Eksp. Rab. Vlyaniya Ioniz. Izluch. Organizm* p. 50 (1967); via *C. A.* **69**, 93417.
2731. W. H. Nyberg and C. C. Cheng, *J. Heterocyclic Chem.* **1**, 1 (1964).
2732. R. A. Nyquist (to The Dow Chemical Co.), U.S. 3,231,564 (1966).
2736. S. Oae and N. Furukawa, *Bull. Chem. Soc. Japan* **38**, 62 (1965).
2737. A. E. Oberth and R. S. Bruenner, *Trans. Soc. Rheol.* **9**, 165 (1965).
2738. A. E. Oberth, *Phot. Sci. Eng.* **6**, 216 (1962).
2738a. P. Obrecht and J. W. Woenckhaus, *Krebsforsch. Krebsbekaempf.* **6**, 138 (1967).
2739. C. O'Brien, *Chem. Rev.* **64**, 81 (1964).
2740. S. J. O'Brien and W. J. Van Loo, Jr., *Textile Res. J.* **31**, 340 (1961).
2741. E. Ochiai and H. Mitarashi, *Chem. & Pharm. Bull.* (*Tokyo*) **12**, 1495 (1964); via *C. A.* **62**, 9102.
2742. C. H. Ockey, *Abhandl. Deut. Akad. Wiss. Berlin, Kl. Med.* No. 1, p. 47 (1960); via *C. A.* **55**, 4661.
2743. C. H. Ockey, *J. Genet.* **55**, 525 (1957).
2743a. P. W. O'Connell (to Upjohn Co.), U.S. 3,272,696 (1966).
2744. R. Oda, M. Miyanoki, and M. Okano, *Bull. Chem. Soc. Japan* **35**, 1910 (1962).
2745. R. Oda, M. Miyanoki, and M. Okano, *Bull. Chem. Soc. Japan* **35**, 1915 (1962).
2746. Y. Oda, *Asahi Garasu Kenkyu Hokoku* **13**, 39 (1963); via *C. A.* **60**, 3160.
2747. A. C. Oehlschlager, P. Tillman, and L. H. Zalkow, *Chem. Commun.* p. 596 (1965).
2748. A. C. Oehlschlager and L. H. Zalkow, *J. Org. Chem.* **30**, 4205 (1965).
2749. A. C. Oehlschlager and L. H. Zalkow, *Chem. Commun.* p. 70 (1965).
2750. A. C. Oehlschlager and L. H. Zalkow, *Chem. Commun.* p. 5 (1966).
2751. H. Oertel and H. Rinke (to Farbenfabriken Bayer), U.S. 3,232,908 (1966); Ger. 1,153,161 (1963).
2752. R. C. O'Gee and H. M. Woodburn, *J. Am. Chem. Soc.* **73**, 1370 (1951).
2753. Y. Ohara, Japan. 12,232 ('60); via *C. A.* **55**, 10914.
2754. M. Ohta and H. Kato, *Nippon Kagaku Zasshi* **78**, 1400 (1957); via *C. A.* **54**, 511.
2754a. M. Ohtsuru and K. Tori, *J. Mol. Spectry.* **27**, 296 (1968).
2754b. S. Oida and E. Ohki, *Chem. Pharm. Bull.* (*Tokyo*) **16**, 764 (1968).
2755. A. Oka, *Arch. Pathol. Anat. Physiol.* **214**, 149 (1913).
2755a. K. Okawa, T. Kinutani, and K. Sakai, *Bull. Chem. Soc. Japan* **41**, 1353 (1968).
2756. M. Okawara *et al.*, *Kogyo Kagaku Zasshi* **69**, 766 (1966); via *C. A.* **65**, 20236.
2757. G. Oláh, I. Kuhn, and G. Kovács-Bruckner, *J. Org. Chem.* **22**, 979 (1957).
2758. G. A. Oláh and P. J. Szilagyi, private communication (1967).
2759. Olea-Centre, Fr. 1,442,286 (1966); via *C. A.* **66**, 40708.
2760. J. N. Olin, *Ind. Eng. Chem.* **55** (9), 10 (1963).
2761. G. L. Oliver *et al.*, *J. Am. Chem. Soc.* **80**, 702 (1958).
2762. H. C. Olsen (to National Starch and Chemical Corp.), U.S. 2,946,705 (1960); Brit. 898,999 (1962).
2763. K. Onoue, Y. Yagi, and D. Pressman, *Immunochemistry* **2**, 181 (1965).
2764. M. Opris, *Materiale Plast.* **2**, 339 (1965); via *C. A.* **64**, 19856.
2765. Oriental Rayon Co., Japan. 1947 ('53); via *C. A.* **48**, 4856.
2766. K. Orita, M. Sato, and Y. Iwakura, *Kogyo Kagaku Zasshi* **64**, 1404 (1961); via *C. A.* **57**, 3285.

2767. W. Oroshnik and R. A. Mallory (to Ortho Pharmaceutical Co.), U.S. 2,811,525 (1957).

2767a. C. E. O'Rourke, L. B. Clapp, and J. O. Edwards, *J. Am. Chem. Soc.* **78**, 2159 (1956).

2768. P. S. Orphandis, *Ann. Inst. Phytopathol. Benaki* [N.S.] **5**, 260 (1963); via *Rev. Appl. Entomol.* **A54**, 51.

2769. P. S. Orphandis, C. D. Soultanopoulos, and M. G. Karendeinos, *Ann. Inst. Phytopathol. Benaki* [N.S.] **5**, 323 (1963); via *Rev. Appl. Entomol.* **A54**, 51.

2770. P. S. Orphandis and P. G. Patsacos, *Ann. Inst. Phytopathol. Benaki* [N.S.] **5**, 305 (1963); via *Rev. Appl. Entomol.* **A54**, 52.

2771. R. S. Orr *et al.*, *Textile Res. J.* **34**, 192 (1964).

2772. L. Orthner, W. Luce, and G. Wagner (vested in Alien Property Custodian), U.S. 2,390,165 (1945); Swiss 224,641 (1943); Ger. 902,256 (1954).

2772a. Osaka Kinzoku Industry Co., Ltd., Japan. 5899 ('63); via *C. A.* **59**, 11724.

2773. Osaka University, Japan. 4973 ('63); via *C. A.* **58**, 10302.

2774. H. Osborg, D. Horvitz, and A. H. Pope (to Chemirad Corp.), U.S. 2,824,791 (1958).

2775. H. Osborg, D. Horvitz, and A. H. Pope (to Chemirad Corp.), U.S. 2,995,032 (1960).

2776. H. Osborg, D. Horvitz, and A. H. Pope, U.S. 3,133,845 (1964).

2777. H. Osborg (to Chemirad Corp.), U.S. 3,325,346 (1967); Brit. 1,108,546 (1968).

2778. H. Osborg, J. W. Brook, and A. Goldstein (to Chemirad Corp.), U.S. 3,298,902 (1967); Brit. 1,082,554 (1967).

2779. Y. Oshiro *et al.*, *Kogyo Kagaku Zasshi* **68**, 2113 (1965); *C. A.* **64**, 14291.

2780. Y. Oshiro, T. Agawa, and S. Komori, *Technol. Rept. Osaka Univ.* p. 541 (1967).

2781. Y. Oshiro *et al.*, *Kogyo Kagaku Zasshi* **68**, 2121 (1965); via *C. A.* **64**, 14292.

2782. Y. Oshiro *et al.*, *Kogyo Kagaku Zasshi* **68**, 2217 (1965); via *C. A.* **64**, 14292.

2783. Y. Oshiro, K. Yamamoto, and S. Komori, *Yuki Gosei Kagaku Kyokai Shi* **24**, 945 (1966); via *C. A.* **66**, 37706.

2784. W. Ostertag and J. Haake, *Z. Vererbungslehre* **98**, 299 (1966).

2785. N. Otsuji *et al.*, *Nature* **184**, Suppl. 14, 1079 (1959).

2786. G. F. Ottmann, R. P. Alexander, and E. H. Kober (to Olin Mathieson Chemical Corp.), U.S. 3,157,638 (1964); Fr. 1,364,322 (1964); Belg. 635,058 (1963); Brit. 1,038,675 (1966); Neth. 294,907 (1965).

2787. G. F. Ottmann *et al.*, *Inorg. Chem.* **3**, 753 1964).

2788. G. F. Ottmann and H. Hooks, *J. Med. Chem.* **9**, 962 (1966); G. F. Ottmann and H. Hooks (to Olin Mathieson Chemical Corp.), U.S. 3,324,112 (1967); Can. 774,582 (1967).

2789. G. F. Ottmann *et al.* (to Olin Mathieson Chemical Corp.), U.S. 3,136,754 (1964).

2790. G. F. Ottmann *et al.* (to Olin Mathieson Chemical Corp.), U.S. 3,197,464 (1965).

2791. M. T. Ouye, R. S. Garcia, and D. F. Martin, *J. Econ. Entomol.* **58**, 1018 (1965).

2792. I. M. Ovcharova and E. S. Golovchinskaya, *Zh. Obshch. Khim.* **34**, 3274 (1964); *J. Gen. Chem. USSR* (*English Transl.*) **34**, 3290 (1964).

2793. C. G. Overberger and M. Tobkes, *J. Polymer Sci.* **A2**, 2481 (1964).

2794. C. G. Overberger, H. Ringsdorf, and N. Weinshenker, *J. Org. Chem.* **27**, 4331 (1962).

2794a. T.-Y. Owen, *Acta Chim. Sinica* **26**, 140 (1960); via *Chem. Zentr.* No. 2, abstr. 1068 (1965).

2795. K. Oyamada and Y. Sato, *Takamine Kenkyusho Nempo* **9**, 17 (1957); via *C. A.* **55**, 1564.

2796. K. Oyamada and S. Morimura, *Takamine Kenkyusho Nempo* **12**, 41 (1960); via *C. A.* **55**, 6459.

2797. V. N. Oyer and W. Szybalski, *Science* **145**, 55 (1964).

2798. Y. Y. Ozol and G. Y. Vanags, *Zh. Obshch. Khim.* **33**, 3154 (1963); *J. Gen. Chem. USSR* (*English Transl.*) **33**, 3080 (1963).

2798a. Pacific Research Laboratory, Fr. 1,480,068 (1967); via *C. A.* **68**, 14175.

2799. A. Padwa and L. Hamilton, *J. Am. Chem. Soc.* **87**, 1821 (1965).

2800. A. Padwa and L. Hamilton, *Tetrahedron Letters* p. 4363 (1965).

2801. A. Padwa and L. Hamilton, *J. Heterocyclic Chem.* **4**, 118 (1967).

2802. A. Padwa and L. Hamilton, *J. Am. Chem. Soc.* **89**, 102 (1967).

2803. A. Padwa and L. Hamilton, *J. Org. Chem.* **31**, 1995 (1966).

2804. A. Padwa, L. Hamilton, and L. Norling, *J. Org. Chem.* **31**, 1244 (1966).

2805. R. R. Painter and W. W. Kilgore, *J. Econ. Entomol.* **57**, 154 (1964).

2806. R. R. Painter and W. W. Kilgore, *J. Insect Physiol.* **13**, 1105 (1967).

2807. J. Palmquist and L. E. LaChance, *Science* **154**, 915 (1966).

2808. W. W. Pandler and A. G. Zeiler, *J. Org. Chem.* **32**, 2425 (1967).

2808a. N. V. Pankova, *Genetika* No. 6, 62 (1967); via *C. A.* **67**, 107164.

2809. O. A. Pan'shin, V. P. Nechiparenko, and R. G. Kostyanovskii, *Izv. Akad. Nauk SSSR, Ser. Khim.* p. 228 (1966); *Bull. Acad. Sci. USSR, Div. Chem. Sci.* (*English Transl.*) p. 210 (1966).

2810. Z. B. Papanastassiou and T. J. Bardos, *J. Med. Pharm. Chem.* **5**, 1000 (1962).

2810a. Z. B. Papanastassiou and T. J. Bardos (to Armour Pharmaceutical Co.), U.S. 3,201,313 (1965); Fr. 1,220,665 (1961); Brit. 911,764 (1962); Can. 680,196 (1964).

2811. Z. B. Papanastassiou and R. J. Bruni, *J. Org. Chem.* **29**, 2870 (1964).

2811a. T. Z. Papoyan, I. I. Chervin, and R. G. Kostyanovskii, *Izv. Akad. Nauk SSSR, Ser. Khim.* p. 1530 (1968); via *C. A.* **69**, 95760.

2812. L. A. Paquette (to Upjohn Co.), U.S. 3,200,111 (1965); Neth. appl. 6,409,655 (1965); Belg. 652,389 (1965); Brit. 1,067,249 (1967).

2813. L. A. Paquette and W. C. Farley, *J. Am. Chem. Soc.* **89**, 3595 (1967).

2814. L. A. Paquette (to Upjohn Co.), U.S. 3,177,204 (1965).

2815. L. A. Paquette (to Upjohn Co.), U.S. 3,213,098 (1965).

2816. L. A. Paquette (to Upjohn Co.), U.S. 3,251,841 (1966); Belg. 652,709 (1965); Neth. appl. 6,410,134 (1965).

2816a. L. A. Paquette (to Upjohn Co.), U.S. 3,303,194 (1967).

2817. L. A. Paquette (to Upjohn Co.), U.S. 3,316,299 (1967).

2817a. L. A. Paquette (to Upjohn Co.), U.S. 3,372,161 (1968); Belg. 652,918 (1964); Neth. appl. 6,410,599 (1965); Brit. 1,070,205 (1967); Fr. 1,451,218 (1966); Ger. 1,263,005 (1968).

2818. R. E. Parcell, *Chem. & Ind.* (*London*) p. 1396 (1963).

2819. C. E. Pardo, Jr., U.S. 2,817,602 (1957).

2820. O. E. Paris and P. E. Fanta, *J. Am. Chem. Soc.* **74**, 3007 (1952).

2821. J. C. Parish and B. W. Arthur, *J. Econ. Entomol.* **58**, 699 (1965).

2822. R. E. Parker and N. S. Isaacs, *Chem. Rev.* **59**, 737 (1959).

2823. R. P. Parker, D. R. Seeger, and E. Kuh (to American Cyanamid Co.), U.S. 2,606,900 (1952); Can. 491,652 (1953); Brit. 715,861 (1954).

2824. R. P. Parker, D. R. Seeger, and E. Kuh (to American Cyanamid Co.), U.S. 2,606,901 (1952); Can. 491,493 (1953); Brit. 715,422 (1954).

2825. R. P. Parker, D. R. Seeger, and E. Kuh (to American Cyanamid Co.), U.S. 2,606,902 (1952); Can. 491,995 (1953).

2826. R. P. Parker, D. R. Seeger, and E. Kuh (to American Cyanamid Co.), U.S. 2,663,705 (1953); Can. 491,653 (1953).

2827. P. F. Pascoe and W. A. Sherbrock-Cox, *J. Appl. Chem.* **13**, 564 (1963).

2828. G. Pataki and A. Niederwieser, *J. Chromatog.* **29**, 133 (1967); G. Pataki *et al.*, *Chromatographia* **1**, 406 (1968).

2829. J. B. Patrick and J. S. Webb (to American Cyanamid Co.), U.S. 3,140,293 (1964); Belg. 624,559 (1963); Brit. 1,003,092 (1965); Fr. M2980 (1965).

2830. D. K. Pattilloch and C. Polowczyk (to Michigan Research Laboratories, Inc.), U.S. 2,957,796 (1960).
2831. D. K. Pattilloch (to Electro-Chem Fiber Seal Corp.), U.S. 3,016,325 (1962).
2832. D. K. Pattilloch (to Michigan Research Laboratories, Inc., and Electro-Chem Fiber Seal Corporation), U.S. 3,027,295 (1962).
2833. D. K. Pattilloch (to Michigan Research Laboratories, Inc., and Electro-Chem Fiber Seal Corporation), U.S. 3,060,079 (1963).
2833a. S. K. Paufler and R. H. Foote, *J. Reprod. Fertil.* **14**, 348 (1967).
2834. R. Paul and S. Tchelitcheff, *Bull. Soc. Chim. France* p. 736 (1958).
2835. M. Paulshock and J. C. Watts (to du Pont de Nemours and Co.), U.S. 3,310,469 (1967).
2836. Z. N. Pazenko, *Ukr. Khim. Zh.* **24**, 632 (1958); via *C. A.* **53**, 12281.
2837. R. M. Peck, R. K. Preston, and H. J. Creech, *J. Org. Chem.* **26**, 3409 (1961).
2838. R. J. Peffer (to Minnesota Mining and Manufacturing Co.), U.S. 3,258,452 (1966); Brit. 1,086,601 (1967).
2839. S. W. Pelletier and P. C. Parthasarathy, *J. Am. Chem. Soc.* **87**, 777 (1965).
2840. H. M. Pellett, *Dissertation Abstr.* **25**, 742 (1964).
2841. S. S. Pelosi, Jr. and R. E. Lyle, *Abstr. Papers, 147th Am. Chem. Soc. Meeting, Philadelphia, 1964* p. N-47.
2842. W. Pense and H. Bestian (vested in Alien Property Custodian), U.S. 2,341,413 (1944).
2843. W. R. Pepia and H. B. Yuoka (to Interchemical Corp.), U.S. 3,171,826 (1965).
2844. J. R. W. Perfect, *J. Soc. Dyers Colourists* **74**, 829 (1958).
2845. R. M. Perkins, G. L. Drake, Jr., and W. A. Reeves, *U.S. Dept. Agr., ARS* **ARS 72-32** (1964).
2846. R. M. Perkins, G. L. Drake, Jr., and W. A. Reeves, *Ind. Eng. Chem., Prod. Res. Develop.* **1**, 281 (1962).
2847. R. M. Perkins, G. L. Drake, Jr., and L. H. Chance, *Am. Dyestuff Reptr.* **52**, P521 (1963).
2848. R. M. Perkins, G. L. Drake, Jr., and W. A. Reeves, *Am. Dyestuff Reptr.* **54**, P540 (1965).
2849. T. D. Perrine and W. R. Landis, *J. Polymer Sci., Part A-1* **5**, 1933 (1967).
2850. T. D. Perrine and P. F. Goolsby, *J. Polymer Sci.* **A3**, 3031 (1965).
2851. S. B. Pershad and M. B. Naidu, *J. Econ. Entomol.* **59**, 948 (1966).
2851a. I. V. Persianova, *Puti Sinteza Izyskaniya Protivoopukholevykh Preparatov . . .,* p. 99 (1962); via *C. A.* **57**, 15246.
2852. M. Pesson and M. Joannic, *Compt. Rend.* **259**, 4716 (1964).
2853. M. Pestel, *Presse Med.* **64**, 1474 (1956); via *C. A.* **51**, 4571.
2854. H. G. Petering and G. J. Van Giessen, *J. Pharm. Sci.* **52**, 1159 (1963).
2855. S. Petersen, W. Gauss, and E. Urbschat, *Angew. Chem.* **67**, 217 (1955).
2856. S. Petersen, W. Gauss, and G. Domagk (to Schenley Industries), U.S. 2,913,453 (1959); Brit. 866,434 (1961).
2856a. L. Petit and P. Touratier, *Bull. Soc. Chim. France* p. 1136 (1968).
2857. P. Petkov and E. Manolov, *Farmatsiya (Sofia)* **13**, 17 (1963); via *C. A.* **60**, 2919.
2857a. D. F. Petrov *et al., Tr. Moskv. Obshchestva Ispytatelei Prirody, Otd. Biol.* **22**, 278 (1966); via *C. A.* **68**, 93754.
2858. K. A. Petrov, A. I. Gavrilova, and V. P. Korotkova, *Zh. Obshch. Khim.* **36**, 853 (1966); *J. Gen. Chem. USSR (English Transl.)* **36**, 868 (1966).
2859. K. A. Petrov, A. I. Gavrilova, and V. P. Korotkova, *Zh. Obshch. Khim.* **32**, 915 (1962); *J. Gen. Chem. USSR (English Transl.)* **32**, 904 (1962).
2860. K. A. Petrov, A. I. Gavrilova, and M. M. Butilov, *Zh. Obshch. Khim.* **35**, 1856 (1965); *J. Gen. Chem. USSR (English Transl.)* **35**, 1850 (1965).

2861. K. A. Petrov, A. I. Gavrilova and V. P. Korotkova, *Zh. Obshch. Khim.* **32**, 1978 (1962); *J. Gen. Chem. USSR (English Transl.)* **32**, 1958 (1962).
2862. K. A. Petrov *et al.*, *Zh. Obshch. Khim.* **31**, 3076 (1961); *J. Gen. Chem. USSR (English Transl.)* **31**, 2867 (1961).
2862a. K. A. Petrov, R. A. Baksova, and L. V. Khorkhoyanu, *Khim. Org. Soed. Fosfora . . .*, p. 170 (1967); via *C. A.* **68**, 114691.
2863. K. A. Petrov, A. I. Gavrilova, and V. P. Korotkova, U.S.S.R. 170,973 (1965); via *C. A.* **63**, 9990.
2864. G. R. Pettit, S. K. Gupta, and P. A. Whitehouse, *J. Med. Chem.* **10**, 692 (1967).
2865. G. R. Pettit, J. A. Settepani, and R. A. Hill, *Can. J. Chem.* **43**, 1792 (1965).
2866. R. G. Pews, *Abstr. Papers, 153rd Am. Chem. Soc. Meeting, Miami Beach, 1967* abstr. O–73.
2867. E. Pfeil and U. Harder, *Angew. Chem.* **79**, 188 (1967); *Angew. Chem. Intern. Ed. Engl.* **6**, 178 (1967).
2868. E. Pfeil and U. Harder, *Angew. Chem.* **77**, 505 (1965); *Angew. Chem. Intern. Ed. Engl.* **4**, 518 (1965).
2869. E. Pfeil and K. Milzner, *Angew. Chem.* **78**, 677 (1966); *Angew. Chem. Intern. Ed. Engl.* **5**, 667 (1966).
2869a. Chas. Pfizer & Co., Brit. 1,067,390 (1967).
2869b. B. Philipp, H. Lang, and J. Stieler, *Faserforsch. Textiltech.* **18**, 568 (1967); via *C. A.* **68**, 41128; *ibid.* **19**, 217 (1968); via *C. A.* **69**, 11522.
2870. F. S. Philips, *Pharmacol. Rev.* **2**, 281 (1950).
2871. F. S. Philips *et al.*, *Am. J. Physiol.* **155**, 295 (1948).
2872. F. S. Philips and J. B. Thiersch, *J. Pharmacol. Exptl. Therap.* **100**, 398 (1950).
2873. F. S. Philips, H. S. Schwartz, and S. S. Sternberg, *Cancer Res.* **20**, 1354 (1960).
2874. C. R. Phillips, *Am. J. Hyg.* **50**, 280 (1949).
2876. Phillips Petroleum Co., Brit. 985,614 (1965); Neth. 294,833 (1966).
2877. Phillips Petroleum Co., Ger. 1,170,674 (1964); Brit. 944,538 (1963).
2878. L. G. Picklesimer and T. F. Saunders (to United States Dept. of the Air Force), U.S. 3,305,551 (1967).
2879. H. A. Piggott and F. S. Statham (to Imperial Chemical Industries), U.S. 2,163,807 (1939); Brit. 475,095 (1937); Fr. 821,604 (1937).
2880. M. N. Pimenova *et al.*, *Vestn. Leningr. Univ., Ser. Biol.* **4**, 153 (1964); via *C. A.* **66**, 62982.
2881. R. A. Pingree, *Am. Dyestuff Reptr.* **35**, P124 (1946).
2882. J. Pinte, M. Coupez, and P. Rochas (to Institut Textile de France), U.S. 2,893,892 (1959); Brit. 781,489 (1957); Can. 540,861 (1957); Ger. 1,036,201 (1958).
2883. J. R. Piper, C. R. Stringfellow, Jr., and T. P. Johnston, *J. Med. Chem.* **9**, 911 (1966).
2884. P. G. Piquett and J. C. Keller, *J. Econ. Entomol.* **55**, 261 (1962).
2885. A. G. Pittman, *Textile Res. J.* **33**, 953 (1963).
2885a. A. G. Pittman, *U.S. Dept. Agri. Res. Serv. ARS* **ARS 74-29**, 35 (1964).
2886. A. G. Pittman and R. E. Lundin, *J. Polymer Sci.* **A2**, 3803 (1966).
2887. A. G. Pittman and W. L. Wasley, *Am. Dyestuff Reptr.* **53**, P366 (1964); Pittman and Wasley (to U.S. Department of Agriculture), U.S. 3,300,274 (1967); Can. 771,684 (1967).
2887a. K. Pitts and P. Calott, *Pulp Paper Mag. Canada* **68**, T367 (1967).
2888. Pittsburgh Plate Glass Co., Brit. 912,118 (1962).
2889. Pittsburgh Plate Glass Co., Neth. appl. 6,607,487 (1966); via *C. A.* **66**, 86734.
2890. R. A. Pizzarello, A. F. Schneid, and P. Resnick (to Interchemical Corp.), U.S. 3,133,950 (1964).

2891. R. A. Pizzarello, A. F. Schneid, and J. J. De Lucia (to Interchemical Corp.), U.S. 3,288,783 (1966); Brit. 1,108,735 (1968).

2892. R. A. Pizzarello, A. F. Schneid, and J. J. De Lucia (to Interchemical Corp.), U.S. 3,297,677 (1967).

2893. F. W. Plapp, Jr. et al., J. Econ. Entomol. **55**, 607 (1962).

2894. R. N. Platonova and V. V. Sakharov, Genetika No. 3, 56 (1965); via C. A. **64**, 11564.

2895. R. H. A. Plimmer and W. J. N. Burch, Biochem. J. **31**, 398 (1937).

2896. K. F. Plitt (to U.S. Department of Commerce), U.S. 2,985,609 (1961).

2897. R. A. Ploeger and W. E. F. Rupprecht (to The Dow Chemical Co.), U.S. 3,317,473 (1967).

2898. A. E. Pohland, R. C. Badger, and N. H. Cromwell, Tetrahedron Letters p. 4369 (1965).

2899. A. E. Pohland et al., J. Am. Chem. Soc. **87**, 2510 (1965).

2903. A. I. Polazhaeva and A. A. Grushina, Farmakol. i Toksikol. **22**, 533 (1959); via C. A. **54**, 17718.

2904. G. Poles, Ind. Carta (Milan) **9**, 1 (1955); via C. A. **49**, 14320.

2905. C. B. Pollard and R. F. Parcell, J. Am. Chem. Soc. **73**, 2925 (1951).

2905a. Polymer Corp., Ltd., Brit. 1,110,632 (1968); Fr. 1,510,328 (1968).

2906. K. Ponsold and H. Groh, Chem. Ber. **98**, 1009 (1965).

2907. K. Ponsold and D. Klemm, Chem. Ber. **99**, 1502 (1966).

2908. K. Ponsold, Chem. Ber. **97**, 3524 (1964).

2908a. I. A. Poplavskaya, A. D. Dembitskii, and M. I. Goryaev, Zh. Obshch. Khim. **37**, 805 (1967); J. Gen. Chem. USSR (English Transl.) **37**, 755 (1967).

2909. Z. V. Popova and V. G. Nemets, Tr. Leningr. Tekhnol. Inst. im. Lensoveta **40**, 180 (1957); via C. A. **54**, 19693.

2910. Z. V. Popova and D. M. Yanovskii, Zh. Prikl. Khim. **33**, 186 (1960); J. Appl. Chem. USSR (English Transl.) **33**, 182 (1960).

2911. Z. V. Popova and D. M. Yanovskii, U.S.S.R. 125,037 (1959); via C. A. **54**, 11578.

2912. F. D. Popp and E. Cullen, Chem. & Ind. (London) p. 1911 (1961).

2913. F. J. Poschmann, Tappi **40**, 487 (1957).

2913a. F. J. Poschmann, Pulp Paper Mag. Canada **69**, T210 (1968).

2914. I. Y. Postovskii, E. I. Grinblat, and L. F. Trefilova, Zh. Obshch. Khim. **31**, 400 (1961); J. Gen. Chem. USSR (English Transl.) **31**, 363 (1961).

2915. W. J. Potts, Spectrochim. Acta **21**, 511 (1965).

2916. D. H. Powers, Jr., V. B. Schatz, and L. B. Clapp, J. Am. Chem. Soc. **78**, 907 (1956).

2917. D. H. Powers, Jr., Dissertation Abstr. **15**, 1314 (1955).

2918. E. L. Powers, C. A. Raper, and J. H. Pomeroy, Arch. Biochem. Biophys. **56**, 297 (1954).

2919. K. S. V. R. V. Prasadarao, Dissertation Abstr. **26**, 2482 (1965).

2920. C. Prelini, Fibre Colori **17**, 49 (1967); via C. A. **66**, 76837.

2921. R. K. Preston et al., J. Med. Chem. **7**, 471 (1964).

2922. W. C. Preusse (to Olin Mathieson Chemical Corp.), U.S. 3,168,514 (1965).

2923. C. C. Price, P. R. Koneru, and R. Shibakawa, J. Med. Chem. **11**, 1226 (1968).

2923a. C. C. Price et al., Biochem. Biophys. Acta **166**, 327 (1968).

2924. C. P. Priesing and S. J. Mogelnicki (to The Dow Chemical Co.), U.S. 3,259,569 (1966).

2925. C. P. Priesing and S. J. Mogelnicki (to The Dow Chemical Co.), U.S. 3,259,570 (1966).

2926. W. Pritzkow and D. Timm, J. Prakt. Chem. [4] **32**, 178 (1966).

2926a. Proban Ltd., Brit. 1,126,432 (1968).

2927. Procter and Gamble, Belg. 702,495 (1968); S. Afr. 67/4902; Brit. 1,111,708 (1968); Fr. 1,506,349 (1967).

2928. M. Prostenik, N. P. Salzman, and H. E. Carter, *J. Am. Chem. Soc.* **77**, 1856 (1955).
2929. L. D. Protsenko *et al.*, *Probl. Organ. Sinteza, Akad. Nauk SSSR, Otd. Obshch. i Tekhn. Khim.* p. 319 (1965); via *C. A.* **64**, 6597.
2930. L. D. Protsenko, K. A. Kornev, and Yu. I. Bogodist, *Puti Sinteza i Izyskaniya Protivo-opukholevykh Preparatov* . . . p. 182 (1962); via *C. A.* **58**, 4491.
2931. L. D. Protsenko, K. A. Kornev, and Yu. I. Bogodist, *Ukr. Khim. Zh.* **27**, 357 (1961); via *C. A.* **56**, 3433.
2932. L. D. Protsenko, *Zh. Obshch. Khim.* **35**, 368 (1965); *J. Gen. Chem. USSR (English Transl.)* **35**, 368 (1965).
2933. L. D. Protsenko and Yu. I. Bogodist, *Zh. Obshch. Khim.* **33**, 537 (1963); *J. Gen. Chem. USSR (English Transl.)* **33**, 530 (1963).
2934. L. D. Protsenko and K. A. Kornev, *Ukr. Khim. Zh.* **24**, 636 (1958); via *C. A.* **53**, 12266.
2935. L. D. Protsenko and L. A. Negievich, *Zh. Obshch. Khim.* **35**, 1564 (1965); *J. Gen. Chem. USSR (English Transl.)* **35**, 1567 (1965).
2936. L. D. Protsenko and N. Ya. Skul'skaya, *Zh. Obshch. Khim.* **33**, 2284 (1963); *J. Gen. Chem. USSR (English Transl.)* **33**, 2225 (1963).
2938. L. D. Protsenko and N. Ya. Skul'skaya, *Zh. Obshch. Khim.* **34**, 2233 (1964); *J. Gen. Chem. USSR (English Transl.)* **34**, 2244 (1964).
2939. L. D. Protsenko and E. A. Svyatnenko, *Zh. Obshch. Khim.* **37**, 2517 (1967); via *C. A.* **69**, 26945.
2939a. L. D. Protsenko and E. A. Svyatnenko, *Zh. Obshch. Khim.* **38**, 590 (1968); via *C. A.* **69**, 43587.
2940. L. D. Protsenko, G. I. Derkach, and A. V. Kirsanov, *Zh. Obshch. Khim.* **31**, 3433 (1961); *J. Gen. Chem. USSR (English Transl.)* **31**, 3200 (1961).
2941. L. D. Protsenko and N. Ya. Skul'skaya, *Ukr. Khim. Zh.* **32**, 1198 (1966); via *C. A.* **66**, 37496.
2942. L. D. Protsenko and Yu. I. Bogodist, *Ukr. Khim. Zh.* **32**, 867 (1966); via *C. A.* **66**, 2531.
2942a. J. E. Purdie and R. A McIvor, *Biochim. Biophys. Acta* **128**, 590 (1966).
2943. G. I. Pustoshkin and F. Yu. Rachinskii, *Zh. Organ. Khim.* **2**, 1259 (1966); *J. Org. Chem. USSR (English Transl.)* **2**, 1254 (1966).
2943a. G. I. Pustoshkin, F. Yu. Rachinskii, and N. M. Slavachevskaya, U.S.S.R. 218,181 (1968); via *C. A.* **69**, 76661.
2943b. R. Puttner, W. Kaiser, and K. Hafner, *Tetrahedron Letters* p. 4315 (1968).
2944. D. J. Pye and G. F. Schurz (to The Dow Chemical Co.), U.S. 2,853,444 (1958).
2944a. H. P. Raaen and F. E. Kraus, *J. Chromatogr.* **35**, 531 (1968).
2945. T. Rabek, J. Malcgewski, and A. Tanska, *Przemysl Chem.* **37**, 596 (1958); via *C. A.* **53**, 14385.
2946. G. C. Rabotti and G. Mayr, *Giorn. Ital. Chemioterap.* **5**, 75 (1958); via *C. A.* **54**, 7265.
2947. W. J. Rabourn and W. L. Howard, *J. Org. Chem.* **27**, 1039 (1962).
2948. W. J. Rabourn (to The Dow Chemical Co.), U.S. 3,236,835 (1966).
2949. W. J. Rabourn (to The Dow Chemical Co.), U.S. 3,247,185 (1966) and 3,321,465 (1967).
2950. W. J. Rabourn (to The Dow Chemical Co.), U.S. 3,285,909 (1966).
2951. F. Yu. Rachinskii and N. M. Slavachevskaya, *Tiolovye Soedin. v. Med.* . . . p. 23 (1959); via *C. A.* **54**, 24368.
2952. F. Yu. Rachinskii, N. M. Slavachevskaya, and D. V. Ioffe, *Zh. Obshch. Khim.* **28**, 2998 (1958); *J. Gen. Chem. USSR (English Transl.)* **28**, 3027 (1958).
2952a. R. Radeglia, *Spectrochim. Acta* **A23**, 1677 (1967).

2953. R. F. W. Raetz and M. J. Gruber (to Olin Mathieson Chemical Corp.), U.S. 3,163,640 (1964).

2954. R. F. W. Raetz and A. D. Bliss, *J. Heterocyclic Chem.* **3**, 20 (1966).

2955. R. F. W. Raetz (to Olin Mathieson Chemical Corp.), U.S. 3,138,585 (1964); Belg. 631,036 (1963); Fr. 1,360,419 (1964); Brit. 996,506 (1965).

2956. R. F. W. Raetz and M. J. Gruber, *J. Med. Chem.* **9**, 144 (1966).

2957. R. F. W. Raetz and C. J. Grundmann (to Olin Mathieson Chemical Corp.), U.S. 2,858,306 (1958).

2958. R. F. W. Raetz (to Olin Mathieson Chemical Corp.), U.S. 3,113,129 (1963).

2959. R. F. W. Raetz (to Olin Mathieson Chemical Corp.), U.S. 3,180,793 (1964).

2960. R. F. W. Raetz and A. D. Bliss (to Olin Mathieson Chemical Corp.), U.S. 3,325,566 (1967).

2961. R. F. W. Raetz and M. J. Gruber (to Olin Mathieson Chemical Corp.), U.S. 3,314,848 (1967).

2962. M. A. Raftery and R. D. Cole, *Biochem. Biophys. Res. Commun.* **10**, 467 (1963); *J. Biol. Chem.* **241**, 3457 (1966).

2963. K. S. Rai, *Biol. Bull.* **127**, 119 (1964); *Cytology* **29**, 346 (1964).

2964. D. N. Raine, *J. Pharm. Pharmacol.* **14**, 614 (1962).

2965. P. Rajagopalan and C. N. Talaty, *J. Am. Chem. Soc.* **88**, 5048 (1966).

2966. V. M. Rakova, A. D. Chinaeva, and A. Ya. Berlin, *Zh. Obshch. Khim.* **29**, 3962 (1959); *J. Gen. Chem. USSR (English Transl.)* **29**, 3922 (1959).

2967. G. M. Rambosek (to Minnesota Mining and Manufacturing Co.), U.S. 3,223,681 (1965).

2968. G. M. Rambosek (to Minnesota Mining and Manufacturing Co.), U.S. 3,378,399 (1968).

2969. V. Rancelis and A. Baranauskaite, *Genetika* No. 6, p. 70 (1966); via *C. A.* **65**, 9354.

2969a. V. Rancelis and V. Jacunskaite, *Lietuvos TSR Aukstuju Molyklu Mokslo Darbai Biol.* **7**, 117 (1967); via *C. A.* **69**, 84192.

2969b. V. Rancelis and N. Jurgelaityte, *Lietuvos TSR Aukstuju Molyklu Mokslo Darbai Biol.* **7**, 109 (1967); via *C. A.* **69**, 84191.

2970. D. I. Randall and W. Schmidt-Nickel (to General Aniline and Film Corp.), U.S. 3,261,824 (1966); Belg. 641,606 (1964); Fr. 1,387,141 (1965); Japan. 23,984 ('65); Brit. 1,037,166 (1966).

2971. K. Randerath, *Angew. Chem.* **74**, 780 (1962); *Angew. Chem. Intern. Ed. Engl.* **1**, 553 (1962).

2972. K. Randerath, *Biochim. Biophys. Acta* **61**, 852 (1962).

2973. K. Randerath and E. Randerath, *J. Chromatog.* **22**, 110 (1966).

2974. I. A. Rapoport, *Vopr. Obshch. Prom. Toksikol., Leningrad, Sb.* p. 67 (1963); via *C. A.* **63**, 13918.

2975. I. A. Rapoport, *Byul. Moskv. Obshch. Ispyt. Prir., Otd. Biol.* **67** (1), 96 (1962); via *C. A.* **56**, 15987.

2976. I. A. Rapoport, *Byul. Moskv. Obshch. Ispyt. Prir., Otd. Biol.* **67** (4), 109 (1962); via *C. A.* **58**, 3714.

2977. I. A. Rapoport, *Federation Proc.* **22**, Trans. Suppl. T547 (1963).

2977a. L. B. Rapp and I. I. Kuzmenko, U.S.S.R. 162,588 (1964); via *Chem. Zentr.* No. 44, abstr. 2451 (1965).

2978. R. H. Ratcliffe and S. S. Ristich, *J. Econ. Entomol.* **58**, 1079 (1965).

2979. H. Rath, *Reyon, Zellwolle, Chemiefasern* **9**, 85 (1959); *C. A.* **53**, 13581.

2980. H. Rath, "Lehrbuch der Textilchemie," 2nd ed. Springer, Berlin, 1963.

2981. H. Rath, Ger. 929,963 (1955); *C. A.* **52**, 3356.

2982. H. M. Rauen and G. Hess, *Z. Physiol. Chem.* **317**, 10 (1959).

2983. H. M. Rauen and G. Hess, *Z. Physiol. Chem.* **317**, 19 (1959).

2984. H. M. Rauen and H. Palla, *Arzneimittel-Forsch.* **16**, 40 (1966).

2985. H. M. Rauen and A. Reisch, *Arzneimittel-Forsch.* **14**, 752 (1964).

2986. H. M. Rauen, A. Reisch, and H. Schriewer, *Arzneimittel-Forsch.* **14**, 176 (1964).

2987. H. M. Rauen and W. Hengst, *Arzneimittel-Forsch.* **15**, 892 (1965).

2988. H. M. Rauen, *Arzneimittel-Forsch.* **14**, 855 (1964).

2989. H. M. Rauen, K. Norpoth, and H. Schriewer, *Angew. Chem.* **80**, 621 (1968); *Angew. Chem. Intern. Ed. Engl.* **7**, 627 (1968).

2990. A. E. Raymond (to Minnesota Mining and Manufacturing Co.), U.S. 3,090,106 (1963).

2992. A. I. Razumov, E. A. Markovich, and O. A. Mukhacheva, *Khim. i Primenenie Fosfororgan. Soedin., Akad. Nauk SSSR Kazansk. Filial, Trudy 1-oi Konf.* p. 194 (1955); via *C. A.* **52**, 237.

2993. A. I. Razumov, O. A. Mukhacheva, and E. A. Markovich, *Zh. Obshch. Khim.* **27**, 2389 (1957); *J. Gen. Chem. USSR (English Transl.)* **27**, 2450 (1957).

2994. J. Read, *Radiobiol., Proc. 3rd Australasian Conf., Sydney, 1960* p. 27. Butterworth, London and Washington, D.C., 1961; via *C. A.* **57**, 7575; J. Read, *Intern. J. Radiation Biol.* **3**, 95 (1961); R. Wakonig-Vaartaja and J. Read, *Radiation Botany* **2**, 53 (1962).

2995. Reanal Finomvegyszergyar, Brit. 987,496 (1965); Austrian 229,291 (1963).

2998. D. L. Rector and R. E. Harmon, *J. Org. Chem.* **31**, 2837 (1966).

2999. C. T. Redemann (to The Dow Chemical Co.), U.S. 3,234,229 (1966); Brit. 957,277 (1963); Fr. 1,353,714 (1964).

3000. E. Reeder and L. H. Sternbach (to Hoffmann-La Roche Inc.), U.S. 3,141,890 (1964).

3001. E. Reeder and L. H. Sternbach (to Hoffmann-La Roche Inc.), U.S. 3,144,439 (1964).

3002. E. Reeder and L. H. Sternbach (to Hoffmann-La Roche Inc.), U.S. 3,243,427 (1966).

3003. W. A. Reeves and J. D. Guthrie (to U.S. Department of Agriculture), U.S. 2,795,569 (1957).

3004. W. A. Reeves and J. D. Guthrie, *Ind. Eng. Chem.* **48**, 64 (1956).

3005. W. A. Reeves and V. R. Bourdette, *Textile Ind.* **128** (1), 105 (1964).

3006. W. A. Reeves *et al.*, *Textile Res. J.* **27**, 260 (1957).

3007. W. A. Reeves, G. L. Drake, Jr., and C. L. Hoffpauir, *J. Am. Chem. Soc.* **73**, 3522 (1951).

3008. W. A. Reeves, G. L. Drake, Jr., and C. L. Hoffpauir (to U.S. Department of Agriculture), U.S. 2,636,880 (1953).

3009. W. A. Reeves, J. R. Corley, and J. D. Guthrie (to U.S. Department of Agriculture), U.S. 2,751,278 (1956).

3010. W. A. Reeves and J. D. Guthrie (to U.S. Department of Agriculture), U.S. 2,809,941 (1957).

3011. W. A. Reeves, L. H. Chance, and G. L. Drake, Jr. (to U.S. Department of Agriculture), U.S. 2,859,134 (1958).

3012. W. A. Reeves, L. H. Chance, and G. L. Drake, Jr. (to U.S. Department of Agriculture), U.S. 2,889,289 (1959).

3013. W. A. Reeves, J. D. Guthrie, and G. L. Drake, Jr. (to U.S. Department of Agriculture), U.S. 2,906,592 (1959).

3014. W. A. Reeves, J. D. Guthrie, and L. H. Chance (to U.S. Department of Agriculture), U.S. 2,912,412 (1959).

3015. W. A. Reeves, G. L. Drake, Jr., and J. D. Guthrie (to U.S. Department of Agriculture), U.S. 2,915,480 (1959).

3016. W. A. Reeves, L. H. Chance, and G. L. Drake, Jr. (to U.S. Department of Agriculture), U.S. 2,917,492 (1959).

3017. W. A. Reeves, G. L. Drake, Jr., and J. D. Guthrie (to U.S. Department of Agriculture), U.S. 2,933,367 (1960).

3018. W. A. Reeves, G. L. Drake, Jr., and J. D. Guthrie (to U.S. Department of Agriculture), U.S. 3,084,017 (1963).

3019. W. A. Reeves and J. D. Guthrie (to U.S. Department of Agriculture), U.S. 2,772,188 (1956).

3020. Reggiani S. P. A., Brit. 903,820 (1962).

3021. R. M. Reinhardt et al., Textile Res. J. 29, 802 (1965).

3022. R. M. Reinhardt and J. D. Reid (to U.S. Department of Agriculture), U.S. 2,938,765 (1960).

3023. E. J. Reist, I. G. Junga, and B. R. Baker, J. Org. Chem. 25, 1673 (1960).

3024. E. J. Reist et al., J. Org. Chem. 26, 2139 (1961).

3024a. R. H. Reitsema, J. Am. Chem. Soc. 71, 2041 (1949).

3025. R. E. Reizin and A. Tupuraine, Tr. Inst. Lesokhoz. Probl. i Khim. Drevesiny, Akad. Nauk Latv. SSR 25, 107 (1963); via C. A. 60, 8225.

3026. W. A. Remers, R. H. Roth, and M. J. Weiss, J. Org. Chem. 30, 2910 (1965).

3026a. W. A. Remers and M. J. Weiss, J. Med. Chem. 11, 737 (1968).

3027. W. B. Renfrow et al., J. Org. Chem. 33, 150 (1968).

3028. E. Rerabkova and E. Hermanova, Neoplasma 6, 145 (1959).

3029a. Research Foundation for Practical Life, Japan. 10,230 ('67); via C. A. 67, 90652.

3030. P. Resnick and J. J. R. Luzzi (to Interchemical Corp.), U.S. 3,028,377 (1962).

3031. P. Resnick and H. S. Bender, Abstr. Papers, 147th Am. Chem. Soc. Meeting, Philadelphia, 1964 p. N-17.

3032. P. Resnick et al., Armed Services Technical Information Agency Rept. (U.S.) AD 250,307 (1960); AD 253,802 and AD 258,248 (1961).

3032a. P. Reynaud, R. C. Moreau, and P. Fodor, Compt. Rend. C266, 632 (1968).

3033. W. B. Reynolds (to Phillips Petroleum Co.), U.S. 3,074,917 (1963).

3034. W. F. Reynolds, Jr., and L. A. Lundberg (to American Cyanamid Co.), U.S. 2,772,969 (1956).

3035. W. F. Reynolds, Jr. (to American Cyanamid Co.), U.S. 3,332,834 (1967).

3036. Rhône-Poulenc S. A., Neth. appl. 6,504,563 (1965); Belg. 662,656 (1965); via C. A. 64, 11228.

3036a. U. Riboni and L. Bartolucci (to "Montecatini" Societa . . .), U.S. 3,116,406 (1964); Brit. 881,981 (1961); Ger. 1,124,917 (1962).

3037. S. A. Rice and M. Nagasawa, "Polyelectrolyte Solutions," p. 416. Academic Press, New York, 1960.

3038. W. Ried, H. Hillenbrand, and G. Oertel, Ann. Chem. 590, 123 (1954).

3039. S. S. Ristich, R. H. Ratcliffe, and D. Perlman, J. Econ. Entomol. 58, 929 (1965).

3040. S. S. Ristich and B. Stearns (to Olin Mathieson Chemical Corp.), U.S. 3,208,905 (1965).

3041. S. H. Roach and J. A. Buxton, J. Econ. Entomol. 58, 802 (1965).

3042. E. J. Roberts, C. P. Wade, and S. P. Rowland, Abstr. Papers, 154th Am. Chem. Soc. Meeting, Chicago, 1967 abstr. E-40.

3043. J. Robins (to Atlas Chemical Industries), U.S. 3,221,055 (1965).

3044. J. Robins, Dissertation Abstr. 20, 1194 (1959).

3044a. R. K. Robins et al., J. Am. Chem. Soc. 83, 2574 (1961).

3045. D. B. Rochlin, H. Goepfert, and J. Damnavits, Surg., Gynecol. Obstet. 121, 774 (1967).

3046. I. S. Rodynyuk, Selek. Mikrobov, Akad. Nauk SSSR, Sibirsk . . . p. 108 (1965); via C. A. 64, 14628.

3047. Roehm and Haas, A.-G., Ger. 857,495 (1952); C. A. 52, 10188.

3048. Roehm and Haas G.m.b.H., Belg. 653,521 (1965); via *C. A.* **64**, 14009; Ger. 1,237,720 (1967).
3049. Roehm and Haas Co., Brit. 969,962 (1964); Ger. 1,180,997 (1964).
3050. G. Roehrborn, *Z. Vererbungslehre* **93**, 1 (1962).
3051. G. Roehrborn, *Experientia* **16**, 523 (1960).
3052. D. B. Rollins and H. N. Calderwood, *J. Am. Chem. Soc.* **60**, 2751 (1938).
3053. A. G. Romankova, M. V. Fursenko, and A. D. Kommunarskaya, *Mikrobiologiya* **33**, 582 (1964); via *Biol. Abstr.* **46**, 35294.
3054. N. B. Romanova, *Antibiotiki* **12**, 114 (1967); via *C. A.* **66**, 73495.
3055. N. B. Romanova and S. I. Alikhanyan, *Antibiotiki* **11**, 984 (1966); via *Nucl. Sci. Abstr.* **21**, 22825.
3055a. N. B. Romanova, *Tr. Mosk. Obshch. Ispyt. Prir., Otd. Biol.* **22**, 130 (1966); via *C. A.* **68**, 102863.
3056. J. M. Romeo, *Rev. Clin. Españ.* **50**, 382 (1953); via *C. A.* **48**, 3555.
3057. C. S. Rondestvedt, Jr. and S. J. Davis, *J. Org. Chem.* **22**, 200 (1957).
3057a. C. A. Root *et al.*, *Abstr. Papers, 156th Am. Chem. Soc. Meeting, Atlantic City, 1968* abstr. INOR-145.
3058. W. E. Rosen, V. P. Toohey, and A. C. Shabica, *J. Am. Chem. Soc.* **79**, 3167 (1957).
3058a. W. E. Rosenberg (to Enthone, Inc.), U.S. 3,393,135 (1968); Fr. 1,488,707 (1967).
3059. D. H. Rosenblatt, P. Hlinka, and J. Epstein, *Anal. Chem.* **27**, 1290 (1955).
3060. D. Rosenthal *et al.*, *J. Org. Chem.* **30**, 3689 (1965).
3061. N. Rosenthal and L. Citarel (to Thiokol Chemical Corp.), U.S. 3,335,116 (1967).
3062. A. Rosowsky, *Chem. Heterocyclic Compds.* **19**, Part 1, 270 (1964).
3063. A. Rosowsky, *Chem. Heterocyclic Compds.* **19**, Part 1, 316 (1964).
3064. J. G. Ross, G. Holm, and C. H. Chen, *Proc. S. Dakota Acad. Sci.* **40**, 170 (1961).
3065. S. D. Ross, *J. Am. Chem. Soc.* **69**, 2982 (1947).
3066. S. D. Ross, J. J. Bruno, and R. C. Peterson, *J. Am. Chem. Soc.* **85**, 3999 (1963).
3067. W. C. J. Ross, *J. Chem. Soc.* p. 183 (1949); J. L. Everett and W. C. J. Ross, *ibid.* p. 1972.
3068. W. C. J. Ross, "Biological Alkylating Agents." Butterworth, London and Washington, D.C., 1962.
3069. C. M. Rosser (to American Viscose Corp.), U.S. 2,828,237 (1958).
3069a. S. Rossi, T. Bacchetti, and S. Maiorana, *Gazz. Chim. Ital.* **92**, 1367 (1962).
3069b. J. A. Rothfus and M. J. A. Crow, *Biochim. Biophys. Acta* **160**, 404 (1968).
3070. C. S. Rowland, F. Varron, and A. Varron (to Interchemical Corp.), U.S. 3,028,349 (1962).
3071. H. Rudzick, *Ber.* **34**, 3543 (1902).
3072. H. Ruebner, *Arzneimittel-Forsch.* **15**, 796 (1965); via *C. A.* **63**, 11339.
3073. S. Ruhemann and E. W. Watson, *J. Chem. Soc.* **85**, 1170 (1904).
3074. H. Ruile, *SVF Fachorgan Textilveredlung* **19**, 767 (1964); via *J. Soc. Dyers Colourists* **81**, 69.
3074a. P. Rumpf, *Bull. Soc. Chim. France* [5] **5**, 871 (1938).
3075. P. Rumpf, *Compt. Rend.* **204**, 592 (1937).
3076. W. Rundel and E. Mueller, *Chem. Ber.* **96**, 2528 (1963).
3077. J. D. Rushmere (to du Pont de Nemours and Co.), U.S. 3,296,105 (1967).
3078. V. Rusignuolo and L. Lucchetti (to "Montecatini" Societa . . .), U.S. 3,091,536 (1963); Ital. 602,490 (1959); Brit. 868,158 (1961); Ger. 1,136,209 (1962).
3079. R. J. Rutman, F. S. Lewis, and W. D. Bloomer, *Science* **153**, 1000 (1966).
3080. A. K. Ruzhentsova, A. M. Chivireva, and N. G. Leiferova, *Med. Prom. SSSR* **16**, 46 (1962); via *C. A.* **60**, 6702.
3081. W. H. Ryan and V. K. Walworth (to Polaroid Corp.), U.S. 2,868,077 (1959).

3083. W. Rzeszotarski and Z. Ledochowski, *Roczniki Chem.* **37**, 913 (1963); via *C. A.* **60**, 1697.
3084. A. Sabaneyev, *Ann. Chem.* **178**, 109 (1875).
3085. T. M. H. Saber, *Dissertation Abstr.* **26**, 2505 (1965).
3086. G. Sacca, E. Stella, and R. Magrone, *Riv. Parassitol.* **25**, 207 (1964); via *C. A.* **65**, 20776.
3087. G. Sacca and E. Stella, *Riv. Parassitol.* **25**, 279 (1964).
3088. G. Sacca, *Riv. Parassitol.* **25**, 295 (1964); via *Rev. Appl. Entomol.* **55B**, 130.
3088a. H. Saeki, T. Iwashige, and E. Ohki, *Chem. Pharm. Bull.* (*Tokyo*) **16**, 188 (1969).
3088b. D. Saika and D. Swern, *J. Org. Chem.* **33**, 4548 (1968).
3089. G. Sakauchi and C. W. DeWitt, *Transplantation* **5**, 248 (1967).
3090. O. L. Salerni and R. N. Clark, *J. Med. Chem.* **9**, 778 (1966).
3091. A. R. Sallmann and R. Pfister (to J. R. Geigy A.-G.), U.S. 3,152,127 (1964); Fr. 1,304,789 (1962) and M1740 (1963); Swiss 385,225 (1965) and 399,476 (1966); Japan. 1935 ('64); Ger. 1,163,841 (1964); Brit. 1,006,559 (1965); Indian 79,045 (1963); Hung. 150,718 (1960) and 151,182 (1963).
3091a. T. V. Sal'nikova and N. N. Zoz, *Supermutageny, Akad. Nauk SSSR, Inst. Khim. Fiz.* p. 121 (1966); via *C. A.* **67**, 41104.
3092. G. Salomon, *Trans. Faraday Soc.* **32**, 153 (1936).
3093. G. Salomon, *Helv. Chim. Acta* **17**, 851 (1934).
3094. G. Salomon, *Rec. Trav. Chim.* **68**, 903 (1949).
3095. G. Salomon, *Helv. Chim. Acta* **16**, 1361 (1933).
3096. J. Sam and T. C. Snapp, Jr., *J. Pharm. Sci.* **53**, 1364 (1964).
3097. J. Sambeth and F. Grundschober, *Angew. Chem.* **77**, 718 (1965); *Angew. Chem. Intern. Ed. Engl.* **4**, 693 (1965).
3098. S. Samenhof, *Am. J. Med.* **34**, 609 (1963).
3099. B. Sander and F. Becke (to Badische Anilin- und Soda-Fabrik), U.S. 3,280,108 (1966); Belg. 661,085 (1965); Fr. 1,427,431 (1965); Neth. appl. 6,503,187 (1965); Brit. 1,099,992 (1968).
3100. I. Sandescu, *Arch. Roumaines Pathol. Exptl. Microbiol.* **26**, 181 (1967); via *C. A.* **67**, 81444.
3101. Sandoz Ltd., Swiss 388,498 (1965); *C. A.* **63**, 13453.
3102. Sandoz A.-G., Neth. appl. 6,703,461 (1967).
3103. Sandoz Ltd., Belg. 687,335 (1967); Fr. 1,503,443 (1967).
3104. J. M. Sandri and E. K. Fields [to Standard Oil Co. (Indiana)], U.S. 3,280,032 (1966) and 3,328,391 (1967).
3105. Sankyo Co., Ltd., Japan. 475 ('58); via *C. A.* **53**, 1252.
3106. Sankyo Co., Ltd., Japan. 1480 ('58); via *C. A.* **53**, 1253.
3107. Sankyo Co., Ltd., Japan. 2787 ('58); via *C. A.* **53**, 5285.
3108. Sankyo Co., Ltd., Japan. 3068 ('59); via *C. A.* **54**, 13089.
3109. Sankyo Co., Ltd., Japan. 3069 ('59); via *C. A.* **54**, 13145.
3110. Sankyo Co., Ltd., Japan. 6269 ('59); via *C. A.* **54**, 14267.
3111. Sankyo Co., Ltd., Japan. 8424 ('57); via *C. A.* **52**, 14693.
3112. Sankyo Co., Ltd., Japan. 9030 ('60); via *C. A.* **55**, 9348.
3113. Sankyo Co., Ltd., Japan. 9327 ('57); via *C. A.* **52**, 15588.
3114. Sankyo Co., Ltd., Japan. 9779 ('60); via *C. A.* **55**, 9348.
3115. Y. Sanno and K. Tanaka, *Chem. & Pharm. Bull.* (*Tokyo*) **8**, 753 (1960); via *C. A.* **55**, 15501.
3116. S. Sarel and H. Leader, *J. Org. Chem.* **23**, 330 (1958).
3117. S. Sarel, J. T. Klug, and F. D'Angeli, *Tetrahedron Letters* p. 1553 (1964).
3118. S. Sarel and H. Leader, *J. Am. Chem. Soc.* **82**, 4752 (1960).

3119. S. Sarel, A. Taube, and E. Breuer, *Chem. & Ind.* (*London*) p. 1095 (1967).
3120. K. V. Sarkanen, *in* "Wet Strength in Paper and Paperboard" (J. P. Weidner, ed.), Tappi Monograph Ser. No. 29, p. 38. Technical Association of the Pulp and Paper Industry, New York, 1965.
3121. K. V. Sarkanen, F. Dinkler, and V. Stannett, *Tappi* **49**, 4 (1966).
3121a. Yu. F. Sarychev, *Genetika* No. 8, p. 30 (1967); via *C. A.* **68**, 102611.
3121b. T. Sasaki and Y. Yoshioka, *Bull. Chem. Soc. Japan* **41**, 1258 (1968).
3122. H. Sato and M. Nagai, Japan. 8192 ('57); via *C. A.* **52**, 21209.
3123. H. Sato and M. Nagai, Japan. 8193 ('57); via *C. A.* **52**, 21209.
3124. Y. Sato, *Takamine Kenkyusho Nempo* **9**, 15 (1957); via *C. A.* **55**, 1564.
3125. Y. Sato *et al.*, *Takamine Kenkyusho Nempo* **10**, 34 (1958); via *C. A.* **55**, 1564.
3125a. N. V. Sazonov and A. A. Kropacheva, *Khim.-Farm. Zh.* **1** (8), 32 (1967); via *C. A.* **68**, 114541.
3126. F. C. Schaefer, J. Y. Geoghegan, and D. W. Kaiser, *J. Am. Chem. Soc.* **77**, 5918 (1955).
3127. F. C. Schaefer, *J. Am. Chem. Soc.* **77**, 5922 (1955).
3128. F. C. Schaefer, *J. Am. Chem. Soc.* **77**, 5928 (1955).
3129. H. Schaffner, *Z. Ges. Textil-Ind.* **65**, 849 (1963); via *J. Textile Inst.* **54**, A778.
3130. V. B. Schatz, *Dissertation Abstr.* **15**, 1315 (1955).
3131. V. B. Schatz and L. B. Clapp, *J. Am. Chem. Soc.* **77**, 5113 (1955).
3132. P. Scheiner, *J. Am. Chem. Soc.* **90**, 988 (1968).
3133. P. Scheiner, *J. Org. Chem.* **30**, 7 (1965).
3134. P. Scheiner and W. R. Vaughan, *J. Org. Chem.* **26**, 1923 (1961).
3135. P. Scheiner, *J. Org. Chem.* **32**, 2022 (1967).
3136. P. Scheiner, *J. Am. Chem. Soc.* **88**, 4759 (1966).
3137. P. Scheiner, *J. Org. Chem.* **32**, 2628 (1967).
3137a. P. Scheiner, *Tetrahedron* **24**, 349 (1968).
3138. Schenley Industries, Inc., Can. 582,602 (1959); Brit. 826,533 (1960); Ger. 1,080,560 (1960).
3139. O. Scherer and M. Schmidt, *Chem. Ber.* **98**, 2243 (1965).
3140. Schering A.-G., Ger. 1,211,228 (1966); Belg. 667,643 (1965); Fr. 1,441,326 (1966); *C. A.* **64**, 16146.
3141. Schering A.-G., Fr. 1,480,997 (1967); Japan. 6358 ('67); via *C. A.* **67**, 21901; Ger. 1,232,800 and 1,243,488 (1967); via *C. A.* **67**, 96335.
3142. J. Scherzer *et al.*, *Inorg. Chem.* **5**, 847 (1966).
3143. H. H. Scheunert and H. J. Eckert, *Zellstoff Papier* **10**, 174 (1961); *C. A.* **59**, 15484.
3144. E. D. Schilling and F. M. Strong, *J. Org. Chem.* **22**, 349 (1957).
3145. E. Schipper *et al.*, *J. Med. Pharm. Chem.* **4**, 79 (1961).
3146. P. Schlack (to I. G. Farbenindustrie), U.S. 2,131,145 (1938).
3147. P. Schlack (to I. G. Farbenindustrie), U.S. 2,136,928 (1938).
3148. P. Schlack (to I. G. Farbenindustrie), U.S. 2,202,169 (1940).
3149. P. Schlack (to W. H. Duisberg), U.S. 2,261,294 (1941).
3150. P. Schlack (to W. H. Duisberg), U.S. 2,291,061 (1942).
3151. H. Schlaepfer and A. Margot (to J. R. Geigy A.-G.), U.S. 2,558,273 (1951); Swiss 270,826 (1951).
3152. L. H. Schlager, *Arch. Pharm.* **296**, 217 (1963).
3153. R. Schlitt, *Anal. Chem.* **35**, 1063 (1963).
3154. R. Schmeisfurth and W. Schwartz, *Naturwissenschaften* **41**, 42 (1954).
3155. C. H. Schmidt, D. A. Dame, and D. E. Weidhaas, *J. Econ. Entomol.* **57**, 753 (1964).
3156. F. Schmidt, *Ber.* **55**, 1581 (1922).
3157. J. Schmidt, *Ber.* **34**, 3536 (1902).

3158. L. H. Schmidt *et al.*, *Cancer Chemotherapy Rept. Suppl.* **2**, 1 (1965).
3159. W. Schmitt, R. Purrmann, and P. Jochum (to ESPE Fabrik Pharmazeutischer Praeparate), U.S. 3,107,427 (1963); Swiss 382,918 (1964); Ger. 1,146,617 (1963).
3160. I. R. Schmolka and P. E. Spoerri, *J. Am. Chem. Soc.* **79**, 4716 (1957).
3161. F. Schneider, J. Hamsher, and R. E. Beyler, *Steroids* **8**, 553 (1966).
3162. W. Schneider and E. Kaemmerer, *Arch. Pharm.* **299**, 846 (1966).
3163. W. A. Scholtens Chemische Fabrieken N. V., Ger. 1,187,599 (1965); Brit. 815,358 (1959).
3164. G. Schrader (to Farbenfabriken Bayer), U.S. 3,184,465 (1965); Ger. 1,099,532 (1961); Swiss 386,411 (1965).
3165. K. Schrage, *Tetrahedron* **23**, 3033 (1967).
3166. K. Schrage, *Tetrahedron* **23**, 3039 (1967).
3167. K. Schrage, *Tetrahedron Letters* p. 5795 (1966).
3168. D. C. Schroeder *et al.*, *J. Org. Chem.* **27**, 1098 (1962).
3169. H. Schroeder, J. R. Reiner, and T. A. Knowles, *Inorg. Chem.* **2**, 393 (1963).
3170. H. Schroeder, J. R. Reiner, and T. L. Heying, *Inorg. Chem.* **1**, 618 (1962).
3171. H. Schroeder and C. Grundmann, *J. Am. Chem. Soc.* **78**, 2447 (1956).
3172. H. Schroeder *et al.*, *J. Org. Chem.* **27**, 2580 (1962).
3173. W. Schroeder (to Upjohn Co.), U.S. 3,306,821 (1967).
3174. W. H. Schuller and D. C. Guth (to American Cyanamid Co.), U.S. 2,958,682 (1966).
3175. E. M. Schultz and J. M. Sprague, *J. Am. Chem. Soc.* **70**, 48 (1948).
3176. E. M. Schultz, C. M. Robb, and J. M. Sprague, *J. Am. Chem. Soc.* **69**, 188 (1947).
3177. E. M. Schultz, C. M. Robb, and J. M. Sprague, *J. Am. Chem. Soc.* **69**, 2454 (1947).
3178. G. Schulz and K. Mehnert, *Kunststoffe* **41**, 237 (1951); *C. A.* **45**, 10664.
3179. R. C. Schulz and J. Loflund, *Angew. Chem.* **72**, 771 (1960).
3180. H. S. Schwartz, J. E. Sodergren, and F. S. Philips, *Science* **142**, 1181 (1963).
3181. R. Schwyzer, *Helv. Chim. Acta* **35**, 1903 (1952).
3182. R. Schwyzer (to Ciba, Ltd.), U.S. 2,785,191 (1957); Brit. 749,122 (1956).
3182a.J. J. Scigliano, H. H. Weyland, and E. E. Hamel (to Aerojet-General Corp.), U.S. 3,364,259 (1968).
3183. F. L. Scott and E. Flynn, *Tetrahedron Letters* p. 1675 (1964).
3184. J. D. Sculley and N. H. Cromwell, *J. Org. Chem.* **16**, 94 (1951).
3185. S. Searles *et al.*, *J. Am. Chem. Soc.* **78**, 4917 (1956).
3185a.T. P. Seden and R. W. Turner, *J. Chem. Soc., C, Org.* p. 876 (1968).
3186. D. R. Seeger and A. S. Tomcufcik, *J. Org. Chem.* **26**, 3566 (1961).
3187. D. R. Seeger and A. S. Tomcufcik (to American Cyanamid Co.), U.S. 3,134,784 (1964); Brit. 885,370 (1962); Fr. 1,296,542 (1962); Ger. 1,222,505 (1966).
3188. D. R. Seeger and A. S. Tomcufcik (to American Cyanamid Co.), U.S. 3,226,382 (1965).
3189. D. R. Seeger and A. S. Tomcufcik (to American Cyanamid Co.), U.S. 3,226,377 (1965).
3189a.W. Seelinger *et al.*, *Angew. Chem.* **78**, 913 (1966); *Angew. Chem. Intern. Ed. Engl.* **5**, 875 (1966).
3190. H. Segal and C. G. Skinner, *J. Org. Chem.* **27**, 199 (1962).
3191. L. Segal and F. V. Eggerton, *Textile Res. J.* **33**, 739 (1963).
3191a.L. Segal (to U.S. Department of Agriculture), U.S. 3,393,968 (1968).
3192. A. Seher, *Ann. Chem.* **575**, 153 (1952).
3193. R. Sehring and K. Zeile (to C. H. Boehringer Sohn), U.S. 3,134,801 (1964); Ger. 1,146,486 (1963); Brit. 932,011 (1963); Neth. 107,782 (1964).

3194. Seiko Chemical Industry Co., Japan. 2924 ('67).
3195. V. Seke, *Chem. Ind.* (*Zagreb*) **10** (7) (*Photochem. Ind.*) F-71 (1961); via *Chem. Zentr.* p. 15831 (1952).
3196. M. Sekino, A. Nishihara, and Y. Mineki, Japan. 3293 ('57); via *C. A.* **52**, 5702.
3197. Sekisui Chemical Co., Ltd., Japan. 17,661 ('65).
3198. Sekisui Chemical Co., Ltd., Japan. 5006 ('68).
3199. G. Semenza, *Helv. Chim. Acta* **43**, 1057 (1960).
3200. F. W. Semmler, *Ber.* **37**, 950 (1904).
3201. M. Semonsky and A. Cerny, *Chem. Listy* **47**, 281 (1953); via *C. A.* **49**, 233.
3202. M. Semonsky and A. Cerny, *Chem. Listy* **47**, 469 (1953); via *C. A.* **48**, 3245.
3203. A. E. Senear, M. M. Rapoport, and J. B. Koepfli, *J. Biol. Chem.* **167**, 229 (1947).
3204. Y. Senkosho, Japan. 5998 ('64).
3205. S. Sentein, *Experientia* **12**, 257 (1956).
3206. F. H. Sexsmith (to Johnson and Johnson), U.S. 3,122,447 (1964).
3207. R. R. Shagidullin *et al.*, *Materialy 1-oi* [*Pervoi*] *Konf. Molodykh Nauchn. Rabotnikov g. Kazani, Sekt. Khim., Kazan, Sb. 1959* p. 137. Kazan, U.S.S.R., 1960; via *C. A.* **58**, 10876.
3207a. R. R. Shagidullin, *Izv. Akad. Nauk SSSR, Ser. Fiz.* **22**, 1079 (1958); via *C. A.* **53**, 861.
3208. R. R. Shagidullin, *Izv. Kazansk. Filiala, Akad. Nauk SSSR, Ser. Khim. Nauk* **6**, 123 (1963); via *C. A.* **59**, 14767.
3208a. R. R. Shagidullin and N. P. Grechkin, *Zh. Obshch. Khim.* **38**, 150 (1968); *J. Gen. Chem. USSR* (*English Transl.*) **38**, 148 (1968).
3209. F. V. Shallcross, *Dissertation Abstr.* **19**, 2244 (1959).
3210. E. M. Shamaeva, *Tr. Inst. Eksperim. i Klinich. Onkol., Akad. Med. Nauk SSSR* **2**, 128 (1960); via *C. A.* **59**, 9223.
3211. M. Y. Shandala, M. D. Solomon, and E. S. Waight, *J. Chem. Soc.* p. 892 (1965).
3212. N. C. Shane and H. G. Weiland (to Arkansas Co.), U.S. 3,236,672 (1966).
3213. N. C. Shane and H. G. Weiland, U.S. 3,336,157 (1967).
3214. G. N. Shangin-Berezovskii, *Izv. Akad. Nauk SSSR, Ser. Biol.* p. 859 (1965); via *Nucl. Sci. Abstr.* **20**, 14334.
3215. B. Sharma, *Izv. Timiryazevsk. Sel'skokhoz. Akad.* p. 127 (1965); via *C. A.* **64**, 5463; *Dokl. TSKhA* **102**, 245 (1965); via *C. A.* **65**, 9354; *Genetika* No. 1, p. 45 (1966); via *C. A.* **65**, 2598.
3216. B. Sharma, *Supermutageny, Akad. Nauk SSSR, Inst. Khim. Fiz.* p. 143 (1966); via *C. A.* **67**, 41107.
3217. I. Ya. Sharov, *Supermutagency, Akad. Nauk SSSR, Inst. Khim. Fiz.* p. 184 (1966); via *C. A.* **67**, 41110; *Tr. Mosk. Obshchestva Ispyt. Prir., Otd. Biol.* **23**, 126 (1967); via *C. A.* **67**, 88164.
3218. V. S. Shashkov *et al.*, *Farmakol. i Toksikol.* **30**, 109 (1967); via *C. A.* **66**, 102316.
3219. J. G. Shaw and M. Sanchez-Riviello, *Ciencia* (*Mex.*) **22**, 17 (1962); via *C. A.* **58**, 10673.
3220. J. G. Shaw and M. Sanchez-Riviello, *J. Econ. Entomol.* **58**, 26 (1965); cf. J. G. Shaw *et al.*, *ibid.* **60**, 992 (1967).
3221. N. S. Shcheglova, *Genetika* No. 2, p. 143 (1965); via *Nucl. Sci. Abstr.* **20**, 22658.
3222. J. C. Sheehan and J. H. Beeson, *J. Am. Chem. Soc.* **89**, 362 (1967).
3223. J. C. Sheehan and J. H. Beeson, *J. Am. Chem. Soc.* **89**, 366 (1967).
3224. J. C. Sheehan and I. Lengyel, *J. Am. Chem. Soc.* **86**, 1356 (1964).
3225. J. C. Sheehan and J. W. Frankenfeld, *J. Am. Chem. Soc.* **83**, 4792 (1961).
3226. D. P. Sheetz (to The Dow Chemical Co.), U.S. 3,134,740 (1964).
3227. Y. N. Sheinker, E. M. Peresleni, and G. I. Braz, *Zh. Fiz. Khim.* **29**, 518 (1955); via *C. A.* **50**, 12655.

3228. Y. N. Sheinker and E. M. Peresleni, *Zh. Fiz. Khim.* **32**, 2112 (1958); via *C. A.* **53**, 6760.

3228a. Shell International Research Maatschappij, Brit. 1,096,320 (1967).

3228b. Shell International Research Maatschappij, N.V., Neth. appl. 6,611,538 (1968).

3229. Shell Research Ltd., Fr. addn. 81,370 (1963); *C. A.* **60**, 2767.

3229a. T. E. Shellenberger, W. A. Skinner, and J. M. Lee, *Toxicol. Appl. Pharmacol.* **10**, 69 (1967).

3230. E. J. Shepherd and J. A. Kitchener, *J. Chem. Soc.* p. 2448 (1956).

3231. E. J. Shepherd and J. A. Kitchener, *J. Chem. Soc.* p. 86 (1957).

3232. J. K. Sherman and E. Steinberger, *Proc. Soc. Exptl. Biol. Med.* **103**, 348 (1960).

3233. M. Sherman and R. B. Herrick, *Toxicol. Appl. Pharmacol.* **9**, 279 (1966).

3234. R. P. Shibaeva and L. O. Atovmyan, *Dokl. Akad. Nauk SSSR* **160**, 334 (1965); *Soviet Physics Doklady* (*English Transl.*) **10**, 4 (1965).

3235. M. Kh. Shigaeva, V. D. Swertseva, and R. M. Dyjubanova, *Tr. Inst. Mikrobiol. Virusol., Akad. Nauk Kaz. SSR* **8**, 86 (1965); via *C. A.* **64**, 7087.

3235a. A. Shimizu, *Bull. Textile Res. Inst. Japan. Govt.* **37**, 81 (1956); via *Textile Technol. Dig.* **16**, 2987.

3236. M. B. Shimkin, *Cancer* **7**, 410 (1954).

3237. M. B. Shimkin, *J. Natl. Cancer Inst.* **36**, 915 (1966).

3239. H. Shinohara and S. Nagasawa, *Japan. J. Appl. Entomol. Zool.* **8**, 123 (1964); **9**, 162 (1965).

3240. Shionogi and Co., Ltd., Japan. 9826 ('67).

3241. Shionogi and Co., Ltd., Japan. 21,146 ('66); via *C. A.* **66**, 85651.

3242. Shionogi and Co., Ltd., Japan. 6337 ('67); Brit. 1,084,607 (1967).

3243. Shionogi and Co., Ltd., Neth. appl. 6,514,295 (1966); Fr. 1,452,541 (1966); Brit. 1,084,609 (1967); Japan. 9827 ('67).

3245. Shionogi and Co., Ltd., Neth. appl. 6,515,376 (1966); Belg. 672,932 (1966); Fr. 1,469,250 (1967); Japan. 10,231 ('67); Brit. 1,093,906 (1968).

3246. Shionogi and Co., Ltd., Fr. 1,461,846 (1966); Brit. 1,090,546 (1967).

3248. Shionogi and Co., Ltd., Brit. 1,090,686 (1967); Japan. 9056 ('68).

3248a. A. V. Shirodkar, *Dissertation Abstr.* **28B**, 4519 (1968).

3249. P. K. Shkvarnikov, M. I. Kulik, and I. V. Chernyi, *Tsitol. Genet. Akad. Nauk Ukr. SSR* **1**, 23 (1967); via *C. A.* **66**, 102323.

3251. P. K. Shkvarnikov, M. I. Kulik, and V. T. Safonova, *Dokl. Akad. Nauk SSSR* **164**, 1161 (1965); via *C. A.* **64**, 3977.

3252. P. K. Shkvarnikov, *Dokl. Akad. Nauk SSSR* **59**, 1337 (1948); via *C. A.* **42**, 7373.

3253. J. N. Short and C. C. Bice (to Phillips Petroleum Co.), U.S. 3,150,209 (1964).

3254. J. N. Short and C. C. Bice (to Phillips Petroleum Co.), U.S. 3,257,248 (1966).

3255. R. J. Shozda and J. A. Vernon, *J. Org. Chem.* **32**, 2876 (1967).

3256. D. Shukelene and Yu. Degutis, *Zh. Obshch. Khim.* **34**, 1221 (1964); *J. Gen. Chem. USSR* (*English Transl.*) **34**, 1207 (1964).

3257. B. N. Sidorov, N. N. Sokolov, and V. S. Andreev, *Genetika* No. 1, p. 112 (1965); via *C. A.* **64**, 5463; *ibid.* No. 7, p. 124 (1966); via *C. A.* **66**, 550.

3258. K. K. Sidorova, N. P. Kalinina, and L. P. Uzhintseva, *Genetika* No. 2, p. 136 (1965); via *Nucl. Sci. Abstr.* **20**, 22657.

3259. K. K. Sidorova, *Genetika* No. 6, p. 81 (1966); via *C. A.* **65**, 9354.

3260. J. Sieber, *Ber.* **23**, 326 (1890).

3261. Siegfried A.-G., Fr. 1,266,431 (1961): via *Chem. Zentr.* No. 38, abstr. 1580 (1964).

3262. Siemens-Schuckertwerke A.-G., Fr. 1,425,274 (1966); Brit. 1,059,281 and 1,068,150 (1967); Ger. 1,262,591 (1968).

3263. F. S. Sievenpiper and L. S. Zielinski (to Allied Chemical Co.), U.S. 3,208,814 (1965).

3264. S. D. Silver and F. P. McGrath, *J. Ind. Hyg. Toxicol.* **30**, 7 (1948).

3265. Simes S.p.A., Brit. 894,820 (1962).

3266. J. A. Simms (to du Pont de Nemours and Co.), U.S. 3,261,796 (1966); Belg. 636,350 (1964); Fr. 1,367,214 (1964); Neth. 296,850 (1965); Japan. 8577 ('66); Brit. 1,056,079 (1967).

3267. H. Simon and G. Apel, *Z. Naturforsch.* **11b**, 693 (1956).

3268. Z. Simon and I. Badilescu, *Biochem. Biophys. Res. Commun.* **21**, 1 (1965).

3268a. R. A. Simone and L. W. Fancher (to Stauffer Chemical Co.), U.S. 3,392,215 (1968); Neth. appl. 6,616,268 (1967); Belg. 689,830 (1967); Fr. 1,500,721 (1967).

3269. M. Simonetta, N. V. DiModrone, and G. Favini, *Gazz. Chim. Ital.* **80**, 129 (1950).

3270. M. Simonetta, N. V. DiModrone, and G. Favini, *Gazz. Chim. Ital.* **79**, 800 (1949).

3271. M. Simonetta, N. V. DiModrone, and G. Favini, *Gazz. Chim. Ital.* **79**, 814 (1949).

3271a. S. Singh *et al.*, *Indian J. Chem.* **6**, 12 (1968).

3272. B. Singh and E. F. Ullman, *J. Am. Chem. Soc.* **89**, 6911 (1967).

3272a. A. P. Sineokov, F. N. Gladysheva, and V. S. Etlis, *Zh. Org. Khim.* **4**, 284 (1968); via *C. A.* **68**, 104644.

3272b. A. P. Sineokov, F. N. Gladysheva, and V. S. Etlis, *Khim. Geterotsikl. Soedin., Akad. Nauk Latv. SSR* p. 370 (1968); via *C. A.* **69**, 96529.

3273. A. P. Sineokov, V. N. Gladysheva, and V. S. Etlis, *Khim. Geterotsikl. Soedin., Akad. Nauk Latv. SSR* p. 567 (1968); via *C. A.* **69**, 96538.

3273a. J. Sjoedin, *Hereditas* **48**, 565 (1962).

3274. E. L. Skau, R. M. Mod, and F. C. Magne (to U.S. Department of Agriculture), U.S. 3,219,659 (1965) and 3,294,802 (1966).

3275. W. A. Skinner and H. C. Tong, *Experientia* **24**, 924 (1968).

3276. W. A. Skinner *et al.*, *J. Med. Chem.* **10**, 120 (1967).

3277. W. A. Skinner *et al.*, *J. Org. Chem.* **26**, 148 (1961).

3278. W. A. Skinner *et al.*, *J. Med. Chem.* **9**, 520 (1966).

3279. W. A. Skinner *et al.*, *J. Med. Chem.* **9**, 605 (1966).

3280. W. A. Skinner *et al.*, *J. Med. Chem.* **8**, 647 (1965).

3281. W. A. Skinner, H. F. Gram, and B. R. Baker, *J. Org. Chem.* **25**, 953 (1960).

3282. W. A. Skinner, M. G. M. Schelstraete, and B. R. Baker, *J. Org. Chem.* **24**, 1827 (1959).

3283. W. A. Skinner, M. Cory, and J. I. DeGraw, *J. Med. Chem.* **10**, 1186 (1967).

3284. S. S. Skorokhodov *et al.*, *Zh. Obshch. Khim.* **31**, 3626 (1961); *J. Gen. Chem. USSR* (*English Transl.*) **31**, 3382 (1961).

3285. M. F. Sloan *et al.*, *Tetrahedron Letters* p. 2945 (1964).

3285a. A. E. Sloboda and A. W. Vogel, *Cancer Chemotherapy Rept.* **24**, 7 (1962).

3286. R. K. Smalley, *J. Chem. Soc., C, Org.* p. 80 (1966).

3287. R. J. Smat, *Dissertation Abstr.* **B27**, 1831 (1966).

3288. E. E. Smissman, R. P. Quintana, and J. H. Biel, *Abstr. Papers, 139th Am. Chem. Soc. Meeting, St. Louis, 1961* p. N-35.

3289. B. C. Smith and J. A. C. Berube, *Can. Entomol.* **98**, 1005 (1966).

3290. C. N. Smith, *Advan. Chem. Ser.* **41**, 36 (1963).

3291. C. N. Smith, G. C. LaBrecque, and A. B. Borkovec, *Ann. Rev. Entomol.* **9**, 269 (1964).

3292. F. F. Smith, A. L. Boswell, and T. J. Henneberry, *J. Econ. Entomol.* **58**, 98 (1965).

3293. G. H. Smith (to Minnesota Mining and Manufacturing Co.), U.S. 3,162,617 (1964).

3294. G. H. Smith (to Minnesota Mining and Manufacturing Co.), U.S. 3,060,048 (1962).

3295. G. H. Smith (to Minnesota Mining and Manufacturing Co.), U.S. 3,115,474 (1963); Brit. 938,113 (1963).

3296. G. H. Smith (to Minnesota Mining and Manufacturing Co.), U.S. 3,115,482 (1963); Can. 684,207 (1964).

3297. G. H. Smith (to Minnesota Mining and Manufacturing Co.), U.S. 3,115,490 (1963).
3298. G. H. Smith (to Minnesota Mining and Manufacturing Co.), U.S. 3,162,618 (1964); Fr. 1,273,547 (1961); Brit. 956,007 (1964); Can. 679,361 (1964).
3299. G. H. Smith (to Minnesota Mining and Manufacturing Co.), U.S. 3,240,720 (1966).
3300. J. R. L. Smith and D. J. Waddington, *Anal. Chem.* **40**, 522 (1968).
3301. L. Smith and B. Platon, *Ber.* **55**, 3143 (1922).
3302. L. H. Smith, ed., "Synthetic Fiber Developments in Germany" (PB 7416). Textile Res. Inst., New York, 1946.
3303. N. L. Smith and H. H. Sisler, *J. Org. Chem.* **26**, 5145 (1961).
3304. P. A. S. Smith and E. E. Most, Jr., *J. Org. Chem.* **22**, 358 (1957).
3305. B. J. Smittle, J. B. Schmidt, and G. S. Burden, *J. Econ. Entomol.* **59**, 1419 (1966).
3306. D. D. Smolin, L. M. Razbitnaya, and Yu. M. Viktorov, *Zh. Obshch. Khim.* **34**, 3713 (1964); *J. Gen. Chem. USSR (English Transl.)* **34**, 3762 (1966).
3307. G. Smolinsky and B. I. Feuer, *J. Org. Chem.* **31**, 1423 (1966).
3308. G. Smolinsky, *J. Am. Chem. Soc.* **83**, 4483 (1961).
3310. J. Smrt *et al.*, *Collection Czech. Chem. Commun.* **22**, 262 (1957); *Chem. Listy* **51**, 112 (1957).
3311. J. Smrt *et al.*, *Experientia* **13**, 291 (1957).
3312. J. Smrt, J. Beránek, and J. Sicher, Czech. 87,649 (1958); via *C. A.* **54**, 8852.
3314. J. Smrt and J. Sicher, Czech. 87,656 (1958), J. Smrt, J. Beránek, and J. Sicher, U.S. 2,943,092 (1960); Brit. 854,922 (1960).
3315. J. Smrt, Czech. 87,660 (1958); Brit. 855,444 (1960); Ger. 1,093,367 (1960); J. Smrt, J. Beránek, and J. Sicher, U.S. 2,958,691 (1960).
3316. H. F. Smyth, Jr., C. P. Carpenter, and C. S. Weil, *J. Ind. Hyg. Toxicol.* **31**, 60 (1949).
3317. H. F. Smyth, Jr. and C. P. Carpenter, *J. Ind. Hyg. Toxicol.* **30**, 63 (1948).
3318. H. F. Smyth, Jr., J. Seaton, and L. Fischer, *J. Ind. Hyg. Toxicol.* **23**, 259 (1941).
3320. L. A. Snyder and I. I. Oster, *Mutation Res.* **1**, 437 (1966).
3321. Societa Farmaceutici Italia, Fr. 1,335,310 (1963); Brit. 959,263 (1964).
3322. Societa per Azioni Ferraria, Ital. 572,862 (1958); via *C. A.* **54**, 22120.
3323. Société Industrielle de la Cellulose S. A., Brit. 794,858 (1958).
3324. Société les laboratoires Dausse, Fr. M3013 (1963); Brit. 1,058,675 (1967); Belg. 648,317 (1964); Neth. appl. 6,405,907 (1965).
3325. Société Rhodiacéta, Neth. appl. 6,607,297 (1966); Fr. 1,481,537 (1967); Brit. 1,109,756 (1968).
3326. Société Rhodiacéta, Fr. 1,014,009 (1956); *C. A.* **53**, 11856.
3327. Société Rhodiacéta, Fr. 1,437,455 (1966); Neth. appl. 6,607,371 (1966); Brit. 1,109,755 (1968); Ger. 1,260,786 (1968).
3328. M. Soekawa, *Proc. 16th Intern. Vet. Congr., Madrid, 1959* Vol. 2, p. 457; via *C. A.* **54**, 21302.
3328a. U. Soenksen and W. Sanne (to Badische Anilin- und Soda-Fabrik), U.S. 3,350,340 (1967).
3329. L. M. Soffer and E. Carpenter, *Textile Res. J.* **24**, 847 (1954).
3330. J. D. Solomon, *J. Econ. Entomol.* **59**, 1528 (1966).
3331. A. H. Soloway *et al.*, *J. Med. Pharm. Chem.* **5**, 1371 (1962).
3332. Solvay et Cie, Belg. 624,416 (1963); *C. A.* **60**, 9146; Fr. 1,372,363 (1964); Neth. 285,808 (1965).
3333. H. Sommer and F. Linke, *Teintex* **27**, 289 (1962); via *C. A.* **57**, 12754; *Textile-Rundschau* **16**, 622 (1961); via *J. Textile Inst.* **53**, 207.
3334. H. Sommer, *Melliand Textilber.* **43**, 507 (1962); *C. A.* **57**, 6162.
3334a. H. Sommer, H. Bestian, and D. Bergmann (to Farbwerke Hoechst), U.S. 3,399,110 (1968); Ger. 1,261,744 (1968).

3335. A. A. Sommerville and J. J. R. Luzzi (to Interchemical Corp.), U.S. 3,296,200 (1967).
3336. S. Sonnerskog, *Acta Chem. Scand.* **10**, 467 (1956).
3337. S. Sonnerskog, *Acta Chem. Scand.* **11**, 573 (1957).
3338. P. E. Sonnet, *J. Org. Chem.* **32**, 248 (1967).
3339. P. E. Sonnet and A. B. Bořkovec, *J. Org. Chem.* **31**, 2962 (1966).
3340. M. Sorkin, *Textil-Rundschau* **16**, 612 (1961); *C. A.* **56**, 4986.
3340a. I. N. Sorochkin *et al.*, U.S.S.R. 216,698 (1968); via *C. A.* **69**, 96442.
3341. P. E. Soto and J. B. Graves, *J. Econ. Entomol.* **60**, 550 (1967).
3342. P. L. Southwick and W. L. Walsh, *J. Am. Chem. Soc.* **77**, 405 (1955).
3343. P. L. Southwick and D. R. Christman, *J. Am. Chem. Soc.* **74**, 1886 (1952).
3344. P. L. Southwick and R. J. Shozda, *J. Am. Chem. Soc.* **82**, 2888 (1960).
3345. P. L. Southwick *et al.*, *J. Am. Chem. Soc.* **84**, 4299 (1962).
3346. P. L. Southwick and R. J. Shozda, *J. Am. Chem. Soc.* **81**, 5435 (1959).
3347. J. R. Sowa, *Dissertation Abstr.* **26**, 5046 (1966).
3348. H. L. Spell, The Dow Chemical Company, private communication (1967).
3349. H. L. Spell, *Anal. Chem.* **39**, 185 (1967).
3350. A. J. Speziale and E. G. Jaworski, *J. Org. Chem.* **25**, 722 (1960).
3351. A. J. Speziale and E. G. Jaworski, *J. Org. Chem.* **25**, 728 (1960).
3352. A. J. Speziale *et al.*, *Abstr. Papers, 149th Am. Chem. Soc. Meeting, Detroit, 1965* p. P-44; *J. Am. Chem. Soc.* **87**, 3460 (1965).
3353. G. Spielberger, *in* "Methoden der organischen Chemie" (Houben-Weyl) 4th ed. (E. Mueller, ed.), Vol. 11, Part 1, p. 83. Thieme, Stuttgart, 1957.
3354. J. D. Spivack (to J. R. Geigy A.-G.), U.S. 2,931,804 (1960); Indian 68,216 (1960); Can. 637,452 (1962); Brit. 921,994 (1963); Ger. 1,156,414 (1963).
3355. Sponcel Ltd. *et al.*, Brit. 914,421 (1963).
3356. R. M. Srivastava, K. Weissman and L. B. Clapp, *J. Heterocyclic Chem.* **4**, 114 (1967).
3357. H. A. Staab, W. Rohr, and A. Mannschreck, *Angew. Chem.* **73**, 143 (1961).
3358. H. A. Staab and H. Merdes, *Chem. Ber.* **98**, 1134 (1965).
3359. H. A. Staab and W. Rohr, *Chem. Ber.* **95**, 1298 (1962).
3360. M. Staeuble, K. Weber, and P. Hugelshofer (to Ciba Ltd.), U.S. 3,157,653 (1964); Deering Milliken Research Corp., Belg. 610,527 (1962); Brit. 996,068 (1965).
3361. H. Stamm, *Angew. Chem.* **74**, 694 (1962); *Angew. Chem. Intern. Ed. Engl.* **1**, 509 (1962).
3362. H. Stamm, *Arch. Pharm.* **299**, 965 (1966).
3363. H. Stamm, *Angew. Chem.* **77**, 546 (1965); *Angew. Chem. Intern. Ed. Engl.* **4**, 524 (1965).
3364. H. Stamm, *Chem. Ber.* **99**, 2556 (1966).
3364a. H. Stamm, *Ann. Chem.* **716**, 121 (1968).
3365. L. Stangalini, Ital. 484,325 (1953); *C. A.* **49**, 11312; Fr. 1,048,846 (1953).
3366. V. T. Stannett, *in* "Surfaces and Coatings Related to Paper and Wood" (R. H. Marchessault and C. Sklar, eds.), p. 269. Syracuse Univ. Press, Syracuse, New York, 1967.
3367. W. Starck, H. Starck, and F. Schulde (to Farbwerke Hoechst), U.S. 2,901,443 (1959); Brit. 834,883 (1960); Can. 639,848 (1962); Ger. 1,031,511 (1958).
3367a. B. P. Stark and A. J. Duke, "Extrusion Reactions." Pergamon, New York, 1967.
3368. Stauffer Chemical Co., Neth. appl. 6,603,199 (1966); Brit. 1,096,744 (1967); Fr. 1,475,997 (1967).
3369. Stauffer Chemical Co., Neth. appl. 6,616,268 (1967); Belg. 689,830 (1967); Fr. 1,500,721 (1967).
3370. R. J. Stedman, A. G. Swift, and J. R. E. Hoover, *Tetrahedron Letters* p. 2525 (1965).
3371. G. A. Stein *et al.*, *J. Chem. Soc.* p. 5002 (1963).

3372. E. Steinberger *et al.*, *Endocrinology* **65**, 40 (1959).

3373. R. C. Steinhauer (to Stauffer Chemical Co.), U.S. 3,034,919 (1962).

3374. I. D. Steinman, V. N. Iyer, and W. Szybalski, *Arch. Biochem. Biophys.* **76**, 78 (1958).

3375. W. D. Stephens *et al.*, *J. Chem. Eng. Data* **8**, 625 (1963).

3376. L. H. Sternbach, E. Reeder, and G. A. Archer, *J. Org. Chem.* **28**, 2456 (1963).

3377. S. S. Sternberg, F. S. Philips, and J. Scholler, *Ann. N.Y. Acad. Sci.* **68**, 811 (1958).

3378. C. L. Stevens *et al.*, *J. Med. Chem.* **8**, 1 (1965).

3379. C. L. Stevens *et al.*, *J. Org. Chem.* **29**, 3146 (1964).

3380. C. L. Stevens and P. M. Pillai, *J. Am. Chem. Soc.* **89**, 3084 (1967).

3381. J. P. Stevens and Co., Inc., Belg. 626,797 (1963); Fr. 1,381,230 (1964); Neth. 287,504 (1965); Brit. 1,043,341–1,043,344 (1966).

3382. J. P. Stevens and Co., Inc., S. Afr. 67/3514.

3383. J. P. Stevens and Co., Inc., Brit. 1,034,937 (1966).

3384. J. P. Stevens and Co., Inc., Neth. appl. 6,605,633 (1966); Brit. 1,082,916 (1967).

3384a. J. P. Stevens and Co., Inc., Brit. 1,109,946 (1968).

3385. J. H. Stevenson, *Abstr. Papers, 20th S.W. Reg. Am. Chem. Soc. Meeting, Shreveport, La., 1964* p. 52.

3386. J. M. Stewart, *J. Am. Chem. Soc.* **76**, 3228 (1954).

3387. Stockholms Superfosfat Fabriks A/B, Swed. 148,559 (1955); via *C. A.* **50**, 2679.

3388. E. L. Stogryn and S. J. Brois, *J. Org. Chem.* **30**, 88 (1965).

3389. E. L. Stogryn and S. J. Brois, *J. Am. Chem. Soc.* **89**, 605 (1967).

3390. M. A. Stolberg, J. H. O'Neill, and T. W. Jauregg, *J. Am. Chem. Soc.* **75**, 5045 (1953).

3391. R. Stollé, *J. Prakt. Chem.* [2] **67**, 143 (1903).

3392. W. N. Stoops and A. L. Wilson (to Carbide and Carbon Chemicals Corp.), U.S. 2,403,960 (1946).

3393. R. A. Strecker and A. S. Tompa, *Am. Chem. Soc., Div. Polymer Chem. Preprints* **8**, 567 (1967); *J. Polymer Sci., Part A-1* **6**, 1233 (1968).

3395. A. Streitweiser, Jr., *Chem. Rev.* **56**, 682 (1956).

3396. A. Streitwieser, Jr. and S. Pulver, *J. Am. Chem. Soc.* **86**, 1587 (1964).

3397. A. Streitwieser, Jr., "Solvolytic Displacement Reactions," p. 105. McGraw-Hill, New York, 1962.

3398. V. V. Strelko and Z. Z. Vysotskii, *Sintez i Fiz.-Khim. Polimerov, Akad. Nauk Ukr. SSR . . .* p. 66 (1964); via *C. A.* **62**, 9242.

3399. V. V. Strelko, P. P. Gushkin, and Z. Z. Vysotskii, *Dokl. Akad. Nauk SSSR* **153**, 619 (1963); *Proc. Acad. Sci. USSR, Chem. Sect.* (*English Transl.*) **151-153**, 968 (1963).

3400. V. V. Strelko and Z. Z. Vysotskii, *Inst. Khim. Vysokomolekul. Soedin., Sb. Statei* p. 30 (1964); via *C. A.* **62**, 9242.

3401. U. Stroele and E. Thomich (to Zellstofffabrik Waldhof), U.S. 3,119,731 (1964); Belg. 608,996 (1962); Ger. 1,136,199 (1962); Can. 698,086 (1964).

3403. G. W. Strother, Jr. (to The Dow Chemical Co.), U.S. 3,303,144 (1967); Belg. 691,891 (1967); Ital. 787,349 (1967); Fr. 1,506,897 (1967).

3404. G. W. Strother, Jr. (to The Dow Chemical Co.), U.S. 3,303,158 (1967).

3405. G. W. Strother, Jr. (to The Dow Chemical Co.), U.S. 3,316,210 (1967).

3406. G. W. Strother, Jr. (to The Dow Chemical Co.), U.S. 3,346,533 (1967).

3407. B. M. Sturgis (to du Pont de Nemours and Co.), U.S. 2,299,938 (1942).

3408. V. I. Sudenko, *Mikrobiol. Zh., Akad. Nauk Ukr. RSR* **26** (3), 37 (1964); via *C. A.* **65**, 20548.

3409. T. J. Suen and A. M. Schiller (to American Cyanamid Co.), U.S. 2,646,419 (1953).

3410. T. J. Suen (to American Cyanamid Co.), U.S. 2,688,607 (1954).

3410a. Y. Sugiya *et al.*, *Ann. Rept. Takamine Lab.* **12**, 218 (1960); via *Chem. Zentr.* No. 5, abstr. 1170 (1965).

3411. H. Suhr, *Ann. Chem.* **689**, 109 (1965).
3412. H. B. Sullivan and A. R. Day, *J. Org. Chem.* **29**, 326 (1964).
3413. A. Sumida *et al.*, Japan. 10,399 ('57); via *C. A.* **52**, 21150.
3413a. Sumitomo Atomic Power Industry Co., Japan. 8878 ('66); via *C. A.* **65**, 18723.
3414. Sumitomo Chemical Co., Ltd., Japan. 19,358 ('65); via *C. A.* **63**, 16363.
3415. Sumitomo Chemical Co., Ltd., Japan. 218 ('55); via *C. A.* **50**, 16867.
3416. Sumitomo Chemical Co., Ltd., Japan. 918 ('60); via *C. A.* **54**, 19539.
3417. Sumitomo Chemical Co., Ltd., Japan. 1713 ('66).
3418. Sumitomo Chemical Co., Ltd., Japan. 4234 ('62); via *C. A.* **59**, 2833.
3419. Sumitomo Chemical Co., Ltd., Japan. 5706 ('65); via *C. A.* **62**, 16273.
3420. Sumitomo Chemical Co., Ltd., Japan. 6349 ('65); via *C. A.* **63**, 1799.
3421. Sumitomo Chemical Co., Ltd., Japan. 14,650 ('64).
3422. Sumitomo Chemical Co., Ltd., Japan. 15,363 ('63); via *C. A.* **60**, 2770.
3424. Sumitomo Chemical Co., Ltd., Japan. 19,567 ('61); via *C. A.* **57**, 13776.
3425. Sumitomo Chemical Co., Ltd., Japan. 21,793 ('66); via *C. A.* **66**, 105852.
3426. Sumitomo Chemical Co., Ltd., Japan. 29,844 ('64); via *C. A.* **62**, 11782.
3427. Sumitomo Chemical Co., Ltd., Belg. 640,748 (1964); Ger. 1,260,474 (1968).
3428. Sumitomo Chemical Co., Ltd., Japan. 10,575 ('65), 18,745 and 18,746 ('65); Belg. 640,798 (1964); Brit. 996,107 (1965).
3429. Sumitomo Chemical Co., Ltd., Fr. 1,535,414 (1968).
3430. Sumitomo Chemical Co., Ltd., Japan. 13,637 ('66).
3431. Sumitomo Chemical Co., Ltd., Japan. 6274 ('67); via *C. A.* **67**, 54622.
3432. Sumitomo Chemical Co., Ltd., Japan. 6272 ('67); via *C. A.* **67**, 54620.
3433. Sumitomo Chemical Co., Ltd., Japan. 13,018 ('67); via *C. A.* **67**, 109166.
3434. Sumitomo Chemical Co., Ltd., Japan. 13,019 ('67); via *C. A.* **67**, 109167.
3435. Sumitomo Chemical Co., Ltd., Japan. 13,020 ('67); via *C. A.* **67**, 109168.
3437. G. Sunagawa, K. Murayama, and N. Yoshida, *Yakugaku Zasshi* **77**, 1173 (1957); via *C. A.* **52**, 6304.
3438. G. Sunagawa, Y. Sato, and H. Nakano, *Yakugaku Zasshi* **77**, 1176 (1957); via *C. A.* **52**, 6304.
3439. E. S. Sutton, Jr. and C. W. Vriesen (to Thiokol Chemical Corp.), U.S. 3,193,421 (1965); Brit. 1,014,048 (1965); Ger. 1,222,418 (1966); Fr. 1,395,058 (1965).
3440. H. Suyama and M. Uzumaki, *Seni-i Gakkaishi* **17**, 1073 (1961); via *C. A.* **56**, 4982.
3441. K. Suzuki and H. Matsui, Japan. 1954 ('66); via *C. A.* **64**, 19850.
3442. L. E. Sventsitskaya, A. A. Kropacheva, and S. I. Sergievskaya, *Zh. Obshch. Khim.* **28**, 1601 (1958); *J. Gen. Chem. USSR* (*English Transl.*) **28**, 1650 (1958).
3443. M. Svoboda *et al.*, *Chem. Listy* **49**, 1351 (1955); *Collection Czech. Chem. Commun.* **20**, 1426 (1955).
3444. G. E. Swailes, *J. Econ. Entomol.* **59**, 596 (1966).
3445. C. G. Swain and C. B. Scott, *J. Am. Chem. Soc.* **75**, 141 (1953).
3446. N. Swanson and J. B. Lovett (to The Dow Chemical Co.), U.S. 3,295,930 (1967).
3447. R. W. Swanson (to Air Products and Chemicals Co.), U.S. 3,146,236 (1964).
3448. G. Swift and D. Swern, *J. Org. Chem.* **32**, 511 (1967).
3449. G. Swift and D. Swern, *J. Org. Chem.* **31**, 4226 (1966).
3450. M. P. Sykes, S. Philips, and D. A. Karnovsky, *Med. Clin. N. Am.* **40**, 837 (1956).
3450a. M. P. Sykes *et al.*, *Cancer* **6**, 142 (1953).
3451. G. Szeimies and R. Huisgen, *Chem. Ber.* **99**, 491 (1966).
3452. J. Szmuszkovicz, *J. Am. Chem. Soc.* **82**, 1180 (1960).
3453. W. Szybalski, *Develop. Ind. Microbiol.* **1**, 231 (1960); Z. Lorkiewicz and W. Szybalski, *J. Bacteriol.* **82**, 195 (1961).
3454. W. Szybalski, *Ann. N. Y. Acad. Sci.* **76**, 475 (1958).

3455. C. W. Tabor and S. M. Rosenthal, *J. Pharmacol. Exptl. Therap.* **116**, 139 (1956).
3456. T. Taguchi, M. Kojima, and T. Muro, *J. Am. Chem. Soc.* **81**, 4322 (1959).
3457. T. Taguchi and M. Eto, *J. Am. Chem. Soc.* **80**, 4075 (1958).
3458. T. Taguchi and S. Kasuga, *Chem. & Pharm. Bull.* (*Tokyo*) **13**, 241 (1965); via *C. A.* **63**, 6963.
3459. T. Taguchi and M. Kojima, *J. Am. Chem. Soc.* **81**, 4316 (1959).
3460. T. Taguchi, O. Komori, and M. Kojima, *Yakugaku Zasshi* **81**, 1233 (1961); via *C. A.* **56**, 7128.
3461. T. Taguchi and M. Eto, *Pharm. Bull.* (*Tokyo*) **5**, 88 (1957); via *C. A.* **51**, 17777.
3462. T. Taguchi, O. Komori, and M. Kojima, *Yakugaku Zasshi* **81**, 1229 (1961); via *C. A.* **56**, 7293.
3463. T. Taguchi and M. Kojima, *J. Am. Chem. Soc.* **78**, 1464 (1956).
3464. T. Taguchi and M. Kojima, *Chem. & Pharm. Bull.* (*Tokyo*) **7**, 103 (1959); via *C. A.* **54**, 22551.
3465. T. Taguchi and M. Kojima, *J. Am. Chem. Soc.* **81**, 4318 (1959).
3467. Taisho Pharmaceutical Co., Ltd., Japan. 23,007 ('65); via *C. A.* **64**, 6496.
3468. H. Takagi, Y. Inazu, and R. Takeda, *Takamine Kenkyusho Nempo* **11**, 150 (1959); via *C. A.* **55**, 3823.
3471. M. Takebayashi, *Sci. Rept.* (*Osaka Univ.*) **11**, 7 (1962); via *C. A.* **61**, 12098.
3473. M. Takebayashi and Y. Inaba, *Sci. Rept.* (*Osaka Univ.*) **13**, 17 (1964); via *C. A.* **63**, 13183.
3474. Takeda Chemical Industries, Ltd., Japan. 20,018 ('61); via *C. A.* **57**, 13642.
3475. Takeda Chemical Industries, Ltd., Japan. 6540 ('64); via *C. A.* **61**, 13406.
3475a. Takeda Chemical Industries, Ltd., Japan. 14,848 ('64).
3476. Takeda Chemical Industries, Ltd., Japan. 25,334 ('65); via *C. A.* **64**, 12610.
3477. Takeda Chemical Industries, Ltd., Japan. 26,817 ('65); via *C. A.* **64**, 9637.
3478. Takeda Chemical Industries, Ltd., Fr. 1,518,056 (1968).
3479. Takeda Pharmaceutical Industries Co., Japan. 3489 ('50); via *C. A.* **47**, 5963.
3479a. S. Takemura, Y. Ueno, and S. Sega, *Kinki Daigaku Yakugakubu Kigo* No. 5, p. 13 (1967); via *C. A.* **69**, 86540.
3480. I. Takizaki and J. Okito (to Toyo Rayon Co.), U.S. 3,189,404 (1965).
3481. E. R. Talaty, A. E. Dupuy, Jr., and A. E. Cancienne, Jr., *J. Heterocyclic Chem.* **4**, 657 (1967).
3481a. E. R. Talaty and A. E. Dupuy, Jr., *Chem. Commun.* p. 790 (1968).
3482. P. B. Talukdar and P. E. Fanta, *J. Org. Chem.* **24**, 526 (1959).
3483. P. B. Talukdar and P. E. Fanta, *J. Org. Chem.* **24**, 555 (1959).
3484. L. E. Tammelin, *Acta Chem. Scand.* **11**, 1738 (1957).
3485. Y. L. Tan and D. R. Cole, *Clin. Chem.* **11**, 58 (1965).
3486. Tanabe Seiyaku Co., Ltd., Japan. 2060 ('67); via *C. A.* **66**, 104920.
3487. Tanabe Seiyaku Co., Ltd., Japan. 13,222 ('61); via *C. A.* **56**, 7279.
3488. Tanabe Seiyaku Co., Ltd., Japan. 18,949 ('66); via *C. A.* **66**, 37792.
3489. K. Tanaka, *J. Pharm. Soc. Japan* **70**, 212 and 220 (1950); via *C. A.* **44**, 7273.
3490. K. Tanaka and T. Sugawa, *J. Pharm. Soc. Japan* **72**, 1548 and 1551 (1952); via *C. A.* **47**, 8682.
3490a. M. Tanaka *et al.*, *Biochem. Biophys. Res. Commun.* **16**, 422 (1964).
3491. H. Tanida, T. Tsuji, and T. Irie, *J. Org. Chem.* **31**, 3941 (1966).
3491a. S. Tanifuji, *J. Fac. Sci.*, *Hokkaido Univ.*, *Ser. V* **8**, 143 (1962); via *C. A.* **60**, 12384.
3492. H. Taniyama, *Sogo Rinsho* **9**, 343 (1960); via *C. A.* **54**, 15703.
3493. A. Taral, *Ind. Textile* (*Paris*) No. 809, 280 (1954); via *C. A.* **48**, 14222.
3494. N. D. Tarasenko, *Izv. Sibirsk. Otd. Akad. Nauk SSSR, Ser. Biol.-Med. Nauk* No. 1, p. 35 (1963); via *C. A.* **59**, 13088.

3495. N. D. Tarasenko, *Izv. Sibirsk. Otd. Akad. Nauk SSSR, Ser. Biol.-Med. Nauk* No. 12, p. 133 (1964); via *C. A.* **60**, 13806; but cf. *Chem. Zentr.* No. 12, abstr. 1101 (1965).
3496. N. D. Tarasenko, *Radiobiologiya* **3**, 427 (1963); via *C. A.* **60**, 8325.
3497. N. D. Tarasenko, *Radiobiologiya* **4**, 770 (1964); via *C. A.* **62**, 3041.
3498. D. S. Tarbell and D. K. Fukushima, *J. Am. Chem. Soc.* **68**, 2499 (1946).
3499. D. S. Tarbell and P. Noble, *J. Am. Chem. Soc.* **72**, 2657 (1950).
3500. D. S. Tarbell and D. P. Cameron, *J. Am. Chem. Soc.* **78**, 2731 (1956).
3501. V. A. Tartakovskii, O. A. Luk'yanov, and S. S. Novikov, *Izv. Akad. Nauk SSSR, Ser. Khim.* p. 2246 (1966); *Bull. Acad. Sci. USSR, Div. Chem. Sci. (English Transl.)* p. 2186 (1966); *Dokl. Akad. Nauk SSSR* **178**, 123 (1968); *Doklady Chem. (English Transl.)* **178**, 21 (1968); U.S.S.R. 202,958 (1967); via *C. A.* **69**, 59084.
3501a. V. S. Tatarinskii *et al.*, *Sovrem. Metody Khim.* . . . p. 253 (1967); via *C. A.* **68**, 46024.
3502. K. Taube and K. Boeckmann (to Farbenfabriken Bayer), U.S. 2,912,296 (1959); Ger. 954,686 (1956).
3503. P. Tautu and L. Stanescu, *Acta Unio Intern. Contra Cancrum* **20**, 96 (1964); via *C. A.* **61**, 16677.
3504. L. D. Taylor, *J. Appl. Polymer Sci.* **6**, S13 (1962).
3505. L. D. Taylor (to Polaroid Corp.), U.S. 3,165,495 (1965).
3506. T. W. J. Taylor, J. S. Owen and D. Whittaker, *J. Chem. Soc.* p. 206 (1938).
3508. Teikoku Rayon Co., Ltd., Japan. 11,424 ('62); via *Chem. Zentr.* No. 31, abstr. 3071 (1965).
3509. J. Temple, *Compt. Rend.* **259**, 1717 (1964).
3510. A. Teramoto, M. Morimoto, and Y. Nishijima, *J. Polymer Sci., Part A-1* **5**, 1021 (1967).
3511. G. C. Tesoro and S. B. Sello, *Textile Res. J.* **34**, 523 (1964).
3512. G. C. Tesoro and S. B. Sello (to J. P. Stevens and Co.), U.S. 3,197,463 (1965); Fr. 1,323,045 (1963); Brit. 1,000,194 (1965).
3513. G. C. Tesoro (to J. P. Stevens and Co.), U.S. 3,165,375 (1965); Brit. 1,000,508 (1965); Ger. 1,265,114 (1968).
3513a. G. C. Tesoro, *Textilveredlung* **2**, 435 (1967).
3514. G. C. Tesoro (to J. P. Stevens and Co.), U.S. 3,279,882 (1966).
3515. G. C. Tesoro (to J. P. Stevens and Co.), U.S. 3,285,798 (1966).
3516. E. Testa, L. Fontanella, and V. Aresi, *Ann. Chem.* **676**, 151 (1964).
3517. F. N. Teumac (to The Dow Chemical Co.), U.S. 3,234,127 (1966).
3518. F. N. Teumac (to The Dow Chemical Co.), U.S. 3,318,870 (1967).
3519. F. N. Teumac (to The Dow Chemical Co.), U.S. 3,271,430 (1966).
3519a. D. Teves, *ATCP (Mexico)* **6** (2), 155 (1966); via *C. A.* **67**, 3891.
3520. Y. Tezuka, *Seni-i Gakkaishi* **17**, 948 (1961); via *C. A.* **56**, 7529.
3521. Y. Tezuka, *Seni-i Gakkaishi* **17**, 802 (1961); via *C. A.* **55**, 24564.
3522. Y. Tezuka, *Seni-i Gakkaishi* **17**, 940 (1961); via *C. A.* **56**, 4987.
3523. Y. Tezuka, *Seni-i Gakkaishi* **17**, 944 (1961); via *C. A.* **56**, 4987.
3523a. S. F. Thames *et al.*, *J. Am. Oil Chem. Soc.* **45**, 277 (1968).
3523b. S. F. Thames, J. E. McClosky, and P. L. Kelly, *J. Heterocyclic Chem.* **5**, 749 (1968).
3524. A. M. Theiss, *Arch. Toxikol.* **21**, 67 (1965).
3525. M. Theunis, *Bull. Sci., Acad. Roy. Belg.* [5] **12**, 785 (1926).
3526. H. Thiele and L. Langmaack, *Z. Physik. Chem. (Leipzig)* **207**, 118 (1957).
3527. H. Thiele and K. H. Gronau, *Makromol. Chem.* **59**, 207 (1963).
3528. H. Thiele and L. Langmaack, *Z. Physik. Chem. (Leipzig)* **206**, 394 (1957).
3529. H. Thiele and L. Langmaack, *Z. Naturforsch.* **12b**, 14 (1957).
3530. H. Thiele, K. Hoppe, and G. Moll, *Kolloid-Z.* **85**, 45 (1962).
3531. H. Thiele and H. S. V. Levern, *J. Colloid Sci.* **20**, 679 (1965).

3532. H. Thiele, Ger. 1,249,517 (1967); via *C. A.* **67**, 109390.

3533. K. Thinius and D. Weichert, Ger. (East) 27,163 (1964); via *C. A.* **61**, 12155.

3534. Thiokol Chemical Corp., Brit. 970,459 (1964); Fr. 1,366,026 (1964).

3537. Thiokol Chemical Corp., Neth. appl. 6,402,557 (1964); Belg. 645,138 (1964); Brit. 1,029,225 (1966); Fr. 1,385,127 (1965); Japan. 16,865 ('66).

3537a. W. Thoma and H. Rinke (to Farbenfabriken Bayer), U.S. 3,393,180 (1968).

3538. Dr. Karl Thomae G.m.b.H. Chemisch-pharmazeutische Fabrik, Brit. 807,826 (1959).

3538a. D. Karl Thomae, G.m.b.H., Brit. 1,057,612 (1967).

3539. L. C. Thomas and R. A. Chittenden, *Spectrochim. Acta* **20**, 467 (1964).

3540. A. L. Thompson, T. J. Hardwick, and C. A. Winkler, *Can. J. Res.* **26B**, 181 (1948).

3541. G. Thompson and R. F. Lambert (to Thiokol Chemical Corp.), U.S. 3,268,544 (1966).

3542. H. W. Thompson and G. P. Harris, *J. Chem. Soc.* p. 301 (1944).

3543. H. W. Thompson and W. T. Cave, *Trans. Faraday Soc.* **47**, 951 (1951).

3544. Thuringesche Zellwolle A.-G. and Zellwolle u. Kunstseide-Ring, Ger. 722,944 (1942); *C. A.* **37**, 5081.

3545. C. C. Thurman, Jr., J. S. Scruggs, and F. N. Teumac (to The Dow Chemical Co.), U.S. 3,341,476 (1967).

3546. J. T. Thurston, FIAT Final Rept. No. 960 (1946) (PB 48,437); *Bib. Sci. Ind. Rept. (U.S.)* **4**, 763.

3547. P. T. Thyrum and A. R. Day, *J. Med. Chem.* **8**, 107 (1965).

3547a. G. V. D. Tiers, *in* "High Resolution Nuclear Magnetic Resonance Spectroscopy" (J. W. Emsley, J. Feeney, and H. Sutcliffe, authors), Vol. II, Appendix B. Pergamon Press, Oxford, 1966.

3548. E. Tietze, *in* "Methoden der organischen Chemie" (Houben-Weyl) 4th ed. (E. Mueller, ed.), Vol. 11, Part 2, p. 234. Thieme, Stuttgart, 1958; private communication to H. Bestian.

3551. J. F. Tilney-Bassett, *J. Chem. Soc.* p. 2517 (1962).

3551a. N. I. Timin, *Dokl. TSKHA* No. 132, p. 187 (1967); via *C. A.* **69**, 74543.

3551b. N. I. Timin, *Dokl. TSKHA* No. 137, p. 57 (1967); via *C. A.* **69**, 74541.

3552. J. Timmermans, *Bull. Soc. Chim. Belges* **61**, 393 (1952).

3553. M. Tisler, *Arch. Pharm.* **291**, 457 (1958).

3554. G. T. Tisue, S. Linke, and W. Lwowski, *J. Am. Chem. Soc.* **89**, 6303 (1967).

3555. Toa Synthetic Chemical Industry Co., Ltd., Japan. 20,638 ('66).

3556. Toa Synthetic Chemical Industry Co., Ltd., Japan. 5222 ('68).

3557. F. Toda and K. Akagi, *Tetrahedron Letters* p. 3695 (1968).

3558. E. Toegel, *Textil-Rundschau* **16**, 707 (1961); *C. A.* **56**, 4989.

3559. Toho Rayon Co., Ltd., Japan. 3370 ('57); via *C. A.* **52**, 5476.

3560. Toho Tayon Co. Ltd., Japan. 3379 ('57); via *C. A.* **52**, 5476.

3561. Tokai Seiyu Kogyo Co., Japan. 3493 ('62); via *Chem. Zentr.* No. 12, abstr. 3077 (1965).

3562. N. Tokita and K. Kanamaru, *Kogyo Kagaku Zasshi* **59**, 824 (1956); *J. Polymer Sci.* **27**, 255 (1958).

3563. Tokuyama Soda Co., Ltd., Japan. 9436 ('60); via *C. A.* **55**, 8703.

3563a. Tokuyama Soda Co., Ltd., Japan. 2347 ('68).

3564. Tokyo Cellophane Paper Co., Ltd., Japan. 3464 ('62); via *Chem. Zentr.* No. 14, abstr. 3072 (1965).

3565. Tokyo Cellophane Paper Co., Ltd., Japan. 17,590 ('60); via *C. A.* **55**, 22820.

3565a. Tokyo Cellophane Paper Co., Ltd., Japan. 10,490 ('61); via *Chem. Zentr.* No. 12, abstr. 2508 (1964).

3566. W. S. Tolgyesi and J. F. Krasny, *Textile Res. J.* **37**, 298 (1967).

3567. H. Tolkmith, *Ann. N. Y. Acad. Sci.* **136**, 59 (1966).

3568. H. Tolkmith, E. C. Britton, and C. F. Holoway (to The Dow Chemical Co.), U.S. 2,802,823 (1957).
3569. H. Tolkmith, E. C. Britton, and C. F. Holoway (to The Dow Chemical Co.), U.S. 2,802,824 (1957).
3570. W. M. Tolles and W. D. Gwinn, *J. Chem. Phys.* **42**, 2253 (1965).
3571. D. A. Tomalia, *J. Heterocyclic Chem.* **3**, 384 (1966).
3571a. D. A. Tomalia (to The Dow Chemical Co.), U.S. 3,404,172 (1968).
3572. D. A. Tomalia and J. N. Paige, *J. Heterocyclic Chem.* **4**, 178 (1967).
3573. D. A. Tomalia, *Tetrahedron Letters* p. 2559 (1967).
3574. D. A. Tomalia and D. P. Sheetz, *J. Polymer Sci.*, Part *A*-1 **4**, 2253 (1966).
3575. R. Tondeur, R. Sion, and E. Deray, *Bull. Soc. Chim. France* p. 2493 (1964).
3576. A. V. Topchiev, U.S.S.R. 165,166 (1964); via *C. A.* **62**, 5297.
3577. A. Toppozada, S. Abdallah, and M. E. Eldefrawi, *J. Econ. Entomol.* **59**, 1125 (1966).
3578. K. Tori *et al.*, *Tetrahedron Letters* p. 869 (1965).
3579. K. Tori *et al.*, *Tetrahedron Letters* p. 2921 (1966).
3580. W. F. Tousignant and C. Moore (to The Dow Chemical Co.), U.S. 3,200,088 (1965).
3581. H. Tovey, *Textile Res. J.* **31**, 185 (1961).
3582. Toyo Rayon Co., Ltd., Japan. 290 ('65); via *C. A.* **63**, 5819.
3583. Toyo Rayon Co., Ltd., Japan. 787 ('67); via *C. A.* **67**, 22831.
3584. Toyo Rayon Co., Ltd., Japan. 2275 ('67); via *C. A.* **67**, 54982.
3585. Toyo Rayon Co., Ltd., Japan. 2400 ('56); via *C. A.* **51**, 9179.
3586. Toyo Rayon Co., Ltd., Japan. 4791 ('63); via *C. A.* **59**, 14157.
3587. Toyo Rayon Co., Ltd., Japan. 17,054 ('64); via *C. A.* **62**, 1785.
3588. Toyo Rayon Co., Ltd., Japan. 9437 ('63); Fr. 1,321,038 (1963); Brit. 991,572 (1965).
3589. Toyo Rayon Co., Ltd., Japan. 24,719 ('63); via *C. A.* **60**, 6982.
3590. Toyo Rayon Co., Ltd., Japan. 16,407 ('67); via *C. A.* **68**, 88037.
3591. Toyo Rayon Co., Ltd., Japan. 17,083 ('67); via *C. A.* **68**, 79420.
3592. Toyo Rayon Co., Ltd., Japan. 17,868 ('63); via *C. A.* **60**, 6978.
3593. Toyo Rayon Co., Ltd., Japan. 18,319 ('63); via *C. A.* **59**, 10284.
3594. Toyo Rayon Co., Ltd., Japan. 18,562 ('63); via *C. A.* **60**, 3151.
3595. Toyo Rayon Co., Ltd., Japan. 18,568 ('63); via *C. A.* **60**, 1884.
3596. Toyo Rubber Industry Co., Ltd., Japan. 4692 ('63); via *C. A.* **59**, 6540.
3597. Toyo Spinning Co., Ltd. and Sumitomo Chemical Industry Co. Ltd., Japan. 19,173 ('67).
3598. Toyo Spinning Co., Ltd., Japan. 543 ('67); via *C. A.* **67**, 33657.
3599. Toyo Spinning Co., Ltd., Japan. 16,464 ('62); via *C. A.* **59**, 12696.
3600. Toyo Spinning Co., Ltd., Japan. 24,591 ('63); via *C. A.* **60**, 5697.
3601. T. Toyoda, T. Suyama, and S. Kanao, *Yakugaku Zasshi* **83**, 856 (1963); via *C. A.* **60**, 1832.
3602. E. G. Trams, *Anal. Chem.* **30**, 256 (1958).
3603. T. G. Traylor, *Chem. & Ind.* (*London*) p. 649 (1963).
3604. L. M. Trefonas and R. Majeste, *Tetrahedron* **19**, 929 (1963).
3605. L. M. Trefonas, R. Towns, and R. Majeste, *J. Heterocyclic Chem.* **4**, 511 (1967).
3605a. L. M. Trefonas and T. Sato, *Abstr. Papers, 152nd Am. Chem. Soc. Meeting, New York, 1966* abstr. V-183.
3606. L. M. Trefonas and R. Majeste, *J. Heterocyclic Chem.* **2**, 80 (1965).
3607. L. M. Trefonas and J. Couvillion, *J. Am. Chem. Soc.* **85**, 3184 (1963).
3608. L. M. Trefonas and R. Towns, *J. Heterocyclic Chem.* **1**, 19 (1964).
3609. G. S. Trick and C. A. Winkler, *Can. J. Chem.* **30**, 915 (1952).
3609a. H. G. Trieschmann, L. Reuter, and W. Arend (to Badische Anilin- und Soda-Fabrik), U.S. 3,036,974 (1962); Brit. 784,059 (1957); Ger. 1,094,454 (1960).

3610. H. G. Trieschmann, L. Reuter, and W. Arend (to Badische Anilin- und Soda-Fabrik), U.S. 2,831,018 (1958); Ger. 1,081,473 (1960); Brit. 784,058 (1957).
3611. D. J. Triggle, *Advan. Drug. Res.* **2**, 173 (1965).
3612. V. W. Tripp, E. R. McCall, and R. T. O'Connor, *Am. Dyestuff Reptr.* **52**, P598 (1963).
3613. E. R. Trotman, "Dyeing and Chemical Technology of Textile Fibers." Chas. Griffin, London, 1964.
3614. P. E. Trout, *Tappi* **34**, 539 (1951).
3615. W. E. Truce and D. G. Brady, *J. Org. Chem.* **31**, 3543 (1966).
3616. W. E. Truce, J. E. Parr, and M. L. Gorbarty, *Chem. & Ind. (London)* p. 660 (1967).
3617. R. Truhaut and G. Deysson, *Compt. Rend.* **240**, 1568 (1955).
3618. R. Truhaut and G. Deysson, *Bull. Assoc. Franç. Étude Cancer* **44**, 221 (1957).
3619. R. Truhaut *et al.*, *Clin. Chim. Acta* **8**, 235 (1963).
3620. R. Truhaut and G. Deysson, *Compt. Rend. Soc. Biol.* **154**, 718 (1960).
3621. R. Truhaut and G. Deysson, *Compt. Rend.* **254**, 3760 (1962); G. Deysson and R. Truhaut, *Ann. Pharm. Franç.* **20**, 670 (1962).
3622. G. Tsatsas, C. Sandris, and D. Kontonassios, *Bull. Soc. Chim. France* p. 3100 (1964).
3623. Y. S. Tsizin and N. A. Preobrazhenskii, *Zh. Obshch. Khim.* **33**, 2873 (1963); *J. Gen. Chem. USSR (English Transl.)* **33**, 2800 (1963).
3624. K. C. Tsou and K. Hoegerle, *J. Med. Chem.* **6**, 47 (1963).
3625. K. C. Tsou, K. Hoegerle, and H. C. F. Su, *J. Med. Chem.* **6**, 435 (1963).
3626. K. C. Tsou (to Borden Co.), U.S. 3,119,790 (1964).
3627. K. C. Tsou *et al.*, *J. Pharm. Sci.* **56**, 484 (1967).
3628. K. C. Tsou (to Borden Co.), U.S. 3,166,590 (1965).
3629. S. Tsuboyama, K. Tsuboyama, and M. Yamagita, *Rika Gaku Kenkyusho Hokoku* **41**, 194 (1965); via *C. A.* **62**, 14079.
3630. S. Tsuboyama, *Bull. Chem. Soc. Japan* **38**, 354 (1965).
3631. S. Tsuboyama, *Bull. Chem. Soc. Japan* **39**, 698 (1966).
3632. S. Tsuboyama, *Bull. Chem. Soc. Japan* **35**, 1004 (1962).
3633. C. M. Tsung and H. Fraenkel-Conrat, *Biochemistry* **5**, 2061 (1966).
3634. Y. Tsunoda (to Asahi Chemical Industry Co.), U.S. 3,184,281 (1965); Brit. 990,406 (1965); Ger. 1,225,857 (1966).
3635. A. Tulinsky, *J. Am. Chem. Soc.* **84**, 3188 (1962).
3636. A. Tulinsky and J. H. van den Hende, *J. Am. Chem. Soc.* **89**, 2905 (1967).
3637. S. D. Turk *et al.*, *J. Org. Chem.* **29**, 974 (1964).
3638. A. B. Turner *et al.*, *J. Am. Chem. Soc.* **87**, 1050 (1965).
3638a. A. N. Turner and R. E. Lutz, *J. Heterocyclic Chem.* **5**, 437 (1968).
3639. T. E. Turner, V. C. Fiora, and W. M. Kendrick, *J. Chem. Phys.* **23**, 1966 (1955).
3640. T. E. Turner *et al.*, *J. Chem. Phys.* **21**, 564 (1953).
3641. UCB (Union Chimique-Chemische Bedrijven S.A.), Neth. appl. 6,607,402 (1966); via *C. A.* **66**, 105652.
3641a. UCB (Union Chimique-Chemische Bedrijven S.A.), Belg. 699,763 (1967).
3642. A. Uffer, *Experientia* **10**, 76 (1954).
3643. P. S. Ugrymov, *Tekstilna Prom. (Sofia)* **20** (7), 45 (1960); via *J. Textile Inst.* **52**, A381.
3644. F. C. Uhle, *J. Org. Chem.* **32**, 1596 (1967).
3645. Ukrainian Sci-Res. Sanitary-Chem. Inst. Health Ministry Ukrainian SSR, U.S.S.R. 162,149 (1964); via *C. A.* **61**, 13327.
3646. Ukrainian Sci.-Res. Sanitary-Chem. Inst. Health Ministry Ukrainian SSR, U.S.S.R. 162,533 (1964); via *C. A.* **61**, 13282.

3647. G. D. Ullyot and J. F. Kerwin, *in* "Medicinal Chemistry" (F. F. Blicke and C. M. Suter, eds.), Vol. 2, p. 234. Wiley, New York, 1956; J. P. D. Graham, *J. Med. Pharm. Chem.* **2**, 499 (1960).

3648. H. Ulrich (to General Aniline and Film Corp.), U.S. 2,222,200 (1940); I. G. Farbenindustrie A.-G., Brit. 509,334 (1939); Ger. 721,931 (1940); included in Belg. 429,331 (1939).

3649. H. Ulrich and K. Kuespert (to I. G. Farbenindustrie), U.S. 2,185,480 (1940); Ger. 697,761 (1940); Brit. 488,553 (1938); Fr. 830,220 (1938); Belg. 424,955 (1938).

3650. H. Ulrich and W. Harz (to I. G. Farbenindustrie), U.S. 2,182,306 (1939); Belg. 415,413 (1936); Fr. 805,905 (1936); Brit. 461,354 (1937); Neth. 45,673 (1937); Ger. 665,791 (1938).

3651. H. Ulrich (to I. G. Farbenindustrie), U.S. 2,206,273 (1940); Brit. 460,888 (1937); Fr. 807,146 (1937); Ger. 665,790 (1938); Neth. 44,232 (1938).

3652. H. Ulrich and K. Kuespert (to General Aniline and Film Corp.), U.S. 2,242,490 (1941).

3653. H. Ulrich (to General Aniline and Film Corp.), U.S. 2,272,489 (1942).

3654. H. Ulrich (to General Aniline and Film Corp.), U.S. 2,296,225 (1942); I. G. Farbenindustrie A.-G., Brit. 466,346 (1957); Fr. 810,395 (1937) in part; Ger. 656,934 (1938).

3655. H. Ulrich (to General Aniline and Film Corp.), U.S. 2,296,226 (1942).

3656. H. Ulrich, E. Ploetz, and E. Nold (vested in the Alien Property Custodian), U.S. 2,348,039 (1944); I. G. Farbenindustrie A.-G., Ger. 766,083 (1953).

3657. H. Ulrich (to I. G. Farbenindustrie), U.S. 2,382,185 (1944); Brit. 466,270 (1937); Fr. 810,395 (1937); Ger. 711,408 (1941).

3658. H. E. Ungnade and L. W. Kissinger, *J. Org. Chem.* **30**, 354 (1965).

3659. United States Rubber Co., Neth. appl. 6,605,525 (1966); via *C. A.* **66**, 95055.

3660. Upjohn Co., Japan. 2903 ('66).

3662. Upjohn Co., Ger. 1,122,671 (1962); Brit. 975,771 (1964); Fr. 1,434,922 (1966).

3663. Upjohn Co., Neth. appl. 6,618,213 (1967).

3664. Upjohn Co., Japan. 9019 ('66).

3665. Upjohn Co., Fr. 1,377,390 (1964); Brit. 1,043,142 (1966).

3666. Upjohn Co., Brit. 1,066,254 (1967).

3666a. Upjohn Co., Brit. 1,102,495 (1968).

3667. G. Ya. Uretskaya, E. I. Rybkina, and G. P. Men'shikov, *Zh. Obshch. Khim.* **30**, 327 (1960); *J. Gen. Chem. USSR (English Transl.)* **30**, 350 (1960).

3668. J. J. Ursprung (to Upjohn), U.S. 3,270,018 (1966); Brit. 1,088,942 (1967); Neth. appl. 6,501,753 (1965); Fr. 1,452,008 (1966); Can. 758,592 (1967).

3669. H. R. Usala and L. E. Wolinski (to du Pont de Nemours and Co.), U.S. 3,228,823 (1966); Belg. 636,357 (1964); Fr. 1,372,077 (1964); Brit. 1,002,231 (1965).

3670. D. A. Usher, *J. Am. Chem. Soc.* **90**, 363 (1968).

3671. D. A. Usher, *J. Am. Chem. Soc.* **90**, 367 (1968).

3672. K. Uzu, Y. Harada, and S. Wakaki, *Agr. Biol. Chem.* **28**, 388 (1964); via *C. A.* **61**, 14622.

3672a. T. A. Valega and J. C. Ingangi, *J. Chem. Eng. Data* **12**, 457 (1967).

3673. S. A. Valeva, *Radiobiologiya* **4**, 451 (1964); via *C. A.* **61**, 8609; *Genetika* No. 2, p. 106 (1965); via *Nucl. Sci. Abstr.* **20**, 22656.

3674. J. G. Vandenbergh and D. E. Davis, *J. Wildlife Management* **26**, 366 (1962).

3674a. J. L. van der Minne, P. H. J. Hermanie, and C. Douwes (to Shell Oil Co.), U.S. 3,380,970 (1968).

3675. J. L. van der Minne, P. H. J. Hermanie, and C. Douwes (to Shell Oil Co.), U.S. 3,210,169 (1965); Belg. 612,088 (1962); Ger. 1,257,484 (1967).

3676. H. G. P. van der Voort (to Shell Oil Co.), U.S. 3,267,034 (1966); Austral. 54,679/59; Brit. 869,084 (1961); Indian 69,700 (1961); Neth. 100,023 (1961).

3677. H. G. P. van der Voort and M. Krukziener (to Shell Oil Co.), U.S. 3,130,161 (1964); Austral. 54,680/59; Indian 69,701 (1961); Brit. 898,056 (1962); Neth. 101,069 (1962); Ger. 1,211,739 (1966).

3678. H. G. P. van der Voort (to Shell Oil Co.), U.S. 3,189,546 (1965), and U.S. 3,277,128 (1966); Belg. 599,944 (1961); Fr. 1,279,081 (1961); Brit. 940,606 (1963); Can. 656,519 (1963); Ger. 1,211,740 (1966); Indian 75,230 (1961).

3679. R. L. Van Etten and A. T. Bottini, *J. Chromatog.* **21**, 408 (1966).

3680. A. E. Van Hoof and R. M. Hart (to Gevaert Photo-Producten), U.S. 3,234,025 (1966); Ger. 1,095,120 (1960); Brit. 907,739 (1962).

3681. A. E. Van Hoof, R. M. Hart, and J. F. Willems (to Gevaert Photo-Producten), U.S. 3,174,859 (1965); Ger. 1,104,334 (1961); Belg. 595,323 and 595,324 (1961).

3682. G. van Nederveen, *Ingenieur* (*Utrecht*) **62**, Mk 1 (1950); via *C. A.* **44**, 5589.

3683. L. Vargha and B. Dumbovich, U.S. 3,152,147 (1964); Gyógyszeripari Kutato Intezet, Ger. 1,151,514 (1963); Brit. 811,510 (1959) and 864,235 (1961); Hung. 146,033 (1960); Swiss 349,266 (1960) and 356,774 (1961).

3684. L. Vargha, L. Toldy and E. Kasztreiner, *Acta Chim. Acad. Sci. Hung.* **19**, 295 (1959).

3685. L. Vargha, *Naturwissenschaften* **42**, 582 (1955).

3686. L. Vargha *et al.*, *J. Chem. Soc.* p. 805 (1957).

3687. L. Vargha, O. Fehér, and S. Lendvai, *J. Chem. Soc.* p. 810 (1957).

3688. G. S. Vasil'ev, I. I. Guseinov, and M. F. Shostakovskii, *Zh. Obshch. Khim.* **34**, 1216 (1964); *J. Gen. Chem. USSR* (*English Transl.*) **34**, 1211 (1964).

3689. W. R. Vaughan and M. S. Habib, *J. Org. Chem.* **27**, 324 (1962).

3690. W. R. Vaughan *et al.*, *J. Org. Chem.* **26**, 2392 (1961).

VEB Farbenfabrik Wolfen, see Farbenfabrik Wolfen.

3691. J. A. Verdol (to Sinclair Research, Inc.), U.S. 3,036,003 (1962); Japan. 23,961 (1964); Fr. 1,322,673 (1963).

3693. Vereinigte Papierwerke Schickedanz and Co., Ger. 1,056,916 (1959); *C. A.* **56**, 2618.

3694. Vereinigte Papierwerke Schickedanz and Co., Ger. 1,217,196 (1966); *C. A.* **65**, 4098.

3695. T. L. M. Vermehren, Dan. 85,906 (1958); via *C. A.* **53**, 11261.

3696. G. B. Vermont (to du Pont de Nemours and Co.), U.S. 3,261,799 (1966).

3697. S. G. Vestermann, U.S.S.R. 170,680 (1965); via *C. A.* **63**, 10092.

3698. W. H. J. Vickers, *European Polymer J.* **3**, 199 (1967).

3699. C. Viel and P. Rumpf, *Compt. Rend.* **252**, 3815 (1961).

3700. K. Vierling, H. Oettel, and G. Wilhelm (to Badische Anilin- und Soda-Fabrik), U.S. 3,006,912 (1961); Austrian 202,126 (1959); Belg. 595,668 (1961).

3700a. E. A. Vitalis (to American Cyanamid Co.), U.S. 3,329,637 (1967).

3701. M. Vitan, M. Ionescu, and V. Niculescu, *Rev. Chim.* (*Bucharest*) **16**, 200 (1965); via *C. A.* **64**, 3410.

3702. M. G. Vladimirova and A. A. Petrov, *Zh. Obshch. Khim.* **16**, 2141 (1946); via *C. A.* **42**, 108.

3703. E. Vogel *et al.*, *Angew. Chem.* **76**, 785 (1964); *Angew. Chem. Intern. Ed. Engl.* **3**, 642 (1964).

3704. F. Vogel, *Arch. Julius Klaus-Stift. Vererbungsforsch. Socialanthropol. Rassenhyg.* **36**, 149 (1961); via *C. A.* **59**, 5654.

3705. O. Vohler, *Chem. Ber.* **91**, 1161 (1958).

3706. G. von Schweinichen, *Materie Plastiche* **18**, 15 (1952); via *C. A.* **46**, 5355.

3706a. H. von Tobel (to Sandoz Ltd.), U.S. 3,187,007 (1965); Ger. 1,208,022 (1966); Fr. addn. 74,695 (1961).

3707. L. I. Vorob'eva *et al.*, *Vestn. Mosk. Univ.*, *Ser. VI: Biol.*, *Pochvoved.* **22** (4), 41 (1967); via *C. A.* **67**, 106163.

3708. M. G. Voronkov, L. A. Fedotova, and D. Rinkis, *Khim. Geterotsikl. Soedin.*, *Akad. Nauk Latv. SSSR* p. 722 (1965); *Chem. Heterocyclic Compounds (English Transl.)* **1**, 488 (1965); U.S.S.R. 165,449 (1964); via *C. A.* **62**, 6461.

3709. M. G. Voronkov, L. A. Fedotova, and D. O. Rinkis, *Khim. Geterotsikl. Soedin.*, *Akad. Nauk Latv. SSSR* p. 794 (1965); *Chem. Heterocyclic Compounds (English Transl.)* **1**, 538 (1965).

3710. M. G. Voronkov, L. A. Fedotova, and D. O. Rinkis, U.S.S.R. 166,680 (1964); via *C. A.* **62**, 10340.

3711. M. G. Voronkov, L. A. Fedotova, and G. F. Evdokimova, U.S.S.R. 166,697 (1964); via *C. A.* **62**, 14726.

3711a. M. G. Voronkov, L. A. Fedotova, and D. O. Kudinya, *Khim. Geterotsikl. Soedin.*, *Akad. Nauk Latv. SSR* p. 256 (1968); via *Chem. Zentr.* No. 62, abstr. 508 (1968).

3712. M. G. Voronkov and L. A. Fedotova, *Khim. Geterotsikl. Soedin.*, *Akad. Nauk Latv. SSSR*, p. 545 (1966); *Chem. Heterocyclic Compounds (English Transl.)* **2**, 408 (1966).

3713. A. A. Vredenskii, T. N. Masalitinova, and Y. A. Katin, *Zh. Fiz. Khim.* **40**, 1968 (1966); *Russ. J. Phys. Chem. (English Transl.)* **40**, 1050 (1966).

3714. C. W. Vriesen (to Thiokol Chemical Corp.), U.S. 3,177,101 (1965); Fr. 1,361,712 (1964); Brit. 998,829 (1965); Ger. 1,231,146 (1966).

3715. C. W. Vriesen (to Thiokol Chemical Corp.), U.S. 3,214,30 (1965).

3716. A. F. Wagner and C. O. Gitterman, *Antibiot. Chemotherapy* **12**, 464 (1962).

3717. E. F. Wagner, *Z. Ges. Textil-Ind.* **65**, 731 (1963); *C. A.* **60**, 1882.

3718. H. Wagner and H. Berg, *J. Electroanal. Chem.* **1**, 61 (1959–1960).

3719. H. Wagner and H. Berg, *J. Electroanal. Chem.* **2**, 452 (1961).

3720. T. Wagner-Jauregg and L. Zirngibl, *Ann. Chem.* **668**, 30 (1963).

3721. T. Wagner-Jauregg, *Angew. Chem.* **72**, 493 (1960).

3722. T. Wagner-Jauregg *et al.*, *J. Am. Chem. Soc.* **77**, 922 (1955).

3723. T. Wagner-Jauregg, *Helv. Chim. Acta* **44**, 1237 (1961).

3724. T. Wagner-Jauregg, J. J. O'Neill, and W. H. Summerson, *J. Am. Chem. Soc.* **73**, 5202 (1951).

3725. P. Wahl, *J. Polymer Sci.* **29**, 375 (1958).

3726. S. Wakaki *et al.*, *Antibiot. Chemotherapy* **12**, 469 (1962).

3727. S. Wakaki *et al.*, *Antibiot. Chemotherapy* **8**, 228 (1958).

3728. P. Walker and W. A. Waters, *J. Chem. Soc.* p. 1632 (1962).

3729. B. M. Wall (to Thiokol Chemical Corp.), U.S. 3,250,829 (1966).

3730. A. T. Wallace, *Abstr. Papers, 59th Ann. Conv., Assoc. S. Agr. Workers, Inc. (USA)*, *Jacksonville, Fla., 1962* p. 68; via *Plant Breed. Abstr.* **33**, 2790; also *Use Induced Mutations Plant Breed., Rept. FAO IAEA Tech. Meeting, Rome, 1964* p. 237. Pergamon Press, Oxford, 1965; via *C. A.* **65**, 20483.

3731. K. Wallenfels and W. Draber, *Angew. Chem.* **70**, 313 (1958).

3732. K. Wallenfels and W. Draber, *Ann. Chem.* **667**, 55 (1963).

3733. K. Wallenfels and W. Draber, *Tetrahedron* **20**, 1889 (1964).

3734. W. E. Walles, *Chem. Eng. News* **42** (29), 36 (1964).

3735. A. L. Walpole *et al.*, *Brit. J. Pharmacol.* **9**, 306 (1954).

3736. A. Walpole, *Ann. N.Y. Acad. Sci.* **68**, 750 (1958).

3737. C. H. Wang and S. G. Cohen, *J. Am. Chem. Soc.* **79**, 1924 (1957).

3738. C. H. Wang and S. G. Cohen, *J. Org. Chem.* **26**, 3301 (1961).

3739. C. H. Wang and S. G. Cohen, *J. Am. Chem. Soc.* **82**, 4688 (1960).

3739a. G. E. Waples, Jr. (to The Dow Chemical Co.), U.S. 3,383,373 (1968); Belg. 708,173 (1968).

3740. R. A. Ward, L. C. Rutledge, and L. H. Bell, *Mosquito News* **25**, 470 (1965).
3741. K. A. Watanabe and J. J. Fox, *J. Org. Chem.* **31**, 211 (1966).
3742. N. L. Watkins, Jr. (to Minnesota Mining and Manufacturing Co.), U.S. 3,159,600 (1964).
3743. N. L. Watkins, Jr., and R. M. McCurdy (to Minnesota Mining and Manufacturing Co.), U.S. 3,182,040 (1965); Brit. 1,000,501 (1965).
3744. N. L. Watkins, Jr. and R. M. McCurdy (to Minnesota Mining and Manufacturing Co.), U.S. 3,182,041 (1965) and 3,281,498 (1966).
3745. N. L. Watkins, Jr. (to Minnesota Mining and Manufacturing Co.), U.S. 3,198,770 (1965).
3746. N. L. Watkins, Jr. and R. M. McCurdy (to Minnesota Mining and Manufacturing Co.), U.S. 3,301,835 (1967).
3747. W. A. F. Watson, *Z. Vererbungslehre* **95**, 374 (1964).
3748. J. S. Webb *et al.*, *J. Am. Chem. Soc.* **84**, 3185 (1962).
3749. J. S. Webb *et al.*, *J. Am. Chem. Soc.* **84**, 3187 (1962).
3750. V. J. Webers, *J. Appl. Polymer Sci.* **7**, 1317 (1963).
3750a. V. J. Webers (to du Pont de Nemours and Co.), U.S. 3,338,164 (1967).
3751. R. Wegler, *in* "Methoden der organischen Chemie" (Houben-Weyl), 4th ed. (E. Mueller, ed.), Vol. 14, Part 2, p. 568. Thieme, Stuttgart, 1958.
3752. J. Wegmann (to Ciba Ltd.), U.S. 3,043,649 (1962); Austrian 202,549 (1959); Brit. 1,065,961 (1967); Ger. 1,133,339 (1962).
3753. H. L. Wehrmeister, *J. Org. Chem.* **30**, 664 (1965).
3754. D. E. Weidhaas and C. H. Schmidt, *Mosquito News* **23**, 32 (1963).
3755. D. E. Weidhaas *et al.*, *Proc. N. J. Mosquito Extermin. Assoc.* **48**, 106 (1961).
3756. D. E. Weidhaas, *Nature* **195**, 786 (1962).
3757. C. L. Weidner and I. R. Dunlap (to The Dow Chemical Co.), U.S. 2,995,512 (1961); Austral. 154,799 (1954); Brit. 723,868 (1955); Can. 526,590 (1956).
3758. J. Weightman and J. P. Hoyle, *J. Am. Med. Assoc.* **189**, 543 (1964).
3759. G. Weimann and K. Randerath, *Experientia* **19**, 49 (1963).
3760. R. Weingand and V. Ostwald, U.S. 2,709,138 (1955).
3761. E. K. Weisburger, *Public Health Rept.* (*U.S.*) **81**, 772 (1966).
3762. A. Weissberger and H. Bach, *Ber.* **65B**, 631 (1932).
3763. A. Weissberger and H. Bach, *Ber.* **64B**, 1095 (1931).
3764. G. Weitnauer, *Gazz. Chim. Ital.* **81**, 156 (1951).
3765. J. N. Wells, A. V. Shirodkar, and A. M. Knevel, *J. Med. Chem.* **9**, 195 (1966).
3767. J. W. Welt *et al.*, *J. Org. Chem.* **31**, 1543 (1966).
3769. H. Wenker, *J. Am. Chem. Soc.* **57**, 2328 (1935).
3770. L. M. Werbel *et al.*, *J. Med. Chem.* **6**, 637 (1963).
3771. E. R. Werner (to du Pont de Nemours and Co.), U.S. 3,282,879 (1966).
3772. S. R. West and F. E. Dollarhide (to The Dow Chemical Co.), U.S. 3,302,717 (1967).
3773. T. J. West and J. L. Dewey (to The Dow Chemical Co.), U.S. 3,042,641 (1962); Fr. 1,334,447 (1963); Brit. 953,959 (1964); Ital. 670,516 (1964); Ger. 1,217,029 (1966); Can. 732,652 (1968).
3774. M. Westergaard, *Experientia* **13**, 224 (1957).
3775. F. Weygand *et al.*, *Chem. Ber.* **99**, 1932 (1966).
3776. G. P. Wheeler, *Cancer Res.* **22**, 651 (1962).
3777. G. B. White, *Nature* **210**, 1372 (1966).
3778. L. A. White, U.S. 3,310,530 (1967).
3778a. L. A. White, U.S. 3,354,103 (1967).
3778b. L. A. White, U.S. 3,352,801 (1967).
3779. L. A. White, U.S. 3,313,779 (1967).

3779a. M. L. White (to American Cyanamid Co.), U.S. 3,284,238 (1966).

3780. R. E. Whitfield, W. L. Wasley, and A. G. Pittman (to U.S. Department of Agriculture), U.S. 3,372,978 and 3,385,653 (1968); Belg. 664,664 (1965); Neth. appl. 6,506,829 (1965); Fr. 1,455,905 (1966); Brit. 1,113,604 (1968).

3781. H. W. Whitlock, Jr. and G. L. Smith, *Tetrahedron Letters* p. 1389 (1965).

3782. H. W. Whitlock, Jr. and G. L. Smith, *J. Am. Chem. Soc.* **89**, 3600 (1967).

3783. A. Wicklein, *Faserforsch. Textiltech.* **8**, 230 (1957).

3784. H. Wieland, *Ber.* **37**, 1148 (1904).

3785. T. Wieland and E. Bokelmann, *Ann. Chem.* **576**, 20 (1952).

3786. T. Wieland *et al.*, *Chem. Ber.* **85**, 1035 (1952).

3787. W. Wigman, *Mededel. Vezelinst. TNO* **83**, 1–40 (1947); via *C. A.* **44**, 9679.

3787a. M. Wikler *et al.*, *Science* **163**, 75 (1969).

3788. S. Wilcox *et al.*, *J. Chem. Phys.* **21**, 563 (1953).

3789. R. H. Wiley *et al.*, *J. Org. Chem.* **21**, 686 (1956).

3790. R. H. Wiley and C. L. De Silva, *J. Org. Chem.* **21**, 841 (1956).

3791. H. Wilfinger (to Badische Anilin- und Soda-Fabrik), U.S. 3,009,831 (1961); Brit. 853,240 (1960).

3792. H. Wilfinger, *Wochbl. Papierfabrik.* **76**, 135 (1948); *C. A.* **42**, 8472.

3793. H. Wilfinger, *Papier* **2**, 265 (1948); *C. A.* **43**, 403; **44**, 10317.

3794. H. Wilfinger, *Angew. Chem.* **62**, 405 (1950).

3794a. H. Wilfinger and W. Auhorn, *Wochenbl. Papierfabr.* **96** (7), 201 (1968); via *POST-J* **3**, 1715.

3795. B. G. Wilkes and W. A. Denison (to Carbide and Carbon Chemicals Corp.), U.S. 2,381,020 (1945).

3796. L. C. Willensens and G. J. M. VanderKerk, *J. Organometal. Chem. (Amsterdam)* **4**, 34 (1965).

3797. I. Williams and B. M. Sturgis (to du Pont de Nemours and Co.), U.S. 2,290,262 (1942).

3798. L. G. Williams, M. S. Thesis, Oklahoma State University, 1968; K. D. Berlin, L. G. Williams, and O. C. Dermer, *Tetrahedron Letters* p. 873 (1968).

3799. D. H. Williamson and A. W. Scopes, *Proc. Intern. Union Physiol. Sci., 22nd Intern. Congr., Leiden 1962* Vol. 1, p. 759. Excerpta Med. Found., Amsterdam, 1962; via *C. A.* **59**, 7895.

3800. G. R. Williamson and B. Wright, *J. Polymer Sci.* **A3**, 3885 (1965).

3802. A. L. Wilson (to Carbide and Carbon Chemicals Corp.), U.S. 2,475,068 (1949).

3803. A. L. Wilson (to Carbide and Carbon Chemicals Corp.), U.S. 2,553,696 (1951).

3804. A. L. Wilson (to Carbide and Carbon Chemicals Corp.), U.S. 2,318,729 (1943).

3805. A. L. Wilson (to Carbide and Carbon Chemicals Corp.), U.S. 2,318,730 (1943).

3806. A. L. Wilson, *Univ. Pittsburgh Bull.* **40**, 326 (1944); via *Brit. Abstr.* Part A ii, p. 24 (1945).

3807. B. W. Wilson (to The Dow Chemical Co.), U.S. 3,203,910 (1965); Belg. 643,454 (1964); Brit. 1,037,965 (1966); Ital. 714,262 (1966); Can. 761,539 (1967); Fr. 1,392,629 (1965); Japan. 8828 ('68).

3808. R. H. Wilson, *Textile Res. J.* **32**, 424 (1962).

3809. J. W. Wilt, J. M. Kosturik, and R. C. Orlowski, *J. Org. Chem.* **30**, 1052 (1965).

3810. J. W. Wilt *et al.*, *J. Org. Chem.* **31**, 1543 (1966).

3811. E. Windemuth, H. von Brachel, and G. von Finck (to Farbenfabriken Bayer), U.S. 3,267,077 (1966); Ger. 1,112,286 (1961); Brit. 919,861 (1963).

3812. E. Winterfeldt and H. Pruess, *Chem. Ber.* **99**, 450 (1966).

3813. E. Winterfeldt and H. Pruess, *Angew. Chem.* **77**, 679 (1965); *Angew. Chem. Intern. Ed. Engl.* **4**, 689 (1965).

3813a. E. Winterfeldt and J. M. Nelke, *Chem. Ber.* **101**, 2381 (1968).

3813b. E. Winterfeldt and J. M. Nelke, *Chem. Ber.* **101**, 3163 (1968).

3814. F. Winternitz, M. Mousseron, and R. Dennilauler, *Bull. Soc. Chim. France* p. 382 (1956).

3814a. Wintershall A.-G. and Chemische Fabrik Stockhausen A.-G., Ger. 1,267,631 (1968).

3815. E. L. Wittle *et al.*, *J. Am. Chem. Soc.* **75**, 1694 (1953).

3816. H. P. Wohnsiedler and E. L. Kropa (to American Cyanamid Co.), U.S. 2,582,613 (1952); Can. 530,726 (1956).

3817. H. P. Wohnsiedler and E. L. Kropa (to American Cyanamid Co.), U.S. 2,582,614 (1952); Can. 534,951 (1956).

3818. H. P. Wohnsiedler and E. L. Kropa (to American Cyanamid Co.), U.S. 2,582,730 (1952).

3819. H. P. Wohnsiedler and E. L. Kropa (to American Cyanamid Co.), U.S. 2,784,166 (1957).

3820. F. Wolf, *Plaste Kautschuk* **14** (2), 85 (1967).

3820a. F. Wolf and K. Stelzner, *Zesz. Nauk. Univ. Poznaniu, Mat., Fiz., Chem.* No. 11, 77 (1967); via *C. A.* **69**, 97406.

3821. F. J. Wolf and D. M. Tennent (to Merck and Co.), U.S. 3,308,020 (1967); Brit. 929,391 (1963).

3822. L. Wolff, *Ann. Chem.* **399**, 274 (1913).

3823. N. Wolff and T. B. Pitrolffy-Szabo (to A. E. Staley Manufacturing Co.), U.S. 3,238,171 (1966).

3824. F. Wolfheim, *Ber.* **47**, 1450 (1914).

3824a. P. B. Woller and N. H. Cromwell, *J. Heterocyclic Chem.* **5**, 579 (1968).

3825. E. H. Wollerman, *S. Lumberman* **207** (2585), 119 (1963).

3827. J. W. Wood and P. T. Mora, *J. Org. Chem.* **26**, 2115 (1962).

3828. H. M. Woodburn and B. G. Pautler, *J. Org. Chem.* **19**, 863 (1954).

3829. W. M. Wooding (to American Cyanamid Co.), Can. 578,353 (1959).

3830. W. M. Wooding and T. J. Suen (to American Cyanamid Co.), U.S. 2,646,368 (1953).

3831. W. M. Wooding (to American Cyanamid Co.), U.S. 2,887,405 (1959).

3832. W. M. Wooding (to American Cyanamid Co.), U.S. 2,918,386 (1959).

3833. R. J. Woodman, *Nature* **209**, 1362 (1966).

3834. C. W. Woods, A. B. Bořkovec, and F. M. Hart, *J. Med. Chem.* **7**, 371 (1964).

3835. C. W. Woods and A. B. Bořkovec (to U.S. Department of Agriculture), U.S. 3,197,465 (1965).

3836. C. W. Woods and A. B. Bořkovec (to U.S. Department of Agriculture), U.S. 3,180,792 (1965).

3837. C. W. Woods and M. Beroza (to U.S. Department of Agriculture), U.S. 3,126,315 (1964); Interchemical Corporation, Belg. 630,315 (1963); S. African 63/1855; Neth. 291,032 (1965); Fr. 1,352,399 (1964).

3838. C. Wunderly, *Nature* **177**, 586 (1956).

3839. M. Wuokko, *J. Pharm. Belg.* [N.S.] **13**, 513 (1958).

3840. O. B. Wurzburg and E. D. Mazzarella (to National Starch and Chemical Corp.), U.S. 3,102,064 (1963).

3840a. K. D. Wuu and W. F. Grant, *Can. J. Genet. Cytol.* **8**, 471 (1966).

3841. V. P. Wystrach, D. W. Kaiser, and F. C. Schaefer, *J. Am. Chem. Soc.* **77**, 5915 (1955).

3842. V. P. Wystrach and D. W. Kaiser (to American Cyanamid Co.), U.S. 2,520,619 (1950).

3843. A. K. Yalynskaya, *Latvijas PSR Zinatnu Akad. Vestis* No. 7, p. 48 (1966); via *C. A.* **66**, 579.

3844. A. K. Yalynskaya, *Latvijas PSR Zinatnu Akad. Vestis* No. 18, p. 127 (1966); via *C. A.* **66**, 62810.

3845. H. Yamaguchi and A. J. Miah, *Radioisotopes (Tokyo)* **13**, 472 (1964); via *Nucl. Sci. Abstr.* **19**, 7140.

3846. K. Yamazaki and H. Tokui, *Bull. Chem. Soc. Japan* **38**, 2174 (1965).

3847. S.-H. Yang and Y.-K. Li, *Hua Hsueh Tung Pao* p. 449 (1964); via *C. A.* **62**, 1617.

3848. Yawata Iron and Steel Co., Ltd., Japan. 15,459 ('63); via *C. A.* **60**, 7735.

3849. K. B. Yim, *Korean Forest. Soc. J.* **3**, 43 (1963).

3850. R. H. Yocum and M. M. Joullié, *J. Org. Chem.* **31**, 3823 (1966).

3851. J. H. Yoe, *Publication Board Rept. (U.S.)* PB 16,436 (1941); via *Bibliog. Sci. Ind. Rept.* **1**, 1377 (1946).

3851a. Yokohama Rubber Manufacturing Co. Ltd., Japan. 784 ('67).

3851b. T. Yonezawa and I. Morishima, *J. Mol. Spectry.* **27**, 210 (1968).

3852. T. Yoshida and K. Naito, *J. Chem. Soc. Japan., Ind. Chem. Sect.* **55**, 455 (1952); via *C. A.* **48**, 13625.

3853. Z. Yoshida and K. Nakagawa, *Tetrahedron Letters* p. 3753 (1965).

3854. Yoshitomi Pharmaceutical Industries Ltd., Japan. 13,632 ('61); via *C. A.* **56**, 10157.

3855. J. R. Young and H. C. Cox, *J. Econ. Entomol.* **58**, 883 (1965).

3856. J. R. Young and J. W. Snow, *J. Econ. Entomol.* **60**, 1427 (1967).

3857. R. L. Younger and J. E. Young, *Am. J. Vet. Res.* **24**, 659 (1963).

3858. R. L. Younger and R. D. Radeleff, *Trans. N.Y. Acad. Sci.* [2] **111**, 715 (1964).

3859. R. L. Younger, *Am. J. Vet. Res.* **26**, 991 (1965).

3860. T.-S. Yu, M. S. Thesis, Oklahoma State University, 1966.

3861. J. Yudelson (to Eastman Kodak Co.), U.S. 3,017,280 (1961).

3862. Y. Yukawa and S. Kimura, *Mem. Inst. Sci. Ind. Res., Osaka Univ.* **14**, 191 (1957); via *C. A.* **52**, 2748.

3863. H. Yumoto *et al.* (to Toyo Rayon Co.), U.S. 3,286,009 (1966).

3864. O. A. Yuzhakova, V. F. Bystrov, and R. G. Kostyanovskii, *Izv. Akad. Nauk SSSR, Ser. Khim.*, p. 240 (1966); *Bull. Acad. Sci. USSR, Div. Chem. Sci. (English Transl.)* p. 218 (1966).

3864a. H. M. Zacharis and L. M. Trefonas, *J. Heterocyclic Chem.* **5**, 343 (1968).

3864b. G. N. Zaeva *et al.*, *Toksikol. Novykh Prom. Khim. Vestchestv* **9**, 59 (1967); via *C. A.* **69**, 109631.

3865. G. N. Zaeva *et al.*, *Toksikol. Novykh Prom. Khim. Veshchestv* **8**, 41 (1966); via *C. A.* **67**, 80782; *ibid.* **9**, 50 (1967); via *C. A.* **69**, 109629.

3865a. K. C. Zahn, *Dissertation Abstr.* **B28**, 4956 (1968).

3865b. Zaidan Hojin Seisan Kaihatsu Kagaku Kenkyusho, Japan. 11,785 ('68).

3865c. N. F. Zakharova, *Med. Parazitol. Parazit. Boliz.* **35**, 515 (1966); via *C. A.* **66**, 36804.

3866. L. H. Zalkow *et al.*, *Chem. & Ind. (London)* p. 1556 (1964).

3867. L. H. Zalkow and A. C. Oehlschlager, *J. Org. Chem.* **28**, 3303 (1963).

3868. L. H. Zalkow and C. D. Kennedy, *J. Org. Chem.* **28**, 3309 (1963).

3869. H. Zallen, J. E. Christian, and A. M. Knevel, *J. Pharm. Sci.* **50**, 783 (1961).

3869a. A. Zampieri and J. Greenberg, *Genetics* **57**, 41 (1967).

3870. L. Zannone, *Energia Nucl. Agr.* p. 309 (1963); via *Nucl. Sci. Abstr.* **17**, 38691; *Use Induced Mutatations, Plant Breed., Rept. FAO IAEA Tech. Meeting, Rome, 1964* p. 205. Pergamon Press, Oxford, 1965; via *C. A.* **66**, 44310.

3871. R. K. Zech *et al.*, *Western J. Surg., Obstet. Gynecol.* **62**, 436 (1954).

3872. N. S. Zefirov, P. P. Kadzyauskas, and Yu. K. Yur'ev, *Zh. Obshch. Khim.* **35**, 259 (1965); *J. Gen. Chem. USSR (English Transl.)* **35**, 262 (1965).

3872a. N. S. Zefirov, P. Kadziauskas, and Y. K. Yur'ev, *Khim. Geterotsikl. Soedin.*, *Akad. Nauk. Latv. SSR* p. 47 (1965); *Chem. Heterocyclic Compounds (English Transl.)* **1**, 30 (1965).

3873. R. P. Zelinski and H. L. Hsieh (to Phillips Petroleum Co.), U.S. 3,281,383 (1966).

3874. R. P. Zelinski and C. W. Strobel (to Phillips Petroleum Co.), U.S. 3,108,994 (1963); J. N. Short (to Phillips), U.S. 3,225,089 (1965); Brit. 921,803 (1963).

3875. Zellstofffabrik Waldhof, Brit. 962,939 (1964); Fr. 1,303,882 (1963); Swiss 399,160 (1966).

3876. Zellstofffabrik Waldhof, Ger. 1,186,315 (1965); *C. A.* **63**, 3164.

3878. E. Zerner and M. W. Pollock (to Sun Chemical Corp.), U.S. 2,651,631 (1953).

3879. G. L. Zhdanov, *Tr. Inst. Eksperim. i Klinich. Onkol., Akad. Med. Nauk SSSR* **2**, 137 (1960); via *C. A.* **60**, 1010.

3880. N. K. Zhdanov, N. I. Zharova, and S. I. Alikhanyan, *Radiobiologiya* **5**, 304 (1965) acc. to *C. A.* **63**, 3291.

3881. D. S. Zhuk, P. A. Gembitskii, and V. A. Korgin, *Usp. Khim.* **34**, 1249 (1965); *Russ. Chem. Rev. (English Transl.)* **34**, 515 (1965).

3882. N. Zidermane, *TioTEFA, Akad. Nauk Latv. SSR, Inst. Organ. Sinteza* p. 19 (1961); via *C. A.* **58**, 844.

3883. M. Ziegler and L. Ziegeler, *Talanta* **14**, 1121 (1967).

3884. L. S. Zielinski and F. L. Sievenpiper (to Allied Chemical Corp.), U.S. 3,295,916 (1967).

3885. W. L. Zielinski, Jr. *et al., J. Chromatog.* **29**, 58 (1967).

3885a. H. Zimmerman, G. Pfeiffer, and K. Stetzelberg (to Farbwerke Hoechst), U.S. 3,266,931 (1967); Fr. addn. 83,110 (1964); Japan. 5975 ('64); Brit. 1,017,610 (1966).

3886. H. E. Zimmerman and W. H. Chang, *J. Am. Chem. Soc.* **81**, 3634 (1959).

3887. H. Zollinger, *Angew. Chem.* **73**, 125 (1961).

3888. V. P. Zosimovich and A. F. Androshchuk, *Tsitol. Genet., Akad. Nauk Ukr. SSR* **1**, 42 (1967); via *C. A.* **67**, 61689.

3888a. V. P. Zosimovich, M. K. Safin, and V. E. Demchenko, *Tr. Mosk. Obshchestva Ispyt. Prir., Otd. Biol.* **23**, 306 (1966); via *C. A.* **67**, 88165.

3889. S. V. Zotova, G. V. Loza, and M. Yu. Lukina, *Dokl. Akad. Nauk SSSR* **164**, 1303 (1965); *Proc. Acad. Sci. USSR, Chem. Sect. (English Transl.)* **163-165**, 1016 (1965).

3890. S. V. Zotova, G. V. Loza, and M. Yu. Lukina, *Izv. Akad. Nauk SSSR, Ser. Khim.* p. 2057 (1965); *Bull. Acad. Sci. USSR, Div. Chem. Sci. (English Transl.)* p. 2204 (1965).

3891. S. V. Zotova, G. V. Loza, and M. Yu. Lukina, *Izv. Akad. Nauk SSSR, Ser. Khim.* p. 432 (1967); *Bull. Acad. Sci. USSR, Div. Chem. Sci. (English Transl.)* p. 415 (1967).

3892. N. N. Zoz, N. N. Kozhanova, and T. V. Sal'nikova, *Genetika* No. 2, p. 78 (1967); via *C. A.* **67**, 843.

3893. N. N. Zoz *et al., Dokl. Akad. Nauk SSSR* **163**, 224 (1965); via *C. A.* **63**, 10325.

3894. N. N. Zoz, *Dokl. Akad. Nauk SSSR* **137**, 426 (1961); via *Plant Breed. Abstr.* **32**, 3103.

3895. N. N. Zoz and N. P. Dubinin, *Dokl. Akad. Nauk SSSR* **137**, 704 (1961); via *Plant Breed. Abstr.* **32**, 3105.

3896. N. N. Zoz, *Dokl. Akad. Nauk SSSR* **145**, 187 (1962); via *C. A.* **57**, 12916.

3897. N. N. Zoz, *Dokl. Akad. Nauk SSSR* **136**, 712 (1961); via *Plant Breed. Abstr.* **32**, 3133.

3898. N. N. Zoz, P. V. Kolotenkov, and S. I. Makarova, *Dokl. Akad. Nauk SSSR* **159**, 1397 (1964); via *C. A.* **62**, 9474.

3899. N. N. Zoz, *Supermutageny, Akad. Nauk SSSR, Inst. Khim. Fiz.* p. 93 (1966); via *C. A.* **67**, 41102; T. V. Sal'nikova and N. N. Zoz, *ibid.* p. 121; via *C. A.* **67**, 41104.

3900. S. E. Zurabyan, S. S. Keblas, and I. L. Knunyants, *Izv. Akad. Nauk SSSR, Ser. Khim.* p. 2036 (1964); *Bull. Acad. Sci. USSR, Div. Chem. Sci.* (*English Transl.*) p. 1932 (1964).
3901. E. N. Zvonkova *et al.*, *Zh. Obshch. Khim.* **34**, 3659 (1964); *J. Gen. Chem. USSR* (*English Transl.*) **34**, 3708 (1964).
3902. A. Zwierzak and A. Koziara, *Angew. Chem.* **80**, 285 (1968); *Angew. Chem. Intern. Ed. Engl.* **7**, 292 (1968).

Supplementary References

4000. F. I. Abezganz and S. V. Solokov, *Zh. Obshch. Khim.* **37**, 809 (1967); *J. Gen. Chem. USSR* (*English Transl.*) **37**, 759 (1967).
4001. S. Akerfeldt, *Acta Chem. Scand.* **20**, 1783 (1966).
4002. All-Union Scientific Research Institute of Phytopathology, U.S.S.R. 190,142 (1966); via *C. A.* **67**, 116138.
4003. A. G. Anastassiou, *J. Am. Chem. Soc.* **90**, 1527 (1968).
4004. A. Anhalt and H. Berg, *J. Electroanal. Chem.* **1**, 61 (1960).
4005. Asta-Werke A.-G., S. Afr. 67/3905.
4006. R. S. Atkinson and C. W. Rees, *Chem. Commun.* p. 1230 (1967).
4007. R. S. Atkinson and C. W. Rees, *Chem. Commun.* p. 1232 (1967).
4008. R. Aumann and E. O. Fischer, *Angew. Chem.* **79**, 900 (1967); *Angew. Chem. Intern. Ed. Engl.* **6**, 879 (1967).
4009. J. Aylett and J. Emsley, *J. Chem. Soc., A, Inorg., Phys., Theoret.* p. 1918 (1967).
4010. A. L. J. Beckwith and J. W. Redmond, *J. Am. Chem. Soc.* **90**, 1351 (1968).
4011. H. Berg and K. H. Koenig, *Z. Krebsforsch.* **62**, 495 (1958).
4012. H. Berg and K. H. Koenig, *Anal. Chim. Acta* **18**, 140 (1958).
4013. R. F. Bleiholder and H. Shechter, *J. Am. Chem. Soc.* **90**, 2131 (1968).
4014. S. J. Brois, *J. Am. Chem. Soc.* **89**, 4242 (1967).
4015. S. J. Brois, *J. Am. Chem. Soc.* **90**, 506 (1968).
4016. S. J. Brois, *J. Am. Chem. Soc.* **90**, 508 (1968).
4017. A. B. Bořkovec, S. C. Chang, and A. M. Limburg, *J. Econ. Entomol.* **57**, 815 (1964).
4018. A. T. Bottini and C. P. Nash, *J. Am. Chem. Soc.* **84**, 734 (1962).
4019. N. F. Bukva and G. H. Gass, *Cancer Chemotherapy Rept.* **51**, 431 (1967).
4020. R. N. Castle and S. Takano, *J. Heterocyclic Chem.* **5**, 113 (1968).
4021. T.-H. Chang and F. T. Elequin, *Mutation Res.* **4**, 83 (1967).
4022. E. Cherbuliez *et al.*, *Helv. Chim. Acta* **47**, 2106 (1964).
4023. Z. F. Chmielewicz *et al.*, *J. Pharm. Sci.* **56**, 1179 (1967).
4024. D. D. Christianson, J. W. Paulis, and J. S. Wall, *Anal. Biochem.* **32**, 35 (1968).
4025. Ciba A.-G., Swiss 345,652 (1960); via *Chem. Zentr.* p. 3743 (1961).
4026. R. J. Cicione *et al.*, *Am. Dyestuff Reptr.* **57**, P66 (1968).
4027. J. Cleophax *et al.*, *Compt. Rend.* **C266**, 720 (1968).
4028. W. J. Connick, Jr. and S. E. Ellzey, Jr., *Am. Dyestuff Reptr.* **57**, P71 (1968).
4029. D. G. Constantinescu *et al.*, *Compt. Rend.* **254**, 1665 (1962).
4030. D. B. Cosulich, J. B. Patrick, and R. P. Williams (to American Cyanamid Co.), U.S. 3,332,944 (1967).
4031. N. H. Cromwell, D. B. Capps, and S. E. Palmer, *J. Am. Chem. Soc.* **73**, 1226 (1951).
4032. M. M. Crystal, *J. Econ. Entomol.* **61**, 134 (1968).
4033. M. M. Crystal, *J. Econ. Entomol.* **61**, 140 (1968).
4034. M. A. Dahlem and R. A. Pingree, *Publication Board Rept.* (*U.S.*) PB 1576 (1945).
4035. Dai-Nippon Ink and Chemicals Co., Inc., Japan. 18,474 ('67).
4036. T. B. Davich *et al.*, *J. Econ. Entomol.* **60**, 1533 (1967).
4037. L. E. Davis and R. D. Deanin, *SPE* (*Soc. Plastics Engrs.*) *J.* **24** (1), 59 (1968).

4038. E. V. Dehmlow, *Tetrahedron Letters* p. 5177 (1967).

4039. G. I. Derkach and S. K. Mikhailik, *Khim. Organ. Soedin. Fosfora* ... 59 (1967); via *C. A.* **69**, 2757.

4040. W. J. Dickson and F. W. Jenkins (to Petrolite Corp.), U.S. 3,346,489 (1967).

4041. V. Dishlers, *Latvijas PSR Zinatnu Akad. Vestis* No. 1, p. 95 (1966); via *Plant Breed. Abstr.* **37**, 1605.

4043. G. F. Dregval, A. M. Samuilov, and I. V. Komissarov, *Zh. Obshch. Khim.* **37**, 1885 (1967); *J. Gen. Chem. USSR* (*English Transl.*) **37**, 1795 (1967).

4044. Eastman Kodak Co., Fr. 1,486,986 (1967); via *C. A.* **68**, 74068.

4045. M. Elzinga and C. H. W. Hirs, *Arch. Biochem. Biophys.* **123**, 343 (1968).

4046. T. Endo and M. Okawara, *Makromol. Chem.* **112**, 49 (1968).

4047. D. J. Endsley (to The Dow Chemical Co.), U.S. 3,365,519 (1968).

4048. A. Ermili and A. Floridi, *Farmaco* (*Pavia*), *Ed. Sci.* **22**, 402 (1967); via *C. A.* **68**, 21895.

4049. E. Ettenhuber and K. Ruehlmann, *Chem. Ber.* **101**, 743 (1968).

4050. Farbenfabriken Bayer A.-G., Brit. 919,861 (1963).

4051. Farbenfabriken Bayer A.-G., Ger. 1,099,532 (1961); *C. A.* **56**, 3515.

4052. Farbwerke Hoechst A.-G., Ger. 1,258,604 (1968); via *C. A.* **68**, 50585.

4053. N. Ya. Fedotova, T. T. Buglova, and E. N. Pisarchuk, *Tr. Ukr. Nauchn.-Issled. Inst. Spirt. Likero-Vodochnoi Prom.* **10**, 142 (1965); via *Biol. Abstr.* **48**, 5595.

4054. J. F. Feeman (to Crompton and Knowles Corp.), U.S. 3,334,138 (1967).

4055. D. Felix and A. Eschenmoser, *Angew. Chem.* **80**, 197 (1968); *Angew. Chem. Intern. Ed. Engl.* **7**, 224 (1968).

4056. T. A. Foglia and D. Swern, *J. Org. Chem.* **33**, 766 (1968).

4057. F. W. Fowler and A. Hassner, *J. Am. Chem. Soc.* **90**, 2875 (1968).

4058. M. I. Fremery (to Shell Oil Co.), U.S. 3,342,833 (1967).

4059. D. D. Gagliardi and V. Kenney, *Chem. Specialties Mfrs. Assoc., Proc. Ann. Meeting* **53**, 121 (1966).

4060. P. A. Gembitskii *et al.*, *Izv. Akad. Nauk SSSR, Ser. Khim.* p. 225 (1968); *Bull. Acad. Sci. USSR, Div. Chem. Sci.* (*English Transl.*) p. 228 (1968).

4061. General Tire and Rubber Co., Neth. appl. 6,614,045 (1967); via *C. A.* **68**, 30898.

4062. N. P. Grechkin and L. N. Grishina, *Izv. Akad. Nauk SSSR, Ser. Khim.* p. 2120. (1967); *Bull. Acad. Sci. USSR, Div. Chem. Sci.* (*English Transl.*) p. 2047 (1967).

4063. N. P. Grechkin and R. R. Shagidullin, *Izv. Akad. Nauk SSSR, Otd. Khim. Nauk* p. 2135 (1960); *Bull. Acad. Sci. USSR, Div. Chem. Sci.* (*English Transl.*) p. 1978 (1960).

4064. B. S. Green, *Dissertation Abstr.* **B28**, 100 (1967).

4065. A. G. Grinevich, *Vopr. Mikrobiol., Akad. Nauk Arm. SSR* p. 98 (1966); via *Biol. Abstr.* **48**, 117684.

4066. K. K. Grover, M. K. K. Pillai, and C. M. S. Dass, *Current Sci.* (*India*) **36**, 625 (1967).

4067. G. E. Ham (to The Dow Chemical Co.), U.S. 3,341,568 (1967).

4068. G. E. Ham (to The Dow Chemical Co.), U.S. 3,359,259 (1967).

4069. G. R. Hansen and T. E. Burg, *J. Heterocyclic Chem.* **4**, 653 (1967).

4070. J. A. Harding, *J. Econ. Entomol.* **60**, 1631 (1967).

4071. G. R. Harvey, *J. Org. Chem.* **33**, 887 (1968).

4072. A. Hassner and F. W. Fowler, *J. Am. Chem. Soc.* **90**, 2869 (1968).

4073. H. W. Heine and J. Irving, *Tetrahedron Letters* p. 4767 (1967).

4074. H. W. Heine, A. B. Smith, III, and J. D. Bower, *J. Org. Chem.* **33**, 1097 (1968).

4075. H. W. Heine *et al.*, *J. Org. Chem.* **32**, 2708 (1967).

4076. H. Heslot, *Abhandl. Deut. Wiss. Berlin, Kl. Med.* p. 193 (1962).

4077. Hodogaya Chemical Co., Ltd., Ger. 1,242,219 (1967); via *C. A.* **68**, 30676.

4078. R. E. Humbel, R. Derron, and P. Neumann, *Biochemistry* **7**, 621 (1968).
4079. K. Ichimura and M. Ohta, *Bull. Chem. Soc. Japan* **40**, 1933 (1967).
4080. Imperial Chemical Industries of Australia and New Zealand Ltd., Neth. appl. 6,610,166 (1967); via *C. A.* **68**, 49591; Fr. 1,502,712 (1967); Belg. 684,340 (1967); S. Afr. 66/4044.
4081. S. A. Inkina, L. A. Vol'f, and A. I. Meos, U.S.S.R. 191,043 (1967); via *C. A.* **68**, 30613.
4082. Interchemical Corp., "Propylene Imine" brochure (1966).
4083. S. Z. Ivin *et al.*, *Zh. Obshch. Khim* **37**, 1640 (1967); *J. Gen. Chem. USSR (English Transl.)* **37**, 1556 (1967).
4084. S. Z. Ivin, V. K. Promonenko, and G. V. Konopatova, *Zh. Obshch. Khim.* **37**, 1681 (1967); *J. Gen. Chem. USSR (English Transl.)*, **37**, 1600 (1967).
4085. A. G. Jelinek (to du Pont de Nemours and Co.), U.S. 3,354,036 (1967).
4086. D. E. Johnson, R. H. Quacchia, and A. J. Di Milo, *Ind. Eng. Chem., Prod. Res. Develop.* **6**, 273 (1967).
4087. A. Jones and F. P. Lossing, *Can. J. Chem.* **45**, 1684 (1967).
4088. T. Kagiya *et al.*, *Bull. Chem. Soc. Japan.* **41**, 172 (1968).
4089. D. L. Kenaga (to The Dow Chemical Co.), U.S. 3,362,850 (1968).
4091. K. Kitahonoki, A. Matsuura, and K. Kotera, *Tetrahedron Letters* p. 1651 (1968).
4092. R. F. Klemm, *Can. J. Chem.* **45**, 1693 (1967).
4093. W. Klassen, J. F. Norland, and A. B. Borkovec, *J. Econ. Entomol.* **61**, 401 (1968).
4094. I. M. Klotz and V. H. Stryker, *J. Am. Chem. Soc.* **90**, 2717 (1968).
4095. E. Kobayashi, Japan. 15,003 ('67); via *C. A.* **67**, 118078.
4097. K. Kotera *et al.*, *Tetrahedron* **24**, 1727 (1968).
4098. A. A. Kropacheva, V. A. Parshina, and S. I. Sergievskaya, *Zh. Obshch. Khim.* **30**, 3584 (1960); *J. Gen. Chem. USSR (English Transl.)* **30**, 3552 (1960).
4099. S. J. Kuhn (to The Dow Chemical Co.), U.S. 3,335,130 (1967).
4100. S. J. Kuhn (to The Dow Chemical Co.), U.S. 3,335,132 (1967).
4101. I. I. Kuz'menko, *Fiziol. Aktiv. Veshchestva, Akad. Nauk Ukr. SSR . . .* p. 78 (1966); via *C. A.* **67**, 117242.
4103. G. L'Abbe, *Ind. Chem. Belge* **32**, 541 (1967).
4104. G. C. LaBrecque and C. N. Smith, eds., "Principles of Insect Chemosterilization." Appleton, New York, 1968.
4105. L. E. La Chance and A. P. Leverich, *Ann. Entomol. Soc. Am.* **61**, 164 (1968).
4106. P. Lagally (to Chemirad Corp.), U.S. 3,346,527 (1967); Brit. 1,109,696 (1968).
4107. J. L. Larice, J. Roggero, and J. Metzger, *Bull. Soc. Chim. France* p. 3637 (1967).
4108. K. Laube and E. Nischwitz, *Papier* **22**, 124 (1968).
4109. J. M. Lehn and J. Wagner, *Chem. Commun.* p. 148 (1968).
4110. I. Lengyel and J. C. Sheehan, *Angew. Chem.* **80**, 27 (1968); *Angew. Chem. Intern. Ed. Engl.* **7**, 25 (1968).
4111. N. J. Leonard, D. A. Durand, and F. Uchimaru, *J. Org. Chem.* **32**, 3607 (1967).
4112. N. J. Leonard, E. F. Muth, and V. Nair, *J. Org. Chem.* **33**, 827 (1968).
4113. A. Loveless, *Nature* **167**, 338 (1951).
4114. S. Machida *et al.*, *Kami-pa Gikyoshi* **21**, 432 (1967); via *C. A.* **67**, 118303.
4115. J. F. McGhie and B. T. Warren, *Chem. & Ind. (London)* p. 253 (1968).
4116. M. C. McMaster, Jr., *Dissertation Abstr.* **B28**, 589 (1967).
4117. G. G. Maher, C. R. Russell, and C. E. Rist, *Staerke* **19**, 354 (1967).
4118. M. M. Marciacq-Rousselot and N. Bellavita, *Compt. Rend.* **C265**, 853 (1967).
4119. G. Martini, *Caryologia* **19**, 241 (1966).
4120. V. S. Martynov, A. N. Makarova, and A. Ya. Berlin, *Zh. Organ. Khim.* **3**, 1675 (1967); via *C. A.* **68**, 2877.

4121. A. B. Maslow and N. D. Stepanova, *Genetika* No. 9, p. 27 (1967); via *Nucl. Sci. Abstr.* **21**, 45597.
4122. H. C. Mason *et al.*, *J. Econ. Entomol.* **61**, 166 (1968).
4123. H. C. Mason and F. F. Smith, *J. Econ. Entomol.* **61**, 362 (1968).
4124. R. Mathis-Noel *et al.*, *Compt. Rend.* **B266**, 926 (1968).
4125. J. S. Meek and J. S. Fowler, *J. Org. Chem.* **33**, 985 (1968).
4126. C. E. Mendoza and D. C. Peters, *J. Econ. Entomol.* **61**, 416 (1968).
4127. L. F. Mikheeva and Z. P. Vasil'eva, *Probl. Poluch.-Poluprod. Prom. Organ. Sin.* . . . p. 118 (1967); via *C. A.* **68**, 49213.
4128. A. Mishra, S. N. Rice, and W. Lwowski, *J. Org. Chem.* **33**, 481 (1968).
4129. E. F. Monteiro *et al.*, *Compt. Rend. Soc. Biol.* **161**, 1168 (1967).
4130. A. E. Munson *et al.*, *Cancer Chemotherapy Rept.* **51**, 253 (1967).
4131. M. M. Nawar, *Dissertation Abstr.* **27B**, 44 (1966).
4132. E. E. Nifant'ev and A. I. Zavalishina, *Zh. Obshch. Khim.* **37**, 1854 (1967); *J. Gen. Chem. USSR (English Transl.)* **37**, 1766 (1967).
4133. C. W. Noell and C. C. Cheng, *J. Med. Chem.* **11**, 63 (1968).
4134. H. Nozaki, S. Fujita, and R. Noyori, *Tetrahedron* **24**, 2193 (1968).
4135. Y. Ohshiro, S. Honjoh, and T. Agawa, *Kogyo Kagaku Zasshi* **70**, 1828 (1967); via *C. A.* **68**, 39380.
4136. Y. Oishi and Y. Nakajima, U.S. 3,362,827 (1968).
4137. T. Orav, G. Shangin-Berezova, and I. Orav, *Izv. Akad. Nauk Est. SSR, Biol. Ser.* **17** (1), 20 (1968).
4138. A. Padwa and W. Eisenhardt, *Chem. Commun.* p. 380 (1968).
4139. A. Padwa and L. Hamilton, *Tetrahedron Letters* p. 1861 (1967); A. Padwa, D. Eastman, and L. Hamilton, *J. Org. Chem.* **33**, 1317 (1968).
4140. L. A. Paquette and D. E. Kuhla, *Tetrahedron Letters* p. 4517 (1967).
4141. J. C. Parish and B. W. Arthur, *J. Econ. Entomol.* **58**, 976 (1965).
4142. G. Pataki and H. Zuercher, *J. Chromatog.* **33**, 103 (1968)
4143. J. B. Patrick *et al.*, *J. Am. Chem. Soc.* **86**, 1889 (1964).
4144. R. S. Patterson, C. S. Lofgren, and M. D. Boston, *J. Econ. Entomol.* **60**, 1673 (1967).
4145. H. Paulsen and D. Stoye, *Angew. Chem.* **80**, 120 (1968); *Angew. Chem. Intern. Ed. Engl.* **7**, 134 (1968).
4146. K. A. Petrov *et al.*, *Zh. Obshch. Khim.* **31**, 3081 (1961); *J. Gen. Chem. USSR (English Transl.)* **31**, 2872 (1961).
4147. K. A. Petrov, A. I. Gavrilova, and A. M. Kopylov, *Zh. Obshch. Khim.* **30**, 2863 (1960); *J. Gen. Chem. USSR (English Transl.)* **30**, 2842 (1960).
4148. K. Ponsold and D. Eichhorn, *Z. Chem.* **8**, 59 (1968).
4149. F. D. Popp, E. Cullen, and S. Roth, *Chem. & Ind. (London)* p. 1017 (1962).
4150. L. D. Protsenko and L. A. Negievich, *Ukr. Khim. Zh.* **30**, 1328 (1964); via *C. A.* **62**, 9085.
4151. L. D. Protsenko and K. A. Kornev, *Ukr. Khim. Zh.* **28**, 719 (1962); via *C. A.* **59**, 489.
4152. L. D. Protsenko and K. A. Kornev, *Ukr. Khim. Zh.* **27**, 243 (1961); via *C. A.* **55**, 23481.
4153. G. I. Pustoshkin, *Zh. Organ. Khim.* **4**, 43 (1968); via *C. A.* **68**, 95299.
4154. R. H. Quacchia, *J. Gas Chromatog.* **6**, 253 (1968).
4155. R. H. Quacchia, D. E. Johnson, and A. J. Di Milo, *Ind. Eng. Chem., Prod. Res. Develop.* **6**, 268 (1967).
4156. R. Raetz *et al.*, *Inorg. Chem.* **3**, 757 (1964).
4157. H. M. Rauen and K. Norpoth, *Klin. Wochschr.* **46**, 272 (1968); via *C. A.* **68**, 85898.
4158. W. A. Reeves and J. D. Guthrie, in "Chemical Reactions of Polymers" (E. M. Fettes, ed.), p. 1165. Wiley (Interscience), New York, 1964.

4159. H. Saito et al., J. Am. Chem. Soc. 89, 6605 (1967).
4160. Yu. F. Sarychev, Genetika No. 9, p. 16 (1967); via C. A. 68, 36829.
4161. T. Sasaki and T. Yoshioka, Yuki Gosei Kagaku Kyokai Shi 25, 658 (1967); via C. A. 68, 12788.
4162. W. Schaefer and H. Schlude, Tetrahedron Letters p. 4307 (1967).
4163. P. Scheiner, Tetrahedron 24, 2757 (1968).
4164. O. J. Scherer and J. Wokulat, Z. Naturforsch. 22b, 474 (1967).
4165. W. Schneider, Angew. Chem. 77, 550 (1965); Angew. Chem. Intern. Ed. Engl. 4, 536 (1965).
4166. W. A. Schroeder, J. R. Shelton, and B. Robberson, Biochim. Biophys. Acta 147, 590 (1967).
4167. P. H. Schwartz, Jr., J. Invertebrate Pathol. 7, 148 (1965).
4168. R. M. Scribner (to du Pont de Nemours and Co.), U.S. 3,337,535 (1967).
4169. R. M. Scribner (to du Pont de Nemours and Co.), U.S. 3,342,808 (1967).
4170. R. R. Shagidullin and N. P. Grechkin, Khim. Geterotsikl. Soedin., Akad. Nauk Latv. SSR p. 305 (1967); via C. A. 68, 73603.
4171. R. P. Shibaeva, L. O. Atovmyan, and R. G. Kostyanovskii, Dokl. Akad. Nauk SSSR 175, 586 (1967); Soviet Physics Doklady (English Transl.) 12, 669 (1968).
4172. P. C. Singer, W. O. Pipes, and E. R. Hermann, J. Water Pollution Control Federation 40, R1 (1968).
4173. N. Ya. Skulskaya and L. D. Protsenko, Zh. Obshch. Khim. 37, 2724 (1967); J. Gen. Chem. USSR (English Transl.) 37, 2594 (1967).
4174. R. W. Slater and J. A. Kitchener, Discussions Faraday Soc. 42, 267 (1966).
4175. Smith, Kline and French Laboratories, Brit. 1,081,317 (1967).
4176. C. G. Smith, J. E. Grady, and J. I. Northam, Cancer Chemotherapy Rept. 30, 9 (1963).
4177. H. L. Spell, Abst. Papers, 155th Am. Chem. Soc. Meeting, San Francisco, 1968 abstr. B-53.
4178. L. D. Spicer et al., J. Org. Chem. 33, 1350 (1968).
4179. H. Stamm, Angew. Chem. 77, 738 (1965); Angew. Chem. Intern. Ed. Engl. 4, 714 (1965).

4180. L. A. Suikova, Izv. Akad. Nauk SSSR, Ser. Biol. p. 739 (1966); via Nucl. Sci. Abstr. 21, 12819.
4181. Sumitomo Chemical Co., Ltd., Japan. 26,864 ('67); via C. A. 68, 79055.
4182. P. J. Szilyagi and G. A. Olah, Abst. Papers, 155th Am. Chem. Soc. Meeting, San Francisco, 1968 abstr. N-11.
4183. D. Taber, E. E. Renfrew, and H. E. Tiefenthal, in "Chemical Reactions of Polymers" (E. M. Fettes, ed.), p. 1113. Wiley (Interscience), New York, 1964.
4184. Takeda Chemical Industries, Ltd., Fr. 1,477,050 (1967); via C. A. 68, 49119.
4185. S. Takemura et al., Chem. & Pharm. Bull. (Tokyo) 15, 1322 (1967); via C. A. 68, 12617.
4186. S. Takemura et al., Chem. & Pharm. Bull. (Tokyo) 15, 1328 (1967); via C. A. 68, 29378.
4187. G. C. Tesoro and K. B. Domors, U.S. 3,355,437 (1967).
4188. F. N. Teumac (to The Dow Chemical Co.), U.S. 3,362,996 (1968).
4189. S. F. Thames and L. H. Edwards, J. Heterocyclic Chem. 5, 115 (1968).
4190. A. S. Tompa and R. D. Barefoot, Anal. Chem. 40, 650 (1968).
4191. Toyo Rayon Co., Ltd., Japan. 28,142 ('65).
4192. L. M. Trefonas and T. Sato, J. Heterocyclic Chem. 3, 404 (1966).
4193. V. I. Trofimov and I. I. Chkheidze, Khim. Vys. Energ. 1, 324 and 402 (1967); via C. A. 68, 12244 and 67, 86426.

4194. K. Tsiboyama, S. Tsuboyama, and M. Yanagita, *Rika Gaku Kenkyusho Hokoku* **42**, 19 (1966); via *C. A.* **66**, 29188; *Bull. Chem. Soc. Japan* **40**, 2954 (1967).

4195. R. Valters, S. Valtere, and A. Kipina, *Zh. Organ. Khim.* **4**, 445 (1968); via *C. A.* **68**, 114336.

4196. A. Veillard, J. M. Lehn, and B. Munsch, *Theoret. Chim. Acta* **9**, 275 (1968).

4197. S. I. Veselova, *Antibiotiki* **13**, 127 (1968).

4198. A. A. Volod'kin *et al.*, *Izv. Akad. Nauk SSSR, Ser. Khim.* p. 1592 (1967); *Bull. Acad. Sci. USSR, Div. Chem. Sci.* (*English Transl.*) p. 1531 (1967).

4199. M. G. Voronkov and L. A. Fedotova, *Khim. Geterotsikl. Soedin., Akad. Nauk Latv. SSR* p. 302 (1967); via *C. A.* **67**, 116687.

4200. D. K. Wall *et al.*, *J. Heterocyclic Chem.* **5**, 77 (1968).

4201. A. T. Wallace, R. M. Singh, and R. M. Browning, Atomic Energy Commission (U.S.) Report on Contract AT (40–1)–3092 (1966); via *Nucl. Sci. Abstr.* **21**, 6709.

4202. H. F. Walton, Atomic Energy Commission (U.S.) Report on Contract AT (11–1)–499 (1967); via *Nucl. Sci. Abstr.* **21**, 45194; K. Schimomura, L. Dickson, and H. F. Walton, *Anal. Chim. Acta* **37**, 102 (1967).

4203. H. E. Wave and T. J. Henneberry, *J. Econ. Entomol.* **60**, 1758 (1967).

4204. R. E. Webb and F. F. Smith, *J. Econ. Entomol.* **61**, 521 (1968).

4205. K. Wiesner and A. Philipp, *Tetrahedron Letters* p. 1467 (1966).

4206. J. W. Wilt *et al.*, *J. Org. Chem.* **33**, 694 (1968).

4207. F. P. Woerner, H. Reimlinger, and D. R. Arnold, *Angew. Chem.* **80**, 116 (1968); *Angew. Chem. Intern. Ed. Engl.* **7**, 130 (1968).

4208. G. J. Wright and V. K. Rowe, *Toxicol. Appl. Pharmacol.* **11**, 575 (1967).

4209. D. S. Wulfman *et al.*, *Abst. Papers, 155th Am. Chem. Soc. Meeting, San Francisco, 1968*, abstr. P-29.

4210. T. Yamaguchi (to Yoshitomi Drug Mfg. Co.), Japan. 2190 ('54); via *C. A.* **49**, 14817.

4211. G. H. Yeoman and B. C. Warren, *Vet. Record* **77**, 922 (1965).

4212. D. L. Zybina *et al.*, *Supermutageny, Akad. Nauk SSSR, Inst. Khim. Fiz.* p. 72 (1966); via. *C. A.* **67**, 40306; *Biofizika* **12**, 336 and 549 (1967); via *C. A.* **67**, 8010 and 87757.

Subject Index

A

Acetal group in aziridines, hydrolysis of, 309
Acetylenic compounds
  addition of aziridines to, 136–141
  aziridines from, 83
  ring opening of aziridines with, 246–248
Acid anhydrides (carboxylic)
  acylations of aziridines with,160, 162, 165
    of polyethylenimine with, 336
  cyclic, copolymerization with aziridines, 324
    ring opening of basic aziridines with, 241–243
Acid halides (carboxylic)
  acylation of aziridines with, 160–169
    of polyethylenimine with, 336
  ring opening of basic aziridines with, 241–243
Acids
  as catalysts for polymerizing aziridines, 315–316, 322
  removal with polyethylenimine, 377
  ring opening of activated aziridines with, 248–251
    of basic aziridines with, 206–218, 222–224
  salts with aziridines, 107–113
    with polyethylenimine, 334
  titration of aziridines with, 445
Acrylic polymers, use
  in adhesives, 377
  in coatings, 382, 384–386
  in ion-exchange resins, 377
  in plastics, 368, 370, 372
  in strengthening paper, 361
  in textile printing pastes, 344
Activated aziridines
  biological effects, 394
  definition, 106, 205–206, 248
  isomerization, 278–293
  polymerization and polymers, 321–322, 379

Activated aziridines—*continued*
  reaction with aziridines, 133, 160–161
    with cellulose, 342
1-Acylaziridines
  antimicrobial effects, 401–402
  as antitumor drugs, 434
  chemosterilant effects, 410
  cytostatic effects, 395
  isomerization, 251, 278–293
  as pesticides, 406
  physical properties, 97, 101
  polymerization, 321–322, 326
  preparation, 45, 52–53, 59, 65, 70, 84
  reactions with ring retention, 309, 312–314
  ring opening, 205–206, 241
    with alcohols, 253–254
    with amines, 262–264, 266
    with arenes, 268–269
    with aziridines, 133
    with carbanions, 269
    with carboxylic acids, 257
    with halogens, 268
    with hydrogen halides, 248, 251
    with phenols, 256
    as side reaction, 160–162, 193
    with thiols, 260
  toxicity, 419
  uses in adhesives, 378–379
    in coatings, 382–384
    in paper, 362–363
    in photography, 387–388
    in plastics, 364–365, 368–372
    in synthesis, 392
    in textiles, 344, 347–352, 355–357
Acyl halides, *see* Acid halides
Addition–elimination reactions, 138, 141, 145–153
Adhesives
  laminating, 379–380
  for nonwoven textiles, 381
  for particles, 381
  pressure-sensitive, 378
  for tire cords, 380

O

Oil-repellent finishing of textiles, 356
Olefinic compounds
addition of aziridines to, 136–144
of iodine isocyanate to, 35
formation from aziridines, 293–295
reaction with organic azides, 68–79
ring opening of basic aziridines with, 246–248
Optical activity, 94, 96, 328, 339
Optical bleaching agents for textiles, 359
Oxazolidinium salts, from quaternary aziridinium salts, 272
1,3-Oxazolidines, 136
1,3-Oxazolidin-2-ones
preparation from activated aziridines, 284, 288
pyrolysis, 83–84, 316
reaction with polyethylenimines, 337
Δ^2-1,3-Oxazolines
preparation, 52–53, 162, 244, 259, 282–293, 321
reactions, 84, 322
Δ^2-1,3-Oxazolin-5-ones, 86
Oxidation
of aziridines, 301
not involving aziridine ring, 144–145, 309–310
of unsaturated amines to aziridines, 78
Oxiranes, *see* Epoxides

P

Paper
adhesives for, 379–381
coating with plastic films, 385
detection of polyethylenimine in, 449
ion-exchange materials from, 374–377
pulp freeness, 362
retention aid, 361–362
sizing, 362–363
strength improvement, 360–362
Perfluoroalkyl compounds in water-repellent finishes, 356, 362
Pesticides, 406–407
1-Phenethylaziridine
basicity constant, 108
inversion of nitrogen in, 98
polymers, 319–320, 338

1-Phenethylaziridine—*continued*
preparation, 40, 140, 143
reactions, 233–234, 296, 298
uses, 382
Phenols
ring opening of activated aziridines with, 256–257
of basic aziridines with, 226–227
2-Phenoxyethylamines from phenols and aziridines, 226–227
1-Phenylaziridine
physical properties, 88, 92, 94, 97, 102–103
polymerization and polymers, 325–326, 332, 339
preparation, 39, 153, 156
reactions, 117, 248, 298
uses, 347
Phosphines, ring opening of basic aziridines with, 245
Phosphine oxide
tris(1-aziridinyl)-
abbreviation of name, xiii
as antitumor drug, 440
chemosterilant effects, 408, 411, 414–415
cytostatic effects, 395
determination, 446–448, 449, 451
herbicidal effects, 406
mutagenic effects, 396–399
physical properties, 88
preparation, 173, 177
ring-opening reactions, 133, 259–260, 340
stabilization in solution, 458
toxicity, 417, 421
uses, in adhesives, 378–381
in coatings, 382–383, 385
in paper, 361, 363
in plastics, 368–369, 371–372
in textiles, 343, 347, 349, 351, 353–354, 356, 358–359
tris(2-methyl-1-aziridinyl)-
abbreviation of name, xiii
chemosterilant effects, 408, 411–412, 414–415
determination, 445
mutagenic effects, 396–397, 399
preparation, 177
reactions, 117, 259
toxicity, 421
uses, 344, 368–370, 379, 381, 384

DATE DUE

MAY 1 '73			
GAYLORD			PRINTED IN U.S.A.